PLATE TECTONICS

PLATE TECTONICS

Arthur N. Strahler

Department of Geology
Columbia University
(retired)

Geo•Books Publishing
Cambridge, Massachusetts

This book was set in New Aster in camera-ready copy by the author and printed and bound by Bawden Printing of Eldridge, Iowa. The cover was designed and separated by E A T Design, Cambridge, Massachusetts.

Published by Geo•Books Publishing for Arthur N. Strahler.

(SAN 299-7614)
Geo•Books Publishing
55 Fresh Pond Parkway
Cambridge, MA 02138–3348
Phone: (617) 864-1334
Fax: (617) 876-9836

Publisher's Cataloging-in-Publication
(Provided by Quality Books, Inc.)

Strahler, Arthur Newell, 1918-
Plate tectonics / Arthur N. Strahler. — 1st ed.

p. cm.
Includes bibliographical references and index.
LCCN: 98-75540
ISBN: 0-9668594-4-8

1. Plate tectonics. I. Title.
QE511.4.S87 1998 551.1'36
QBI98-1578

Printed in the United States of America

Dedicated

to

Karl Ver Steeg

and

Charles B. Moke

Abbreviated Table of Contents

Chapter 1 Plate Tectonics— Once Over Lightly

Chapter 2 Continental Drift— Precursor of Plate Tectonics

Chapter 3 Crust/Mantle/Core Lithosphere/Asthenosphere

Chapter 4 The Ocean Floor and Its Sediments

Chapter 5 Igneous Activity and Plate Tectonics

Chapter 6 Seismicity and Plate Tectonics

Chapter 7 Tectonics of the Oceanic Lithosphere

Chapter 8 Subduction Tectonics

Chapter 9 Collision Tectonics and Continental Accretion

Chapter 10 Continental Rifting and Extensional Tectonics

Chapter 11 Sedimentary Basins of the Continents

Chapter 12 Geomorphology and Plate Tectonics

Chapter 13 The Accretion and Breakup of Continents

About the Author

Arthur N. Strahler (b. 1918) received his B.A. degree in 1938 from the College of Wooster, Ohio, and his Ph.D. degree in geology from Columbia University in 1944. He was appointed to the Columbia University faculty in 1941, serving as Professor of Geomorphology from 1958 to 1967 and as Chairman of the Department of Geology from 1959 to 1962. He is a Senior Fellow of the Geological Society of America. He has been cited for his pioneering contributions to quantitative and dynamic geomorphology, contained in over 30 major papers in leading scientific journals. He is the author of 16 textbook titles with 13 revised editions in geology, earth sciences, and related disciplines.

Author's Preface

As a geology major in the late 1930's at the College of Wooster, Ohio, I had two very fine teachers—Karl Ver Steeg and Charles B. Moke. I had found two fields that fascinated me: structural geology, taught by Charlie Moke, and geomorphology, taught by Dr. Ver Steeg, our department head.

In the summer of my junior year I traveled to Wisconsin to seize the rare opportunity to enter the field camp of a widely known teacher, J. Harlen Bretz of the University of Chicago. The camp is ideally located in the Baraboo District, where Precambrian rocks are beautifully exposed for study. Back at the camp, nightly fireside discussions were vigorous, but I never heard a word about "wandering continents," nor about the ideas of a German geophysicist, Alfred Wegener, who had published strong evidence of the separation of continents.

Upon returning to Wooster to finish out my undergraduate program, I found that Dr. Ver Steeg had obtained for me the prestigious Britton Scholarship at Columbia University. Arriving that fall in New York City, I found this new academic environment strange but exciting. Among the many touring geologists who visited our department were some from "down under" and of course each was asked to give us a talk about his latest work. Geologists from South Africa, Australia, and New Zealand were frequent visitors, and we Yankees found their accents amusing. Not so amusing to our faculty were those guests' casual mentions of Wegner's beliefs. However, some of them strongly supported a popular hypothesis that the earth is expanding its diameter, resulting in continents spreading apart and leaving wider sea floors.

As time passed, I completed my courses and exams and had begun to work on my dissertation—a study of the transverse watergaps in the Newer Appalachian Mountains. But now a new faculty member was present: Walter Bucher, a leading figure in structural geology and tectonics. He became my dissertation mentor and I held him in high esteem. In group meetings, Bucher strongly expressed his displeasure with the visitors who supported the spreading apart of the continents. By now I had begun to consider Wegener's theory reasonable, but I must not tell anyone! Wait until the time is right to jump on the bandwagon! In due time, sound evidence of spreading of the mid-ocean floor was to be established by geophysicts as being beyond doubt.

While I was serving on the Columbia Graduate Faculty there arose in 1949 a sister institution of learning, now called the Lamont-Doherty Earth Observatory. It was founded by Maurice Ewing, a seismologist and a professor in our Geology Department. Taking over the use of a splendid estate with endowment that had been given to our university, the observatory was situated on the Palisades of the Hudson and could serve to hold a fine seismograph lab. There were also ample grounds to house several kinds of laboratories for research on materials of the ocean floors. Ewing added several of the finest seismologists. He also attracted young learners to our Geology Department, where some of them came to take geology courses with me. It was apparent that they were absorbing Wegner's theories and were interested in finding new ways to test them. In the Lamont laboratories they helped perform crucial tests that finally succeeded. "Yes," they announced, "the oceanic plates are indeed separating." At that point, Doc Ewing, who had clung to the belief that plates don't spread, now capitulated!

As a professor in the Columbia Geology Department, I was frequently assigned to sit on dissertation commitees of Lamont students, and this required me to read their doctoral theses. What better opportunity could I have to learn in advance a number of the the great discoveries in plate tectonics!

Perhaps you will participate in similar discoveries. Today, those big events are rare, but then you never know. Good Luck!

Arthur N. Strahler
Santa Barbara, California

Reviewers of Chapters in *Plate Tectonics*

I wish to express my gratitude to the reviewers below for their time and effort spent in improving the clarity and accuracy of my text, and for educating me on the fine points of their specialites. The chapters they reviewed are denoted by number.

A.N.S.

The College of Wooster, Ohio
Mark A. Wilson (1-13)
Lori Betisson-Varga (5)
Robert J. Varga (6-10)

Lamont-Doherty Earth Observatory
Marie Tharp (2)

Cornell University, Ithaca
Jack Oliver (6)
Eric Sandvol (6)

U.S. Geological Survey
John Kingston (11)

University of California at Santa Barbara
Edward A. Keller (12)

Colby College, Maine
E. Donaldson Koons (12)

Otago University, Duneda, New Zealand
Peter Koons (12)

A Preview

Purpose, Scope, Level

PLATE TECTONICS is a textbook of basic principles and important data of plate tectonics for use at an intermediate college level. It contains essential material for geology and geophysics majors and minors. It is also recommended for other natural-science majors, especially those in evolutionary biology. The presentation is generally descriptive, with abundant quantitative data, but otherwise non-mathematical.

Prerequisites

Minimum prerequisite: a thorough introduction to general physical geology with lab, covering basic topics in mineralogy, petrology, sedimentology and stratigraphy, structural geology, and geomorphology. Elements of seismology and radiometric age determination are also assumed. A course in historical geology can be useful, but is not essential, beyond furnishing an assumed familiarity the with the sequence of names of eons, periods, and eras of the table of geologic time. (A table of geologic time is given in the Appendix.)

General Plan of Treatment

Chapter 1 is an overview of plate tectonics at a level suitable for persons with little or no geology background, but it should not be skipped over. It makes a good first reading assignment for all. Chapter 2, a historical essay, may be passed over without detriment, but with regret. Chapters 3 and 4 are not plate tectonics, *per se*, but give essential background material. Chapters 5 and 6 emphasize the petrologic and seismologic underpinnings of plate tectonics as fundamental to an understanding of chapters to follow. Chapters 7 through 13 are the main body of Plate Tectonics, following the Wilson model of opening and closing of ocean basins, but taking as the starting point the midoceanic spreading boundaries, where lithosphere is initially generated. Chapter 13, in contrast to those that precede it, is largely focused on the history of the continents. No ordering of chapters can be fully satisfactory, but the plan is to cumulate knowledge in a logical cause-to-effect chain. Thus, for example, rifting of a continent already completed is more meaningful when presented at the end, when continent formation is understood. A simple *Geologic Time Scale* follows the final chapter.

Levels of Difficulty

Every chapter contains some introductory sections and paragraphs that are easily understood by readers with little or no geologic background. Included in some of these are historical vignettes that maintain a discovery theme. These early, more accessible sections are followed by sections at a quantum level higher in technical detail, documented with literature references. In these more advanced parts, an attempt is made to include all the important hypotheses, concepts, and terms appearing in modern plate tectonics research publications. At the same time we try to make this material clear to all geology readers—much as one would find it presented in the better "science news" articles in such journals as *Science, Nature, Science News, GSA Today, Scientific American, American Scientist*, and *Geotimes*. In short, Plate Tectonics is not a treatise for specialists in plate tectonics.

Limits to Scope

We keep in mind that "plate tectonics" refers to large-scale structural phenomena. Tectonics on the small to microscopic scales, appropriate in structural geology, is introduced only where necessary. We also minimize the geochemical aspects of plate tectonics, introducing only what elementary physical chemistry is necessary.

Except in the final chapter, no attempt is made to present systematic chronological and stratigraphic historical geology. Type examples are extracted from the historical record only as needed. A list of references cited in the chapter is placed at end of each chapter. Two indices follow the last chapter: *Index of Subjects* and *Index of Persons*.

Design and Illustrations

The format of Plate Tectonics is best described as a "no-frills" textbook. This means that color rendition is out. Halftones (photos) and other screened illustrations are not used. Illustrations in Plate Tectonics are rendered in sharply defined lines that make clear lecture slides and overheads. This format is consonant with the philosophy that science is in flux, so that texts require frequent, even constant, revision and updating. As any textbook comes off the press it is already outdated in many places and probably contains errors as well.

A Final Note

Plate tectonics is a grand paradigm in earth science that brings together many disparate areas of geology and geophysics in a single focus. It is a complex topic that has been studied at many levels and scales. My purpose in writing this book has been to summarize the major ideas and concepts of plate tectonics in a single volume at a constistant level of presentation. I hope I have acheived my objective and that that you will find the text clear, enlightening, and interesting to read. As note in my *Author's Preface*, plate tectonics is a field that has held my own interest for much of my long career. I hope you will find it as fascinating as I have.

Chapter: 1 Plate Tectonics—Once Over Lightly

Our opening chapter offers an overview of plate tectonics in which only the major parts of the tectonic system are described and the basic processes are stated only in very generalized terms. Much of this overview will be familiar material to those of you who have recently completed a modern introductory course in physical geology. How much is familiar will depend on the extent to which plate tectonics was stressed in that course.

Readers whose first geology course was taken more than three decades ago may find most of this chapter strange new ground. Plate tectonics is, after all, a recent revolution in the geosciences. This new view of earth processes developed swiftly following its rather hesitant start in the 1960s. It has now been fleshed out to achieve high status as a solid paradigm of natural science with enormous power to explain a wide range of empirical observations.

Some geologists ask, however, that the mainframe of plate tectonics still be viewed cautiously and with a tentativeness appropriate to all major theories of science. The brief overview in this chapter can best be thought of as essentially a statement of hypothesis, for we give here little or no attention to corroborative evidence; that will come in later chapters. Here, our descriptions of structures and processes will necessarily be greatly simplified and should be thought of as first approximations, unqualified by the many variations, complexities, and exceptions that will appear upon closer examination.

1.1 The Earth's Concentric Rock Zones

Like the other three inner planets of our solar system—Mercury, Venus, and Mars—Planet Earth is a spherical ball of rock consisting largely of compounds of the elements oxygen, silicon, magnesium, and iron. The four inner planets differ greatly from the four great outer planets—Jupiter, Saturn, Uranus, and Neptune—which are giants by comparison and are composed largely of volatiles, principally liquid or metallic hydrogen and helium and/or ices of methane and ammonia.

The average radius of the earth sphere is about 6400 km (more exactly, 6370 km). Nearly all of this radius is taken up with two zones or regions: a core and a mantle (Figure 1.1). The spherical *core*, with a radius of 3470 km, consists of metallic iron mixed with a small proportion of nickel or of the mineral troilite with the composition FeS. The outer two-thirds of the core is in a liquid state, intensely hot and under enormous confining pressure. There is evidence that the inner portion of the core is solid. Surrounding the core is the *mantle*, a great shell of ultramafic rock nearly 2800 km thick. Thus, the mantle occupies nearly half the earth's radius. The dense mantle rock consists mostly of the elements silicon, oxygen, iron, and magnesium in a solid state; it has a very high temperature and is under great confining pressure.

Extremely thin in comparison with the mantle is the outermost earth shell, the *crust*, ranging in thickness from about 5 to 60 km. If spread evenly over the entire earth, its average thickness would be about 17 km. Such a thin layer cannot be shown to true scale on our cutaway drawing of the earth, Figure 1.1. Rock of the crust differs from that of the mantle in containing substantial proportions of the lighter metals: aluminum, sodium, calcium, and potassium, along with abundant silicon and oxygen. For this reason, crustal rock is less dense than mantle rock, just as a light metal such as aluminum is less dense than a heavy metal such as iron. Mantle rock is, in turn, less dense than the iron-rich mixture of the core. Thus our first generalization about the planetary structure is that it consists of shells that decrease in density outward from the center.

1.2 Continental Crust and Oceanic Crust

Two basic kinds of crust are *continental crust* and *oceanic crust* (Figure 1.2A). Continental crust is much thicker, on the average, than oceanic crust. Whereas continental crust consists in large part of felsic (granitic rock), the oceanic crust consists

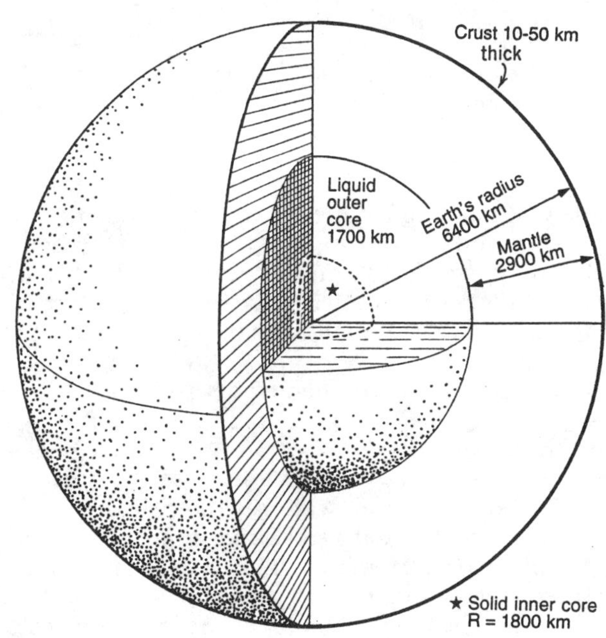

Figure 1.1 Principal zones of the earth's interior. (© A.N. Strahler.)

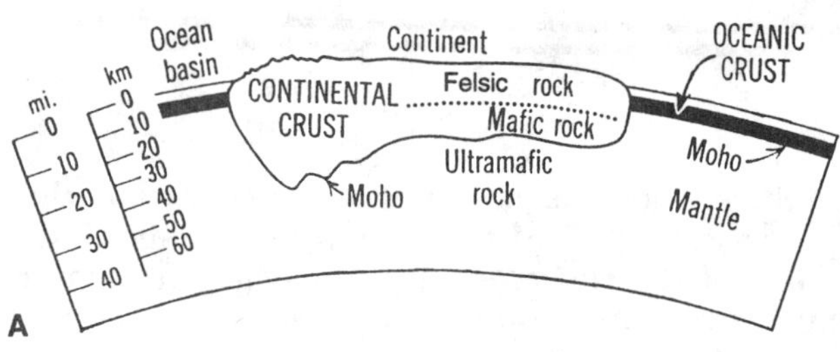

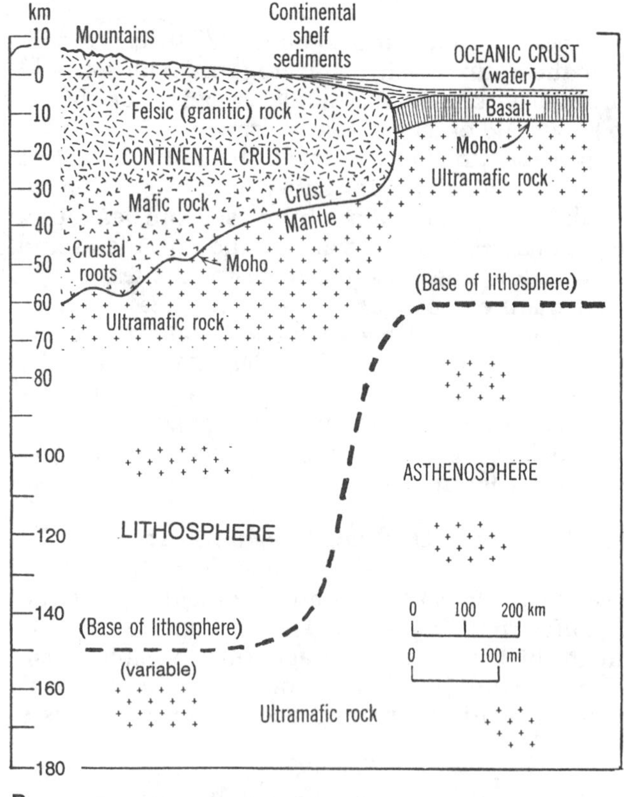

Figure 1.2 Schematic diagram of composition and thickness of crust and mantle under continents and ocean basins. (© A.N. Strahler.)

largely of mafic igneous rock (basalt, gabbro). The lower boundary of the crust is quite sharply defined. It is a discontinuity known as the *Moho*. Usually, the Moho is interpreted as the interface of mafic crustal rock with ultra-mafic mantle rock.

1.3 Lithosphere and Asthenosphere

The three earth rock zones we have described—core, mantle, and crust—differ from one another in chemical composition, which is the primary basis on which each is defined. Superimposed on the outer shells (outer mantle and crust) are layers defined according to the physical state of the rock—whether the rock is hard and brittle or soft and plastic. Depending largely on temperature, the same rock can exist in either of these states or conditions. A close analogy is a bar of cast iron that is strong, hard, and brittle when cold, but comes soft and plastic when heated to a high temperature (Figure 1.3).

In terms of physical state, the earth has an outer layer of rigid, brittle rock known as *lithosphere*. This layer includes the entire crust and a portion of the upper mantle. Thickness of the lithosphere ranges from under 50 to over 125 km, with a rough global average of about 75 km, as shown in Figure 1.4. Below the lithosphere lies the *asthenosphere*, a soft layer in the upper mantle. The word is derived from the Greek root *asthenés*, meaning "weak." The asthenosphere is in a soft condition because its temperature is high—about 1400°C—and close to its melting point (a condition of partial melting may be present.) The rock behaves much like an ingot of white-hot iron that will hold its shape when resting on a flat surface, but is easily formed into bars or sheets when squeezed between rollers.

Below the asthenosphere lies the *mesosphere*; essentially it is the remaining thickness of the mantle. The mesosphere is strong in comparison with the asthenosphere, but is considered to be capable of extremely slow flowage.

Temperature increases steadily inward from the earth's surface, so that the change from lithosphere to asthenosphere is gradual, rather than abrupt. We know from the behavior of earthquake waves as they travel through the outer mantle that the asthenosphere extends to a depth of about 300 km, below which the strength of the mantle rock again begins to increase. The weakest portion of the asthenosphere lies at a depth of roughly 200 km. We present the evidence in detail in Chapter 3.

The important concept you should derive from the above statements is this: The rigid, brittle lithosphere forms a hard shell capable of moving

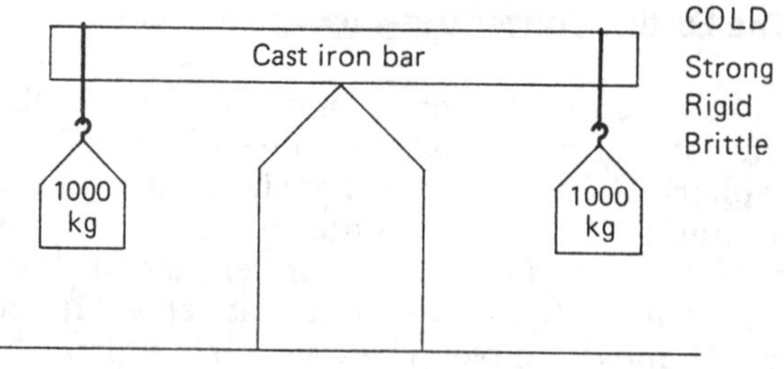

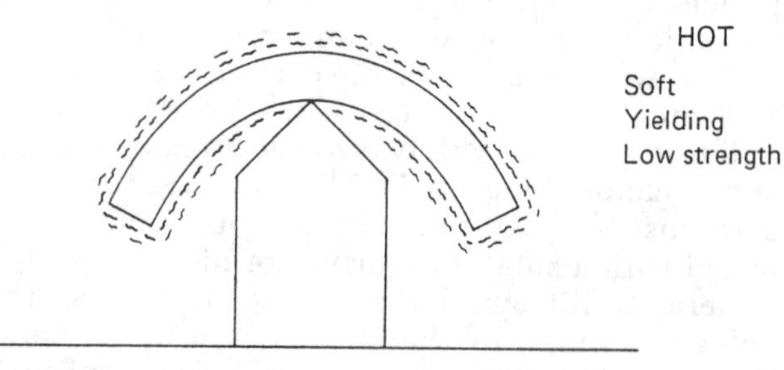

Figure 1.3 A cold bar of cast iron can support heavy weights, though it will snap if overloaded. The same bar heated to redness becomes soft and sags under its own weight. (© A.N. Strahler.)

Figure 1.4 The lithosphere and asthenosphere drawn to true scale. The curvature of the upper diagram fits a circle 30 cm in radius. The thin black line at the top is scaled to represent a thickness of 10 km; it will contain about 98 percent of the earth's surface features, including the ocean floors and high mountains and plateaus. The complete circle below is drawn on a scale one-tenth as great as the upper diagram. Seen in true scale, the lithosphere is a very thin shell compared with the mantle and core. (From A.N. and A.H. Strahler, *Elements of Physical Geography,* 3rd ed. Copyright © 1984 by John Wiley & Sons, Inc. Reproduced by permission of the publisher.)

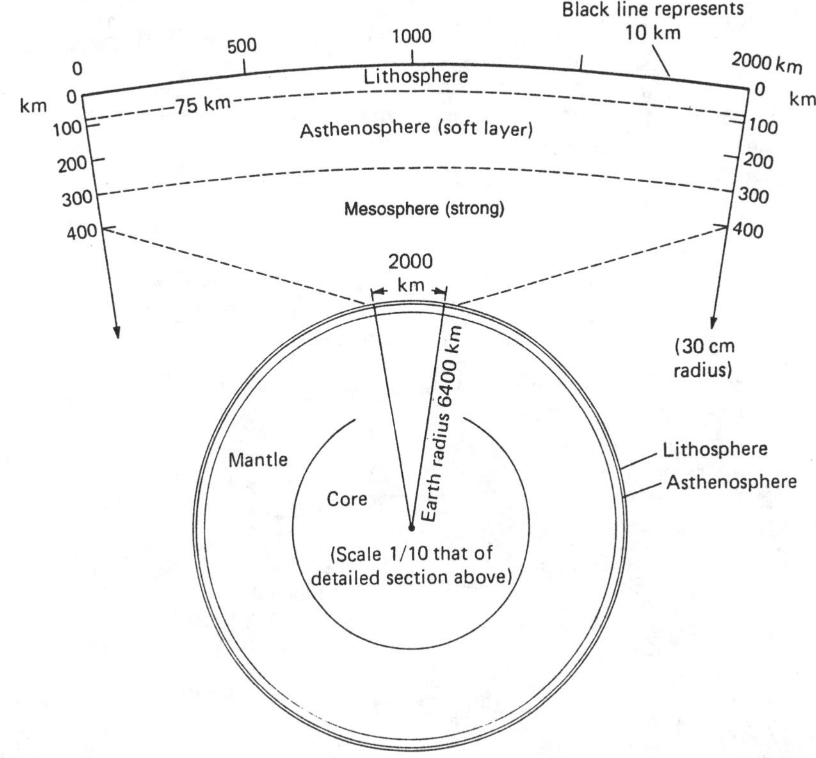

bodily over the soft weak plastic asthenosphere. This motion is exceedingly slow and is distributed through a thickness of many tens of kilometers. A simple model of the motion is a deck of playing cards resting on a tabletop, its top ten cards glued together to form a solid block, representing the lithosphere (Figure 1.5). A horizontal force against the edge of the deck will move the upper block horizontally, while the motion becomes a slipping between the free cards beneath it. The card at the bottom of the deck will remain fixed to the table. Slippage on a great number of very thin parallel layers is described as *shearing*. Layers involved in shearing of the asthenosphere are no thicker than atoms or molecules, so that we could not actually see one layer gliding over another. The entire asthenosphere seems to move by the kind of flow we observe in a tacky liquid-like thick syrup—but the asthenosphere is not a true liquid. (A true liquid has no strength.) It is difficult for us to understand how rock behaves under such conditions as exist in the asthenosphere, where temperatures are very high and the rock is under enormous confining pressure from the weight of the overlying rock. We discuss this subject in greater detail in Chapter 3.

1.4 Continental Lithosphere and Oceanic Lithosphere

Continents, by definition, are crustal masses that rise in surface elevation above sea level. In contrast, the floor of the ocean basins lie at an average depth of some 4 km below sea level. In this case, our zero reference is the surface of the ocean, which tends to form a nearly perfect sphere. [Because of earth rotation, the actual form approximates an oblate ellipsoid, or "flattened sphere."] Figure 1.6 shows the continental surfaces rising above sea level and the ocean-basin floors below that level. Some good scientific evidence has established that the lithosphere under the continents is much thicker than the lithosphere under the ocean basins. The reasons for this

Figure 1.5 The shearing motion of soft rock in the asthenosphere resembles the slip of cards in a deck. We imagine the cards in the upper part of the deck to be glued together so as to move as a solid plate, representing the lithosphere. (© A.N. Strahler.)

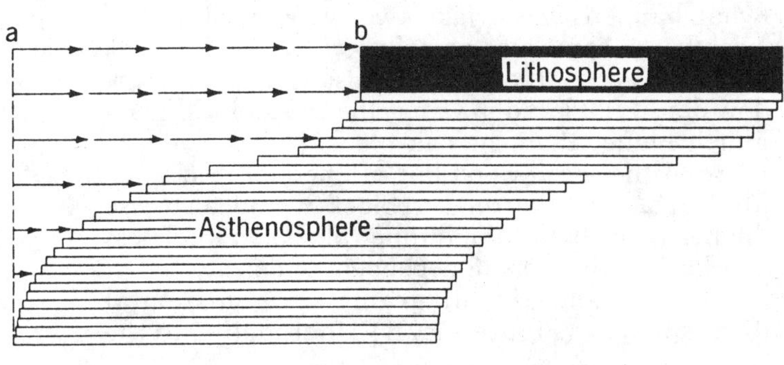

© A.N. Strahler

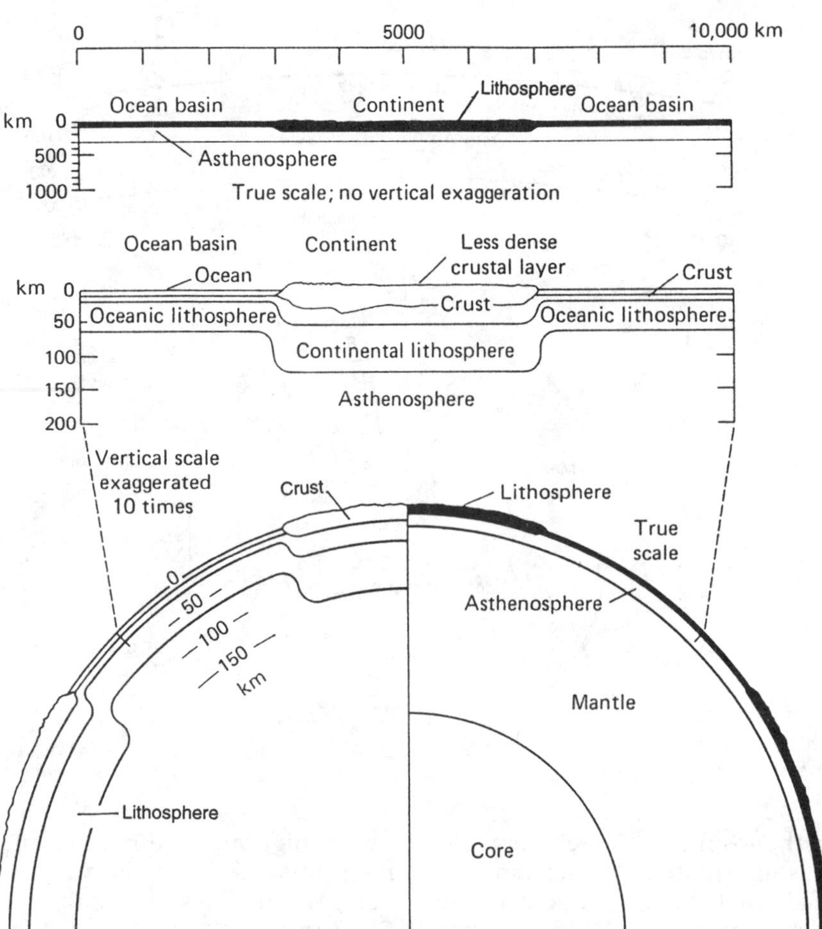

Figure 1.6 Continental lithosphere is thicker than oceanic lithosphere. The crust of the continents is also thicker than the crust of the oceans. For purposes of illustration, the continental lithosphere is shown as being twice as thick as the oceanic lithosphere. (© A.N. Strahler.)

difference in thickness will become clear in later chapters. In these illustrations we show continents to be underlain by a thick layer of *continental lithosphere* and the ocean basins by a thin layer of *oceanic lithosphere*. Keep in mind that the lithosphere/asthenosphere boundary is transitional, rather than sharply defined (as in the case of the Moho.)

Besides being thicker, continental lithosphere is also different in gross rock composition from oceanic lithosphere. Continental lithosphere bears continental crust, which includes an upper felsic (granitic) crustal layer of rock having lower-than-average density (Figure 1.2). Continental lithosphere is, therefore, more buoyant than oceanic lithosphere, and this property contributes to the higher upper surface of a continent. To explain this principle in simple terms, consider what happens if we take two wooden blocks of exactly the same size and shape, one block of oak (a dense wood), the other of balsa (a wood of very low density). Placed in water, the balsa block floats much higher than the oak block. [If both blocks were of the same wood but of unequal thickness, the surface of the thicker block would also rise higher than that of the thinner block; so thickness is a basic factor here, independent of density.]

Our schematic diagram of continental lithosphere (Figure 1.2B) includes in the continental crust an upper felsic layer of lower rock density. Notice that this felsic layer is missing from oceanic crust, and thus also from oceanic lithosphere. As Figure 1.6 shows, the boundary surface of contact of lithosphere and asthenosphere "shadows" or "tracks" the Moho surface above it.

Up to this point, we have presented the earth's internal structure as a completely fixed or stationary set of spherical layers. We turn next to consider motions of one layer with respect to the other; i.e., from statics we turn to dynamics.

1.5 Lithospheric Plates

If the earth consisted of a perfectly spherical lithosphere with no flaws or fractures, it is conceivable that the entire lithosphere could move as a whole shell with respect to the entire sphere beneath it (mantle and core taken as a unit). The entire asthenosphere would absorb the differential motion, or shear. If that kind of motion actually occurred, it would carry as a unit all of the earth's continents and ocean basins. We can visualize a situation in which western Europe might be moving toward the earth's north pole, so that there would come a time when the north pole would be situated in Ireland. At the same time, New Zealand would be nearing

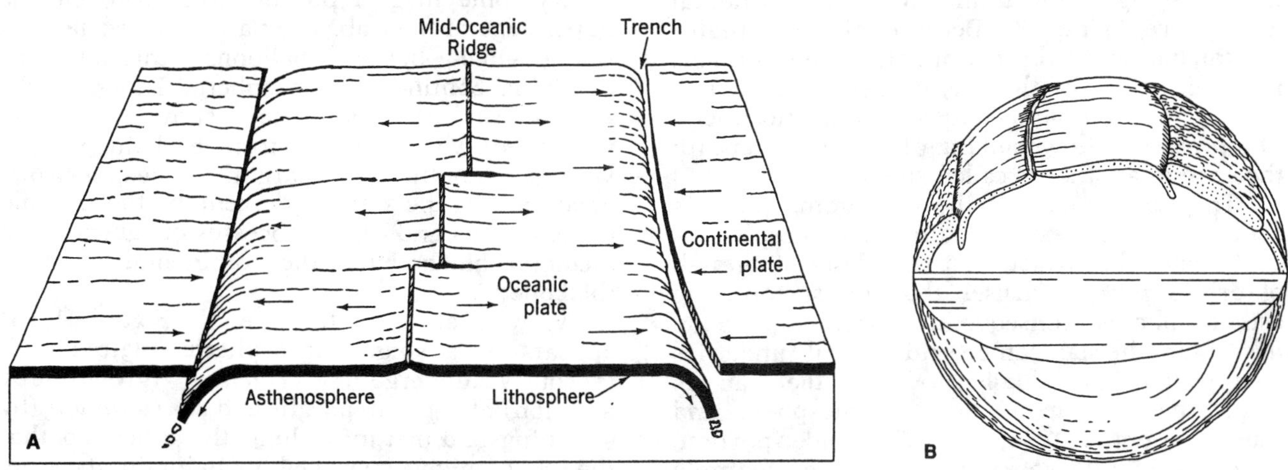

Figure 1.7 (A) Schematic block diagram of lithospheric plates in motion. Earth curvature has been removed. (B) Pictorial rendition of plates on a spherical earth. These diagrams are not to correct depth scale. (© A.N. Strahler.)

the south pole, while the city of Cape Town, South Africa, would be approaching the equator.

It is more realistic to suppose that the brittle lithosphere has tended to break into large sections. There is strong evidence to support the statement that the lithosphere is relatively thin beneath vast areas (notably beneath the deep ocean floors) and relatively thick beneath other areas (notably under the continents). Thin lithosphere might be expected to fracture quite easily, while thick lithosphere would tend to hold together much better under horizontal compression.

In reality, then, breakup of the lithosphere has formed a number of *lithospheric plates*, each having some degree of freedom to move independently of the adjacent plates. Like great slabs of floating ice on the polar sea, lithospheric plates can be seen to be pulling apart in some places and colliding in others. In the case of floating ice, two plates pulling apart leave a widening gap of exposed water. This gap can be filled with new ice as the top of the exposed water freezes. When two ice plates collide, they often come together in crushing impacts that raise great welts, called "pressure ridges." These welts remind us of mountain chains found along the margins of continents. Consider also that when collision occurs between a thick ice plate and a thin ice plate, the latter might be forced down beneath the thick plate. The downdiving thin plate would then melt and its substance would disperse into the surrounding water.

Because ice is less dense than water, an ice plate floats easily and resists being pushed down below the water surface. Thus, it would not be wise to carry the floating-ice-plate model any further in search of a valid model of lithospheric plates. Unlike ice, a given kind of solid rock is denser than the same rock in the molten condition, when the two are compared at the same pressure. Thus, lithosphere carried down into the asthenosphere will be denser than the surrounding rock, which is heated close to melting and may, in fact, be partly molten. A lithospheric plate, then, shows a tendency to sink. Given a suitable opportunity, the free edge of a lithospheric plate may plunge into the asthenosphere, nosediving at a steep angle—but here we are getting ahead of our story line.

1.6 Plate Tectonics and Plate Boundaries

The general theory of lithospheric plates, their relative motions, and their boundary interactions is called *plate tectonics*. The word *tectonics* is a noun meaning "the study of tectonic activity." [Although a plural term, it can be used in either singular or plural construction. Thus it is permissible to say "Plate tectonics is..."] *Tectonic activity*, in turn, refers to all forms of breaking and bending of rock of the lithosphere.

Our next step is to visualize the lithosphere broken into lithospheric plates that move with respect to one another. Figure 1.7 is a pictorial rendition to give the general impression of plates in motion. Figure 1.8 gives details of the major features of plate interactions. In Figure 1.8 we can see two plates, X, and Y, both made up of oceanic lithosphere, pulling apart along a common plate boundary. This activity tends to create a gaping crack in the crust, but magma (molten rock) from the mantle below rises continually to fill the crack. The magma solidifies in the crack and is added to the two edges of the spreading lithospheric plates. In this way, new solid lithosphere is continually formed. At the distant (right) boundary of oceanic plate Y, the oceanic lithosphere is shown to be pushing against a thick mass of continental lithosphere, plate Z. Because of its greater crustal buoyancy, the continental plate remains in place, while the thinner, denser oceanic plate bends down and plunges into the asthenosphere. The process of downsinking of one plate beneath the edge of another is called *subduction*.

The leading edge of the descending plate is cooler than the surrounding asthenosphere—cooler enough, in fact, that this descending slab of brittle rock is denser than its surrounding asthenosphere. Consequently, once subduction has begun, the slab can be said to "sink under its own weight." Gradually however, the slab is heated by the surrounding asthenosphere and thus it eventually softens. The under-portion, which is mantle rock in composition, simply reverts to asthenosphere as it softens. The thin basaltic crust may actually melt and become magma, which tends to rise because it is less dense than the surrounding material. Figure 1.8B shows some magma pockets formed from the upper edge of the slab. They are pictured here as rising like hot-air balloons through the overlying continental lithosphere. Reaching the earth's surface, quantities of magma build volcanoes, which tend to form a chain parallel with the continental margin. A deep *oceanic trench* marks the line of descent of the oceanic plate. By this and other processes of igneous and metamorphic activity, the continental crust is thickened.

Viewed as a unit, plate Y (Figure 1.8B) appears as a single lithospheric plate simultaneously undergoing *accretion* (growth by addition) along one margin and *consumption* (by softening and melting) along the other, so that the plate might conceivably maintain its size, without necessarily expanding or diminishing. Actually, our tectonic model can also call for a plate of oceanic lithosphere either to grow in extent or to diminish to the point of disappear-

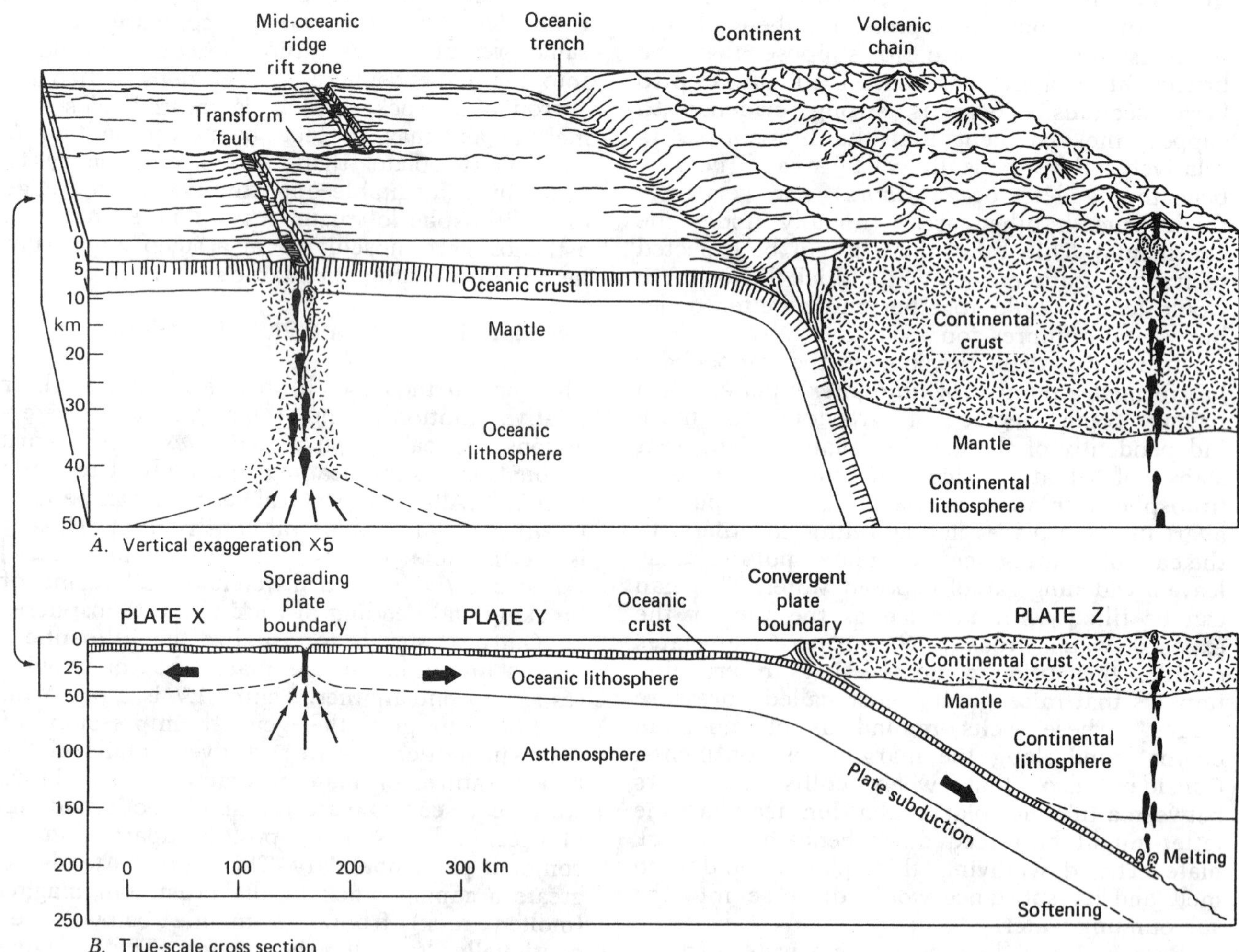

Figure 1.8 Schematic cross sections showing some of the important elements of plate tectonics. Diagram A is greatly exaggerated in vertical scale so as to emphasize surface and crustal features. Only the uppermost 50 km is shown. Diagram B is drawn to true scale and shows conditions to a depth of 250 km. Here the actual relationships between lithospheric plates can be examined, but surface features can scarcely be shown. (© A.N. Strahler.)

ance. We also have models that allow for the creation of new plates of oceanic lithosphere where none previously existed. In this respect, the theory is quite flexible.

We have yet to consider a third type of lithospheric plate boundary. Two lithospheric plates may be in contact along a common boundary on which one plate merely slides horizontally past the other with no motion that would cause the plates to separate or to converge (Figure 1.9). The plane along which motion occurs is a nearly vertical fracture extending far down into the lithosphere; it is called a *transform fault*. The transform fault is a special case of the transcurrent (strike-slip) fault and is used strictly in reference to plate boundaries.

Thus, in summary, there are three major kinds of active plate boundaries:

Spreading boundary (or *Divergent boundary*) New oceanic lithosphere is being formed by accretion of mafic magma as two plates move apart.

Convergent boundary Subduction is in progress; lithosphere is being consumed within the mantle.

Transform boundary Plates are gliding past one another along a transcurrent fault.

Let us put these three boundaries into a pattern to include an entire lithospheric plate. As shown in Figure 1.10, we have visualized a moving rectangular window-like plate, set in the middle of a surrounding stationary plate. The moving plate is bounded by transform faults on two parallel sides. Some familiar mechanical devices come to mind in visualizing this model. One is the sunroof top of an automobile; it has a window that opens by sliding backward along parallel sidetracks to disappear under the fixed roof. Another is the old-fashioned roll-top desk. In Chapter 7, we will investigate the various different arrangements of plate boundaries, which can be curved as well as straight, while individual plates can pivot as they move. Thus, there are many geometric variations to consider.

1.7 The Global System of Lithospheric Plates

The first global map of lithospheric plates appeared in published form in 1968, and there have since been many minor changes and revisions in the map. Boundaries have been relocated and new plates identified; differences have appeared in the naming of plates, as well. Today, however a fairly good consensus exists in the geologic community as to the number and names of the major plates, the nature of their boundaries, and their relative motions. Differences of interpretation persist in many

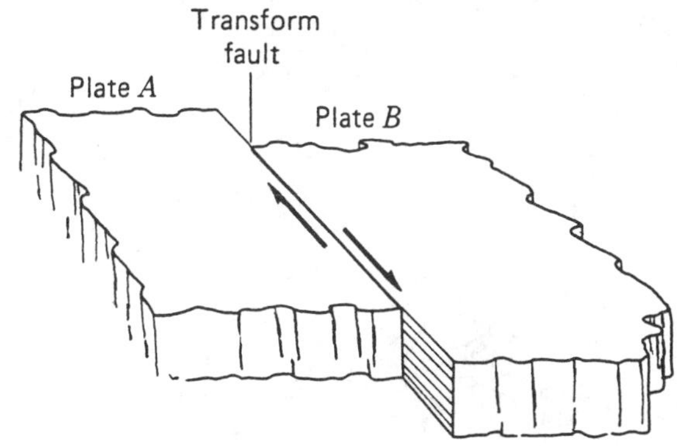

Figure 1.9 A transform fault involves the horizontal motion of two adjacent oceanic lithospheric plates, one sliding past the other. (© A.N. Strahler.)

boundary details. Also, a few sections of certain plate boundaries are of uncertain classification or location.

For a particular lithospheric plate to be identified and named, its boundaries should all be active. In other words, there must be good evidence of present or recent relative motion between the plate and all its contiguous (adjoining) plates.

A generalized map of the global plate system is shown in Figure 1.11. Figure 1.12 is a schematic circular cross section of the lithosphere along a great circle in low latitudes, showing plates and their boundaries. (Maps of Figure 7.30 show many additional details of

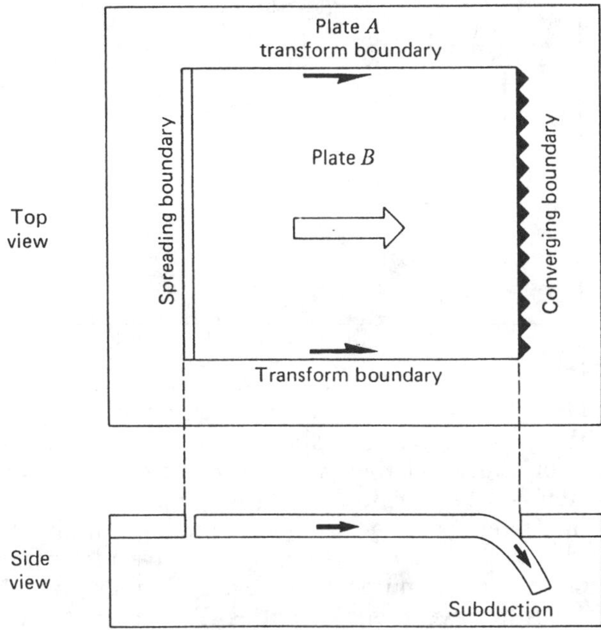

Figure 1.10 A schematic diagram of a single rectangular plate of oceanic lithosphere with four boundaries. (© A.N. Strahler.)

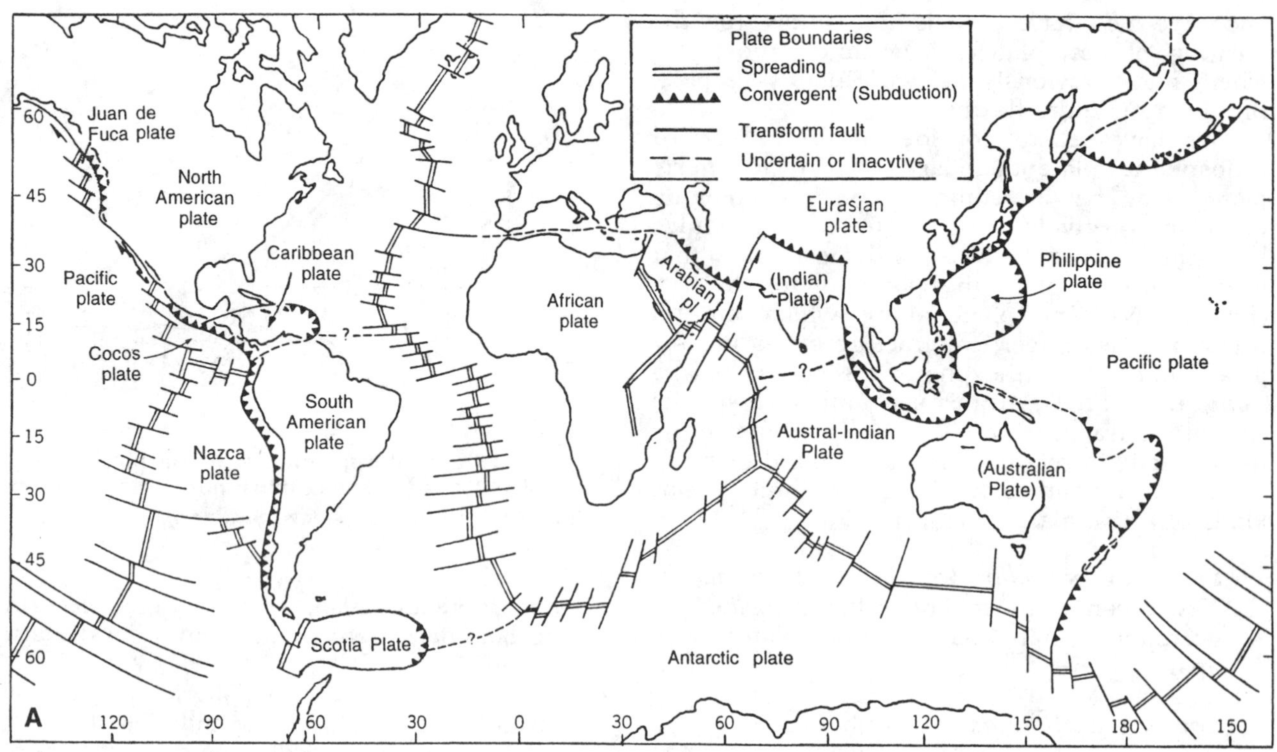

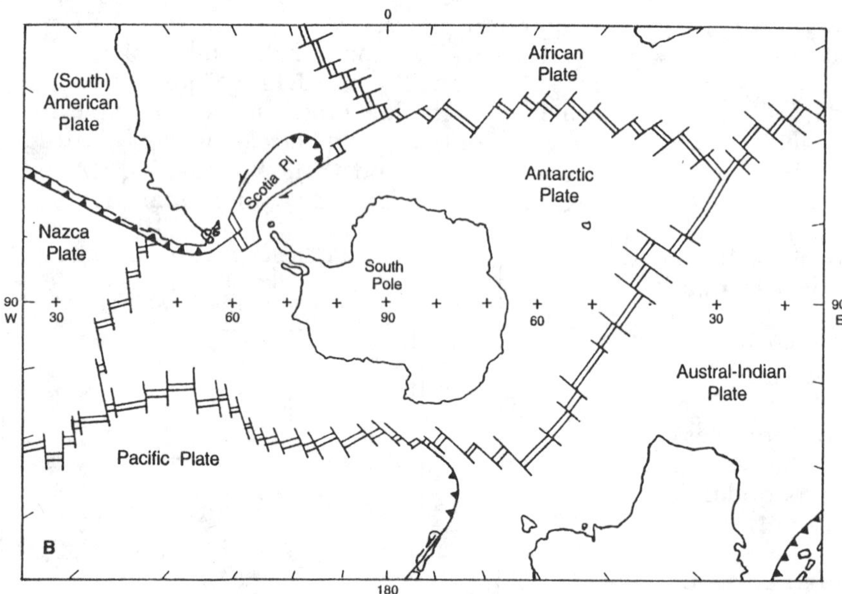

Figure 1.11 (A) Generalized world map of the major lithospheric plates on a Mercator grid. (B) The Antarctic plate on a polar grid. (© A.N. Strahler.)

plate boundaries and their junctions). The lithospheric plate system consists of twelve major plates. Of the twelve, six are of enormous extent—they are the "great plates." The remaining six range from intermediate in size to comparatively small. Geologists have identified and named a number of even smaller plates within the twelve major plates. The great Pacific plate occupies much of the Pacific Ocean Basin and consists almost entirely of oceanic lithosphere. Its relative motion is north-westerly, so that it has a convergent (subduction) boundary along most of its western and northern edge. The eastern and southern edge is mostly spreading boundary. A sliver of continental lithosphere is included, making up the coastal portion of California and all of Baja California. The California portion of the plate boundary is the San Andreas Fault, an active transform fault.

The American plate includes most of the continental lithosphere of North and South America, as well as the entire oceanic lithosphere lying west of the mid-oceanic ridge (Mid-Atlantic Ridge), a spreading boundary that divides the Atlantic Ocean Basin down the middle. For the most part, the western edge of

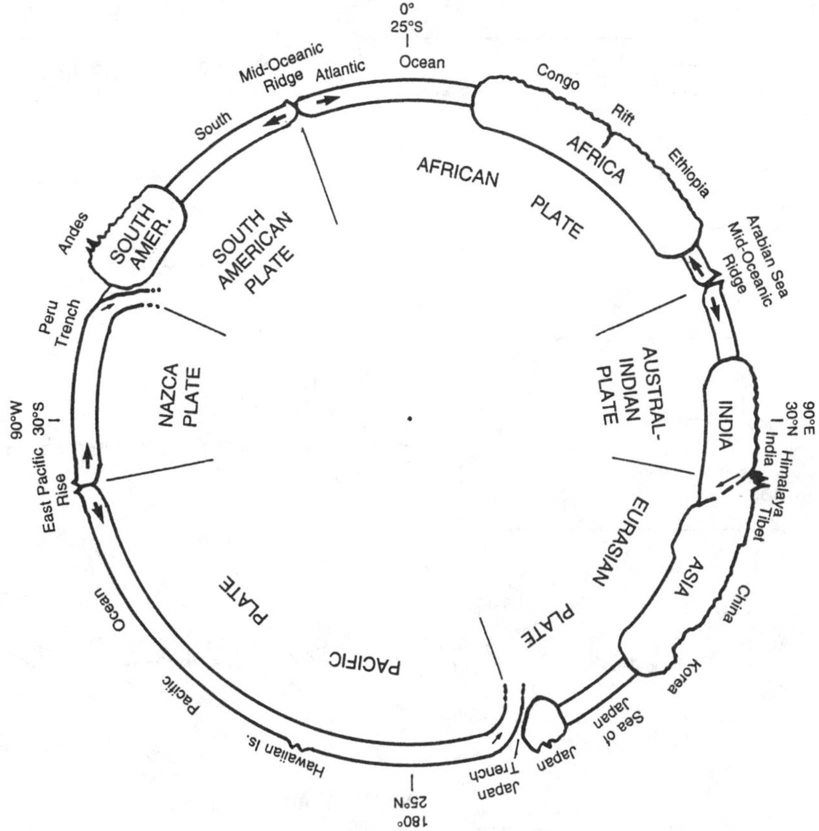

Figure 1.12 Schematic circular cross section of the major plates on a great circle tilted about 30 degrees with respect to the equator. (Drawn by A.N. Strahler. Copyright © 1992 by John Wiley & Sons, Inc. Reprinted by permission of the publisher.)

the American plate is a convergent boundary with active subduction extending from Alaska to northern California and from Central America to southernmost South America. Two sections of transform boundary are also shown: one off the British Columbia coast; the other is the San Andreas fault zone of California. Some geolgists distinguish a North American plate from a South American plate, with the boundary running east-west at about latitude 15°N. That boundary does not, however, appear to be tectonically active and is perhaps an arbitrary line.

The Eurasian plate is largely continental lithosphere, but is fringed on the west, north, and east by belts of oceanic lithosphere. The African plate can be visualized as having a central core of continental lithosphere nearly surrounded by oceanic lithosphere. The Austral-Indian plate (also called the Australian plate) takes the form of an elongate rectangle. It is mostly oceanic lithosphere, but contains two cores of continental lithosphere—Australia and peninsular India. The Antarctic plate has an elliptical outline and is almost completely enclosed by a spreading boundary. The continent of Antarctica forms a central core of continental lithosphere completely surrounded by oceanic lithosphere.

Of the remaining six major plates, the Nazca and Cocos plates of the eastern Pacific are rather simple fragments of oceanic lithosphere bounded by the Pacific mid-oceanic ridge, a spreading boundary, on the west and by a convergent boundary on the east. The Philippine plate is noteworthy as having convergent boundaries on both eastern and western edges. The Arabian plate resembles the "sunroof" model shown in Figure 1.10; it has two transform boundaries and its relative motion is northeasterly. The Caribbean plate also has important transform boundaries on its parallel sides. The tiny Juan de Fuca plate is steadily diminishing in size and will eventually disappear by subduction beneath the American plate. Geologists recognize one or more subplates within certain of the major plates. A *subplate* is a plate of secondary importance set apart from the main plate by a boundary that is uncertain or questionable, either as to its true nature or the level of its activity. An example is the Somalian subplate of the African plate. It is bounded by the East African Rift Valley system and there is good reason to think that this portion of the African plate is beginning to split off and move northeast and will eventually become an independent plate.

1.8 Stages of Ocean-Basin Opening and Closing —The Wilson Cycle

With an overview of plate boundaries and relative motions now in hand, along with a general sketch of the global plate system, it is

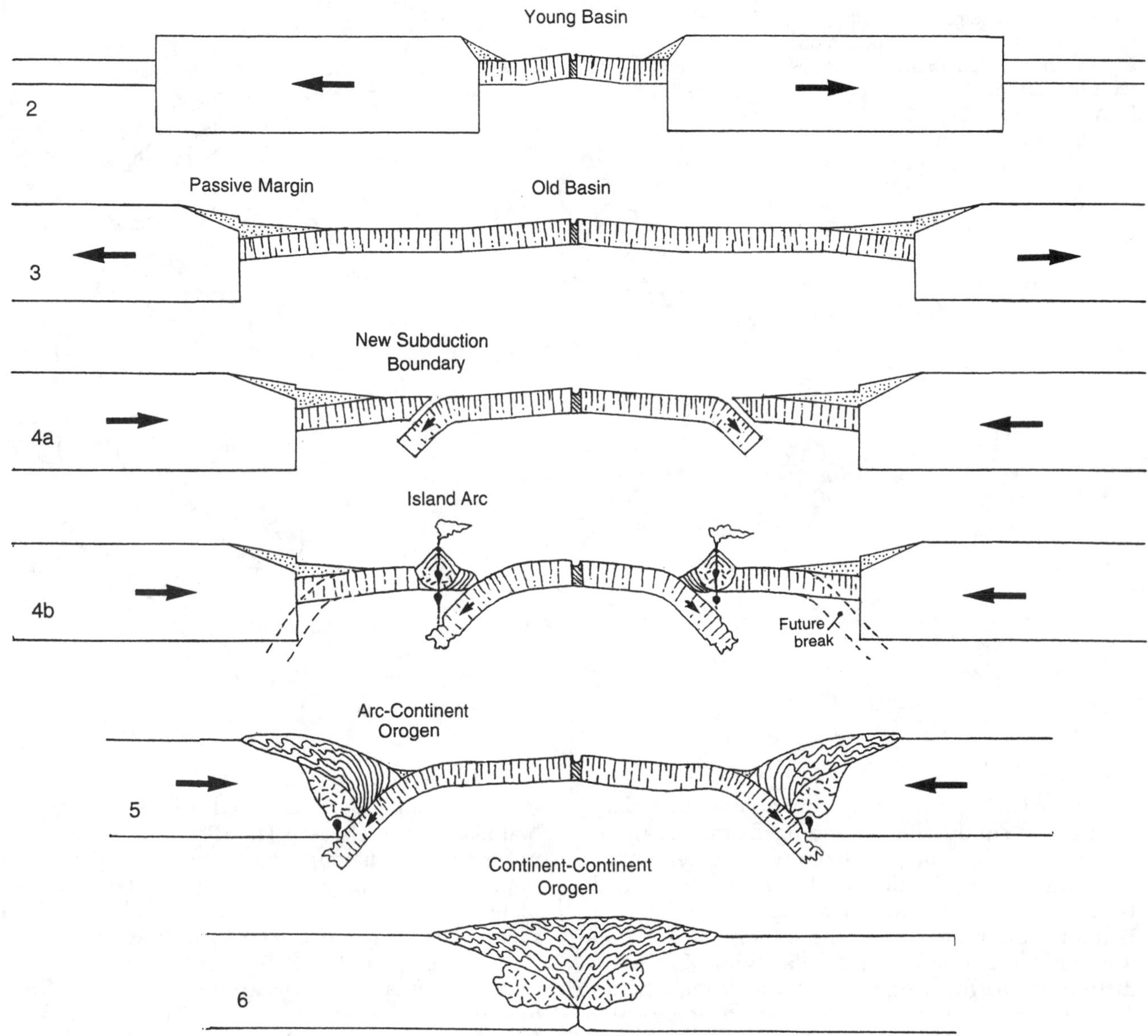

Figure 1.13 Schematic diagrams using iconic graphics to depict stages in the Wilson cycle of opening and closing of an ocean basin. The ocean surface not shown. Stage 1: Continental rifting begins, forming a rift valley that is the embryonic ocean basin. Stage 2: Early stage; a narrow ocean gulf. Stage 3: Late stage, a wide ocean basin with passive continental margins on both sides. Stage 4a: Closing is initiated by the formation of new subduction boundaries in the oceanic lithosphere. Stage 4b: Volcanic island arcs are built adjacent to subduction boundaries. Stage 5: Island-arc collision. New subduction boundary at continental margin allows island arc to collide with continent, producing an orogen. Stage 6: Continental collision produces an orogen above a suture, ending the cycle. (Drawn by A.N. Strahler. Interpreted from descriptions in J.A. Jacobs, R.D. Russell, and J.T. Wilson, *Physics and Geology*, 2nd ed., 1974, Chapter 15, The life cycle of ocean basins, McGraw-Hill, New York, p. 397-470.)

appropriate to put things together into a unified description of the whole dynamic plan of plate tectonics. We do this through the concept that continental lithosphere is rifted apart to form a new, widening ocean basin; that the widening process is halted and then reversed to a narrowing and closing of that basin, ultimately bringing the separated masses of continental lithosphere back into union as a single plate. As the opening and closing of the ocean basin takes place, however, other kinds of tectonic and volcanic activity intervene to create complex new belts of deformed rock called *orogens*, so that the final product is enormously more complex than what existed at the start.

Recognition of this grand cycle of tectonic events bears the name of a distinguished Canadian geologist and geophysicist who first recognized and described the tectonic cycle: Professor J. Tuzo Wilson. In his honor, the full cycle of opening and closing of ocean basins has been named the *Wilson cycle*.

With suitable modifications to bring the original Wilson cycle up to date, the six stages of the cycle are as follows: (Refer to Figure 1.13.)

Stage 1: Rift-valley system, the embryonic stage in continental rifting. Example: the East African rift-valley system.

Stage 2: Narrow ocean gulf, the formation of a young ocean basin. Example: the Gulf of Aden.

Stage 3: Wide ocean basin, fully developed and mature. Example: the Atlantic Ocean basin between Europe and North America. Continental margins in this stage have developed thick accumulations of sediment.

Stage 4a: Beginning of ocean-basin closing with shrinking ocean basin. Example: the Pacific Ocean basin.

Stage 4b: During this stage, initiation of new subduction boundaries entirely within the area of oceanic crust is accompanied by the growth of *volcanic island arcs* (long chains of andesitic volcanoes).

Stage 5: Further closing results in collisions of island arcs with continents, creating orogens that constitute new continental crust. Ocean basin continues to narrow in the late stage of ocean-basin closing. Example: the Mediterranean basin.

Stage 6: Ocean basin closing is complete. Continental collision and terminal orogen completed. Example: the Himalayan arc and Tibetan Plateau.

We next present brief descriptions of the major sedimentary accumulations and orogens produced during the Wilson cycle.

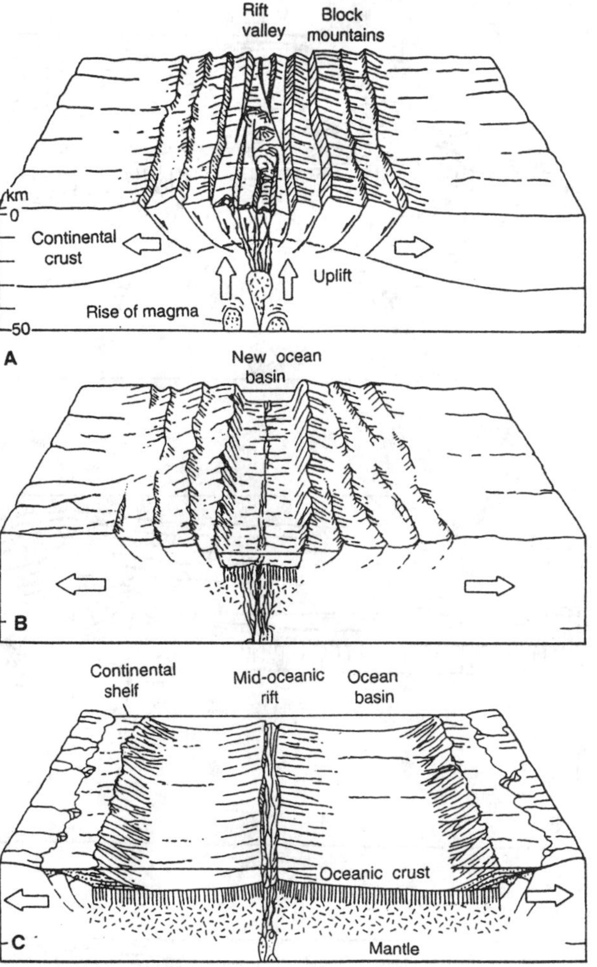

Figure 1.14 Schematic block diagrams showing stages in continental rupture and the opening up of a new ocean basin. The vertical scale is greatly exaggerated to emphasize surface features. (A) The crust is uplifted and stretched apart, causing it to break into blocks that become tilted on faults. (B) A narrow ocean is formed, floored by new oceanic crust. (C) The ocean basin widens, while the stable continental margins subside and receive sediments from the continents. (© A.N. Strahler.)

1.9 Continental Rupture and New Ocean Basins

Stage 1 of the Wilson cycle provides for a most remarkable geologic event—a *continental rupture*, the splitting apart of a plate composed of continental lithosphere. When this occurs, an entire continent is divided into two parts, which begin to separate, as shown in Figure 1.14. First, the underlying mantle is domed up, so that the overlying continental crust is stretched and thinned. As this change occurs, there appears a long narrow valley, called a *rift valley* (Block A). Crustal blocks slip down along a succession of steep normal faults, creating a mountainous landscape. Mafic magma rises in the domed uplift and appears locally within the rift valley to form isolated volcanoes and lava flows.

As separation continues, a narrow ocean appears; down its center runs a spreading plate boundary (Block B). The widening gap in its center is continually filled in with mafic magma rising from the mantle below. The magma solidifies to form new basaltic/gabbroic crust. Plate accretion thus takes place to produce a new ocean basin.

The Red Sea is an example of a young, narrow ocean formed by continental rupture. Its straight, steep coasts are features we would expect after such deformation. The widening of the ocean basin can continue until a large ocean has formed and the continents are widely separated (Block C).

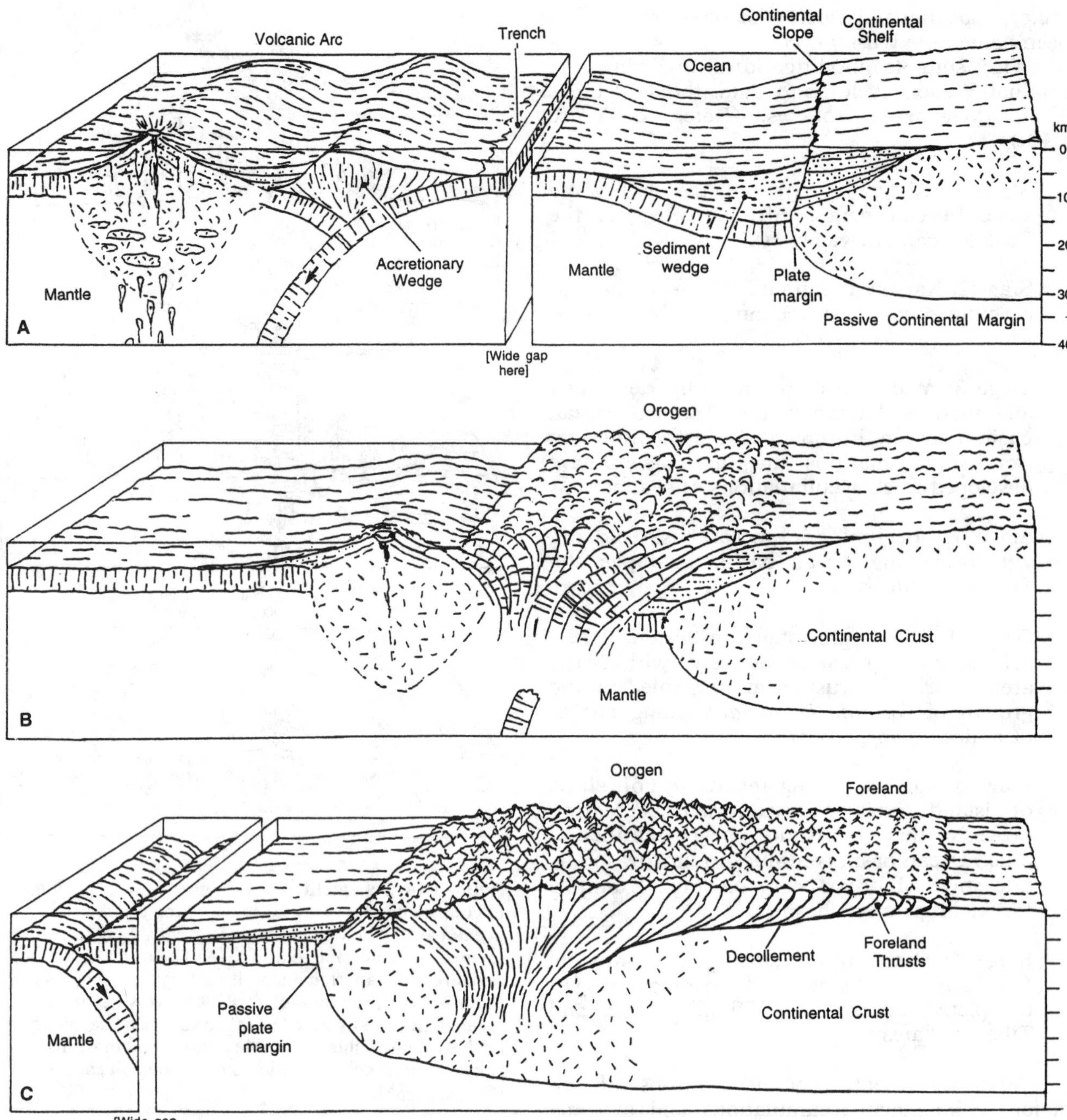

Figure 1.15 Schematic block diagrams showing stages in the formation of an arc-continent collision. (A) (right) Sediment wedges have been deposited in a long period of stability during which the crust has undergone sinking to a lower level. At left, a volcanic island arc. (B) Collision of arc with continent has begun, causing severe tectonic modification of the sediment wedges. (C) Collision completed, forming a great orogen with a thrust sheet extending far into the continent. (© A.N. Strahler.)

1.10 Passive Margins and Their Sediment Wedges

As an ocean basin widens and the oceanic lithosphere travels farther away from the axial spreading boundary, the cooler it becomes. Cooling is accompanied by an increase in rock density, so that the lithosphere slowly sinks to a lower level and the ocean basin correspondingly deepens. While this is going on, sediment derived from the continent is arriving at the coast, from which it is swept into deeper water. The right-hand half of Figure 1.15 shows some details of the sedimentary deposits that have accumulated many tens of millions of years after the new ocean basin began to develop. On the continental margin there has formed a sediment wedge, the surface of which is a continental shelf. At the outer brink of the shelf lies the steep continental slope. Turbidity currents carry shelf sediment down that slope into water of abyssal depths, where it accumulates as a second type of sediment wedge that thins in the direction away from the continent.

This type of continental margin is called a *passive margin*. Slow crustal subsidence continues as the sediment wedges thicken. At the present time, thick sediment wedges border the passive margins that characterize the eastern and western sides of the Atlantic Ocean basin.

1.11 The Development of Volcanic Island Arcs

Stage 4 in the Wilson cycle initiates the closing of the mature ocean basin. For this to happen, at least one new subduction plate boundary is required, and a second may also develop, as shown in Figure 1.13. A deep trench appears and subduction now swallows up oceanic lithosphere, enabling the continents to come closer together, even as spreading continues at the axial plate boundary.

With the passage of time a volcanic island chain begins to form adjacent to the trench. It is built of magma that rises to the surface, forming volcanoes with associated lava and ash accumulations. At the same time rising magma accretes to the underside of the plate by a process called *underplating*. Gradually, underplating forms a deep "keel" beneath the arc, which may undergo partial transformation into continental litho-sphere. A fully developed volcanic arc is shown in the left-hand half of Diagram A of Figure 1.15.

Accompanying the building of the island arc is the accumulation of sediment derived from the mountains of the arc and carried into the adjacent trench. This process is also illustrated in the left half of Diagram A of Figure 1.15. An important function of the subduction process is to develop an *accretionary wedge* (or *prism*) consisting of both terrestrial (continental) sediment and sea-floor sediment. In this case, the terrestrial sediment is derived by erosion from the arc volcanoes built high above sea level. The seafloor sediment, along with some protruding masses of oceanic basalt, is removed from the descending plate by *offscraping*. The accretionary wedge thus consists of severely deformed heterogeneous material. Deeper portions of the wedge are gradually converted into metamorphic rock.

1.12 Arc Continent Collisions

A typical next step in the Wilson cycle is that the volcanic island arc closes with the passive margin, resulting in an *arc-continent collision* and producing an orogen. Diagram B of Figure 1.15 shows how this collision begins. We have depicted an early stage in which the accretionary wedge has been brought under severe compressional tectonic force, causing it to be sliced into slabs separated on high-angle overthrust faults, formed into a fanlike arrangement. This deformed mass is the *orogen*.

Diagram C of Figure 1.15 shows an advanced stage of the arc-continent collision and the orogen it has produced. The orogen is now belt of high, alpine mountains. As it is elevated, erosion by streams and glaciers keeps removing the upper parts of the folds.

In the farthest inland zone, or *foreland*, of the orogen we may find a region of *foreland thrusts*, which make up a comparatively thin thrust sheet. This sheet rides far inland—often many tens of kilometers—on a low-angle thrust fault, or *décollement*. At great depth in the orogen, rocks of the volcanic arc and its accretionary wedge are even more severely deformed, and are converted into metamorphic rock.

The newly-formed continental crust now includes the entire former volcanic arc, so that the new passive margin of the continent lies on what was the outer side of the arc. Here, sediment deposition over the floor of the adjacent oceanic crust is building a new continental shelf. Because the oceanic plate is continuing to push against the extended continent, it develops a new subduction boundary, shown at the far left of Diagram C.

Examples of the arc-continent collision orogen can be found in both eastern and western North America. The relationships shown in Figure 1.15 are patterned in a general way after Paleozoic arc-continent collisions that affected the Appalachian and Ouachita mountain belts (Chapter 9). Another and much more recent example is the Cordilleran Orogeny that (as the name indicates) built the Cordilleran ranges of western North America (Chapter 9). For this reason, the arc-continent collision product is sometimes referred to as a "Cordilleran-type" orogen.

1.13 Continent-Continent Collisions

The final event (Stage 6) of the Wilson cycle sees the two masses of continental lithosphere close in a great *continent-continent collision* that eliminates any intervening oceanic lithosphere and is finalized in a permanent bonding structure, called a *continental suture*. Steps in achieving this terminal orogen are shown in Figure 1.16. Note that the scenario shown here could be accomplished without any prior occurrence of an arc-continent collision. All that is necessary is that a subduction boundary develop closely adjacent to one of the two opposed passive continental margins. Closing brings the sediment wedges of the passive margin (shown at the right in blocks A and B of Figure 1.16) into orogenic contact with the accretionary prism of the opposing continental

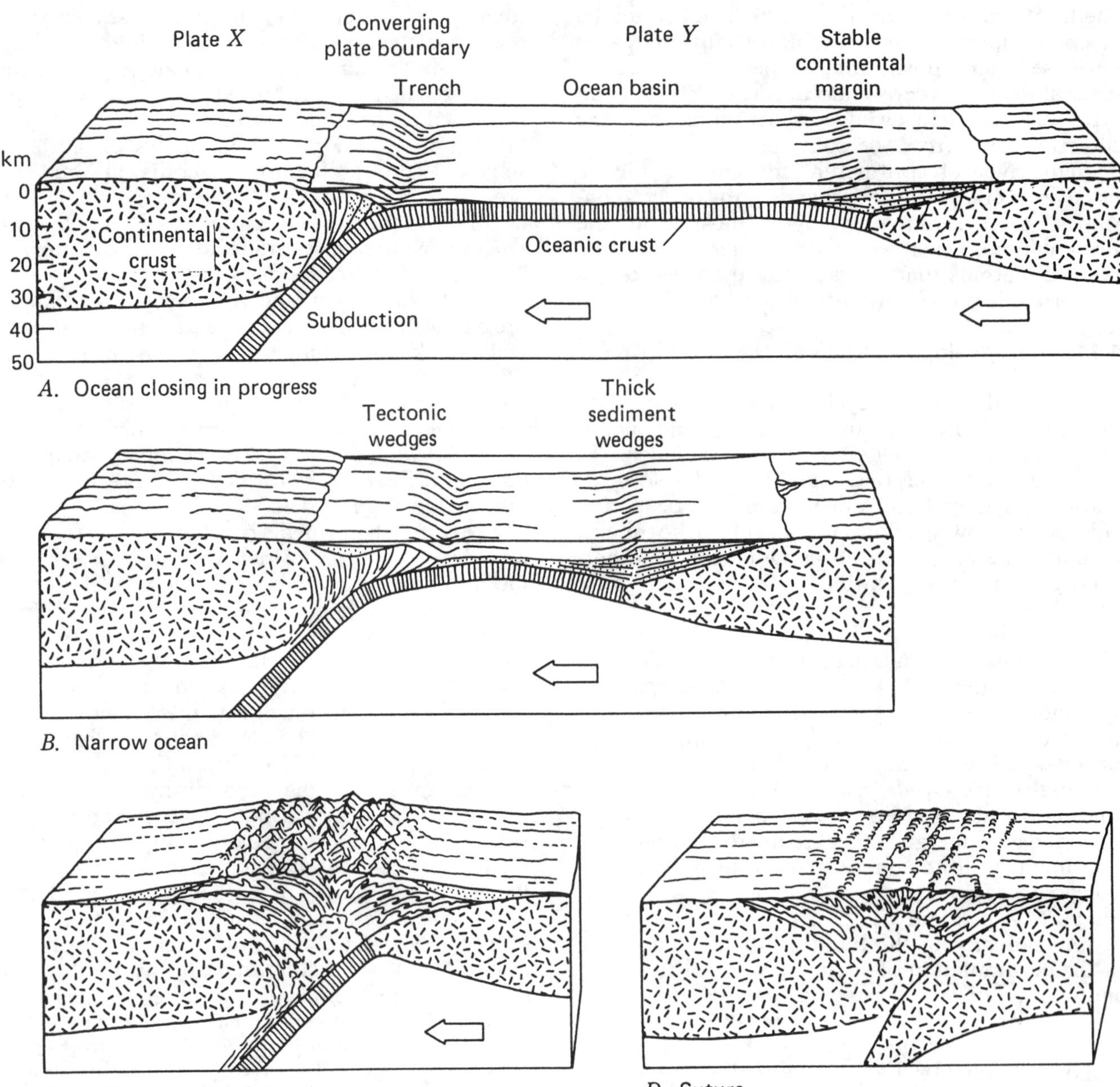

Figure 1.16 Four stages in the collision of two lithospheric plates, starting with closing of an ocean basin and ending in an orogeny that represents a suture between the plates. The vertical scale of these diagrams is greatly exaggerated to emphasize surface features and the difference in thickness between continental crust and oceanic crust. (© A.N. Strahler.)

plate. Intense telescoping ensues, and great piles of thrust sheets can accumulate. Metamorphism occurs on a large scale, and igneous intrusion leads to formation of deep-seated batholiths.

A striking example of a collision orogen and its recently completed suture is the Himalayan-Hindu Kush mountain arc bordering the Indian subcontinent on the north. The deep roots of a few ancient continental sutures can be found today in the interiors of continental shields. One example often cited is the Ural Mountains, a north-south range that serves today as the arbitrary line of geographical demarcation between Europe and Asia. Although sutures are comparatively stable through most of later geologic time, they can be intersected by newer continental rifts that start a new Wilson cycle (see Chapter 11).

1.14 Relative Ages of Continents and Ocean Basins

Our final reference to plate tectonics in this brief introductory overview concerns a deeply significant concept in the interpretation of the history of our planet. We have seen that new oceanic lithosphere is simultaneously being consumed in converging plate boundaries. If so, oceanic lithosphere cannot be very old, measured in terms of the duration of geologic history. In contrast, the patches of continental lithosphere are remarkably enduring, because they are thick, buoyant masses that do not easily undergo subduction. Once formed, continental lithosphere tends to remain, and much of that lithosphere must be very old indeed.

As one collision after another formed new orogens of metamorphic and igneous rock, the continental lithosphere must have grown in areal extent. This would mean, of course, that the continents themselves have increased in total global area, through much geologic time (Chapter 13). We will find convincing evidence that most of the continental crust, which is the uppermost layer of the continental lithosphere, is of great geologic age. Much of it is from 1 to 2½ billion years old, i.e., of Proterozoic age. Some relatively small areas of continental crust are dated as having been formed in the Archean Eon, with ages as old as 3 billion years. In contrast, rock of the ocean floor formed in spreading boundaries has proved to be quite young geologically—nowhere is it older than about 230 million years.

1.15 A World Continent and Its Breaking Apart

Because continental lithosphere and the crust it bears is so long enduring, the continents hold an extremely long and complex geologic history. A typical large continent such as North America is made up of core areas of Precambrian rock that are arranged so as to suggest that several individual small continents came together in collisions to form a single larger continent (Chapter 13). Evidence found in only the last decade or two has supported the hypothesis that there have been several times when all continents, large and small, came together to form a single *supercontinent*, surrounded by a single world-ocean. Following its completion, each supercontinent became unstable because of the overheating of the mantle beneath it. That heating caused a broad doming of the lithosphere, leading to its developing great tensional fractures that steadily widened. Called *continental rifting*, this process gave rise to a number of smaller continents, separated from each other by new oceans floored by young oceanic crust. Of course, this entire process fits into stages of the Wilson cycle as described in earlier paragraphs. We have simply introduced here an added breadth dimension to what was previously illustrated by cross-sections.

Figure 1.17 shows schematically the supercontinent cycle as a closed circuit with three phases. We can begin with an intact supercontinent. There follows a dispersal phase in which the supercontinent comes apart largely along boundaries of the more ancient continents that had previously come together. During dispersal, the individual continents may rotate, and they will receive new arc-continent collisions that will add to their extent. The next phase is one of convergence, in which the continents come together again. Many continent-continent collis-ions occur to weld them all together into another supercontinent. Given, say, 3 Ga (Middle Archean) as the first occurrence of a fully developed supercontinent, there could have been some 6 to 10 such cycles.

The very latest supercontinent that existed is clearly defined by many lines of supporting evidence. The name given to that supercontinent is *Pangea*; to the world-ocean surrounding it, *Panthalassa*. Long before plate tectonics emerged as a dominant theory, Pangea had been reconstructed by geologists and geophysicists who brought together several lines of evidence, including structural geology, paleontology, biogeography, and glacial geology. The development of this concept in the early 1900s is fully presented in Chapter 2 and carried into the plate-tectonics period of the mid-1900s in Chapter 13. In Figure 1.18, we offer a set of global maps published in 1970 by two prominent pioneers of plate tectonics, Robert S. Dietz and John C. Holden. Their maps show Pangea intact in Permian time, its breaking apart through the Mesozoic and Cenozoic eras. Pangea itself had been formed by the joining of two previously completed supercontinents, named Gondwana and Laurasia.

Many minor changes have since made in this early scenario, but its basic validity remains intact. We now live in a time of widespread plate motions in various directions, and these are continuing to separate continents in one part of the globe, while elsewhere bringing continents closer together.

1.16 The Plate Tectonic System

The system of lithospheric plates in motion represents an enormous material flow system powered by an internal energy-flow system. The scheme of the cycling of mineral matter is fairly well understood in a general way, although many details remain speculative.

Figure 1.19 is a schematic diagram or cartoon (not to scale) showing some of the major features of the material flow system. Diagram A shows how a plate of oceanic lithosphere undergoing subduction transfers matter to the margin of the continental lithosphere by volcanic and tectonic processes. Magma formed by melting of the upper surface of the plate rises to penetrate the continental lithosphere and is added to the continental crust in the form of igneous plutons and extrusive masses (volcanoes and lava flows). Offscraping of the upper surface of the subducting plate contributes to the growth

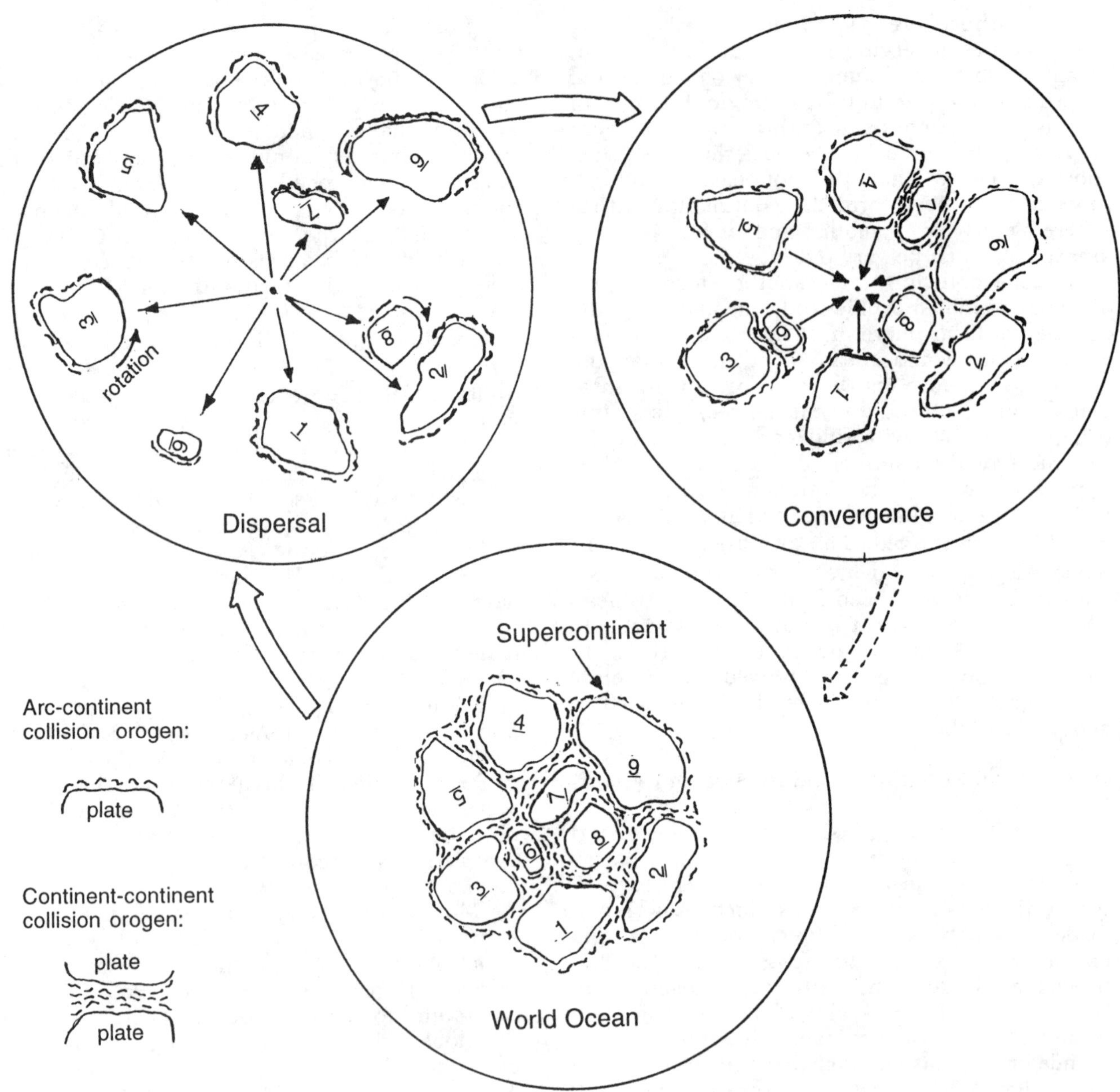

Figure 1.17 Schematic diagram of the supercontinent cycle, shown in three phases. (© A.N. Strahler.)

of the accretionary prism which becomes a permanent addition to the continental crust as metamorphic rock.

The downgoing plate is softened by heating and is eventually reabsorbed into the asthenosphere or deeper mantle. Slow convection currents deep within the asthenosphere, shown here as moving in a direction generally opposite to the plate motion, return the enriched mantle rock to the spreading plate boundaries, but other flow paths may be followed.

Diagram B of Figure 1.19 shows that under certain conditions the dragging action of the downgoing plate tears loose blocks and slabs of the adjacent continental lithosphere. This material is carried down into the asthenosphere. Thus by *tectonic erosion* some felsic rock of the continental crust can enter the mantle and be recycled.

The energy system that causes plate motions is generally agreed to have a source in the phenomenon of radioactivity. Radioactive elements in the crust and upper mantle constantly give off heat. This is a process of transformation of matter into energy. As the temperature of mantle rock increases, the rock expands. Upward motions of less dense material may take place within the convection systems. It is thought that mantle rock is rising steadily beneath the spreading plate boundaries. How this rise of heated rock causes plates to move is not well understood, but one hypothesis states

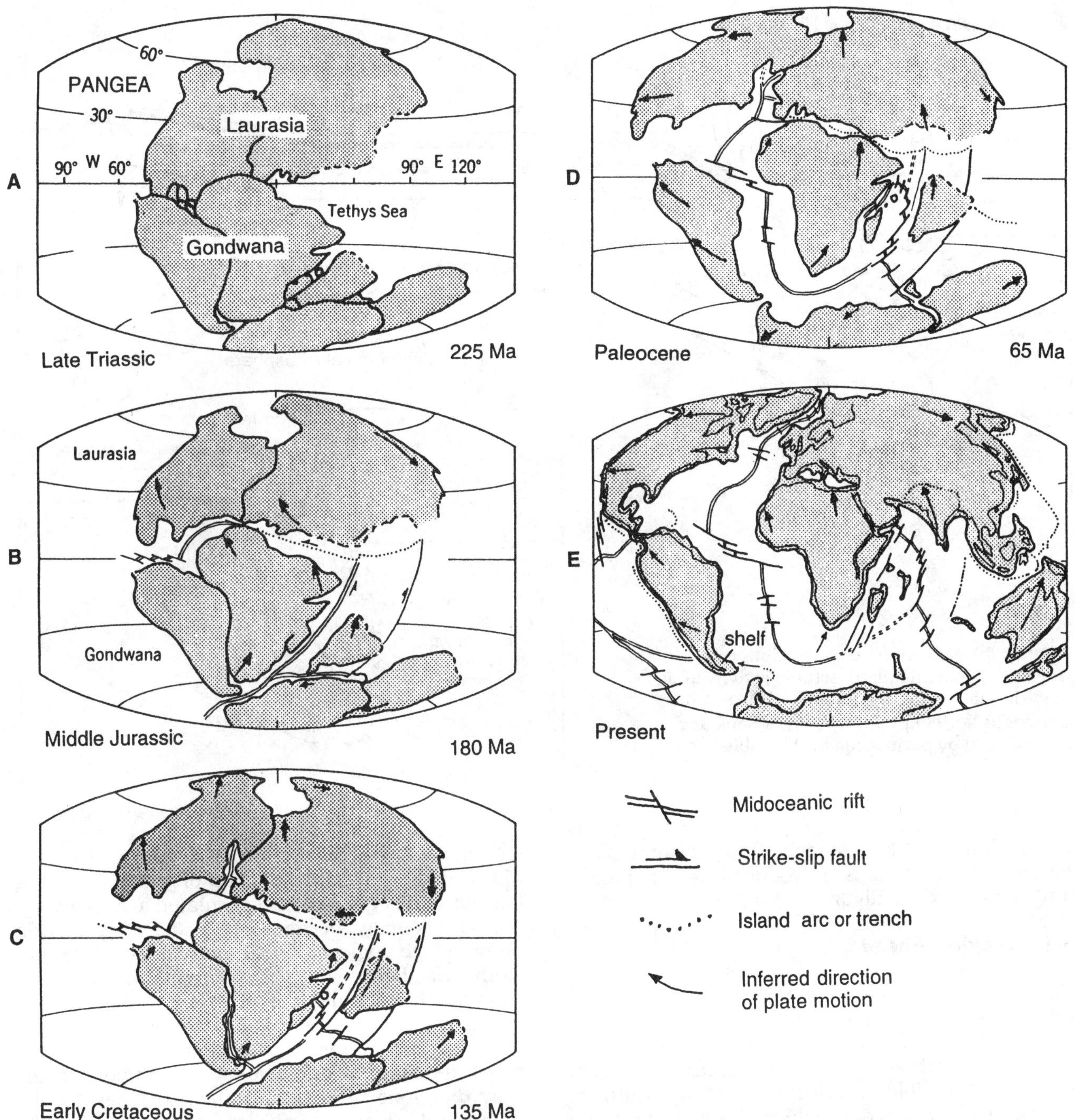

Figure 1.18 Five stages in the breakup of Pangea to form the modern continents. Arrows indicate the directions of motion of the lithospheric plates. The continents are delimited by the 1800-m submarine contour in order to show the true extent of continental lithosphere. (Redrawn and simplified from maps by R.S. Dietz and J.C.Holden, 1970, *Journal of Geophysical Research*, v. 75, p, 4943-4951, Figures 2-6. Copyright © by the American Geophysical Union.)

that as the lithospheric plate is lifted to a higher elevation above the rising mantle it tends to move horizontally away from the spreading axis under the influence of gravity. At the opposite edge of the plate, subduction goes on because the oceanic plate is denser than the asthenosphere through which it is sinking. Motion of the plate exerts a drag on the underlying asthenosphere, setting in motion flow currents in the upper mantle. Thus slow convection currents probably exist in the asthenosphere beneath the moving plates, and may also be present in deeper zones of the mantle. Recent seismic data analysis, known as seismic tomography, is revealing both horizontal and vertical motions within the deep mantle.

[A complete systems analysis of plate tectonics includes an energy-flow system cor-

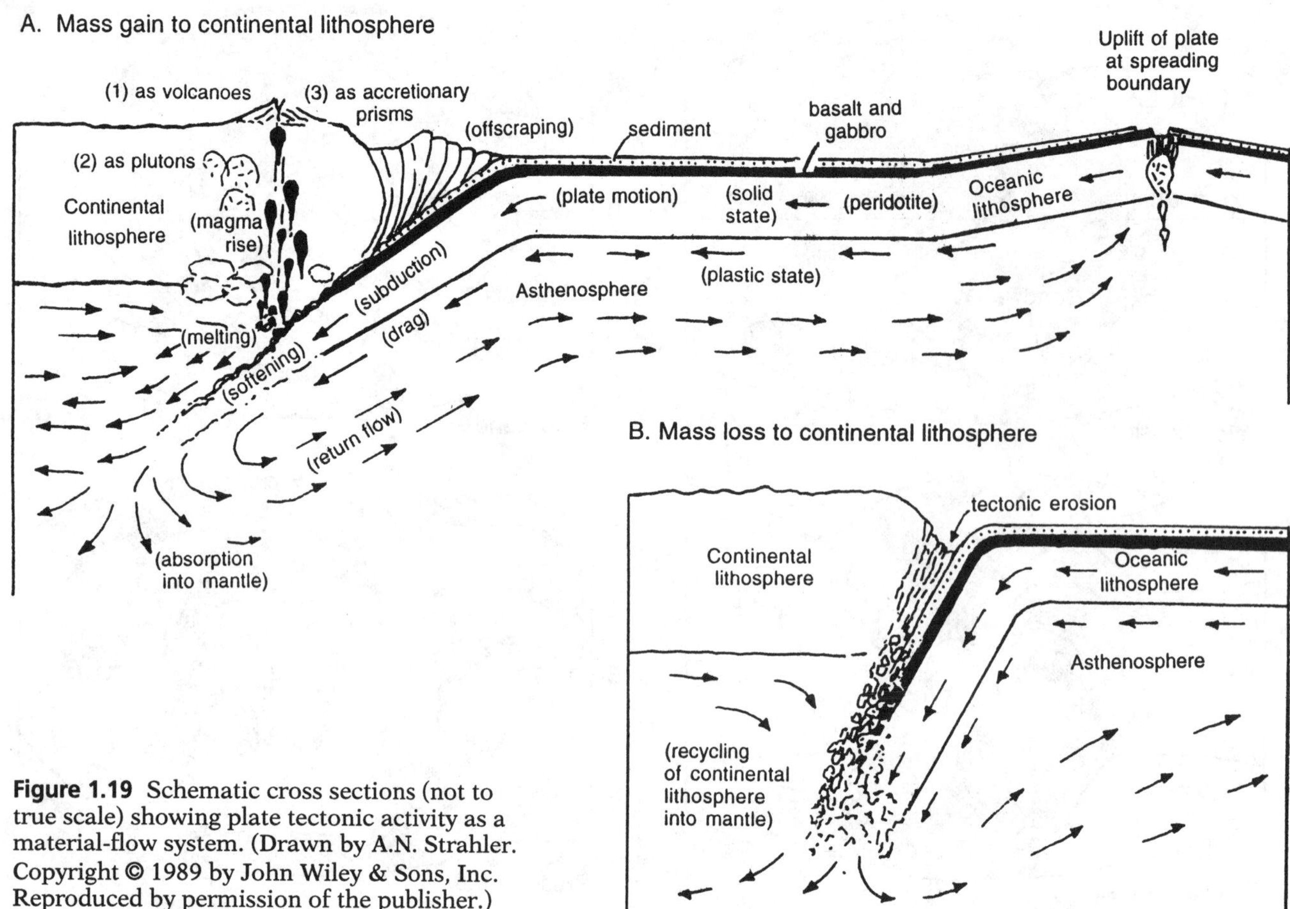

Figure 1.19 Schematic cross sections (not to true scale) showing plate tectonic activity as a material-flow system. (Drawn by A.N. Strahler. Copyright © 1989 by John Wiley & Sons, Inc. Reproduced by permission of the publisher.)

responding to the material-flow system. The energy-flow system is introduced in Chapter 5 and illustrated in Figure 5.44.]

1.11 Looking Ahead

Throughout the later chapters of this book we will develop the many detailed features of what is so hastily skimmed over in this chapter. Most important will be the full inclusion of direct geological field evidence and indirect geophysical evidence on which the plate tectonic theory rests.

First, however, we have inserted as Chapter 2 a historical review of what came before plate tectonics arrived with a bang in the mid-1950s. Many of the separate features of plate tectonics had been recognized or speculated upon over a period of many decades. Indeed, many strong points of geologic evidence had already been put forth in favor of the rifting of a great supercontinent and the drifting apart of its fragments over a time span of some 200 million years. Who were these researchers who had some novel ideas and strong evidence to support them? Why did none of them hit upon the key to the theory of plate tectonics, which was the phenomenon of plate subduction, even though it seemed almost to have been "staring them in the face," so to speak?

SUPPLEMENTRARY REFERENCES

The Emergence of Plate Tectonics as a Science:

Hallam, A., 1973, *A Revolution in the Earth Sciences: From Continental Drift to Plate Tectonics*. Oxford: Clarendon Press.

LeGrand, H.E., 1988, *Drifting Continents and Shifting Theories*. Cambridge, UK: Cambridge Univ. Press.

Marvin, Ursula B., 1973, *Continental Drift: The Evolution of a Concept*. Washington, D.C.: Smithsonian Institution Press.

Schwartzbach, Martin, 1985, *Alfred Wegener: The Father of Continental Drift*. Madison, WI,: Science Tech, Inc.

Sullivan, Walter, 1974, *Continents in Motion: The New Earth Debate*. New York: McGraw-Hill Book Co.

Takeuchi, H., S. Uyeda, and H. Kanamori, 1970, *Debate About the Earth: Approach to Geophysics Through Analysis of Continental Drift*., Rev. Ed., San Francisco: Freeman, Cooper & Co.

Wood, Robert Muir, 1985, *The Dark Side of the Earth*. London: Allen & Unwin.

College-Level Texbooks Featuring Plate Tectonics:

Cox, Allan, and Robert Brian Hart, 1986, *Plate Tectonics: How It Works*. Palo Alto, CA: Blackwell Scientific Publications.

Holmes, Arthur, 1978, *Holmes Principles of Physical Geology*. Third Edition, revised by Doris L. Holmes. New York: John Wiley & Sons.

Kearey, Philip, and Frederick J. Vine, 1990. *Global Tectonics*. Oxford: Blackwell Scientific Publications.

Moores, Eldredge M., and Robert J. Twiss, 1995, *Tectonics*, New York: W. H. Freeman and Company.

Seyfert, Carl K., and Leslie A. Sirkin, 1979, *Earth History and Plate Tectonics*, 2nd Ed. New York: Harper & Row.

Strahler, Arthur N., 1981, *Physical Geology*. New York: Harper & Row.

Wilson, J. Tuzo, Ed., 1970, *Continents Adrift: Readings from the Scientific American*. San Francisco: W.H. Freeman and Company.

Windley, Brian F., 1984, *The Evolving Continents*, 2nd. Ed. New York: John Wiley & Sons.

Chapter: 2 Continental Drift—Precursor of Plate Tectonics

Although modern plate tectonics achieved wide acceptance by the world scientific community within only the past three decades, the concept of breakup of an early supercontinent into two or more fragments, which moved apart to form the modern continents, is many decades old. In this chapter, we review the history of that concept with emphasis on the period 1900-1950, leaving many details of the dramatic breakthrough to the modern paradigm in the two decades 1950-1970 to appropriate places in later chapters.

2.1 Earliest Notions of Former Continental Union

Some historians of geology have cited Francis Bacon (1561-1626) as the earliest writer to suggest a former union of continents. By the year 1620, when Bacon's *Novum Organum* appeared, world maps had became sufficiently accurate to reveal a rough similarity in the outlines of continents on opposite sides of the Atlantic. The possibility of a good fit of these coastlines can be easily seen in Diego Ribera's chart of 1529. In Bacon's time, world charts such as those of Nicholas Sanson depicted these opposing coastlines with remarkable detail (Raisz, 1948, p. 23-29). A. Hallam comments that Bacon "merely pointed out a general conformity of outline of the two continents, both of which tapered southwards, and a certain similarity between the Pacific coast of South America and the Atlantic coast of Africa" (1973, p. 1). Faul and Faul (1983, p. 225) note that Bacon suggested that North and South America may represent remnants of the mythical "lost continent" Atlantis.

Also mentioned as a writer who recognized the former unity of the continents is Father Francois Placet. In his 1668 booklet, titled *La Corruption du Grand et Petit Monde*, the Atlantic Ocean basin is attributed to the catastrophic Flood of Noah, either by downsinking of the intervening landmass (which may have been Atlantis) or an emergence of the American landmass (Faul and Faul, 1983, p. 225). Compte de Buffon offered a similar speculation about 1750, citing as evidence "the similarity of fossils in Ireland and America" (Faul and Faul, 1983, p. 225). Hallam mentions Alexander von Humboldt as having speculated (in the mid-1800s) that the Atlantic basin "was nothing more than a huge valley scooped out by the sea" (1973. p. 1).

Another possible contender for the earliest mention of the former connection of the African continent with South America, followed by their separation, was a German theologian, Theodore Christoph Lilienthal. His text was written in 1756 (Romm, 1994, p. 407). But even this early account was preceded by one published in 1598 by Abraham Ortelius, a prominent cartographer of his time. Details of his document have been reviewed by James Romm in a 1994 article in *Nature*. Ortelius noted that the separation required a "dislocation," rather than the downsinking of a "lost" continent of Atlantis.

2.2 A Fixist View of the Earth's Crust

During the middle 1800s mainstream geologists came to affirm as a geological doctrine what might be called a "fixist view" of the history of the earth's crust. Stated in specific terms, this doctrine held that since the beginning of geologic time ocean basins and continents have retained their identity, i.e., that they have been permanently fixed features. The permanence of ocean basins and continents excludes the possibility that continental crust could have foundered to become oceanic crust or that oceanic crust might have been bodily upraised to form continental crust. The principle of permanence of the ocean basins and continents was strongly advocated by James Dwight Dana (1813-1895).He had become professor of geology at Yale University following his participation in the Wilkes scientific expedition to the Antarctic (1838-1852). As editor of the *American Journal of Science* and author of standard manuals of mineralogy and geology, Dana's influence was powerful among the English-speaking geologists of his time. Dana's ideas have been reviewed by Ursula B. Marvin (1973, p. 38-40). The permanence (fixist) principle went hand-in-hand with the view that the earth cooled from a molten state and that during the cooling process, contraction of the planet took place. Cooling and contraction proceeded unevenly over the earth's surface. Areas that cooled first became the elevated continents; areas that cooled more slowly formed depressions and became the ocean basins. The total scenario might then be described as a "contractionist/fixist" view. Marvin reduces Dana's doctrine of permanence to a slogan: "Once a continent, always a continent; once a basin, always a basin" (1973, p. 39). Later, the doctrine was strongly voiced by Professor Bailey Willis of Stanford University, a leader in tectonic and structural geology through the late 1800s and early 1900s. It was to persist into the 1950s, in spite of competition from the "mobilists" and their hypotheses of vast horizontal motions of continents relative to one another and to ocean basins.

All was not easy going for the contractionist/fixist school, and it was placed under

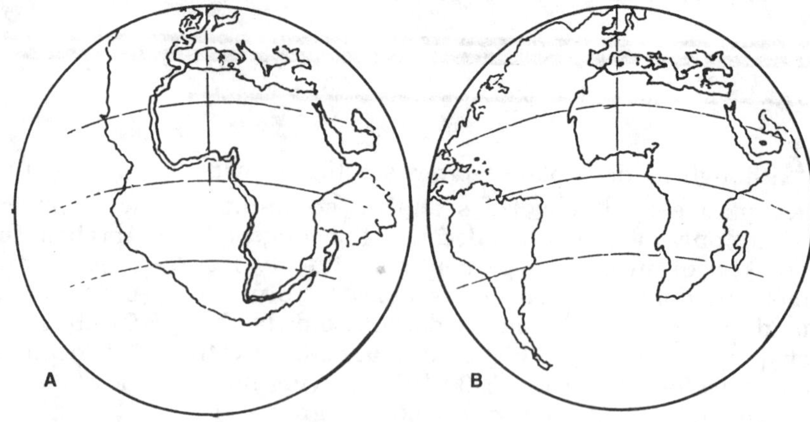

Figure 2.1 Antonio Snider's global maps of 1858 show (A) the continents united in the period between Creation and the Flood of Noah and (B) separation that occurred during that one-year flood. (Courtesy of the Smithsonian Institution Press.)

suspicion even by some of those who supported it. The problem lay in the inadequacy of uniform global contraction to generate horizontal compressional forces in the crust needed to produce great systems of overthrust sheets and nappes. Marvin writes: "Dana himself was less than satisfied with this aspect of his hypothesis. In 1864 he said that he had adopted the concept that contraction was due to cooling because no other force at all adequate had been suggested" (1973, p. 39).

2.3 Nineteenth Century Speculations on Continental Separation

The first specific mention of drifting apart of the continents may have been made in 1857 by Richard Owen, a professor at the University of Indiana, in his book titled *Key to the Geology of the Globe*. A physician as well as a professor of geology and chemistry, Owen was attempting to interpret earth structure according to forces and laws analogous those that governed organic development (Marvin, 1973, p. 40). Using as his planetary model a tetrahedron, of which one face was initially occupied by a single continent, Owen postulated its catastrophic disruption and the separation of the continental fragments, with ocean basins occupying the intervening spaces. (Details are given by Marvin, 1973, p. 40-42.) Faul and Faul describe this work as "obscurely-written," in the context of "a grand and slightly mystical scheme of nature" (1983, p. 225). Perhaps for that reason it should not be taken as a genuinely scientific working hypothesis.

Some historians find the first serious mention of continental separation in a work published in France in 1858 by Antonio Snider-Pellegrini, an American who held the biblical catastrophist view of earth history (Hallam, 1973, p. 2; Marvin, 1973, p. 42-43). Snider's map, showing a landmass labeled "Atlantide" closely fitted to the coastline of Europe and Africa, is reproduced here in simplified form as Figure 2.1A. Snider speculated that during the Flood of Noah the single continent was fractured and pulled apart, separating the Americas from the landmass of the Old World as shown in Figure 2.1B.

Continuing in chronological order, we come to another possible contributor to the concept of large-scale horizontal continental movement. He was Elisée Reclus, little known in English-speaking geological circles, but referred to by some Europeans as the "French Darwin" (Berkland, 1979, p. 189). Reclus accepted the great age of the earth and appears to have had a naturalistic view of earth history. According to Berkland, Reclus "presented evidence for a supercontinent and suggested that there had been connections between France and England, between Greece and Africa,..."and even Europe and America (p. 189). Reclus pointed out the similarities of Africa and South America in terms of their general structure and concluded that "we can not fail to see proof of unity of formation in the two continental masses" (Reclus, 1872, p. 59-60). Elsewhere, he wrote "the continents themselves...are changing places, and are slowly traveling around the circle of the globe" (p. 567). The impression from this and other passages quoted by Berkland is that the entire crust is in very slow zonal motion around the earth, accompanied by "an undulation in the so-called rigid crust of the globe." Separation, i.e., relative lateral movement of one continental unit with respect to another, is not spelled out in these quotations. Nevertheless, Berkland concludes: "It would seem appropriate that Reclus should be recognized in the history of the development of plate tectonic theory as one of its foremost pioneers and, perhaps, as its founder" (p. 192).

Another naturalistic hypothesis of continental separation, this one based on astronomy and physics, was put forward by the English clergyman Reverend Osmond Fisher. In a 1881 work, titled *Physics of the Earth's Crust*, he had postulated that the earth has a "relatively fluid interior...subject to convection currents rising beneath the oceans and falling beneath the continents" (as quoted by Faul and Faul, 1983, p. 226). For a mechanism of continental breakup and separation, Fisher turned to a then-popular hypothesis proposed in 1879 by Sir George Darwin, a leading authority on tidal phenomena, to the effect that the moon was formed by fission from the earth, its bulk derived from what is now the Pacific Ocean basin. In an 1882 article in *Nature*, Fisher proposed as a consequence of this catastrophic event that the subsequent rise of mafic magma into the deep scar would have fragmented the earth's granitic crust and induced the lateral movement of continent-sized fragments of cool granitic crust toward the scar (1882, p. 244). Note that the formation of the moon by fission is a one-shot event in geologic time; that circumstance rules out lateral continental motions at earlier and later times than the singular event, unless another and more general mechanism is postulated also to have operated. (Essentially the same scenario was offered by an American, W.H. Pickering, in 1907.)

In commenting on the Fisher hypothesis, Hallam calls attention to Fisher's "mobilist views" as being atypical of "what might be called the Anglo-American geophysical tradition in the late nineteenth and early twentieth centuries" (1973, p. 3). (He is referring to Dana's view of earth history we have described in earlier paragraphs.) In contrast, Hallam states, the mobilist tradition (crust floating on liquid interior, and hence capable of moving freely), "accorded better with the contemporary Germanic Tradition, which because of the language barrier was not well understood in the English-speaking world" (p. 3). (See also Faul and Faul, 1983, p. 226.) We will encounter this fundamental difference in viewpoints with its unfortunate prejudicial effects as we continue our historical review.

2.4 Edward P. Dutton on Isostasy

The principle of isostasy, well known to all first-year geology students, was destined from its inception to become a guiding concept in all matters of geophysics and tectonics. Archdeacon J.H. Pratt and the British astronomer G.B. Airy had published their papers on the Himalayan gravity problem and the "mountain-root theory" in 1855 (Heiskanen and Vening Meinesz, 1958, p. 126-129). It remained for the American geologist Clarence Edward Dutton (1841-1912) to coin the word "isostasy" and to apply the principle to the earth's figure and the fundamental distinction between continents and ocean basins. This he did in 1889 in a paper titled "On Some of the Greater Problems of Physical Geology." He showed that the principle of isostasy requires that the earth can be expected to have "a deformed figure, bulged where the matter is light and depressed where it is heavy." In this same work, Dutton suggested that although crustal units have different densities, there is an underlying zone within which viscous flow of rock takes place to maintain isostasy (Skinner, 1986, p. 74).

Application of the Airy model of isostasy to the whole earth and to the question of origin of continents and ocean basins fit neatly into Dana's fixist view and provided the supporting physical theory for the doctrine of permanence of continents and ocean basins. It was, however, later to deal a fatal blow to the notion of land bridges of continental crust having foundered to leave ocean basins—a notion that emerged and remained popular with the fixists in succeeding decades.

2.5 The Geological Contributions of Eduard Suess

As our narrative moves into the 1900s, we should stop to take note of the highly influential contributions of the Austrian geologist, Eduard Suess, whose five-volume treatise, *Das Antlitz der Erde* (The Face of the Earth), was published in the years 1904-24. Suess falls into the camp of the contractionists. Likened to a drying apple or prune, the cooling planet developed surface wrinkles that are seen in what we now recognize as the collision orogens. According to Suess, contraction also resulted in local uparching or updoming, which was accompanied by collapse of an arch into a system of fault blocks. Certain of these fault blocks would have remained elevated as horsts; others would have sunk as grabens. Fault-block sinking over very broad up-arched belts could also explain ocean basins. Thus global contraction could account for what we view today as compressional and extensional tectonic forms. Such "vertical tectonics" could also operate over large continental areas as negative and positive epeirogenic movements, resulting in transgressions and regressions of shallow seas. Suess also recognized eustatic changes of sealevel, governed by rising and sinking crustal motions and translocations of sediment.

Suess also discussed crustal evolution in terms of chemical layering. As magma of the molten interior rose to solidify in as crust, it was differentiated into what we today call felsic and mafic igneous rocks. Suess called the former *sal*, a term that was later revised to *sial*, reflecting the compositional dominance of silica and alumina. Mafic rock was named *sima*, the syllable *ma* having the same meaning as in mafic, i.e., "magnesia."

According to Marvin, Suess, following a suggestion made earlier by the Austrian paleontologist Melchior Neumayr, identified "two kinds of continental margins—an Atlantic, or fractured type and a Pacific, or folded, type" (1973, p. 54). Marvin continues:

> Along fractured coastlines geological structures are truncated abruptly, as though the ocean basin were younger than the continental platforms. The Pacific margins, in contrast, are bordered by relatively young, folded mountain ranges and chains of active volcanoes that clearly control the configuration of the coastline itself. (1973, p. 54)

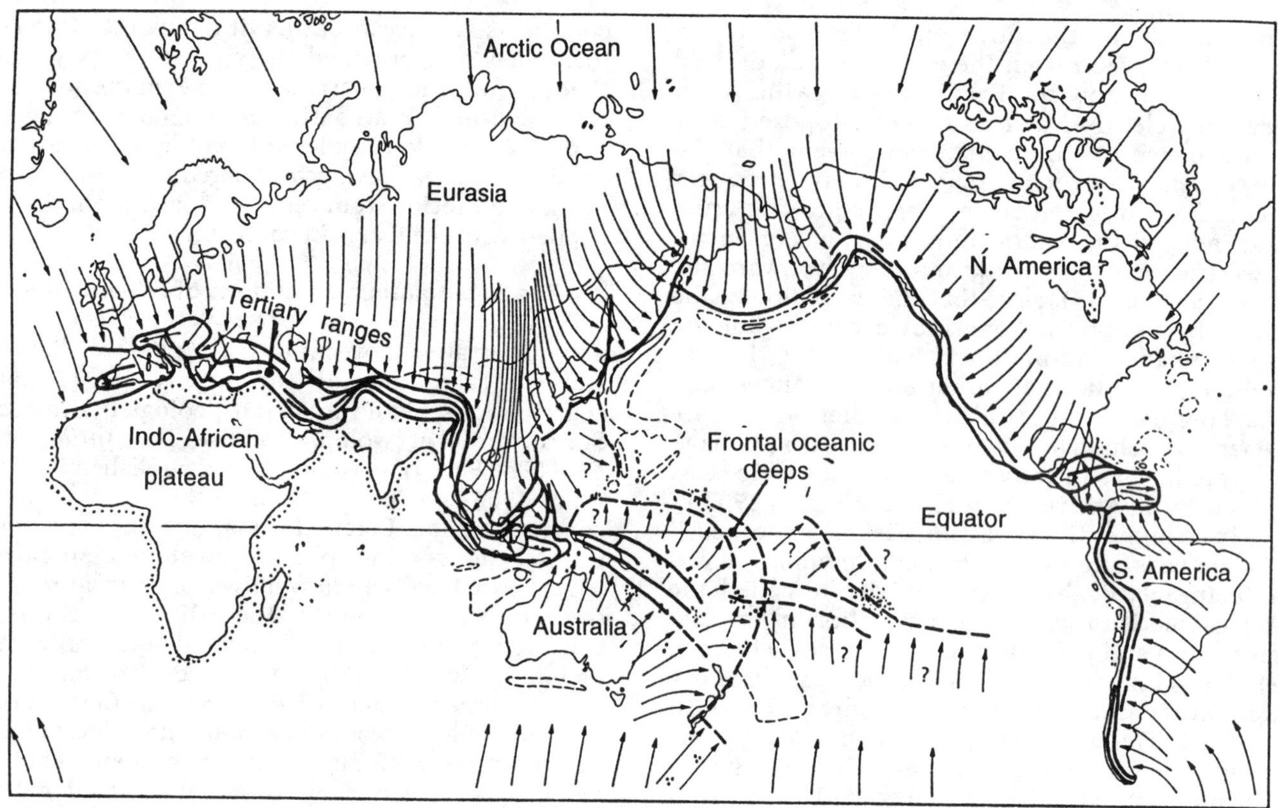

Figure 2.2 Frank B. Taylor's 1910 map showing by arrows the relative amounts and directions of crustal motions, generally from higher to lower latitudes. (From F.B. Taylor, 1910, *Bull, Geol. Soc. Amer.*, v. 21, Figure 7 Used by permission of the Geological Society of America.)

How familiar this classification of continental margins sounds today!

Of course, there remained for Suess the problem of explaining by vertical movements the great thrust sheets and nappes that clearly indicated localized belts of crustal shortening. Marvin presents Suess's explanation as follows:

> Suess pictured the forces resulting from contraction as being resolved into vertical and tangential components. The former cause sinking of crustal segments; the latter result in horizontal compression which pushes blocks together, folding and thrusting forelands against more rigid backlands and causing the hundreds of miles of crustal shortening seen in the Alps and other mountain ranges. (1973, p. 57)

In recognizing the multiple lobate form of Tertiary mountain chains of Eurasia, Suess was obliged to introduce an outward "creep" of felsic rock, but this he limited to a superficial layer and to a narrow peripheral zone (Marvin, 1983, p. 47). Here, he came perilously close to becoming a mobilist.

Suess was aware of the need for former land bridges across what are now deep ocean basins. The similarities of Permian/Triassic and older floras and faunas on today's separated continents required such bridges. Moreover, they served to make one or more unified supercontinents. Suess gave the name *Gondwana-Land* (later *Gondwanaland*) to a southern group of connected continents; it was taken from a region in India known as Gondwana, meaning "Land of the Gonds," and is thus redundant. Collapse of the land bridges in late Mesozoic time brought about isolation of the faunas and floras of certain of the now-separate continents.

The twentieth century mobilists were to challenge the entrenched fixists—a formidable undertaking, indeed. The first to try was an American; his attempt doomed to failure because—like Osmond Fisher—he relied on a singular astronomical event to implement that mobility.

2.6 Taylor's Creeping Crustal Sheets

Frank Bursely Taylor (1860-1938) is best known for his lifelong study of the Pleistocene history of the Great Lakes region, which yielded some seventy publications. His collaboration with Frank Leverett in this research is well known. Little known to today's generation of geologists is Taylor's second interest, which was in astronomy (origin of the solar system) and what we know today as continental drift. Familiar with Suess's contractionist/fixist view, he challenged it on grounds that it gave no satisfactory explanation for the great Tertiary arcuate mountain ranges forming the southern border of Eurasia (G.W. Black, 1979, p. 68-69; Hallam, 1973, p. 3; Marvin, 1973, p. 63-64). It was to the problem of origin of these and the circum-Pacific tectonic arcs that Taylor directed his mobilist hypothesis. His first paper on this subject was published in the *Bulletin of the Geological Society of America*; its title, "Bearing of the Tertiary Mountain Belt on the Origin of the Earth's Plan" (F.B. Taylor, 1910).

Taylor's publications attracted little attention at the time and they have since been virtually ignored. Alfred Wegener, a German mobilist, was to move in only a year or so after Taylor with a theory of continental drift that drew heavy fire from the English-speaking geologists and geophysicists. Taylor's last publication, "Sliding Continents and Tidal and Rotational Forces," is the text of a paper he presented at a 1928 symposium addressed to evaluating Wegener's theory of continental drift. Many interesting details of Taylor's reception by the geological community, and particularly how others related his work to that of Alfred Wegener, are presented by Stanley Totten (1981).

Taylor envisaged a pre-Tertiary earth on which large continents occupied both of the polar regions (Figure 2.2). At the north lay an ancestral combination of Eurasia, Greenland, and North America; at the south, a continent consisting of Antarctica, Australia, and South America. Between them, in an equatorial location, lay the fixed continents of Africa and India. Taylor called upon a "deforming force" to set the two polar continents in a general equatorward motion. These great crustal sheets moved by slow creep over a shear zone. The leading edge of each sheet was deformed into outwardly convex mountain arcs, which were thrust over oceanic crust. Interestingly enough, Taylor took this cue from Suess, who had also explained the Asian mountain arcs as "due to local depression of ocean basins and tangential crustal movement overthrusting the basins" (Black, 1979, p. 68). George W. Black, Jr., writing on Taylor's contribution as a pioneer in the concept of continental drift, states that Suess "later subscribed to the idea that increased oblateness of the earth caused the outflow of superfluous earth-mass from the poles to the equator" (1979, P. 68). Scarcely a fixist view! Taylor seems not to have been able to reconcile such large-scale flowage and overthrusting with a contracting earth (Black, 1979, p. 68). But Taylor was also closely familiar with the Pleistocene history of great continental ice sheets, and it is with these in mind that he formulated his hypothesis of vast, slowly creeping crustal sheets. As the sheets moved away from the polar zones, they left behind widening rifts that became the Arctic Ocean basin and the basin of the Southern Ocean. Both Greenland and Antarctica remained unmoved in their high-latitude locations.

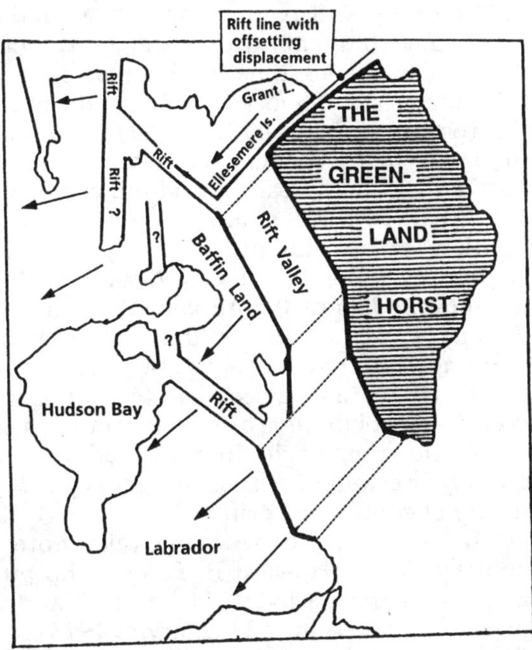

Figure 2.3 Taylor's 1910 sketch map of the Greenland-Labrador region, showing Baffin Bay as a rift valley, or graben, and a transcurrent fault separating Greenland from Ellesmere Island. (Same source as Figure 2.2.Labels replaced. Used by permission the Geological Society of America.)

Taylor included a special map of Greenland in relation to North America, reproduced here as Figure 2.3. Labeled the "Greenland Horst," that crustal unit remained fixed relative to the moving mainland, from which it became separated by a widening rift (now Baffin Bay). Lesser rifts separated Baffin Island from Labrador. Particularly interesting is the transcurrent fault shown as truncating the northern edge of Greenland and separating it from Grant Land and Ellesemere Island; it is recognized today as a major transform fault and goes under the name of the Wegener Fault (Totten, 1981, p. 217).

Taylor seems to have been at a loss to fit the Mid-atlantic Ridge into his hypothesis, but he recognized it as a residual feature marking a rift line along which South America split apart from Africa. The African continent moved eastward in Permian time; the South American continent moved westward much later—in Tertiary and Recent time (Marvin, 1973, p. 63).

For a driving force behind the equatorward creep of the crustal sheets, Taylor called upon an astronomical explanation. In his 1910 paper, he suggested that powerful tidal forces had piled up the ocean waters in a low-latitude girdle, causing the Cretaceous marine transgression deep into continental interiors. On the subject of a causative force behind equatorward crustal creep, his final sentence was to the effect that "one is inclined to reject all internal causes and look to some form of tidal force as the only possible agency" (1910, p.

226).) In 1928, Taylor came out with the clear statement that capture of the moon occurred during Cretaceous time, more than doubling the tidal force and intensifying mountain building in the Tertiary (1928, p. 175). While this unique event in earth history could be invoked to explain Tertiary crustal spreading and the construction of the great Tertiary mountain arc, it would not furnish an explanation of earlier orogenic structures, such as the well-known Paleozoic mountain roots of the Appalachians and western Europe. Taylor's catastrophic hypothesis of cause, seemingly offered in desperation, could not help but cause his entire scenario to be rejected as a plausible explanation of global tectonics through all of known geologic time. Instead, all attention quickly became focused on Alfred Wegener's theory of continental drift.

In passing, we pause to take note of the contribution of Howard B. Baker, who published articles in the period 1911 to 1931 and a book privately printed in 1932 (Marvin, 1973, p. 64-65). Baker's hypothesis of continental separation is cited by some writers as of equal significance to those of Taylor, but clearly it lacks the geological basis and detail found in Taylor's presentation. Baker's catastrophic hypothesis required the origin of the moon by fission, an event occurring in late Miocene time. This event induced the rifting apart of a supercontinent, the fragments of which drifted toward the great Pacific depression. Baker's 1929 reconstruction of the supercontinent looks strangely like Wegener's Pangaea, and is often reprinted in historical accounts of continental drift. Perhaps Baker's dating of the catastrophic event as late Miocene tells us something about the lack of substance behind his presentations.

2.7 Alfred Wegener and His Theory of Continental Drift

Alfred Wegener, son of an evangelical preacher, was born in Berlin, Germany, in 1880. After completing his studies at the universities of Heidelberg, Innsbruck, and Berlin, he took employment as an astronomer. In 1906 he joined a Danish national expedition to the northeast coast of Greenland, serving as official meteorologist. Two years later, he joined the faculty of the University of Marburg, where he taught meteorology and astronomy. From this experience there emerged in 1911 his first book, titled "Thermodynamics of the Atmosphere." For full details of Wegener's life and work, see a 1980 work by the German geologist Martin Schwartzbach, translated into English in 1985.

Wegener wrote that his first concept of continental drift came to him in 1910, as he was examining world maps in a large atlas and was struck by "the congruence of coastlines on either side of the Atlantic" (1966, p. 1). [From this point on, "1966" in reference to Wegener's work, *The Origin of the Continents and Ocean Basins*, is to the 1966 English translation by John Biram of the fourth revised German edition published in 1929.] At first, Wegener paid no attention to the idea, regarding it as improbable, but his interest was rekindled in the fall of 1911 upon learning of paleontological evidence of a former land bridge between Brazil and Africa. Continuing his account, Wegener wrote:

> As a result I undertook a cursory examination of relevant research in the fields of geology and palaeontology, and this provided immediately such weighty corroboration that conviction of the fundamental soundness of the idea took root in my mind. (1966, p. 1)

On January 6, 1912, Wegener made public his ideas in an address before the Geological Association in Frankfurt am Main. A second address, given in Marburg, followed four days later with the title "Horizontal Displacements of the Continents." In the same year his first two publications on this subject appeared; one was a three-part paper in *Petermanns Geographische Mitteilungen*; the other a summary in *Geologische Rundschau* (Wegener, 1912a; 1912b). Both bore the title "The Origin of Continents." By that time, Wegener had left on a second expedition to Greenland. Returning in 1913, he married the daughter of Vladimir Köppen, a distinguished biogeographer and climatologist with whom he later collaborated on climates of the geologic past (Köppen and Wegener, 1924).

With the onset of World War I, Wegener entered the German army as an officer, was twice wounded, and served for the duration of the war. While on sick leave, he wrote a short work (94 pages) titled *Die Enstehung der Kontinente und Ozeane* (*The Origin of the Continents and Oceans*). Published in 1915, it was never widely circulated and existing copies are extremely rare (Marvin, 1973, p, 67). In 1919, Wegener became director of the meteorological research department of the Marine Observatory in Hamburg. A thoroughly revised second edition of *Origin*, containing much new material, was published in 1920 and attracted immediate attention and controversy on the European continent (Marvin, 1973, p. 67). Two years later, critical reviews were written by the British geologist Philip Lake (1922) and the American geologist Harry Fielding Reid (1922). The third edition of Origin appeared in 1922 and was translated into English in 1924 by J.G.A. Skerl (and into four other European languages, as well) drawing much attention from the English-speaking geologists. A fourth edition, published in 1929, was translated into English by John Biram and published in 1966. A fifth and sixth edition appeared in German, but these are essentially unchanged from the fourth edition. In 1924, Wegener was appointed Professor of Meteorology and Geophysics at Graz University in Austria.

In November, 1930, Wegener perished of cold

and exhaustion on the Greenland Ice Sheet while he and a companion were attempting to return on foot from the research station Eismitte (Mid-ice) to the coast, a distance of 400 km, under conditions of blizzard winds and temperatures below -50°C. His body was found later, but left in place to become naturally entombed under successive snowfalls (Schwartzbach, 1985, p. 44-46; Wood, 1985, p. 87).

Had he lived, Wegener would have faced another quarter-century of unrelenting opposition from the strongly entrenched Anglo-American fixists. His theory, like that of Charles Darwin, had two epistemically different themes: (1) that continental separation had occurred; (2) the explanation of how it happened. For Darwin, his first theme—"descent with modification"—had clear sailing; the second—"by natural selection"—was widely greeted with skepticism and came close to foundering. In like manner, Wegener's hypothesis was to be rejected, not for lack of evidence that drift had occurred, but rather for the unacceptability of his proposed mechanical explanation of the drift motion itself and the forces behind it.

2.8 Wegener's Basic Arguments

We begin a review of Wegener's work with consideration of two quite different phases of his initial argument—two sides of a coin, as it were. These are:

I Land Bridges vs. Drift (The question of vertical tectonics.)

II Contraction vs. Drift (The question of horizontal tectonics.)

Under item I, the traditional view of land bridges and their collapse was to be placed in opposition to continental drift. The issue was over vertical tectonics. Under item II, the issue was over the efficacy of the traditional view of global contraction with crustal uparching to explain large-scale tangential movements of the crust, or "horizontal" tectonics. Both sets of arguments were pitted against the prevailing view and from the standpoint of Wegener's theory were negative in approach, but the strategy was to leave only drift as a viable solution. It is essentially a form of the argument from ignorance in which Wegener was saying "You must be wrong, therefore I must be right." Nevertheless, it was a necessary argument, basic to the success of Wegener's hypothesis. He reviewed the argument in his second chapter (1966, p. 5-21).

Against the land-bridge hypothesis, Wegener brought to bear two kinds of physical evidence: geophysical and oceanographic. Fundamental geophysical evidence could be found in crustal structure and isostasy. This he presented in some detail in his fourth chapter (1966, p. 35-60). He

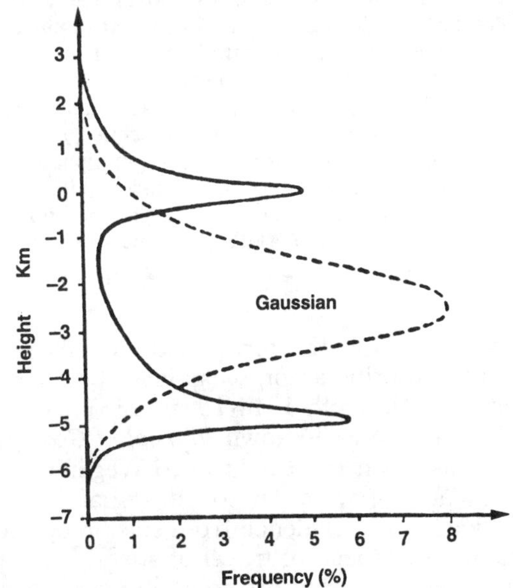

Figure 2.4 Wegener's comparison of the bimodal hypsometric curve of relative global surface elevations (bold line) with a Gaussian normal curve. The area under the two curves is the same. (From the English version of the Fourth Revised Edition of A. Wegener, *Die Enstehung der Kontinente und Ozeane*, published in 1929 by Friedr. Vieweg & Sohn, Braunschweig. Translated by John Biram. Copyright © 1966 by Dover Publications, Inc., New York. Used by permission.)

began with analysis of the global hypsographic curve, showing frequency of surface area as a function of elevation (Figure 2.4). The strongly two-peaked curve he compared with a Gaussian-normal curve, arguing for significance of the bimodal form. This argument was challenged on grounds of erroneous assumption of the Gaussian form (p. 38-39). Nevertheless, Wegener wrote:

> From this we conclude that there were at one time two undisturbed primal levels, and it seems an inevitable deduction that we are dealing with two different layers in the crust when we refer to the continents and the oceans. To put it in rather picturesque terms, the two layers behave like open water and large ice floes (p. 37).

Wegener then turned to crustal structure, using the Airy/Heiskanen model of isostasy and Vening-Meinesz's gravity data to support the model of a denser simatic oceanic crust contrasting with a thicker but less dense continental crust. Figure 2.5 is Wegener's diagram of this relationship at a continental margin. He refers to the presence of a depth of compensation ("the so-called equilibrium level"), at which "all horizontal density differentials vanished." In this area, Wegener was on sound ground by modern standards. He gives no reference to the earlier seminal paper by the American geologist Joseph

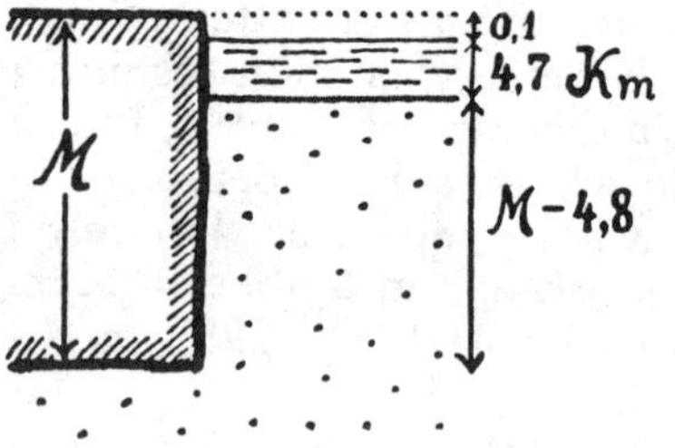

Figure 2.5 Wegener's sketch of the isostatic equilibrium of a block of sial (left) immersed in sima (dot pattern). Ocean water shown by horizontal dashes. The sial block (M), 100 km thick, "floats" in the sima to a depth of 95.2 km (100 minus 4.8 km). (From the English version of the Fourth Revised Edition of A. Wegener, *Die Enstehung der Kontinente und Ozeane*, published in 1929 by Friedr. Vieweg & Sohn, Braunschweig. Translated by John Biram. Copyright © 1966 by Dover Publications, Inc., New York. Used by permission.)

Barrell, in which the term "asthenosphere" was coined to describe a hot, weak layer below a rigid lithosphere (Barrell, 1914-15, p. 965). This work appeared in the well-known *Journal of Geology* and would have been most helpful to Wegener at this point. Wegener went on to cite what was then recently acquired evidence from seismology to the effect that the speed of travel of surface, P, and S waves is significantly different between oceanic crust and continental crust, as would be expected from their postulated chemical contrasts (p. 46-51). At this point Wegener expresses confidence:

> One can therefore see that seismic research as developed recently has arrived by totally different and mutually dependent routes at the conclusion that the ocean floors are of fundamentally different material from that of the continental blocks, and that their material corresponds to a deeper layer in the earth. (p. 51)

What Wegener had accomplished at this point was to make a powerful geophysical argument against the former existence of land bridges composed of continental crust, namely, that had those bridges existed, they could not have collapsed (subsided) to become oceanic crust. That being the case, the bridges could not have existed in the first place. On the other hand, the evidence left open the possibility that continents could have drifted apart; but it also permitted the fixist position of permanent ocean basins that was to prevail until much later.

In concluding these arguments against land bridges, we should note that Wegener introduced another quite different kind of argument to the same end. He wrote, in effect, that we might imagine a time when the land bridges did not exist. What would happen if we then put them in place? "The water displacement of the intercontinental bridges would be so enormous that the level of the world's oceans would rise above that of the whole continental area of the earth and all would be flooded, today's continents and the bridges alike" (p. 13). To appreciate the weight of this conclusion, Wegener asks us to look at his world map of land areas (continental crust?) in Carboniferous time, reproduced here as Figure 2.6. Note that he seems to have selected an equal-area projection (Mollweide's homolographic?), a correct choice for comparing global areas. Wegener gives credit for this idea to Bailey Willis and Albrecht Penck, both of whom were arguing for permanence, not only of the ocean basins, but for the fixed quantity of global water as well, through all known geologic history (p. 13).

All things considered, Wegener laid sound geophysical foundations through his collection of arguments against former land bridges. They were, of course equally sound for both fixist and mobilist hypotheses. The important difference was that whereas Wegener could do very nicely without those bridges, the fixists desperately needed them.

The second part of Wegener's basic argument dealt with the significance of crustal shortening evident from field studies of thrust sheets and nappes in the intensely deformed Tertiary mountain belts, such as the European Alps and the Himalayas. Most fixists of Wegener's time invoked global shrinking (contraction) as the cause of all crustal tectonics. Recall that Eduard Suess was

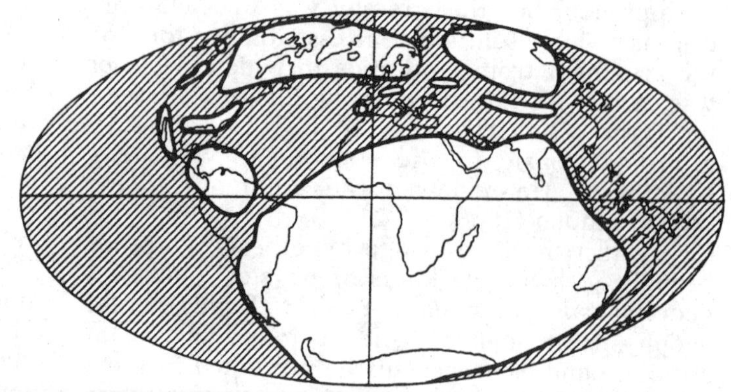

Figure 2.6 Wegener's sketch map of the distribution of water (ruled pattern) and land in the Carboniferous Period according to the then prevalent conception. (From the English version of the Fourth Revised Edition of A. Wegener, *Die Enstehung der Kontinente und Ozeane*, published in 1929 by Friedr. Vieweg & Sohn, Braunschweig. Translated by John Biram. Copyright © 1966 by Dover Publications, Inc., New York. Used by permission.)

one of these, and that he tried to explain block faulting and the downdropping of ocean basins through crustal uparching required by diminishing radius of the earth. The idea was that the cool crust could not shrink appreciably as earth radius diminished, hence that the crust became relatively too large and was forced to rise in some areas in archlike structures. Besides collapse of the arches to produce fault blocks and new ocean basins, the tangential (horizontal) component of gravity tended to move the crust away from the crest of an arch. (Today, this principle is recognized in the ridge-push force that results in plate motion away from the mid-oceanic spreading boundaries.) This tangential force expressed itself in crustal shortening near the edge of a continent, concentrated in the great Tertiary mountain arcs.

Wegener noted that other writers had already discounted Suess's version of great arching; he cites four references to authors "among others, (who) have opposed this quite rightly, claiming that the surface of the earth would have to undergo regular overall wrinkling, just as a drying apple does" (1966, p. 10). Little wrinkles would be allowed, but not big ones; little wrinkles just could not provide the required amount of horizontal movement. The relatively thin crust would not have had the strength to transmit the required stress over 180 great-circle degrees of arc (p. 10). Wegener quotes figures from several contemporary sources as to the proportion of shortening required. Albert Heim, a highly respected student of Alpine geology, had estimated a shortening of from one-quarter to one-eighth of the initial crustal width. The present Alpine chain, 150 km wide, would have been derived from a belt of horizontal crust 600 to 1200 km wide (p. 10). Wegener cites Rudolph Staub, agreeing with Argand "that the compression must have been even greater," and estimating crustal shortening of around 1500 km for the Alps (p. 10-11). Staub comments: "What is involved here is a true continental drift of the African Landmass and an extensive one at that" (Staub, 1924). Wegener (p. 11) quotes another author (Kossmat) as stating: "the formation of mountains must be explained by large-scale tangential movements of the crust, which cannot be incorporated in the scope of the simple contraction theory." This accumulated evidence was indeed powerful, and Wegener exploited it to the point of overkill, but it was wasted on the fixist/contractionists—blinded and deafened as they had been rendered by devotion to their premise.

Wegener next attacked the fixist/contraction ists with a new weapon—radioactivity and radiogenic heat. He scoffingly wrote: "Moreover, even the apparently obvious basic assumption of contraction theory, namely that the earth is continuously cooling, is in full retreat before the discovery of radium" (1966, p. 11-12). Wegener viewed the internal heat system as being in "a state of equilibrium between radioactive heat production in the core and thermal loss into space" (p. 12). Interesting is his further observation that the rate of radiogenic heat production is greater than conduction under the continents, but less than production under the ocean basins. Here were the makings of a heat engine, capable of producing convection currents below the crust, but Wegener failed to use the principle to supply a driving mechanism for his drifting continents. According to Marvin, Osmond Fisher in 1889 "described mountain making and other crustal deformations as due in part to currents in the molten substratum that rise along the median lines of the ocean basins and sink beneath the continental margins" (Marvin, 1973, p. 52). Marvin also notes that besides Fisher, Otto Ampherer in 1906 and Rudolph Staub in 1928 had proposed convection within the mantle to explain mountain building and crustal motions (1973, p. 103). Evidently Wegener did finally get the message. Marvin states:

> The concept of sialic blocks riding passively along in currents of moving sima was not a part of Wegener's model until 1929 when he revised his book for the fourth time. By then he commented favorably on the ideas of Otto Ampherer, John Joly, and others that thermally driven convection currents occur in the mantle and cause the deformation or displacement of the crust (1973, p. 71).

Wegener's rather detailed discussion of ideas voiced in the 1920s of a zone of melting below the crust and of "undercurrents" that carried along the floating crust makes clear that he had every opportunity in his fourth edition to switch to an acceptable theory of the mechanism of continental drift (1966, p. 59-60). Why did he let this golden opportunity pass? Perhaps his mind was too firmly set on demolishing his fixist/contractionist opponents, for at the end of his paragraph on radioactivity he wrote: "In any case, one can see that through these new views the foundation of the contraction theory has been completely removed" (p. 12).

Apropos of the above query, the mystery of Wegener's failure to resort to a thermal convection system deepens when we look back to his 1912 paper published in *Petermanns Mitteilungen*. Wolfgang R. Jacoby, writing on this subject in 1981, cites in the 1912 paper statements of early ideas of Wegener about his drift hypothesis that do not appear in his later works. One of these reads as follows: "The depth variation appears also to suggest that the Mid-Atlantic Ridge should be regarded as the zone in which the floor of the Atlantic, as it keeps spreading, is continuously tearing open and making space for fresh, relatively fluid and hot sima (rising) from depth" (1912a, p. 305). (This is from the English translation by Jacoby, 1981, p. 25). Wegener's words "depth variation" are in reference to a previous sentence in which he says that freshly exposed sima is hotter than old sima, resulting in significant differences in ocean-floor depths. Where could one look for a clearer statement of seafloor spreading along an extensional rift accompanied by the rise of mafic magma within the rift axis? Was Wegener, then, the first to describe seafloor spreading? If so, why did he abandon the idea?

Wegener seems to have felt confident that by means of the arguments we have reviewed he had cleared the way to acceptance of his theory. Orogenesis, with its intense folding and overthrusting, could occur at the leading edge of a moving continent of sial (1966, p. 20). There need be no limit to the distance through which a continent of sial might travel. In summing up his evidence he wrote:

> If the drift theory is taken as the basis, we can satisfy all the legitimate requirements of the land-bridge theory and of permanence theory. This now amounts to saying that there were land connections, but formed by contact between blocks now separated, not by intermediate continents which later sank; there is permanence, but of the area of ocean and area of continent as a whole, but not of individual oceans or continents (p. 21).

2.9 Wegener's Maps of Pangaea and Its Breakup

Although the name Pangaea is universally attributed to Wegener, Marvin writes that the name appears with the spelling of *Pangäa* in both his second and third editions "in a rather offhand manner," and that it never appears as a "specific proper name" or printed on a map (Marvin, 1973, p. 72). Schwartsbach's statement that Wegener named his continent "Pangaea" appears in context with his review of *Die Klimate der geologischen Vorzeit*, authored jointly by Köppen and Wegener in 1924, so perhaps that work contains its first documented text use (Schwartzbach, 1985, p. 92). The name uses the Greek root *gäa* or *gaea* which refers to "earth" or "land"; it comes from *Gaea* (or *Gaia*), the Greek earth-goddess. [In North American, the favored spelling is now "Pangea," which we use in subsequent chapters. However, "Pangaea" continues to be used today in British-authored publications.]

Wegener's 1915 reconstruction of Pangaea is shown in Figure 2.7. He had clearly stated that he took as his continental boundaries the outer limit of the continental shelf (see, for example, Wegener/Skerl, 1924, p. 2). This is approximately the line along which modern cross sections of the passive continental margins place the underlying boundary between continental lithosphere and oceanic lithosphere. Curved lines of long dashes on Wegener's map indicate the strike of the roots of Paleozoic mountain chains. As we do today, the present shorelines of landmasses are shown only for geographic reference to crustal features.

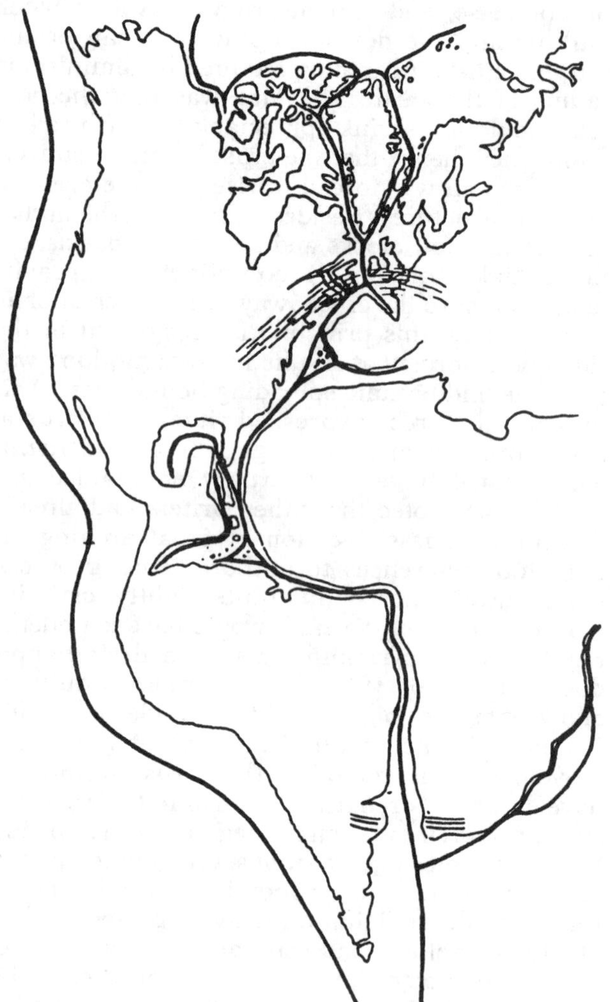

Figure 2.7 Wegener's 1915 map fitting together the continents that today border the Atlantic Ocean basin. The sets of dashed lines show the fit of Paleozoic tectonic structures between Europe and North America and betweem southermost Africa and South America. (From A. Wegener, *Die Entstehung der Kontinente und Ozeane*, First Edition, 1915. Used by permission of Friedr. Vieweg & Sohn, Braunschweig.)

According to Ellen Drake, several of Wegener's critics failed to understand where Wegener drew his continental margins, criticizing him severely for attempting to fit together details of the present coastline. Among them was Professor Schuchert, the distinguished stratigrapher and paleogeographer of Yale University (Drake, 1976, p. 41). Even Alexander Du Toit, a strong supporter of Wegener in the 1930s, made this same mistake (p. 42).

Wegener's second edition (1920) carried the oblique zenithal polar projections shown here as Figure 2.8. Gondwanaland, the southern of the two subcontinents of Pangaea, is especially well shown on this map of Permocarboniferous time.

Wegener's third edition (1922) carried a beautifully rendered set of paleogeographic world maps showing Pangaea in the upper Carboniferous and its continental separation in stages of

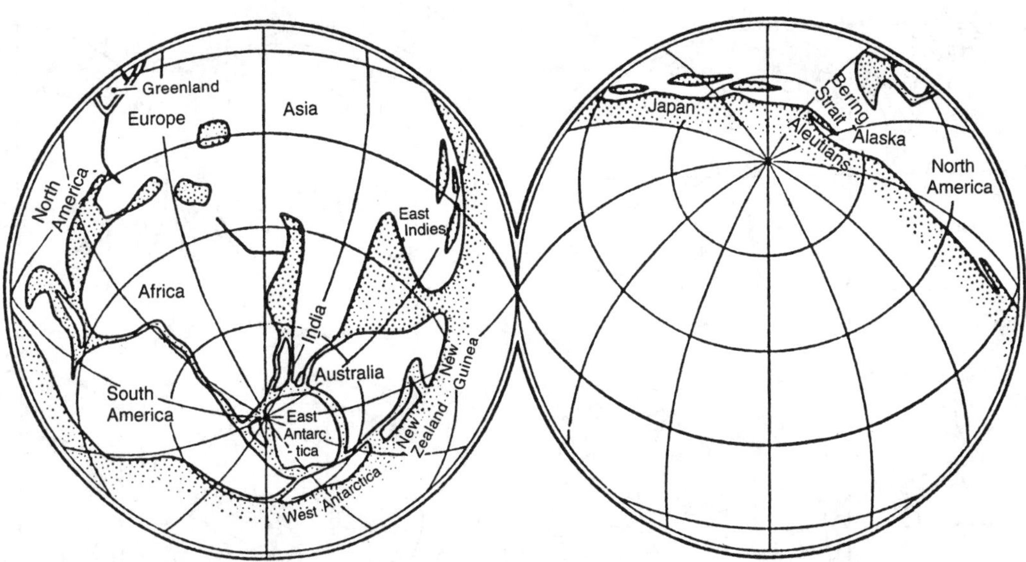

Figure 2.8 Wegener's 1920 map of world continents in Permocarboniferous time. (English labels added.) Notice the clustering of continental masses around the south pole. (From the Second Edition, 1920, of A. Wegener, *Die Entstehung der Kontinente und Ozeane*. Used by permission of Friedr. Vieweg & Sohn, Braunschweig.)

occurrence in the Eocene and Older Quaternary (Early Pleistocene) (Wegener/Skerl, 1922, Figures 1 and 2, p. 6-7). These we reproduce as Figure 2.9. Latitude and longitude selected for the maps is arbitrary, actually being those of present-day Africa, which retains its position through the three stages. Figure 2.10, showing the same stages, uses oblique polar projections of the same stages, and these are particularly useful in overcoming high-latitude shear distortions inherent in the equatorial projection.

By Eocene time, on these maps, the Atlantic ocean was open except for a contact point between Africa and South America. India, still attached to Eurasia, had separated some distance from Madagascar, while a landmass chain was formed by Australia and Antarctica, still attached to the tip of South America. At this point "land bridges" effectively existed so that no major land area was isolated from the others, but migration distances for faunas were stretched out to great distances. By Quaternary time the North and South Atlantic oceans were wide open, and Australia (with New Zealand still attached) was now fully separated from the other continents. For reasons we discuss in later paragraphs, the northern landmasses remain close together far longer than a modern schedule would call for—so close together, in fact, that Wegener proposed that they held a single great Pleistocene ice sheet.

While Wegener was still revising his work, others who came to his support were publishing maps of Gondwanaland. These included du Toit (1921 and 1927,), Michaelsen (1922), and Argand (1924). [See Wegener, 1924, for reference citations. Maps by all three authors appear in Wegener's fourth edition, 1966, p. 72, 85, 117.]

2.10 Wegener's Evidence in Favor of Continental Drift

Wegener offered positive geological arguments supporting a united continent in Paleozoic time. He found the evidence particularly strong for the union of the Gondwanaland fragments. In southernmost Africa, the Swartberg, a range consisting of Paleozoic strata deformed in Permian time and striking east-west, could be found continuing in Argentina (1966, p. 61-62). This arrangement is shown on du Toit's 1927 map reproduced by Wegener as Figure 18, and here as Figure 2.11. The Swartberg structure is indicated by a line of dots. In these matched belts, both the Devonian sedimentary rocks and the Upper Paleozoic glacial conglomerate are folded. Wegener states: "All this is an indication that we have here an elongated ancient fold that traverses the southern tip of Africa, then is continued across South America south of Buenos Aires and finally turns north to join the Andes. Today the fragments of this fold are separated from each other by an ocean more than 6000 km wide" (p. 62). Of this remarkable geologic match across the ocean he observed that "one is reminded of the torn visiting card used as a means of recognition" (p. 62).

Wegener also cited similarities of the vast "gneiss" plateaus found in both Africa and Brazil (p. 63): "This similarity is not confined only to generalities, as is revealed by the conformity between the igneous rocks and between the sedimentary deposits of each area, and by the conformity between the original fold directions" (p. 63). He then drew upon evidence detailed by Brower (1921) and du Toit (1921, 1927). Of the last cited of these works, Wegener commented: "I must

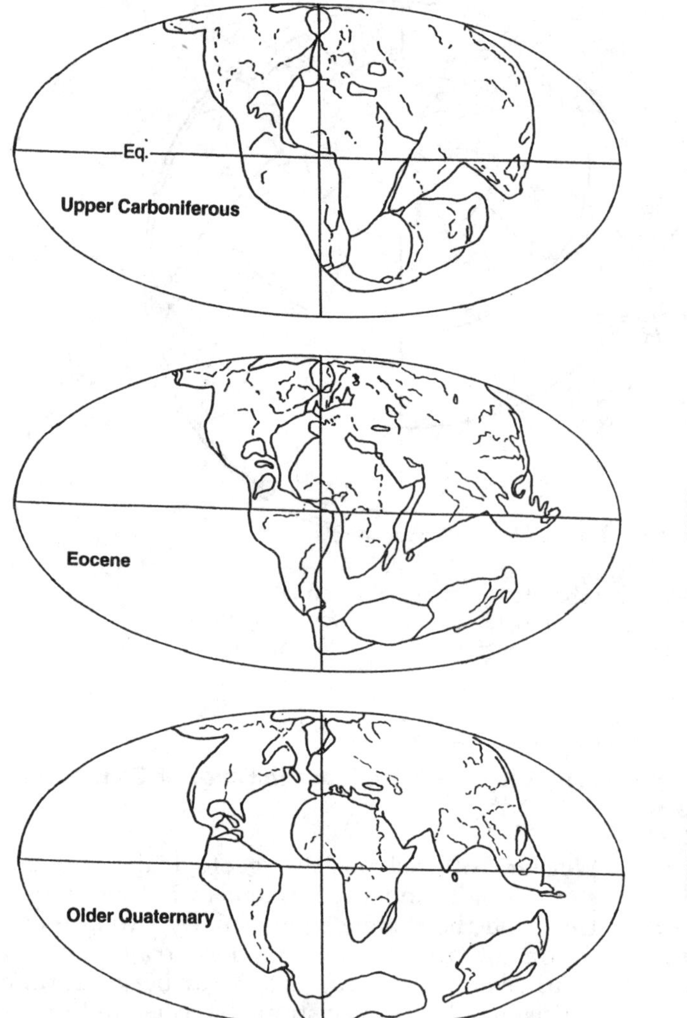

Figure 2.9 Wegener's 1924 maps reconstructing three stages in the history of Pangaea. Details of coastlines and rivers are shown only to aid in relating ancient features to present-day geography. (Redrawn from the Second Edition of A. Wegener, *Die Entstehung der Kontinente und Ozeane*, 1920, as translated by J.G.A. Skerl in 1924. Used by permission of Friedr. Vieweg & Sohn, Braunschweig.

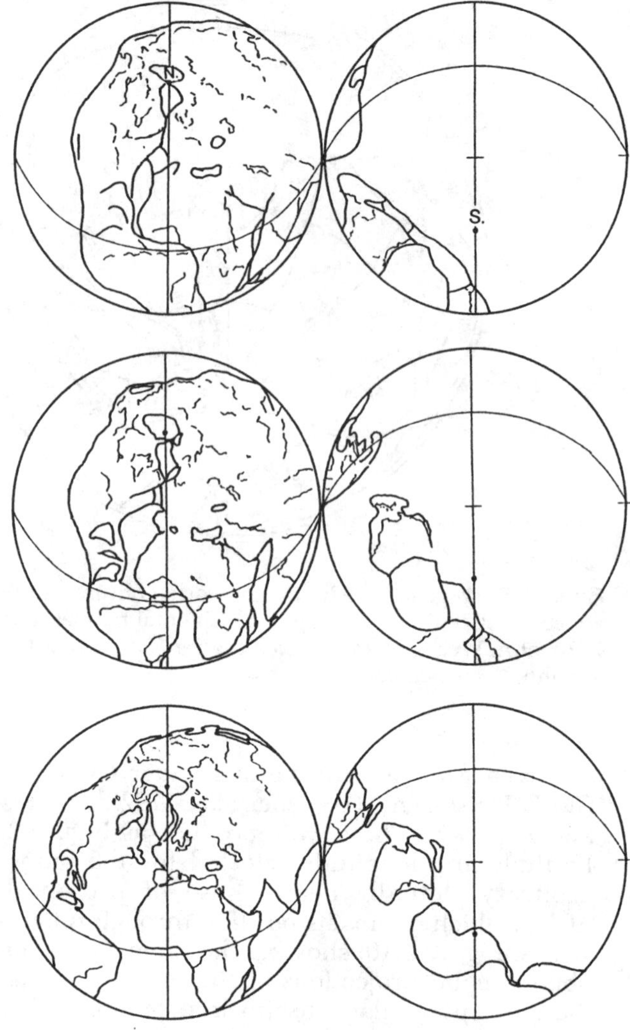

Figure 2.10 Polar projections of the same stages of Pangaea as the maps in Figure 2.9. (Same source as given in Figure 2.9. Used by permission.)

admit that du Toit's book made an extraordinary impression on me, since up till then I had hardly dared to expect so close a geological correspondence between the two continents" (p. 72).

For Laurasia, the northern part of Pangaea, equally striking matches were found in orogens now on the two sides of the Atlantic. Here the Caledonides, orogens of middle Paleozoic time, could be traced from Norway and Great Britain, across to Newfoundland (p. 75). In a similar manner, the Hercynian/Alleghenian fold belt produced at the close of the Paleozoic could be aligned from Europe to North America (p. 74-75). Another match was found in geologic features of northwestern Greenland, correlatable with those in Ellesmere Island, across Smith Sound and the Kennedy Channel, with due allowance for a strike-slip fault (p. 78-79). Wegener's version of Lauge-Koch's map of this area is reproduced here as Figure 2.12.

The significant point about this category of evidence is that most of it was handed to Wegener on a silver platter—so to speak—by reputable geologists whose authority was difficult to challenge. Referring to the European-North American connections, Wegener wrote:

> Of crucial importance here is the fact that, although the blocks must be rejoined on the basis of other features—their outlines, especially—the conjunction brings the continuation of each formation on the farther side into perfect contact with the end of the formation on the near side. It is as if we were to refit the torn pieces of a newspaper by matching their edges and then check whether the lines of print run smoothly across (1966, p. 76-77).

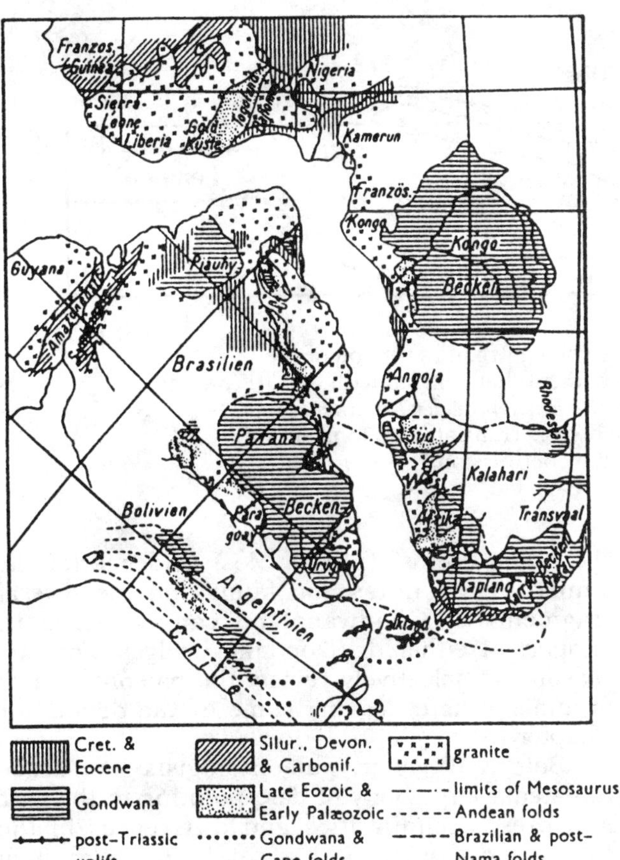

Figure 2.11 Du Toit's map of South America and Africa in their former relative positions in Gondwanaland prior to breaking apart. (From the English version of the Fourth Revised Edition of A. Wegener, *Die Enstehung der Kontinente und Ozeane*, published in 1929 by Friedr. Vieweg & Sohn, Braunschweig. Translated by John Biram. Copyright © 1966 by Dover Publications, Inc., New York. Used by permission.)

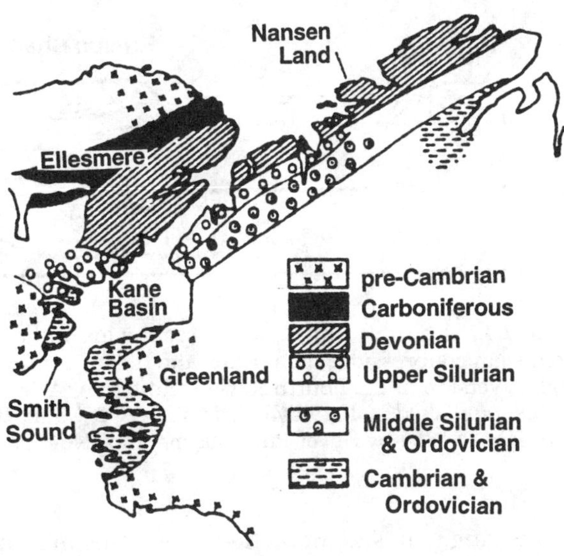

Figure 2.12 Wegener's geologic map of northwestern Greenland and adjacent part of Ellesmere Island, after Lauge-Koch, 1920. (From the English version of the Fourth Revised Edition of A. Wegener, *Die Enstehung der Kontinente und Ozeane*, published in 1929 by Friedr. Vieweg & Sohn, Braunschweig. Translated by John Biram. Copyright © 1966 by Dover Publications, Inc., New York. Used by permission.)

Wegener followed up this analogy with the familiar argument from improbability, namely, that if six different and independent structural features are matched across the gap, the probability of their all matching by pure chance alone is one in a million (p. 77-78).

Always, in connection with these arguments, the crucial question comes at the end: Could land bridges explain the observations equally well? In this case, the answer is a clear "No." Assuming the land bridges to have dropped out, an imagined closing of the ocean basins and cartographic refitting of the continental margins would be expected to show mostly boundary mismatches in the structural trends.

2.11 Wegener on Mountain and Island Arcs

On the subject of the great Tertiary continental mountain arcs of Asia—a prime object of Taylor's hypothesis of creeping sheets of sial—Wegener could fit them into his drift hypothesis under the mechanism of compressional deformation resulting from the motion of the sialic continental masses. For the great series of mountain arcs extending from the Mediterranean to the Himalayas, he seems to have envisioned continental collision of sialic blocks, not much different in concept from the modern view of plate tectonics. He recognized in the Himalayas a compression imposed by the sialic mass of peninsular India, calling it the "Lemurian compression" (p. 82-86). Using Argand's cross section and tectonic map (Argand, 1924), Wegener shows the underthrusting of Indian sial beneath that of Asia, producing the Himalayas and the Tibetan Plateau (our Figure 2.13).

The Pacific continental arcs of the Americas were explained by compressional deformation on the leading edges of the sialic masses as they moved through oceanic sima. Wegener wrote: "In the westward drift of both Americas, their leading edges were compressed and folded by the frontal resistance of the ancient Pacific floor, which was deeply chilled and hence a source of viscous drag. The result was the vast Andean range which extends from Alaska to Antarctica" (1966, p. 20).

For those island arcs of the western and northern Pacific, separated from the mainland by back-arc basins, Wegener had to resort to a special explanation, which he presents in his Chapter 10 (p. 193-197). These arcs, he explains, are trailing features, left behind in the wake of a moving continent. His schematic crustal section and plan, reproduced here as Figure 2.14, shows a thin,

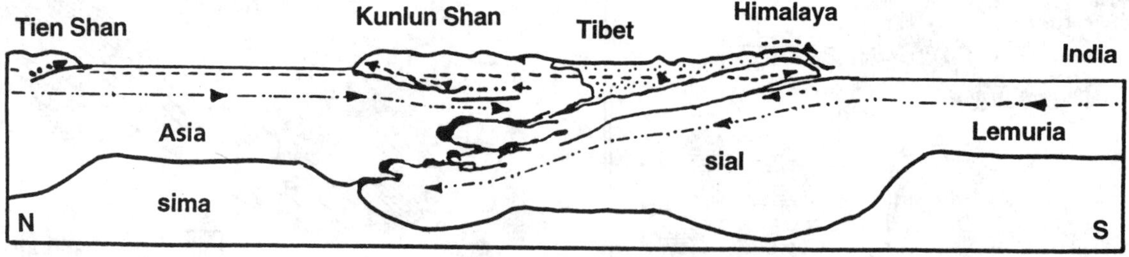

Figure 2.13 A north-south structure section in southern Asia showing Argand's version of the "Lemurian conpression." Lemuria is the Indian continental fragment that collided with Asia. (From the English version of the Fourth Revised Edition of A. Wegener, *Die Enstehung der Kontinente und Ozeane*, published in 1929 by Friedr. Vieweg & Sohn, Braunschweig. Translated by John Biram. Copyright © 1966 by Dover Publications, Inc., New York. Used by permission.)

curved ridge of sial detached from the moving continent and separated from it by a back-arc basin of sima, or in his words, "still-liquid areas of seafloor...exposed as windows" (1966, p. 197). The trench is interpreted as a deep, narrow tensional rift between old sima and old sial.

Besides the splitting off of marginal chains, there is yet another tectonic process in cases where the motion is one of shear between the moving sialic continent and the adjacent sima; here strike-slip faulting produces a "marginal chain" of sial. His example: Baja California and the San Andreas fault (p. 198-99 and Fig. 53).

From the standpoint of our topic, which is that of Wegener's evidence positively favoring his drift hypothesis, his interpretation of the great arcs as either compressional or extensional phenomena cannot be accepted as positive (affirmative) evidence. Instead, this is merely permissive evidence, which is to say that his hypothesis can accommodate the data (by a bit of manipulation on the side), but his explanation is not corroborative evidence that the drift process actually took place. Perhaps this point is borne out by the judgment imposed by modern plate tectonics. In retrospect, Wegener got it right for the south Eurasian collision arcs, but got it all wrong for the circum-Pacific island arcs.

2.12 Paleontological and Biological Arguments

Wegener's fourth edition of *Origin* devotes the sixth chapter to paleontological and biological arguments. It opens with some comments on land bridges versus drift. He thought it preposterous that some biologists continued to think that one hypothesis would work just as well as the other (1966, p. 97). As we stated in earlier paragraphs, Wegener went to great length to present geophysical arguments for the impossibility of land bridges having once existed and then sunken into the depths. He insisted that the idea of a sunken continent "just does not come into the picture. It is simply a matter of choosing between drift theory and the theory of the permanence of the ocean basins" (p. 98). Most evidence for the similarities of floras and faunas on the several fragments of Gondwanaland can be urged in support of either drift or land bridges. For this reason, we selectively review the paleontological arguments here, leaving some of the details for Chapter 13.

Before Wegener, paleontologists had accumulated a large body of data pointing to the past and present similarities and differences in the floras and faunas of certain landmasses now widely separated by deep ocean basins. This information could be organized into a time sequence, i.e., for each period of geologic time

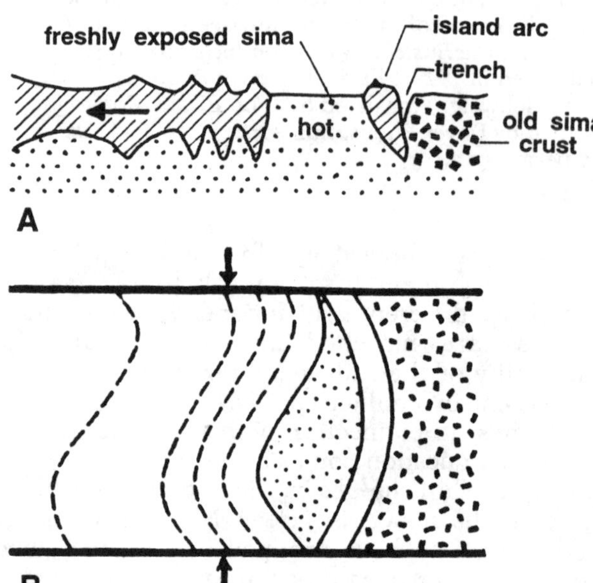

Figure 2.14 Wegener's hypothesis for the origin of Pacific island arcs. (A) Cross section; (B) Plan view. A narrow arc of sial has pulled away from the continent, exposing a new seafloor of hot sima. (From the English version of the Fourth Revised Edition of A. Wegener, *Die Enstehung der Kontinente und Ozeane*, published in 1929 by Friedr. Vieweg & Sohn, Braunschweig. Translated by John Biram. Copyright © 1966 by Dover Publications, Inc., New York. Used by permission.)

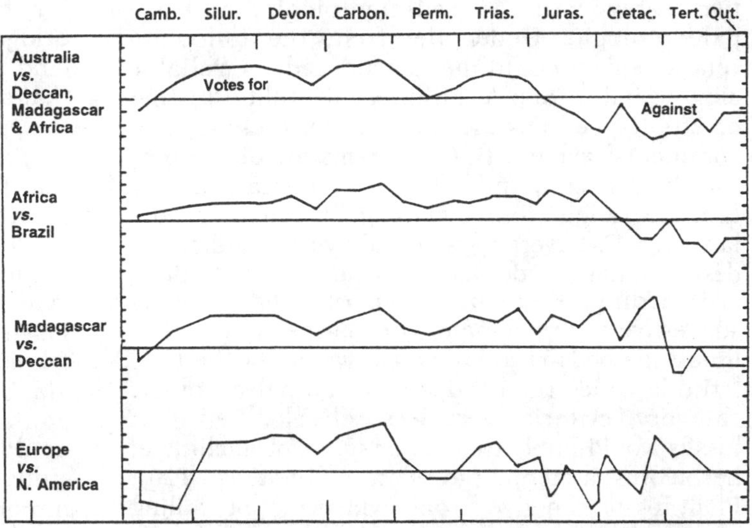

Figure 2.15 Wegener's graph summarizing the "votes" for or against existence of a land bridge through the Phanerozoic. The value plotted is the difference between yes and no votes of 20 scientists. The data were collected by T. Arldt in 1917. (Simplified from the English version of the Fourth Revised Edition of A. Wegener, *Die Enstehung der Kontinente und Ozeane*, published in 1929 by Friedr. Vieweg & Sohn, Braunschweig. Translated by John Biram. Copyright © 1966 by Dover Publications, Inc., New York. Used by permission.)

from Cambrian through Tertiary (Cenozoic). It became clear that within a particular major taxon, the close similarity of organisms on the two now-separate landmasses endured from the evolutionary inception of that taxon through a long span of Phanerozoic time, after which the similarity rapidly diminished. This sequence would lead to the conclusion that union of the landmasses persisted up to a certain point, permitting homogeneity of the flora and fauna to be maintained, but thereafter, evolutionary radiation proceeded independently on each of the widely separate lands to reduce the similarities. On the basis of this information, the paleogeographer would postulate the existence of a land bridge and establish the point in geologic time at which it was destroyed.

In his opening chapter, Wegener had shown a graph of the time schedules compiled independently by twenty scientists on the question of existence or nonexistence of four land bridges (1966, p. 6-8). He used these as a poll and tabulated the "votes" in an illustration partially reproduced here as Figure 2.15. Each graph shows for each of four regions the net number of votes that constituted the majority, whether for or against a land bridge. Wegener interpreted the uppermost graph as showing that the separation of Australia from the land group India-Madagascar-Africa occurred early in Jurassic time. The bridge disappeared at progressively more recent dates for the second and third land pairs. The breakup of Gondwanaland is clearly suggested by the first three graphs, in agreement with what modern plate tectonics has since established. The fourth graph, for the Europe-North America connection, gives a confusing result, suggesting alternating separation and reunion.

One interesting observation made by Wegener was that most biologists who supported the land-bridge hypothesis were in agreement that no trans-Pacific bridge was necessary. Von Ihering had shown such a bridge across the North Pacific in his map of 1927. Another version cited by Wegener is by T. Arldt (1918), who showed a land bridge connecting South America with Australia by way of southern latitudes (p. 111-112). [See Wegener's text for these references cited.] Wegener considered that "the Pacific basin must have existed as such from very ancient geological times" (p. 111). He restated the widely-held concept that very early in its history, the earth possessed a layer of sial over the entire globe, referred to as the "sialsphere" (p. 203-204). Through Precambrian time, by means of a great amount of folding and crustal shortening, large areas of the globe became denuded of sial. "Very probably, it was the area of the Pacific Ocean, generally regarded as very ancient, which was first denuded of its sial cover in this way" (p. 204). With land-bridges across the Pacific safely removed from contention, Wegener could make little use of the massive store of paleontological data in positive support of his drift hypothesis.

2.13 Paleoclimatic Arguments

By the time Wegener was preparing his fourth edition (1929), he had been collaborating for several years with the climatologist, Wladimir Köppen, whose system of world climates was already in use and provided an excellent world map of present climates to which paleoclimates could be referred. In 1924, the two scientists had coauthored a book titled *Die Klimate der geologischen Vorzeit* (The Climates of the Geologic Past), which applied paleoclimatology to the problem of continental drift (Köppen and Wegener, 1924).

The following major conclusions arising from that collaboration were summarized by Wegener in the fourth edition of *Origin* (Wegener, 1966). The idea behind paleoclimatology was that strata may contain evidence of prevailing climate in two categories: (1) sedimentologic, and (2) paleontologic. Under the first, the following relationships could be considered as reliable climate indicators: A. Lithified till (tillite) resting on striated bedrock indicates former presence of a continental glacier. B. Coal seams, requiring peat for their origin, indicate a wet climate in the latitude range from equatorial through middle latitudes. C. Layers of salt and gypsum indicate a desert climate, as do massive sandstones with dune crossbeding. Red coloration of sandstones is suggestive of dry climate. For marine strata, thick limestone beds required warm waters of the low-latitude zones (p. 123-126). In the paleontologic category, criteria were less reliable. Reptilian fossils would imply tropical or subtropical climate; herbivores, a steppe (grassland) climate (p. 126). Plant fossils can give strong evidence of prevailing climate. Wegener pointed out that the plant fossils of lower Tertiary time found in Spitzbergen clearly required a climate about like that of present-day France. Moreover, in Spitzbergen, strata as far back as the Carboniferous contain thick gypsum beds, indicative of tropical desert conditions, and flora of subtropical affinities (p. 127). Of these relationships Wegener wrote:

> This enormous climatic shift...immediately suggests a shift in the position of the poles and the equator, and thus the whole zonal system of climates. In fact, this suggestion is inescapably confirmed by the *equally large, but exactly reversed climatic change experienced by South Africa...in the same period*: in the Carboniferous it was buried under an inland ice sheet, i.e., it then had a polar climate, today a subtropical (p. 127).

Polar wandering was by no means a new idea, as Wegener made clear (p. 128). Among the nineteen authors he cites as having embraced polar wandering are some who also advocated land bridges. The point is, then, that polar wandering in itself could not rule out land bridges. There was, however, something specific about the application of polar wandering that could be the critical tool for favoring continental union without land bridges, but totally discrediting union by means of land bridges. In Wegener's words, "it is undeniable that all early attempts to determine the position of the poles and equator at all points of time have led to absurdities so grotesque that it is no surprise that the concept was suspected to be erroneous" (p. 129).

We consider first the application of this argument against land bridges to a salient one: the evidence of a great continental glaciation in Permocarboniferous time. In South Africa, the Dwyka Formation of Carboniferous age consists of glacial deposits now lithified into a tillite containing numerous striated and faceted boulders. Alexander du Toit spent several years studying this formation and described it in an important paper published in 1921. The tillite reaches a thickness of 300 to 500 m over a large area. Beneath the tillite are some exposures of strongly striated and grooved basalt of Precambrian age. Other occurrences of Permocarboniferous tills and striated surfaces, cited by Wegener, are in the Falkland Islands, Argentina and southern Brazil, India, and Australia (p. 131-32). These localities are shown in Wegener's map, reproduced here as Figure 2.16. On this map, Wegener placed the South Pole at a location he found optimum, i.e., at 50°S, 45°E. He then drew the equator for that pole position, noting that the glaciated areas of South America, India, and Australia lay within about 10 degrees of that line—in a tropical zone not likely to be the site of continental glaciers. Commented Wegener, "It is not necessary to stress that this result is ludicrous" (p. 132). On this "fixist" map of widely separate continents, an enormous missing land bridge would need to be inserted to provide a large, pole-centered landmass. Wegener shows just such an enormous missing landmass on another of his maps, shown as our Figure 2.6.

Wegener put together all the pertinent data of stratigraphy on world paleogeographic maps for the Carboniferous and Permian periods, using his version of Pangaea; these are reproduced here as Figure 2.17. Continental fragments that bear the

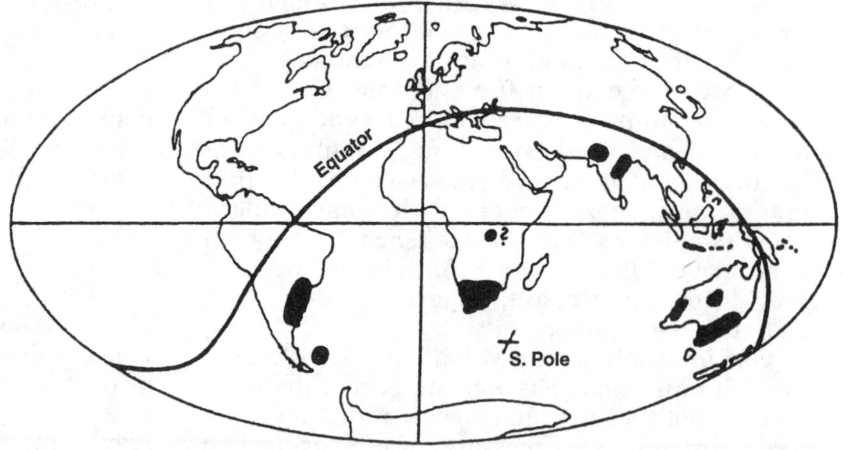

Figure 2.16 Areas in black are where evidences of a Permo-carboniferous glaciation are found today. By rotating the geographic coordinates to produce a different equator and pole (bold line and cross) all glaciated areas fall into the southern hemisphere. (From the English version of the Fourth Revised Edition of A. Wegener, *Die Enstehung der Kontinente und Ozeane*, published in 1929 by Friedr. Vieweg & Sohn, Braunschweig. Translated by John Biram. Copyright © 1966 by Dover Publications, Inc., New York. Used by permission.)

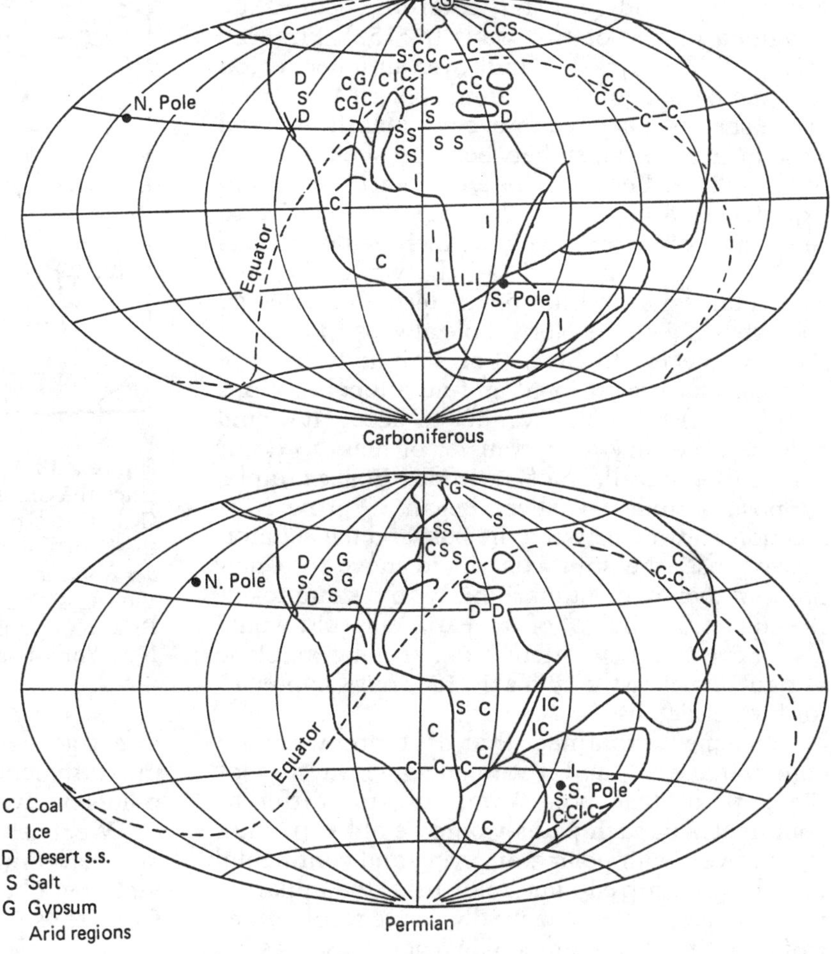

Figure 2.17 Wegener's maps simplified to show locations of ice and sedimentary deposits of Pangaea during the Carboniferous and Permian periods. From these, he fitted to each a new equator and poles, appropriate to the climates indicated by the deposits. (Adapted to English from the English version of the Fourth Revised Edition of A. Wegener, *Die Enstehung der Kontinente und Ozeane*, published in 1929 by Friedr. Vieweg & Sohn,

evidences of glaciation are now neatly nested beneath the pole, including peninsular India (or "Deccan"). Also noteworthy are belts of coals, one close to the equator and another in middle latitudes, while salt and gypsum beds and desert sandstones occupy the two intervening subtropical belts. Note that the North Pole lies out in the Pacific Ocean. The poles are shown to have moved their locations from one period to the next. (Recently constructed paleogeographic maps of these periods are shown in our Chapter 13.) Wegener: "No better corroboration of our theory could be desired" (p. 136).

Not satisfied with the stratigraphic evidence alone, Wegener went to some length to cite opinions of paleobotanists certifying to the wet, equatorial climatic affinity of the Carboniferous plants found in the coal measures (p. 139-44). On a Köppen-Wegener paleobotanical map for the Permocarboniferous he had shown the distribution of *Pectopteris*, a tree fern, selected as representative of the equatorial coal measures. If plotted on the same maps as shown in our Figure 2.17, *Pectopteris* would lie close to the Carboniferous equator. Wegener's comment on this paleogeographic evidence is as follows: "I must repeat that the site of these beds a quarter of a great circle distant from the center of an undoubtedly polar inland ice sheet is an *utterly compelling reason* for believing them to have originated in a climate of equatorial rains; this is quite independent of the problem of continental drift, as I stressed before" (p. 142).

Another important paleobotanical feature is the occurrence of the *Glossopteris flora* in beds resting on tillites of the pole-centered glaciated region. This flora is named for a herbaceous fern, *Glossopteris*, that flourished in bogs in the cold periglacial climate. On Wegener's maps of Carboniferous and Permian times, this evidence strongly reinforces the existence of a single, pole-centered continent.

2.14 Polar Wandering and Continental Drift

As we have already noted, the Köppen-Wegener paleogeographic reconstructions of climates, stratigraphic elements, and biota required two very different kinds of crustal displacement: (1) Continental drift, which is motion of one continental crustal unit relative to another, or to several other units; (2) Polar wandering, in which the entire surface of the earth as a unit is visualized as rotating relative to the earth's axis of rotation. Wegener recognized that polar wandering, which he also called "crustal wandering" and "crustal rotation," could be imagined in one of two ways (p. 152). First, an outer "shell" moves as a unit over an inner region that can be imagined as a solid sphere. Movement of the shell is imagined to occur by plastic or fluid flow in a weak layer between the shell and the inner sphere. Second, the entire earth as a unit experiences a change in the spin axis relative to reference points on the globe; there is no internal relative motion involved. All the while, the spin axis retains its orientation in terms of celestial coordinates, i.e., the North Pole always "points" to *Polaris*, the North Star. (For simplicity, we are disregarding precessional and nutational motions of the axis.) For polar wander to occur, it would only be necessary for a transfer of mass to occur across the parallels of latitude. For example, suppose a huge ice sheet began to grow in a location midway between the pole and the equator. In response, the spin axis would move to a new point of dynamic equilibrium. By the same token the equatorial "bulge" of the earth ellipsoid would also move to a new orientation, keeping its plane at right angles to the spin axis. (See our Chapter 13 for further details.)

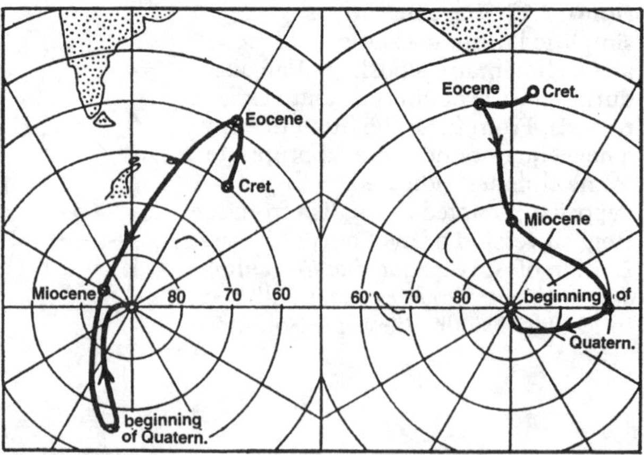

Figure 2.18 Wegener's maps of wandering of the pole since the Cretaceous: (Left) Relative to South America; (Right) Relative to Africa. (From the English version of the Fourth Revised Edition of A. Wegener, *Die Enstehung der Kontinente und Ozeane*, published in 1929 by Friedr. Vieweg & Sohn, Braunschweig. Translated by John Biram. Copyright © 1966 by Dover Publications, Inc., New York. Used by permission.)

Wegener explained that if there were no continental drift, and if we had some way to plot the path of true pole wandering for different continents, all such paths would be alike (p. 149). If, however, both polar wandering and continental drift have occurred simultaneously, the apparent polar wander paths we actually derive would differ from continent to continent. Wegener used as his data the pole positions he and Köppen had estimated from paleoclimate determinations based on geological and paleontological data (see Figure 2.17). He plotted past pole positions from Cretaceous to present. In a pair of maps, reproduced here as Figure 2.18, Wegener shows that the apparent polar wander paths since the Cretaceous are different for South America and Africa (p. 150, Figure 38). The differences in the two paths can be attributed to continental drift motions. In Wegener's time, the use of paleomagnetism as an independent method of locating former pole positions had not yet been discovered, so he could not separate the two effects that might be acting simultaneously to produce the observed wandering curve.

2.15 Rates of Continental Drift—Estimated and Observed

Under the heading of "Geodetic arguments," Wegener's fourth chapter (1966) considers two entirely different approaches to obtaining hard figures as to the rates of continental separation. In the first approach, which was geologic rather than geodetic, he used what were then the going estimates of the durations of geologic epochs or periods and coupled these with estimates of distances of separation. Second, he turned to direct geodetic data, which consisted of repeated measurements of longitudinal differences between points on two continents.

Wegener reviewed the progress of radiometric age determination, which by the mid 1920s was yielding Phanerozoic ages not greatly different from those of the 1960s and later. He first set down a table of elapsed time from the start of each epoch of the Tertiary (Cenozoic) (p. 25). He then made estimates of (a) the total separation distances between each of a number of pairs of coastal points since drift began, and (b) the elapsed time since separation began. These are shown in our Table 2.1, which is adapted from Wegener's table on p. 26, using his figures but revising the wording of the column headings and rearranging the list in increasing order of elapsed time. By comparison with today's estimates and direct geodetic measurements, Wegener's rates are extremely (unreasonably) fast for the North Atlantic separations, diminishing to much slower rates for the distant parts of Gondwanaland. Even these slower rates are greater by a factor of 5 than today's assigned rift-widening rates. The great decrease in rates with elapsed time is striking.

Obviously, we need to look for causes of the discrepancies between Wegener's data and current values. The most obvious place to look first would be at Wegener's schedule of elapsed times on the geologic time scale. These are given in his table on p. 25, and in our Table 2.2. We have placed Wegener's elapsed times in a column between those of Barrell (1917) and Holmes (1933), which bracket him in time. Going back into the Cenozoic (Tertiary), Wegener's times drop drastically in comparison to the others, being on the order of one-fourth of the other values. Thus, we could simply divide Wegener's drift rates for his Eocene

Table 2.1 Wegener's Estimates of Rates of Continental Separation*

Separated continental units	Distance separated (km)	Elapsed time (10^6 yr)	Drift per year (m)
Sabine Island-Bear Island	1070	0.05-0.1	21-11
Cape Farewell-Scotland	1780	0.05-0.1	36-18
Iceland-Norway	920	0.05-0.1	18-9
Madagascar-Africa	890	0.1	9
Newfoundland-Ireland	2410	2-4	1.2-0.6
Tasmania-Wilkes Land	2890	10	0.3
India-southern Africa	5550	20	0.3
Buenos Aires-Cape Town	6620	30	0.2

*Data of A. Wegener, 1966, *The Origin of the Continents and Ocean Basins*. Translated from the 4th revised (1929) German edition by John Biram. New York: Dover Publications, Inc. See p. 26.

Table 2.2 Elapsed Time in Millions of Years Since Start of Epoch or Period through Mesozoic and Cenozoic Eras

	Barrell (1917)	Wegener (1929)	Holmes (1933)	Harland (1989)
Holocene	—	0.01-0.05	—	0.01
Pleistocene (Quat.)	1-1.5	1	1	1.64
Pliocene	7-9	3	15	5.2
Miocene	19-23	6	32	23.5
Oligocene	35-39	10	42	35.5
Eocene + Paleocene	55-65	15	60	65
Cretaceous	120-150	—	128	132
Jurassic	155-195	—	158	208
Triassic	190-240	—	192	245

Sources: See *References Cited* under author name and year.

and Oligocene cases by four, giving rates roughly equivalent to those of modern reckoning (e.g., divide 20 cm/yr by 4, giving 5 cm/yr).

There still remains a glaring discrepancy in the North Atlantic separations, to which Wegener assigns a mere 10,000 to 50,000 years. This means that he visualized the North American landmasses to have been joined together as recently as Late Pleistocene (Wisconsinan) or even at the onset of the Holocene. Confirmation is found in Wegener's map of "Quaternary inland ice, entered on the reconstruction for the period before North America was detached" (1966, legend of Figure 19, p. 77). Describing this map, reproduced here as Figure 2.19, Wegener says that when the existing Pleistocene terminal moraines of North America and northern Europe are plotted on the map "they join without gaps or breaks," (p. 76) and, indeed, he shows just that on his map.

Obviously, delaying the breakup of the northern landmasses until late Pleistocene time would result in deriving enormously rapid rates of separation, i.e., 18-36 m/year. Why did not Wegener assign a much earlier date of breakup than he did? At the risk of being greatly mistaken, we look for a possible answer in the following

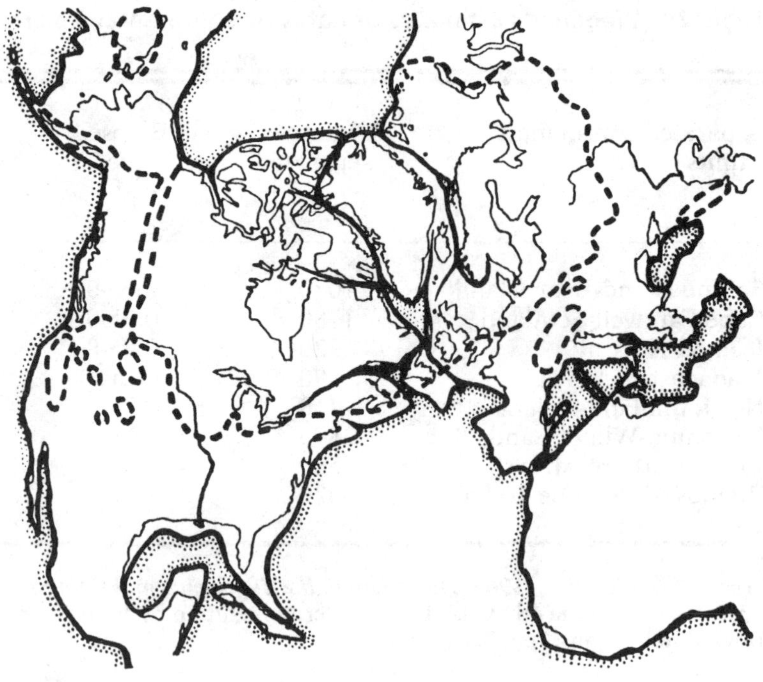

Figure 2.19 Wegener's map of "boundaries of the Quaternary inland ice for the period before North America was detached." (From the English version of the Fourth Revised Edition of A. Wegener, *Die Enstehung der Kontinente und Ozeane*, published in 1929 by Friedr. Vieweg & Sohn, Braunschweig. Translated by John Biram. Copyright © 1966 by Dover Publications, Inc., New York. Used by permission.)

paragraph from Robert Muir Wood's *The Dark Face of the Earth*:

> Immediately after the Great War there was in Germany a flood of pseudo-scientific pamphlets; of myths and magic and of science fiction. There was a clamour for a 'spiritual reorientation' in the face of the tragedy of defeat and the breakdown of government. 'Sensations and imaginative fantasies...would help to conquer gross 'materialism' and its literary counterpart, realism. Wegener's drift could not be assimilated as myth, or not at least in the manner of the most outrageous and successful of the post-war cosmogenies: the '*Welt Eis Lehre*', the creation of an Austrian technician Hans Hörbiger. A large organisation was set up in Germany to proselytise Hörbiger's cosmic history, and an alliance was forged with the Nazi party. In 1925, Hörbiger wrote to all scholars in Germany and Austria stating that 'You now have to choose to be with us or against us'(1985, p. 99-100).

Wood goes on to describe the content of *Welt Eis Lehre*, which explained the Ice Age by the impact of an ice-satellite. Previous impacts of such ice-satellites had occurred at times when Earth peoples had engaged in moral turpitude and racial impurity. Wood gives further details of the scenario (p. 100). He concludes with this paragraph:

> Hörbiger's cosmology offers some insight into Wegener's insistence that Europe and America had been joined to Greenland right into the most recent geological period. Ice lay at the heart of both Hörbiger's and Wegener's histories. If its position was irrational when it was also so integral; Wegener's continental drift could not be sustained without this ingredient. The need to explain the Ice Age; the shadows, however faintly perceived, of some lost North Atlantic continent lie within Wegener's explanation (1985, p. 100).

As a geophysicist, Wegener easily grasped the possibility that precision measurements of longitude, taken at intervals of several years, could lead to recognition of significant and consistent continental drift. He had taken part in such determinations when an assistant on the 1906-1908 Danmark expedition to Greenland. Knowing of earlier longitude measurements from the same station, he looked into the earlier data for indications of increases in longitude of north-eastern Greenland with respect to Europe (p. 26). Determinations of 1823 and 1870 had large standard errors, but they seemed to show separations of 9 and 32 meters per year. These rates were almost unbelievably rapid, but seemingly commensurate with rates he derived by the age-distance method we have described in earlier paragraphs. In 1922, the Danish Survey carried out new longitude determinations in western Greenland using for the first time radio-telegraphy time signals from Europe that greatly reduced the standard error of the determinations (p. 28). Again, the longitude increase of Greenland seemed to confirm continental drift. An even more accurate determination, made in 1922 at Kornok in Godthaab Fiord, and repeated in 1927 yielded an increase in longitude relative to Greenwich equivalent to 0.09 seconds of time, which translated to a drift rate of 36 m/yr (p. 29). In this case the increase was nine times greater than the mean error of the observations, leading Wegener to write: "The result is proof of a displacement of Greenland that is still in progress. As a result of this first precise astronomical proof of a continental drift, which fully corroborates the predictions of drift theory in a quantitative manner, the whole discussion of the theory, in my view, is put on a new footing." (p. 30). Similar observations of the longitude of Cambridge, Massachusetts, vis-à-vis Greenwich suggested a possible annual longitude increase of 0.6 m, but with a relatively large possible error (p. 31). In an appendix, Wegener announced the results of Washington-Paris determinations comparing data of 1913/14 with those of 1927 (p. 217). Again, an increase was found, the annual value being about 0.1 m.

The modern era of determination of differences in ground distance by satellites making use of radar (Laser Geodynamics Satellite, or LAGEOS), begun in 1977 and continued through the 1980s by use of the Very Long Baseline Interferometry (VLBI) method, only began to detect by 1985 possible significant increases in the distance between Massachusetts and Europe. The indicated rate was only about 2 centimeters per year—only 1/1,800 the value Wegener claimed in 1929! Thus something proved to have been very wrong with the geodetic data acquired in Wegener's time. (This topic is continued in Chapter 7).

2.16 Forces Causing Continental Drift

Wegener was well aware of the great difficulties to be anticipated in solving the question of forces causing continental drift. He predicted that "the complete solution to the problem of the driving forces will still be a long time coming" (1966, p. 167). He recognized two forms, or directions, of displacement: (a) westward drift of the continents and (b) their "flight from the poles," or movement from higher to lower latitudes (p. 169). These motions can be described by the words "zonal" and "meridional," respectively, if we may borrow from the terminology of movements of the atmospheric jet streams. The extremely slow meridional drift away from the poles would not be easily recognized because it would be overshadowed by polar wandering. (See Chapter 7.)

Wegener thought that the meridional drift to lower latitudes could be explained through the Eötvös force, recognized in 1913 by an author of that name, but appearing in the literature as early as 1900. This pole-flight force (*Polfluchtkraft*) could be deduced as a result of the oblateness of the rotating ellipsoid applied to a floating body and is the resultant of two opposed forces acting upon the body in slightly different directions. Wegener quotes a full explanation from W. Köppen. (See Wegener, p. 169-174 for details and references.) The pole-flight force reaches its maximum value at the 45th parallel of latitude, where it is one three-millionth as strong as the gravitational force. Among the opinions expressed by various investigators quoted by Wegener, one seems to be firmly expressed, namely, that the pole-flight force is insufficient to have produced the compressional mountain ranges (orogens) that arose along the leading edges of equatorward-drifting continental masses of sial (p. 172). With this opinion, Wegener agreed (p. 174).

Turning to the westward, or meridional component of continental drift, Wegener commented that there is much less to be said about it than about the pole-flight force (p. 175). The possible efficacy of the frictional effect of earth-tides was considered with the highly tentative conclusion that "it nevertheless seems very likely that the most clearly recognizable general movement of the continents, their westerly drift, could be explained by the attractive forces of the sun and moon on the viscous earth" (p. 176).

Wegener then turned to Helmert's hypothesis of the earth's figure being that of a triaxial ellipsoid, in which the equator would be an ellipse rather than a circle. In effect, this geometry results in two opposed, broad crustal arches separated by opposed depressions (as referred to a circular equator). The next step was to suggest that, in response to the need to restore the equilibrium state of a rotating ellipsoid of revolution, sima would tend to flow down the flanks of the arches. Perhaps the opening up of the Atlantic could be explained this way (p. 176-177).

That thought led Wegener to yet another interesting idea, but it applied to pole-flight rather than to westward drift. Polar wandering would displace the equatorial bulge from its equilibrium location on the equator, setting up a gradient that would cause continents to drift. The force, "many times the normal pole-flight force," would act not only on the sial blocks but also on the underlying sima as well. Wegener: "I would like to believe that we have in this deformation of the earth's shape by polar wandering a completely adequate source of power to supply the energy required for folding" (p. 178).

The closing paragraphs of Wegener's Chapter 10 on "displacement forces" contain perhaps its most significant statements; these relate to "the concept of convection currents in the sima" (p. 178). He refers to other authors, including R. Schwinner (1919) and especially G. Kirsch (1928) as having made use of that concept. [See Wegener, 1966, for reference citations.] Both used Joly's idea of radiogenic heat buildup under the continents and its dissipation from the oceanic crust. Wegener states: "Kirsch assumes a circulation of sima beneath the crust: It rises below the continents up to their lower boundary, then flows along under them to the ocean regions, where it flows downwards, returning to the continents after reaching greater depths" (p. 178). This flow system

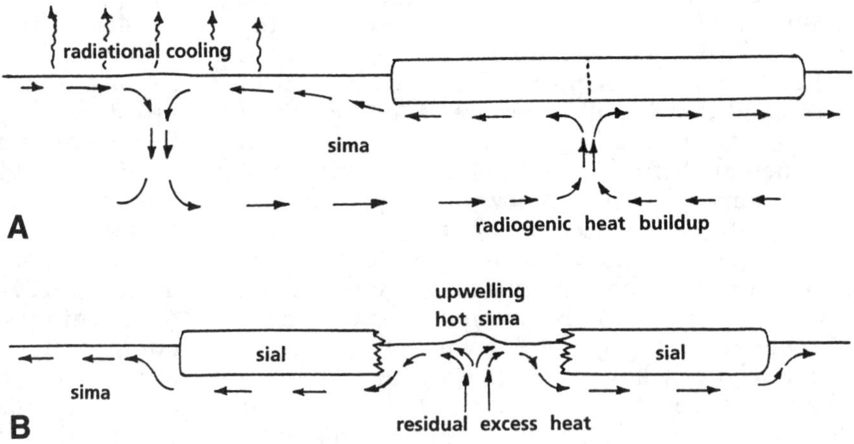

Figure 2.20 (A) Schematic diagram of G. Kirch's 1928 model of hot fluid sima rising and flowing beneath a continent of sial. (B) Deduced consequence of Kirsch's model to include continental rifting and opening of a new ocean basin. (Copyright © by Arthur N. Strahler.)

is diagrammed in our Figure 2.20A. "Because of the resulting friction, he [Kirsch] says, the sima tends to disrupt the continental cover and force the fragments apart" (p. 178). This model of mantle heating, uparching, and continental rifting (to use modern terms) is in vogue today, as we explain in Chapter 10. Of course, Kirsch would have the convection currents converging in a mid-oceanic location, rather than diverging there, as seafloor spreading now requires, so that part of his model would require later rejection. Wegener conceded that Kirsch's model would apply nicely to the breakup of both Gondwanaland and the American-Eurasian landmass (Laurasia) and that it "apparently offers a reasonable explanation of the opening up of the Atlantic Ocean" (p. 178). On the other hand he seemed reluctant to endorse the idea further because "the relatively greater fluidity of the sima, as assumed here, has been regarded as unlikely by the majority of authors to date" (p. 178).

How close Wegener came to adopting a mechanism and driving force that would hold up under the attacks of his critics! But now look a step further to a missing logical deduction that might have been seized upon. If a rising convection current, diverging into two horizontal currents, caused a continent to break into two parts, surely the same divergence of hot sima would have persisted along the midline of the new opening ocean for millions of years, until the excess mantle heat had been dissipated (Figure 2.20B). So therein lay a lightly veiled invitation to embrace the midoceanic spreading concept of today's plate tectonics, it was an opportunity that eluded both Kirsch and Wegener, but was soon to be seized upon by others.

As we bring to a close this review of Wegener's hypothesis of continental drift, and before turning him over to the tender mercies of his contemporaries, it is fitting to quote the final paragraph of his chapter on displacement forces:

> We may, however, assume one thing as certain: *The forces which displace continents are the same as those which produce great fold-mountain ranges*. Continental drift, faults and compressions, earthquakes, volcanicity, transgression cycles and polar wandering are undoubtedly connected causally on a grand scale. Their common intensification in certain periods of the earth's history shows this to be true. However, what is cause and what effect, only the future will unveil (1966, p. 179).

Wegener's vision of a grand new paradigm of earth history that was to arise from the ashes of an outmoded and discredited fixist/contractionist paradigm was to be put on hold for nearly four decades.

2.17 The Response to Wegener's Hypothesis

Reaction to the hypothesis of continental drift while Wegener was alive and revising his work came slowly and hesitatingly at first. We turn first to the negative reaction and its expression, which began to mount some years before his death in 1930, particularly among the Anglo-American geologists who were staunch supporters of the fixist/contractionist view. A few geologists supported the hypothesis and began to amplify and apply it; these we will consider in later paragraphs.

Two strongly unfavorable reviews of the second edition (1920) appeared in 1922. One was by the American geologist Harry Fielding Reid, perhaps best known for his "elastic rebound" theory of the San Francisco earthquake; the other by British geologist Philip Lake. These and other early responses are fully covered by Marvin (1973, p. 82-86) and Wood (1985, p. 73-82).

Most of the significant objections voiced by the Anglo-American critics are covered in a 1928 volume, *Theory of Continental Drift*, representing papers presented and discussion thereof at a symposium held in New York City in 1926 under the auspices of the American Association of Petroleum Geologists. The symposium had been organized by the Dutch petroleum geologist W.A.J.M. van Waterschoot van der Gracht, who seems to have hoped for fair and open discussion of all versions of continental drift. His published "Introduction" runs to 75 pages—about one-third of the entire volume (Van der Gracht, 1928). His elucidation of the contributions of John Joly, Frank B. Taylor, Alfred Wegener, and Reginald A. Daly is detailed and shows a grasp of the major problems involved in explaining horizontal crustal motions, along with the fundamental physical principles involved—an excellent review of the state-of-the-art. Van der Gracht wrote supportively of the drift hypotheses of Taylor, Wegener, Joly, and Daly, stating that he personally was in favor of continental drift, but not necessarily as presented by these writers (p. 75). In contrast were the outspokenly negative contributions of the Anglo-American fixists: Bailey Willis, Rollin T. Chamberlin, J.W. Gregory, and Charles Schuchert. Taylor presented a review of his own hypothesis; Wegener a brief statement in his own behalf. Van der Gracht added a 29-page summary of what the contributors had said.

Here, we give little attention to those objections to Wegener's work that were later to be refuted or rendered specious by evidence supporting the modern version of plate tectonics, nor do we repeat most of the *ad hominem* arguments and insinuations aimed at Wegener. Focus must be on Wegener's greatest problem: the forces and mechanisms capable of driving continental drift and of also causing compressional folding and thrusting of the continental margins.

To dispose first of *ad hominen*, here is number 17 of the 18 "objections" Rollin T. Chamberlin urged against Wegener's hypothesis:

> Wegener's hypothesis in general is of the foot-loose type, in that it takes considerable liberty with our globe, and is less bound by restrictions or tied down by awkward, ugly facts than most of its rival theories. Its appeal seems to lie in the fact that it plays a game in which there are few restrictive rules and no sharply drawn code of conduct. (1928, p. 87).

Bailey Willis had his own *ad hominem* style:

> When we consider the manner in which the theory is presented we find: that the author offers no direct proof of its verity; that the indirect proofs assembled from geology, paleontology, and geophysics prove nothing in regard to drift...; that the fields of related sciences have been searched for arguments that would lend color to the adopted theory, whereas facts and principles opposed to it have been ignored. Thus the book leaves the impression that it has been written by an advocate rather than by an impartial investigator (1928, p.82).

We next concentrate on the objections (a) to blocks of sial moving (drifting) through the sima in which they "floated" with a low freeboard, and (b) to sialic blocks experiencing folding (crumpling) at the leading edge when moving through sima. Both of these points had previously been addressed by the distinguished British physicist, Harold Jeffreys, in his 1924 book *The Earth, Its Origin, History, and Physical Constitution*. Of the symposium contributors, only one—Chester R. Longwell—refers to that work, but nowhere in the symposium volume is Jeffreys's argument fully presented; nevertheless it has priority. Jeffreys had pinpointed the most serious flaw in Wegener's proposal, namely, the inadequacy of the forces invoked by Wegener to accomplish either the drift of the continents or the formation of compressional mountain ranges. Longwell, following Jeffreys, noted that "the discrepancy between the work performed in making mountains and the forces assumed for the task is very great. Jeffreys has computed that the forces charged with moving the Americas westward amount to 1/100,000 dyne per square centimeter; the force necessary to make the Rocky Mountains is 1,000,000,000 dynes per square centimeter" (1928, p. 151). (Longwell references the last sentence to Jeffreys, 1924, p. 261.)

Marvin states Jeffreys's continuing argument as follows:

> It is an impossible hypothesis, said Jeffreys, that a "small force can not only produce indefinitely great movement, given a long enough time, but that it can overcome a force many times greater acting in the opposite direction for the same time." He made the point that if sima is the weaker layer and will allow continents to plough through it like ships sailing before the wind, then it will not crumple their prows--even less will it keep them sailing. And he added that even Wegener's ice floes are never deformed by the resistance of open water but only by collision with other ice fields or by running aground in bottom sediment, a truly resistant medium (1973, p. 87).

On the problem of moving blocks of sial, Willis pointed out that the forces invoked to cause westward drift "would act more effectively on the denser sima than on the lighter sial, in the proportion of the densities. How is it, then, that the lighter continental mass is drawn forward by a lesser force through the denser sub-oceanic mass, which remains stationary under a stronger pull?" (1928, p. 78)

Longwell argued that, even if we accept the

premise that the deep sima in which the sialic raft was floating behaves as a true viscous fluid and hence might allow the sial to drift through it, surely the uppermost zone of the sial under the ocean floors would be in a strong, rigid, crystalline state. This rigid zone (which we would now identify as lithosphere) "must be at least 30 miles thick." Longwell then asked: "Are we to believe that this material, superior in strength, is displaced like a liquid by the floating sial?" (1928, p. 150) He would not emphatically say that such a lateral displacement is not possible but merely "that in the light of all our knowledge in geophysics and geology the conception is improbable in the highest degree" (p. 150). In short, a thick, rigid surface layer of sima would prohibit the drift of blocks of sial.

On the problem of the folding of sial in the leading edge of a continental block, Willis challenged the concept on the grounds that for the sial to float as a block, the medium in which it floats—the sima—must be the more yielding of the two. Why, then, should the moving floating body be forced to yield? This is essentially the argument that had been made by Jeffreys, using the simile of a ship's prow being crumpled by the water through which it plows. For his simile, Willis chose the patently absurd picture of a "leaden chisel thrust into steel" (1928, p. 78). For the sial to yield, he argued, it would have to be weaker than the sima, but that would reverse Wegener's essential postulate. Clearly, opposite postulates could not be allowed. There could be either continental drift or marginal folding, but not both under one consistent physical model of sima and sial. Longwell cited the same difficulty: "The inconsistency of Wegener's argument is obvious. In order to conceive that the continents may be propelled at all, we must assume that the sima is devoid of strength with relation to secular forces. Therefore there could be no resistance, no back thrust, to fold the mountains" (1928, p. 150-51).

Many pages would be needed to cover adequately all the objections urged by authors of the 1928 AAPG symposium against Wegener's hypothesis of continental drift. Suffice it to say that Wegener's evidence that drift had occurred on a large scale remained in contention and many geologists found it convincing. On the other hand, Wegener's proposed mechanism for continental drift and the origin of marginal fold systems stood thoroughly rejected by the weight of physics. For lack of a plausible mechanism, his entire hypothesis was discredited by all but a few. There were, however, some geologists discerning enough to realize that evidence favoring the proposition that drift had occurred can be judged sound and convincing in the absence of an explanation. One of these was the South African geologist, Lester C. King, who said: "The driftist is no more obliged to adduce a mechanism to prove the fact of drift than the user of an electric appliance is obliged to define the nature and mechanism of electricity" (1957, p. 79). After all, the Copernican heliocentric solar system of 1543, strongly suggested by Galileo's astronomical observations of 1632, received wide acceptance without a physical explanation being available. Not until a half century later did Newton come forward with the explanatory laws of gravitation and motion (1687).

For those readers wishing to investigate further the response of the geological community to Wegener's theory, Henry Frankel, viewing the debate from the standpoint of the philosophy of science, has analyzed the cognitive aspects of the sharply negative responses of specialists in the various fields involved (1976).

In retrospect, perhaps the most significant lesson of the entire debate lies in the role of geophysics—vis-à-vis that of traditional geology—as the prime mover of scientific discovery in this precursory phase of a new understanding of the workings of the solid earth. Wegener was trained in geophysics, which today formally includes the subjects of gravity, geodesy, terrestrial magnetism, tectonophysics, and seismology. Wegener turned naturally to evidence from geophysics. Without these investigative tools, the paradigm of global plate tectonics could not have emerged. This may seem to be an overstatement, but it follows from the observation that classical geology, including such conventional fields as stratigraphy, structural geology, petrology, and geochemistry, were in a comparatively high state of development by the mid-1900s, insofar as description of the continental crust is concerned. Although enormous piles of descriptive data had accumulated in those fields, their interpreters were powerless to explain such enigmatic features as the melanges of Newfoundland and California and the ophiolitic suites in continental sutures. In chapters to come, geophysics will emerge as the key to an understanding of the processes of plate tectonics.

2.18 Alternative Drift Hypotheses of the 1920s

While Wegener's hypothesis of continental drift was undergoing revision and gaining support from some geoscientists but harvesting scathing criticism from others, two quite different models of earth evolution involving lateral motions of continents were put forward for serious consideration. One was by an American geologist, Professor Reginald Alsworth Daly of Harvard University; the other by John Joly, Professor of Geology at Trinity College, Dublin, Ireland.

Daly's hypothesis, often referred to as the "theory of continental sliding," was contained in his 1926 book, *Our Mobile Earth*. Daly, as did Taylor, focused on the Tertiary (Cenozoic) mountain and island arcs, i.e., upon compressional tectonics. He was a contractionist and favored the concept of great crustal arches, or "continental domes," raised by contraction. The idea is quite similar to that put forward by Eduard Suess in the early 1900s. The raised areas were composed of sialic (granitic) crust and may have earlier been grouped into a primitive continent, or "land hemisphere" (Daly, 1926, p. 274). This granitic crustal mass, upon breaking into fragments, yielded a number of tilted crustal blocks. Daly described what happened next:

> The continents appear to have slid down-hill, to have been pulled down over the earth's body, by mere gravity; mountain structures appear to be the product of enormous, slow *landslides*. Each chain has been folded at the foot of a crust block of continental dimensions, which was not quite level, but slightly tilted (1926, p. 263).

The important contribution made by Daly perhaps lies in his concept of a weak underlying glassy layer of hot basalt that could easily permit the lateral movement of an overlying strong, rigid layer consisting of the granitic layer and an underlying zone of crystallized basalt. The crystalline basalt layer was present over the entire earth. This structure is shown in his diagram (1926, p. 269), reproduced here as Figure 2.21. The same crust/mantle relationship had been described much earlier by Joseph Barrell (1914-15), who proposed the terms "lithosphere" and "asthenosphere" for the rigid and weak layers, respectively, but Daly did not use these terms until much later. Daly wrote: "The physical nature of the substratum, the material just below the crust, is of crucial importance. Because it is hot glass it offers but very small resistance to slow sliding of the crust-fragment of the dome; in a sense, the *substratum is slippery*" (p. 269).

Daly's vision of how fold-mountain belts arise is shown in his figure. A geosyncline (troughlike body of sedimentary strata) occupies a broad crustal depression (Diagram A). The crust at the margin of the depression fractures under the loading stress and creates a downplunging crustal slab, the leading part of which breaks off and sinks into the hot glassy substratum (Diagram B). As this happens, the tilted plate (at right) slides "downhill" under gravity to crumple the geosyncline into folds (i.e., into a compressional orogen).

While Daly's mountain-building process shows some similarities to that of Taylor, the difference lies in the repeatability of the fracture-and-slide mechanism. This kind of event occurred repeatedly through geologic time; it was the process by which an initial, globally complete granitic layer (covered by the world ocean, Panthalassa) became coalesced into a single thick granitic continent. The resulting high "dome" of granitic rock broke under its own weight into fragments and the parts separated under gravity to move toward the lower-lying Pacific region (Marvin, 1973, p. 98). This event occurred in Mesozoic time and agrees more or less with Wegener's schedule.

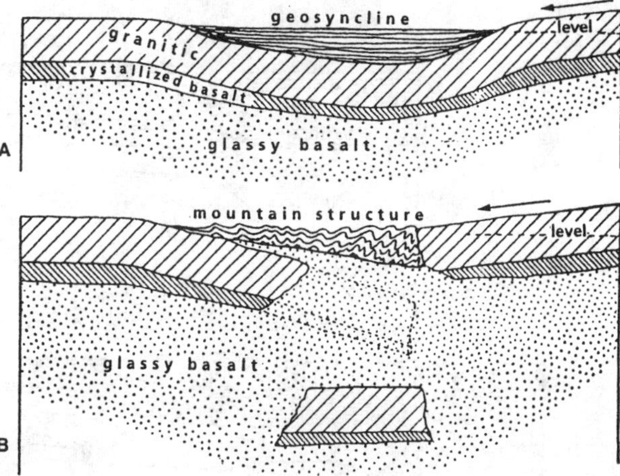

Figure 2.21 R.A. Daly's drawings illustrating his theory of "continental sliding." Postulated densities (g/cm^3) are as follows: granite, 2.65; crystallized basalt, 3.00; glassy basalt, 2.80-2.85. (From R.A. Daly, 1926, *Our Mobile Earth*, Charles Scribner's Sons. Reproduced by permission of the publisher.)

In looking at Daly's diagram, we may be tempted to see it as a precursor to the modern concept of formation of a new subduction plate boundary within oceanic lithosphere. The difference, of course, is that Daly shows continental lithosphere breaking and foundering under compression, an event ruled out by plate tectonics on grounds of crustal density. What Daly can be justifiably credited with is adopting Barrell's static lithosphere-asthenosphere model and imposing on it great lateral motions of the lithosphere over the asthenosphere.

Joly's major contribution to continental drift was to emphasize the role of radiogenic heat in crustal processes, particularly in powering a sequence of tectonic events then known as geologic "revolutions." These catastrophic events required great lateral motions of continents, but Joly was not a supporter of slow inter-continental drift in the style of Wegener (Van der Gracht, 1928, p. 42). As we noted earlier in presenting Kirsch's model of convection currents, Joly's exposition of the role of radiogenic heat could have been used by Wegener to formulate a physically acceptable continent-moving force, but that link was never forged.

Joly's hypothesis (1925) is fully presented by Van der Gracht (1928, p. 42-54); we sketch it very briefly here. Radiogenic heat accumulates in the sima beneath the sialic continents. The heat has no way to escape, except downwards, because of the great thickness of the overlying rock. As a consequence, melting occurs first in the upper levels of the sima, then progresses deeper into the sima. This creates, in effect an "ocean" of liquid

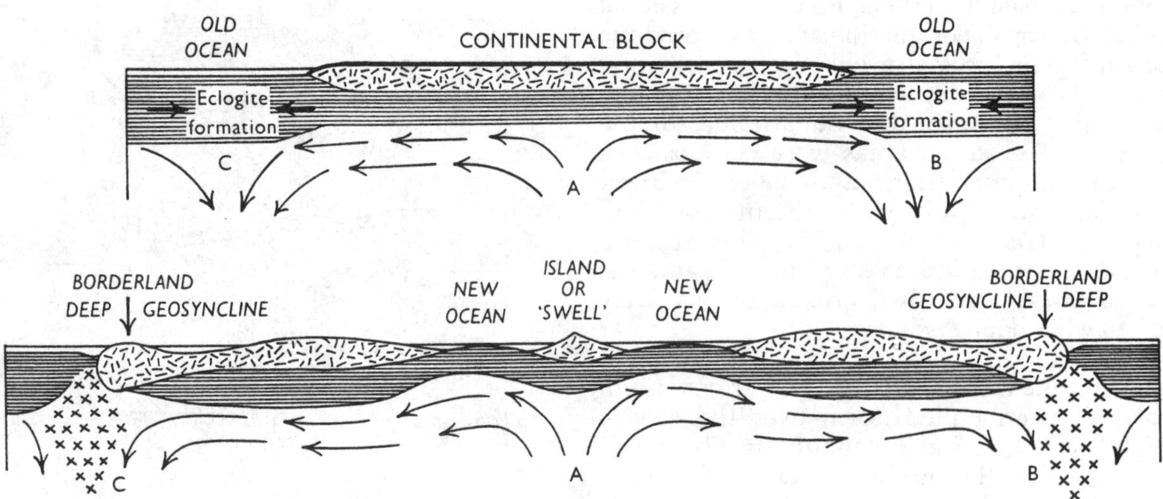

Figure 2.22 A model of mantle convection introduced in 1929 by Arthur Holmes. Extension of the continental crust is shown to have resulted in the opening of new ocean basins. (From A. Holmes, 1928-1929, Radioactivity and Earth Movements, *Trans. Geological Society of Glascow*, v. 18, p. 559-606, Figures 2 and 3.)

sima on which the crystalline sial layer above can float. If the accumulation of radiogenic heat were to continue, an "impossible" situation would arise. This crisis is averted when the layer of liquid magma extends beneath not only the continents but also under the entire layer of crystalline sima beneath the ocean basins. Now, heat is dissipated upward through the thin oceanic sima, while at the same time a circulation system of convection currents would be set up in the molten zone to transfer the heat from the subcontinental source to the oceanic sink. The floating solid crust could now respond to tide-raising forces, resulting in its westward drift, carrying along the sialic continents. Further dissipation of excess heat would result when the sialic masses (a) moved laterally away from their former positions or (b) broke into fragments, forming new inter-continental oceans. Thus continental drift comes about. Liquifaction of the lower zone of the sial would cause the continents to sink to a lower equilibrium position, resulting in flooding (transgression) of those land surfaces.

Joly's mechanism for generating compressional orogens (fold belts) at the continental margins is stated in rather vague terms. In his brief contribution to the 1928 AAPG symposium, he states that, besides tidal forces, "other disintegrating forces would probably arise out of the contraction and expansion of the outer crust which occurs at each great revolution" (1928, p. 88). Those changes would be mainly in the oceanic crust. He concludes:

> Here, accordingly, the mountain-building forces originate. That the force which wrinkled the western side of North and South America would be competent to shift these continents as a whole, supposing sufficient inequality of thrusts at opposite continental margins, seems highly probable (p. 88).

2.19 Convection Currents Come to the Aid of Continental Drift

Following Wegener's death in 1930, the hypothesis of continental drift was to be carried through the next decade by two fully sympathetic geologists: Arthur Holmes and Alexander du Toit. Both were to make use of convection currents below the crust to supply the competent driving force so conspicuously lacking in Wegener's presentation.

Arthur Holmes (1890-1965) had achieved wide recognition and a high level of respect within the geological community for his pioneering work in radiometric age determination. Beginning his education in physics at Imperial College, London, under R.J. Strutt (later to become Lord Rayleigh), Holmes developed an interest in radioactivity as applied to geology. Strutt had encouraged him to investigate the uranium-lead method of radiometric age determination, a project Holmes pursued to the point that he became the leading authority on age determination (Holmes, 1913). His first detailed time scale of the Phanerozoic periods was published in 1933 (see our Table 2.2)

Holmes investigated Wegener's hypothesis rigorously from the standpoint of the forces involved and in the late 1920s published a paper presenting his own model of the upper earth layers and their physical behavior (Holmes, 1928-29). In Holmes's model, the "crust" is a crystalline (solid) zone that includes the granitic "continental blocks"

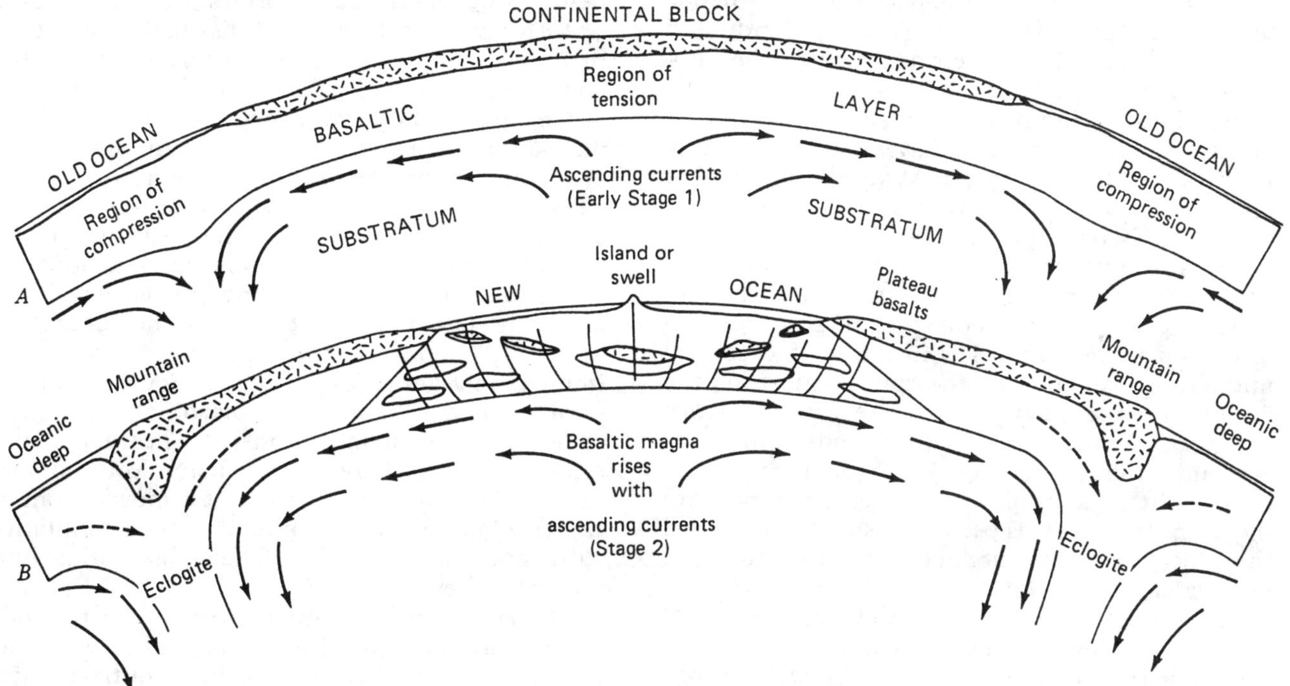

Figure 2.23 Published in 1944, this drawing illustrates Arthur Holmes's updated hypothesis of mantle convection currents as the driving force for continental drift and the opening of a new ocean basin. (From A. Holmes, 1944, *Principles of Geology*, Reproduced by permission of Thomas Nelson and Sons, Ltd.)

as well as a continuous basaltic layer that underlies both the continents and ocean basins. At a depth of 40 to 80 km, Holmes's "crust" grades down into a "substratum" that is glassy, has no permanent strength, and is capable of slow continuous flowage (Holmes, 1933, p. 187). Barrell's terms "lithosphere" and "asthenosphere" would apply, respectively, to Holmes's "crust" and "substratum." Holmes's cross-sectional diagrams showing crust and substratum are reproduced here as Figures 2.22 and 2.23; these are his 1928-29 and 1944 versions, respectively. The earlier version is clearly explained in his own figure legend, and restated in the third and last edition of his famed geology textbook, revised by Doris L. Holmes:

> Diagrams to illustrate a convective-current mechanism for 'engineering' continental drift and the development of new ocean basins, proposed by A. Holmes in 1928, when it was thought that the oceanic crust was a thick continuation of the continental basaltic layer (horizontal line shading). (*Above*) A current ascending at A spreads out laterally, extends the continental block and drags the two main parts aside, provided that the obstruction of the old ocean floor can be overcome. This is accomplished by the formation of eclogite at B and C, where sub-continental currents meet sub-oceanic currents and turn downwards. Being heavy, the eclogite is carried down, so making room for the continents to advance. (*Below*) The foundering masses of eclogite at B and C share in the main convective circulation and, melting at depth to form basaltic magma, the material rises in ascending currents: e.g. at A, healing the gaps in the disrupted continent and forming new ocean floors (locally with a swell of old sial left behind, such as Iceland). (Holmes, 1928-1929, p. 579; 1978, p. 640.)

Holmes explained that at the continental margin compression against the oceanic crust would thicken the basaltic layer ("region of compression" in Figure 2.23). Thickening would be accompanied by an increase in pressure and temperature, altering the basalt to eclogite, which is denser and would tend to sink. The eclogite would break off in blocks that would sink into the substratum, increasing the downward speed of the convection current. (The "blocks" are shown by X's in Holmes's drawing, seen in our Figure 2.22.) In this way, room would be made for the continental block to advance. The downsinking would also account for the ocean deeps, or trenches. Compression of the edge of the continental block against the oncoming oceanic crust would have caused the granitic layer to thicken greatly (by thrust faulting and folding), resulting in the rise of a mountain range with a deep root (1933, p. 189).

Holmes's drawing located the rising convection current beneath the central part of the continental block because the production of radiogenic heat is most intense within the granitic layer. Like Joly before him, he supposed the heat would be unable to escape upwards and would be conducted downward, raising the temperature of the substratum. At sufficiently high temperatures, he wrote, the substratum would reach a condition of no strength; i.e., it would behave as a viscous fluid. Holmes's 1928-29 diagram showed the granitic layer to be rifted, whereas the basaltic layer beneath it is not shown to be broken. Moreover, Holmes shows no magma rising through the basaltic crust and reaching the surface. This, then, is not a picture of seafloor spreading as found in modern plate tectonics. The insertion of a residual midoceanic island with the same pattern as the granitic rock scarcely seems correct as analogous to Iceland or any of the basaltic islands of the mid-oceanic ridge. Moreover, his island shows no central rift. Placing descending currents beneath the deeps (trenches) is perhaps a small step toward the concept of plate subduction destined to come years later.

It is interesting to look at the later version of the 1928-29 drawings appearing in the first edition (1944) of Holmes's *Principles of Physical Geology* (see our Figure 2.23). Beneath the "new ocean," fragments of sialic crust are shown to have foundered to become inclusions in the new section of the basaltic layer (marked off by opposed lines slanting outward at left and right). Sets of oblique curved lines suggest either (a) normal faults or (b) accreted portions of new crust. Whether the single vertical line in the center is intended to represent a midoceanic rift is not made clear. Altogether, this diagram is more enigmatic than elucidative. Whether it can be justifiably claimed as the earliest description of seafloor spreading along an axial crustal rift is questionable; an affirmative answer is perhaps permitted, but not easy to defend.

Years later, speaking to the above question, Arthur A. Meyerhoff nominated Arthur Holmes as "originator of (the) spreading ocean floor hypothesis" (1968, p. 6563). This he did on the basis of the 1928-29 diagram we have analyzed. Replies by Robert S. Dietz and Harry H. Hess accompanied Meyerhoff's paper (p. 6567, 6569). Commented Dietz: "Holmes' concept is not really sea-floor spreading. He resorts to thinning of the crust rather than creating new oceanic crust at the mid-ocean swell and destroying it in trenches in the conveyor belt fashion of seafloor spreading." Hess commented that Holmes's model and that of modern sea-floor spreading "have very little in common except for a propelling mechanism of mantle convection." (The modern concept of seafloor spreading is covered in our Chapter 7.)

Comparing Holmes's model with that of Kirsch (1928), quoted by Wegener (1929, p. 178) and illustrated in our Figure 2.20, reveals a possible serious defect in the former. Kirsch, following Joly, had the heated basalt move out into the ocean basin, where it could be cooled, become denser, and thus set in motion a sinking current. Holmes, by locating his sinking eclogite currents directly below thickened crust, offers no comparable opportunity for external heat dissipation, and thus provides no single great thermal sink for completing the energy-flow cycle. In 1933, Holmes wrote: "Excess heat from the substratum is (thus) discharged (a) by cooling due to thinning of the crust and consequent development of basins, geosynclines or ocean floors over the sites of ascending currents; (b) by the heating-up and remelting of crustal materials carried down in descending currents; and (c) by igneous activity of all kinds" (1933, p. 188-89). Note, however, that under (a), cooling through the ocean floor immediately above the rising hot current would perhaps tend to damp the horizontal convection rather than to sustain it. Under (b), heating up and remelting at depth, the heat of fusion would simply be absorbed into the system, not removed from it. Under (c) there may be doubt as to the quantitative sufficiency of this mode of heat dissipation into the atmosphere.

Reliance upon the phase change to produce eclogite and the downdrag of blocks of eclogite to power the down-current appears contrived and little more than an *ad hoc* device. Note that, elsewhere, Holmes stated that the dense eclogite facies "is sucked down by downward-flowing currents" (1933, p. 189). On the question of continental rifting, Hallam (1973, p. 30) states that "Holmes preferred a model whereby such rifts are formed under compression rather than tension, as was widely assumed." This comment seems strange in view of Holmes's provision for arching and extensional rifting above the rising convection current.

Despite these possible negative points, it is generally agreed that Holmes had made substantial progress in explaining continental drift through the dynamics of mantle convection. Much to his credit, Holmes seems to be the first to suggest that the continental margins bordered by oceanic trenches are the loci of downward movement of crustal material. No hint is given, however, of a subducting crustal plate. It is especially significant that Holmes locates his driving convection cell beneath the continental lithosphere, whereas modern plate tectonics locates the driving convection cell beneath the oceanic lithosphere.

Alexander L. du Toit (1878-1948), a leading geologist of South Africa, had made extensive field investigations of the geology of the various parts of Suess's Gondwanaland. Upon learning of Wegener's hypothesis, du Toit had accepted continental drift as almost "a self-evident truth" (Wood, 1985, p. 107). His 1937 volume, *Our Wandering Continents*, was dedicated to Wegener and to reinforcing the geological evidence of formerly united continents. Instead of a single Pangaea, du Toit identified two supercontinents: *Laurasia* and *Gondwana*, but these were contiguous from the Mediterranean region to the Himalayas. The du Toit map of Gondwana is reproduced here as Figure 2.24. It is interesting for

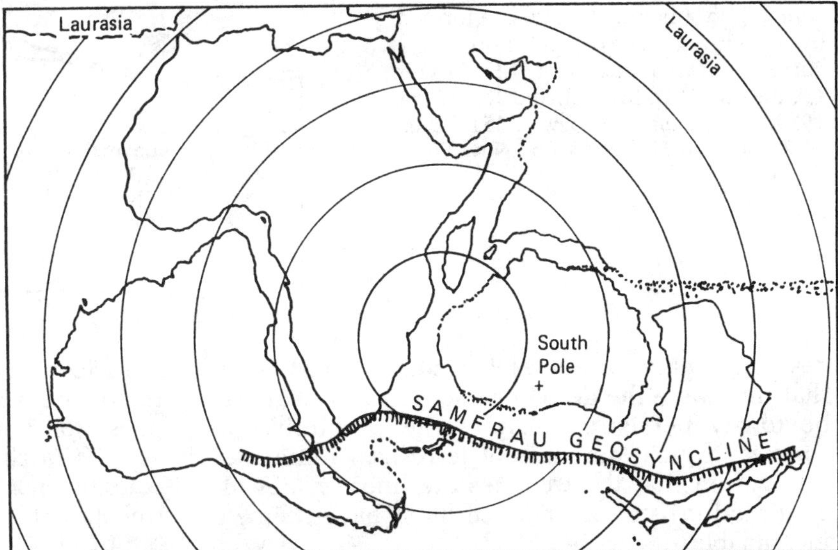

Figure 2.24 Alexander du Toit's 1937 reconstruction of Pangaea showing the position of the SAMFRAU geosyncline. (From A. du Toit, 1937, *Our Wandering Continents*, Figure 7. Oliver & Boyd, Ltd. Edinburgh. Reproduced by permission.)

his drawing of the Paleozoic "Samfrau geosyncline," traced continuously from South America, across southernmost Africa to eastern Australia. (The name is an acronym: "S-AMerica-aFRica-AUstralia.) As to the Permian glaciation of Gondwana, du Toit considered it to have consisted of a time-succession of smaller icecaps appearing first in Argentina and subsequently in South Africa, India, and Australia.

What is perhaps most significant in du Toit's view of global geology is that he pictured the ocean basins as underlain by sial (Marvin, 1973, p. 107-108). This interpretation, which is seen in his diagrams (reproduced here as Figure 2.25), was grossly out of step with the then-prevailing consensus of a sima floor. The du Toit model of drift used convection currents in the sima, rising and diverging in the middle region of the continents, and causing extensional rifting. The convection cell is closed by return flow at relatively shallow depth. Thickening and folding at the continental margin forced the sial down into a trench ("fosse") or foredeep. However, du Toit seems not to have carried out the mid-continent rifting in his lower diagram to the point of great continental separation, demanded by the comparison of his Gondwana with the present geography. Had he tried to do so, he would have encountered extreme difficulty in flooring such new, widening basins with sial. Perhaps he could have accomplished this flooring by downdropping of a succession of sialic fault blocks, as if tiles were being laid down continuously. In that case, his continents would have become progressively narrower, since he had no mechanism of adding to them at the same rate at their opposite margins.

2.20 Mantle Convection and the Tectogene

Early attempts to explain systems of alpine nappes through mantle convection form an interesting phase of geology that emerged just prior to plate tectonics. The problem attracted the attention of some of the best geologists and geophysicists during the 1920s through the 1940s. They focused on the great Cenozoic mountain arcs, such as the European Alps and the circum-Pacific island arcs and mountain arcs bordered by deep trenches. As we have seen, these arcs had been interpreted by a succession of speculators—among them Taylor, Wegener, Argand, Joly, Daly, and Holmes—as compressional features obviously requiring considerable crustal shortening and thickening. The fixists who opposed Wegener's continental drift were also required to explain these orogenic belts, and this they claimed was easily accomplished through the hypothesis of earth contraction—as wrinkles in the skin of a

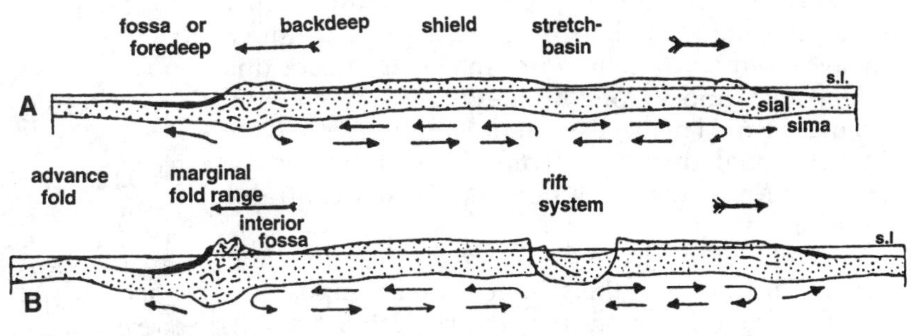

Figure 2.25 Du Toit's drawings showing his ideas of the stretching of the sial by drag of convection currents to produce a rift valley and also to cause compressional shortening and folding of sial to produce a fold mountain range with an adjacent "deep." (From A. du Toit, 1937, *Our Wandering Continents*. Oliver & Boyd, Ltd., Edinburgh. Reproduced by permission.)

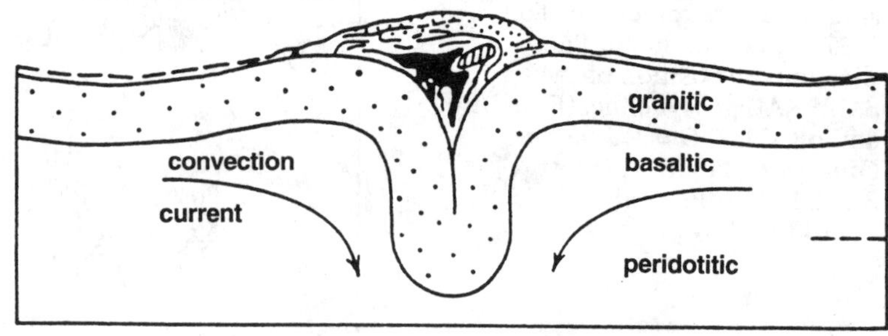

Figure 2.26 Imagined tectogene formed by converging mantle convection currents. (Based on data of H.H. Hess in J.A. Jacobs, R.D. Russell, and J.T. Wilson, 1959, *Physics and Geology*, p. 351, Figure 15.2. McGraw Hill Book Co., New York.)

desiccated plum or apple. Particularly puzzling at that time were the deep oceanic trenches, that are obviously persisting despite the proximity of sources of great amounts of terrestrial sediment. The notion that the trenches are linear zones of continual crustal subsidence must have seemed inescapable.

The contribution of Dutch geodesist F.A. Vening Meinesz was especially important in the pre-plate-tectonics period of the 1920s and 1930s. In 1923 he had made the first of several submarine traverses along the East Indies arc in order to measure and map the gravity field associated with the Java (Sunda) trench. His completed map showed a strong negative gravity anomaly belt lying just north of the trench axis (Heiskanen and Vening Meinesz, 1958, p. 373-377). [See Chapter 3 for an explanation of gravity anomalies.]

For Vening Meinesz, implication of the linear negative isostatic anomaly was that a large mass of crust had been forced down into the mantle and was being held there against its natural tendency to rise. The structure envisioned to explain this situation was a deep downfold (or downbuckle) of the crust. In 1936 it was named a *tectogene* by Ph.H. Kuenen, who had produced this structure in laboratory models using mixtures of paraffin and wax floating on water. The term as well as the structure itself was favored by Princeton professor H.H. Hess in 1938 (see Fairbridge, 1966, p. 937 for reference citations). Hess's model of a tectogene is reproduced here as Figure 2.26. Notice that the deep downward invagination of the crust has caused intense folding of alpine nappes in strata above the tectogene.

Vening Meinesz favored the action of mantle convection currents as the mechanism of forming and maintaining the tectogene and its negative isostatic gravity anomalies. His theoretical model, shown here as Figure 2.27, shows a rising current beneath the tectogene axis and mantle flow diverging beneath the lithosphere so as to move away from the tectogene in both directions (Heiskanen and Vening Meinesz, 1958, p. 439 and Figure 11-6). This flow system is directly opposite in rotational direction from those indicated by Hess and others who used scale-model experiments.

Much later, through seismic refraction and reflection studies of the structure and composition of the crust beneath the Puerto Rico trench, Maurice Ewing and J. Worzel showed that no tectogene root exists and that isostatic compensation is essentially present across the trench zone (Fairbridge, 1966, p. 937). The same conclusion applied to the Java trench and other trenches of subduction zones.

In 1939, David Griggs of Harvard University published the results of an experiment using a mechanical model correctly scaled to simulate a convection current system capable of inducing a downbuckle in a floating crust. The lithosphere was simulated by a mixture of sand and heavy oil; the mantle by a viscous water-glass. Parallel cylinders lying horizontally within the "mantle" were rotated in opposite directions, setting up currents that were able to drag the floating layer into an axis of convergence to produce a downbuckle (Figure 2.28). In what may seen as a presaging of the idea of subduction, Griggs found that with one cylinder held stationary the drag of the other also produced a downbuckle, but it was asymmetrical and matter accumulated as a "mountain range." In both cases, Griggs could observe what seemed to be underthrusting of the arriving material beneath the accumulating mass.

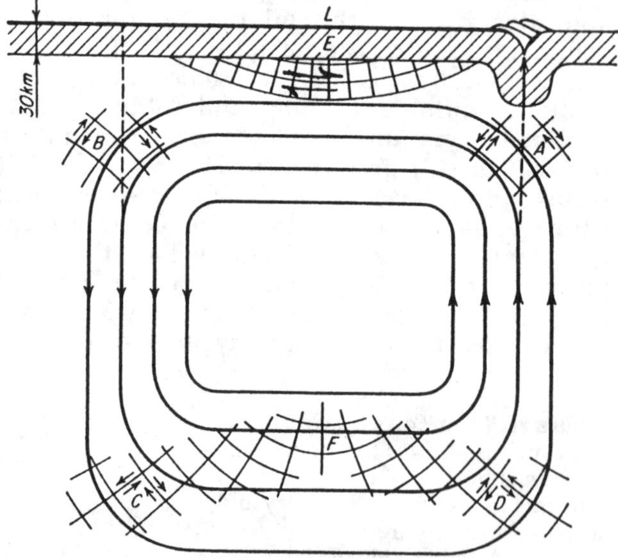

Figure 2.27 Cross section of possible mantle convection system beneath an imagined tectogene. (From J.A. Jacobs, R.D. Russell, and J.T. Wilson, 1959, *Physics and Geology*, p. 350, Figure 16.1. McGraw Hill Book Co., New York. Reproduced by permission of the publisher.)

2.21 The 1940s and 1950s—Two Decades of Relative Quiet

To the contributions of Holmes and du Toit, we add brief mention of that of Amadaus W. Grabau, an American paleontologist and stratigrapher who adopted continental drift after the models proposed by Taylor and Wegener. In his major work, *The Rhythm of the Ages* (1940), he carried back the reconstructions of Pangaea to early Paleozoic time, drawing a series of paleogeographic maps from Cambrian time to the present. In these, he showed the shifting position of Pangaea relative to the poles. Details of Grabau's work are presented by Marvin (1973, p. 114). Grabau's reconstructions seemed to attract little favorable comment. His reputation remained secure, however, through his numerous valuable scholarly contributions to paleontology and stratigraphy.

The relative quiet on the subject of continental drift was broken in 1943 by the noted American vertebrate paleontologist, George G.Simpson, who rather scathingly denounced the claim of the drift supporters that the distribution of fossil vertebrates supported their hypothesis. Simpson's extensive exposition of the case favored narrow and fluctuating isthmian connections (land bridges) or other means of across-water transferences of faunas.

A remarkable idea that resurfaced in the 1950s was that the earth, instead of shrinking, as the contractionists had thought for so long, was instead expanding. Continental separation could be explained by an expanding earth, and this would not require the continents to move relative to the earth sphere. The hypothesis had been promoted in 1933 by a German, O.C. Hilgenberg, who drew attention by preparing an illustration showing three globes of increasing diameter; the smallest showed almost no ocean at all. The new proponent of this hypothesis was Samuel W. Carey, a Tasmanian geologist, who published his version in 1958. The original earth had about half the diameter of the present earth; its surface area was about one-quarter as great. As a result, it rotated much more rapidly than today, and the gravitational pull at the surface was much greater (Marvin, 1973, p. 152). Volumetric expansion of the matter deep within the earth was attributed to a relaxation of an originally dense packing of atomic nuclei. Expansion of the earth caused tangential extensional stresses over the entire rigid crust, which broke apart into continents. Whereas these new continents remained unchanged in size, ocean basins that lay between them grew steadily in area. Of course, compressional stresses capable of major crustal deformation and shortening in mountain belts proved difficult to explain under the expansion hypothesis. The expansion theory became popular as evidence of midoceanic crustal spreading became stronger, while at the same time subduction had not been proposed to dispose of older crust. For that reason, expansion was adopted in 1958 and held for period of several years by Bruce C. Heezen, whose studies of the submarine topography of the Atlantic seemed to demand a widening ocean. (See Chapter 7 and Figure 7.22.)

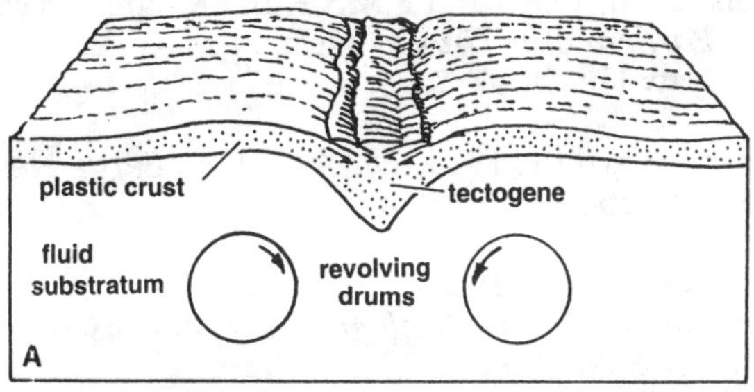

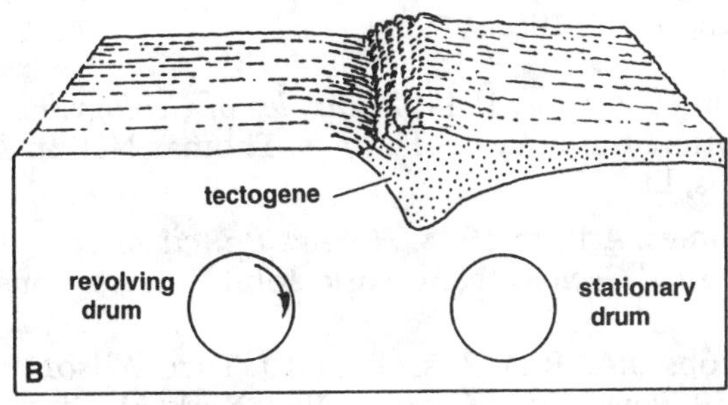

Figure 2.28 Tectogenes produced in a model experiment by David Griggs. (From D. Griggs, 1938, *Amer. Jour of Science*, v. 237. Copyright © 1939 by *The American Journal of Science*. Used by permission.)

The decades 1940-60 were anything but dull and uneventful from the standpoint of significant discoveries in geophysics and submarine geology. To the contrary, much was happening to prepare for the coming of the new paradigm, plate tectonics. One of these lines of discovery was about the nature of the earth's crust and mantle—particularly about the oceanic crust—making use of data coming from new seismic and gravity exploration methods put in practice immediately after the end of World War II (Chapter 3). Another field that got an early start was submarine geology. Mapping of the topography of the ocean floor began in earnest using multiple profiles from the precision depth recorder, while coring and seismic reflection began to reveal the thickness and composition of ocean floor sediments (Chapter 4). Seismic data from the vicinity of the great system of foredeeps (trenches) and island arcs began to disclose evidence of a mysterious slanting zone of deep-focus earthquakes (Chapter 5).

Our historical review is by no means ended; instead, it has now split into several parallel paths of discovery. The field of paleomagnetism with its important discoveries about polar wandering grew rapidly in the mid-1950s, providing strong evidence that continental drift had occurred.

REFERENCES CITED

Argand, E., 1924, La tectonique de l'Asie. *Extrait du Compte Rendus du XIIIe Congrès Géologique International 1922*, Liège.

Bacon, Francis, 1620, *The New Organon and Related Writings*. (F.H. Anderson, ed.). New York, Liberal Arts Press, 292 pp.

Bacon, Francis, 1620, *Novum Organum*. (G. Kitchin, trans., 1855). Oxford: Oxford University Press.

Baker, Howard B., 1932, *The Atlantic Rift and Its Meaning*, Detroit (privately printed).

Barrell, Joseph, 1914-1915, The strength of the earth's crust. *Jour. of Geology*, v. 22, p. 28-48, 145-165, 209-236, 289-314, 441-468, 537-555, 655-683, 729-741; v. 23, p. 27-44, 425-443, 499-515.

Barrell, Joseph, 1917, Rhythms and the measurements of geologic time. *Bull., Geol. Soc. of Amer.*, v. 28, p. 745-904.

Berkland, James O., 1979, Elisee Reclus—neglected geologic pioneer and first (?) continental drift advocate. *Geology*, v. 7, p. 189-192.

Black, George W., Jr., 1979, Frank Bursley Taylor—forgotten pioneer of continental drift. *Jour. of Geologic Education*, v. 27, p. 67-70.

Carey, Samuel W., 1958, The tectonic approach to continental drift. Pages 177-355 in *Continental Drift—A Symposium*, S.W. Carey, convener, Hobart: University of Tasmania.

Chamberlin, Rollin T., 1928, Some of the objections to Wegener's theory. Pages 83-87 in Van der Gracht, 1928.

Daly, Reginald A., 1926, *Our Mobile Earth*. New York: Charles Scribner and Sons.

Drake, Ellen T., 1976, Alfred Wegener's reconstruction of Pangea. *Geology*, v. 4, p. 41-44.

du Toit, Alex. L., 1921, The Carboniferous glaciation of South Africa, *Geol. Soc. South Africa Trans.*, v. 24, p. 188-227.

du Toit, Alexander L., 1927, *A Geological Comparison of South America with South Africa.* Publication No. 381. Washington, D.C.: Carnegie Institution of Washington.

du Toit, Alexander, 1933. *Our Wandering Continents: An Hypothesis of Continental Drift.* Edinburgh: Oliver and Boyd, Ltd.

Dutton, Clarence E., 1889, On some of the greater problems of physical geology. *Bull., Washington Philosophical Soc.*, series B, v. 11, p. 51-64.

Fairbridge, R.W., 1966, Trenches and related deep troughs. Pages 929-939 in R. W. Fairbridge, Ed., 1966, *Encyclopedia of Oceanography*. New York: Reinhold Publishing Co.

Faul, Henry, and Carol Faul, 1983, *It Began with a Stone.* New York: John Wiley & Sons.

Fisher, Osmond, 1881, *Physics of the Earth's Crust*. London: Macmillan.

Fisher, Osmond, 1882, On the physical cause of the ocean basins. *Nature*, v. 25, p. 243-244.

Frankel, Henry, 1976, Alfred Wegener and the specialists. *Centaurus*, v. 20, p. 305-324.

Grabau, Amadeus, 1940, *The Rhythm of the Ages, Earth History in the Light of the Pulsation and Polar Control Theories.* Peking: Henri Vetch.

Griggs, David, 1939, A theory of mountain making. *Amer. Jour. of Science*, v. 237, p. 611-650.

Hallam, A., 1973, *A Revolution in the Earth Sciences: From Continental Drift to Plate Tectonics*. Oxford: Clarendon Press.

Harland, W.B., et al, 1989, *A Geologic Time Scale 1989*. Cambridge: Cambridge University Press.

Heiskanen, W.A., and F.A. Vening Meinesz, 1958, *The Earth and Its Gravity Field.* New York: McGraw-Hill Book Co.

Holmes, Arthur, 1913, *The Age of the Earth.* New York: Harper.

Holmes, Arthur, 1928-29, Radioactivity and earth movements. *Trans. Geological Soc. of Glascow*, v. 18, p. 559-606.

Holmes, Arthur, 1933, The thermal history of the earth. *Washington Academy of Sciences Journal*, v. 23, p. 169-195.

Holmes, Arthur, 1944, *Principles of Geology*, First Edition. Sunbury-on-Thames: Thomas Nelson & Sons, Ltd.

Holmes, Arthur, 1978, *Holmes Principles of Physical Geology*. New York: John Wiley & Sons.

Jacobs, J.A., R.D. Russell, and J. Tuzo Wilson, 1959, *Physics and Geology*. New York: McGraw-Book Co.

Jacoby, Wolfgang R., 1981, Modern concepts of earth dynamics anticipated by Alfred Wegener in 1912. *Geology*, v. 9, p. 25-27.

Jeffreys, Harold, 1924, *The Earth: Its Origin, History and Physical Constitution.* (1929, Second Edition) Cambridge: Cambridge University Press.

Joly, John, 1925, *The Surface of the Earth.* Oxford: Clarendon Press.

Joly, John, 1928, Continental movement. Pages 88-89 in Van der Gracht, 1928.

King, Lester C., 1957, __?__ *Proc. Geological Soc. of London,* p. 79.

Kirsch, G., 1928, *Geologie und Radioaktivität.* Vienna and Berlin: Springer.

Köppen, W., and A. Wegener, 1924, *Die Klimate der geologischen Vorzeit.* Berlin: Verlag von Gebrüder Borntraeger.

Lake, Philip, 1922, Wegener's displacement theory. *Geological Magazine.* v. 59, p. 338-346.

Longwell, Chester, 1928, Some physical tests of the displacement hypothesis. Pages 145-157 in Van der Gracht, 1928.

Marvin, Ursula B., 1973, *Continental Drift: The Evolution of a Concept.* Washington, D.C.: Smithsonian Institution Press.

Meyerhoff, Arthur A., 1968, Arthur Holmes: originator of spreading ocean floor hypotheses. Replies by Robert S. Dietz and H.H. Hess. *Jour. of Geophysical Research,* v. 73, p. 6563-6569.

Neumayr, Melchior, 1895, *Erdgeschicte,* v. 2. *Beschreibende Geologie,* 2nd Ed. Leipzig und Wien: Bibliographisches Institut.

Owen, Richard, 1857, *Key to the Geology of the Globe; An Essay.* Philadelphia: Lippincott.

Pickering, William H., 1907, The place of the origin of the Moon—the volcanic problem. *Jour. of Geology,* v. 15, p. 23-38.

Placet, Francois, 1668, *La Corruption du Grande et Petit Monde.* Paris: Alliot.

Raisz, Erwin, 1948, *General Cartography.* 2nd. Ed. New York: McGraw-Hill, Book Co.

Reclus, Elisée, 1872, *The Earth.* (American edition translated by B. Woodward; H. Woodward, Ed.) New York: Harper & Brothers.

Reid, Harry Fielding, 1922, Drift of the earth's crust and displacement of the pole. *Geographical Review,* v. 12, p. 672-674.

Romm, James, 1994, A new forerunner for continental drift. *Nature,* v. 367, p. 407-408.

Schwinner, R., 1919, Vulkanismus und Gebirgsbildung: Ein Versuch. *Zeitschrift fur Vulkanologie,* v. 5. p. 176-230.

Schwartzbach, Martin, 1980 (1985), *Alfred Wegener: The Father of Continental Drift.* English Ed., 1985, Carla Love, Tr. Madison, Wisc.: Science Tech, Inc.

Shea, James H., Ed., 1985, *Continental Drift.* Benchmark Papers in Geology, v. 88. New York: Van Nostrand Reinhold Co.

Simpson, George Gaylord, 1943, Mammals and the nature of continents. *Amer. Journal of Science,* v. 241, p. 1-31.

Skinner, Brian J., 1986, Can you really believe the evidence? Two stories from geology. *American Scientist,* v. 74, p. 401-409.

Snider-Pellegrini, Antonio, 1858, *La Création et Ses Mystères Dévoilés.* Paris: Franck and Dentu.

Staub, Rudolph, 1924, Der Bau der Alpen. *Beiträge zur geologische Karte der Schweiz,* N.F., No. 52, Bern, Switzerland.

Suess, Eduard, 1904-1924, *The Face of the Earth.* 5 vols., Oxford: Clarendon Press.

Taylor, Frank B., 1910, Bearing of the Tertiary mountain belts on the origin of the earth's plan. *Bull., Geol. Soc. Amer.,* v. 21, p. 179-226.

Taylor, Frank B., 1928, Sliding continents and tidal and rotational forces. Pages 158-177 in Van der Gracht, 1928.

Totten, Stanley M., 1981, Frank B. Taylor, plate tectonics, and continental drift. *Jour. of Geological Education,* v. 29, p. 212-220.

Van Der Gracht, W.A.J.M. Waterschoot, Ed., 1928, *Theory of Continental Drift.* Tulsa, Okla.: Amer. Assoc. of Petroleum Geologists.

Wegener, Alfred, 1912a, Die Enstehung der Kontinente. *Petermanns Geographische Mitteilungen,* p. 185-195, 253-256, 305-309. English translation of excerpts of the above by Rhodes W. Fairbridge, p. 147-164 in Shea, 1985.

Wegener, Alfred, 1912b, Die Enstehung der Kontinente. *Geologische Rundschau,* v. 3, no. 4, p. 276-292.

Wegener, Alfred, 1915, *Die Enstehung der Kontinente und Ozeane.* 1st Ed., ; 2nd Ed., 1920; 3rd Ed., 1922; 4th Ed., 1924; 4th Ed., revised, 1929; 5th Ed., revised by Kurt Wegener, 1936. Braunschweig, Germany: Friedrich Vieweg & Sohn.

Wegener, Alfred, 1924, *The Origin of Continents and Ocean Basins*. Translated from the 3rd (1922) German edition by J.G.A. Skerl. London: Methuen and Co.; New York: E.P. Dutton.

Wegener, Alfred, 1966, *The Origin of the Continents and Ocean Basins*. Translated from the 4th revised (1929) German edition by John Biram. New York: Dover Publications, Inc.

Willis, Bailey, 1928, Continental drift. Pages 76-82 in Van der Gracht, 1928.

Wood, Robert Muir, 1985, *The Dark Side of the Earth*. London: George Allen & Unwin.

Chapter: 3 Crust/Mantle/Core—Lithosphere/Asthenosphere

An understanding of plate tectonics is founded in large part on existing knowledge of the earth's interior. For that reason it is appropriate to review what is known or inferred about the major concentric zones of the earth. Our purpose in this chapter is to describe the internal structure and composition of the earth and to investigate the dynamic properties of its zones. This information will provide a data bank that can be drawn upon in following chapters introducing plate tectonics as the active agent that has played the leading role in forming and differentiating the rock structures found today in the crust of the earth.

As explained in Chapter 1, there are two frames of reference in which to treat the earth shells, or spheres. The system of crust/mantle/core lies in the frame of reference of chemical (petrologic) constitution of these parts and is associated with the physical property of density. The system of lithosphere/asthenosphere/mesosphere lies in the frame of reference of temperature/pressure dependent properties—principally strength and viscosity. As we have observed in Chapter 1, the two systems lie superimposed in the region of the crust and outer mantle, a circumstance that makes for some difficulty in keeping straight the relationships between the two systems.

Seismology has been the principal tool of investigation of the earth's interior, and we assume that the reader comes prepared with at least a general, nonmathematical knowledge of first principles of seismology.

3.1 Pressure, Temperature, and Density in the Earth's Interior

Graph A of Figure 3.1 shows the increase of confining pressure to the earth's center, where it reaches about 3500 kilobars (kb). Matter at the earth's center has no weight, because it is being attracted outward equally in all directions by the mass of the sphere that surrounds it, but the confining pressure is greatest here because the weight of the entire earth mass is directed toward that one point.

Figure 3.1, Graph B, shows the profile of temperature increase with depth, which is rapid in the first 200 km of depth. The rate of increase falls off sharply below this depth. Through the core, temperature increase is very gradual and reaches a maximum estimated to be about 2775°K at the earth's center.

Increase in density, shown in Graph C of Figure 3.1 is fairly steady with depth through the mantle, but makes an abrupt jump where the iron core is encountered. Measurement of the average density of the earth as a whole requires a knowledge of both its mass and its volume. The earth's mass was determined in 1798 by the distinguished English physicist, Lord Cavendish, who was able to measure the universal gravitational constant by means of a delicate instrument, the torsion balance. This constant allows the gravitational equation of Newton to be solved. The earth's radius and volume were already quite accurately known from geodetic surveys. Thus we have the two necessary quantities:

Earth's mass: 5.975×10^{27} gm
(round to 6×10^{27} gm)

Earth's volume: 1.08×10^{27} cm^3
(round to 1.1×10^{27} cm^3)

Dividing mass by volume gives us a density of about 5.5 gm/cm^3. This figure is just over twice the density of granite (2.6 gm/cm^3). Iron, in comparison, has a density of nearly 8 gm/cm^3. [For convenience throughout this and later chapters, density values will be given without the necessary units of mass and volume. This treatment is numerically the same as for *specific gravity*, a dimensionless quantity requiring no statement of units; it is the ratio of density of a mineral or rock to the density of pure water at 4°C, taken as equal to 1.00.]

Geologists many decades ago reasoned that because the greater part of known rock of the earth's crust is of the density of granite (2.6) or basalt (3.0), values that are much less than the global average, density must increase greatly toward the earth's center. The most reasonable conclusion was that there exists a core of high density, in the range of 10 to 12. This reasoning was strongly supported by the astronomer's determination of another physical quantity: the earth's moment of inertia. The core is usually considered to be composed largely of iron, because if iron were compressed in the earth's center under 2000 to 3000 kb of confining pressure, it would decrease in volume and undergo a density increase from 8.0 to 11.0. Independent supporting evidence for an iron core was found in the composition of meteorites, one class of which is composed of iron. (Details of core composition are given in a later section of this chapter.)

Between the outermost layer (the crust) and the earth's core (i.e., throughout the mantle) density must range somewhere between 4.0 and 6.0. Rocks that fit this requirement are peridotite and dunite, both ultramafic and composed largely of olivine. Their density at the surface is about 3.3, but would be increased to an acceptable value under the known confining pressures.

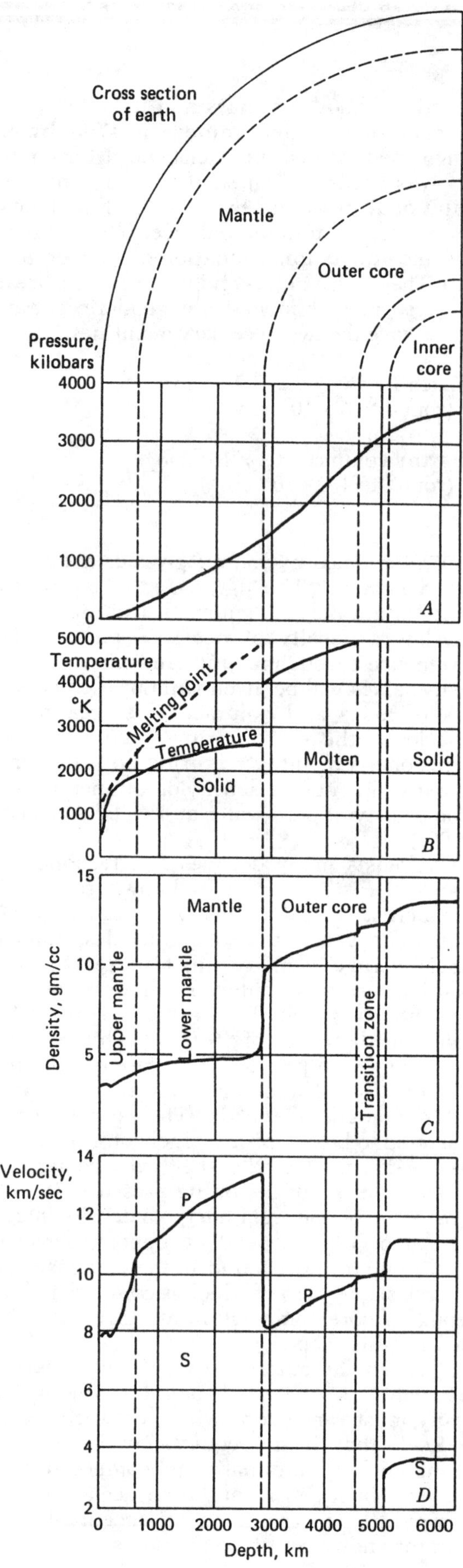

Figure 3.1 (A) Increase in pressure with depth in the earth. (B) Increase in temperature with depth. (C) Increase in density with depth. (D) Velocity of P and S waves. (Based on data of K.E. Bullen, B.A. Bolt, and others. Drawing copyright by © by Arthur N. Strahler)

3.2 Composition of the Crust

A knowledge of the granite-gabbro series of igneous rocks can be put to use to describe the composition of the earth's crust. In Chapter 1, we presented the crustal layers in a very general way, emphasizing rock density. Figure 1.2 showed the crust of the continental lithosphere as being thicker than the crust of the oceanic lithosphere. Moreover, the continental crust was shown to have a less dense upper layer, not present in the oceanic crust.

Figure 3.2 shows further details of the crust and its composition. The *oceanic crust*, on the average about 6 km thick, is composed of mafic igneous rock of the composition of basalt and gabbro. The upper part is basalt, which solidified from lava reaching the seafloor in the spreading plate boundary between two oceanic lithospheric plates. The same magma, solidifying the lower part of the crust, below the basalt, consists of gabbro, the intrusive equivalent of basalt.

The *continental crust* averages some 30 to 35 km in thickness generally, but extends down to depths of 65 km or more beneath the high plateaus and mountain belts. An upper, felsic rock zone grades into a basal, mafic zone. Except in a few places, no sharp boundary separates these layers. The upper, felsic layer, often described by the term *granitic rock*, has a chemical composition about that of granite or granodiorite, with a density of about 2.7 near the surface. Much of it is intrusive rock of granitic composition or metamorphic rock derived from granite. (Sedimentary rock, which covers the granitic layer in many places, makes up only a very small percentage of the volume of the crust.) Although little is known with certainty about the composition of the lower, mafic zone of the continental crust, it is usually considered to have a chemical composition similar to basalt and gabbro. The mafic zone should not, however, be visualized as a continuation of the oceanic crust, nor should it be thought to have had a similar origin. The mafic lower zone of the continental crust is probably vastly older than the mafic oceanic crust, just as the upper, felsic layer is also undoubtedly vastly older than the upper basaltic layer of the oceanic crust. The contact between the crust and mantle is typically a sharply defined boundary, called the *Moho*; it is described below.

3.3 Seismic-Wave Speeds and Rock Varieties

A principle of seismology that can be put to use to reveal the nature of the earth's interior is that P and S earthquake waves travel faster through

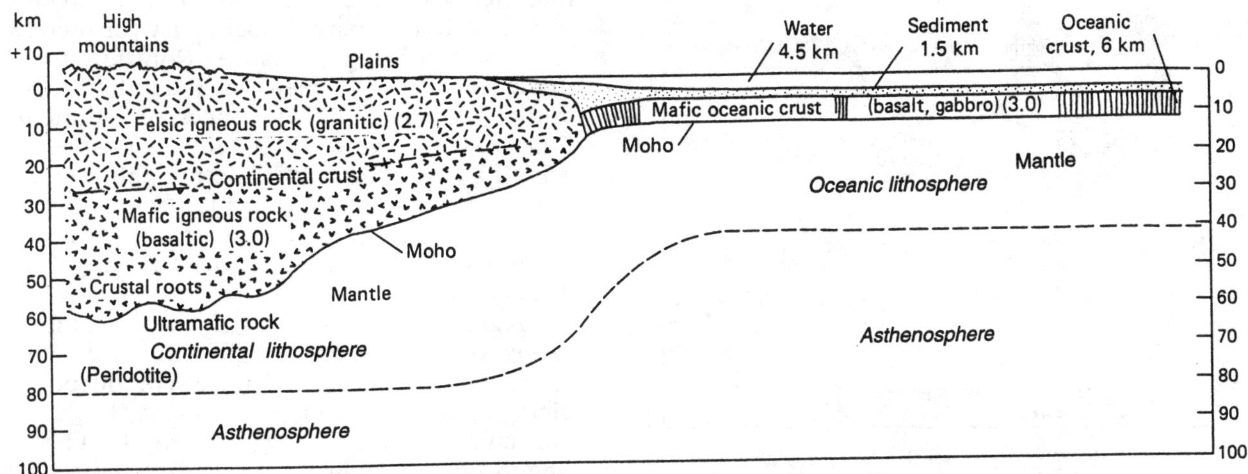

Figure 3.2 Schematic cross section of the crust beneath the continents and ocean basins. The vertical scale of the drawing is greatly exaggerated. Figures in parentheses give density. (Copyright © by Arthur N. Strahler.)

highly rigid material than through less rigid material. The word *rigidity* applies only to elastic solids, and it refers to the degree of resistance the body offers to shearing forces. Steel and rubber are both elastic, but steel has a much greater rigidity because it bends very much less than rubber under the same deforming stress. [As used in seismology, "rigidity" corresponds with the *shear modulus*, a measure of the resistance of an elastic solid to shearing deformation. P-waves are also influenced by the *bulk modulus*, which measures ratio of compressive stress to resulting volume change by dilatation.]

Crustal rocks in general have a high degree of rigidity, whether composed of crystallized or glassy mineral matter, but there is quite a marked variation among different rocks. Rigidity can be measured by the physicist in the laboratory, not only under the conditions of the earth's surface, but also under great confining pressures and high temperatures such as those which might be expected many kilometers deep in the earth.

Because the rigidity of rocks determines the velocity of earthquake waves and because the velocity of these waves at various depths can be calculated from seismograms, it is possible to make fairly good guesses concerning the kinds of rock deep in the earth's crust and mantle. Figure 3.3 lists several rock types and their densities under surface conditions. Sand, clay, and silt layers, made up of non-cemented grains, have low rigidity. Shale, sandstone, and limestone have moderate rigidity, followed by granite and other felsic igneous rocks. Diabase and gabbro, mafic rocks which have greater density than granite, have about one-third higher rigidity than granite. Next come the ultramafic rocks, pyroxenite and dunite, with about twice the rigidity of granite and considerably greater density.

As Figure 3.3 shows, the speed of earthquake P-waves corresponds with this same series; slowest in sand, silt, or clay, and increasingly faster in the sedimentary rocks, in granite, basalt and gabbro, and in pyroxenite and dunite. Dolomite, although a sedimentary rock, is exceptional in that it has wave speeds as great as basalt.

3.4 Seismic Waves and Crustal Structure

Most of our information on the general structure and composition of the crust has come from observations of seismic-wave behavior. The crust is distinguished from the mantle by the presence of a rather abrupt and clearly defined change in velocity of seismic waves, indicating that there is a corresponding abrupt change in rigidity of the rock from crust to mantle. A change in rigidity indicates in turn an abrupt change in mineral composition or in the physical state of the rocks. [For basic principles of seismic waves, see Fowler, 1990, p. 76-85.]

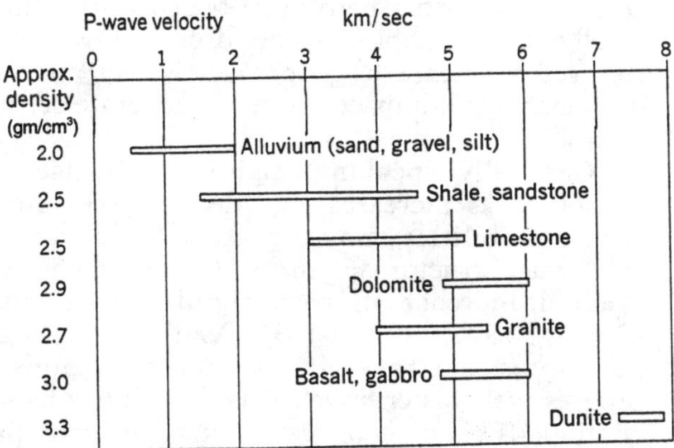

Figure 3.3 Speed of travel of P-waves in various types of rocks (Based on data of M.B. Dobrin, 1960, *Introduction to Geophysical Prospecting*, McGraw-Hill, New York.)

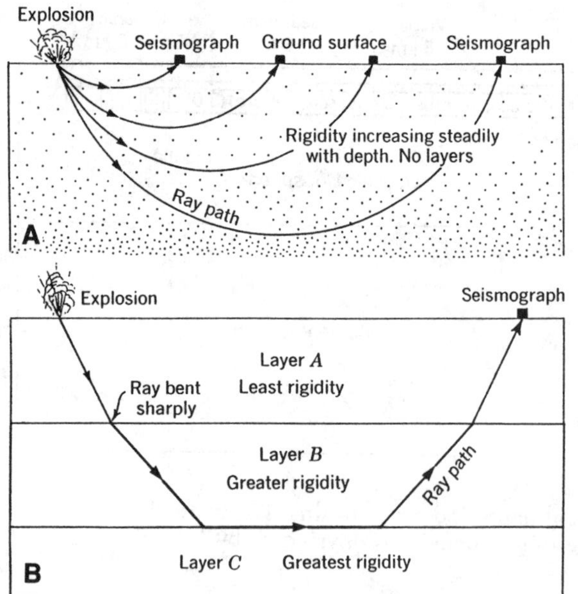

Figure 3.4 Bending of seismic waves as they travel through rock layers of differing degrees of rigidity. (After M.B. Dobrin, 1960, *Introduction to Geophysical Prospecting,* McGraw-Hill, New York.)

Where an earthquake has a focus close to the surface and is located not more than a few hundred kilometers from the seismograph station, the seismic body waves (P waves and S waves) do not penetrate the earth more than about 100 km before they are turned back toward the surface and thus reach the seismograph. Interpretation of the complex wave records will reveal the velocities at which the waves travel at different depths.

The times and places of natural earthquakes are unpredictable except in a very general way. Therefore, the best source of seismic information about the shallow zones of the earth is from human-made shocks. One of the older methods is to make use of blasts set off at rock quarries and to record them with portable seismographs at various distances from the source. In analyzing shallow zones for possible petroleum-bearing structures, small dynamite explosions are used. The waves are received by means of geophones. Newer methods use mechanical impact devices to generate seismic waves.

Generally speaking, rigidity of crust and mantle rocks increases with depth. Very simply, two possibilities may be considered for the subsurface structure. Figure 3.4A shows the case of gradual increase in rock rigidity with depth (Stacey, 1977, p. 145-163). As the body wave penetrates the rock, it encounters regions of progressively faster travel. This change results in a continuous bending, or *refraction*, of the wave path in such a way as to turn it toward a path parallel with the surface. Continued upward bending of the path causes the wave to return to the surface. Continuous refraction of this type might indicate that the rock becomes more rigid at depth because of increasing density associated with increase of load or confining pressure. Continuous linear increase in wave speed with depth is actually found in some thick sequences of sediment, for example, in the Gulf Coast geocline (Dobrin, 1960, p.77-78). Continuous refraction might also indicate that the rock is changing gradually in composition to denser minerals, for example, from felsic to more mafic rock, without any abrupt discontinuity.

Figure 3.4B shows the case in which there exist layers of rock, each of uniform rigidity within itself, but with each successive deeper layer changing abruptly to higher rigidity. In this case a particular *ray* of the body wave travels in a straight line through each layer but is refracted sharply as it enters the next layer. When the ray strikes a new layer at a certain critical angle, it travels along the contact between layers (the interface) for a certain distance and is then turned upward to return to the surface. When the seismograms of several recording stations are compared, the subsurface paths of the seismic waves can be reconstructed and the speeds of wave travel estimated for different depths. The program is known as the *seismic refraction method* (Dobrin, 1960, p. 69-104). This information in turn makes possible the selection of rock varieties whose physical properties fit the observed wave speeds. (The refraction method should not to be confused with the seismic reflection method, explained below.)

Body waves of both shallow earthquakes and surface explosions show quite definitely that, as a first approximation or generalization, the continents consist of an upper layer, the *crust*, averaging about 35 km thick, resting upon quite different rock of the mantle. As indicated in Figure 3.5, the upper part of the continental crust consists largely of felsic (granitic) rock, while the lower part is largely mafic (basaltic, gabbroic) rock.

It is known that the P-waves near the surface travel at about 6 km/sec, which is expected in granitic rock, and that this velocity increases gradually or by one or more abrupt steps to the base of the crust, where it is about 7 km/second. This wave speed is to be expected in basaltic/gabbroic rock at this depth. At about 35 km, on the average, the P-wave speed increases abruptly to 8.0 km/sec or somewhat greater, a speed to be expected of an ultramafic rock, such as peridotite. (S-waves undergo a corresponding speed increase with depth.) This surface of sudden increase in wave speed, which separates the crust above from the mantle below, is the *Mohorovicic discontinuity*, named after the Croatian seismologist, Andrija Mohorovicic, who first recognized the discontinuity in 1910 from the records of shallow-focus earthquakes (Shea, 1985, p. 237). It has become accepted practice to designate this discontinuity as the *M-discontinuity*, or simply as the *Moho*.

3.5 Structure of the Oceanic Crust

The nature of the oceanic crust remained obscure until the 1930s. The distinguished seismologist, Beno Gutenberg, in a 1927 publication, had assumed that a sialic (felsic) crust, 20-25 km thick, underlies the floors of the Atlantic and Indian ocean basins, whereas that underlying the Pacific basin is totally composed of sima (mafic rock) (Shea, 1985, p. 244). This distinction between two very different kinds of oceanic crust may have had its roots in the earlier hypothesis of origin of the Pacific basin by formation of the moon by fission, leaving a great depression that quickly became filled by basaltic lavas (see Chapter 2). The other major ocean basins, in contrast, were thought to be down-sunken parts of an original sialic (granitic) crust of the earth.

The exploration geophysicist E.L. De Golyer suggested in 1932 that "Seismic reflection and refraction methods that had been widely used on land would be ideal for investigating the geology of the ocean bottoms and margins." He pointed out that both geophones and explosions could be located near the surface, thus taking advantage of water's excellent sound transmission (Shea, 1985, p. 249). This suggestion was followed up by Maurice Ewing, A.P. Crary, and H.M. Rutherford (1937), who developed a workable method for taking seismic refraction observations at sea. A research vessel was used in conjunction with a small boat to place geophones on the ocean bottom. This exploration was limited to the continental shelves. In 1941, E.C. Bullard and T.F. Gaskell used hydrophones placed near the sea surface (Shea, 1985, p. 255).

A salient event was the 1950 report by Maurice Ewing and his associates—J.L. Worzel, J.B. Hersey, Frank Press, and G.R. Hamilton—of seismic refraction data taken in the deep Atlantic northwest of Bermuda. In water depths of about 5 km, the research vessels *Atlantis* and *Caryn* from Woods Hole formed the first two-vessel flotilla to run a line of refraction measurements; it consisted of 42 shots with explosive charges ranging up to 300 pounds. The receiving hydrophone was suspended at a water depth 15 to 30 m. From the calculated wave speeds, the overlying sedimentary layer was found to be about 1,500 m thick; a layer below it was equated to an ultramafic layer previously identified from earthquake seismology, but no granitic layer was found. The Moho was located at a depth of 12 km below sea level, which is only about 5 km below the ocean floor. In the same year, Maurice Ewing and Frank Press examined the data of surface earthquake waves that had passed across ocean basins, and these verified the existence of a thin sediment layer underlain by a relatively thin oceanic crust. In this respect the Atlantic and Pacific ocean basins appeared similar in crustal layering (Ewing and Press, 1950, 1952; see also Shea, 1985, p. 265).

Crustal layers typical of the North Atlantic Ocean basin are shown schematically in Figure 3.5. Beneath a thickness of about 4.5 km of seawater is a thin layer of unconsolidated deep-sea sediment, averaging about 0.5 km. Beneath the sediment is a rock layer about 1.5 km thick with P-wave speed in the range from 4.5 to 5.5 km/sec. This basement layer might represent either basaltic lava formed at the spreading plate boundary in the mid-oceanic region, or consolidated sediments, or

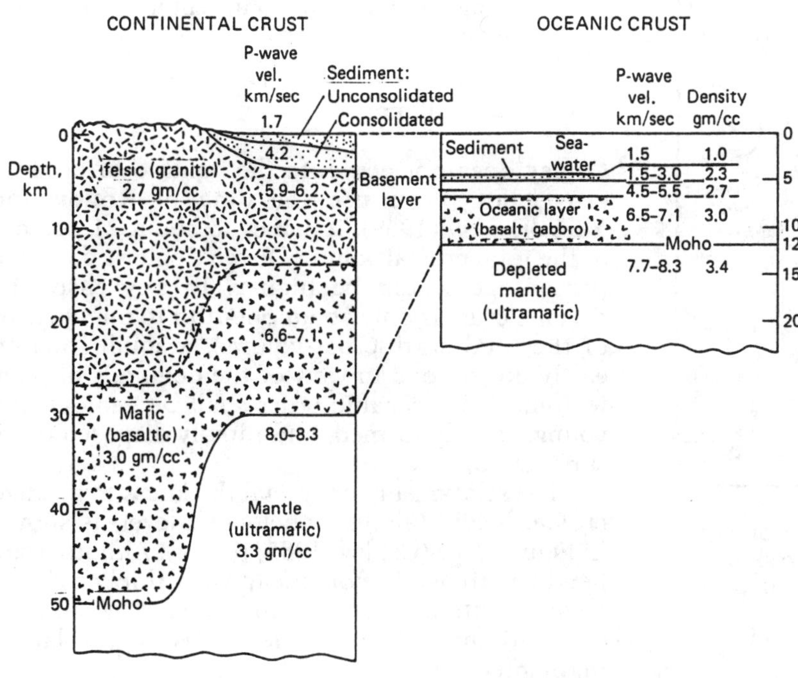

Figure 3.5 Compositions and seismic P-wave velocities of the continental crust and oceanic crust. (Copyright © by Arthur N. Strahler.)

both. Its density is on the order of 2.7. The next layer, called the oceanic layer, shows a P-wave speed of 6.5-7.1 km/sec and a density of 3.0. It could be interpreted as consisting of basalt or its coarse-grained igneous equivalent, gabbro, also formed during lithospheric plate accretion at the spreading boundary. The Moho is encountered at an average depth of 12 km—much shallower than beneath the continental crust. Here the P-wave speed jumps to between 7.7 and 8.3, and the density increases to 3.4 in ultramafic rock of the mantle.

3.6 Thickness and Extent of the Crust

Figure 3.6 is a 1982 world map showing crustal thickness in kilometers, using isopachs (lines of equal thickness) (Soller, et al., 1982). Much of the oceanic crustal thickness is less than 7 km, and some parts of the midoceanic ridge show values less than 4 km. Under the continents, thickness is typically from 40 to 50 km, but data are generally lacking for much of South America, Africa, Australia, and Antarctica. Much greater thicknesses (60 to 70 km) are found locally, e.g., beneath the Andes and under the Himalayas and the contiguous Tibet Plateau.

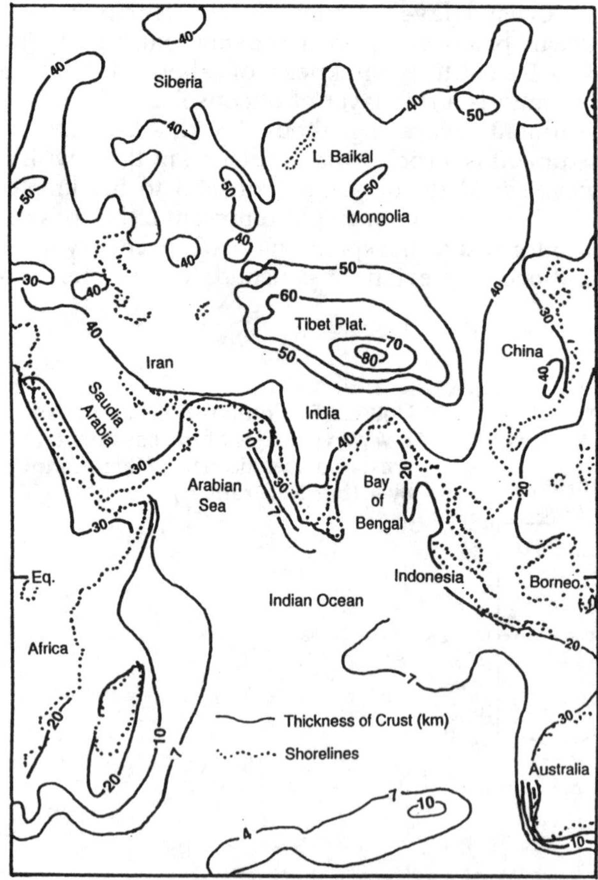

Figure 3.6 Portion of world map of thickness of the earth's crust. It is focused on southern Asia to show crustal thicknesses beneath the Tibetan Plateau. (From David R. Soller, R.D. Ray, and R.D. Brown, 1982, *Tectonics*, v. 1, p. 125-149, Plate 1. Copyright © by the American Geophysical Union.)

A map of crustal thickness of North America, based on seismic data, was published in 1989 by Walter D. Mooney and Laurence W. Braile. It is reproduced here as Figure 3.7. The map includes boundaries of the geological provinces, from which it is clear that the greatest crustal thicknesses are in the Precambrian shield regions.

Over the past three decades, several attempts have been made to summarize the entire earth's crust in terms of area occupied by three or more kinds or classes of crust (Wyllie, 1971, p. 148-49). In addition to the two largest classes—oceanic crust and continental crust—a third class was designated as "transitional" or "subcontinental"; it is found mostly along the passive continental margins. Figure 3.8 is an example of a summation made in 1969 by Ronov and Yaroshevskiy. It included three subclasses of continental crust; these recognize the thickness or absence of a sedimentary layer overlying the granitic layer.

In a report published in 1984, J. Graham Cogley presented a revised assessment of the global extent of continental crust based on a vast amount of data, including that from reflection and refraction seismology and from magnetic and gravity profiling (Cogley, 1984). Cogley's map of the global extent of continental crust is shown here as Figure 3.9. His continent/oceanic-crust boundary includes what we have described above as transitional or subcontinental crust. Fourteen continents are identified, the continent-continent contacts are drawn on basis of plate boundaries. Four microcontinents are included on the list. A few of the statistics from this survey are as follows:

Total area of continents: 210.4×10^6 km^2 or 41% of the earth's surface.

Average thickness of continental crust: 36 km.

Total volume of continental crust: 7.2×10^9 km^3.

Cogley does not compute the volume of oceanic crust, but if we use the data of Ronov and Yaroshevskiy (1969), it comes to about 21 percent of the total crustal volume. From Cogley's data, the percentage would be higher. In any case, the oceanic crust is only about one-fifth to one-quarter of the total earth-crust volume, a small fraction easily understood in view of the demands of plate tectonics that oceanic crust shall be geologically young, rapidly formed, and rapidly disposed of by subduction.

The relationship of crustal thickness to average crustal height (above or below sealevel) is shown in Figure 3.10 (Cogley, 1985, p. 114). Although the height increase is not linear with thickness, the close positive relationship is what would be expected under the principle of isostasy (explained in Chapter 11).

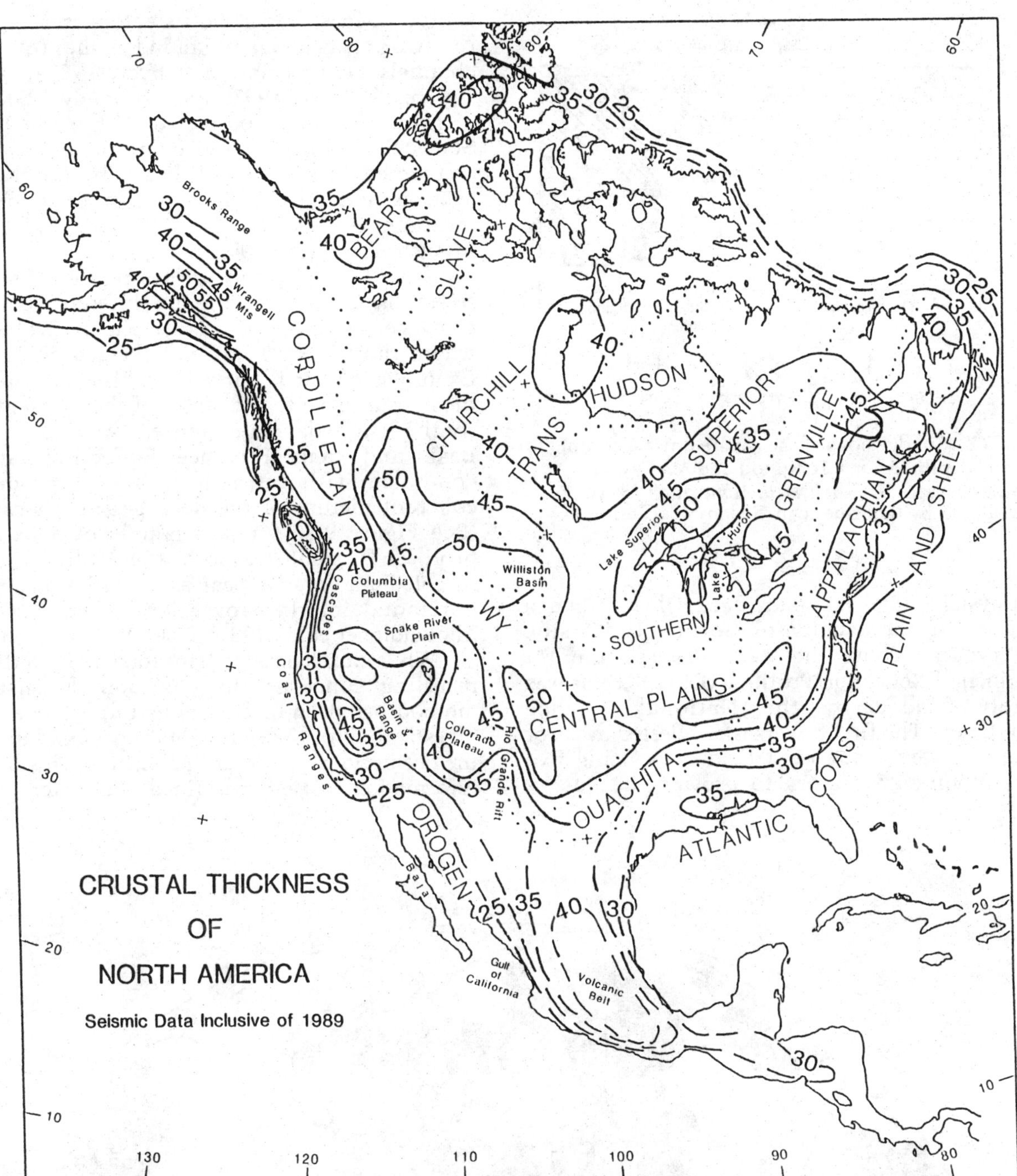

Figure 3.7 Contour map of crustal thickness (km) of North America. Geological provinces are outlined in broken line. (From W.D. Mooney and L.W. Braile, 1989, p. 41, Figure 1B, in *The Geology of North America*, vol. A, Boulder CO: The Geological Society of America. Reproduced by permission of the authors and the publisher.)

3.7 Seismic Reflection Probes of the Continental Crust

The *seismic reflection method,* which is the most extensively used of all geophysical prospecting methods, gives a clearer and more detailed picture of crustal structure than the refraction method (Dobrin, 1960, p. 105). Distances to layer interfaces can be determined with great precision by observing the travel times of seismic waves generated at or near the surface and reflected back from geologic features such as stratigraphic contacts and faults. A single shot will provide data for many such reflecting features. When a sequence of shots is delivered at short intervals along a line of traverse, there results a cross-sectional image of geologic structures.

A program to use reflection seismology as a probe deep into the continental crust was begun in 1975 under the leadership of the distinguished

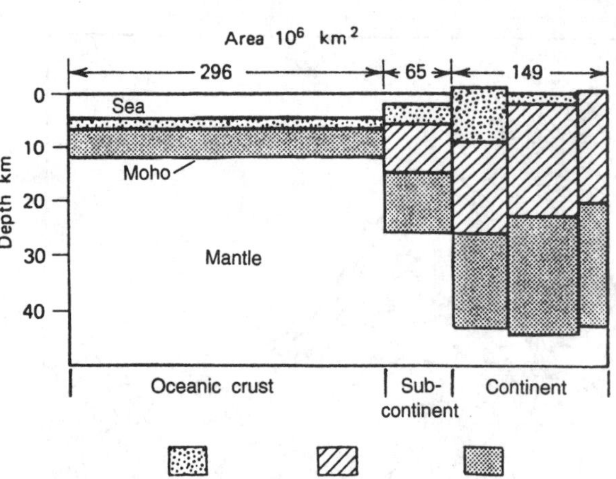

Figure 3.8 Subdivisions of the earth's crust according to area and depth. (After A.B. Ronoff and A.A. Yaroshevskiy, 1969, *Geophysical Monograph 13,* p. 37, Copyright © by the American Geophysical Union.)

geophysicist (seismologist) Jack Oliver, then a member of the faculty of Cornell University. The program bore the name Consortium for Continental Reflection Profiling (COCORP). It was largely funded by the National Science Foundation. The first traverses of selected areas of the crust were made by a field crew using five truck-mounted vibrators to provide the energy sources. More than 2000 detectors, serving as a receiving array about 10 km in length, provided 96 channels of information (Oliver, 1982a, p. 161; 1982b; 1983). By 1993, approximately 12,000 km of lines had been completed within the United States. Similar seismic reflection studies have been conducted in the United States by government agencies and universities, and in other countries—for example LITHOPROBE in Canada and ACORP in Australia (Oliver, 1993, p. 22).

The COCORP program has produced seismic reflection profiles from many different geological provinces of continental crust. Figure 3.11 shows where the COCORP profiles have been located. Examples of particularly interesting profiles are those transverse to the strike of the northern and southern Appalachians and east-west across the Basin and Range Province. Reflection data are combined with refraction data to produce a coherent picture of the deep geologic structure. (See Figure 9.10 for an example of a COCORP profile.) In some traverses the Moho is clearly revealed, and may appear as a continuous, nearly horizontal interface over large distances. (See Allmendinger et al., 1987, p. 308.)

While our reference here to seismic reflection profiling concerns the continental crust, the method has been of enormous importance in the investigation of the sedimentary accumulations of the ocean floors and marginal basins. This class of information is briefly described in Chapter 4.

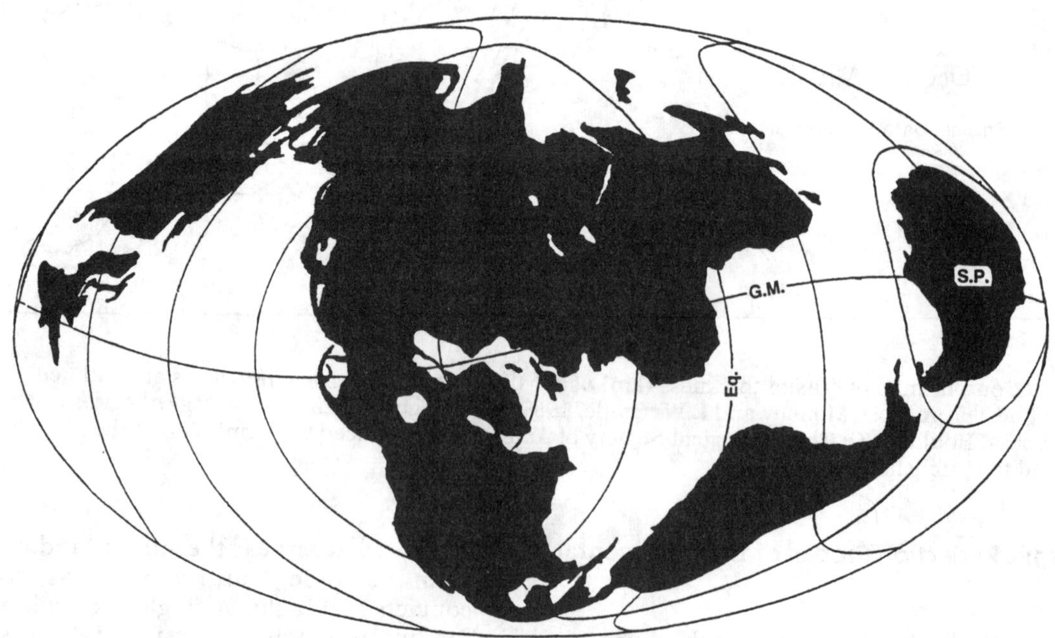

Figure 3.9 Map of the global extent of continental crust, including continent-continent boundaries and showing oceanic windows. The microcontinents are Jan Mayen and Rockall, in the North Atlantic: Agulhas, off southern Africa; and Seychelles, in the Indian Ocean. The map is on a Briesemeister equal-area projection centered at 60°N, 10°E. (Redrawn from J. Graham Cogley, 1984, *Annual Reviews of Geophysics and Space Physics,* v. 22, no. 2, p. 105, Figure 2. Used by permission.)

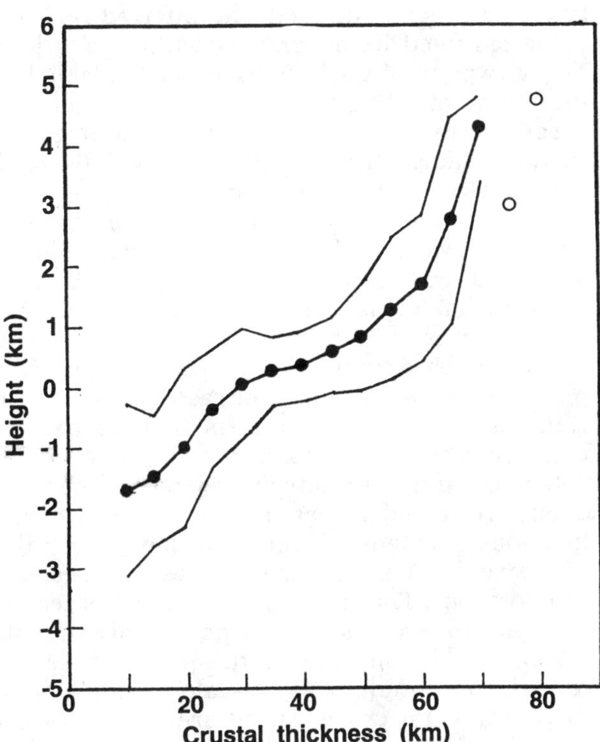

Figure 3.10 Continental height as a function of crustal thickness. Upper and lower lines connect points of one standard deviation from plotted points. (From Cogley, 1984, p. 114. Same source as for Figure 3.8. Used by permission.)

3.8 Deep Drilling of The Continental Crust

The idea of drilling a hole to reach the Moho and bring up rock samples for direct analysis was put forward in 1957 by the American Miscellaneous Society (AMSOC), described as "an esoteric organization with branches throughout the United States and in some foreign countries" (Lill and Maxwell, 1959, p. 1407). AMSOC was approached by Walter Munk and Harry Hess with the proposition that such a hole should be drilled. As a result of informal discussions a committee was organized in 1958 within the National Academy of Sciences-National Research Council and funded by the National Science Foundation. Understandably, the object of the project immediately became known as the *Mohole*, but it never materialized. Logically, the Mohole was to be placed in oceanic crust, and sites in the Central Pacific were specified. It was imagined that the drilling would be done from a vessel of a type then in use for offshore petroleum exploration (Lill and Maxwell, 1959, p. 1409-1410; Hess, 1959). Funding of engineering studies was continued under the Office of Naval Research. Test holes were drilled in relatively shallow offshore depths from the drilling barge, *Cuss I*. One such hole, off the west coast of Puerto Rico, obtained a 1,000-foot core that consisted entirely of serpentine (*ONR Research Reviews*, June, 1963). As late as 1966, planning continued for a gigantic drilling rig that was to drill through the Moho in four closely-spaced holes on the Pacific Floor (Walter Sullivan, *New York Times*, April 26, 1966). Although the Mohole was never drilled, deep-sea drilling was to become a major tool of scientific exploration under the Deep Sea Drilling Project, begun in 1968 (see Chapter 4).

A proposal to drill deep holes in the continental crust surfaced in 1975, when a working group sponsored by the Carnegie Institution of Washington drew up plans and published its report under the editorship of Eugene M. Shoemaker (Hammond, 1975).

The first deep hole to be drilled was begun in the Soviet Union in 1970 on the Kola Peninsula, 250 km north of the Arctic Circle. By 1989 it had reached a depth of over 12 km and was then the world's deepest hole. It had passed through the Proterozoic shield rocks and was into Archean rocks. Here, the seismic Moho lies at a depth of 9 km, but in passing below that level no mafic (basaltic) rock was found (Kozlovsky, 1984, p. 98),

Figure 3.11 Deep seismic reflection profiles surveyed in the contiguous 48 United States by COCORP as of 1993. (From Oliver, 1993, *Geotimes*, v. 38, no. 2, p. 22. Reproduced by permission of Jack Oliver and the Institute for the Study of Continents (INSTOC), Cornell University.)

nor was any encountered when 12 km was reached.

Under auspices of the U.S. Continental Scientific Drilling Program (CSDP), Robert Hatcher, Director, it was proposed in 1985 that a deep hole be drilled into the Paleozoic orogenic belt of the Southern Appalachians to reach a depth of over 7 km so as to pass through low-angle thrust faults revealed by COCORP seismic profiling. This project became known as the Appalachian Ultradeep Core Hole (ADCOH).

By 1987, U.S. deep drilling had come under the direction of a private nonprofit corporation, Deep Observation and Sampling of the Earth's Continental Crust (DOSECC). Its first project was to drill in Cajon Pass, California, close to the San Andreas fault, with the aim of observing the state of stress along earthquake-producing faults. The goal had been to reach a depth of 5 km, but drilling was suspended in 1988 at a depth of 3.5 km. DOSECC planned for future projects that included holes in the Katmai caldera of Alaska and another near Creede, Colorado, in the Southern Rockies (DOSECC, 1987). These and other projects had specific scientific aims appropriate to the unique geology of each crustal locality; they were not intended to pierce the Moho. DOSECC also took over the ADCOH project, but it was abandoned for lack of funds.

By 1988, deep drilling programs had been implemented in France, Sweden, and West Germany. The German project, titled Bundesrepublik Deutchland Tief Bohrprogramm (KTB), was begun with a hole in the Oberpfalz region on the western margin of the Bohemian massif. Here, a hole 14 km deep was expected to pass through three tectonomorphic zones, or terranes, formed by a plate collision of mid-Carboniferous date (320 Ma). By late 1994, when a depth of 9 km had been reached, drilling was terminated because of a heavy inflow of brines (Kerr, 1994).

By 1989, the deep drilling program of the Soviet Union had been expanded to 11 deep holes, and the Soviet Minister of Geology had proposed a large, world-scale deep-drilling program to be known as GLOBUS. It was to include 50 deep holes that were to serve as nodal points of a network of geophysical transects, crossing all the continents and ocean basins.

By 1991, the United States CSPD had down-scaled its drilling program to shallower holes carefully selected for specific academic research goals. In late 1993, plans were drawn up for an International Continental Drilling Program (ICDP) (Swinbank, 1993: Elders, 1994).

3.9 The Continental Crust and Moho As Geological Entities

Thus far, our definition and description of the crust has been from the standpoint and data of seismology, with petrologic labels being applied to layers seismically defined, the inferred rock type being assumed homogeneous within each layer. This viewpoint of the crust is understandable from the history of seismic refraction exploration of the oceanic crust in the 1950s by research groups, such as Maurice Ewing and his associates of the Lamont Geological Obervatory.

Recall that whereas under the deep ocean floors the Moho is found at a relatively shallow depth (12 km), beneath the continents it ranges from 30 km to as deep as 50 km (Figure 3.5). Oceanic crust has been comparatively recently formed by basaltic magma rising along spreading plate boundaries. In contrast, most of the continental crust is an ancient body of rock put together in numerous collisions that have severely deformed and metamorphosed both preexisting crustal rock and newer oceanic crust. Repeated invasions of magmas from below have added their intrusive bodies of varied sizes, shapes, and compositions. This complex interaction of tectonic and igneous processes explains why accumulated seismic reflection data of the past two decades reveals a multitude of "fine-scale" features within the continental crust. These are in the form of local layerlike discontinuities as well as local massive variations, altogether described as "inhomogeneities."

We now see various pictorial diagrams that attempt to show typical crustal inhomogeneities inferred to be present. One such diagram, reproduced here as Figure 3.12, was presented in 1983 by geophysicist Jack Oliver, with the following explanation:

> Figure [3.12] illustrates a general change in thinking about the structure of the continental crust over the last few decades. On the left is the traditional, but now outdated crustal model... Few earth scientists consider this model realistic anymore.
>
> The section on the right of Figure [3.12] is probably a more realistic model of the crust. It was suggested by Smithson (1978), and features an upper layer of supracrustal rocks and grantitic intrusions, a middle migmatitic layer, and a deep andesitic layer overlying the mantle.
>
> A critical point is that, although there is a sort of vertical zonation comparable to that of the model on the left, there is also considerable lateral variation within a zone and within the crust in general. (Oliver, 1983, p. 277)

Notice that in Smithson's model, the Moho beneath continental crust is shown as a sharp horizontal interface and that the mantle is shown as a homogeneous body. More recent studies have challenged that simplicity. Oliver has elsewhere

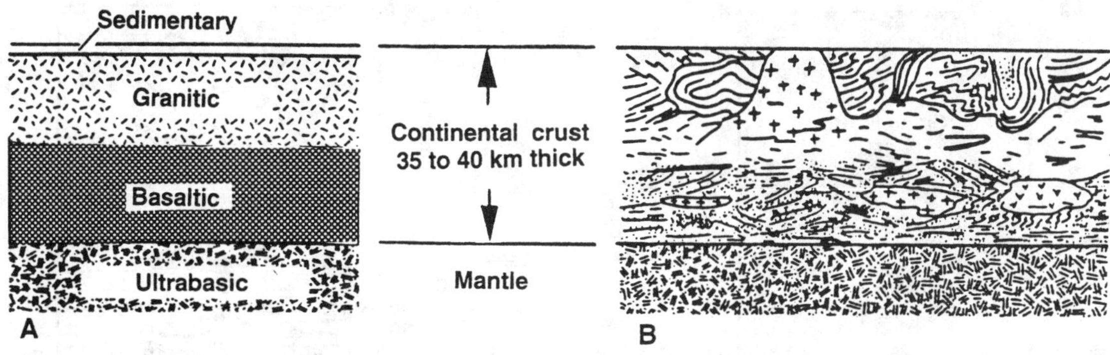

Figure 3.12 (A) Traditional but outdated model of continental crust consisting of a thin layer of sediment overlying a granitic layer of about half crustal thickness, in turn overlying a basaltic layer of about half crustal thickness, with the mantle beneath. (B) Modified from Smithson's generalized crustal model (1) showing three zones including an upper zone of supracrustal and granitic rocks, a middle migmatitic zone and a lower andesitic zone with the mantle beneath. Later variations are a key point of this model. (Figure and legend reprinted with permission from Jack Oliver, 1982, *Science*, v. 216, p. 691, Figure 1. Copyright © 1982 by the American Association for the Advancement of Science.)

editorialized on a need to distinguish between a seismologic boundary and one based on other physical/chemical criteria. He has observed that other terms recently used, such as "petrological Moho" and "geochemical Moho," only tend to lead us into a "semantic abyss" (Oliver, 1988, p. 291).

Geochemists and petrologists have attempted to interpret the indications of inhomogeneities in the light of new findings in experimental laboratory studies of minerals under high confining pressures and at high temperatures, such as those assumed to exist deep in the crust and in the upper mantle. From this newer research there has arisen a distinction between the "seismic Moho," which is a wave-velocity discontinuity, and a geologic feature that is the actual lithologic boundary between the mafic rock of the lower part of the crust and the ultramafic rock that underlies it. This petrologic crust/mantle boundary has been designated the *CMB* (Griffin and O'Reilly, 1987, p. 241).

Direct geologic evidence of what lies deep in the continental crust and upper mantle is available in a few rare localities where, because of intense deformation followed by deep erosion, a sequence of rocks can be traced from upper crust to lower crust and even into what may be the mantle. One example is in the Ivrea Zone of the Alps; others are found in Canada, Africa, and Australia (Oliver, 1983, p. 278). (Exposures of sequences from oceanic crust into oceanic mantle are abundant in the form of ophiolitic suites, described in Chapter 5.) Direct evidence of rocks of the CMB region in its present location is also provided by actual rock samples, and these can come from very deep drill holes or as rock fragments brought to the surface by special geologic processes, including the rise of magmas carrying up solid fragments that are now exposed as xenoliths. Diatremes (explosion pipes) are also deemed capable of bringing up mineral grains or crystals from the mantle.

3.10 Geologic Features of the Crust-Mantle Transition

Earlier, we identified the rock of the mantle directly below the Moho as peridotite in the case of oceanic crust. The general rock name "peridotite" refers to a coarse-grained, plutonic igneous rock composed chiefly of olivine, with (or without) other mafic minerals, and as such it is classed as an ultramafic rock. (Dunite, composed entirely of olivine, falls under the more general designation of peridotite.) The density of peridotite is 3.3, so the rock is a suitable candidate for nomination as the material composing the mantle immediately underneath the Moho.

An alternative to assigning peridotite to the zone immediately below the Moho is found in the concept of *phase transition*, in which a mineral (or suite of minerals), subjected to increasing temperature and/or pressure, undergoes a reordering of its components to become a mineral (or mineral suite) of greater density. Applying this concept to the mantle, it has been proposed that the mafic gabbroic rock of the crustal zone above the seismic Moho extends below the Moho for some distance—say 15 km—into the mantle, but with a higher P-wave speed because it has undergone a phase transition to eclogite. The idea was put forward by J.F. Lovering in 1958 and G.C. Kennedy in 1959 (Wyllie, 1971, p. 68-69, 72). Figure 3.13 shows such an arrangement. It is established by experimentation that the phase change from mafic granulite (composition of gabbro) to eclogite is accompanied by an increase in P-wave speed on the order of 0.5 to 1.0 km/sec (Griffin and O'Reilly, 1987, p. 243). The phase change is reversible, hence the Moho could move downward as well as upward with environmental pressure/temperature changes.

More recent findings have challenged the concept of the Moho as a single abrupt interface. A

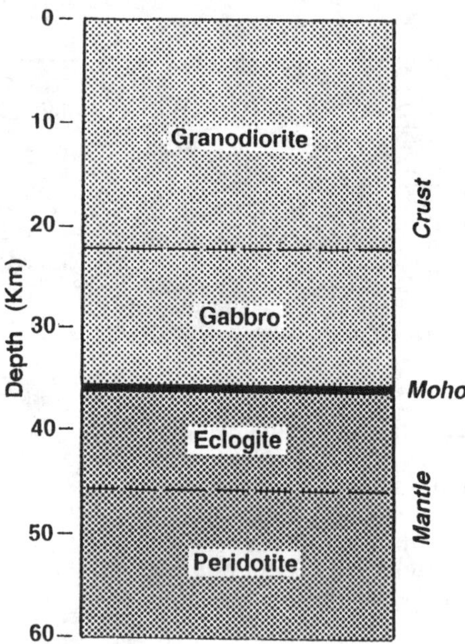

Figure 3.13 A model of the layers of the crust and mantle showing a phase transition from gabbro to eclogite at the seismic Moho. (From Peter J. Wyllie, 1971, *The Dynamic Earth,* p. 70, Figure 5-6. Copyright © 1971 by John Wiley & Sons, New York. Used by permission.)

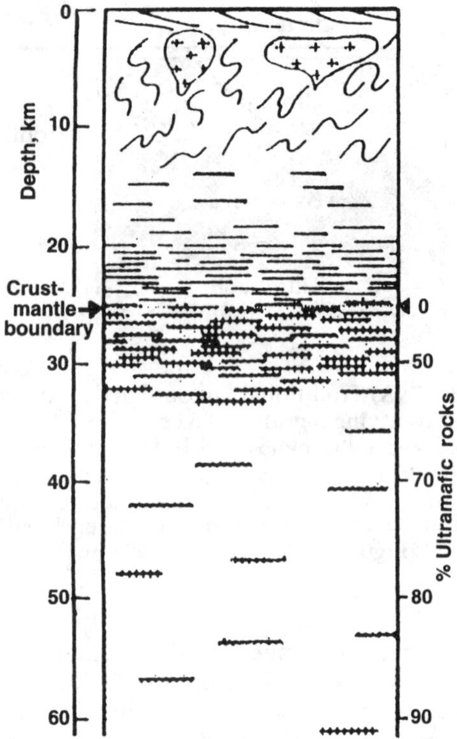

Figure 3.14 A model for the crust-mantle transition. Horizontal lines represent sill-like layers of intruded mafic rock. (Redrawn from W.L. Griffin and S.Y. O'Reilly, 1987, *Geology,* v. 15, p. 242, Figure 2. Used by permission of the Geological Society of America and the authors.)

newer model for the crust/mantle boundary (CMB), described in 1987 by W.L. Griffin and Suzanne Y. O'Reilly, is reproduced here as Figure 3.14. Both above and below the CMB are shown sill-like layers of intruded mafic rock, separated from one another both vertically and horizontally. These mafic layers decrease in proportion both upward and downward from the CMB, which arbitrarily separates mafic crust from ultramafic mantle. The result is an overall transition from dominantly mafic to dominantly ultramafic rock.

3.11 Structure and Composition of the Mantle

Figure 3.1D shows the changes in speed of P-waves and S-waves with increasing depth in the earth. Both curves are upwardly convex in the mantle, showing that the rate of increase in wave speed lessens with depth.

Through most of the earth's mantle, which has a total thickness of nearly 2900 km, the speed of earthquake waves is so high that only a very rigid and dense rock, such as the crustal rock peridotite, will satisfy the observed conditions. Thus, it is presently accepted that the mantle consists of solid ultramafic rock.

Based on the behavior of seismic waves, the mantle is usually subdivided into two major parts: *upper mantle* and *lower mantle* (Conde, 1989, p. 40-42). The upper mantle, composed of rock of the composition of peridotite, extends from the base of the crust to a depth of about 660 km (Figure 3.15).

In the upper mantle, at a depth between 370 and 410 km, a sharp increase in P-wave speed occurs, suggesting a sudden increase in rock density (Figure 3.16). Rather than attribute this seismic discontinuity to an abrupt change in chemical composition of the mantle rock, geochemists favor a phase transition caused by the pressure/temperature increase. Olivine, which is the major mineral component of peridotite, is capable of undergoing just such a phase transition to the spinel crystal structure, which is in the isometric system. The phase change has been demonstrated by laboratory experiments conducted under appropriate conditions of pressure and temperature (Willie, 1971, p. 111-37; 1975, p. 57; McKenzie, 1983, p. 75). This phase transition, to which we can assign a depth close to 390 km, results in a density increase of about 10 percent.

Below the 410-km discontinuity, P-wave velocity and density increase gradually and uniformly to a depth of about 660 km. Here, at the boundary between upper mantle and lower mantle, another strong seismic discontinuity occurs, shown in the sharp increase in P-wave velocity (Figure 3.16). It is inferred that at this critical depth pressure is so great that a phase transition occurs from spinel structure to perovskite structure, accompanied by another density

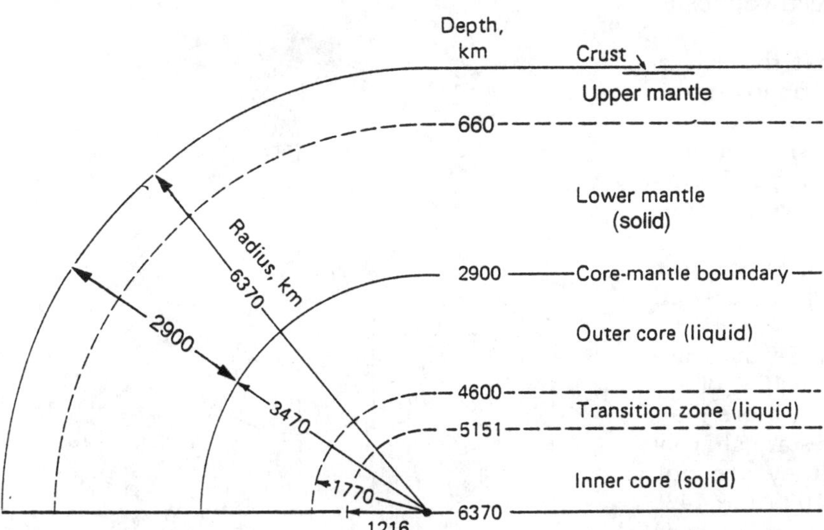

Figure 3.15 Dimensions of the earth's mantle and core. (Copyright © by Arthur N. Strahler.)

increase of about 10 percent (McKenzie 1983, p. 67). Laboratory experiments, using a laser-heated diamond-anvil cell producing pressures up to 127 gigapascals and temperatures above 2000 K, have shown that olivine, pyroxene, and garnet (the dominant minerals of the upper mantle) transform to the perovskite structure along with minor oxides (Knittle and Jeanloz, 1987, p. 668). Within the lower mantle, seismic wave velocity increases rather smoothly, as Figure 3.1D shows, indicating that the perovskite phase persists to the base of the mantle.

3.12 The Earth's Core

We complete the general description of the earth's system of spherical zones with a brief statement of structure and composition of the core. Study of seismograms has confirmed the existence of a spherical core at the earth's center and has added insight into its physical nature. If the earth were in a solid state entirely throughout, both P-waves and S-waves would travel through the center in all possible directions, and the body waves of any large earthquake could be recorded by a

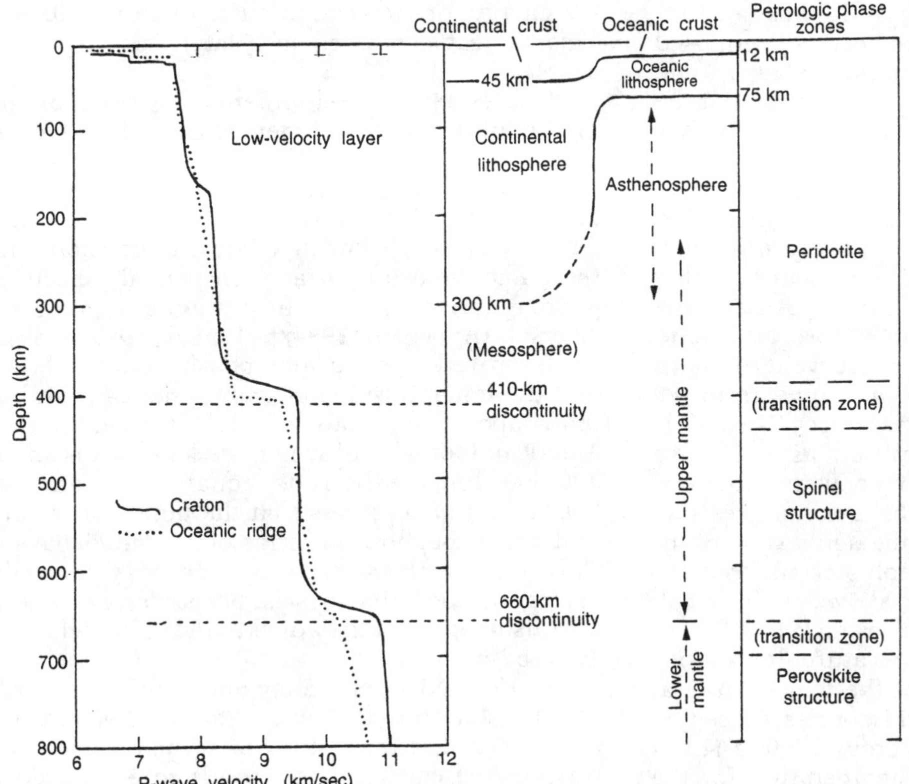

Figure 3.16 Zones of the upper and lower mantle in relation to seismic wave velocities. (Based on data of Wyllie, 1971, Conde, 1989, Archambeau et al., 1968, and other sources.)

seismograph located on the globe directly opposite the focus.

It was soon found, however, that there is a large region on the side of the globe opposite the earthquake focus where S-waves are not received. Evidently they are prevented from passing through the core (Figure 3.1). Laboratory experiments demonstrate that shear waves, or S-waves, cannot be sent through a liquid; hence, the conclusion that the earth's core is in a liquid state in contrast to the surrounding mantle, which is in a solid state.

As shown in Figure 3.17, direct S-waves are received only within a distance of about 103° of arc from the earthquake source (somewhat more than one hemisphere). Because the P-waves are sharply refracted as they enter the core, they are not directly received in a zone between 103° and 143° distant from the focus. Neither are S-waves received there, since they do not travel through the core. Only surface waves and complex reflected waves can be received in this *shadow zone*. A zone beyond 143° receives only P-waves passing through the core, complex reflected waves, and surface waves.

From the extent of the shadow zone, the earth's core is calculated to have a radius of 3470 km, a little more than half the earth's total radius (Figure 3.15). That the core boundary is quite sharply defined is known because the P-waves of high frequency are reflected back to the surface from this boundary.

Using our calculation of the earth's average density (5.5), we may guess that the outer region of the core is composed largely of liquid iron of high density (10 to 12), under enormous pressure and at a high temperature. Although it was at first thought that the liquid outer core is composed almost entirely of metallic iron, there is now some doubt about this, and it seems more likely that the iron is alloyed with a small proportion of another element, which may be carbon, silicon, or sulfur.

Evidence from earthquake seismology also revealed that the inner part of the core, outward to a radius of about 1220 km, behaves very differently from the rest of the core. Notice in Figure 3.1 that the P-wave speed makes an abrupt increase at the boundary between liquid outer core and solid inner core. Although the S-wave curve terminates at the mantle-core boundary, it reappears in the solid inner core. This inner-core S-wave is produced by energy transmitted as a P-wave through the liquid zone and reconverted to an S-wave in the solid zone. This behavior suggests an inner solid state, rather than the liquid state of the outer core. It seems reasonably certain that the inner core is composed of iron alloyed with a small amount of a heavier metal such as nickel.

High-pressure high-temperature laboratory experments yield estimates of the temperature at the outer surface of the liquid core as exceeding 4,800 K, and an estimate of around 7,000 K has been offered as a maximum temperature for the

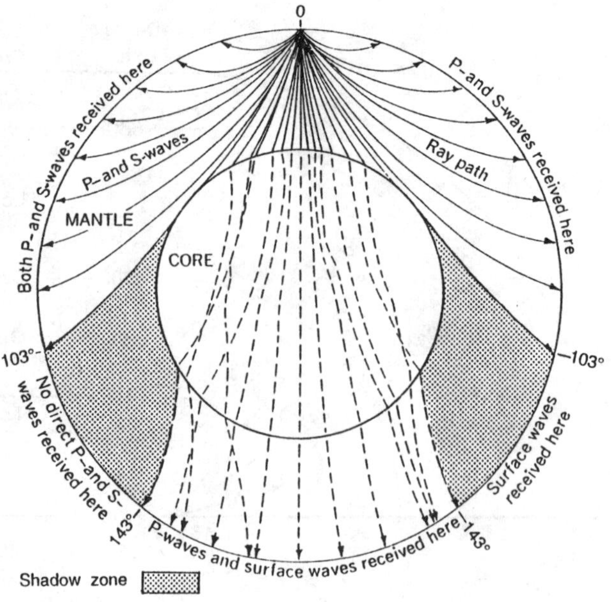

Figure 3.17 Diagrammatic representation of many possible ray paths from a single earthquake source. (Adapted from Gutenberg, 1951, *Internal Constitution of the Earth,* New York: Dover Publ. Co. Used by permission of the publisher.)

inner core (Williams et al., 1987). A sharp temperature drop from 4,800 K at the outer core surface to about 2,700 K at the adjacent base of the mantle has an important bearing on speculations about convective motions in the mantle. It is now postulated that heat from the outer core passing into the base of the mantle may provide most of the energy for convection currents in the mantle. This subject is treated in a later section of this chapter.

Subsequent developments in seismologic methodology revealed departures of the core/mantle boundary (CMB) from a perfectly smooth ellipsoidal surface (Dziewonski and Woodehouse, 1987, p. 45). The CMB appears to have relief features up to 10 km in vertical dimension, and these may be of importance in several aspects of geomagnetism, including magnetic polarity reversals (Anderson, 1984, p. 16: Lay, 1989, p. 49).

Improved seismic methods have also shown that the inner core is not truly spherical, but has the shape of a prolate ellipsoid (resembling an American football), of which the long axis is about 200 km longer than its equatorial diameter. Seismology also reveals that the inner core is not uniform throughout in terms of seismic behavior. This means that the inner core is laterally heterogeneous in its physical properties, i.e., that it is anisotropic. (Dziewonski and Woodehouse, 1987, p. 45-46).

In 1996, Xiaodong Song and Paul G. Richards of the Lamont-Doherty Earth Observatory announced that their study of seismic waves that traverse the earth's inner (solid) core revealed a systematic variation over a period of three decades. They concluded that the phenomenon was best explained as a rotation of the inner core in the same direction as the whole earth, but at a slightly faster rate. This difference of rate is about one degree per year (Song and Richards, 1996, p. 221; Whaler and Holm, 1966, p. 205; Monastersky, 1996, p. 36).

This section concludes a brief description of the earth's concentric zones as static features. Now that we have made a rapid journey downward from the crust through the mantle to the surface of the core, it is necessary to return to the earth's surface to begin an investigation into the dynamics of these layers. How do they respond to unbalanced forces? What rheological properties allow these materials to move—laterally or vertically, or in closed loops?

3.13 Lithosphere and Asthenosphere

Chapter 1 included a general description of both the lithosphere and the asthenosphere (Figures 1.3, 1.4, 1.5 and 1.6). We explained that the lower limit of the brittle (rigid) zone does not represent a change in rock composition, but rather a change in physical properties. Recall from the analogy of the iron bar that if one end of a cast-iron bar is held in a furnace, it becomes white hot and soft; farther out along the bar, the iron is red hot and not so soft; toward the cool end the iron is hard and brittle. In a similar way, the behavior of rock changes gradually upward in a transition from the asthenosphere to the lithosphere.

In Chapter 2, we mentioned Joseph Barrell's introduction in 1914 and 1915 of the terms "lithosphere" and "asthenosphere," and Reginald Daly's adoption of the same concept in 1926 in his model of a brittle crustal layer underlain by a weak layer of hot basalt (see Figure 2.21). Barrell had introduced the asthenosphere in these words: "It is a real zone between the lithosphere above and the centrosphere below.... It needs a distinctive name. Its comparative weakness is its distinctive feature. It may therefore be called the sphere of weakness—*the asthenosphere*" (1914, p. 659 and Figure 14). (The term derives from the Greek word *asthenes*, meaning "weak".) He gave the thickness of the lithosphere as 120 km and that of the "slightly plastic" asthenosphere as about 600 km (p. 680).

Rock in the mantle below the lithosphere, including both the asthenosphere and all of the mantle below it, behaves as both an elastic solid and a plastic solid. Matter possessing these remarkable properties has been called an *elasticoviscous* substance—it can be both elastic and fluid-like at the same time, depending on whether the forces that tend to deform it are applied and released suddenly (as if struck a sharp blow) or applied steadily (as under the force of gravity). In the first case, illustrated by deforming stress alternately applied and restored by seismic body waves, the substance undergoes elastic strain when the stress is applied and the strain is elastically restored when the stress is removed. In the second case, illustrated by placing a constant load stress on the substance, yielding is continuous by viscous flow (as in a Newtonian fluid). In viscous flow, the rate of flow (i.e., the strain rate) is directly proportional to applied stress. Ideally, viscous flow is induced by a deforming stress of any magnitude greater than zero. The term *Maxwell liquid* is also applied to this elastico-viscous substance (Bates and Jackson, 1987, p. 406).

Because early data of seismology clearly revealed the passage of body waves through the entire mantle, the elasticoviscous model of rock behavior in the asthenosphere was generally accepted during the early 1900s in preference to earlier suggestions that a true fluid layer of molten rock (magma) existed in that zone. Viscosity of the asthenosphere has been estimated as 4×10^{20} poise; that of the mantle beneath it as 10^{22} poise (Cathles, 1987, p. 199).

As an illustration of the elasticoviscous substance, it is said to be possible to make a tuning fork out of cold pitch so rigid that it will vibrate with a musical tone when struck, but if the same fork is left to stand for a long time, it will slowly collapse into a shapeless mass (see Van Der Gracht, 1928, p. 24-25).

A slightly different model of deformational behavior is seen in the *elasticoplastic* substance, in which a threshold value of elastic deformation, the *yield stress*, must be attained before continuous viscous flow takes place. However, the rate of strain is not linear with stress, but increases rapidly as stress increases, so that the stress/strain curve steepens rapidly and quickly becomes asymptotic (Figure 3.18). For the upper mantle, the increase is modeled as logarithmic, with strain proportional to the third power of stress (Post and

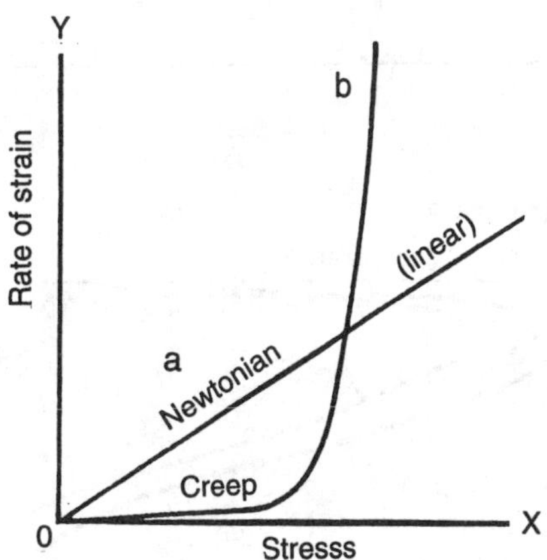

Figure 3.18 Relation of rate of strain to applied stress for (a) Newtonian fluid and (b) elasticoplastic body.(Copyright © by Arthur N. Strahler.)

Griggs, 1973, in Seyfert, 1987, p. 108). The term *viscoelastic* applies specifically to this form of stress/strain behavior (Bates and Jackson, 1987, p. 725).

Presence of a weak or soft layer in the mantle beneath the lithosphere was amenable to detection by seismology because the effect of reduction in rock strength is to slow the velocity of seismic waves, both the P- and S-waves. In 1926, the seismologist Beno Gutenberg showed that wave velocities were diminished in a depth zone about from 100 to 200 km, and he proposed that the cause lay in decreased rigidity of the mantle rock in that zone (Anderson, 1962, p. 52). In 1955, Gutenberg described this zone as a "low-velocity channel" and applied to it the name "asthenospheric channel" (Richter, 1958, p. 269, 273, 279). Interest in this subject was revived with great intensity in the early and middle 1960s, as the theory of plate tectonics was being rapidly put into place. Don L. Anderson of the California Institute of Technology summarized abundant seismic evidence of the low-velocity/low rigidity layer; his summary was widely disseminated through the scientific community in a 1962 article in *Scientific American*.

As Anderson explained, the properties responsible for the low-velocity layer are determined by pressure and temperature in relation to the melting point at increasing depths. Both pressure and temperature increase with depth:

> In general the elasticity of any material decreases as its temperature approaches the melting point. But an increase in pressure raises the melting point and elasticity...and so the two [pressure and temperature] have opposing effects on the proximity to the melting point as well as on the elastic strength of the rock. (Anderson, 1962, p. 58)

Figure 3.19(A) shows how the velocities of S-waves P-waves change with depth, for a selected case. The chosen thickness of the lithosphere is 100 km and for the asthenosphere 150 km (T.H. Jordan and W.S. Fyfe (1976, p. 770). However, partial melting may occur to a depth of 250 km (Wyllie, P.J., 1975, p. 50). Notice that for both waves a sharp reversal marks the upper level of the asthenosphere. Figure 3.19(B) shows the changing in rock strength with increasing depth. The variable Q used here is an anelastic parameter that "coincides satisfactorily with an appropriately normalized viscosity profile" (F.D. Stacey, 1977, p. 308). Strength falls off rapidly in the region of the asthenosphere.

Below about 200 km, the effect of increasing pressure on melting point takes over and the strength curve reverses to increase with depth, so that the asthenosphere gradually gives way to a high-strength mantle zone that has been called the *mesosphere*. In summarizing this three-layer picture in 1968, three seismologists of the Lamont Observatory of Columbia University—Bryan

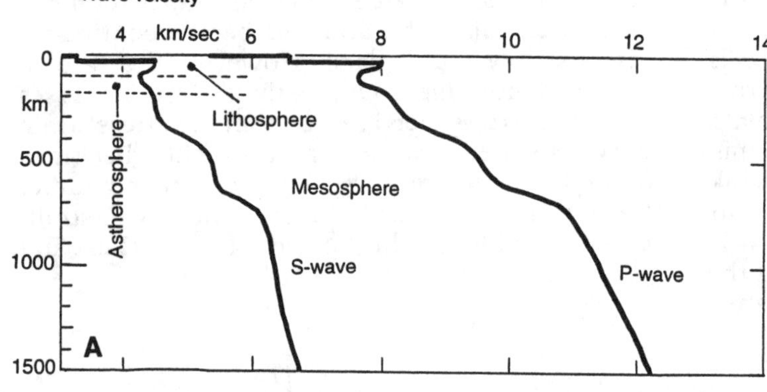

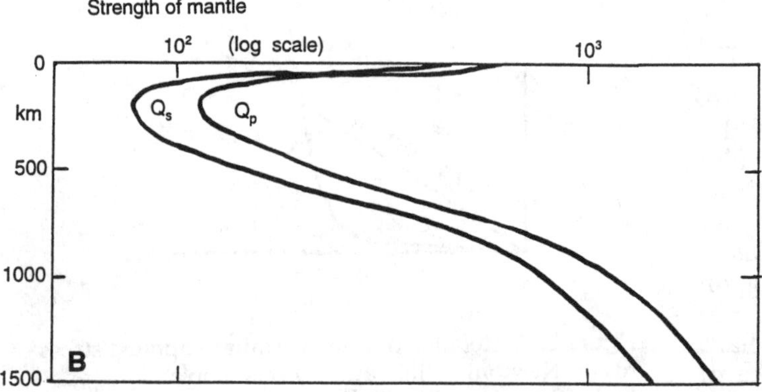

Figure 3.19 Seismic and strength characteristics of the asthenosphere. (A) S-wave and P-wave velocities. (B) A viscosity profile representing the change of strength with depth. (Based on data from Condie, 1989, p. 14, Figure 1.4 and Stacey, 1977, p. 308, Figure 20.21.Used by permission of Pergamon Press and John Wiley & Sons, respectively.)

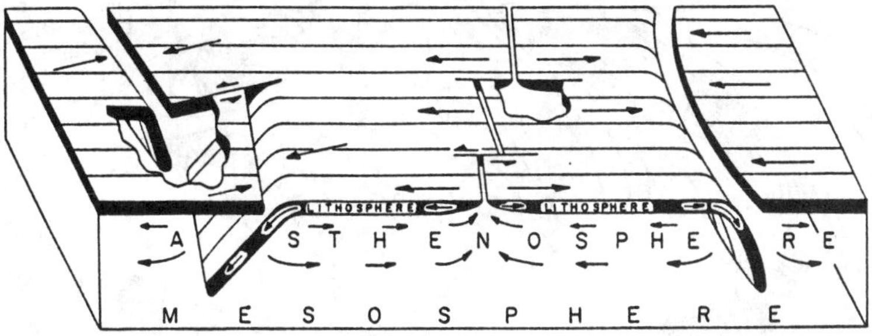

Figure 3.20 A now-classic illustration, first published in 1968, linking the lithosphere, asthenosphere, and mesosphere with the new global tectonics. Arrows on lithosphere indicate relative movements of adjoining "blocks," now known as "plates". Arrows in the asthenosphere represent possbile compensating flow in response to downward movement of segments of lithosphere. (From Bryan Isacks, Jack Oliver, and Lynn R. Sykes, *Jour. of Geophysical Research,* v. 87, p. 5856, Figure 1. Copyright © 1968 by the American Geophysical Union. Used by permssion.)

Isacks, Jack Oliver, and Lynn Sykes—prepared a now-classic illustration, reproduced here as Figure 3.20. Their legend reads: "Block diagram illustrating schematically the configurations and roles of the lithosphere, asthenosphere, and mesosphere in a version of the new global tectonics in which the lithosphere, a layer of strength, plays a key role" (Isacks, Oliver, and Sykes, 1968, p. 71).

The favored interpretation since about 1960 has been that a condition of partial melting exists at least locally in the asthenosphere (Wyllie, 1971, p. 190). As will be explained in Chapter 5, partial melting of mantle rock is thought to provide the magma needed to produce new basaltic rock of the oceanic lithosphere at spreading plate boundaries. Estimates place the proportion of melt in the asthenosphere as on the order of 1% to 10%. Presence of the melt fraction has been used to explain the lower strength of the asthenosphere, as well as the reduced P- and S-wave velocities.

The direct association of partial melting with susceptibility to shear flow has, however, been questioned. In its place the proposal has been offered that physical-chemical properties of the mantle rock determine the rheological properties. This could mean that the actual mantle zone in which most of the plate motion is concentrated may be a relatively thin shear zone (Jordan and Fyfe, 1976, p. 770-771).

Thus far our description of the lithosphere and asthenosphere might seem to suggest that these are two layers of uniform thickness over the entire globe. Recall from Chapter 1 and Figure 1.2, that such is not the case. As shown in Figures 1.2 and 3.16, continental lithosphere is generally much thicker than oceanic lithosphere, a condition easily explained by the great differences in tectonic processes (spreading vs. convergence) that create oceanic and continental lithosphere. We might then guess that the asthenosphere beneath the continental lithosphere may be quite different from that under the oceanic lithosphere.

3.14 The Lithosphere—Its Thickness and Continental Roots

Thickness of the lithosphere can be estimated by indirect methods. One is to use the depth to the top of the low-velocity layer. Alternatively, the rate of surface heat flow can provide an independent indicator of lithospheric thickness, based on the reasonable premise that the lithosphere acts as an insulating cap over the highly heated asthenosphere, and therefore that heat flow is inversely related to depth to asthenosphere. As shown in Figure 3.21, David S. Chapman and Henry N. Pollock correlated surface heat flow with the seismic velocity data separately for oceanic and continental regions, showing that the anticipated

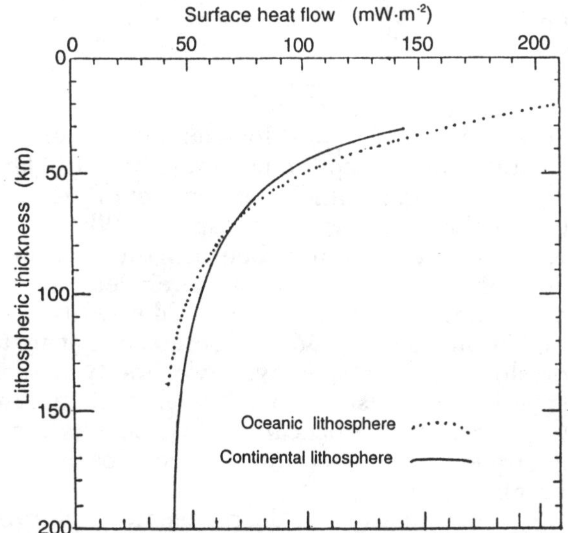

Figure 3.21 Measured rates of surface heat flow compared with estimated lithospheric thickness. (Adapted from Davis S. Chapman and Henry N. Pollack, 1977, *Geology*, v. 5, p. 266. Copyright © by the Geological Society of America. Used by permission.)

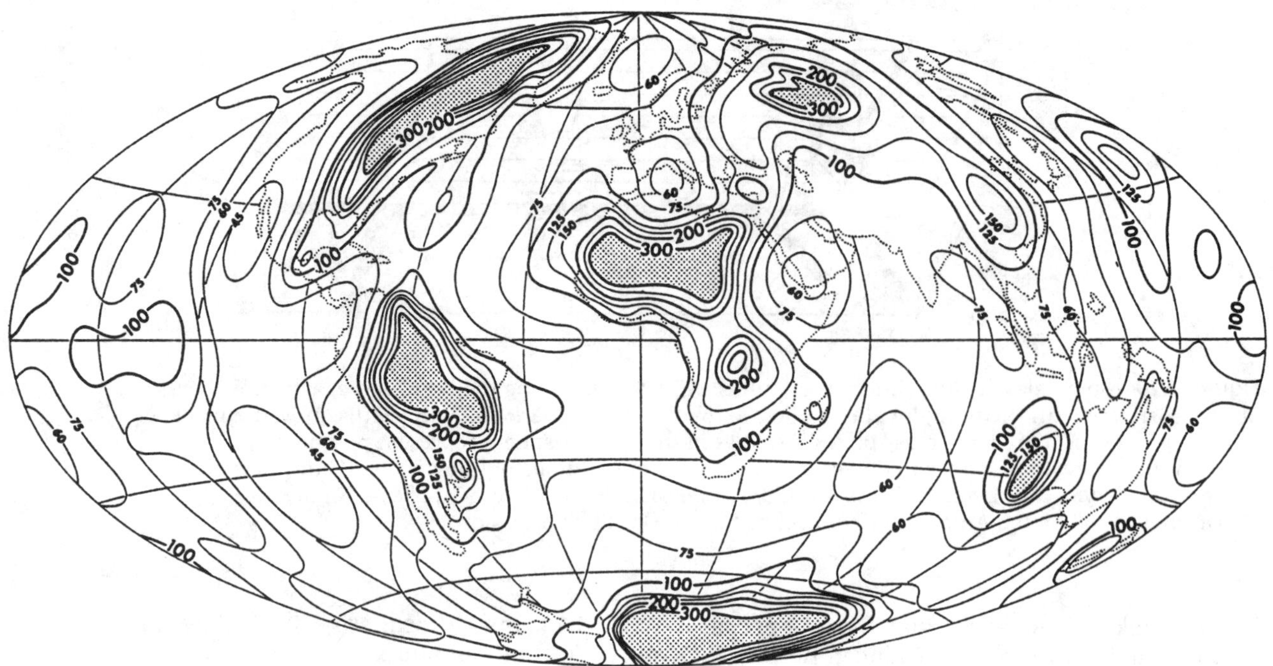

Figure 3.22 World map of the thickness of the lithosphere; isopleths are in kilometers. The thicknesses were determined from the twelfth degree spherical harmonic representation of heat flow. (From D.S. Chapman and H.N. Pollack, 1977. Same source as in Figure 3.21. Used by permission.)

inverse relationship holds rather well for both regions (1977, p. 266).

Figure 3.22 is a world map of thickness of the lithosphere constructed by Chapman and Pollock from their thermal data. A thickness of over 300 km characterizes large areas of the cratons of North America, South America, Africa, and Antarctica, with smaller centers in Eurasia and Western Australia. Thicknesses less than 75 km characterize large areas of the ocean basins, including the active spreading plate boundaries. Low values also lie along parts of the active subduction margins in the western Pacific.

As seismic-wave data accumulated in the 1960s and early 1970s, it became clear that a well-developed continuous low-velocity layer, concentrated in the depth range from 80 to 120 km, is typical of oceanic lithosphere but not of the mantle lying below continental lithosphere. Where a low-velocity layer is found beneath the continental interiors, it is usually weakly developed, or it may not be detected at all. In the middle 1970s, Stuart Sipkin and Thomas Jordan observed that instead of slowing in a shallow, low-velocity asthenospheric zone, seismic waves travel more rapidly in the upper mantle beneath the continents than at equivalent depths beneath the ocean basins (Kerr, 1986b, p. 933).

A new method of deep seismic exploration, known as "tomography," began to be applied in the early 1980s. [Tomography is explained in a following section.] The new data verified the existence of a high-velocity upper-mantle zone extending as deep as perhaps 350 to 400 km beneath the Archean shield rocks (Kerr, 1986, p. 933-934). At a depth of 100 km, the association of high velocities with ancient cratonal areas of the continents, in contrast with low velocities of broad areas beneath oceanic lithosphere, is quite striking. At 300 km, these associations seem to persist in some areas but not in others, while at 500 km the correlation disappears (Dziewonski and Anderson, 1984, p. 488, Figure 5). Newer analyses using larger numbers of observations revealed details of zones of relatively high velocity extending from 250 to 350 km beneath the continents (Kerr, 1986b, p. 933; Anderson et al., 1992; Polet and Anderson, 1995).

In 1979, Thomas H. Jordan, a seismologist, proposed a global classification of the earth's crust into seven major types with which variations in the thermal and seismic properties of the underlying lithosphere and asthenosphere might be correlated, leading to a better understanding of lateral (horizontal) inhomogeneities in the upper mantle (Jordan, 1979, p. 94-96). We present this classification by reproducing a representative section of Jordan's world map (Figure 3.23). The seven crustal classes named in the legend are based on plate tectonics and crustal geology. Three classes cover the oceanic crust in terms of its age—young, intermediate, and old. Continental crust consists of three classes: Precambrian shields and platforms, Phanerozoic platforms, and Phanerozoic orogenic zones. A seventh, or transitional type occupies a zone between the oceanic and continental types and includes both passive margins and subduction plate boundaries. Figure 3.24 shows typical geotherms of four of the crustal types. Figure 3.25 shows seismic and thermal

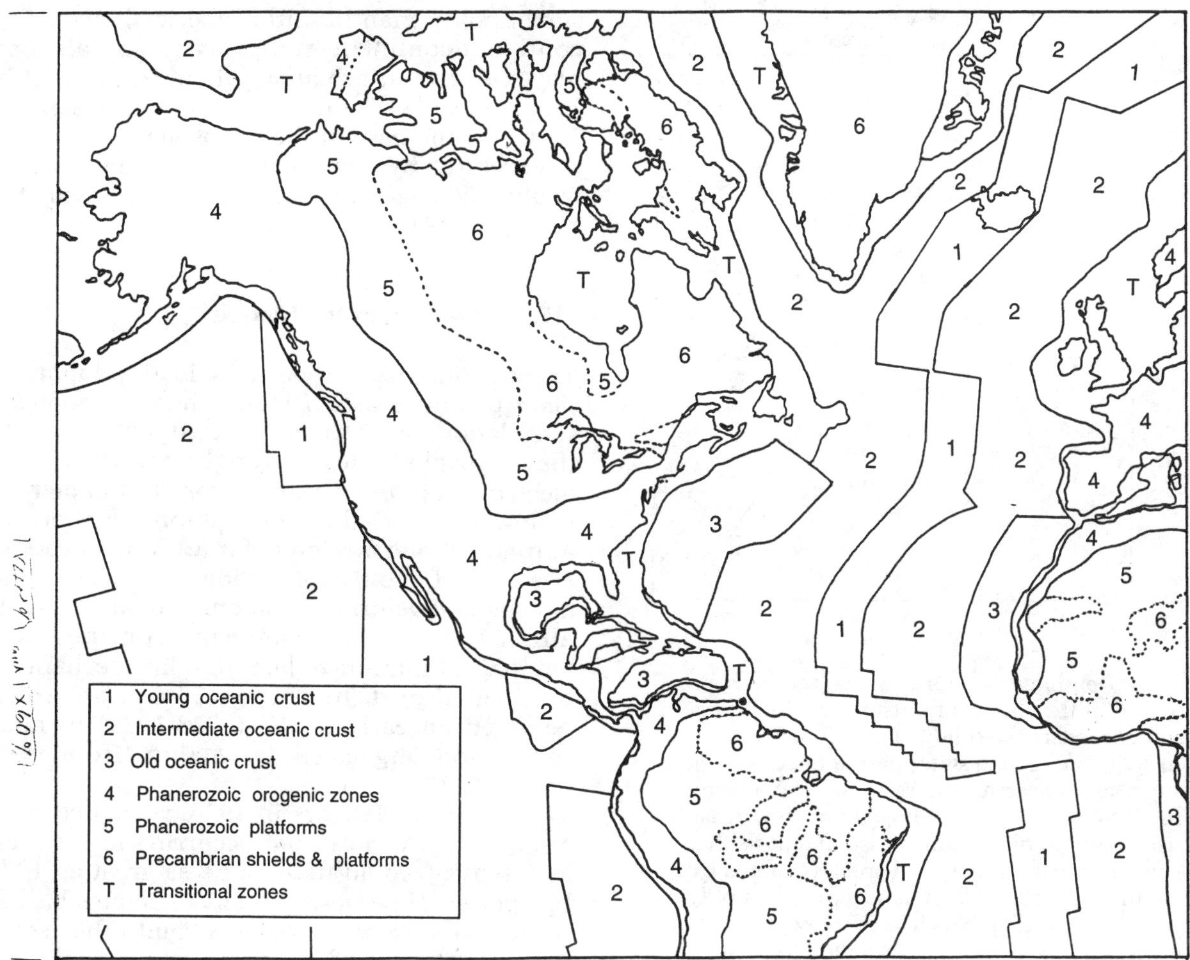

Figure 3.23 Portion of a world map showing six major types of crust according to the system of tectonic classification devised by Thomas H. Jordan. (From T.H. Jordan, 1979, *Scientific American*, v. 240, no. 1, p. 94-95. Copyright © by Allen Beechel. Used by permission.)

properties of the 6 main types; specifically, (A) travel time of vertical S-waves from a depth of 700 km to the surface and (B) rate of surface heat flow. (See Chapter 5 for information on radiogenic heat sources and surface heat flow rates.) In paragraphs below we focus mainly on the differences between the end types, contrasting lithosphere of the Precambrian shields with that of the oceanic crust.

The expressions "continental roots" and "deep continental structure" have come into frequent use to apply to that part of the upper mantle through which S-wave velocities continuously increase downward in the depth range 250 to 350 km, while temperature increases from 1,400 to over 1,500°C. Jordan recognizes that only the upper 100 to 150 km of continental rock is strong, rigid lithosphere and that part of the high-velocity layer below that depth is asthenosphere in the sense of possessing weakness by reason of its high temperature. To replace the system name "lithosphere/ asthenosphere," which would be a misnomer in the absence of a clearly defined weak layer of partial melting, the name *tectosphere* was proposed by Jordan (1979, p. 98). The term had been previously used by W. Jason Morgan for what we now call lithosphere (Morgan, 1968, p. 1980). The tectosphere is postulated by Jordan to move more or less as a unit, despite the ability of the weak lower region to yield by slow shear flow. The weak lower tectosphere does not, however, participate in convection current flow systems, as does the suboceanic asthenosphere. As shown in Jordan's illustration, adapted as here as Figure 3.26A, the base of the tectosphere rises to shallower depths as the continental margin is approached and it merges with the lithosphere/asthenosphere boundary beneath the ocean basin. Figure 3.26B shows by isotherms in the same cross section that the lower part of the tectosphere is substantially cooler than mantle rock at the same depths beneath the ocean basin. This relative coolness would tend to make the continental tectosphere denser than surrounding mantle at the same depth. The continental tectosphere is, however, postulated to have distinctive chemical properties, one of them being that it is enriched in magnesium, a development that occurred in Archean time by partial melting and differentiation to produce basaltic magma that moved upward through the shallower lithosphere to form

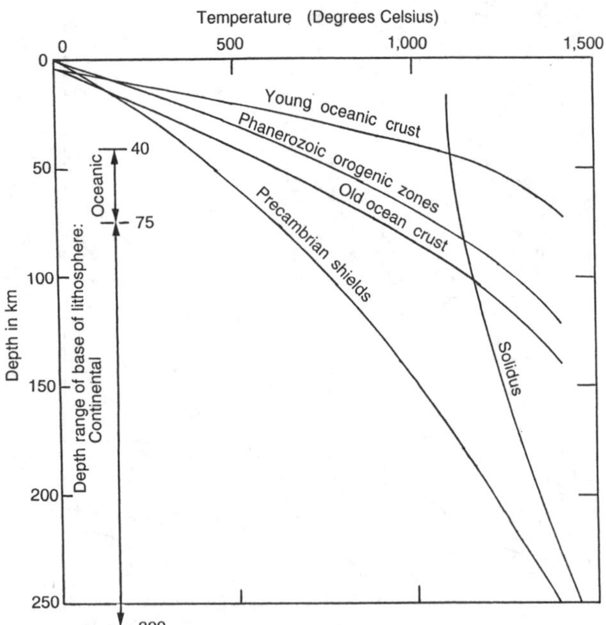

Figure 3.24 Depth/temperature curves (geotherms) beneath four of the classes of crust shown in Figure 3.22. As a geotherm nears the solidus curve (boundary between solid and melted state) partial melting begins, resulting in sharp decreases in seismic wave velocity. Thus, the asthenosphere is shallow under new oceanic crust, deeper under old oceanic crust, and possibly absent under Precambrian shield crust. (Adapted from T.H. Jordan, 1979, *Scientific American*, v. 240, no. 1, p. 96. Copyright © by Allen Beechel. Used by permission.)

continental crust (Kerr, 1986b, p. 934). Magnesium enrichment would have tended to reduce the density of the deep layer in comparison with the undifferentiated mantle rock, and this would have offset the increased density resulting from the lower temperature. Loss of volatiles also occurred at this time. The result was to produce a mantle layer that was less dense than unaffected surrounding mantle. Lithospheric thickening by continent/continent collisions might also have played a part in producing the deep roots (Kerr, 1986b, p. 934). The depth of 350 km, assigned by Jordan to the base of the tectosphere, is regarded as excessive by some petrologists and chemists, who would suggest a lower limit of 200 km (Kerr, 1986b, p. 934).

3.15 Convection In the Mantle

Throughout the early stages in development of plate tectonics as a general theory, geophysical speculation about the forces sustaining motion of the lithosphere was strongly centered on the mechanism of *mantle convection*. In Chapter 2, we reviewed early ideas of Osmond Fisher, Otto Ampherer, and Rudolph Straub on the possible existence of mantle convection currents capable of moving and deforming the crust. It was noted that Alfred Wegener had commented on these ideas, but did not introduce them into his mechanism of continental drift. In Chapter 2, we also critically reviewed an early model (1928-1929) of mantle convection suggested by Arthur Holmes (see Figure 2.22).

Sir Harold Jeffreys in 1928 calculated that to prohibit convection from occurring in the mantle its viscosity would need to be as great as 10^{26} or 10^{27} poises. However, viscosity estimates based on isostatic recovery of the crust and other sources gave an estimate of mantle viscosity on the order of 10^{22}, which is low enough to permit convection with even slight density differences from place to place (Holmes, 1978, p. 711).

Convection, as the term is used in physical science, simply means the spontaneous rising and sinking of fluid masses because of density differences from one place to another. In most cases, convection in a fluid body serves to transport heat from one point in the system to

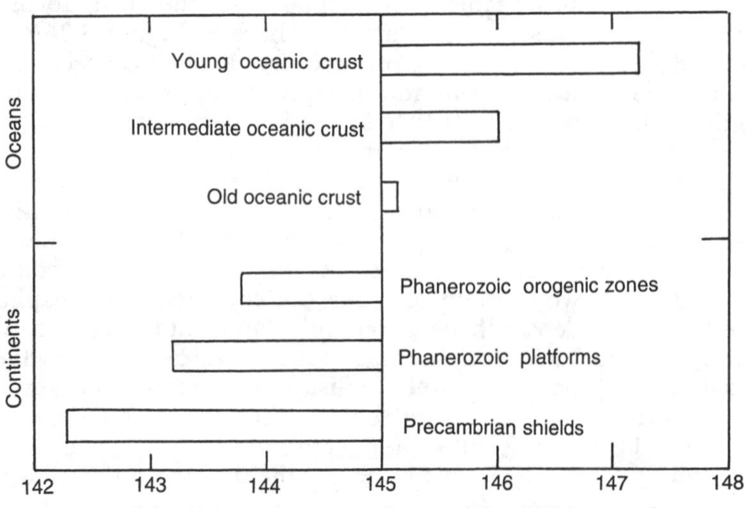

Figure 3.25 Time of travel of S waves vertically from 700 km depth to surface. Six kinds of crust listed are same as those shown in Figure 3.21. The data are plotted arithmetically to right and left of the median value. (From T.H. Jordan, *Scientific American*, v. 240, no. 1, p. 103. Copyright © by Allen Beechel. Used by permission.)

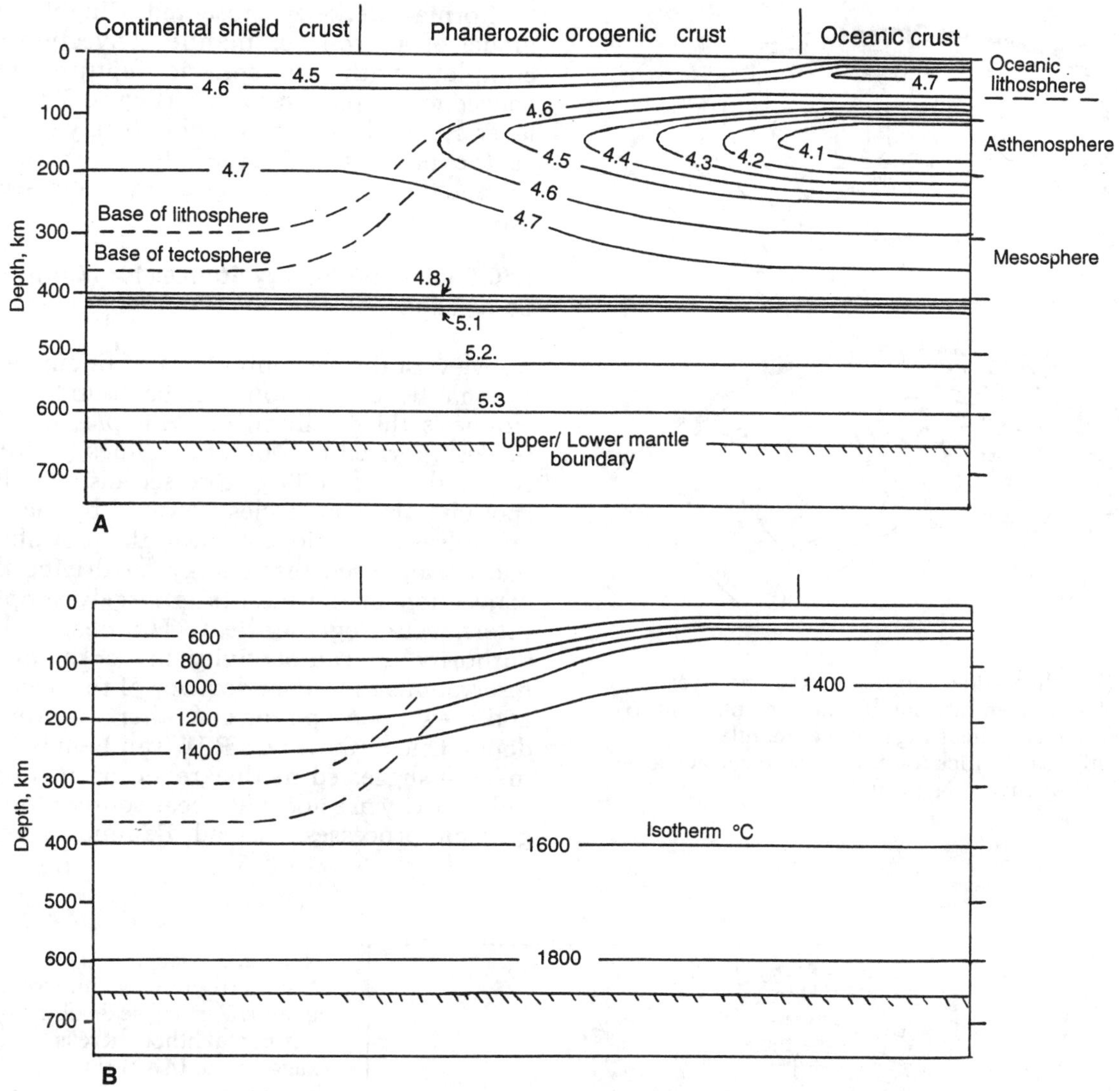

Figure 3.26 Cross sections through the upper mantle showing (A) the transition of seismic wave velocities, and (B) temperatures grading from oceanic crust (right) to continental shield crust (left). (Adapted from T.H Jordan, *Scientific American*, v. 240, no. 1, p. 93, 104. Copyright © by Allen Beechel. Used by permission.)

another—from source to sink—and can be designated as *thermal convection*. Simple thermal convection can be illustrated by a container of water placed over a flame. Application of intense heat at the bottom of the water body produces a warm water mass of low density, which rises to the top where heat is dissipated through radiation, conduction, or transformation from the liquid state to the vapor state. Sinking currents of cooler water replace the rising warm water. Another example of thermal convection is the annual overturn of water in lakes of middle latitudes, occurring at the onset of winter as surface cooling generates a layer of denser water that sinks to the bottom, setting in motion a convection system (Strahler, 1971, p. 219-220). Carefully controlled laboratory experiments with various fluids, such as melted paraffin, show that sustained convection takes the form of *convection cells*. The heated fluid rises within the center of the cell and descends in the boundary zone between cells. The cells are typically of hexagonal outline and more or less equal in size. For experimental substances behaving as Newtonian fluids, the typical vertical and horizontal dimensions of a single cell are about equal; i.e., a one-to-one ratio (Uyeda, 1978, p. 180).

Through the early decades of plate tectonics, two basic models of large-scale mantle convection competed for attention: (A) A single convecting layer affecting the entire thickness of the mantle; (B) A two-layer system in which upper mantle and lower mantle contained independent convection systems, their separating boundary being located at the 660-km seismic discontinuity (O'Nions et al., 1980, p. 232). Figure 3.27 is a simple sketch (not to scale) of these two models of mantle convection. In 1982, Walter Alvarez of the University of

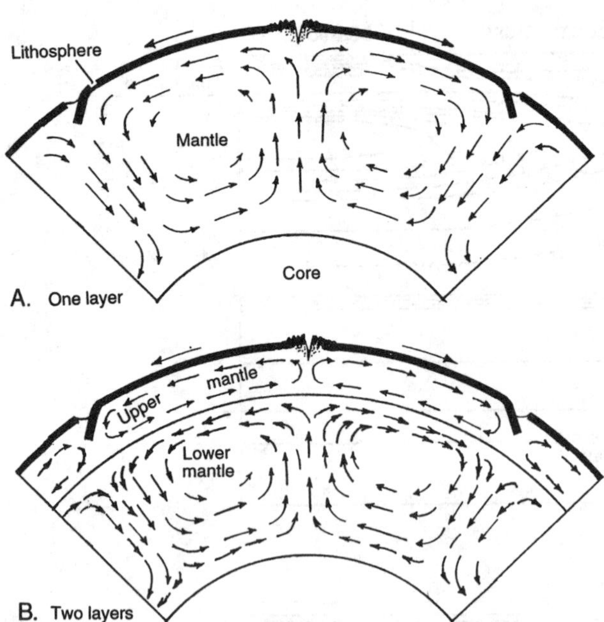

Figure 3.27 Schematic diagrams of (A) a one-layer convection system embracing the entire mantle and (B) a two-layer system consisting of upper mantle and lower mantle. Layer thicknesses are not to correct scale. (Copyright © by Arthur N. Strahler.)

California—Berkeley presented a highly detailed model of a two-layer mantle convection system complete with lithospheric features relating convection to plate tectonics (Figure 3.28). A two-layer system has since become firmly established as the paradigm. Further details, revealed by seismic tomography, are given in a later section of this chapter.

3.16 Radiogenic Energy Sources for Mantle Convection

A review of the early problems of finding a source for mantle convection can be found in Arthur Holmes's third edition of *Principles of Physical Geology*, revised by Doris L. Holmes (1978). Since Joly in the early 1900s expressed his hypothesis of sporadic orogenic cycles powered by the buildup and release of radiogenic heat, the prevailing view had presupposed that energy for driving thermal convection in the mantle is largely supplied by internal radiogenic heat. Holmes, a leading authority on radioactivity in rocks, expressed reservations as to the adequacy of this heat source and drew upon opinions of others to express this doubt. One of these was R.W. van Bemmelen, who in 1954 suggested neither relict original heat nor radioactivity are adequate heat sources for driving geologic processes. Instead, Bemmelen turned to

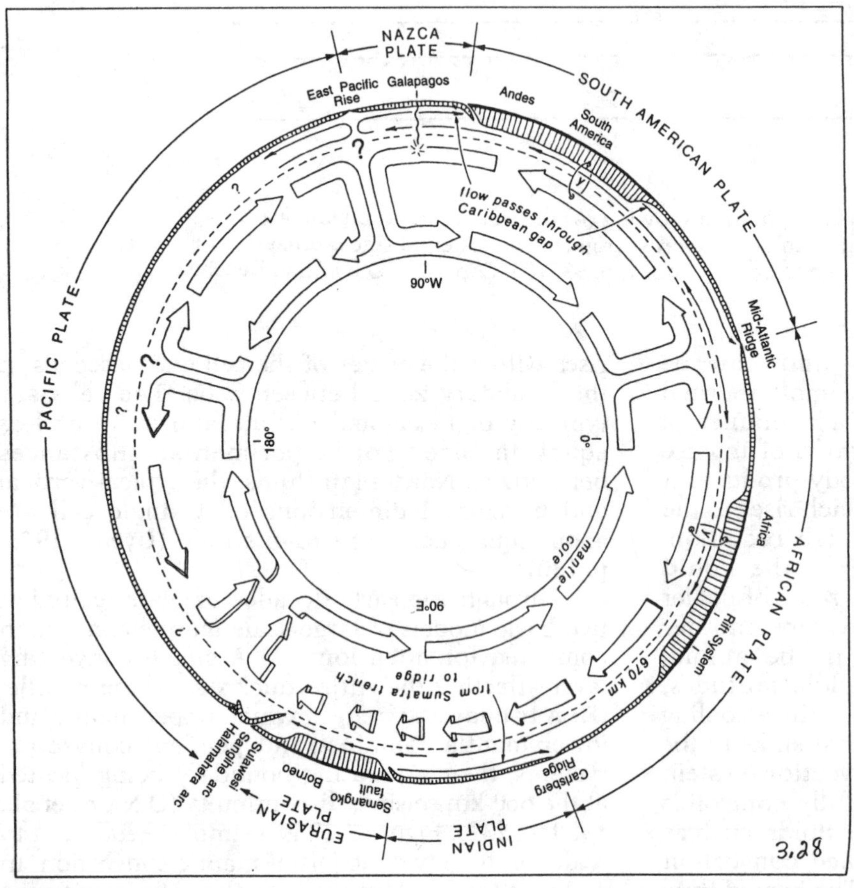

Figure 3.28 Schematic cross section of the earth in the vicinity of the equator. Vertical scale of the continental lithosphere is exaggerated. Use of three-dimensional arrows in the lower mantle allows components of motion toward or away from the viewer to be indicated. (From W. Alvarez, 1982, *Jour. of Geophysical Research*, v. 87, p. 6704, Figure 4. Copyright © 1982 by the American Geophysical Union. Reproduced by permission of author and publisher.)

the liberation of "inter-atomic energy" as a result of changes of temperature and pressure deep in the mantle (Holmes, 1978, p. 710). His reference here is to the existence of phase changes resulting in steplike increases in density with depth; these we have described in earlier paragraphs. The basic idea is that a reduction of confining pressure will allow reversal of the phase changes with concomitant release of stored energy. Holmes presented a calculation of the energy locked up in the lower mantle, close to the core-mantle boundary.

In his earlier pages, Holmes had favorably reviewed the expanding-earth hypothesis (p. 702-707). It included the proviso that expansion occurred in the core, which consisted of "degenerate material" that underwent a phase change at the outer core boundary to produce new mantle rock. The rate of radial expansion had been estimated as 0.25 mm/y. Using these assumptions, Holmes was able to compute the approximate amount of energy released by the phase change as 2.5×10^{29} ergs per year. "Some of this energy will be used in raising the temperature of the materials along the mantle/core boundary, so helping to maintain convection currents in the mantle" (p. 710).

With the subsequent discreditation of the expanding-earth hypothesis, Holmes's internal non-radiogenic energy source was eliminated. It was replaced in later years by newer models of mantle composition, structure, and internal motion. One of these, based on neodymium isotopic data, calls for depletion in the upper mantle of its original store of the principal heat-producing radionuclides of K, U, and Th and their concentration in the continental crust. Depletion is limited to the upper mantle, about 700 km thick.

Donald J. De Paolo has described conditions in the lower mantle as follows:

> The lower mantle, however, still retains its original allotment of these elements. Consequently, it appears that the heat-production elements have not been concentrated near the planet's surface as had been previously thought, but rather that most (up to 75%) are still retained deep within the earth. It also provides a picture of the convecting upper mantle being heated from below. This arrangement affects both the modeling of convection in the mantle and the degree to which radiogenic heat production in the earth can be the driving force for convection and its surface manifestation—plate tectonics (De Paolo, 1981, p. 139).

This view of the historical (evolutionary) difference between upper and lower mantle was expressed by D.P. McKenzie: "There are now several lines of evidence suggesting all scales of convection that have been observed in the upper mantle are confined to a layer whose lower boundary is no deeper than 700 km" (1983, p. 74). Elaborating, McKenzie stated:

> The observed isotopic ratios show that the crust has been extracted from about a third of the mass of the mantle. In other words, only a third of the material in the mantle, thoroughly mixed, is needed to account for the relative abundances of the elements and their isotopes in the continents. Since a third of the mantle lies between the base of the crust and a depth of 700 kilometers, the composition of the crust and the mantle is consistent with the idea that convection in the upper 700 kilometers of the mantle is physically separated from any convection in the lower mantle. Moreover, because much of the continental crust has existed for at least two billion years, there must have been only limited transport between the upper mantle and the lower mantle in that period (p. 76).

A review of a 1985 workshop on mantle dynamics and structure, authored by Paul G. Silver, Richard W. Carlson, Peter Bell, and Peter Olsen, included the following paragraph:

> The most simplistic of the geochemically layered mantle models involves a depleted upper mantle...overlying an undepleted (bulk earth) lower mantle. To stabilize such a system against destructive overturn requires a compositional density contrast between the layers of greater than 3 percent, thus requiring differences in the major element abundances of the layers as well. In addition, stable two-layer convection in such a system would produce a major thermal boundary layer at the interface, with a several-hundred-degree jump across a relatively narrow depth interval (Silver et al., 1985, p. 1197.)

The 660-km boundary between upper and lower mantle is established by a rather abrupt increase in P-wave velocity, as shown in Figure 3.16. [This feature is identical with the "700-km depth" described in the foregoing paragraphs.] A sharp increase (about 10 percent) in mantle density at this boundary is attributed to a phase change from spinel structure to perovskite structure. Where such a sharp density increase exists, physical mixing of mantle rock across the discontinuity is prevented, or made difficult. We see this effect in the oceanic thermocline, above which mixing of the warm water layer through wave-generated turbulence readily occurs, while the colder denser water remains undisturbed.

The hypothesis of a lower mantle still endowed with its original heat-producing radioisotopes was not accepted by all geologists. Don L. Anderson's alternative scenario called for a lower mantle "depleted in the radioactive and crust-forming elements" (1984a, p. 347).

The question of existence of a convection current system in the lower mantle can be treated as independent of the question of whether the lower mantle is depleted or undepleted of the original supply of radiogenic elements.

3.17 Seismic Tomography of the Mantle

Thus far, our description of the mantle has been simplified by a first approximation of horizontal physical uniformity, or homogeneity, in its layers and their boundaries with one another and with the core. We now turn to a more realistic picture that introduces departures from that assumed form, and these could conceivably range from broad-scale undulations in layer boundaries to quite "foreign" bodies that penetrate the layers in a more-or-less vertical (crosscutting) orientation. The latter would include downsinking subducted plates as well as rising stalklike plumes.

Seismic tomography began to come to widespread public attention in the early 1980s. A 1984 article in *Scientific American*, bearing the title "Seismic Tomography," authored by Don L. Anderson and Adam M. Dziewonski, explained the technique used, likening it to the medical X-ray technique of computer-aided tomography, or CAT scanning, then coming into wide use. Seismic tomography requires computer analysis of enormous volumes of collected arrival times of seismic waves from many different sources at many receiving points over the globe. These wave paths crisscross one another and can thus reveal velocity anomalies and locate their positions within the mantle. Body waves are most useful in locating anomalies in the lower mantle, while surface waves are effective for finding anomalies in the upper mantle. Within a given anomaly zone, the wave speed may be either increased or slowed, depending upon the nature of the physical anomaly present. For example, in the upper mantle, masses of cold, downsinking subducted lithosphere are revealed by a cluster of fast wave speeds. An ascending mantle current, such as might represent a rising hot mantle plume, can also be detected. Speed anomalies can also reveal horizontal currents in the mantle and indicate their directions of flow.

One of the greatest impacts of seismic tomography has been to strengthen evidence for the existence of vertical components of mantle flow that are capable of exchanging substantial amounts of mineral matter between the lithosphere and the deep mantle, and even extending to the very floor of the lower mantle. Science writer Richard A. Kerr, in a 1988 review of developments aired by geochemists and geophysicists, reported that seismic tomography has shown that slabs of subducted lithosphere can actually pierce the 660-km density barrier to enter the lower mantle, and that the possibility exists that this same slab material can descend to the base of the lower mantle. Tomographic images obtained by seismologist Thomas Jordan and his students in the early 1980s showed slabs beneath the western Pacific as having descended several hundred kilometers below the pierced barrier (Kerr, 1990, p. 302). Independent confirmation of these observations was obtained in 1991 by Yoshio Fukao and colleagues of Nagoya University in Japan (Kerr, 1991, p. 1096; Fukao, 1992). Their seismic tomography revealed that whereas some slabs in the western Pacific flatten out and move horizontally above the discontinuity, other slabs were observed to have pierced the barrier and descended to a depth of 1200 km; in so doing, the masses had become deformed. (See also Monastersky, 1992, p. 132.) In 1993, Paul J. Tackley of the California Institute of Technology found that in creating computer model simulations of a slab descent into the mantle, the slab material tended to pile up above the 660-km barrier, and only occasionally was punctuated by a "flushing" of great masses of rock down through the boundary (Monastersky, 1993, p. 133). This result suggests the possibility that the timing of major tectonic events—collisions or continental riftings, for example—may be in some manner influenced or controlled by these "flushings."

Slab material that has reached the floor of the lower mantle might be expected to accumulate in direct contact with the extremely hot outer core surface. Horizontal mantle currents might also drag this material along the core surface to new locations. Upon being heated and its density lowered, blobs of the heated rock might then begin to rise, forming mantle plumes, and these would be capable of piercing the 660-km barrier, and finally reaching the crust as hotspots. A diagram of these vertical exchanges prepared by Paul Silver et al. (1985) and used by Kerr (1988; 1990) is reproduced here as Figure 3.29. The postulated ability of slabs and plumes to pierce the 660-km discontinuity was not intended to suggest that large-scale mixing of the upper and lower mantle takes place. On the contrary, it was supposed that very little convectional mixing would be expected, even over long spans of time.

In 1994, a new dimension was added to total picture of slab descent and plume rise through the upper and lower mantle zones. In an article in *Nature*, M. Stein of the Hebrew University in Jerusalem and A.W. Hoffmann of the Max Planck Institute of Mainz focused on the observation that earth history has been characterized by "punctuated episodes of enhanced exchange between the lower and upper mantle" (1994, p. 63). Besides replenishing the upper mantle with trace elements, these episodes would have stimulated rapid growth of the continental crust through the plate mechanism of the compressional orogen. Stein and Hoffman named this phase the *MOMO episode* (Mantle Overturn and Major Orogenies). Their scenario, previously observed by others (S. Moorebath, 1978; Reymer and Schubert, 1984, 1986) also requires long alternative periods in

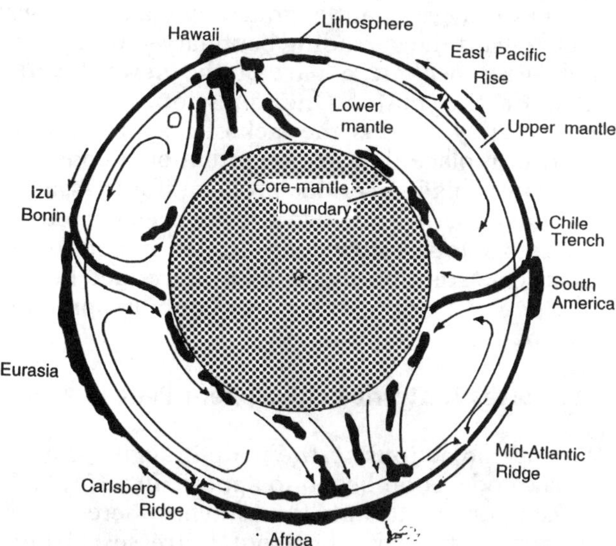

Figure 3.29 Schematic global diagram suggesting possible exchanges of rock material between upper and lower mantle by downsinking subducted lithosperhic plates and rising mantle plumes. (From Paul Silver et al., ____________ Used by permission.)

which the two-layer mantle system prevailed while little new continental crust was being formed—presumably because most of the oceanic crust was being recycled into the mantle. To this phase, Stein and Hoffman applied the name *Wilson Period*. Figure 3.30 is their diagram of the two episodic phases.

For new crust to be formed at high rates required the upwelling of numerous large mantle plumes originating near the base of the lower mantle, piercing the 660 km discontinuity, and continuing through the upper mantle. This one-layer mantle plume system would also include the sinking of subduction slabs through the 660 km discontinuity to mix with the lower mantle, a phenomenon we have described in earlier paragraphs as a "flushing" activity. The rising plumes would bring intense heat flow upward into the asthenosphere and lithosphere. Beneath oceanic lithosphere, the result would be to increase the production of new island arcs, and these would end up in arc-continent collisions. This activity is one form of compressional orogeny. Beneath the continental lithosphere, the rising plumes would bring up heat that would accumulate beneath the crust, causing crustal uplift that would lead to continental rifting and finally to continental breakup. Reuniting of the continental fragments by continent-continent collisions would be the final phase of the entire MOMO episode of accelerated continental crustal generation. [All of these plate activities are described in detail in following chapters. See Chapter 6 for slab pnetration into lower mantle.]

As these new scenarios involving the entire mantle down to its contact with the core were being proposed and debated during the 1990s, an important parallel debate had been in progress. Does the viscosity (stiffness) of mantle rock maintain throughout its entire depth a sufficiently low viscosity to permit these postulated upward and downward flows? Two schools of thought have debated this question: (A) A relatively low viscosity prevails throughout the entire depth; (B) The downward increase in viscosity becomes very large as the base of the mantle is approached. In supporting (A) it can be argued that the downward increase in rock temperature (tending to reduce the viscosity) is offset by the increase of pressure (tending to increase the viscosity) (Kerr, 1996, p. 1053).

Traditional practice for some decades had been to estimate viscosity at great depth through measurements of small variations in gravity observed at the earth's surface. This information was combined with records of rates of rebound of areas formerly covered by icesheets. This practice had suggested little increase of viscosity with depth. However, introducing mantle data observed by seismic imagery has changed the viscosity model. Bradford Hager and his colleagues at MIT concluded that viscosity in the lower mantle must be on the order of 30 times greater than in the upper mantle (Kerr, 1996, p. 1053).

3.18 Convection Systems in the Asthenosphere

When applying the concept of thermal convection to tectonics of the oceanic lithosphere, it is important to keep in mind that the brittle lithosphere must be included within any large upper-mantle convection system. Suppose that we have devised a model convection system using a waxlike substance that quickly solidifies when exposed at the free upper surface of the liquid. We could thus produce a miniature replica of a

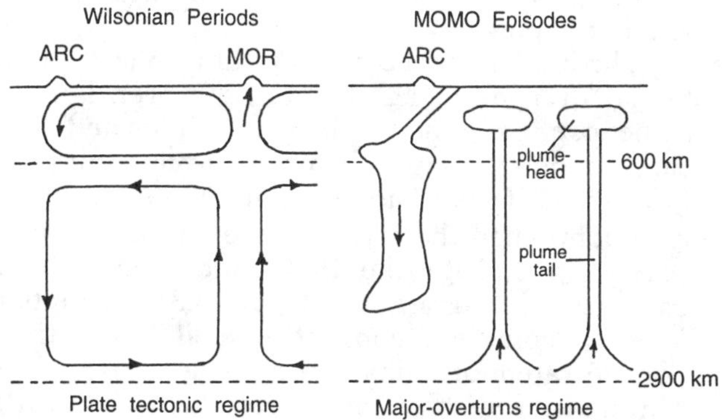

Figure 3.30 Schematic diagrams of Wilson periods and MOMO episodes. (From M. Stein and A.W. Hofman, 1994, *Nature*, v. 372, p. 4, Figure 1. Reproduced by permission of the authors and Macmillan Magazines Ltd.)

lithospheric plate. The plate would come into existence by solidification of the molten wax as it emerges from a rising convection cell and spreads laterally. Our plate of solid wax would then move with the underlying fluid wax until it came to a descending convection zone. Here the wax plate would bend down and begin its descent, but the edge would quickly melt as it absorbed heat from the surrounding molten wax. The point is that the wax plate is an integral part of the matter that makes up this convection system. It is that part of the convecting mass that changes from a fluid state to a solid state and back to a fluid state because of cooling and reheating. In the same way, an oceanic lithospheric plate in motion represents the uppermost part of a convection system, which is thus not merely confined to the soft asthenosphere below the plate. (It is conceivable that other, smaller and more limited convection systems, or .cells, within the mantle might operate without involving the lithosphere in the mass-transport system.)

Operation of a thermal convection cell requires that the fluid rise beneath the source point or line of divergence of the surface layer and that the fluid sink beneath the point or line of convergence. This flow path could not be otherwise, given the upward flow of heat from its deep source. Horizontal motions from source to sink are thus dictated by the rising and falling streams. Because the rising fluid is warmer than the sinking fluid, we may expect a corresponding inequity of surface elevation, with the surface gradient descending from the source toward the sink. Thus heat energy has been transformed into gravitational potential energy, some fraction of which is directed horizontally. When we add a solid layer of lithosphere to the system, we can think of the solid slab as "sliding down hill." The question then arises as to whether the slab exerts a drag on the underlying fluid mantle, or whether the fluid beneath is moving more rapidly than the slab and exerts a "downhill" drag on the overlying slab. These questions are covered in our next section and in Chapter 7.

The fundamental concept of lithospheric plates being "dragged along" by strong currents in the asthenosphere beneath them was inherited from early models proposed before plate tectonics was introduced. (See Chapter 9.) It was an idea that also dominated the early years of plate tectonics, persisting through the 1960s and even into the early 1970s. Diagram A of Figure 3.31 attempts to show a complete convection cell, its activity concentrated principally in the asthenosphere. Through the mechanism of boundary shear, it is seen dragging along the oceanic plate above it and also bringing shear force to bear in pulling the subducting plate down into the asthenosphere. Return flow extends through the entire depth of the upper mantle, but is heavily concentrated in the asthenosphere. The material cycle is completed as the softened lower edge of the plate merges with the mesospheric mantle, gradually making its way back toward the spreading boundary—there to rise and again become a part of the newly-forming edge of the plate. One question that might immediately arise is the lack of a source of heat input to replace that lost by radiational cooling of the plate. This is a serious problem if it is assumed that the upper mantle has already been depleted of its radioisotopes, now concentrated in continental crust. One solution might be to introduce heat by conduction from a rising and laterally spreading current in the lower mantle.

3.19 Forces That Drive Lithospheric Plates

Weighty objections to the plate-dragging convectional model soon began to appear. In 1971, W.M. Elsasser objected that "the asthenosphere may be too soft to transmit horizontal stresses to move plates" (Seyfert, 1987, p. 101). In 1973, a Soviet geophysicist, E. Artyushkov, brought forth some strong theoretical evidence not only against the drag-force mechanism, but even questioning the need to ascribe a significant role to asthenospheric currents. Seiya Uyeda, a geophysicist at the University of Tokyo, describes this challenge laid down by Artyushkov:

> He argued convincingly that the viscosity of the asthenosphere, particularly under oceanic areas, should be one or two orders of magnitude smaller than the usually assumed value, estimated from the postglacial rebound for Scandinavia and North America. Therefore, the mechanical force exerted at the bottom of the lithosphere owing to flows in the asthenosphere would be much too weak to be significant. He maintained that, although there may indeed be flows in the asthenosphere, they are of no importance to plate motion. Whether Artyuskhov was absolutely right or not, the general question of the driving mechanism seemed to require far more serious thought (Uyeda, 1971, p. 190).

Consider, then, an alternative basic hypothesis implied by these objections, namely, that oceanic lithospheric plates are driven by forces other than mantle drag, but with the possibility that the plates may actually induce weak current flow in the adjacent asthenosphere (just as anyone can do in a tub of water by sweeping horizontal motions of one's cupped hand). These weak currents would serve to bring mantle rock back to the spreading plate boundary to complete a material cycle. Diagram B of Figure 3.31 shows such a model devised by G. Schubert and associates (1978). A zone of return flow in the asthenosphere is opposite in direction to that of the plate. Plate drag reverses that flow close to the base of the plate (which is a transitional zone), and the underside of the plate is nourished during the process, resulting in thickening of the lithosphere with increased

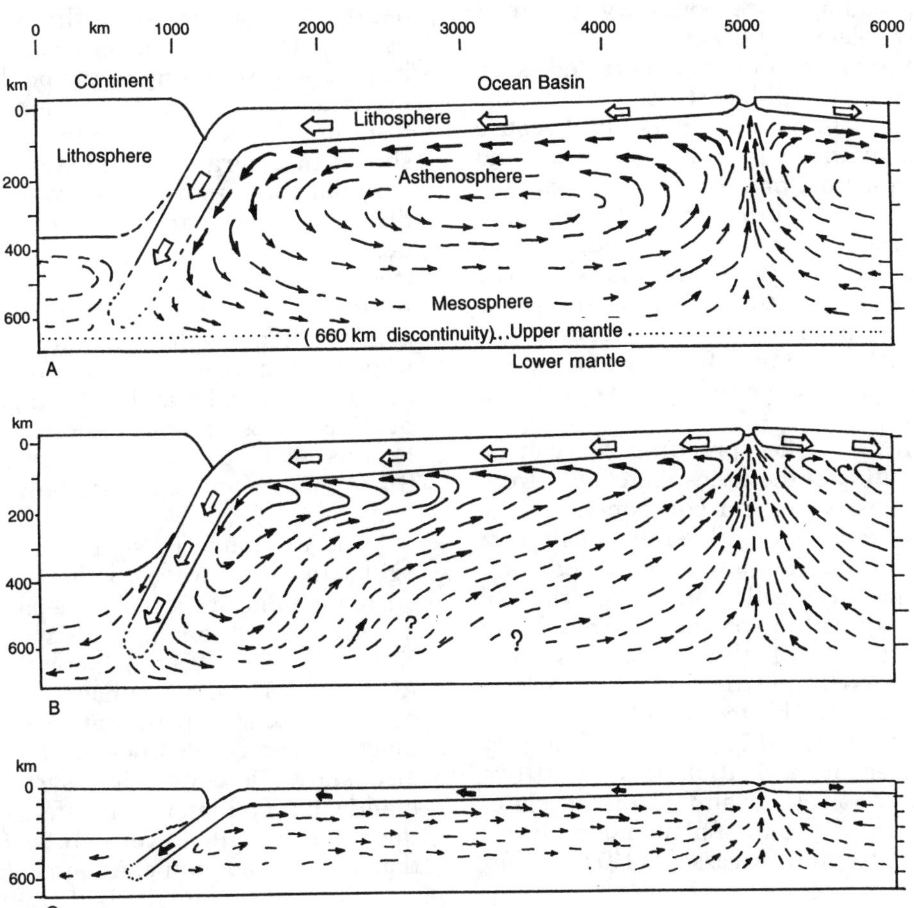

Figure 3.31 Schematic cross sections showing two models of asthenospheric convection systems. (A) Convection current forces plate to move. (B) Plate driven by independent secondary forces; sets up shallow return flow in asthenosphere. (C) Diagram B to true scale. (Copyright © by Arthur N. Strahler.)

distance from the spreading boundary. Schubert's model called for resupply of the upper mantle by slow upward mass flow from the lower mantle, a mechanism that is in disagreement with the idea of a barrier to mixing at the lower-upper mantle boundary.

If convection currents do not provide driving forces directly to the undersides of plates, we need to look to other mechanisms, and this leads us to consider a list of possible alternative plate-driving forces. Here we follow the terminology introduced in 1975 by D. Forsyth and S. Uyeda. A lucid discussion of these forces is given by Uyeda in his popular book, *The New View of the Earth* (1978, p. 190-201).

The change in viewpoint about plate-driving forces seems to have occurred at about the same time it was realized that a subducting plate is not being forced by some external pressure to descend into the asthenosphere, but rather that it sinks spontaneously because it is denser than the surrounding asthenosphere. (We discuss this topic at some length in Chapter 8.) This driving force, caused by density differences, or "negative buoyancy," has been called the *slab pull force* (Forsyth and Uyeda, 1975; Chapple and Tullis, 1977, p. 1970). Seismic evidence, which we present in Chapter 6, shows that the upper part of the descending slab is being subjected to tensional stress, so that "pull" is appropriate in that sense. In another sense, however, the word "pull" may be unfortunate, because it further implies that the downplunging slab can also pull the horizontally moving section of the plate, as a locomotive pulls a train. This connotation has been seriously questioned on several points (Seyfert, 1987, p. 102-103). One of these is that a thin, cold, brittle plate is comparatively weak in terms of transmitting tensional stress; under tension it would easily fail by rifting apart. Another significant point is that some of the large plates have only a very small percentage of the perimeter in subduction boundary. In those cases, another driving force than "pull" must be sought.

During subduction, the descending plate must displace mantle rock of the asthenosphere, and this might induce a return flow within the asthenosphere in a direction generally opposite to that of the horizontal plate above it. As shown in Figure 3.31, diagram B, this return flow, which is greatly diffused and extremely slow, would ultimately transport mantle rock to a position beneath the spreading plate boundary, where it would rise to complete the flow cycle.

Rising hot mantle rock concentrated as a narrow, but very long, wall-like structure under the active spreading-plate boundaries could, because of its lower density than surrounding mantle, tend to exert a lifting action, or vertical force, perhaps capable of elevating the lithosphere. In this way, mass would be elevated and given potential energy of position, relative to regions on either side. The newly-formed oceanic lithosphere would stand higher than older lithosphere that is cooler and denser at increasing distance from the spreading axis, giving the plate a slope to both its upper and lower surfaces.

Thus, uplifting at the spreading rift can be visualized as a tilting of the lithosphere away from the spreading axis, so that a component of the gravitational force is directed laterally away from the axis. This lateral component is called *ridge push force* and has been called on as the principal driver of plate spreading of the oceanic lithosphere. The efficacy of this force has been questioned by Forsyth and Uyeda (1975) "whose calculations show it to be too small by itself to move a plate" (Seyfert, 1987, p. 103). A contrary opinion was given by R.M. Richardson and two colleagues, based on an examination of plate-driving forces using a system of plate models based on predicted intraplate stresses (1976). They stated:

> Intraplate stress calculated for models in which viscous drag drives plates in the direction of their present absolute motions provides a poor fit to observation, whereas models in which drag is purely resistive can provide an acceptable fit (p. 1855). The net driving push at spreading centers is found to be at least comparable in magnitude to other forces acting on the lithosphere and in particular is 0.7 to 1.5 times the net driving pull at convergence zones (p. 1847)

The ridge-push mechanism is attractive because the oceanic plates show both surface slope and lithospheric thickening away from the spreading axis. Furthermore, rigid plates should have the capability of transmitting compressional stress over long distances.

The dike-like rise of magma into a spreading boundary in the lithosphere has been called on to produce a lateral force capable of pushing the plates apart (Seyfert, 1987, p. 103-104). If this force exists and is important in magnitude, it can be seen as augmenting the gravitational ridge push force.

The great depth to which subducting plates retain their identity sets constraints in designing a global system of convection currents limited to the upper mantle and extending no deeper than the 660-km seismic discontinuity. These slabs serve as solid partitions extending from the surface to depths below the lower limits of the asthenosphere. Oceanic lithosphere of the slab reverts by heating and softening to the pool of upper-mantle material, which can be imagined to move away from the slab to complete the convection cycle, as shown in diagrams A and B of Figure 3.31. This material could move away from the plate in either direction, and can thus be imagined to pass beneath the thick continental lithosphere (tectosphere) in the depth range 400-650 km. Although mantle viscosity in this zone is much greater than in the oceanic asthenosphere, an important current of mass transport has been postulated to exist and to be capable of transport over distances of several thousands of kilometers. In this way, the material of recycled oceanic lithosphere can reach distant spreading plate boundaries.

The existence of such a deep current, analogous in some ways to the deep ocean-bottom currents, might reflect the rheological principle of an elasticoplastic substance in which strain rate rises very sharply with increasing stress. Walter Alvarez (1982, p. 6704) has incorporated the idea of such a basal upper-mantle current in his global diagram, reproduced here as Figure 3.28. Alvarez also shows a convection system in the lower mantle, but no material transfer is indicated across the upper-mantle/lower-mantle boundary, other than an isolated plume. An important idea possibly contained in this model is that entire plates along with their underlying asthenosphere and tectosphere are perhaps carried along bodily by a basal upper-mantle current. Alvarez' diagram suggests this idea by showing the drifting apart of the South American and African plates as being related to basal currents moving in opposite directions. Alvarez also shows a coupling of upper and lower mantle motions under these plates, and this locks together the continental lithosphere with a lower-mantle convection system. This possible role of lower-mantle convection currents in the total system of plate motions is treated in Chapter 7.

3.20 Tectonic Activity—Future and Past

The total picture we have drawn thus far in this chapter seems to show that the oceanic lithosphere acts as a machine that directly generates the main share of activity of global plate tectonics. The continental lithosphere tends to remain intact through eons of time, even when a large continent breaks apart. The smaller continental fragments tend to retain their high freeboard and internal structure, and in time reunite to reconstruct a new and larger continent (Chapter 13). Underplating tends to thicken the ancient continents, while subaerial erosion reduces the continental surfaces.

Where large areas of both continental and oceanic lithosphere lie within the same plate, joined in a passive continental margin, their relative motion is one and the same in both direction and speed. How such a composite plate is driven is by no means clear at this time and invites speculation on the possible existence of controlling mantle currents below the asthenosphere.

The great depth to which the base of the continental lithosphere extends in the mantle is a factor that might seem to reduce its mobility. Some geologists have envisioned that continental lithospheric plates will eventually become "grounded" on denser, stronger, mantle and will not be able to move freely, if at all. As the rate of internal heat production slowly declines, the asthenosphere can be expected to become generally thinner. As that happens, plate motions will become slower. The freedom of subducting slabs to plunge deeply into the asthenosphere may gradually be reduced. Both tectonic and volcanic activity should gradually diminish. By the same reasoning, looking back into geologic time when the asthenosphere may have been hotter and thicker, plate motions may have been even more rapid, causing more intensive tectonic and volcanic activity than occurs today.

3.21 Isostasy and the Lithosphere

Because the asthenosphere is capable of yielding slowly when subjected to very small unbalanced stresses, it behaves much like a true fluid. In that sense, the lithosphere can be thought of as floating upon the asthenosphere, much as a layer of sea ice floats on the ocean. Continental lithosphere floats because of the lower density of the thick granitic upper zone of the crust and the possible presence of a deep tectospheric layer of relatively lower density than adjacent mantle rock at the same level.

A floating solid object comes to rest with a certain proportion of its bulk submerged and the remaining portion above the liquid surface. The Archimedes principle requires that a floating object displace a volume of liquid having the same mass as the entire floating object. If an object has a density half that of the liquid, it will float at rest with half its volume below the liquid surface and half above.

When applied to the lithosphere, the principle of a mass floating at rest in a supporting liquid is referred to as the principle of *isostasy*. This word comes from the Greek words *isos*, equal, and *stasis*, standing still. Isostasy requires that a particular column of the lithosphere be physically free to rise or sink; i.e., if not structurally supported by contact with surrounding lithosphere, it must float in an equilibrium state on the underlying asthenosphere. Over most areas of the earth, including the ancient continental cratons and the young ocean floors, equilibrium required by isostasy exists or is closely approached. In other words, *isostatic equilibrium* prevails broadly on a global scale. There are specific exceptions to this generalization, most of them related to the recent disappearance of glacial ice.

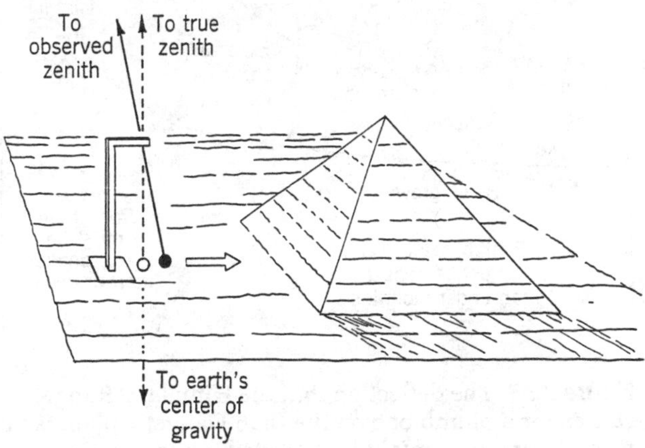

Figure 3.32 A plumb bob will be deflected by a pyramid on a plain. (Copyright © by Arthur N. Strahler.)

The circumstances under which the concept of isostasy came into focus are rather interesting and unusual. The story behind it is sometimes called the "Indian mystery." It involves a commonplace instrument called the plumb bob, used by masons to make sure that a brick wall is vertical and by surveyors to make sure their instrument is precisely located over a reference point on the ground. The plumb bob normally points close to the earth's center of mass. Let us now imagine a smooth, low plain on which an enormous pyramid has been built, as shown in Figure 3.32. The mass of rock in the pyramid will exert a gravitational attraction on the plumb bob, which will seem to be pulled toward the pyramid, deflecting the plumb line slightly from the vertical attitude. Knowing the dimensions of the pyramid and the density of the rock of which it is built, we can predict quite precisely the amount of deflection of the plumb bob.

As to the "Indian mystery," well over a century ago, the British geodesist Sir George Everest was engaged in triangulation surveys involving the precise measurement of the length of a reference line—a base line—on the Indo-Gangetic Plain in north India. To the north rises the greatest of continental mountain ranges, the Himalaya, culminating in many peaks over 7 km above sea level. Knowing the dimensions of the range and the average density of rocks exposed in it. Everest computed the amount by which the plumb bob should be deflected toward the range from a given distance away. To his surprise, the plumb bob was attracted far less than the calculated amount (Figure 3.33).

The importance of Everest's discovery was soon realized by two contemporaries, Sir George Airy, Astronomer Royal of England, and J.H. Pratt, Archdeacon of Calcutta. In 1850, they offered a general explanation that has since been one of the most powerful influences in the development of geologic hypotheses. It was immediately obvious to both of these men that if

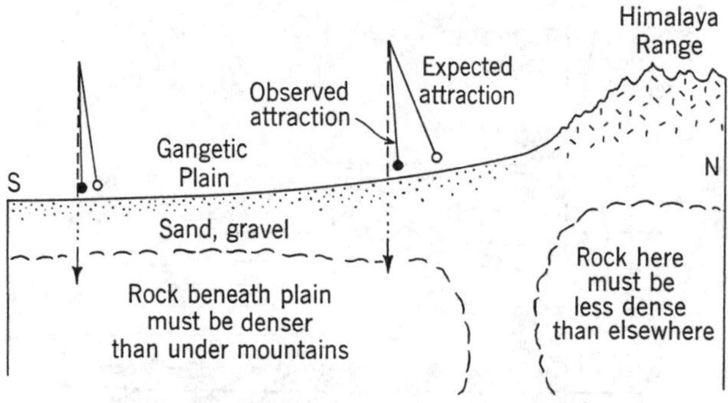

Figure 3.33 The deflection that the Himalaya Range causes for a plumb bob on the Indo-Gangetic plain is not nearly as great as might be expected for so large a mountain mass. (Copyright © by Arthur N. Strahler.)

the plumb bob is not deflected toward the mountains in the amount expected, it is because the crustal rock lying deep beneath the mountains is less dense than in the surrounding crust and that this lack of density largely makes up for the additional volume of the mountains.

Airy's hypothesis, proposed in 1855, can be demonstrated by a simple physical model, shown in Figure 3.34A. Suppose that we take several blocks, or prisms, of a metal such as copper. Although all prisms have the same dimensions of cross section, they are cut to varying lengths. Because copper is less dense than mercury, the prisms will float in a dish of that liquid metal. If all blocks are floated side by side in the same orientation, the longest block will float with the greatest amount rising above the level of the mercury surface, and the shortest block will have its upper surface lowest. With all blocks now floating at rest, it is obvious that the block rising highest also extends to greatest depth. Airy supposed that the rock of which high mountains are composed extends far down into the earth to form *mountain roots* composed of less dense rock; i.e., this crustal rock protrudes downward into a location normally occupied by denser mantle rock. Under a low-lying plain, the root of less dense rock will be shallow. Figure 3.35A shows how the depth, w, of the base of the block is related to the height, h, of the block in terms of the densities of the block and the supporting fluid (McNutt, 1987, p. 355). As shown in Figure 3.34A, the profile of the base of a row of blocks of different lengths will be a mirror image of the surface profile but with exaggerated relief.

Pratt's alternative hypothesis, proposed in 1859, is illustrated by a similar demonstration model (Figure 3.34B, but it is complicated by the need to use prisms of different kinds of metals, each with a different density. These prisms, although of the same cross-sectional area, are cut into lengths such that all prisms have the same weight (mass). The dense metals silver and lead have short prisms, while the less dense metals

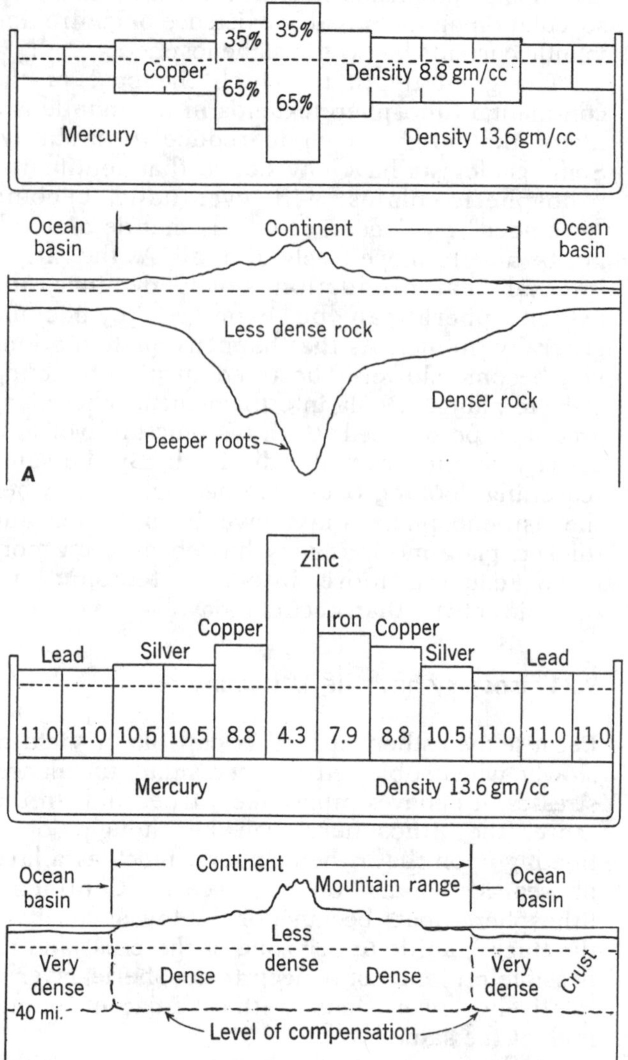

Figure 3.34 (A) The Airy hypothesis of mountain roots is suggested by the equilibrium positions of blocks of the same density. (B) According to the Pratt hypothesis, crustal elements have different densities. (Copyright © by Arthur N. Strahler.)

copper, iron, and zinc have longer prisms, that of zinc being much the longest. If we now float these prisms in a pan of mercury, they will all come to rest with their bases at the same depth below the free fluid surface level. Each prism is displacing a volume of fluid equal to its own weight. Figure 3.35 shows how the topographic height, h, relative to the thickness of the reference layer, Zp, is related to the density ratio (McNutt, 1987. p. 355).

For both Airy and Pratt models there exists at some depth a horizontal surface above which the amount of mass contained in any vertical column is everywhere the same. The least possible (shallowest) depth for such a surface is called the *compensation depth*. For the Pratt model, the compensation depth lies at the common base of the prisms, whereas in the Airy model, it will lie at the level of the base of the longest prism, and for all shorter prisms the mass of a prism of the fluid must be included to equalize the overlying mass.

In reality, neither Airy nor Pratt model is to be expected in pure form, because the crust and upper mantle are laterally inhomogeneous both in terms of petrology and of the thicknesses of layers or bodies of a given kind of rock. Thus the oceanic lithosphere, as compared to the continental lithosphere, is composed of denser rock contained in thinner crustal layers. The isostatic equilibrium of oceanic lithosphere is thus a product of two independently variable factors (density and thickness), both conspiring to yield a lower position relative to the sea level reference than is possible for the continents, which combine crustal layers of less dense rock with greater thicknesses of those layers.

Suppose, now, that under the Airy demonstration model we slice off a piece of the top of the longest prism. The prism will rise and come to rest in a new position with the top surface lower than before and the bottom at a shallower depth. The ratio of volumes above and below the mercury surface level will remain the same. If, on the other hand, we should add a small prism of copper to the longest block it would sink and come to a new position of rest. The top of the longer prism would now stand higher than before, but the bottom would sink deeper.

The effect of unloading and loading a floating prism is seen in epeirogenic movements of the cratons caused by long-continued removal and deposition of rock. Figure 3.36 shows removal by denudation of mountains (left), transport of the sediment, and sediment accumulation on a low plain (right). With each increment of removal and deposition the mountains rise a bit and the adjacent plain sinks a bit, but in each interval of time the mountain does not rise quite as high as formerly, nor does the surface of the plain sink to quite as low a level as formerly. After a vastly long time the mountain and plain will reach nearly the same level.

Underneath the mountains, the elastico-viscous rock of the asthenosphere will flow slowly inwards from the surrounding mantle to occupy the space vacated by the rising block, just as the mercury in the model flows in beneath the rising copper prism. Of course, as this newly introduced plastic material rises it comes into a region of reduced temperature and cools to become strong—that is, it becomes a part of the lithosphere. Similarly, under the sinking plain the brittle rock mass is forced down into the region of the asthenosphere, but here it is heated and becomes plastic itself, forming a part of the plastic zone. This excess material at depth must slowly flow horizontally to escape. It seems only logical that it will move toward the region under the rising mountains. Changes in load on the earth's surface are thus balanced, or compensated for, by slow flowage of the asthenosphere.

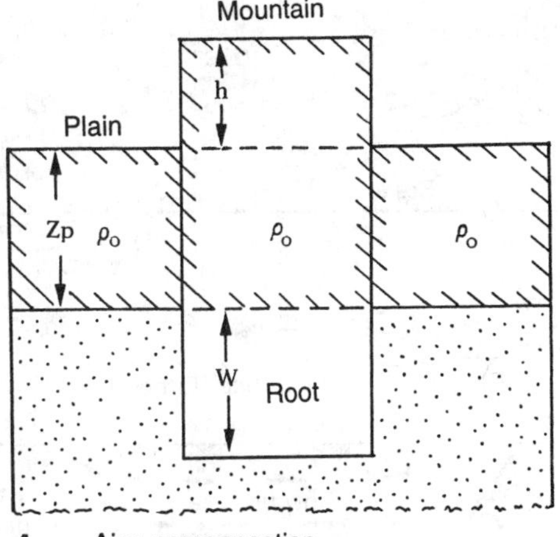

A Airy compensation

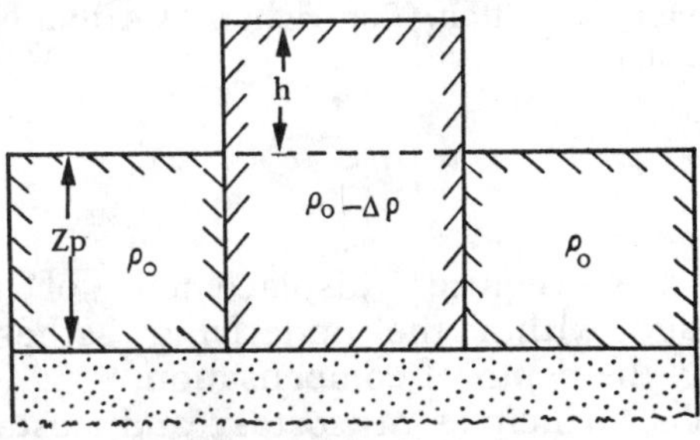

B Pratt compensation

$$W = \frac{\rho_o h}{\rho_m - \rho_o} \qquad \Delta\rho = \rho_o \frac{h}{Zp + h}$$

Airy — Pratt

- h = topographic height above upper reference surface
- W = root depth below lower reference surface
- Zp = thickness of reference layer
- ρ_o = density of reference rock layer
- ρ_m = density of underlying rock
- $\Delta\rho_o$ = density difference between prism and reference layer

Figure 3.35 Relation of topographic height and root depth to relative density of block and supporting fluid. (Based on data of M.K. McNutt, 1987.)

Loading of the crust, requiring isostatic compen-sation by crustal sinking to a new equilibrium level, occurs not only when sediment from an adjacent region is deposited, but also when an overlying layer of ocean water, lake water, or ice is added or thickened. When that layer is thinned or removed, crustal rise occurs. The negative or positive change in crustal level occurs as elastic deformation in the lithosphere,

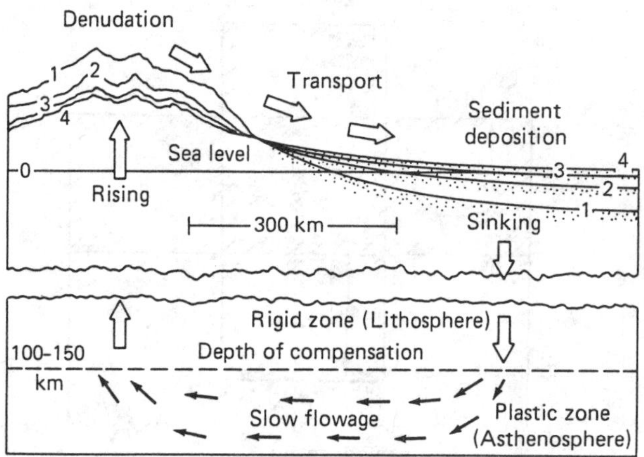

Figure 3.36 Isostatic compensation takes place when rock is either removed by denudation or added by sediment deposition. (Copyright © by Arthur N. Strahler.)

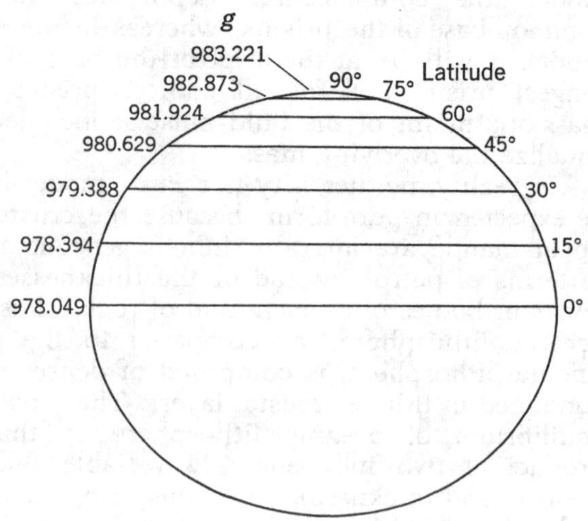

Figure 3.37 The combined effect of earth rotation and oblate earth form results in an increase in the values of normal sea-level gravity from the equator to the poles. These are standard values used in correcting gravity readings. (Copyright © by Arthur N. Strahler.)

and this requires displacement of mass by flowage within the underlying asthenosphere, below the depth of compensation.

The principles of isostasy and isostatic equilibrium are applied in several of our later chapters.

3.22 Gravity and Its Measurement

In addition to seismology, geophysical investigation of the lithosphere makes use of the variations in the value of gravity over the earth's surface. A brief note here on the terminology to be used may be helpful. First is the distinction between "gravitation" and "gravity." *Gravitation* refers to the general principles and universal law describing the mutual attraction and acceleration between any two masses. *Gravity,* as used here in the geophysical context, can be defined as "the resultant force on any body of matter at or near the Earth's surface due to the attraction by the Earth and to its rotation about its axis" (Bates and Jackson, 1987, p. 288). Actually, "gravity," uas used here means specifically the *acceleration of gravity (g)*. [Since force is defined dimensionally as mass times acceleration, a unit of mass is selected and becomes a constant, leaving acceleration as the working variable.]

Precise measurements of the acceleration of gravity (*g*) at the earth's surface have been of great value in interpreting the structure of the continental crust. The study of place-to-place differences in the value of *g* is a major branch of geophysics and has been intensively pursued by geophysicists the world over for many decades. To make clear how extremely small variations in gravity are used as a research tool, we need to review some basic information relating to *g* and its measurement.

A pendulum clock provides one of the basic mechanisms for the measurement of the acceleration of gravity, *g*, at the earth's surface. The beat-rate, or period, of a pendulum of a given length depends upon the value of gravity. If the earth were a true sphere, perfectly uniform in density throughout, and did not rotate on its axis, *g* would be everywhere the same. A pendulum clock would keep perfect time no matter where on the earth's surface it was located. But because the earth rotates (spins) on its axis, *g* is affected in two ways.

First, earth rotation sets up an outward or centrifugal force that tends to counteract gravity. A small portion of the gravitational force, acting as a centripetal force, balances the centrifugal, or outward force. This effect is greatest at the equator and decreases to zero at the poles. At the equator the centripetal force is about 1/289 as great as the gravitational force. This means that an object that now weighs 288 kg at the equator would weigh 289 kg if the earth were not rotating.

A second effect of earth rotation is that the centrifugal force causes a spherical earth to be deformed into an *oblate ellipsoid*. As compared to a sphere, the equatorial diameter of an oblate ellipsoid is increased at the same time that the length of polar axis is shortened. On an ellipsoidal earth, points located at the equator are farther from the center of the earth's mass than points near the poles. The ellipsoidal form by itself causes gravity to increase slightly from a minimum value at the equator to a maximum value at the poles. The effect is to diminish the value of gravity at the equator by 1/547 of the value it would have at the pole.

We must now add the two effects, as follows:

$$\frac{1}{289} + \frac{1}{547} = \frac{1}{189}$$

In practical terms, then, an object that weighs 189 kg at the north pole will weigh only 188 kg if taken to a sea-level point on the equator. The sum of the two effects is used as a single term in stating the standard value of gravity as a function of latitude, as shown in Figure 3.37.

For use as a research tool of geophysics, gravity must be measured with extreme precision, and this requires a world standard of reference. A world standard station for all gravity measurements was set up at Potsdam, Germany, located at a latitude of about 52°N. There, the value of 981.274 cm/sec^2 was determined for the acceleration of gravity. The unit of gravity, known as the *gal* (named for Galileo), is equal to 1 cm/sec^2. Because gravity differences over the earth's surface are very small, the thousandth part of a gal, termed the *milligal*, is used as the unit for stating differences in gravity measurements. Thus, the standard Potsdam value of gravity is equivalent to 981,274 milligals.

Once the standard value of gravity was established at Potsdam, it was possible to set up a standard system of gravity values according to latitude, from the equator to the poles, taking into account the effects of earth oblateness and rotation. A simple formula is used to determine the standard value at any given latitude. As Figure 3.37 shows, *normal sea-level gravity* ranges from a minimum of 978.049 cm/sec^2 at the equator to 983.221 cm/sec^2 at the poles, the difference being 5.172 cm/sec^2 or 5172 milligals.

Gravity is measured at permanent standard stations with a pendulum apparatus designed for extremely precise gravity measurements. Pendulums may also be used to make relative gravity measurements, that is, to observe differences in gravity from one point to another. In its simplest form, a pendulum apparatus would be a single pendulum so constructed that its length remains absolutely constant. When the length is held constant, differences in period from one place to another reflect differences in gravity. Actually, one pendulum is not enough in the precision gravity apparatus, because its motion disturbs the housing from which it is hung. To cancel out the effects of such disturbances, two pendulums may be swung simultaneously in opposite phase in a single instrument housing.

A second instrument, valued for its compactness, is the *gravimeter*. It uses the spring balance as its basic mechanism. A weight is hung from a coiled spring. Change in length of the spring is proportional to the change in acceleration of gravity. Slight changes in spring length are amplified by a combination of mechanical, optical, and electrical means. The gravimeter must be calibrated against a series of base stations so that the differences in spring length can be interpreted into gravity values.

3.23 Correcting Gravity Readings

Suppose that we have calibrated a portable gravimeter at a base station and have taken the instrument to a distant field location—perhaps in a mountainous region—where we have set it up and taken a reading of gravity. For what reasons might this gravity reading differ from that of the base station? Base station readings are in terms of normal sea-level gravity, taking into account only the earth's ellipsoidal form and its rotation. "Normal sea-level gravity" thus represents an earth-model in which the land areas are assumed to be reduced to smooth surfaces at sea level while the ocean basins are assumed to be filled to sea level with crustal rock. Moreover, the density of crustal rock is assumed to be equal everywhere over the globe and to increase downward in density uniformly or in a succession of uniform layers.

When our gravimeter has been taken to a higher elevation than that of the base station, it will register a lower value of gravity simply because it is farther from the earth's center. The correction for elevation, known as the *free-air correction*, can be obtained by solving a simple formula. As a rough approximation we can say that the value of gravity decreases about 0.3 milligal for each meter of ascent. This correction is added to the gravimeter reading.

A second correction to be made on our gravity reading is required by the earth's gross surface configuration. Where a high mountain or plateau exists, a large mass of rock lies above sea level. This mass exerts a gravitational pull of its own. Therefore, gravity at the imaginary ellipsoid surface will be somewhat less beneath high continental masses than on an open plain at the ellipsoid surface, all other conditions being the same.

The correction for effects of masses lying above the ellipsoid surface or for deficiencies of mass below that level is termed the *Bouguer correction*. It was named after Pierre Bouguer, a leader of an early eighteenth-century geodetic expedition to Peru. The Bouguer correction for mass distribution with respect to the ellipsoid surface is made with the assumption of a horizontal rock slab of uniform density. Usually, a density of 2.67 g/cm^3 is assumed for the rock slab. To make the correction, we need to know only the thickness of material between the earth's solid surface and the ideal ellipsoid. Using a formula, subtraction is made from the gravimeter reading obtained on the elevated land surface. The Bouguer correction amounts to about 0.1 milligal per meter of rock thickness.

A third correction takes into account the presence of local topographic features such as a nearby mountain or an adjacent valley. These features will either subtract from or add to the value of the gravimeter reading. A *topographic correction* is therefore made in addition to the Bouguer correction, because the latter assumes that the land surface on which the gravimeter rests is a horizontal surface, i.e., a featureless plain.

After applying all the corrections thus far noted, we may find that the observed value of gravity still does not agree with the normal sea-level gravity. A difference between observed and predicted gravity values is, in general, termed a *gravity anomaly*. In this case, it is termed the *Bouguer anomaly*. Under mountains and plateaus, the Bouguer anomaly has a negative value, so that the plotted profile of the gravity traverse across country "mirrors" the topographic profile (see Figure 3.38). When an anomaly is found, a cause other than those already taken into account must be sought to explain the discrepancy.

3.24 Isostatic Gravity Anomalies

Suppose you were to join a party of geophysicists in a traverse across the United States from the Pacific to the Atlantic coast. Stopping frequently to take gravity readings with a portable gravimeter, you apply the corrections we have listed, calculating the Bouguer anomaly for each station. After plotting these anomaly values against the line of traverse, you compare the resulting *gravity anomaly profile* with the topographic profile, as shown in Figure 3.38B. You would be struck by the fact that strong negative Bouguer anomalies coincide with the Sierra Nevada and Rocky Mountains. You also observe that negative anomalies are large in the Basin-and-Range region that lies between them. Over the interior lowland and Appalachian Plateau, the isostatic anomaly values (C) are almost always negative and rather uniformly small, but there is a marked increase in the negative value beneath the Appalachian Mountains. If the traverse were carried out over the Atlantic Ocean basin, it would show a switch to a strong, uniform positive Bouguer anomaly.

The significance of the Bouguer anomaly we observe in this profile across a continent and over an ocean basin is simply this: We made a wrong assumption about the way rock density is distributed in the crust and upper mantle. We had been assuming that there exist horizontal rock layers of constant thickness, and that within each layer, density is the same in all horizontal directions. We were also assuming that density increases progressively downward from one layer to the next. Evidently, the assumption about constant thickness of each layer does not hold valid. Using information we have previously presented, based on seismology concerning crustal structure and thickness and of the depth to the Moho (Figure 3.5), we could have predicted what the problem is. A profile of the Moho would show deep crustal roots beneath the Rockies (cross-hatched "crystalline basement"). These roots consist of rock less dense than average for this depth. The crystalline basement is shallow over the interior lowland region, but again shows a deepening beneath the Appalachians.

Obviously, a further correction, beyond the Bouguer and topographic corrections, is needed for our gravity readings. To make this correction, we must use seismic evidence allowing us to establish the thickness and density of the crustal layers and mantle. An *isostatic correction* is needed. For this purpose, a set of vertical crustal columns is laid out, and the correction is calculated for each column.

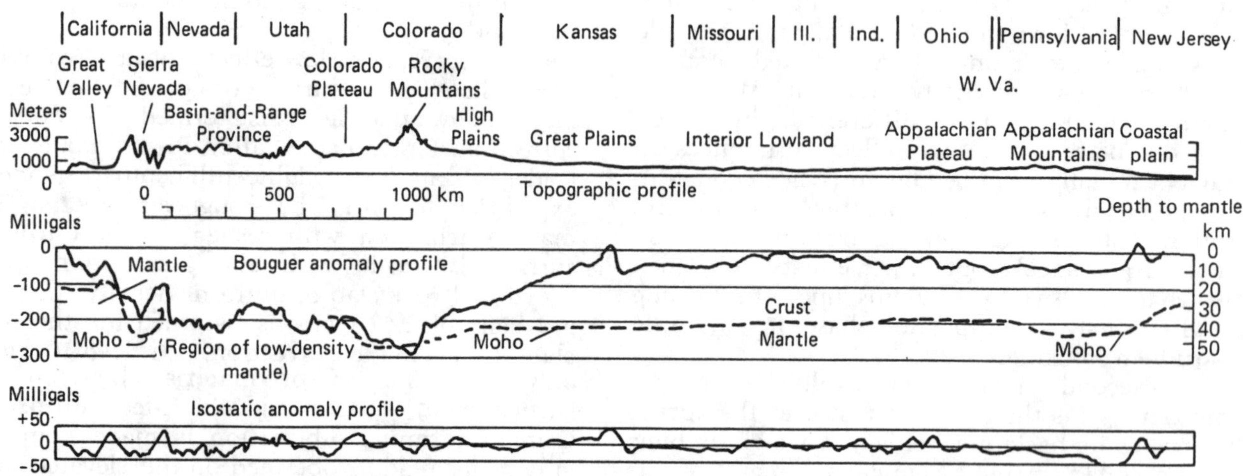

Figure 3.38 Topographic and gravity anomaly profiles crossing the United States from west to east. (Adapted from G.P. Woollard, 1966, *The Earth Beneath the Continents, Monograph 10,* p. 560; used by permission of the American Geophysical Union.)

The first step is to make assumptions about a column whose surface coincides with sea level. For example, we might choose to assume that this crustal column has a depth of 30 km and an average density of 2.9 g/cm^3 (Figure 3.39). An assumed value for density of the mantle rock beneath is 3.3 g/cm^3. Next, it is assumed that for each increase of 1 km in surface elevation with respect to sea level, the base of the column is lengthened by 7.5 km. Figure 3.39 shows such columns for elevations of 3, 2, and 1 km (left to right). Depth of compensation is double the crustal column length and exceeds 100 km under the longest column. A model of oceanic crust is also shown, for comparison.

After the isostatic crustal model is set up, the next step is to calculate a gravity correction based upon the masses of the columns. This isostatic correction is subtracted from the Bouguer correction, leaving a much smaller anomaly known as the *isostatic gravity anomaly*. If the crustal model is a correct one and the condition of isostasy prevails, this anomaly should have zero value. In actual fact, computed isostatic anomalies ranging from -30 to +30 milligals characterize most of the surface of the continents. This small range is seen in the isostatic anomaly profile in Figure 3.38C. The anomalies take the form of small "hills" and "depressions." They reflect place-to-place differences in rock density caused by the presence of local crustal rock masses of various dimensions, compositions, and structures. On the whole, however, much, if not most, of the earth's crust and lithosphere, both continental and oceanic, is found to be near isostatic equilibrium.

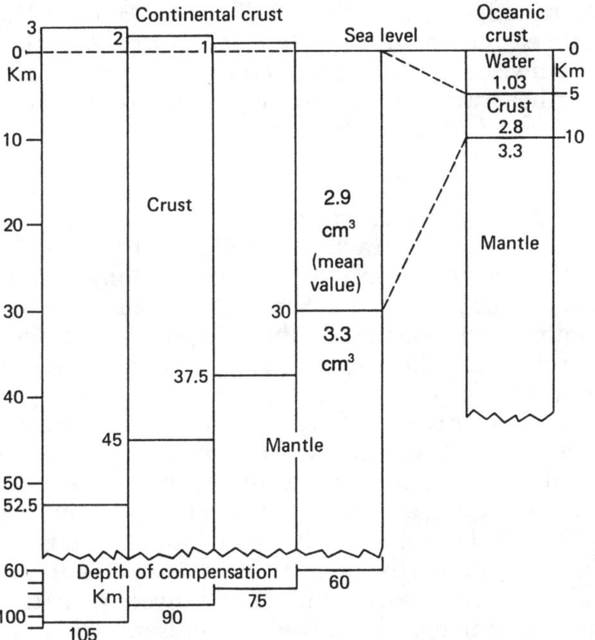

Figure 3.39 Simplified Airy isostatic model of crust. (Based on data of G.P. Woollard, 1966. *The Earth Beneath the Continents, Monograph 10*, Washington, D.C., American Geophysical Union, p. 563.

3.25 The Geoid and Global Geoidal Maps

Surface variations in the value of the acceleration of gravity, *g*, can be presented in the form of the *geoid*, an idealized global surface that can be defined as the equipotential surface in the terrestrial gravity field that concides with undisturbed mean sea level extended through the continents. If it were possible to crisscross all continents with a gridwork of sea-level canals, or better still, of sea-level tunnels, and somehow do away with the fluctuations in sea level due to tides and winds, the sea water would everywhere come to rest to define the geoid.

Figure 3.40 is a schematic diagram showing that ideally the geoid should lie beneath the ellipsoid surface over the ocean basins, but above that surface beneath the continents. This situation is explained by the reduced pull of gravity at sea level where the excess crustal mass lies above the ellipsoid and the increased pull where mass is displaced below the ellipsoid. Because of lateral inhomogeneities in the crust and mantle, however, one cannot predict the position of the geoid merely by looking at a relief map of the globe.

Departures of the elevation of the geoidal surface are referred to an ideal earth ellipsoid. Estimates of the dimensions of the ellipsoid of reference were made as early as 1830 and revised at intervals based on surface measurements of

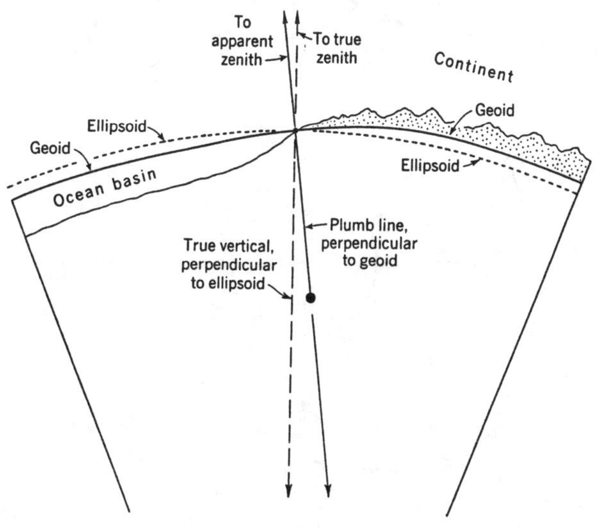

Figure 3.40 Diagrammatic and highly exaggerated cross section showing the relation between ellipsoid and geoid under continents and over ocean basins. (Based on data of W.A. Heiskanen and F.A. Vening Meinesz (1958), *The Earth and its Gravity Field*, New York, McGraw-Hill, p. 237, Figure 8-5.)

arcs of longitude (Strahler, 1971, p. 152-53). When the first orbiting satellites became operational in the late 1950s, more precise measurements were immediately possible. By the mid-1970s, the value of earth flattening had been established as one part in 298.25, and with the equatorial diameter exceeding the polar diameter by 42.77 km (King-Hele, 1976, p. 1295). Using this ellipsoid of reference, harmonic analysis of satellite data yielded in 1974 the meridional profile of the geoid shown here in Figure 3.41. Departures from the ellipsoidal profile range from +20 m at the north pole to –25 m at the south pole (King-Hele, 1976, p. 1295). This figure was widely publicized in the news media as a "pear-shaped" earth.

Satellite data also made possible complete and greatly improved world maps of geoidal heights. Figure 3.42 is one such map, published in 1981, and making use of combined satellite and terrestrial data resources. In order to reveal tectonic features to greatest advantage, it uses an ellipsoid of reference that is in hydrostatic equilibrium and for which the flattening is 1/299.639. The geoid was calculated from spherical harmonics with approximately 100-km spatial resolution (Rapp, 1981; Chase, 1985, p. 98-99). In 1983, a world map was produced by the NASA Goddard Space Flight Center using a one-degree grid and a contour interval of 2 m (Taylor et al, 1983). This map is much too detailed to be reproduced at the size of facing book pages, but we show selected portions in Figure 3.43.

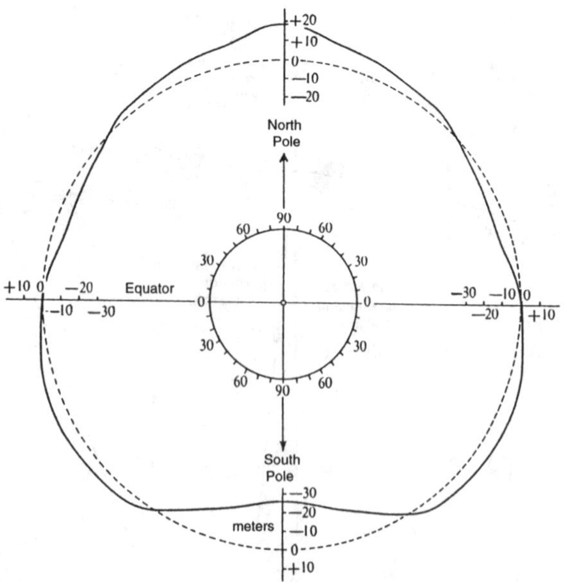

Figure 3.41 Meridional profile of the geoid (solid Line) relative to the ellipsoid of reference. (Courtesy of Desmond King-Hele, Space Department of the Royal Aircraft Establishment, England, 1976, in *Science*, v. 192, p. 1295. Used by permission.)

3.26 The Geoid and Plate Tectonics

Some relatively small-scale features of the geoidal contours are obviously directly related to configuration of the lithospheric plate boundaries. For example, some of the trench/island-arc boundaries are defined by scarp-like gradients or by lines of small closed depressions. The great Himalayan suture shows as a south-facing scarp, and similar features mark the Zagros suture and the Aegean subduction boundary. Depressions of the geoid coinciding with crustal depressions under the Labradorian and Fenno-Scandinavian centers of load of Pleistocene ice-sheets are also clearly defined. (See Figure 12.25.)

It soon became apparent, however, that large-scale (long-wave) undulations in the geoid seem unrelated to present tectonic features of the lithosphere. These departures are thought to represent areas below which lie zones of excess or deficient mass deep within the mantle, and "are dominated by density distributions supported by very large-scale convective processes" (Chase, 1985). One conspicuous example is a very large geoidal depression centered in the Indian Ocean, due south of the Indian peninsula, and bottoming at -100 m (Figure 3.42). Another huge depression lies over Antarctica. The North Atlantic Ocean shows a great east-to-west gradient from a high off the coast of western Europe to a deep low off the North American coast. This feature completely obscures the symmetrical tectonic form of the Atlantic basin with its axial spreading boundary and opposing passive continental margins. In the North Pacific, a southwest-to-northeast gradient leads from a great high over the Philippines-Borneo-New Guinea region to a low off the North American northwest coast that continues to deepen northeastward to a bottom over the crustally depressed Hudson Bay region. This continuous gradient extends across the entire Pacific plate.

Geodesist Clement P. Chase states: "The geoid is more sensitive to deep mass distributions than is gravity" (1985, p. 101). Figure 3.43 shows steplike features along active continental margins, whereas because of isostatic compensation of the components of those boundaries, the gravity signature averages to zero (1985, p. 101).

In his review of geological significance of the geoid, Chase states that "the earth's gravity field is proving a most fruitful tool for investigating a variety of geologic problems" (1985, p. 113). One of his concluding statements reads: "The earth's gravity field is dominated by a large, deep, slowly changing convective pattern that is not closely linked to present-day upper mantle convection in the form of plate tectonics, but that is related to the source of hotspots and possibly to past plate boundary configurations" (p. 113-14).

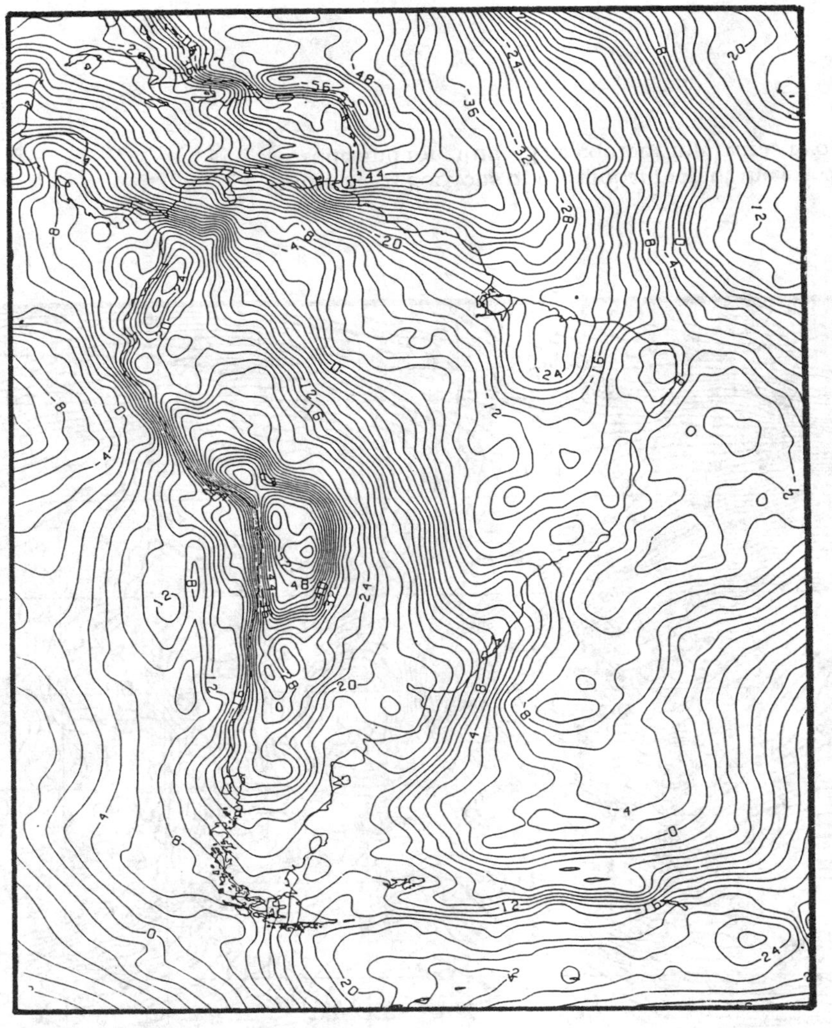

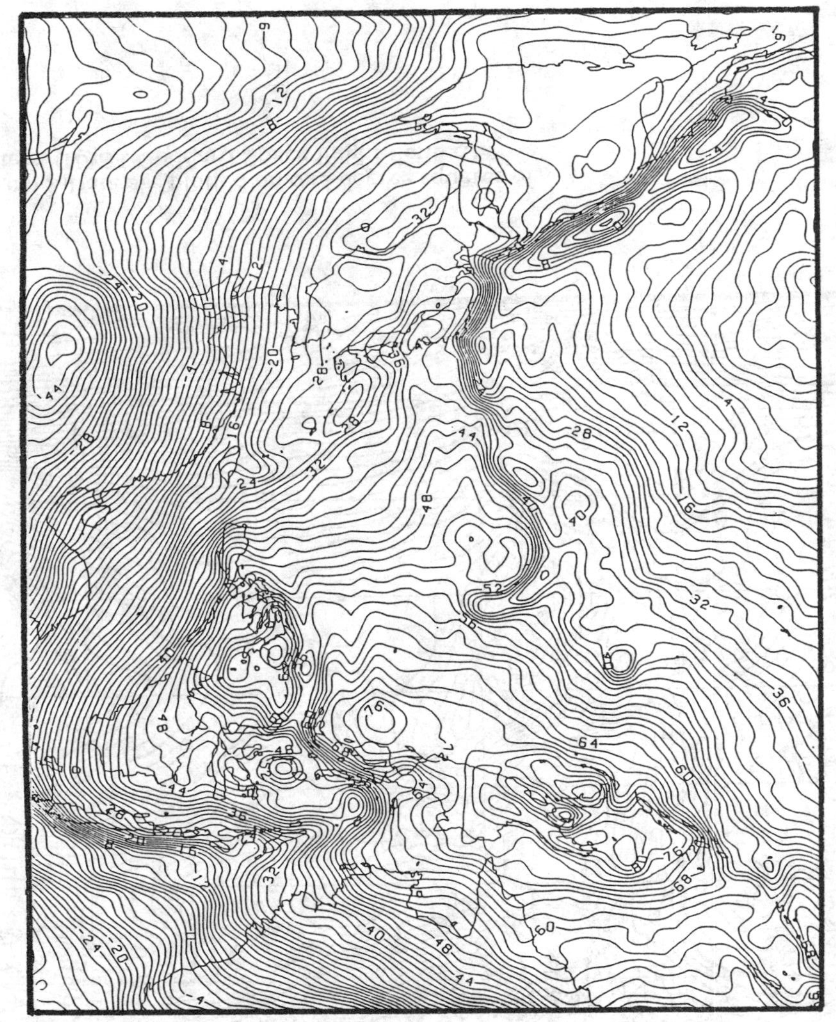

Figure 3.42 Map of the global geoid calculated from spherical harmonics with approximately 100-km spatial resolution. Cylindrical equidistant projection. (From R. Rapp. 1981, Ohio State Univ. Dept. of Geodetic Science, Survey Report 322. Used by permission.)

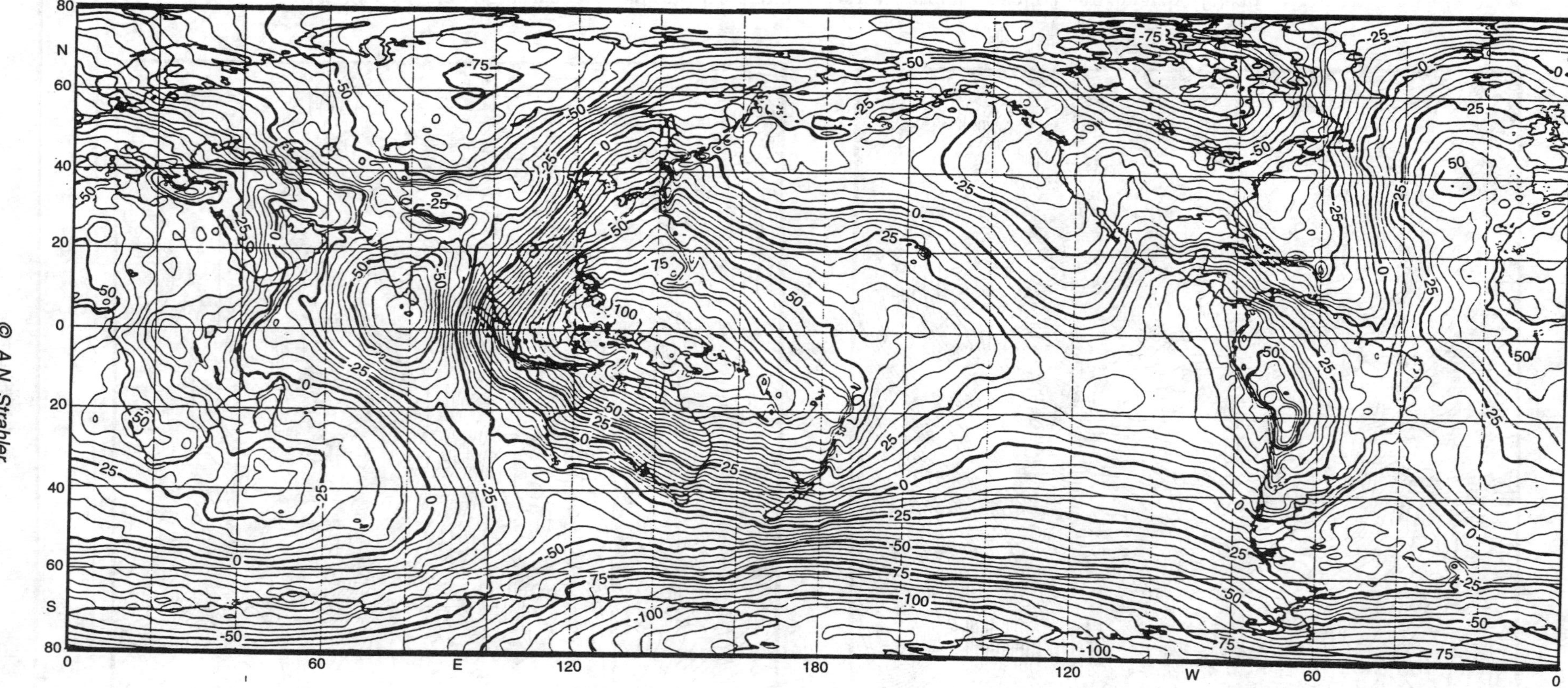

Figure 3.43 Portions of the global map of the gravity geoid. Data are plotted on one-degree squares of latitude and longitude. The contour interval is two meters. (NASA Goddard Space Flight Center.)

REFERENCES CITED

Allmendinger, K.D., et al., 1987, Deep seismic reflection characteristics of the continental crust. *Geology*, v. 15, p. 304-310.

Alvarez, Walter, 1982, Geological evidence for the geographical pattern of mantle return flow and the driving mechanism of plates. *Jour. Geophysical Res.*, v. 87, p. 6697-6710.

Anderson, Don L., 1962, The plastic layer of the earth's mantle. *Scientific American*, July 1962, p. 52-59.

Anderson, Don L., 1984a, The earth as a planet: Paradigms and paradoxes. *Science*, v. 223, p. 347-355.

Anderson, Don L., 1984b, The earth's interior is the new frontier. *Geotimes*, v. 29, no. 9, p. 16-17.

Anderson, Don. L., and Adam M. Dziewonsky, 1984, Seismic tomography. *Scientific American*, v. 251, no. 4, p. 60-68

Anderson, D.L., T. Tanimoto, and Y.-S. Zhang, 1992, Plate tectonics and hotspots: The third dimension. *Science*, v. 256, p. 1645-1651.

Archambeau, C., E.A. Flinn, and D.G. Lambert, 1969, Fine structure of the upper mantle. *Jour. Geophysical Res.*, v. 74, p. 5825-5865.

Artyushkov, E.V., 1973, Stresses in the lithosphere caused by crustal thickness inhomogeneities. *Jour. Geophysical Res.*, v. 78, p. 7657-7708.

Barrell, Joseph, 1914-15, The strength of the earth's crust. *Jour. of Geology*, vol. 22, p. 28-48, 145-165, 209-236, 289-314, 441-468, 537-555, 655-683, 729-741; vol. 23, 27-44, 425-443, 499-515.

Bates, Robert L., and Julia A. Jackson, Eds., 1987, *Glossary of Geology*. Alexandria VA: Amer. Geological Institute.

Cathles, L.M., 1987, Determination of the earth's viscosity. Pages 198-202 in Seyfert, 1987.

Chapman, David S., and Henry N. Pollack, 1977, Regional geotherms and lithospheric thickness. *Geology*, v. 5, p. 265-268.

Chapple, William M., and Terry E. Tullis, 1977, Evolution of the forces that drive the plates. Alexandria, Virginia, *Jour. Geophysical Res.*, v. 82, p. 1967-1984.

Chase, Clement G., 1985, The geological significance of the geoid. *Annual Reviews of Earth & Planetary Sciences*, vol. 13, p. 97-117.

Cogley, J. Graham, 1984, Continental margins and the extent and number of the continents. *Reviews of Geophysics and Space Physics*, v. 22, no. 2, p. 101-122.

Condie, Kent C., 1989, *Plate Tectonics & Crustal Evolution*. Oxford: Pergamon Press.

DePaolo, Donald J., 1981, Nd isotopic studies: Some new perspectives on earth evolution and structure. *EOS*, v. 62, no. 14, p. 137-140.

Dobrin, Milton B., 1960, *Introduction to Geophysical Prospecting*. 2nd Ed., New York: McGraw-Hill Book Co.

DOSECC Investigators and Staff, 1987, DOSECC continental scientific drilling program. *EOS*, v. 68, p. 545-546.

Dziewonski, Adam M., and Don L. Anderson, 1984, Seismic tomography of the earth's interior. *American Scientist*, vol. 72, p. 483-494.

Dziewonski, Adam M., and John H. Woodehouse, 1987, Global images of the earth's interior. *Science*, v. 236, p. 37-48.

Elders, Wilfred A., 1994, Planning the International Scientific Drilling Program, *EOS*, v. 75, no. 45, p. 530-531.

Elsasser, W.M., 1971, Two-layer model of upper-mantle circulation. *Jour. Geophysical Res.*, v. 76, p. 4744-4753.

Ewing, M., A.P. Crary, and H.M. Rutherford, 1937, Geophysical investigations in the emerged and submerged Atlantic coastal plain: Part I - Methods and results. *Bull., Geol. Soc. Amer.*, v. 48, p. 753-802.

Ewing, M., J.L. Worzel, J.B. Hersey, Frank Press, and G.R. Hamilton, 1950, Seismic refraction measurements in the Atlantic Ocean basin. (Part one). *Seismological Soc. of Amer. Bull.*, v. 40, p. 233-242.

Ewing, Maurice, and Frank Press, 1950, Crustal structure and surface-wave dispersion. *Seismological Soc. Amer. Bull.*, v. 40, p. 271-280.

Ewing, Maurice, and Frank Press, 1952, Crustal structure and surfacewave dispersion, Part II, Solomon Islands earthquake of July 29, 1950. *Seimological Soc. of Amer. Bull.*, v. 42, p. 315-325.

Forsyth, D., and Seiya Uyeda, 1975, On the relative importance of the driving forces of plate motions. *Royal Astron. Soc. Geophys. Jour.*, vol. 41, p. 1-38.

Fowler, C.M.R., 1990, *The Solid earth: An Introduction to Global Geophysics*. New York: Cambridge Univ. Press.

Fukao, Yoshio, 1992, Seismic tomography of the earth's mantle: geodynamic implications. *Science*, v. 258, p. 1069.

Griffin, W.L., and Suzanne Y. O'Reilly, 1987, Is the continental Moho the crust-mantle boundary? *Geology*, v. 15, p. 241-244.

Hammond, Allen L., 1975, Exploring the continent by drilling: a new proposal. *Science*, v. 189, p. 35.

Hess, H.H., 1959, The AMSOC hole to the earth's mantle. *Trans. Amer. Geophysical Union*, v. 40, p. 340.

Holmes, Arthur, 1978, *Holmes Principles of Physical Geology*. Third Ed., revised by Doris L. Holmes. New York: John Wiley & Sons.

Isacks, Bryan, Jack Oliver, and Lynn R. Sykes, 1968, Seismology and the new global tectonics. *Jour. Geophysical Res.*, vol. 73, p. 5855-5899.

Jordan, Thomas H., 1979, The deep structure of the continents. *Scientific American*, v. 240, no. 1, p. 92-107.

Jordan, Thomas H., and William S. Fyfe, 1976 Lithosphere-asthenosphere boundary. Penrose Conference Report, *Geology*, vol. 4, p. 770-772.

Kennedy, G.C., 1959, The origin of continents, mountain ranges, and ocean basins. *American Scientist*, v. 47, p. 491-504.

Kerr, Richard A., 1986a, Sinking slabs puncture layered mantle model. *Science*, vol. 231, p. 548-49.

Kerr, Richard A., 1986b, The continental plates are getting thicker. *Science*, v. 232, p. 933-934.

Kerr, Richard A., 1988, The mantle's structure—having it both ways. *Science*, v. 240, p. 175.

Kerr, Richard A., 1990, A generational rift in geophysics. *Science*, v. 248, p. 300-302.

Kerr, Richard A., 1991, New hints of deep slabs. *Science*, v. 252, p. 1069.

Kerr, Richard A., 1994, German super-deep hole hits bottom. *Science*, v. 266, p. 545.

Kerr, Richard A., 1996, Putting stiffness in the Earth's mantle. *Science*, v. 271, p. 1053-1054.

King-Hele, Desmond, 1976, The shape of the earth. *Science*, v. 192, p. 1293-1300.

Knittle, Elise, and Raymond Jeanloz, 1987, Synthesis and equation of state of (Mg,Fe)SiO3 perovskite to over 100 gigapascals. *Science*, v. 235, p. 668-670.

Kozlovsky, Ye. A., 1984, The world's deepest well. *Scientific American*, v. 251, no. 6, p. 98-104.

Lay, Thorne, 1989, Structure of the core-mantle transition zone: a chemical and thermal boundary layer. *EOS*, v. 70, no. 4, p. 49-59.

Lay, Thorne, 1994, Deep earth structure. *Geotimes*, v. 39, no. 6, p. 13-15.

Lill, Gordon G., and Arthur E. Maxwell. 1959, The earth's mantle. *Science*, v. 129, p. 1407-1410.

Lovering, J.F., 1958, The nature of the Mohorovicic discontinuity. *Transactions Amer. Geophysical Union*, v. 39, p. 947-955.

McKenzie, D.P., 1983, The earth's mantle. *Scientific American*, vol. 249, no. 3, p. 67-78.

McNutt, Marcia K., 1987, Isostasy. Pages 354-358 in Seyfert, 1987.

Monastersky, Richard, 1989, Inner space. *Science News*, v. 136, p. 266-268.

Monastersky, Richard, 1992, Hitting a deep barrier within the planet. *Science News*, v. 141, p. 132-133.

Monastersky, Richard, 1993, Mixing Earth's mantle with a delayed flush. *Science News*, v. 143, p. 133.

Monastersky, Richard, 1996, Putting a new spin on the Earth's core. *Science News*, v. 150, p. 36.

Mooney, Walter D., and Lawrence W. Braile, 1989, The seismic structure of the continental crust and upper mantle. Pages 39-52 in *The Geology of North America, Volume A*. Boulder CO: The Geological Society of America.

Morgan, W. Jason, 1968, Rises, trenches, great faults, and crustal blocks. *Jour. Geophysical Res.*, v. 73, p. 1959-1982.

O'Nions, R.K., P.J. Hamilton, and Norman M. Evenson, 1980, The chemical evolution of the earth's mantle. *Scientific American*, v. 242, no. 5, p. 120-133.

Oliver, Jack, 1982a, Exploration of the continental basement the world over by seismic reflection profiling: a goal for the solid earth sciences. *EOS*, v. 63, p. 161.

Oliver, Jack, 1982b, Probing the structure of the deep continental crust. *Science*, v. 216, p. 689-695.

Oliver, Jack, 1983, Exploring the geological structure of the continental crust. *Jour. of Geological Education*, v. 31, p. 277-294.

Oliver, Jack, 1988, Opinion. *Geology*, v. 16, p. 291.

Oliver, Jack, 1993, COCORP probes continental depths. *Geotimes*, v. 38, no. 6, p. 21-22.

Polet, J., and Don L. Anderson, 1995, Depth extent of cratons as inferred from tomographic studies. *Geology*, v. 256, p. 205-208.

Rapp, R.H., 1981, The earth's gravity field to degree and order of 180 using *Seasat* altimeter data, terrestrial gravity data, and other data. *Ohio State University Geodedic Science Survey*, Report No. 322.

Richardson, R.M., S.C. Solomon, and N.H. Sleep, 1976, Intraplate stress as an indicator of plate tectonic driving forces. *Jour. Geophysical Res.*, v. 81, p. 1847-1856.

Richter, Charles F., 1958, *Elementary Seismology*, San Francisco: W.H. Freeman.

Ronov, A.B. and A.A. Yaroshevskiy, 1969, Chemical composition of the earth's crust. *In The Earth's Crust and Upper Mantle*, P.J. Hart, Ed., Geophysical Monograph 13, Washington, D.C.: Amer. Geophysical Union.

Schubert, G., D.A. Yuen, C. Fiordevaux, L. Fleitout, and M. Souriaw, 1978, Mantle circulation with partial shallow return flow: effects on stresses in oceanic plates and topography of the sea floor. *Jour. Geophysical Res.*, v. 83, p. 745-758.

Seyfert Carl K., Ed., 1987, *The Encyclopedia of Structural Geology and Plate Tectonics*. New York: Van Nostrand Reinhold Co.

Seyfert, Carl K., 1987, Convection and the movement of plates. Pages 99-113 in Seyfert, 1987.

Shea, James H., Ed., 1985, *Continental Drift*. Benchmark Papers in Geology, vol. 88, New York: Van Nostrand Reinhold Co.

Silver, P.G., R.W. Carlson, P. Bell, and P. Olsen, 1985, Mantle structure and dynamics. *EOS*, v. 66, no. 48, p. 1195-1198.

Smithson, S.B., 1978, Modeling continental crust; structural and chemical constraints. *Geophysical Research Letters*, v. 5, p. 749-752.

Soller, D.R., R.D. Ray, and R.D. Brown, 1982, A new global crustal thickness map, *Tectonics*, vol. 1, p. 125-149.

Song, Xiaodong, and Paul G. Richards, 1996, Seismological evidence for differential rotation of the Earth's inner core. *Nature*, v. 382, p. 221-224.

Stacey, Frank D., 1977, *Physics of the Earth*, 2nd ed. New York: John Wiley & Sons.

Stein, M., and A.W. Hofman, 1994, Mantle plumes and episodic crustal growth. *Nature*, v. 372, p. 63-68.

Strahler, Arthur N., 1971, *The Earth Sciences*, 2nd. ed. New York: Harper & Row.

Swinbank, David, 1993, Nations urged to unite on drill costs. *Nature*, v. 365, p. 482.

Uyeda, Seiya, 1978, *The New View of the Earth*. Revised edition. San Francisco: W.H. Freeman and Company.

Van Bemmelen, R.W., 1954, *Mountain Building*, The Hague: Martinus Nijhoff.

Van Der Gracht, W.A.J.M. Waterschoot, Ed., 1928, *Theory of Continental Drift*. Tulsa, OK: Amer. Assoc. of Petroleum Geologists.

Weisburd, Stefi, 1986, Plunging plates cause a stir. *Science News*, v. 130, p. 106-109.

Whaler, Kathy, and Richard Holme, 1996, Catching the inner core in a spin. *Nature*, v. 382, p. 205-206.

Williams, Quentin et al., 1987, The melting curve of iron to 250 gigapascals: A constraint on the temperature at earth's center. *Science*, v. 236, p. 181-182.

Wyllie, Peter J. 1975, The earth's mantle. *Scientific American*, v. 232, no. 3, p. 50-63.

Wyllie, Peter J., 1971, *The Dynamic Earth: Textbook in Geosciences*. New York: John Wiley & Sons.

Chapter: 4 The Ocean Floor and Its Sediments

Until shortly after World War II, the world ocean concealed in its black depths the secrets of plate tectonics. Oceanic lithospheric plates are the great driving wheels of the plate tectonic system, but from spreading boundaries to subduction boundaries, their very existence was scarcely even suspected until research on oceanography and submarine geology got well underway. Submarine geology as a subject is often brushed over very lightly in the introductory physical geology course, but it is a subject thoroughly enmeshed with plate tectonics—hence this chapter. Besides bedrock geology and topography of the ocean floors, great importance attaches to the comparatively young sediments that cover most of its bedrock surface. All of these topics need to be reviewed, if for no other reason that oceanic igneous and sedimentary materials have made possible the growth of continents through geologic time.

Built into the theory of plate tectonics is the concept that the ocean basins are young in contrast to the continental cratons, which are very old. Oceanic lithosphere forms quite rapidly, geologically speaking, along the spreading mid-oceanic boundaries, but is rapidly disposed of as it dives beneath the continental lithosphere in subduction zones. Thus, while oceanic crust cannot be very old, it can certainly be very young—so young, in fact, that some of it is even younger than you or I. If we calculate on the basis of sea-floor spreading at a rate of 5 cm per year, and also assume that new oceanic crust must form at the same rate in order to keep the gap between the plates filled, a belt of new crust 1 m wide will have formed since the birth of a person who today is 20 years old.

Perhaps because the ocean basins are the young portions of the earth, it is logical that we have elected to examine their plate tectonics in Chapters 7 and 8, before turning to tectonics affecting the relatively ancient continents. In this chapter, we investigate the ocean basins in terms of their broad configuration, their relief features, and the sediments that form within them. With this information in hand, we can turn more confidently to matters of plate tectonics affecting the oceanic lithosphere and its plate boundaries.

4.1 Ocean Basins and Continents

The first-order relief features of the earth are the continents and ocean basins. A detailed relief map of the earth and its ocean floors shows immediately that the natural limits of the continents are much larger and more regular than a conventional map showing only the oceanic shoreline. Broad shelves and platforms border the continents in many places. These shallow border zones typically show an abrupt outer edge and a steep drop to deep ocean floors.

To get a generalized picture of the earth's solid surface form we can examine the depth-area graph shown in Figure 4.1. The graph shows the proportion of surface lying between equal units of vertical distance, or elevation, each unit being a kilometer. The length of each horizontal bar is proportional to the percentage of surface area found within each one-kilometer elevation zone.

The graph shows most of the surface as concentrated in two general zones: (1) on the continents between sea level and 1 km elevation, and (2) on the floors of the ocean basins from about 3 to 6 km below sea level. This graph also tells us that in a general way the continents are broad, tablelike areas whose edges slope away rapidly to the deep ocean floor. Although the floor does not lie entirely within a single elevation zone, vast flat areas are typical.

Today the ocean basins are full to the brim with water, so that the oceans overlap considerable areas of the continental margins to produce shallow seas bordering the shores. A true picture of the continents in relation to the ocean basins emerges when the ocean level is imagined to be dropped some 180 m to uncover these shallow continental shelves and inland seas. When the area lying above the 180-m submarine contour is included with the lands, it will be found that the continents make up about 35% of the total earth's surface area and the ocean basins about 65% (Figure 4.2). The reasons for a two-level form of the earth's solid surface have already been explained in chapters 1 and 3. Perhaps the most generally satisfactory definition of *continents* and *ocean basins* is that the continents are high-standing surfaces underlain by felsic continental crust, whereas the ocean basins are low-lying surfaces underlain by mafic oceanic crust.

4.2 Visiting the Ocean Floor

Even today, few persons get a chance to see the deep ocean floor at close range. Undersea photographs, taken by a special type of camera lowered to the seafloor from a ship, first became available for research use in the 1940s. Direct observation and bottom sampling are now commonplace, thanks to a fleet of *manned submersibles*—undersea vessels capable of withstanding the enormous confining pressure at depths greater than 3 km. In a historic major expedition to the floor of the Mid-Atlantic rift in 1974, three submersibles from the United States and France made 47 dives to study an active seafloor spreading zone. We review the petrological findings of this international study,

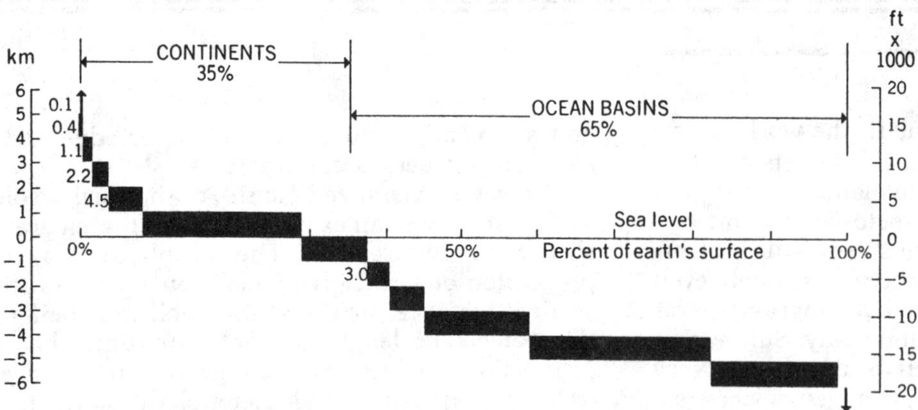

Figure 4.1. The length of each bar represents the percentage of surface area in each one-km elevation zone of the earth's solid surface. (Copyright © by Arthur N. Strahler.)

project FAMOUS, in Chapter 7. Scientists in the submersibles took many photographs of the features they saw and collected many samples of rocks and sediments. *Alvin*, a manned submersible operated by the Woods Hole Oceanographic Institution, was one of the vessels taking part in that project.

Even the deepest points of the ocean floor—the bottoms of trenches above subduction zones—have been visited by manned diving vessels called *bathyscaphes*, suspended from cables. Two French bathyscaphes, the *Trieste* and the *Archimede*, carried out many such deep dives. In 1960, the *Trieste* reached the deepest point humans have yet gone on the ocean floor, 11,033 m, in the Marianas Trench of the western Pacific ocean.

4.3 Charting the Ocean Floor

The making of detailed maps of the ocean floor lagged far behind the mapping of the continental surfaces. In the early decades of oceanographic research, depth sounding of the ocean bottom had to be done by lowering a heavy weight on a thin steel cable until the weight reached bottom, when the depth could be equated to the length of cable. Because this was a slow and costly process, our knowledge of the seafloor was scanty until World War II, when naval vessels began to use a continuously recording sounding apparatus, the *precision depth recorder* (PDR). It makes use of a sound-emitting device attached to the bottom of the ship. Pulses of sound are sent down through the water from the ship's hull and are reflected from the ocean floor back to the ship, where they are picked up by a microphone. The method, called *echo sounding*, uses an automatic recording device to indicate the time required for sound waves to reach the bottom and return. Reflections are plotted continuously by a writing instrument to inscribe the profile of the ocean bottom (Figure 4.3). By allowing the precision depth recorder to operate continuously while the ship travels, a profile across the seafloor is obtained, but this information can only be used to make seafloor maps if the exact position of the ship is known at all times. With navigational satellites now available, precise positioning of a vessel is no problem. Echo sounding enormously increased our knowledge of the configuration of the ocean floors within a span of only two decades, and thus the mid-twentieth century can truly be viewed as a golden age of undersea exploration.

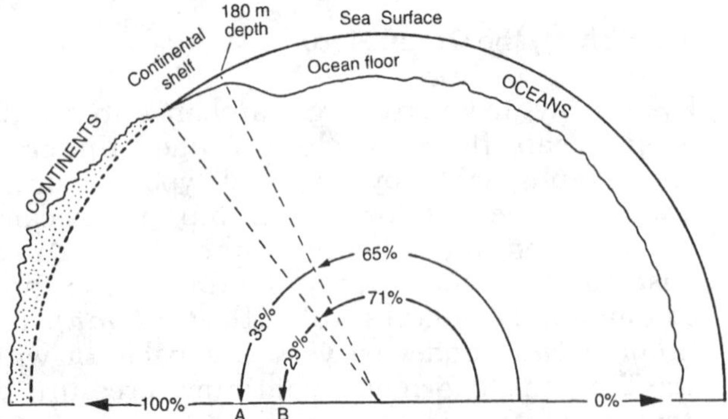

Figure 4.2 A schematic semicircular graph to compare relative global surface areas of continents and ocean basins: (A) with the continental shelves included with the continents; (B) with the shelves included with the oceans. (Copyright © by Arthur N. Strahler.)

Starting about in 1978, a quantum jump was made possible in sonic reflection mapping of the ocean floor by the development of a new high-resolution side-scanning system. Developed in England, *Gloria* was a two-sided sonar scanner towed behind a research vessel and capable of covering a swath of seafloor up to 60 km in width. It was capable of defining surface features as small as about 50 m across (Searle, Francis, Hilde, et al., 1981). *Gloria* was quickly followed by *SeaMARC*, also a deep-towed sidescan sonar; it was developed by U.S. and Canadian agencies with funding by oil companies. Its extremely clear and detailed images became known to the public during the search for the sunken *Titanic*. These scanners measure the intensity of acoustic energy returned from the ocean floor and yield an image similar to that of an aerial photograph. About the same time, *SeaBeam* came on the scene, developed by the U.S. Navy. Like the primitive ancestor we described in earlier paragraphs, it is an echo sounder, reading the travel-time of reflected sound rays. Unlike that ancestor, it uses multiple transducers and 40 receivers permanently attached to a ship's hull; these operate over a swath 43 degrees of arc in width (Farre, Kappel, and Shor, 1983). Used for the production of topographic maps of the seafloor, SeaBeam's output has given extremely precise and detailed contours of great value in scientific research on submarine landforms.

The mid-1990s brought a surprise bounty of seafloor topographic data that can safely be hailed as a quantum jump in our knowledge of that realm (Monastersky, 1995, p. 410). A U.S. Navy *Geosat* mission, classed as "secret," had been in progress from 1985 to 1990; its data unavailable to scientists. This geodetic satellite was equipped with radar altimeters capable of revealing features of seafloor topography. The radar beams are reflected from the sea surface, the height of which varies with the local intensity of gravity. These gravity anomalies, in turn mimic directly the height of the seafloor beneath. For example, a seamount rising 2000 m above the surrounding abyssal plain produces a "bump" in the sea surface about 2 m high (Amer. Geophysical Union, 1995, p. 5).

In 1990, the Navy declassified a portion of the Geosat data covering a small area south of lat. 60°S. It was immediately evident that the gravity anomalies reveal seafloor landforms, such as transform faults, with "unprecedented accuracy and resolution" (Marks, McAdoo, and Sandwell, 1991, p. 145; Sandwell and McAdoo, 1990). Early in 1995, the Navy released all of the Geosat data, and scientists quickly began to prepare detailed maps of the seafloor. A similar observation program, begun by the European Space Agency (ERS-1) in 1991, had also been producing data that closely matched that obtained by Geosat. David Sandwell, a marine geophysicist of the Scripps Institution of Oceanography and Walter Smith of the National Oceanic and Atmospheric Administration (NOAA) used a complex modeling algorithm to produce a map "that resolves the seafloor topography 30 times better than any previous effort" (Amer. Geophysical Union, 1995, p. 5). Marcia K. McNutt, a geophysicist at the Massachusetts Institute of Technology, was quoted as saying these new data sets "will further the study of the ocean basins in the same way that the Hubble [Space] Telescope has promoted the study of the cosmos" (Lawler, 1995, p. 727). [For full-color examples of these gravity "images" see Monastersky, 1995, *Science News*, vol. 148, p. 411.]

Although our book is about enormous lithospheric plates and the large tectonic features their motions generate, accurate knowledge of the fine-scale features of the ocean floor gathered by use of remote-sensing scientific instruments can prove indirectly useful in solving puzzling problems in plate tectonics. For example, accurate descriptions of seafloor features such as volcanic cones, lava flows, and fresh fault scarps along a midocean spreading ridge contribute to an understanding of the growth of new oceanic crust, while descriptions of sediment bodies accumulating in active trenches help us understand how the subduction process generates new bodies of metamorphic rock.

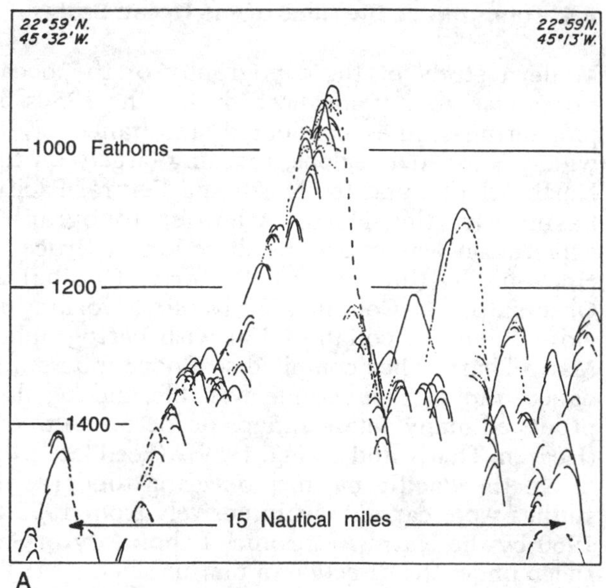

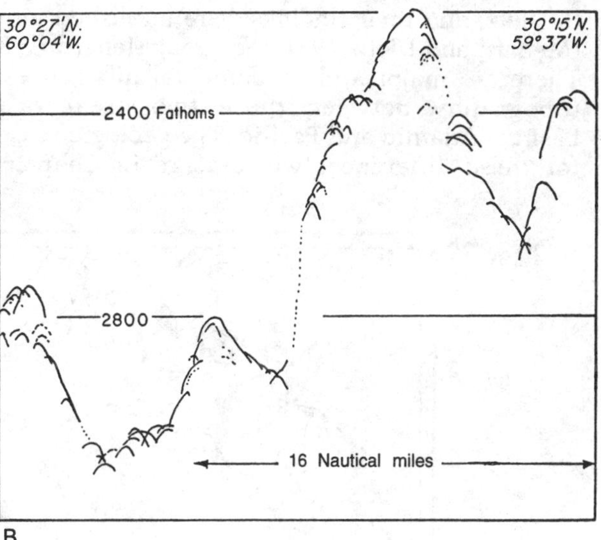

Figure 4.3 Tracings of two of the early sonic records made by a precision depth recorder in the North Atlantic Ocean. The actual sea floor does not consist of a series of rounded "domes," as the profiles seem to show. Diffraction of the sound waves from sharp peaks produces these "hyperbolic echos". (A) Rift zone of the Mid-Atlantic Ridge at lat. 23°N. (B) Abyssal hills southeast of the Bermuda Rise, lat. 30.5°N. (From B.C. Heezen, M. Tharp, and M. Ewing, 1959, *The Floors of the Oceans*, Geological Society of America Spec. Paper 65, p. 64, Figure 28, p. 92, Figure 44. Reproduced with permission of the publisher, the Geological Society of America, Boulder, Colorado USA. Copyright © 1959.)

4.4 Topographic Divisions of the Ocean Basins

Modern study of the topography of the ocean floors was greatly advanced during the 1950s by pioneering studies conducted simultaneously in widely separated regions, focusing largely on the North Atlantic and the North and Central Pacific basins. In the North Atlantic, topographic exploration was under the direction of Bruce C. Heezen of the Lamont-Doherty Geological Observatory at Columbia University, working in close scientific collaboration with cartographer Marie Tharp. They compiled seafloor topographic data as rapidly as it became available, and together produced many detailed maps of the ocean floors (Heezen, Tharp, and Ewing, 1959). (See Plate I.)

In the Pacific basin, pioneering topographic studies were carried out intensively from 1950 to 1960 by the Naval Electronics Laboratory in San Diego under the direction of marine scientist H.W. Menard, who subsequently joined the faculty of the Scripps Oceanographic Laboratory in La Jolla. Menard worked in close collaboration with Robert S. Dietz, and their findings were published jointly (Menard and Dietz, 1951 and 1952; Menard, 1986). There are major and fundamental differences of topography between these two great ocean basins—Atlantic and Pacific. The geologic reasons for these differences will emerge in Chapter 5.

In 1959, Heezen and Tharp published a system of submarine landform classification. (*Landform* refers to the geometrical configuration of the solid earth's surface, whether exposed to the atmosphere or covered by water.) In their system, the topographic features of the ocean basins fall into three major divisions: (1) the continental margins, (2) the ocean-basin floors, and (3) the mid-oceanic ridge (Heezen, Tharp, and Ewing, 1959). As the terms themselves make clear, the continental margins lie in belts directly adjacent to the continents, and the mid-oceanic ridge divides the typical ocean basin roughly in half, with one part of the basin on either side of the ridge. Figure 4.4 shows a map and a typical transverse profile of these major topographic divisions as they apply to the North Atlantic basin. Figure 4.5 is a schematic block diagram idealizing the major features.

The explanation for symmetry of the ocean-basin topography is familiar through our model of continental rifting and the opening up of an ocean basin through seafloor spreading (see Figure 1.14). Figure 4.6 is a map of the physiographic provinces of the western and central North Atlantic ocean basin. It applied the classification prepared in 1959 by Bruce Heezen and Marie Tharp at a time just prior to the arrival of plate tectonics as the new paradigm.

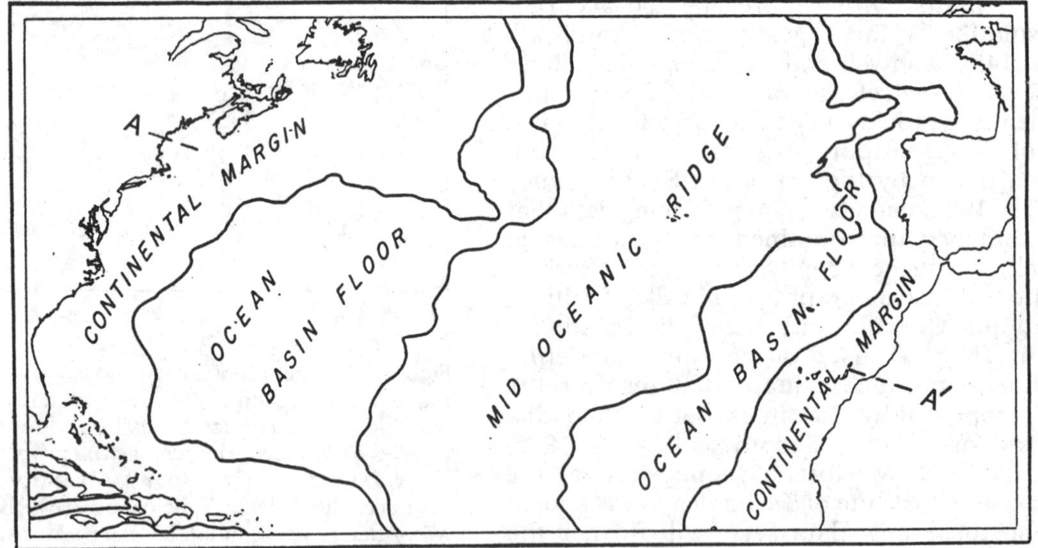

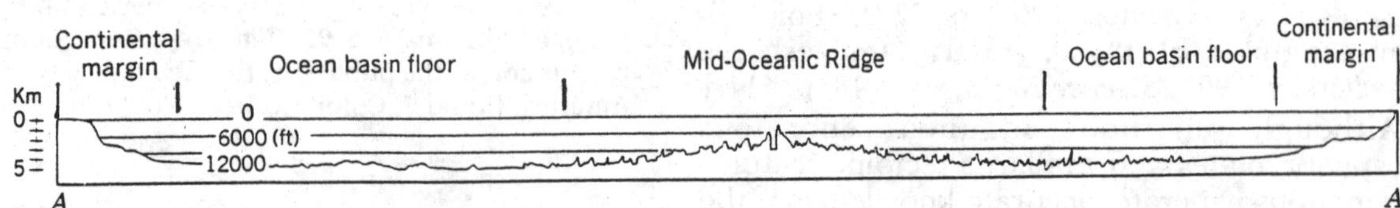

Figure 4.4 Outline map of the major divisions of the North Atlantic Ocean basin, with representative profile from New England to the Sahara coast of Africa. Vertical exaggeration about 40 times. (After B.C. Heezen, M. Tharp, and M. Ewing, 1959, *The Floors of the Oceans,* Geological Society of America Spec. Paper 65, p. 16, Figure 9. Reproduced with permission of the publisher, the Geological Society of America, Boulder, Colorado USA. Copyright © 1959.)

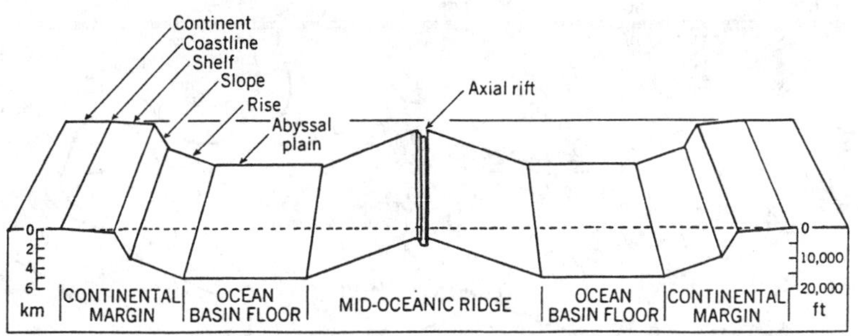

Figure 4.5 This idealized block diagram shows the major units of the North Atlantic Ocean basin as symmetrically placed on both sides of the central ridge axis. (Copyright © by Arthur N. Strahler.)

4.5 The Continental Margins

Perhaps the best known and most easily studied of the units within the continental margins is the *continental shelf*, which fringes the continents in widths from a few kilometers to more than 300 km. The shelves have very smooth and gently sloping floors, and for the most part are covered with water less than 180 m deep. A particularly fine example is the continental shelf of the eastern coast of the United States (Figure 4.7).

Along the seaward margin the continental shelf gives way quite abruptly to the *continental slope*. Although the actual inclination of the slope with respect to the horizontal is only some 2° to 3° along the passive margins of the Atlantic basin, this appears quite precipitous on highly exaggerated profiles (Figure 4.8). Steepness of the slope differs among the continental slopes of different origins. For example, off the Florida coast, where the slope exposes carbonate rock, the steepness is markedly greater. (For a full description of observed variations in slope, see Pratson and Haxby, 1996.)

Notching the continental slope are *submarine canyons*, which may be visualized as resembling gullies cut by erosion in the side of a hill, but on an enormous scale (see Figure 4.6). The continental slope drops from the sharply defined brink of the shelf to depths of 1400 to 3200 m. Here the slope lessens rapidly, though not abruptly, and is replaced by the *continental rise*, a surface of much gentler slope, gradually decreasing in steepness toward the flat ocean-basin floor. Ranging in width from perhaps 200 to 500 km, the continental rise has generally moderate to low relief. [*Relief* refers to the magnitude of local differences in elevation from point to point.] At its outer margin, the continental rise reaches a depth of 5000 m, where it may be in direct contact with the deep floor of the ocean basin.

For future reference, it is important at this point to make clear that deep beneath the continental shelf lies continental crust, so that the shelf lies within the boundary of the continents. In contrast, deep beneath the continental rise lies oceanic crust. Thus the geologic boundary between oceanic and continental crust can be drawn between shelf and rise. This boundary is shown and labeled in Figure 4.7. (See also Chapter 3 and Figure 3.2.)

4.6 The Ocean-Basin Floor

Second of the major topographic divisions of the ocean basins is the extensive region of basin floor, generally lying in the depth range of 4500 to 5500 m. The ocean-basin floor contains three classes of forms: abyssal plains and hills, oceanic rises, and seamounts.

An *abyssal plain* is an area of the deep ocean floor having a flat bottom with the very faint slope of less than one part in 1000 (a drop of one meter in a horizontal distance of 1000 m). Characteristically situated at the foot of the continental rise, the abyssal plain is present in all ocean basins. Examples are the Hatteras and Nares Abyssal plains at depth of roughly 5500 m (Figure 4.8). The nearly perfect flatness is explained by the confirmed observation that the abyssal plains are surfaces formed by long-continued deposition of very fine sediment. (See Plate I-A.)

Abyssal hills are small hills rising to heights of a few tens of meters to a few hundred meters above the ocean-basin floor and may be so numerous as to occupy nearly all the floor. Isolated abyssal hills are well developed in the North Atlantic basin along the mid-ocean side of the great abyssal plains.

Yet another characteristic topographic unit of the ocean-basin floor is the *oceanic rise*, an area hundreds of kilometers in breadth over which the surface rises several hundred meters above the surrounding abyssal plains. Within the rise, relief may range from subdued to very rugged. An example is the Bermuda Rise (or Bermuda Plateau), shown in the lower right corner of Figure 4.6 and in profiles A and B of Figure 4.8. In places, this rise consists of hills 40 to 100 m high and 3 to 16 km wide. Along the eastern edge, the rise is broken by a series of scarps 550 to 1600 m high. Located near the center of the Bermuda Rise is a pedestal or platform 80 by 130 km at its base, upon which the islands of Bermuda are situated.

Perhaps the most fascinating of the strange features of the ocean basins are the *seamounts*, isolated peaks rising 1000 m or more above the floor. Although seamounts also occur on the continental rises, they are most conspicuous on the ocean-basin floors. A good example from the Atlantic basin is the Kelvin Seamount Group, forming a row of conical peaks extending across the continental rise for 1000 km southeastward

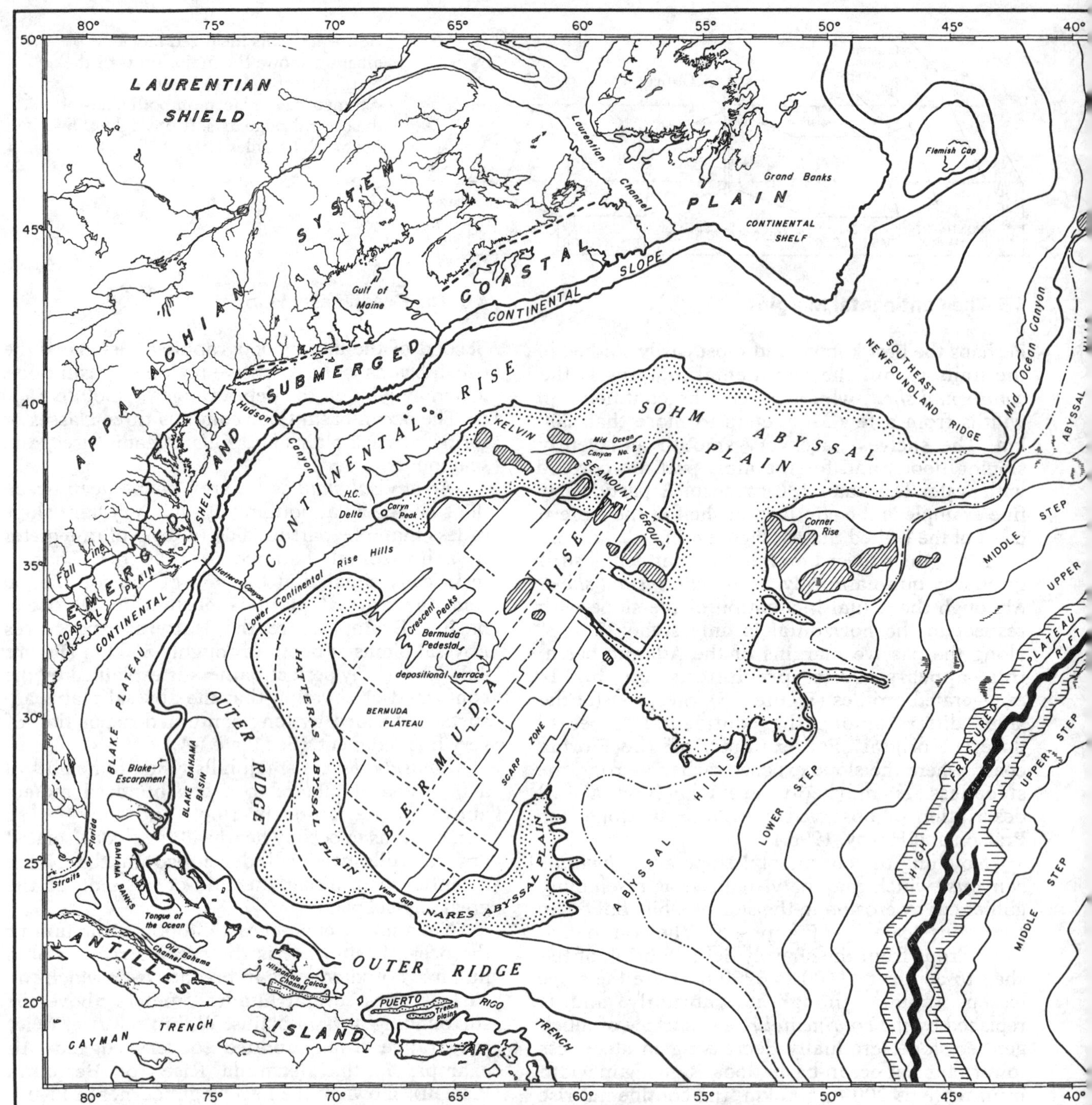

Figure 4.6 Bruce Heezen's 1959 map of the physiographic provinces of the North Atlantic ocean basin. (From B.C. Heezen, M. Tharp, and M. Ewing, 1959, *The Floors of the Oceans,* Geological Society of America, Spec. Paper 65, Plate 20. Reproduced with permission of the publisher, the Geological Society of America, Boulder, Colorado USA. Copyright © 1959.)

Figure 4.7 A representative profile of the continental margin subdivisions of the western North Atlantic ocean basin. It is typical of the sector lying between Georges Bank and Cape Hatteras.(Modified from B.C. Heezen, M. Tharp, and M. Ewing, 1959, *The Floors of the Oceans,* Geological Society of America, Spec. Paper 65, Figure 15, p. 26. Reproduced with permission of the publisher, the Geological Society of America, Boulder, Colorado USA. Copyright © 1959.) →

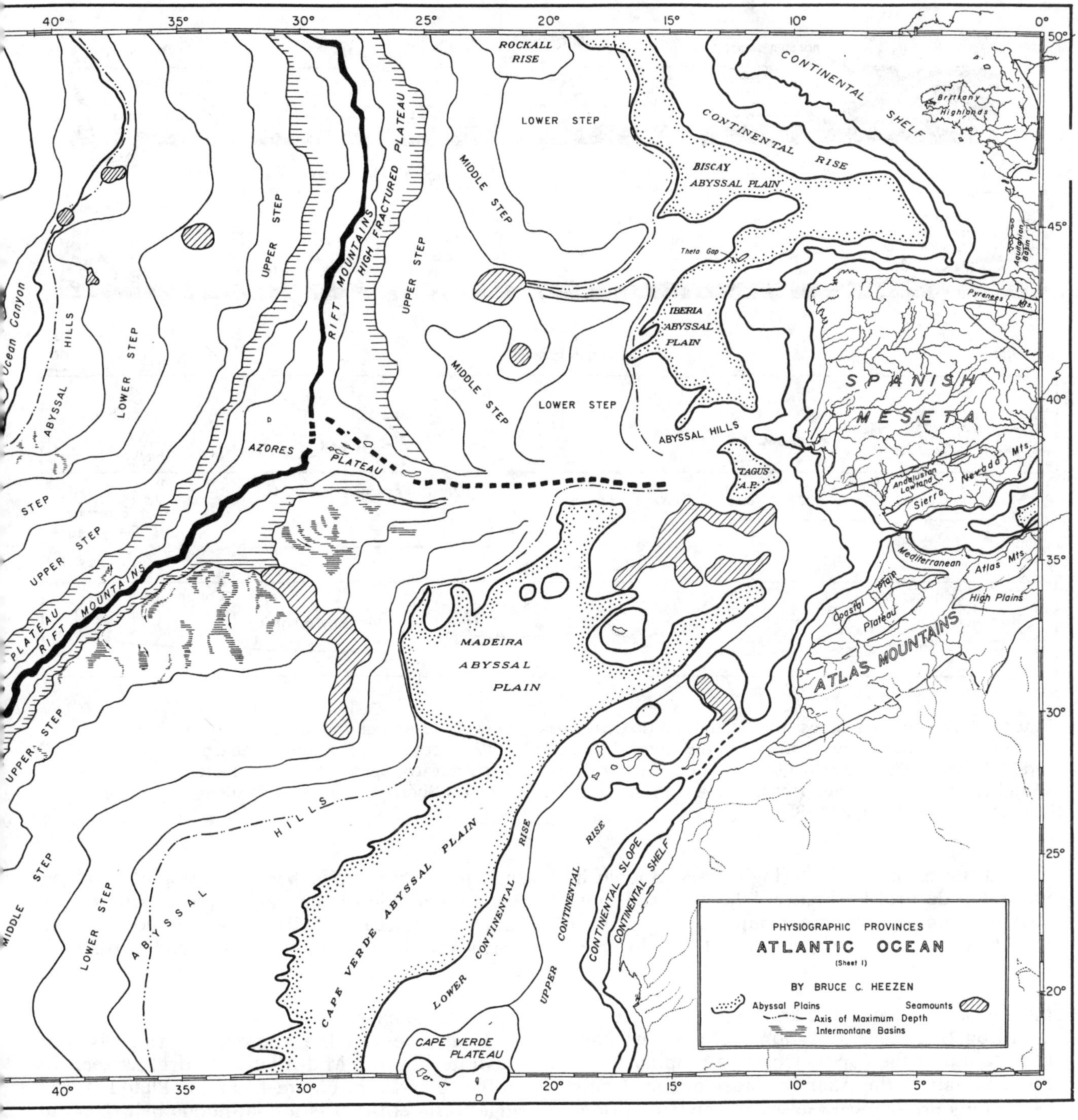

PHYSIOGRAPHIC PROVINCES
ATLANTIC OCEAN
(Sheet I)
BY BRUCE C. HEEZEN

Abyssal Plains
Seamounts
Axis of Maximum Depth
Intermontane Basins

ROCKALL RISE
LOWER STEP
MIDDLE STEP
UPPER STEP
RIFT MOUNTAINS
HIGH FRACTURED PLATEAU
CONTINENTAL SHELF
CONTINENTAL RISE
BISCAY ABYSSAL PLAIN
Theta Gap
IBERIA ABYSSAL PLAIN
ABYSSAL HILLS
TAGUS A.P.
AZORES PLATEAU
Ocean Canyon
MADEIRA ABYSSAL PLAIN
CAPE VERDE ABYSSAL PLAIN
LOWER CONTINENTAL RISE
UPPER CONTINENTAL RISE
CONTINENTAL SLOPE
CAPE VERDE PLATEAU
Brittany Highlands
Aquitanian Basin
Pyrenees Mts.
SPANISH MESETA
Andalusian Lowland
Sierra Nevada Mts.
Mediterranean Coastal Plain
Atlas Mts.
High Plains
Plateau
ATLAS MOUNTAINS

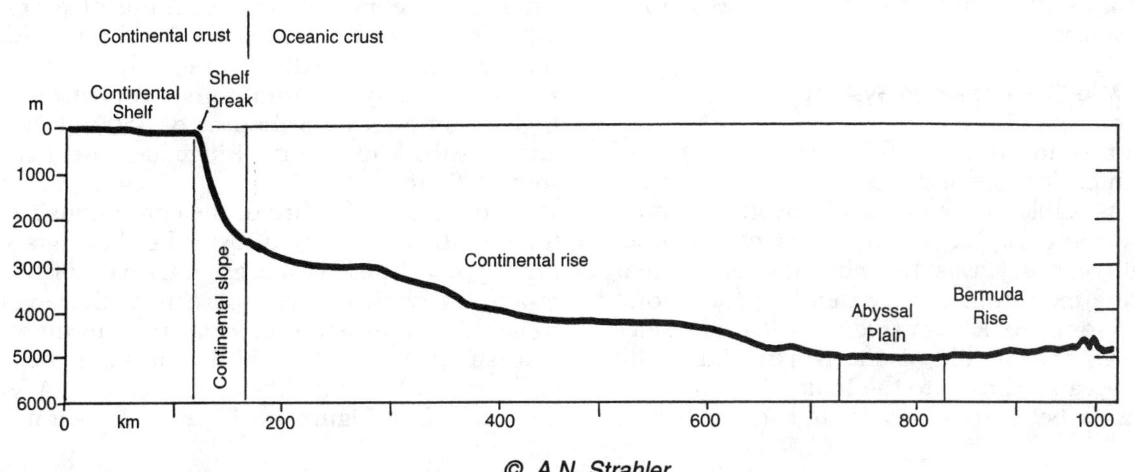

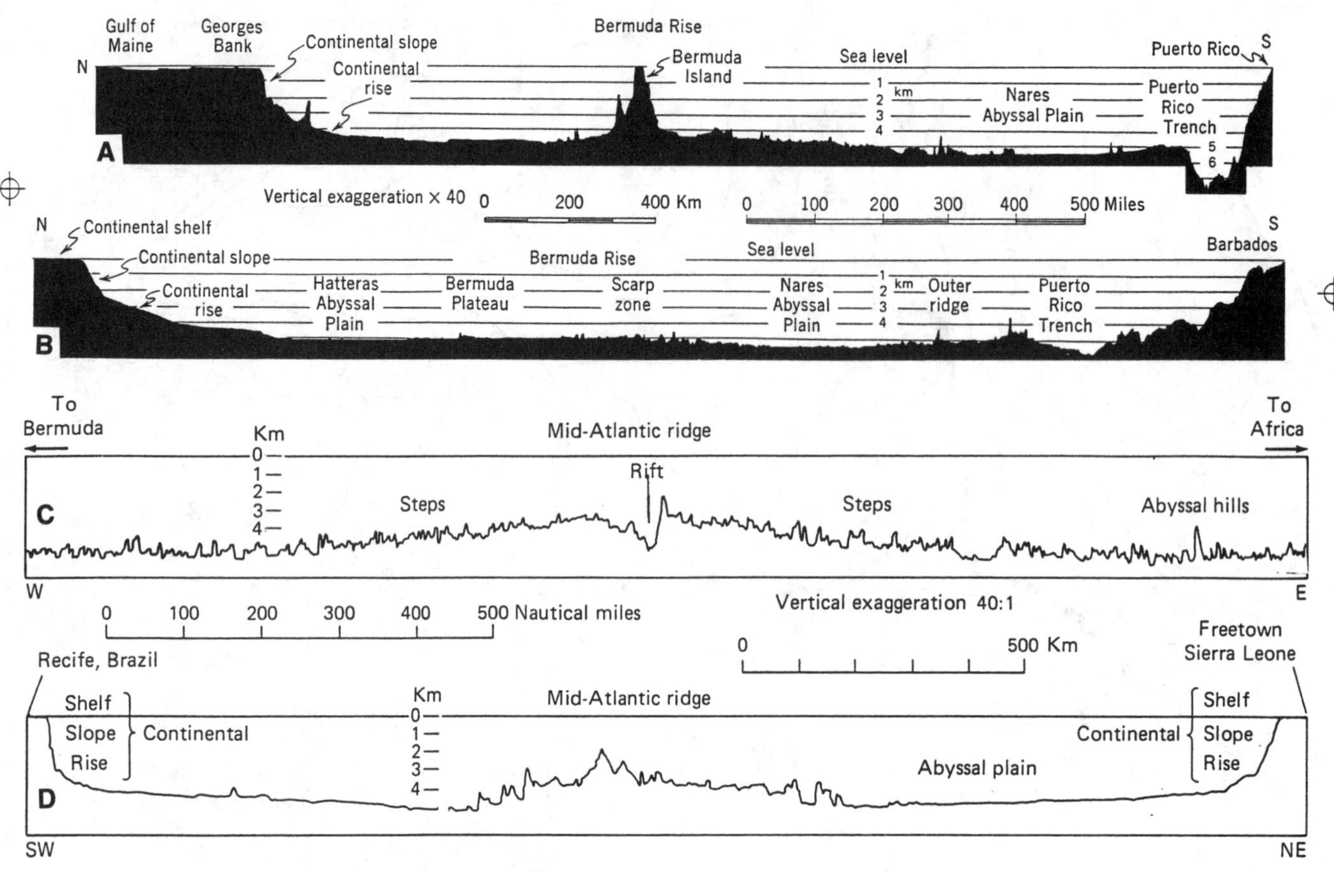

Figure 4.8 Four profiles across the North Atlantic Ocean basin showing several characteristic features of the Atlantic Ocean floor. Profiles A and B trend N-S; C and D, E-W. (From B.C. Heezen, M. Tharp, and M. Ewing, 1959, *The Floors of the Oceans*, Geological Society of America, Special Paper 65, Plates 27 and 22. Reproduced with permission of the publisher, the Geological Society of America, Boulder, Colorado USA. Copyright © 1959.)

toward the Bermuda Rise (Figure 4.6) Shown in natural-scale profile (Figure 4.9), even the most striking seamount of this group may not appear particularly impressive (few mountains do when thus presented), but its bulk is apparent when we note that the seamount rises almost 3300 m above the abyssal plain and is 40 km wide at the base.

Altogether, several hundred seamounts have been found in the Pacific Ocean, a number vastly greater than in the Atlantic. Most of the Pacific seamounts are conical and extremely steep sided (see Figure 4.28). These are identified as extinct basaltic volcanoes.

4.7 The Mid-Oceanic Ridge System

We turn now to the third of the major divisions of the ocean basins, the *mid-oceanic ridge*. One of the most remarkable of the major discoveries coming out of oceanographic explorations of the mid-twentieth century was the charting of a great submarine mountain chain extending for a total length of some 70,000 km (Figure 4.10). The ridge runs down the middle of the North and South Atlantic ocean basins, into the Indian Ocean basin, then passes between Australia and Antarctica to enter the South Pacific basin. Turning north along the eastern side of the Pacific basin, where it is named the East Pacific Rise, the ridge contacts the North American continent at the head of the Gulf of California. The mid-oceanic ridge also extends from the North Atlantic Ocean basin into the Arctic Ocean basin.

Ruggedness of the mid-oceanic ridge is well illustrated by the Mid-Atlantic Ridge, as seen in profiles C and D of Figure 4.8 and in Plate I-B. The ridge in its entirety is a continuous belt, 2000 to 2400 km wide, in which the summits of submarine hills from abyssal plains on both sides rise toward the central, or median, line, where the ridge summits reach mountainous proportions. The higher summits lie at depths of 1500 to 2000 m, and thus the Mid-Atlantic Ridge has a net height of some 3000 m.

A distinctive feature of the continuous ridge in the Atlantic basin is that instead of having a single high crest line, as many narrow continental mountain chains have, there is a characteristic trenchlike depression, or *axial rift*, running quite consistently down the mid-line of the highest part of the ridge. This rift shows well in Figure 4.3A and on profile C of Figure 4.8. Figure 4.11 is a modern

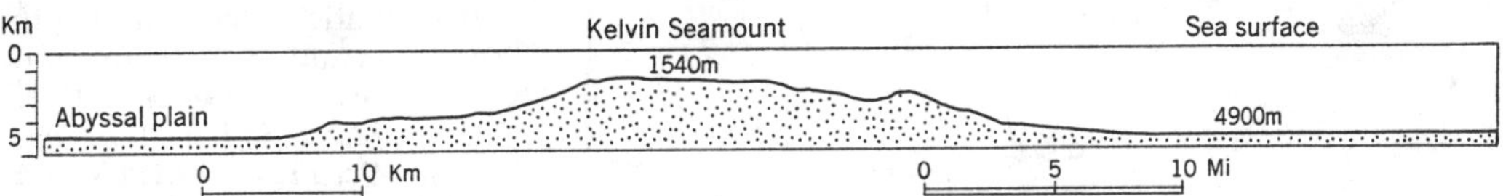

Figure 4.9 Kelvin Seamount shown in true-scale profile (After B.C. Heezen, M. Tharp, and M. Ewing, 1959, *The Floors of the Oceans*, Geological Society of America Special Paper 65, p. 77, Figure 34. Reproduced with permission of the publisher, the Geological Society of America, Boulder, Colorado USA. Copyright © 1959.)

outline map showing a large part of the Mid-Atlantic Ridge. The ridge is segmented in to many parts by what may appear to be transforms (strike-slip faults). [These features are explained on later pages.]

The axial rift of the Mid-Atlantic Ridge was discovered in 1955 by Marie Tharp while she was plotting E-W transverse profiles of the ridge for her new topographic diagram of the sea floor, a portion of which is shown in Plate I-B. Deep V-notches in three consecutive profiles of the ridge summit were obviously displaying a continuous V-shaped north-south valley. Landforms of this kind strongly suggested a pulling apart of the crust. Heezen supported this interpretation, but it was not published until 1956. Tharp also made the crucial discovery that on a world map showing the epicenters of earthquakes, the locations of shallow-depth earthquakes coincided with known sections of the Mid-Atlantic Ridge, and some even fell within the central rift. Because crustal fracturing, an active tectonic process, must generate earthquakes, epicenters of those earthquakes could be used to trace the mid-oceanic ridge over its entire global extent, whether the topography had been explored or not. Tharp later wrote about this deduction:

> Heezen recognized this correlation of a central valley and earthquakes as a valid one. Using earthquake epicenters where there were no soundings, plotting of the position of the valley was continued about the globe. The extension of the valley into the Gulf of Aden and southward into the rift valley of East Africa finally convinced Heezen in mid-1953 that the Mid-Oceanic Rift valley was a globe encircling, tensional feature throughout its 70,000 kilometers length. (1982, p. 22)

This discovery of a correlation of earthquakes with the axial rift did, indeed, present independent

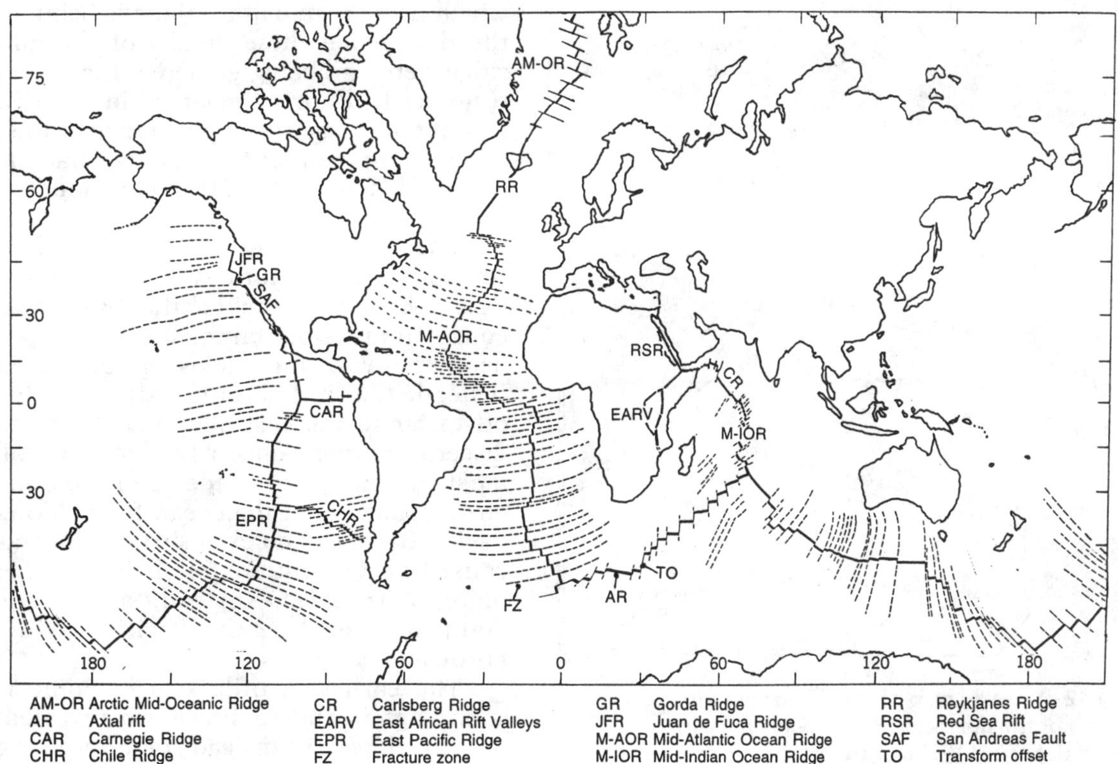

Figure 4.10 Generalized map of the mid-oceanic ridge system and related major fracture zones. (Copyright © by Arthur N. Strahler.)

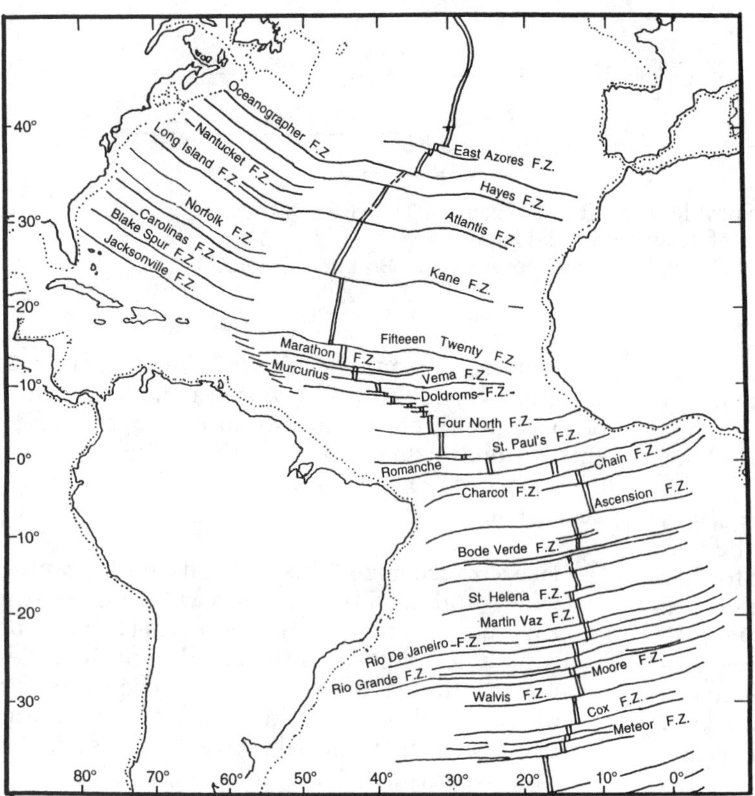

Figure 4.11 A modern map of of the Mid-Atlantic Ridge outlining the ridge segments and the "fracture zones" that extend away from it.(Simplified from map of *Magnetic Lineations of the Earth's Ocean Basins*,1989, compiled by S.C. Cande, et al, Copyright 1989 by the American Association of Petroleum Geologists. All rights reserved.)

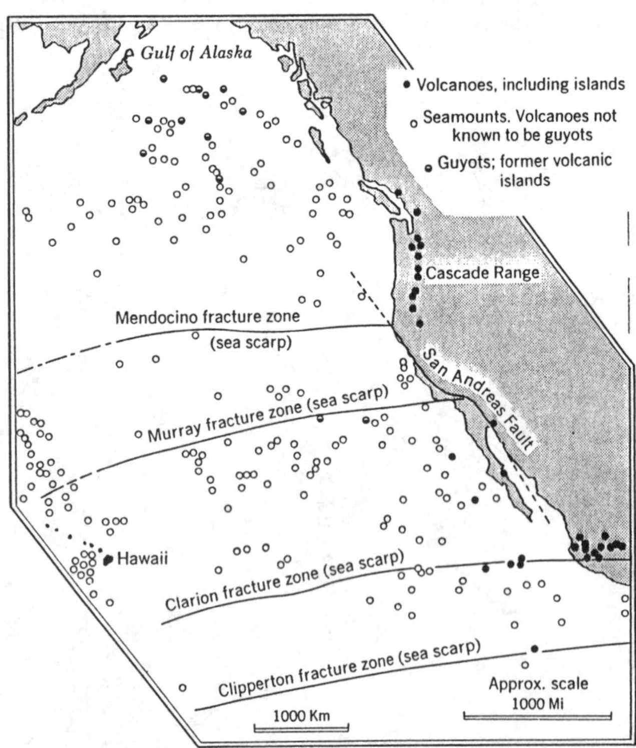

Figure 4.12 An early map of fracture zones and seamounts of the northeast Pacific Ocean basin. (Based on data of H.W. Menard. After J.A. Jacobs, R.D. Russell, and J.T. Wilson, 1959, *Physics and Geology*, New York, McGraw-Hill, p. 273, Figure 12-18. Used by permission.)

proof that the axial rift is a site of crustal faulting of one kind or another. Today, we recognize the axial rift as a spreading plate boundary along which new oceanic lithosphere is being formed. At the time when these details of the mid-oceanic ridge were just being gathered, the theory of plate tectonics had not yet emerged in its present form. Despite the suggestive appearance of the axial rift, strong independent evidence had not been marshalled in the 1950s to demonstrate active seafloor spreading.

The floor of the Pacific Ocean basin offers some important contrasts with that of the Atlantic Ocean basin. In the Pacific basin there is no conspicuous mountainous axial ridge centered neatly between the enclosing continental coasts. Instead, the mid-oceanic ridge is a broad rise, offset far to the east of the center line. Even to discern the ridge, one has to look carefully on the most recent maps made from remote sensing terrain imagery of the ocean floor. Moreover, the Pacific Basin has no extensive continental margins consisting of continental shelf devoid of active plate boundaries. Instead, active subduction boundaries enclose the Pacific basin on west, north, and east sides.

The earliest profile sets of sonic reflection soundings in the Pacific basin revealed no mid-oceanic ridge, but instead some very long, sharply defined narrow ridges, or escarpments, trending east-west across the ocean floor. These ridges are nearly parallel to one another and are broadly

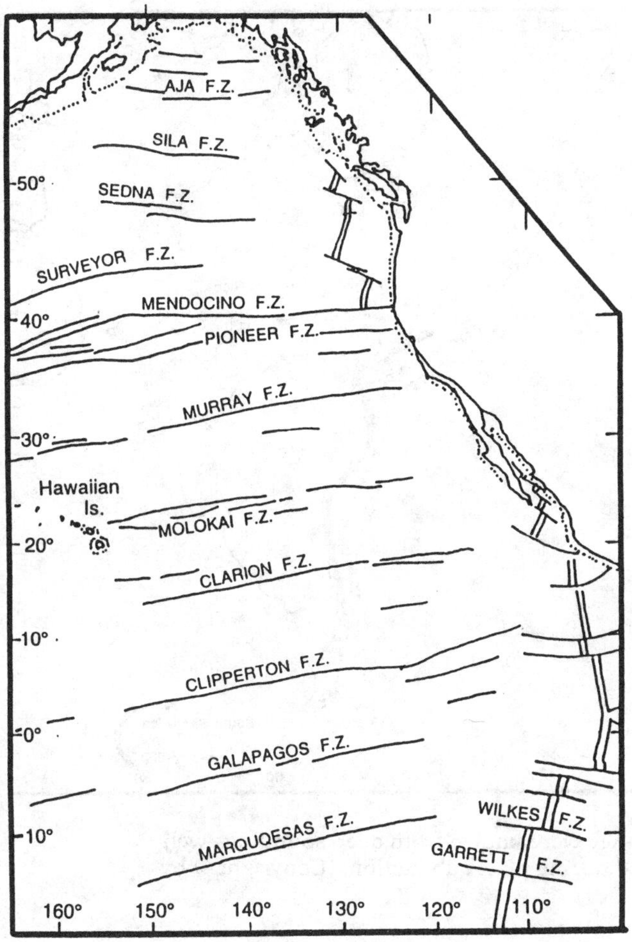

Figure 4.13 A modern map of of the northeast Pacific basin outlining the ridge segments and the "fracture zones" that extend away from it.(Simplified from map of *Magnetic Lineations of the Earth's Ocean Basins*,1989, compiled by S.C. Cande, et al, Copyright 1989 by the American Association of Petroleum Geologists. All rights reserved.)

curved in plan, approximating small circles with a common pole. Such were the findings made by Menard and his Scripps Institution colleagues in the series of exploratory voyages starting in 1950. Focusing attention on what is now the Mendocino ridge on the 40th parallel north, they made several crossings and recrossings with the echo sounder. What they learned was that this strange feature was "a low asymmetrical ridge tilted south, a narrow trough, a steep scarp 6,000 feet high, a ridge tilted north, and a low swale, and ended up in a relatively shallow region" (Menard, 1986, p. 59). Upon their return to San Diego, the press announced that the scientists had found a new kind of sea-floor "mountain range." In coauthorship with Dietz, Menard published a report of their findings in the May 1952 issue of the *Journal of Geology* (Menard and Dietz, 1952). Continued years of sonic surveying revealed an entire set of parallel ridges, but with considerable variation in form and height and in the depth of the abyssal sea-floor from which they rose. Figure 4.12 is a map made in the early 1950s showing four of the ridges mapped by Menard's group. (Notice that there is no hint of a mid-oceanic ridge.) At that time, a leading hypothesis was that the ridges are fault structures of some sort, hence earning the name "fracture zone" (FZ), a practice that persists today. These ridges are aseismic, except where a segment of the ridge is an active transform fault.

"Fracture zone" ridges were not at first noticed in the Atlantic Ocean basin, because the rugged topography of the Mid-Atlantic Ridge obscures their presence. It was, however, soon found that the axial rift is broken into many segments, the ends of which appear to be offset along transverse fault lines (Figure 4.11). This arrangement of offset segments is particularly striking in the equatorial zone of the Atlantic Ocean, where a single offset displaces the main axial rift by as much as 600 km. Later, the "fracture zones" extending far out from the ridge offsets were identified and found to extend both east and west to the limits of the abyssal sea floor. Their extent is clearly shown in Figure 4.11.

Today we recognize that only short sections of "fracture zones"—those located between offset ends of the axial ridge—are true transform faults marking sections of the active boundary between lithospheric plates. Moreover, the "fracture zones" typically extend many hundreds of kilometers out on either side of the offset ends of the axial rift. For example, in the eastern North Pacific basin, "fracture zones" over 5000 km long extend from points close to the west coast of North America to as far west as the Hawaiian islands (Figure 4.13). In Chapter 7, we interpret these "fracture zones" as crustal features formed at the ends of the transform faults, where volcanic activity is continuously building up a lengthening embankment.

4.8 Trenches and Island Arcs

So far, our description of landforms of the ocean floors has been limited to basins bounded by tectonically stable continental margins. Another class of ocean-floor landforms is associated with active subduction zones, where plates are being consumed as they dive into the asthenosphere.

The deepest points on the ocean floors occur in long, narrow *trenches*, also referred to as *foredeeps*, commonly with maximum depths of 7500 to 9000 m (Figure 4.14). Almost invariably, the trenches lie immediately adjacent to and on the oceanward side of submarine ridges—the *island arcs*—or close to coastal mountain ranges of the continental margins—the *mountain arcs*.

Deep trenches virtually surround the deep Pacific Ocean basin floor on three sides: east, north, and west. Trenches of the western North Pacific are particularly striking. Deepest of all may be the Marianas Trench, where a record depth of 11,033 m has been measured. At least five other Pacific trenches have maximum depths over 10,000 m. These trenches have widths of 40 to 120 km and lengths of 500 to over 4500 km. Longest of

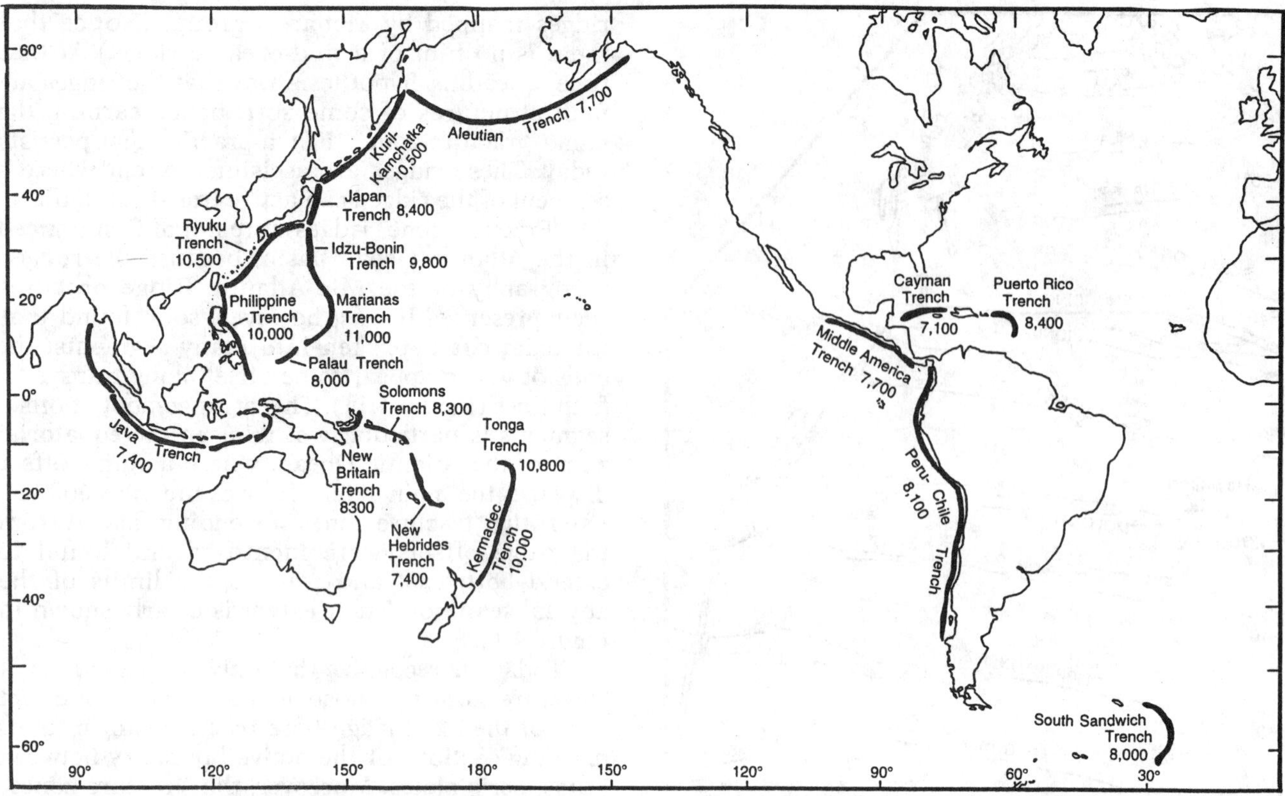

Figure 4.14 Simplified map of the major ocean trenches as they were known from deep soundings well before the theory of plate tectonics explained them as formed during plate subduction. (Copyright © by Arthur N. Strahler.)

all is the Peru-Chile Trench, off the west coast of South America, extending for 5900 km (Plate I-C). It is particularly striking because of the proximity and great height of the Andes range, a volcanic mountain arc that lies only a short distance to the east.

In Chapter 1 we explained volcanic island arcs and mountain arcs as built by magma rising from sources close to the upper surfaces of downbent plate margins plunging into the asthenosphere. By far the greatest development of volcanic island arcs is along the northern and western sides of the Pacific Ocean basin (Figure 4.14). The Aleutian Islands form a great volcanic arc adjacent to the Aleutian Trench. Multiple arcs characterize the western Pacific basin between Japan and New Guinea. Yet another great arc-trench system runs through the Indonesian islands of Sumatra and Java, bordered on the south by the curving Java Trench.

In the western Pacific region of multiple arcs, small but deep ocean basins lie between a given arc and the continental mainland, or between two island arcs. These small ocean basins are called *backarc basins*. One example is the Sea of Japan, between the Japan arc and the Asiatic mainland; another is the basin lying west of the Marianas arc but east of the Ryukyu arc (Figure 4.14).

The wide range of classes of landforms that make up the abyssal floors of the oceans implies varied formative processes. Some features are obviously related to active plate boundaries and are either tectonic or volcanic in origin. Others are related to the erosion of the seafloor or the accumulation of sediments.

4.9 Probing the Ocean Floor

Since the 1870s, oceanographers have taken samples of materials from the ocean floors. At first this could be done only by means of dredges that scraped off a thin layer and brought it to the surface for examination.

By the 1930s, information about the sediment layer as a stratigraphic entity began to be obtained by the process of *coring*, which is simply vertical penetration by a long section of pipe that cuts a cylindrical sample, or *core*. The method is called *piston coring*. Brought to the surface, the core is extruded and gives a complete cross section of the layer. Cores up to 30 m long are readily obtained, then cut in half longitudinally, revealing the bedded structure and permitting small interior samples to be taken for microscopic examination and chemical and physical analysis.

A great advance in deep sampling of the sediment of the ocean floor came in the late 1960s through the use of oil-well drilling methods. The drilling equipment was mounted on a special 10,000-ton vessel, the *Glomar Challenger*, built with the capability of drilling into the ocean floor to a depth of 750 m, in water depths as great as 7000

m. Not only could the drill pass through a sediment layer, but it could obtain cores of the solid crustal rock beneath.

Glomar Challenger looked like an oil-drilling rig, mounted on an ordinary ship's hull. The drilling rig was like other land-based oil rigs, but the hull was unlike that of a typical commercial vessel. The difference lies in an elaborate positioning mechanism, by means of which a vessel can maintain its exact position during the laborious job of drilling. Four motors stabilize the drilling vessel by directing water jets from tunnels in the hull. They are computer-controlled and respond instantly to the pitching and rolling motions the vessel experiences in heavy seas. A flexible drill string is capable of accommodating a considerable motion of the platform. It is even possible for the drill to be withdrawn, the bit replaced, and the hole again found and penetrated.

Called the most successful scientific expedition in the history of science, the long voyage of the *Glomar Challenger* that began in 1968 enabled scientists to probe the floor of every ocean except the Arctic. Hundreds of holes were drilled and over 50,000 m of core samples recovered. In these cores are found a historical record of the sediments of the ocean basins undreamed of a few decades ago.

The program of the *Glomar Challenger* was at first under the supervision of the Deep Sea Drilling Project (DSDP) of the National Science Foundation. The costs ran to some $10 million per year, but the scientific results made the outlay seem a bargain. After seven years of operation, the program of *Glomar Challenger* entered a new phase. Although international participation had always been included in DSDP, 1976 saw the beginning of the International Phase of Ocean Drilling (IPOD), with regular staff representations from the Soviet Union, France, Great Britain, Japan, and West Germany. Each nation pledged to contribute $1 million annually to the IPOD operating budget.

With the change to an international scientific program, the drilling program was redirected to concentrate upon deep holes penetrating hundreds of meters into the basaltic crust—a remarkable feat where the ocean water is 4000 m deep.

In 1985, after 15 years of service, the aging *Glomar Challenger* was replaced by the *JOIDES Resolution*, a much larger and stronger vessel. Its program had been renamed as the Ocean Drilling Program (ODP). Carrying double the complement of scientists, a longer drill string, and using its capability to perform in both arctic and antarctic waters where sea ice had been a problem, the *Resolution* embarked upon a long series of highly rewarding legs. In 1987, Leg 118 succeeded in coring a long section of olivine-rich gabbro belonging to the top of the upper mantle. It was taken from a 500-m hole drilled in an uplifted block along the Atlantic II Fracture Zone in the Southwest Indian Ridge. Although a 2-km-deep hole was drilled in the eastern Pacific Ocean, it failed to achieve the elusive goal of coring into the gabbroic layer of the upper mantle beneath a normal deep section of oceanic crust.

An important step forward during the ODP program was the introduction of a new technique of gaining information about the rock record held in the walls of the drill hole (Pezard and Lovell, 1990, p. 709). It is a high-resolution electrical imaging system, named Formation Micro-Scanner (FMS), developed by the Schlumberger Corporation especially for the ODP, and first used in 1989. Fine details of such structures as graded bedding of turbidites, for example, are recorded with remarkable clarity. These records are particularly valuable in filling information gaps where a drill core has not been recovered intact.

4.10 Seismic Reflection Profiles

A different type of information about the sediments of the ocean floors comes from application of the *seismic reflection* principle. In a manner somewhat like that of the precision depth recorder, the impulse from a small explosion is sent to the ocean bottom and reflected from the bottom and from layered structures below the bottom. As in the case of the echo sounder, the returning waves are picked up by a hydrophone and recorded on paper. In a *seismic profiler traverse*, explosions or other forms of sudden energy release are made at ten-second intervals along the line of the ship's course, and a profile results showing the contact of sediment with bedrock, as well as certain reflecting horizons within the sediment. The method was developed in the mid-1960s by Professor Maurice Ewing, John E. Ewing, and co-workers of the staff of the Lamont-Doherty Geological Observatory. Seismic reflection profiling soon began to yield a remarkably clear picture of the distribution and thickness of the sediment layer over the ocean floors.

One type of sediment accumulation, seen on both flanks of the mid-oceanic ridge with its strong relief, is *ponding* of sediment in isolated topographic basins (Figure 4.15). Notice that sediment is lacking near the ridge axis but thickens outward toward the flanks, where sediment thicknesses up to 500 to 600 m are present.

A different type of sediment accumulation is shown in Figure 4.16. Here the ocean floor is a smooth abyssal plain at a depth of over 5000 m, grading eastward into the rising flank of the Mid-Atlantic Ridge. The sediment accumulation, over 3000 m thick in places, forms a continuous blanket (Ewing, Ludwig, and Ewing, 1964).

Seismic reflection profiles taken in the late 1960s began to provide valuable new information on tectonic processes in trench floors. Figure 4.17 compares a section of the Peru-Chile trench barren of sediments (A) with a section partly filled with

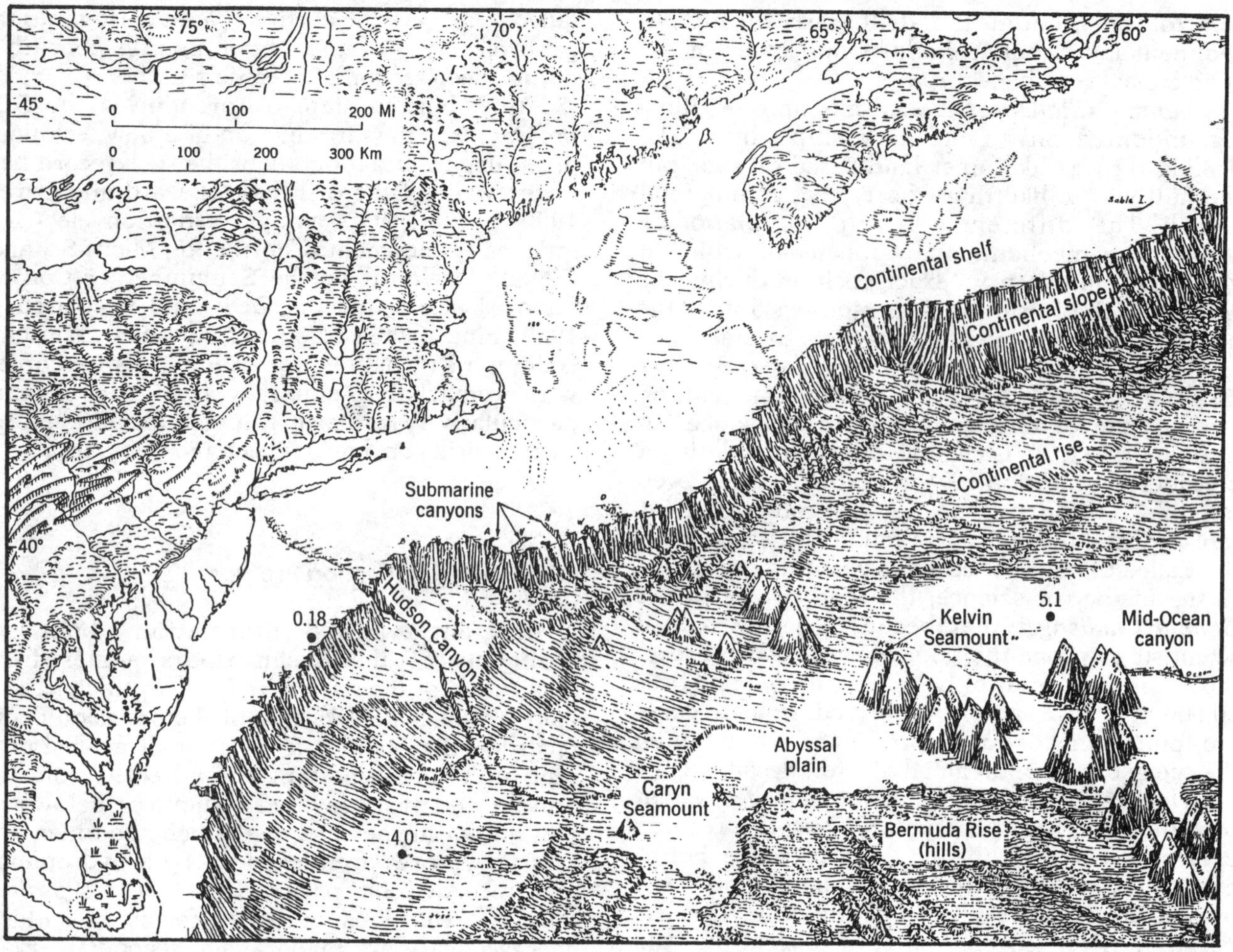

75°
70°
65°
60°
45°
40°
0 100 200 Mi
0 100 200 300 Km
Sable I.
Continental shelf
Continental slope
Continental rise
Submarine canyons
Hudson Canyon
0.18
5.1
Kelvin Seamount
Mid-Ocean canyon
Abyssal plain
Caryn Seamount
Bermuda Rise (hills)
4.0

Diagram A The ocean floor adjacent to the North American Continental Shelf.

0 100 200 Mi
0 100 200 300 Km

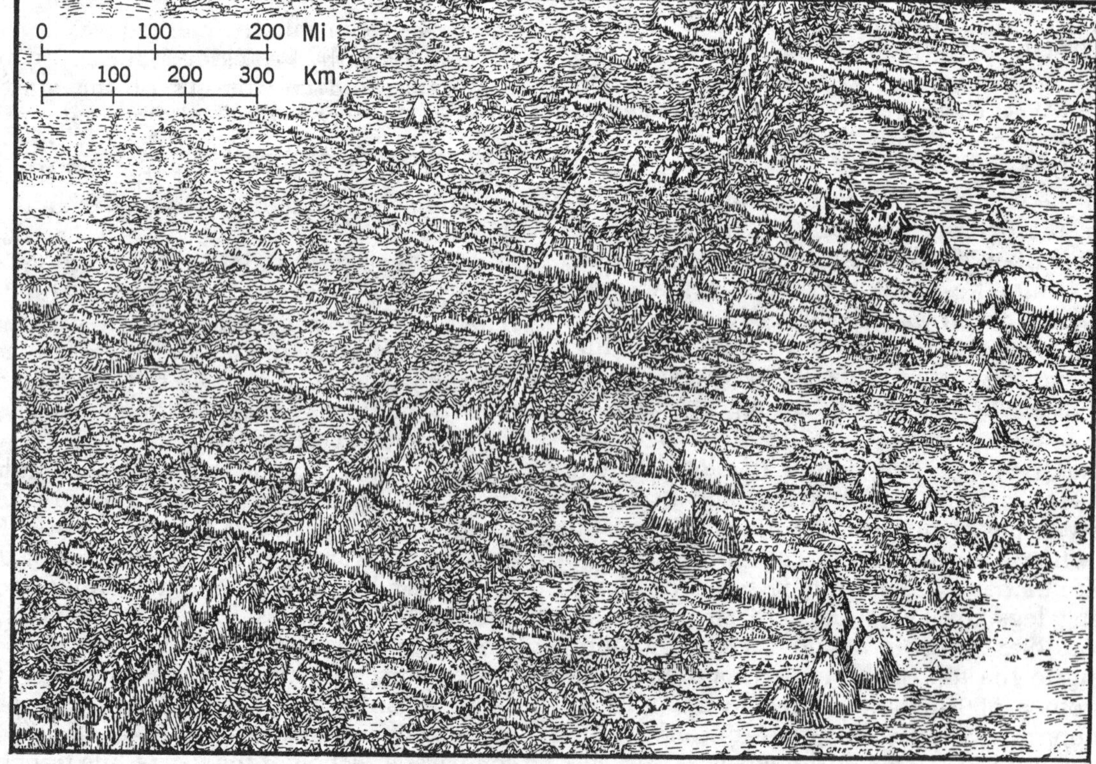

Diagram B. Relief features along the Mid-Atlantic Ridge in the vicinity of the Azores Islands.

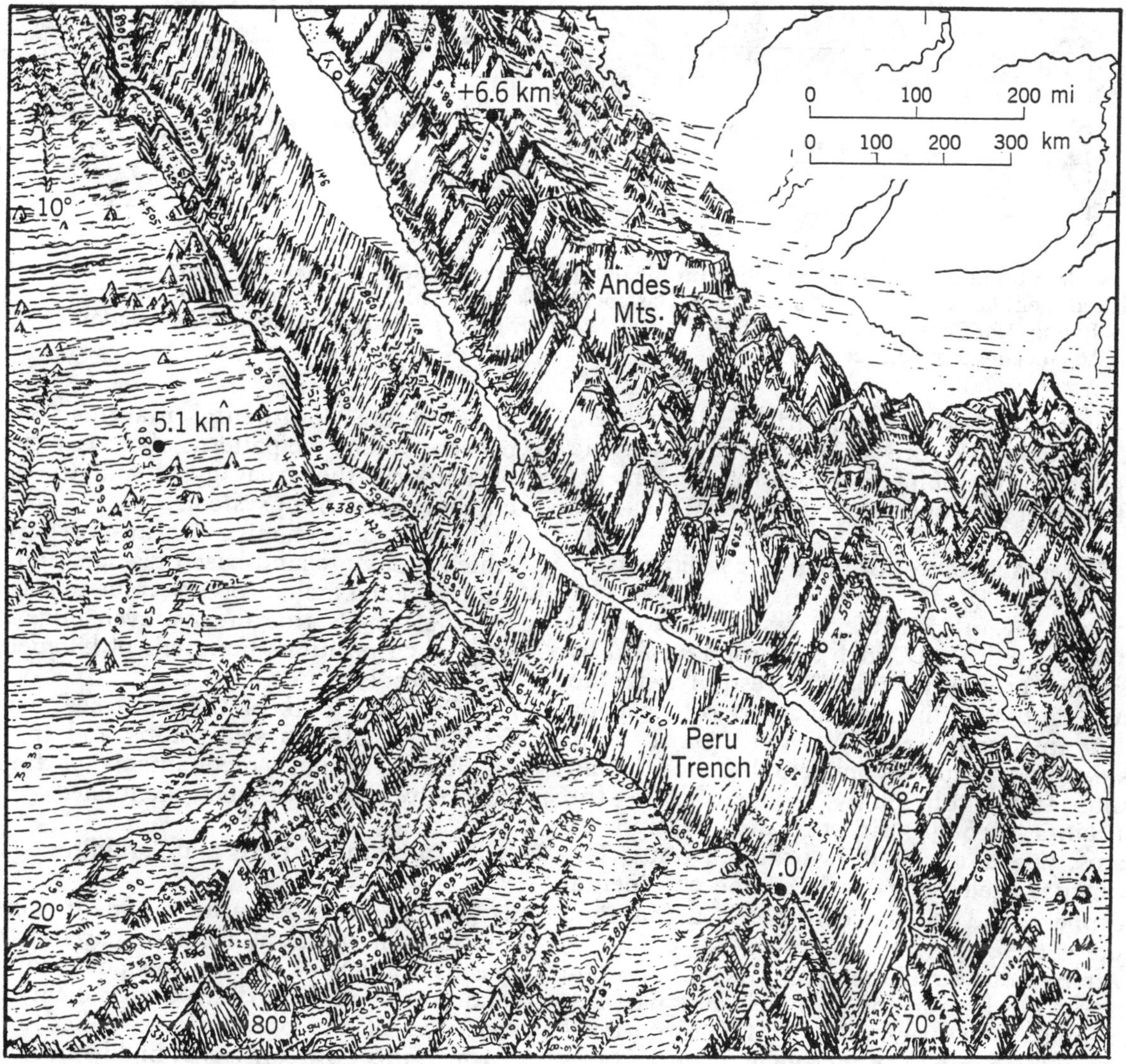

Diagram C The Peru-Chile Trench, off the west coast of South America.

PLATE I

We have selected three portions of the *Physiographic Diagram of the Oceans*, drawn by Marie Tharp of the Lamont-Doherty Observatory of Columbia University. A separate map was drawn for each of the major oceans. The set of six maps was completed and revised during the period from 1957 through 1971 (Tharp, 1982, p. 22-23). The raw data consisted of sound echoes produced by the precision depth recorder, and these were obtained by Bruce Heezen and other marine scientists from ships at sea.

Working together, Tharp and Heezen adopted a system of landscape depiction similar to that developed by Armin K. Lobeck and Erwin Raisz in preparing terrain maps during WW-II. Slopes and summits are rendered in stylized three-dimensional forms,using a strong vertical exaggeration. This graphic device made it possible for the first time ever for humans to visualize the unseen landscape of about two-thirds of the earth's solid surface.

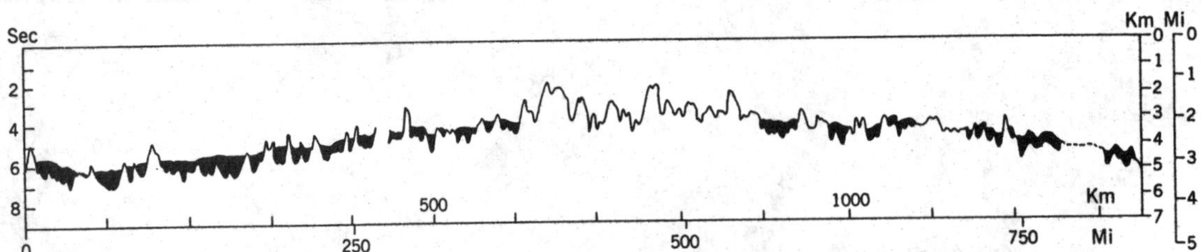

Figure 4.15 A tracing of a seismic reflection profile obliquely crossing the Mid-Atlantic Ridge at about 40° N. Sediment deposits shown in solid black. Basement rock (bedrock) lies beneath. (After J. Ewing and M. Ewing, 1967, *Science*, v. 156, p. 1591, Figure 2. Used by permission of the American Association for the Advancement of Science.)

near-horizontal layers of terrestrial sediments (B). In Chapter 8 (Figure 8.3) we show seismic reflection profiles of intensely deformed sediments in a trench of the Sunda arc in Indonesia.

4.11 Terrestrial Sources of Deep-Sea Sediments

There are several possible terrestrial sources of deep-ocean sediments, such as those revealed by the seismic profiler method. "Terrestrial" refers to sources on the continental land surfaces or along continental coastlines. We will omit from consideration the thick continental-shelf sediment accumulations obviously derived from the continents through direct transportation by streams, waves, and shallow-water currents. The continental shelf wedge rests on the continental lithosphere and can be considered a marginal feature of the continent.

Atmospheric circulation provides an important transport mechanism for extremely fine particles from lands to the deep oceans. Mineral particles are raised high into the atmosphere by dust storms in the tropical deserts in latitudes 10° to 30° north and south. High-level tropical easterly winds carry these particles far westward over the adjacent oceans, where they may settle to the ocean surface or may be carried down in raindrops. Another important source of atmospheric dusts is from volcanic eruptions, emitting minute shards of volcanic glass. The vaporization of comets and meteors in the upper atmosphere also contributes dust particles.

Transport by surface ocean currents is an obvious means for the wide distribution of very fine suspended particles derived from sources close to the continental margins. Suspended particles follow the patterns of oceanic circulation, particularly the great gyres and the Antarctic circumpolar current system.

A related mechanism is transport by icebergs, which break off land-based glaciers and float far out to sea and melt, dropping mineral fragments of many sizes. By this means, even huge boulders may reach positions hundreds of kilometers from the nearest land.

The great bulk of the thick sediment layers found beneath abyssal plains and in trenches requires transport mechanisms of far greater capability than those so far mentioned.

4.12 Turbidity Currents and Turbidites

By far the most capable sediment-transporting mechanism operating in many parts of the ocean basins is a type of current flow powered by gravity and flowing directly down the gradient of sloping portions of the ocean floor. Called a *turbidity current*, this flow consists of highly turbid (muddy) water moving swiftly in a long, narrow tongue. A turbidity current requires a source mass of soft sediment occupying a high position at the brink of a steep submarine slope. Collapse of a mass of sediment causes it to become a turbid liquid (process of liquefaction) with a density greater than the surrounding clear seawater. Under the force of gravity, the denser mixture moves directly downslope, as a tongue, to reach an adjacent seafloor plain or depression where the turbid water spreads out into a thin sheet and comes to rest.

The turbidity current is just one variety of *density current*, a class that includes any gravity-

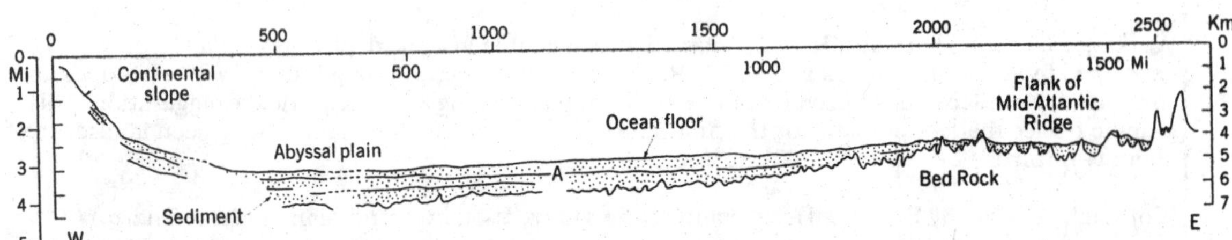

Figure 4.16 Sketch of seismic reflection profile of the Argentine Basin of the South Atlantic, off Buenos Aires at latitude 36°-38° S. (After M. Ewing, W.J. Ludwig, and J.I. Ewing, 1964, *Jour. of Geophysical Res.*, v. 69, p. 2011. Figure 6. Used by permission of the American Geophysical Union.)

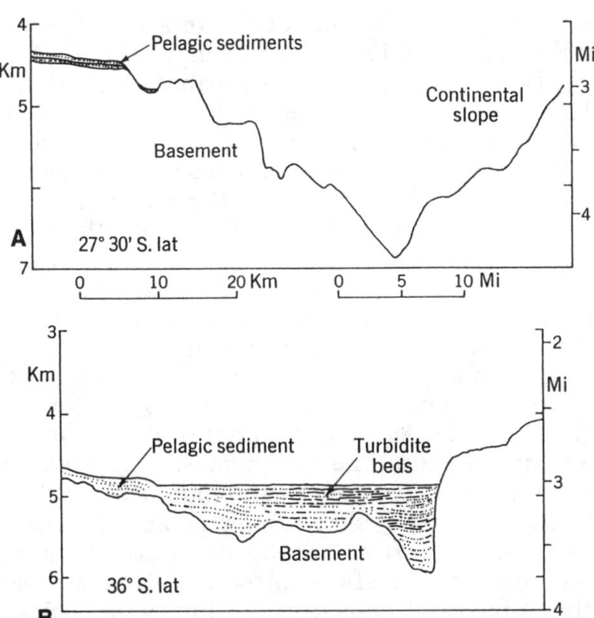

Figure 4.17 Sketches of seismic reflection profiles of two sections of the Peru-Chile Trench. (A) Barren trench. (B) partially filled trench. (After D.W. Scholl, R. von Huene, and J.B. Ridlon, 1968, *Science*, v., 159, p. 870, Figure 2. Used by permission of the American Association for the Advancement of Science.)

powered current of a denser fluid flowing to lower levels beneath a less dense fluid. Turbidity currents repeatedly occur from the same source areas and their deposits accumulate in numerous thin sheets to reach great total thicknesses. In the accumulation process, hills or other topographic irregularities of the bedrock surface are gradually buried until ultimately an abyssal plain is formed. The sediments thus accumulated are classified as *turbidites*.

The deposit of a single turbidity-current flow is represented by a distinctive unit layer of sediment called a *turbidite*. Within this turbidite is an arrangement of layers changing in texture from coarse at the bottom to fine at the top. Typically, the basal zone of the turbidite also shows a distinctive particle size arrangement known as *graded bedding*, characterized by a continuous upward reduction in grain size that may range from coarse sand or gravel to fine sand. The arrangement is illustrated in Figure 4.18. You can simulate graded bedding in the laboratory by placing a clean mixture of fine pebbles, coarse and fine sand, and coarse silt in a tall glass cylinder filled with water. Upend the cylinder and shake it vigorously, then allow it to stand upright. The rain of particles reaching the base of the container will be assorted in the same manner as in graded bedding. Above the basal graded zone, the typical turbidite consists of sand in parallel and rippled laminations. Close to the top is fine sandy to silty clay. The topmost layer is made up of clay-size particles.

As a turbidity current advances, it passes over the soft clay layer that forms the top of the previous turbidity current deposit. The force of the fresh turbulent current digs into the soft clay bed, creating distinctive *scour marks*. On a bedding surface, these appear as elongate cuplike or troughlike indentation. The scour marks are later filled by coarse sediment of the bottom zone of the next turbidity-current deposit. Much later, after the entire turbidite sequence has become lithified and finally exposed as an outcrop on the continental surface, the molds of scour marks appear on the undersides of the coarse sandy beds as *sole marks*. Geologists use scour marks and related current-formed features to determine the direction of the flow of ancient turbidity currents.

Turbidity currents were first recognized in connection with submarine canyons of the Atlantic continental slope of North America, mentioned earlier in this chapter (see Figure 4.6). These remarkable gully-like features score the continental slopes surrounding the Atlantic and Indian ocean basins in large numbers and have attracted the curiosity of geologists for decades. Figure 4.19 is a block diagram of the Baltimore and Wilmington canyons, along with intervening branching canyons and gullies, carefully constructed from data obtained in 1984 by the GLORIA sidescan sonar system (McGregor, 1984, p. 276). Most geologists now consider it quite unlikely that these features could have been carved by terrestrial streams, so they have sought an explanation in processes taking place within the oceans. Turbidity currents formed from softened and disintegrated shelf sediment are considered a major agent in carving the canyons and their tributary gullies. This activity was probably concentrated in interglacial stages when sealevel was substantially lowered.

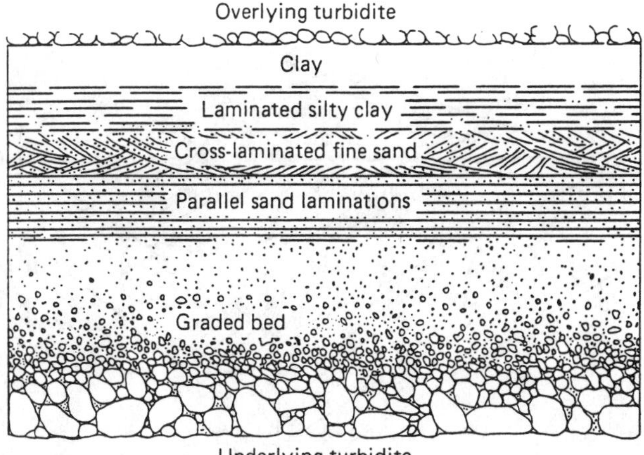

Figure 4.18 A schematic cross section through a single turbidite showing the typical structure. Above the basal layer of graded bedding are laminated sand and silt layers, topped by a clay layer. (Copyright © by Arthur N. Strahler.)

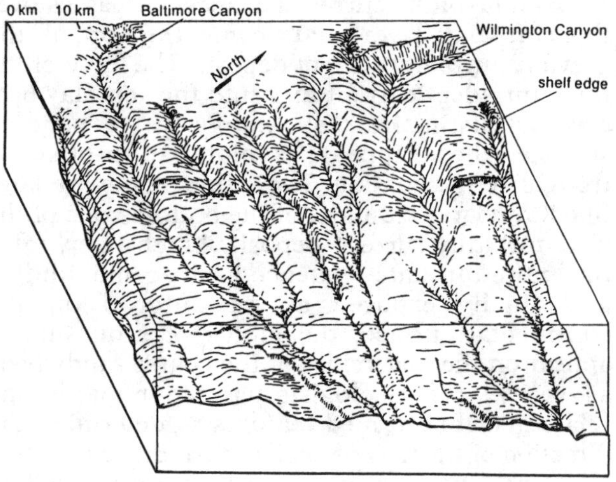

Figure 4.19 Terrain drawing of a section of the Atlantic continental slope showing the Baltimore and Delaware submarine canyons and intervening canyon-and-gully systems. (From B.A. McGregor, 1984, *American Scientist*, v. 72, p. 276, Figure 2. Used by permission of Sigma Xi The Scientific Research Association.)

It remained for a chance earthquake to set off a chain of events that could document a single turbidity current in action. In 1929, a turbidity current crossing the continental slope and rise off the Grand Banks of Newfoundland was sufficiently powerful to break in succession several transatlantic cables lying in its path. From a knowledge of the exact time each cable broke, Bruce Heezen and Maurice Ewing determined the velocity of the turbidity current, which was found to have decreased from 100 km per hour where the bottom gradient was 1 in 170, to 23 km per hour where the gradient was only 1 in 2000. The turbidity current was set off by the earthquake shock, causing unconsolidated sediments of the continental slope to lose strength and to mix with seawater to produce a highly turbid suspension. The turbid tongue ultimately spread out upon the abyssal plain, forming a layer of sediment averaging 1 m thickness over an area of perhaps 200,000 sq km (Heezen and Ewing, 1954).

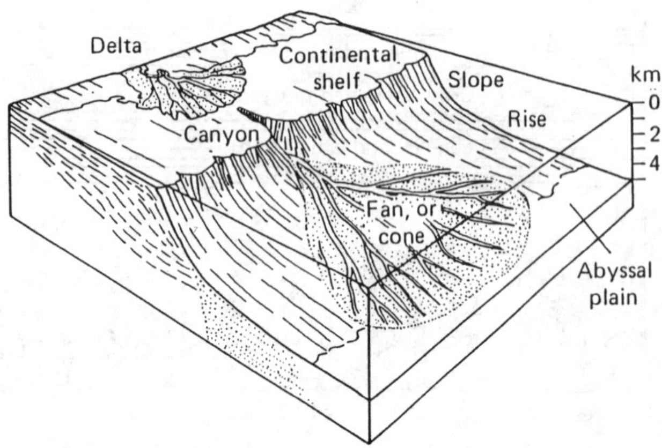

Figure 4.20 Block diagram of a deep-sea fan formed at the base of a continental slope and extending far out upon the deep ocean floor. (Copyright © by Arthur N. Strahler.)

Deltas of major rivers contribute exceptionally large amounts of sediment to the continental shelf on which they emerge. A major submarine canyon is often present, representing a seaward extension of the river channel across the outer shelf. For example, both the Hudson River and the Congo River have major submarine canyons. Sediment carried by turbidity currents from the steep outer slopes of the continental shelf in the vicinity of the river delta build a *submarine fan* (or *submarine cone*) that slopes gently away from the base of the continental slope for many hundreds of kilometers (Figure 4.20). At the outer limit of the fan may lie an abyssal plain. The two greatest submarine fans are those of the Ganges-Brahmaputra and Indus rivers. Figure 4.21 shows outline maps of these two fans. Also important are the Mississippi River fan, built out upon the floor of the Gulf of Mexico, and the Amazon River fan. Turbidity deposits of submarine fans are from several hundreds to a few thousand meters thick. These great fans seem not to be undergoing sediment deposition today, since turbid river water from river floods does not extend seaward out over the fans. This observation indicates that the fans were built during interglacial stages when sea level was much lower (Gibbs, 1981, p. 78).

4.13 Mid-Ocean Deep-sea Channels

A most remarkable flow-channel phenomenon of the abyssal ocean floor was discovered in the early 1950s as a product of extended reflection profile exploration (Heezen, Tharp, and Ewing, 1959, p. 66). First named a *mid-ocean canyon* (and subsequently changed to *mid-ocean channel*), it was identified as a narrow channel on the extremely flat North Atlantic floor that lies east of Newfoundland and the Maritime Provinces; it extends roughly from lat. 55°N. to 35°N. As Figure 4.22 shows, the channel was drawn to link up to the north with a large converging system of submarine canyons on the continental slopes of Newfoundland and Greenland. It is thought be a water-carved channel that carries excess flows of turbidity currents from the contributing slope channels. It ends in the Sohm Abyssal Plain (Nares Deep) at -5 km depth. Profiles across the channel show it to be steep-sided and flat-floored, about 2 km wide, with virtually zero component of surface slope toward it on the plain that flanks it. The drop in gradient in the final 1000 km is about 0.5 km, for a ratio of 1 in 2000. Similar deep-sea channels have been mapped in abyssal plains of the eastern North Atlantic, the South Atlantic, and the eastern North Pacific (Shepard, 1973, p. 376, 382).

As new technologies have greatly increased the ability of oceanographers to map the ocean floor, new details of the deep submarine channels have come into view. A good example is from one part of the same region as that shown in Figure 4.22.

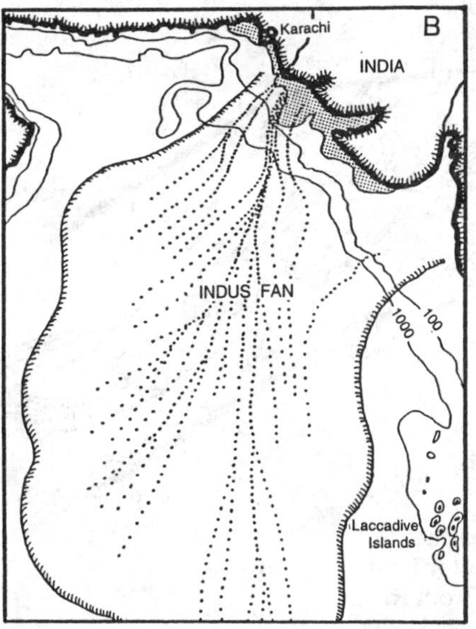

Figure 4.21 Outline maps of the Ganges-Brahmaputra and Indus fans. Dotted lines show distributary channels on the fan surfaces. The stippled areas close to the shoreline are areas of turbid water produced by river floods. Depths are in meters. (From R. J. Gibbs, 1981, *Geology*, v. 9, p. 78. Reproduced with permission of the publisher, the Geological Society of America, Boulder, Colorado USA. Copyright © 1959.)

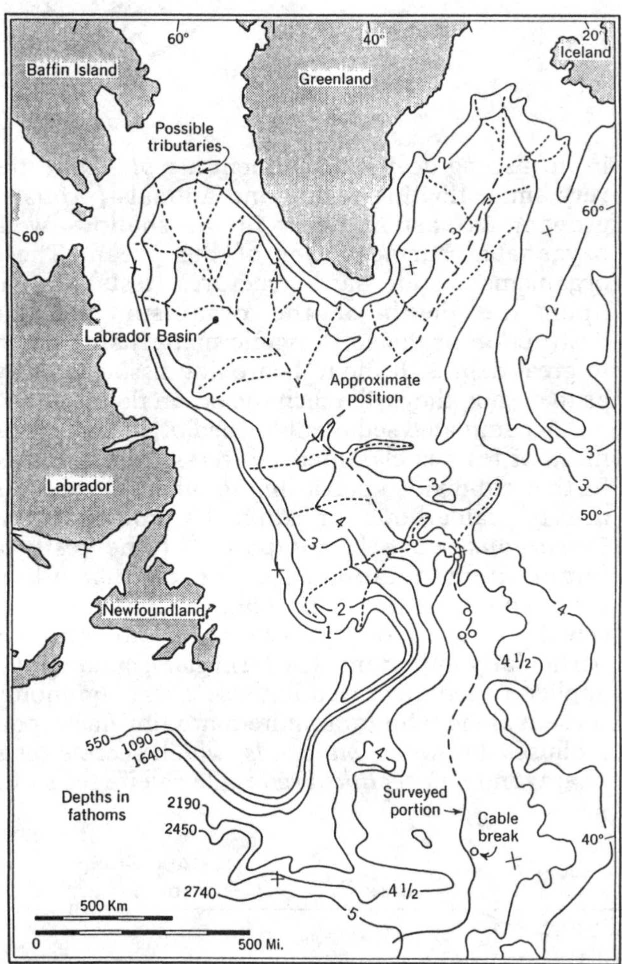

Figure 4.22 This map of the northwest Atlantic Mid-Ocean Canyon and its tributary channels was produced shortly after its discovery by analysis of 48 cross sections taken by precision depth recorder in 1952. (From B.C. Heezen, M. Tharp, and M. Ewing, 1959, *The Floors of the Oceans*, Geological Society of America Spec. Paper 65, p. 67, Figure 29. Reproduced with permission of the publisher, the Geological Society of America, Boulder, Colorado USA. Copyright © 1959.)

Figure 4.23 shows details of the channeled floor of the Labrador Basin. Channels with pointbars and levees are clearly revealed.

4.14 Contourites

The deep bottom currents that flow parallel with the western continental margin of the North Atlantic Ocean basin (and possibly of the Pacific Ocean basin) are also important transporters of sediment at depths of 3000 to 6000 m (see Figure 4.24). The western boundary undercurrent flows over the continental rise at speeds of 10 to 20 cm/sec carrying silt and clay and building important sediment accumulations. Sediment transported by this geostrophic current is probably brought down the continental slope and rise by turbidity currents. The bottom current is capable of winnowing out fine particles from sand of medium and coarse grades originally deposited by turbidity currents. Evidence of current transportation is seen in *ripple marks*, photographed in many places on the ocean floor where the bottom currents operate. The direction of water flow indicated by the ripple marks is known to coincide with the measured direction of the bottom current.

Sediments deposited by contour currents are called *contourites*, to set them apart from turbidites. In contrast to turbidites, which show a large range in particle grade size and a distinctive graded bedding, contourites are formed of well-sorted fine sediment. Figure 4.24 is a schematic diagram showing a lenslike body of contourites underlying the continental rise. The thickness of the deposit is on the order of 500 m. The diagram also shows a layer of sediment deposited beneath the antarctic bottom current. This kind of contourite deposit forms on the very gentle outermost slope of the continental rise, where it grades into the abyssal plain.

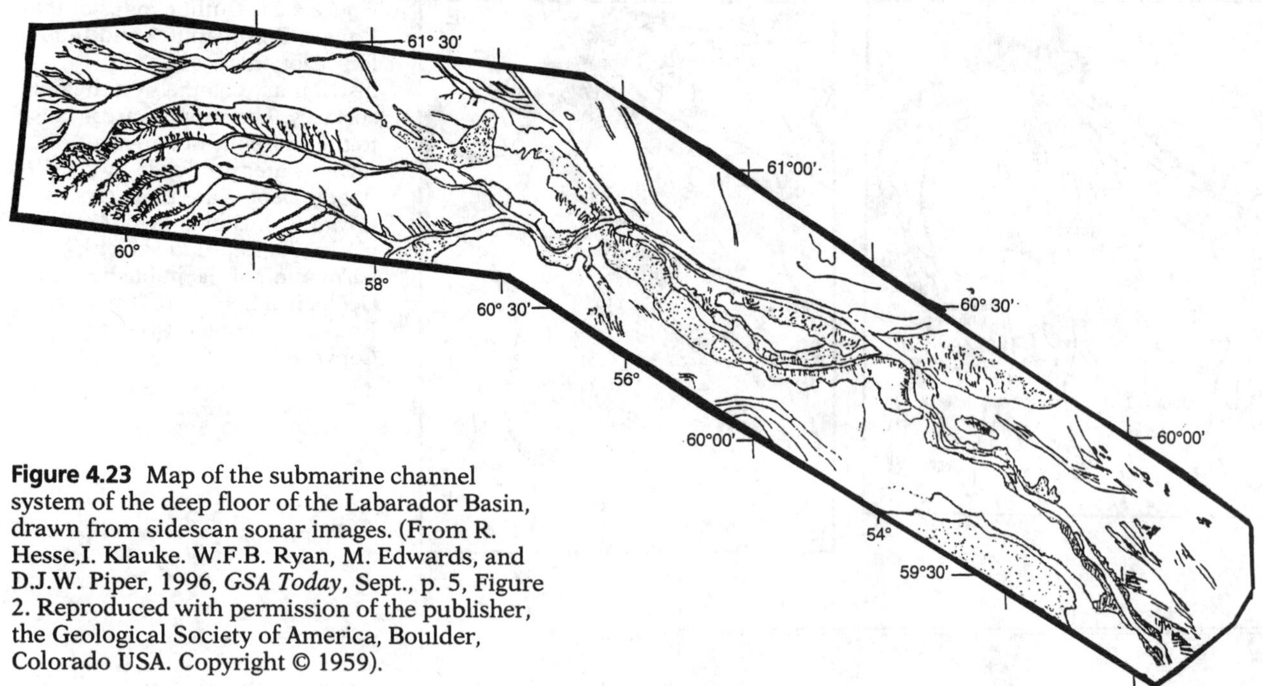

Figure 4.23 Map of the submarine channel system of the deep floor of the Labarador Basin, drawn from sidescan sonar images. (From R. Hesse,I. Klauke. W.F.B. Ryan, M. Edwards, and D.J.W. Piper, 1996, *GSA Today*, Sept., p. 5, Figure 2. Reproduced with permission of the publisher, the Geological Society of America, Boulder, Colorado USA. Copyright © 1959).

All of the minor seabed sediment forms we have mentioned above—turbidites, graded bedding, scour and sole marks, contourites, and ripple marks—play an important secondary role in plate tectonics research, since their presence in highly deformed structures of orogens can shed light on the processes of plate subduction and the formation of new masses of continental crust.

4.15 Composition of the Deep-Sea Sediments

Four main groups of deep-sea sediments are shown in Table 4.1. These recognize both the sediment transport mechanisms and the compositions of the sediments. Other and more rigorous classifications are available (Boggs, 1994). Our first group, the *biogenic-pelagic sediments*, consists principally of calcareous or siliceous mineral matter secreted by organisms. The word *pelagic* (from the Greek word *pelagikos*, for sea) simply means "originating in, or derived from, the ocean." The pelagic organisms of most importance in furnishing deep-sea sediment are *plankton*, the very small floating plants and animals (protists) growing in vast numbers in the shallow, well-oxygenated surface layer of the ocean. These organisms secrete hard structures (tests) which, upon the death of the organism and the destruction of the soft organic matter, sink down to great depths. If the tests are not dissolved away as they sink, they will reach the ocean floor.

Accumulated sediment formed of 30 percent or more of tests is classified as *deep-sea ooze* and is further subdivided according to whether the tests are of calcareous or siliceous composition. *Calcareous ooze* is composed of the tests of foraminifera, pteropods, or coccoliths, all of calcareous composition. *Foraminifera* are one-celled organisms, of which the genus *Globigerina* is particularly important. The term *globigerina ooze* is applied to sediment rich in these tests. Commonly present along with foraminifera are tiny gastropod molluscs, known as *pteropods*, which secrete tests of aragonite. *Coccoliths* are fragile calcite tests of a

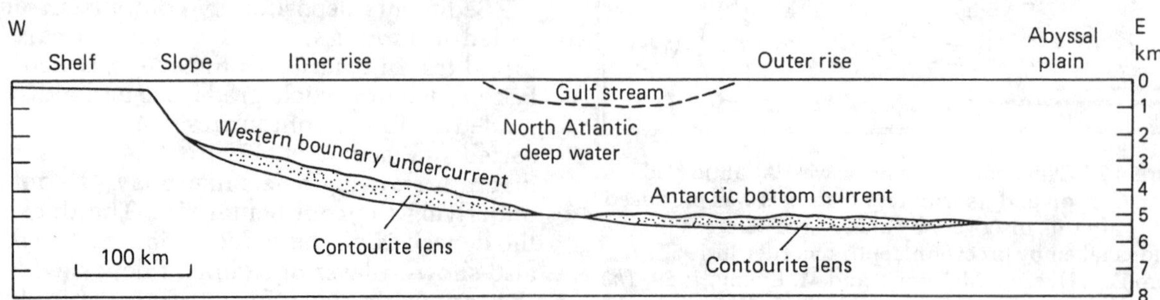

Figure 4.24 Cross section of the continental slope and rise, showing lenses of contourites formed by bottom currents. (After B.C. Heezen, C.D. Hollister, and W.F. Ruddiman, 1966, *Science*, vol. 152, Figure 3, p. 505. Used by permission of the American Association for the Advancement of Science)

Table 4.1 Classification of Deep-Sea Sediments*

I Biogenic-Pelagic Sediments
- Oozes
  - Calcareous ooze
  - Siliceous ooze
- Organic compounds

II Pelagic-Detrital Sediments
- Brown clay (Red clay)
- Glacial-marine sediment
- Volcanic ash

III Bottom-Transported Detrital Sediments
- Turbidites
- Contourites
- Terrigenous muds

IV Hydrogenic Sediments
- Montmorillonite
- Zeolites (Phillipsite)
- Manganese nodules

*Source: Based in part on a classification by K. Turekian, 1968, *Oceans*. Englewood Cliffs, NJ, Prentice-Hall, Table 3-1.

type of algae (microscopic plants) and are an abundant constituent of the very-fine grained calcareous oozes.

At a depth of about 3500 to 5500 m lies the *calcium carbonate compensation depth* (CCD), at which calcium carbonate begins to dissolve in seawater (Figure 4.25). The average depth is 4500 m. Few calcareous tests reach bottom at depths more than 5000 m. Consequently, bottom areas with high proportions of calcium carbonate are quite closely correlated with topographically high areas of the ocean basins. In the Atlantic Ocean, concentration of calcium carbonate is high along the axis of the Mid-Atlantic Ridge, but is relatively low on the abyssal basins on either side. Rate of biological productivity, which tends to be high in areas of warm ocean currents and in zones of upwelling, also influences the actual depth of the CCD.

Siliceous ooze, consisting of 30 percent or more of siliceous tests, is derived from a number of organisms, of which the *diatoms* and *radiolaria* are most important. These are microscopic one-celled organisms within the Kingdom *Protoctista* (Protists). Both secrete ornate siliceous tests with radial symmetry. Siliceous oozes are found largely in two oceanic zones—between latitudes 45°-60° in both hemispheres, and in limited portions of the equatorial Pacific Ocean.

Rate of accumulation of oozes has been estimated as 1 to 5 cm per 1000 years. Both calcareous and siliceous oozes usually contain substantial amounts of inorganic clays.

Under the heading of biogenic-pelagic sediments, we can also include organic matter that escapes decomposition and becomes incorporated into muds on the floors of deep basins, where anaerobic conditions (the absence of oxygen) prevail. This environment is comparatively rare today. An example of such a basin is the Black Sea, over 2200 m deep and almost completely cut off from the Mediterranean Sea. Here, under stagnant bottom conditions, oxygen is depleted and a black mud rich in organic matter is deposited. Over the oceans generally, water circulation is adequate to bring oxygen to even the deepest places, allowing destruction of organic matter as it sinks or upon its arrival at the bottom.

Pelagic-detrital sediments are particles of non-biogenic matter that have settled to the bottom from the near-surface layer above. As we have already explained, such particles may be brought from continental locations as suspended matter in surface ocean currents or in icebergs drifting with those currents. Volcanic and terrestrial dusts carried by winds also furnish detrital matter to the ocean surface, as does the vaporization of comets and meteors in the overlying outer atmosphere. It is obvious that the mineral composition of these detrital sediments can be quite complex, with the proportions of the components depending upon geologic nature of the sources and distances from those sources.

The most widespread of pelagic-detrital sediments is *brown clay*, which is a soft plastic material with a greasy feel. This clay typically is low in calcium carbonate (less than 30%) and consists for the most part of clay minerals, among them illite, chlorite, and kaolinite, derived from

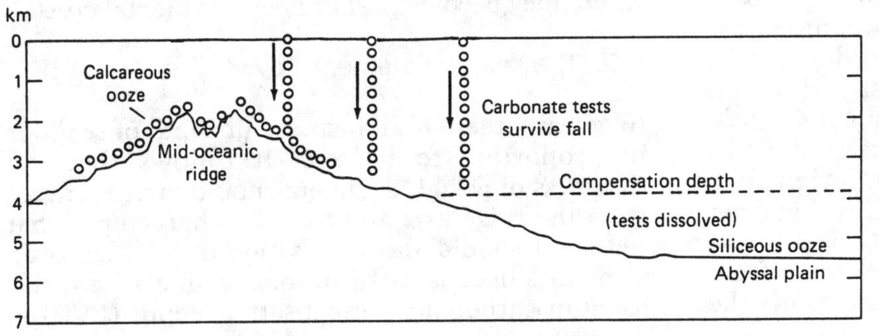

Figure 4.25 A schematic diagram showing that carbonate tests begin to dissolve at the compensation depth and will fail to reach the ocean floor below about 4 km. (Copyright © by Arthur N. Strahler.)

continental sources. Montmorillonite may be present and is thought to have been derived by alteration of volcanic materials after their deposition. Quartz in minute grains is abundant in some brown clays and there may be minor amounts of feldspars and micas, all derived from continental surfaces. Rate of accumulation of brown clay is extremely slow and has been estimated at 0.1 to 1 mm per 1000 years.

The relative abundances of kaolinite and chlorite in brown clay change with geographical position in a manner that reflects conditions of origin of those minerals. Kaolinite, which is produced by silicate rock weathering in warm, humid climates of low latitudes, is 5 to 15 times more abundant than chlorite in the Atlantic Ocean in the latitude range 20°N. to 20°S. Chlorite, which is easily destroyed in a warm climate, becomes two to four times more abundant than kaolinite in latitudes poleward of about 45°. Illite, produced from the alteration of micas, shows its greatest abundances near the continents, from which it is derived. Quartz shows concentrations in the lee of tropical deserts, from which it is brought by easterly winds, and in middle to high latitude locations, where it can be attributed to an abundance of freshly pulverized rock produced by Pleistocene continental glaciation.

On deep ocean floors in both Arctic and Antarctic waters, we find sediments that appear to have been brought by icebergs from continental glaciers. Designated as *glacial-marine sediments*, they consist of silt with some clay and are formed of finely ground fresh rock. Consequently, they show little oxidation or mineral alteration. Glacial-marine sediments were evidently far more widespread in area of deposition during stages of glaciation, for they have been found buried beneath globigerina ooze forming today.

As we have already stated, fine volcanic ash travels widely as dust in the atmosphere. Dust from a single great volcanic explosion achieves global distribution and can be expected to produce a very thin pelagic sediment layer simultaneously in many parts of the world ocean. Horizons of volcanic ash have been found in many sediment cores, and there is no doubt that a definable layer up to several hundreds of kilometers in extent can be associated with a single volcanic eruption. Ash horizons are represented in deep-sea sediment by concentrations of glass shards, highly susceptible to mineral alteration.

Bottom-transported detrital sediments have been described earlier and include thick accumulations of turbidites and contourites. Bordering the continents, in a zone along the upper and middle continental slope, are found *terrigenous muds*, apparently brought to the deep ocean floor by bottom currents. *Terrigenous* means "originating on land." The terrigenous muds are silty, but finer grained than most turbidites, and their silt and lack of complete oxidation set them apart from brown clay. Colors of the terrigenous muds may be blue, green, black, or red. Blue and green colors result from the presence of ferrous iron oxide and reflect a deficiency of oxygen, or a lack of time for oxidation to have occurred. Red muds, colored by ferric iron oxide, show complete oxidation of iron, but this probably occurred during transport on the lands. Black muds, as we have already noted, have a relatively high organic content and show a depositional environment of stagnant water with little oxygen present.

Hydrogenic sediments of the deep ocean floors include minerals formed by alteration in place or reformed from other minerals. Perhaps the most important alteration product is the clay mineral *montmorillonite* (a type of *smectite*). This mineral group is derived from volcanic materials, including volcanic ash and basaltic rock exposed on the ocean floor. A second alteration product is *phillipsite*, a silicate mineral of the zeolite group, also derived from volcanic materials of basaltic composition. Phillipsite, a hydrous alumino-silicate of calcium, sodium, and potassium, forms in minute needlelike crystals that may constitute as much as 50 percent or more of the bottom sediment in parts of the central Pacific Ocean basin, where basaltic volcanic rocks are abundant. This mineral is rare near the bordering continents and is not found in the other oceans.

The deep-sea sediments we have described here in some detail are of great importance for the interpretation of global environmental conditions. Cores of these deposits show alternations of various types of sediment, each reflecting certain physical and chemical conditions of the ocean waters or a certain set of climatic conditions prevailing in the atmosphere. For example, a thick accumulation of turbidites could reflect a glacial stage in which vast amounts of sediment were being brought to the brink of the continental shelf. Particular species of foraminifera are associated with water temperature of a given range. By studying species variations in layers of calcareous ooze, we can derive a record of changing atmospheric temperatures. Deep-sea sediments get involved in plate tectonics through activities that take place in subduction zones. Here the deep-sea sediment is offscraped from the down plunging plate, metamorphosed, and added to the accretionary prism by understuffing. Later tectonic events of arc-continent collision and suturing commonly result in these accretionary prisms being lifted on overthrust faults during telescoping, where they become part of new continental crust.

4.16 The Pelagic Sediment Cover

In general, there is an increase in depth of seafloor in proportion to its age. It follows that the thickness of pelagic sediment should increase away from the ridge axis and that the character of that sediment should show a change from calcareous ooze to siliceous ooze beyond a line where the calcium carbonate compensation depth (CCD) is

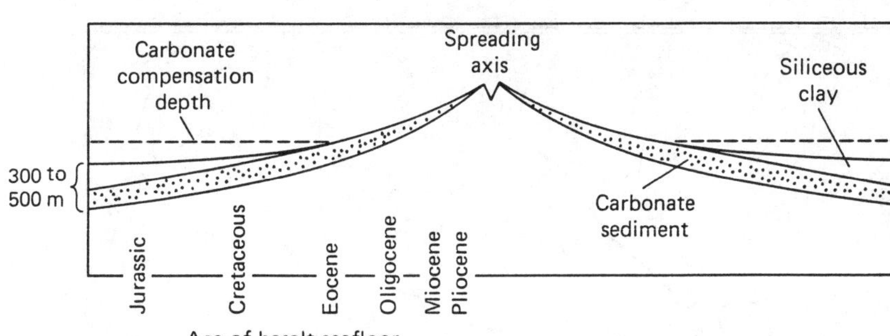

Figure 4.26 A schematic cross section showing the thickening of pelagic seafloor sediment away from a spreading plate boundary. The vertical scale (thickness) of the sediment layers is enormously exaggerated. (Copyright © by Arthur N. Strahler.)

exceeded. The predicted increase in thickness of the sediment layer overlying the basaltic floor became very evident from the numerous deep-sea sediment cores extracted by scientists aboard the *Glomar Challenger*. Figure 4.26 is a schematic diagram showing the increase in sediment thickness and the change in sediment type with increasing distance from the ridge axis. Until the compensation depth is reached, carbonate sediment thickens rapidly, but thereafter remains the same thickness as it becomes buried under pelagic clay, which increases gradually in thickness. In cores drilled into the oldest parts of the western North Pacific Ocean floor, where bedrock is of Lower Cretaceous or Upper Jurassic age, the thickness of clays equals or exceeds the thickness of the underlying carbonate layers, while the total thickness of the sediment layer exceeds 500 m.

4.17 Guyots, Atolls, and Plate Tectonics

Earlier in this chapter we described seamounts that rise from the deep ocean floor, often arranged in long chains. Most of the seamount chains in the Pacific Ocean basin are located far from the subduction plate boundaries. In Chapter 5 we explain these features as products of mantle plumes, rising to penetrate the oceanic lithosphere and crust to form basaltic volcanoes. Given a program of intermittent upsurges of magma, combined with a steady motion of the lithospheric plate, a chain of volcanoes is formed. Figure 4.27 illustrates this concept. We explain in Chapter 5 that as new oceanic lithosphere is formed along a spreading rift and moves away from the rift, it sinks lower because of increased rock density brought on by cooling. Thus the ocean floor deepens, and objects of fixed height, such as extinct volcanoes, originally rising above the ocean surface as islands become fully submerged. While above sealevel, or close to it, two kinds of landform shaping processes can be effective: (1) marine erosion and truncation by wave action; (2) construction of coral reefs.

In high latitudes where corals do not thrive, truncation of an island may be completed, and as submergence brings the summit below wave base, there results a variety of flat-topped seamount called a *guyot* (Palmer, 1966). The name, honoring Arnold Guyot, a nineteenth-century Swiss-American geologist, was given to this landform by Princeton geologist Harry H. Hess. He first recognized its existence while observing echo-sounder traces on a naval vessel cruising the Pacific ocean and published his findings in 1946

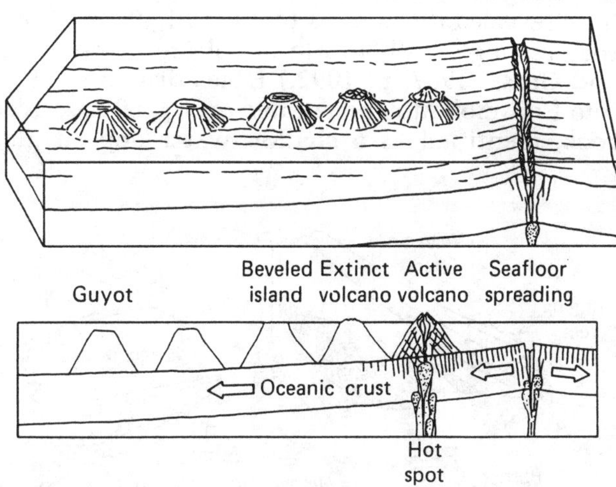

Figure 4.27 Schematic diagram of a hot spot producing a chain of volcanic islands as the oceanic plate moves away from a spreading rift. Beveled extinct volcanoes are submerged to become guyots. Ocean depth and height of volcanoes are enormously exaggerated. (Copyright © by Arthur N. Strahler.)

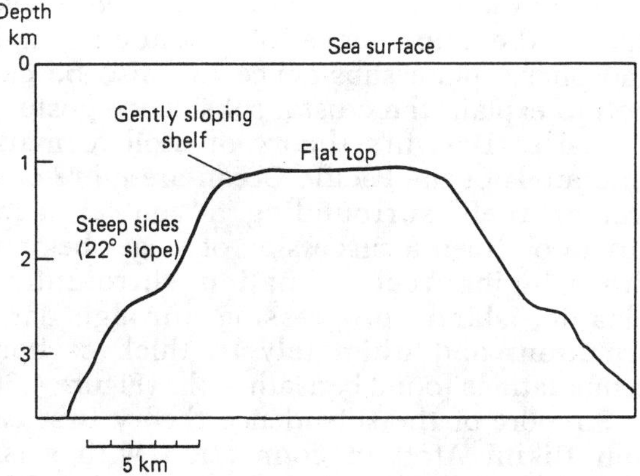

Figure 4.28 Profile of the first Guyot to be discovered in the Pacific Ocean basin (1944). The location of this flat-topped seamount is about lat. 9° N, long. 163° E. (Adapted from H.H. Hess, 1946, *American Journal of Science*, v. 244, p. 772. Reproduced by permission of the publisher.)

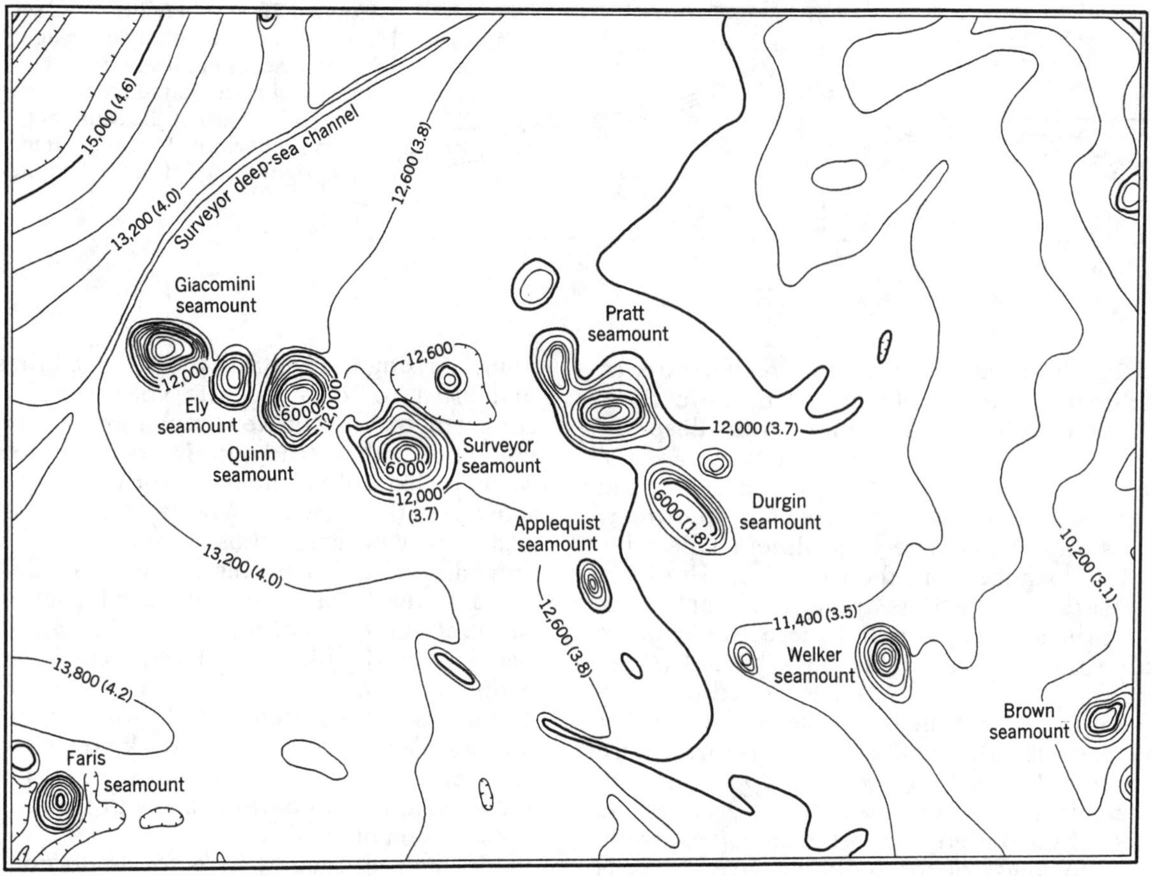

Figure 4.29 An early U.S. Navy bathymetric chart of the Gulf of Alaska. It shows ten seamounts rising from an abyssal plain. Quinn and Welker seamounts are guyots. Note the deep-sea channel lying close to the slope descending into the Aleutian Trench (upper left).(Contours in feet; km in parentheses.)

(Figure 4.28). Figure 4.12 shows the location of seamounts of the northeast Pacific Ocean, some of which are identified as guyots. Figure 4.29 is a bathymetric chart showing some details of seamounts in the Gulf of Alaska, some of which are guyots, rising from an abyssal plain.

Using the series of events described above to explain the subsidence of seamount chains, lithospheric plate subsidence can also be called upon to explain the crustal subsidence postulated in Charles Darwin's theory of atoll formation. Coral atolls of the Pacific Ocean are more or less circular reefs surrounding a central lagoon. Darwin outlined a succession of stages beginning with fringing reef formation surrounding a volcanic island, progressing through lagoon formation, and ultimately to thick carbonate accumulations found beneath atolls (Figure 4.30).

Support of the subsidence theory first came from Bikini Atoll in connection with seismic refraction studies carried out there after World War II. As shown in Figure 4.31, there is strong indication of the presence of more than 1500 m of calcareous deposits beneath the atoll. A drill hole penetrated 760 m of reef materials identified as formed in shallow water, beneath which is a possible volcanic core. If the seismic data are being correctly interpreted, there is no escape from the conclusion that reef growth kept pace with slow subsidence over a long period.

Core borings of several Pacific Ocean atolls, including Funafuti, Eniwetok, Bikini, and Midway, have revealed thicknesses of 200 to 1,400 m of reef rock resting on a platform of volcanic rock (Ladd and Gross, 1967, p. 1092.) Holes drilled in 1952 into Eniwetok Atoll penetrated over 1200 m of reef rock, identified as a shallow-water deposit and

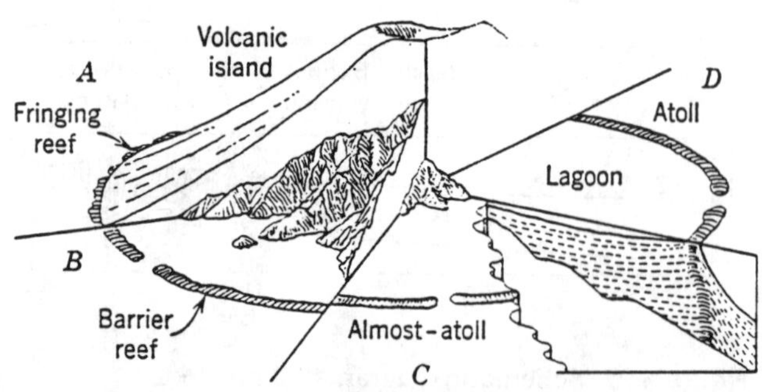

Figure 4.30 Stages in the development of an atoll, according to the subsidence theory. (Adapted from W.M. Davis, 1916, *Scientific Monthly*, v. 2, no. 5, p. 23, Figure 13.)

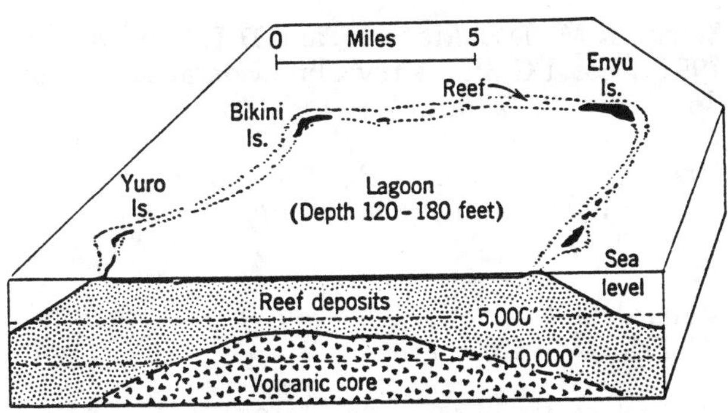

Figure 4.31 Block diagram of Bikini Atoll, Pacific Ocean. (Based on data of M. Dobrin and others.)

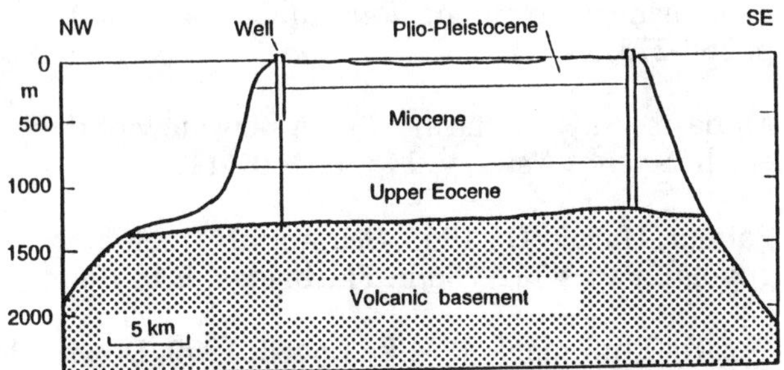

Figure 4.32 A cross section of Eniwetok Atoll, based on borings and seismic refraction soundings. (From Arthur H. Saller, *Geology*, v. 12, p. 219, Figure 4. Reproduced with permission of the publisher, the Geological Society of America, Boulder, Colorado USA. Copyright © 1959).

clearly representing the upbuilding of a submerging reef (Figure 4.32). Age of the reef rock was found to be progressively greater with depth. That below 850 m was of Upper Eocene age, 36 million years old or more (Saller, 1984, p. 219).

These observations have made virtually certain the origin of atolls through slow subsidence of volcanic islands. A volcanic island, following cessation of its constructional activity, was reduced by erosion and planed off by wave action to have a flattened summit, serving as a platform for reef growth. Continued slow subsidence allowed the reef to build upward and maintain itself.

Atolls can undergo drowning where the subsidence rate is too fast to allow corals to build their reefs upward and thus keep pace and survive. When this happens, guyots are formed. In some cases, it may be possible to identify a sunken atoll by the presence of a topographic rim, but the rim may easily be confused with a volcanic crater rim.

To close this chapter, we present a remarkable set of profiles of the earth's solid surface along four parallels of latitude spanning North America and the Atlantic Ocean Basin (Figure 4.33). With earth curvature removed, the profiles show strikingly the basic elevation disparities between continental crust and oceanic crust with respect to mean sea level.

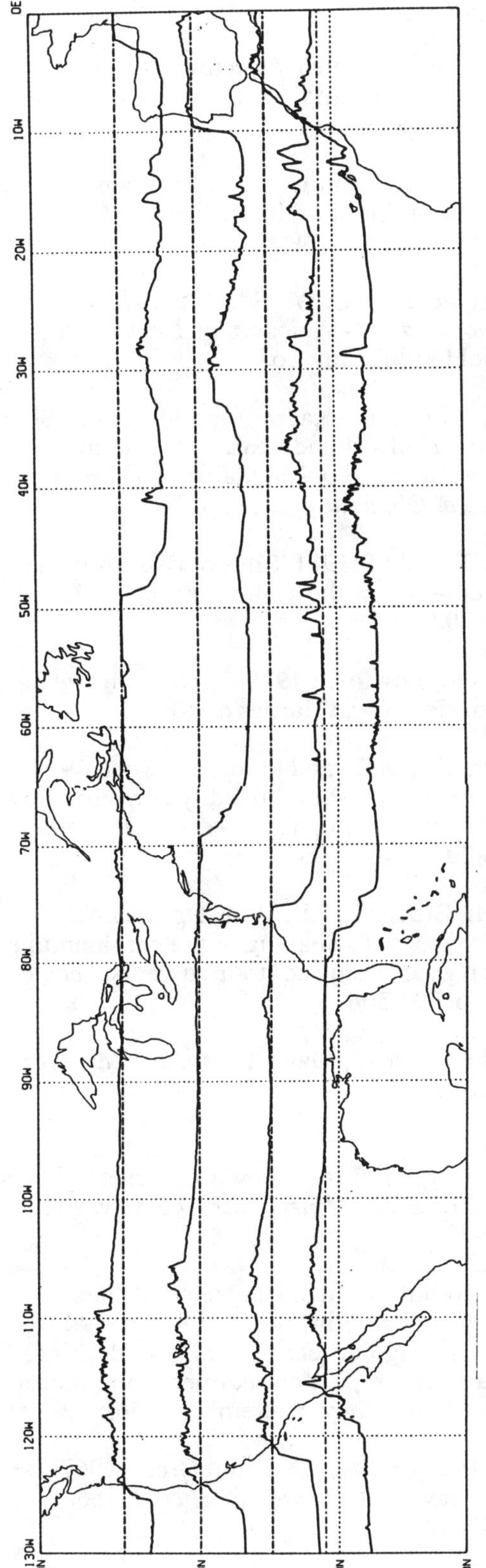

Figure 4.33 Topographic profiles across North America and the Atlantic ocean basin along four parallels of latitude: 31°, 35°, 40°, and 45°. (Digital bathymetric data of the U.S. Navy and the National Geophysical Data Center, Boulder, CO. Published in *EOS*, v. 63, no. 37, 1982. Used by permission of the American Geophysical Union, Peter W. Sloss, and J.R. Heirtzler.)

REFERENCES CITED

Amer. Geophysical Union, 1995, New map of seafloor mirrors surface. *Earth in Space*, vol. 8, no.4, p. 405.

Boggs, Sam, Jr., 1995, *Principles of Sedimentology and Stratigraphy*, 2nd. ed. Englewood Cliffs, NJ:Prentice Hall.

Ewing, M., W.J. Ludwig, and J.I. Ewing, 1964, Sediment distribution in the oceans. *Jour. Geophysical Res*., v. 69, p. 2003-2032.

Fairbridge, Rhodes W., Ed., 1966, *The Encyclopedia of Oceanography*. New York: Reinhold Publishing Co.

Farre, John, Ellen Kappel, and Alexander Shor, 1983, SeaMARC I and SeaBeam: instant seafloor topography. *Yearbook of the Lamont-Doherty Geological Observatory*, v. 9, p. 7-11.

Gibbs, Ronald J. 1981, Sites of river-drained sedimentation in the ocean. *Geology*, v. 1, p. 193-202.

Hamilton, Edwin L., 1973, *Submarine Geology*, 3rd. ed. New York: Harper & Row.

Heezen, Bruce C., and Maurice Ewing, 1954, Further evidence for a turbidity current following Grand Banks earthquake. *Deep-Sea Research*, v. 1, p. 193-202.

Heezen, Bruce C., C.D. Hollister, and W.F. Ruddiman, 1966, Shaping of the continental rise by deep geostrophic contour currents. *Science*, v. 152, p. 502-508.

Heezen, Bruce C., Marie Tharp, and Maurice Ewing, 1959, *The Floors of the Oceans*. Special Paper 65, Geological Society of America.

Hess, Harry H., 1946, Drowned ancient islands of the Pacific Basin. *Amer. Jour. of Sci*., v, 244, p. 772-791.

Hesse, Reinhard, Ingo Klaukem, William B.F. Ryan, Margo B. Edwards, and David J.W. Piper, 1996, Imaging Laurentide Ice Sheet drainage into the deep sea: Impact on sediments and bottom water. *G.S.A. Today*, September 1996, p. 3-9.

Ladd, Harry S., and M. Grant Gross, 1967, Drilling on Midway Atoll, Hawaii. *Science*, v. 156, p. 1088-1094.

Lawler, Andrew, 1995, Sea-floor data flow from postwar era. *Science*, v. 270, p. 727.

Marks, K.M., D.C. McAdoo, and D.T. Sandwell, 1991, Geosat GM data reveal new details of ocean floor. *EOS*, v. 72, no. 13, p. 145-146.

McGregor, Bonnie A., 1984, The submarine continental margin, *Amer. Scientist*, v. 72, p. 275-281.

Menard, H.W., 1986, *The Ocean of Truth*. Princeton NJ: Princeton Univ. Press.

Menard, H.W., and R.S. Dietz, 1951, Submarine geology of the Gulf of Alaska. *Bull., Geol. Soc. of Amer.*, v. 62, p. 1263.

Menard, H.W., and R.S. Dietz, 1952, Mendocino submarine escarpment. *Jour. of Geology*, v. 60, p. 266-278.

Monastsersky, Richard, 1995, A new view of the earth. *Science News*, v. 148, p. 410-411.

Palmer, Harold D., 1966, Seamounts (including guyots). Pages 782-786 in Fairbridge, Ed., 1966.

Pezard, Philippe, and Mike Lovell, 1990, Downhole images. *EOS*, v. 71, no. 20, p. 709, 718.

Pratson, Lincoln F., and Willilam F. Haxby, 1996, What is the slope of the U.S. continental slope? *Geology*, v. 24, p. 3-6.

Saller, Arthur H., 1984, Petrologic and geochemical constraints on the origin of subsurface dolomites. *Geology*, v. 12, p. 217-220.

Sandwell, D.T., and D.C. McAdoo, 1988, High-accuracy hig-resolution gravity profiles from 2 years of the Geosat Exact Repeat Mission. *Jour. Geophysical Res*., v.95, p. 3049-3060.

Scrutton, R.A., and M. Talwani, Eds., 1982, *The Ocean Floor*. New York: John Wiley & Sons.

Searle, R.C., T.J.G. Francis, T.W.C. Hilde, et al., 1981, 'Gloria' side-scan sonar in the East Pacific. *EOS*, v. 62, no. 12, p. 121-122.

Tharp, Marie, 1982, Mapping the ocean floor. Pages 19-31 in R.A. Scrutton and M. Talwani, Eds., 1982, *The Ocean Floor*. New York: John Wiley & Sons.

Chapter: 5 Igneous Activity and Plate Tectonics

Taking stock of what we have covered, Chapter 1 offered a brief overview of plate tectonics, whereas Chapter 2 might be described as a history of "tectonics without plates." Chapters 3 and 4 provided important background information and gave little attention to plate tectonics. Chapter 3 described the concentric earth layers largely in static terms. But we also included mantle convection, which might be thought of as the dynamo of plate tectonics. Chapter 4, describing the ocean floors, covered formative processes of some of the secondary morphological features, but left for later discussion the tectonics of the first-order landforms.

As the title of this chapter suggests, it is the first of a core series that delves into the field of plate tectonics. Although this chapter focuses on igneous processes, they are examined in the framework of lithospheric plates and their boundaries.

5.1 Early Thermal History of the Earth

To provide a background for the subject of igneous activity in relation to plate tectonics, we go back in time to the origin of our earth as a planet. Modern hypotheses of the earth's origin favor the process of accretion of the earth and other planets through the contraction and condensation of an interstellar cloud of gases and dust, often referred to as a primitive *solar nebula* (Hunten, 1993, p. 915). The nebula was similar in composition to that of the sun, which is largely hydrogen and helium, but with a small proportion of heavier elements. It was from these heavier elements that the planets were to be formed.

We are interested here primarily in the *inner planets*: Mercury, Venus, Earth, Mars—listed in order of increasing orbital distance out from the sun (Figure 5.1). These four are also called the *terrestrial planets*. Because their chemical compositions are somewhat like that of the solid Earth, they are also called the "rock planets," (or "rocky planets"). Diameter, mass and density of each are as follows:

	Diameter 10^3 km	Mass relative to Earth	Mean density g/cm^3
Mercury	4.9	0.06	5.4
Venus	12.2	0.80	5.2
Earth	12.7	1.00	5.5
Mars	6.8	0.11	4.0

Note that while there are large disparities among the four in size and mass, the spread in mean density is comparatively small. They also differ considerably in internal structure and composition (Figure 5.2). If we were to select two of them to be paired as geological "twins," they would be Venus and Earth. The similarity of these twins includes the presence of ongoing volcanic and tectonic activity in their crustal layers.

Details of the condensation of the solar nebula to yield the planets differ quite substantially between two scenarios that have been argued over the past three or four decades. The older of these is a history of *cold homogeneous accretion* (Murray, Malin, and Greeley, 1981, p. 5). The dispersed particles of the nebula began to stick to one another to form larger objects. As the latter swept up smaller particles, they grew rapidly into objects known as *planetesimals*, which were about the size of our Moon (Wetherill, 1991, p. 535; Peterson, 1993). Collisions resulted in merging of these large objects to yield the terrestrial planets. Included in this scenario is the provision that the earth remained "cold" (above the melting point) during the entire accretion process, so that it could be described as chemically homogeneous. Differentiation into core, mantle, and crust came later when, as we explain below, heating of the planet by decay of dispersed radioactive elements led to melting and segregation of layers according to density.

An alternative scenario for the condensation of the nebula goes by the name of *hot heterogeneous accretion* (Murray, Malin, and Greeley, 1981, p. 8-11). A specific chemical model of this hypothesis, called the "equilibrium-condensation model" was put forward in the late 1970s by John S. Lewis of the Department of Earth and Planetary Sciences at M.I.T. (Lewis, 1973, 1974). Lewis's hypothesis addressed the serious problem of explaining important chemical differences among the terrestrial planets, arguing that if the planetesimals were of homogeneous composition, the cold-accretion hypothesis contains no explanation for those planetary differences. First, we note that the planets are postulated to have formed in an extremely hot nebula, rather than a cold one, starting with a nebular temperature of 1600 K, and falling steadily with time.

Next, we need to set up a program of evolution of the solar nebula as a whole, starting with a time when the sun as a star had not yet formed. The dense inner part of the nebula can be called the *protosun*. During contraction, the entire nebula began to spin. As the rate of spinning increased, the nebula took on a flattened shape, thinning along the axis of spin and expanding the diameter of its outer "equatorial" edge. As this rim moved farther out from the shrinking protosun, the

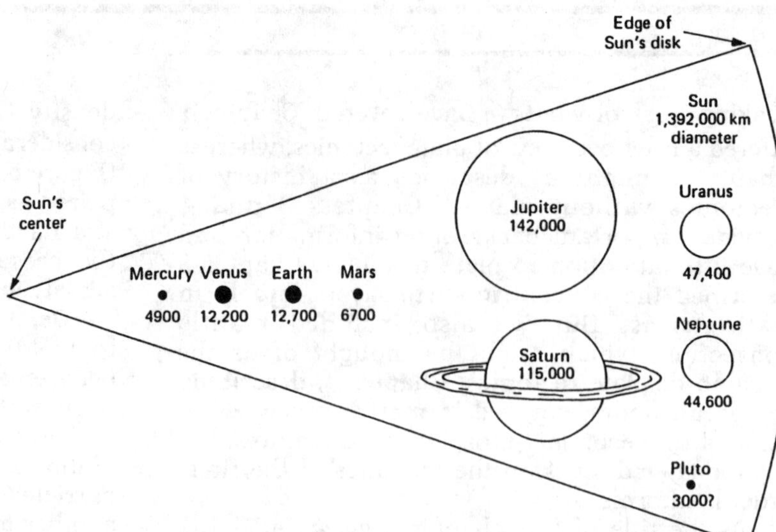

Figure 5.1 Relative diameters (km) of the Sun and planets. (Copyright © by Arthur N. Strahler.)

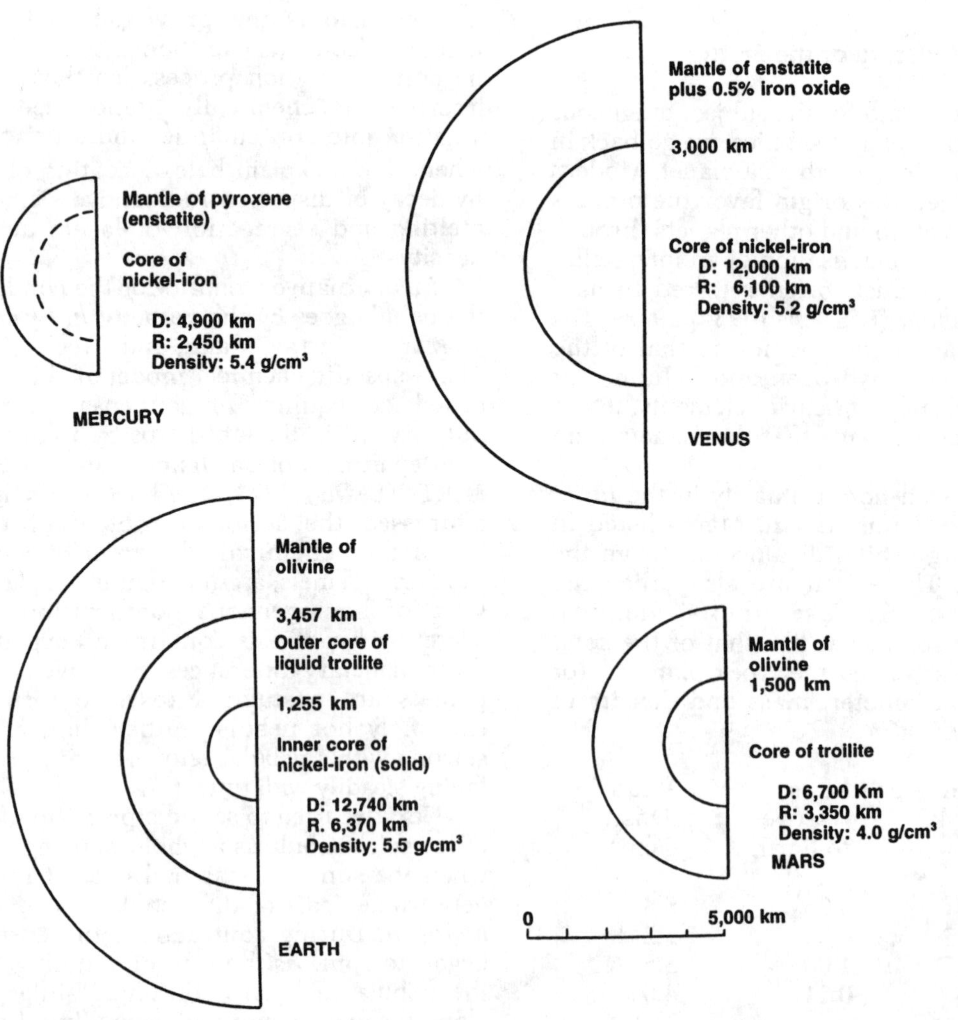

Figure 5.2 Interior structure and composition of the four inner planets. (Copyright © by Arthur N. Strahler.)

Table 5.1 Stages of Condensation from the Solar Nebula

Nebular temperature, K		Chemical activity	Planetary environment	
Above 1600		All nebular matter in gaseous state.		
1600		Condensation of oxides of calcium and aluminum (refractory substances).		
1300		Condensation of nickel-iron alloy.	Mercury	Inner planets
1200	Rock-forming silicate minerals	Condensation of enstatite, a silicate mineral consisting of silicon-oxide and magnesium.		Inner planets
1200 to 490	Rock-forming silicate minerals	Metallic iron unites with oxygen to form iron-oxide, which in turn reacts with enstatite to form olivine, a silicate of iron and magnesium.		Inner planets
1000	Rock-forming silicate minerals	Feldspars, a silicate mineral class, form by combination of silicon-oxide with aluminum, sodium, and calcium.	Venus	Inner planets
680	Water-rich silicate	Hydrogen-sulfide gas combines with metallic iron to form troilite, an iron-sulfur compound.	Earth	Inner planets
550	Water-rich silicate	Molecules of gaseous water (water vapor) unite with silicate minerals of calcium and magnesium to form a water-rich mineral, tremolite.	Mars	Inner planets
425	Water-rich silicate	Water molecules in vapor state unite with olivine to form a water-rich silicate mineral, serpentine.	(Asteroids)	
175	Ices	Molecules of water vapor condense into water-ice.	Jupiter	Outer planets
150	Ices	Ammonia gas unites with water-ice to form an ammonia-ice compound.	Saturn	Outer planets
120	Ices	Methane gas unites with water-ice to form a methane-ice compound.	Uranus Neptune	Outer planets
65	Gases	Argon gas and remaining methane gas condense to solid argon and solid methane.		Outer planets
20	Gases	Condensation of gaseous neon and hydrogen.		
1	Gases	At close to absolute zero, helium gas condenses into liquid helium.		

Data source: John L. Lewis, 1973, Technology Review, vol. 76, no. 1, o. 21-35.

nebular temperature fell within the outer limit of the disk, ultimately dropping to only a few tens of kelvins, whereas the inner part of the nebula remained hot—over 1000 K. Thus a complete gradation of temperature came to exist from a cool outer zone to a hot inner zone.

The basic concepts of the modern heterogeneous condensation hypothesis relate to what happened chemically and physically as temperatures decreased in various zones of the nebular disk. Wherever the nebular temperature remained above 1600 K, all nebular matter was in the gaseous state, but where it fell below that level and continued to fall, condensation of matter from the gaseous state to the liquid or solid state followed a chemical sequence in which different substances were produced at successive temperature zones within the nebula. The chemical sequence based on temperature is given in Table 5.1. The chemical reactions listed here can actually be demonstrated by laboratory experiments. To predict what was going on within the nebular disk at a particular time and place, we need only select the nebular temperature and read from the table the activity appropriate to that temperature. Because the nebular temperature had previously fallen to the specified value, those activities applying to higher temperatures had already occurred in that region, whereas the activities specified for lower temperatures would not yet have occurred.

In the inner nebular zone where temperature was about 1600 K, oxygen was combining with calcium, aluminum, and titantium to form solid dustlike grains of their oxides. These are refractory substances. Somewhat farther out in the zone at 1300 K, the elements iron and nickel were able to condense into minute droplets of nickel-iron alloy. A bit farther out, where the temperature was around 1200 K, a compound of silicon, oxygen, and magnesium was being formed. This is equivalent to the mineral enstatite, of the pyroxene group. Throughout the entire temperature zone from 1200 to 490 K, metallic iron was uniting with oxygen to form iron-oxide, in turn reacting with enstatite to form the equivalent of olivine. In the nebular zone near 1000 K, condensation was allowing formation of the feldspars. In the range from 680 to 425 K, water-rich silicates would be forming. We will not go over the formation temperatures of the volatiles that comprise the outer planets.

Our next step is to set up a scenario for the actual physical formation of the inner planets. Condensation resulted in minute solid grains of microscopic dimensions, and these began to move under gravitational attraction to occupy a flat plane at the equator of the rotating nebula (Figure 5.3). The particles thus began to form a very thin disk. In the process of accretion, the solid grains clotted together to form larger particles that grew rapidly to the size of pebbles, then merged by collisions into the larger masses, or planetesimals, and these in turn collided with one another. Whereas some of the collisions shattered the planetesimals, more gentle collisions allowed them to join into even larger masses, which have been called *protoplanets*. These large masses eventually swept up most of the smaller fragments within their orbits, and thus completed the growth of the primitive inner planets. We might suppose that because of the steady cooling of the nebula, accretion would yield a system of layers of the corresponding components in the temperature series. On the other hand, repeated breakup and reforming of the protoplanets would have given a

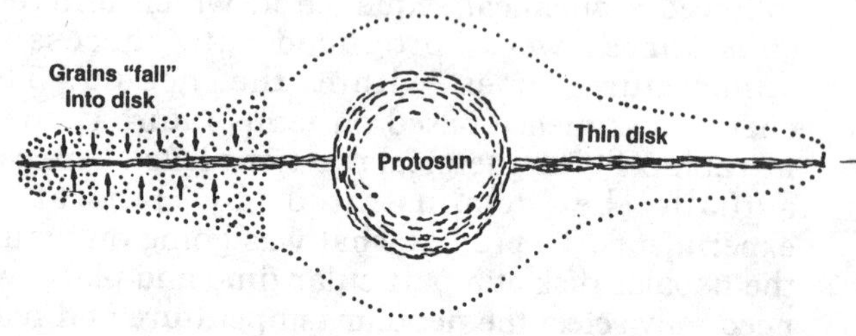

Figure 5.3 Schematic diagram of a stellar nebula with a protostar at its center. (Copyright © by Arthur N. Strahler.)

heterogeneous structure, and this would have required remelting followed by density stratification.

5.2 Natural Radioactivity in the Earth

The discovery of natural radioactivity by Henri Becquerel in 1896, followed by the isolation of radium by Marie and Pierre Curie in 1898, radically altered all scientific thinking about the earth's internal heat. John Joly in 1909 applied the new knowledge of radioactivity to recalculations of the earth's thermal history. Moreover, Joly brought forward the underlying principle that radiogenic heat provides the prime energy source for volcanism, igneous intrusion, and deformation of the earth's crust into mountain belts. Arthur Holmes, a pioneer in establishing the use of radioisotopes in geologic dating, stated: "Apart from the heat inherited from the early days of our planet, the earth is endowed with a source of heat by radioactivity" (1978, p. 707). Radiogenic heat can be stored within the planet as sensible heat, or as potential (gravitational) energy of elevation, or as elastic strain, and these stores can furnish the kinetic energy of plate motions.

We must first accept as a premise that virtually the entire solid earth's supply of radioisotopes was furnished, along with all other elements, at the time the earth was formed. It is most unlikely, however, that the earth, at the time of its formation as a planet about 4.5 Ga, could have contained the same quantity and distribution of radioisotopes that we find today. The obvious reason is that exponential radioactive decay steadily reduces the initial store of radioisotopes. We conclude that the total production of radiogenic heat within the earth was at the maximum level at the time of the earth's formation and has diminished ever since. The relative rates of decay of uranium, thorium, and potassium isotopes are not the same, but are well established for each isotope.

Figure 5.4 is a graph in which time is plotted on the horizontal axis. Time's "arrow" runs left-to-right for a total period of 5 billion years, but is here numbered in reverse order starting at the extreme right as the present (0.0 Ga) and going back to 5.0 Ga. This range accommodates age estimates for the completion of planetary condensation ranging from 4.5 to 5.0 Ga. Rate of radiogenic heat production per year is given on the vertical scale. Values of the total present store of radioisotopes must be estimated as the sum of estimated values of the four major radioisotopes of uranium, thorium, and potassium individually. Note that uranium-235 and potassium-40 have short half-lives in comparison with those of uranium-238 and thorium-232. Referring to the total curve, it is obvious that radiogenic heat production was much greater when the earth was first formed than it is at present—roughly by a factor of from three to six (Mason, 1966, p. 60-61).

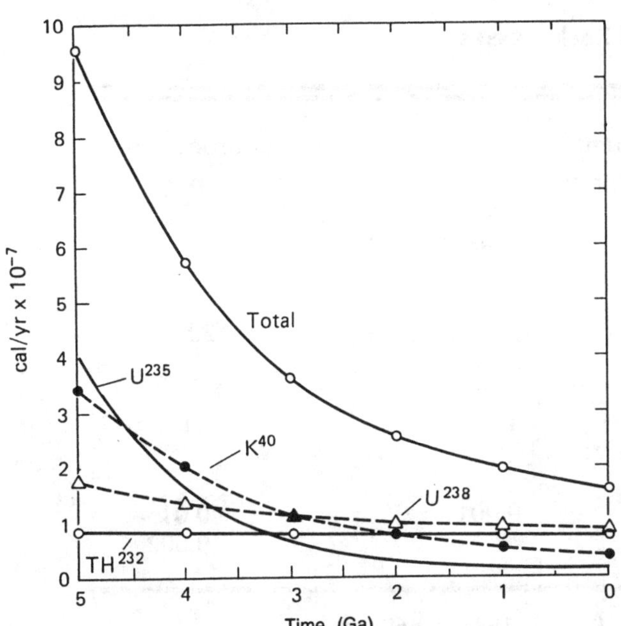

Figure 5.4 Rate of production of radiogenic heat projected back 5 billion years. (Based on data of A.P. Vinogradov, 1961, in *Geochemistry*, as adapted in B. Mason, 1966, *Principles of Geochemistry*, John Wiley & Sons, Inc., New York, p. 61, Figure 3.9.)

The implications of such a history are important in reconstructing the igneous history of the planet.

Our next step is to examine the geochemists' estimates of abundances of the radioisotopes in the common kinds of rock found in the crust today. The data we need are given in Table 5.2. The felsic rock class, including granite, granodiorite and diorite, and their extrusive equivalents, holds by far the largest content (ppm) of the radioisotopes. For the mafic igneous rock class, consisting of gabbro and olivine gabbro, with their extrusive equivalents basalt and olivine basalt, the amounts for all three radioisotopes, are smaller than for the felsic group by factors of one-fifth to one-half. For the ultramafic class—peridotite and dunite—the amounts are very much smaller than for the mafic class, with dunite being much less than peridotite. Looking back to Chapter 3, recall that the continental crust consists of an upper zone of predominantly felsic rock, grading down into a predominantly mafic lower zone, while ultramafic rock makes up the upper mantle. For the ocean basins, the crust consists of basalt overlying gabbro. This zonation is strongly supported by seismic data. From this zonation we may conclude that the radioisotopes are heavily concentrated in the upper part of the continental crust. Table 5.2 also shows the estimates of rates of heat production for the same radioisotopes for the same three rock classes. Figure 5.5 is a simplified graphic presentation of a set of heat production data given by Arthur Holmes (1978, p. 707). Here the large disparity between the felsic class and the mafic class is striking.

For the lower mantle, seismic data point to its content as being ultramafic rock, but this evidence does not permit us to assume that it is as severely depleted of radioisotopes as the upper mantle seems to be. Two opinions on the question were discussed in Chapter 3, with strong statements favoring an undepleted lower mantle (see DePaolo, 1981, and Silver, et al., 1985, for example) and equally forceful statements supporting its depletion (see Anderson, 1984a). The question of mantle depletion is important in formulating hypotheses of ongoing lower mantle convection. Whatever the actual content of radioisotopes in the lower mantle, there is little question that the mantle was at some time in the remote past differentiated from the metallic core, and it is to that first great igneous event we turn next.

5.3 Differentiation of Core and Mantle

We will assume that when the earth's formation by accretion was complete, the radioisotopes were uniformly distributed throughout the entire primitive planet. This conclusion would follow if the silicate minerals and iron are assumed to have been more or less uniformly mixed together by the continuous intensive breakup and reforming of planetesimals and protoplanets. As radiogenic heat accumulated at great depths, the temperature of the solid rock would have been raised to a level

Figure 5.5 A simplified and generalized graph showing the rate of radiogenic heat production within the three rock classes. (Based on data of A. Holmes, 1978, p. 707. Diagram copyright © by Arthur N. Strahler.)

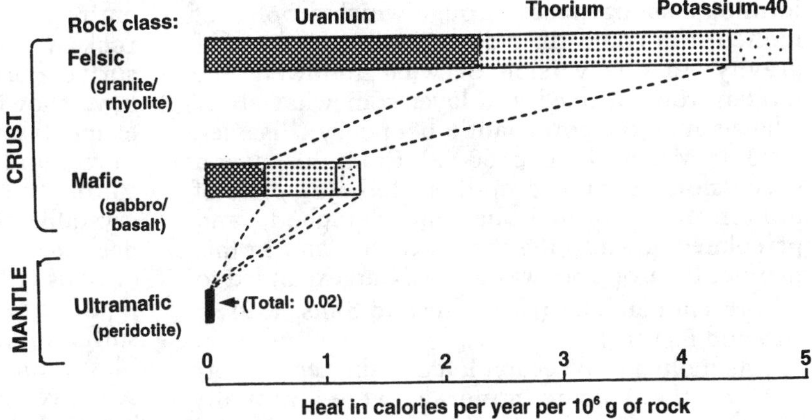

Table 5.2 Radioactive Content and Heat Production of Rock Classes

Rock Class and Name:	Radioisotope Content Parts per million (ppm) Uranium	Thorium	Potassium-40	Heat production 10^{-6} Wm^{-3}
Felsic				
Granite/Rhyolite	3-4	10-16	2	2.5
Mafic				
Gabbro/Basalt	0.5-0.7	2-3	1	1.1
Ultramafic				
Peridotite	0.02	0.06	0.001	0.01
Dunite	0.003	0.01	------	0.002

Data of Arthur Holmes, 1978, p. 707; L. Rybach, 1973, in H.N. Pollack, 1982, p. 469.

Data for constructing Figure 5.5:

Rock Class:	Calories per year per 10^6g of rock Uranium	Thorium	Potassium	Total
Felsic	2.3	2.1	0.5	4.9
Mafic	0.5	0.6	0.2	1.3
Ultramafic	0.01	0.01	0.0002	0.02

Data of Arthur Holmes, 1978, p. 707.

close to the melting point (Mason, 1966, p. 60-62). At a certain point in time, which may have been about one billion years after planetary accretion was completed, the melting point of iron would have been exceeded. This event may have occurred first in a depth zone ranging from 2500 t0 3000 km. The silicate minerals remained crystalline, forming a spongy mass through which droplets of molten iron could filter down under the force of gravity. In one version of what followed, the molten iron collected in a layer somewhat above what is now the core-mantle boundary (Elsasser, 1963, in Mason, 1966, p. 60-62). From this layer a succession of large drop-like blebs (*diapirs*) of molten iron formed, became detached, and percolated down to the earth's center, and in this manner the iron core was formed and expanded to its present diameter (Newsome and Sims, 1991, p. 929 and Figure 2).

As molten iron accumulated in the central core region, the silicate minerals were gradually displaced upward, bringing into play a new factor that would have acted to raise the earth's internal temperature. As the iron sank toward the center, its potential energy would have been converted into kinetic energy of molecular motion in the form of sensible heat. It seems likely that the additional heating was sufficient to cause melting or partial melting of a large proportion of the entire earth. At various times and places, melted rock would have risen as magma toward the surface, bringing up radioisotopes with it. As we have shown, minerals containing the radioactive elements are largely of felsic composition and tend to remain in the liquid state at temperatures lower than the mafic minerals. Cooling and crystallization of the mafic minerals would have been accompanied by a sinking of those mineral crystals (which are denser), leaving the less mafic liquid fraction to solidify closer to the earth's surface. Although such a process of differentiation is speculative, it offers a mechanism for the selective removal of the radioisotopes from the inner earth and their eventual concentration near the surface. So we can at least visualize how, during this great thermal event, the density layering of the earth might have come into existence, resulting in the concentration of metallic iron in the core, a less dense ultramafic rock mantle above it, and a mafic-felsic crust at the top. Some support for the conclusion that the iron core of the earth produces almost no radiogenic heat is found in the analysis of iron meteorites. These fragments of matter are thought to represent the disrupted cores of planetary objects of origin similar to the earth, and they show radioactive minerals in only very small quantities.

During and after the segregation process, the rate of total earth radiogenic heat production was steadily falling. Consequently, along with redistribution of the heat-generating isotopes, the final episodes of deep melting must have become fewer and eventually ceased. Today the earth is thermally stable, in the sense that melting and movement of magma are limited to an extremely shallow layer compared with the earth's total diameter. The inner core and much of the mantle are no longer subject to melting through the accumulation of excess heat, although continued large-scale mantle convection has been possible by slow flowage in a plastic state at temperatures below the melting point (see Chapter 3).

It is fortunate, indeed, that the chemistry of the radioactive elements is such that they would tend to be carried towards the earth's surface throughout its history. If, on the other hand, they had tended to sink and collect near its center, the heat produced by their concentrated activity would have repeatedly melted the earth. Under such conditions, no planetary stability would have been possible throughout geologic history.

As we find conditions today, radiogenic heat production in the core is perhaps negligible, while the rate of surfaceward flow of heat within the upper mantle and crust closely balances the rate of heat production. Only in the soft layer of the upper mantle (the asthenosphere) is local melting and the rise of magma an important ongoing occurrence. It is to that igneous phenomenon we turn next in this chapter.

5.4 An Overview of Global Igneous Activity

The theory of plate tectonics has made possible new interpretations of the places where igneous activity occurs over the globe and the kinds of magmas that have reached shallow depths in the crust or have emerged as extrusives. We begin with a listing of the diverse forms of igneous activity occurring along plate boundaries and within plates. Figure 5.6 is a composite diagram to accompany this list. Figure 5.7 is a world map of volcanoes.

Igneous activity at spreading plate boundaries separating two areas of oceanic lithosphere is predominately one of rise of basaltic magma to make new basaltic dikes and lava flows. This basalt forms the uppermost igneous layer of the oceanic crust (Figure 5.6). Beneath the basalt, a layer of gabbro is formed simultaneously, as large quantities of mafic magma solidify in the space created by plate spreading. Normally, basalt extrusion occurs at a depth of some 2 km below the ocean surface along the mid-oceanic ridge.

Another form of basaltic extrusion occurs within the broad expanses of oceanic lithosphere to form *volcanic island chains* or isolated groups of volcanoes. These are often far distant from plate boundaries; i.e., they are intraplate phenomena. The Hawaiian Islands are an outstanding example. Each volcanic chain and group of this class is thought to have been formed above a magma source called a *hotspot* (also *hot spot*). Geologists have visualized the hotspot as being located over a slowly rising column of heated mantle rock known as a *mantle plume* (Figure 5.6). As we shall explain later in this chapter, whereas the mantle plume and its associated hotspot remain approximately fixed in position relative to the asthenosphere for long periods of time, the overlying oceanic lithospheric plate is drifting past it in continual motion. As a pulse of volcanic activity occurs above the hotspot, a volcanic island, or island group, comes into being, but is then carried away with the moving plate. A short time later, a new pulse of volcanic activity occurs above the hotspot, forming a new volcanic island. In time, a chain of islands results, providing evidence of the direction and the speed of plate motion. (See also guyots and coral atolls, Chapter 4.)

Volcanic islands are also found above active hotspots located on or very close to the spreading plate boundary of the mid-oceanic ridge. A particularly important present-day example is Iceland, which lies over the spreading boundary between the North American plate and the Eurasian plate (Figure 5.7). Here, basalt lavas have been accumulating in large quantities above the Mid-Atlantic Ridge and just east of it. Iceland has several active volcanoes, the larger ones basaltic shield volcanoes, the smaller ones, basaltic cinder cones. (See Figure 5.12.) A second example is the Azores Island group in the central Atlantic, just east of the Mid-Atlantic Ridge. A third example is the Galapagos Islands, a group located not far south of the spreading boundary between the Cocos plate and the Nazca plate. (For these examples, see our global plate map, Figure 7.3.)

Isolated volcanic activity also occurs within continental lithospheric plates, far from presently active boundaries. From a hotspot beneath the continental lithospheric plate, enormous volumes of basaltic magma may rise to the surface, emerging through fissures, and pouring out upon the landscape as thick basalt flows. Called *flood basalts*, these outpourings continue until a total thickness of some thousands of meters of basalt layers have accumulated (Figure 5.6). Comparable to the continental flood basalts in areal extent and volume are large "submarine plateaus" (or

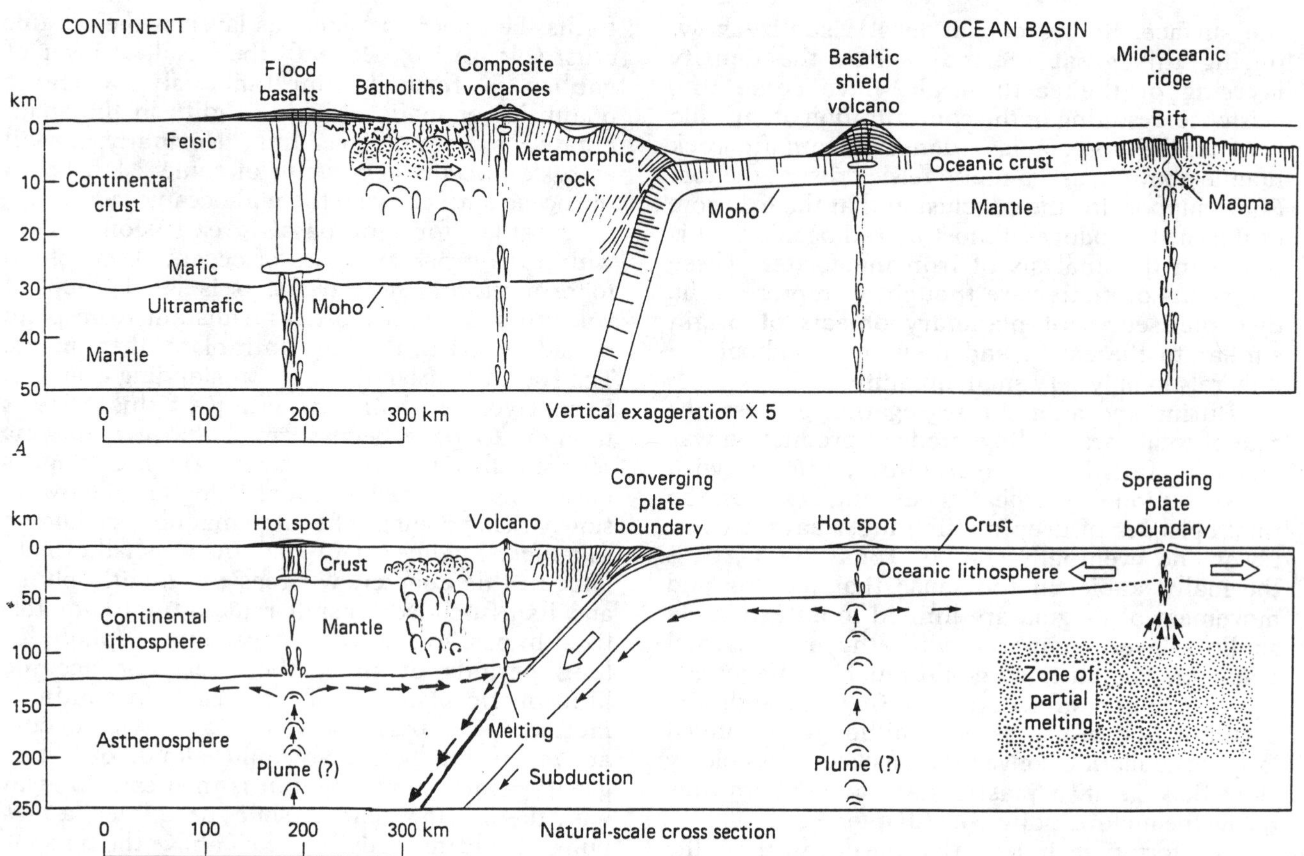

Figure 5.6 Schematic cross sections showing the relationship to plate tectonics of various forms of igneous activity. (A) Cross section with vertical exaggeration to show crustal and surface features of the uppermost 50 km. (B) Natural-scale cross section to show lithospheric plates and asthenosphere in the upper 250 km. (Copyright © by Arthur N. Strahler.)

"submarine platforms") formed of thick layers of basalt flows. These are not shown in Figure 5.6, but are described in detail later in this chapter. (See Basalt Plateaus.)

Besides flood basalts, some small, isolated volcanic areas within the continents are interpreted as igneous activity located over a hotspot. One example is the Yellowstone National Park volcanic area where many hot springs represent hydrothermal activity over a small body of hot magma. Lava flows formerly produced in this area are rhyolites formed from acidic (felsic) magma.

Volcanic eruptions of the more acidic lavas (andesite, rhyolite) that produce stratovolcanoes are largely concentrated directly above descending plates of active subduction zones. *Volcanic arcs* of great andesitic cones, many of them active today, occupy positions above these zones. The subduction zones bounding the Pacific plate generate a great "ring of fire" that borders the Pacific Ocean (Figure 5.7). Volcanic arcs are of two kinds. One is the oceanic volcanic arc, bordered on both sides by oceanic crust. The other is the continental volcanic arc, built upon continental crust, but derived from magma rising from a descending oceanic lithospheric plate of the adjacent subduction plate boundary and from the mantle above the plate (Figure 5.6). Finally on this list of forms of igneous activity, the continental crust contains large masses of felsic plutonic igneous rocks in the form of batholiths (Figure 5.6). The magma for these batholiths is shown as originating in the lower part of the continental crust.

5.5 Magma Formation in the Upper Mantle

There is general agreement among geologists that magma can be formed by the melting of rock in a certain depth zone in the asthenosphere. Evidence from the low-velocity layer of earthquake waves, described in Chapter 3, indicates that the upper mantle under the oceanic crust is closest to its melting point in the depth range of 100 to 200 km (see Figures 3.1B and 3.15). It seems most likely that only a small fraction of the mantle rock in this depth range actually melts, while the larger proportion of the mass remains crystalline. This phenomenon is called *partial melting* (Ernst, 1969, p. 106-109). The melted fraction, which is a liquid less dense than the crystalline fraction, tends to rise through the spongelike crystalline mass and to collect in magma pockets at shallower depth. It is

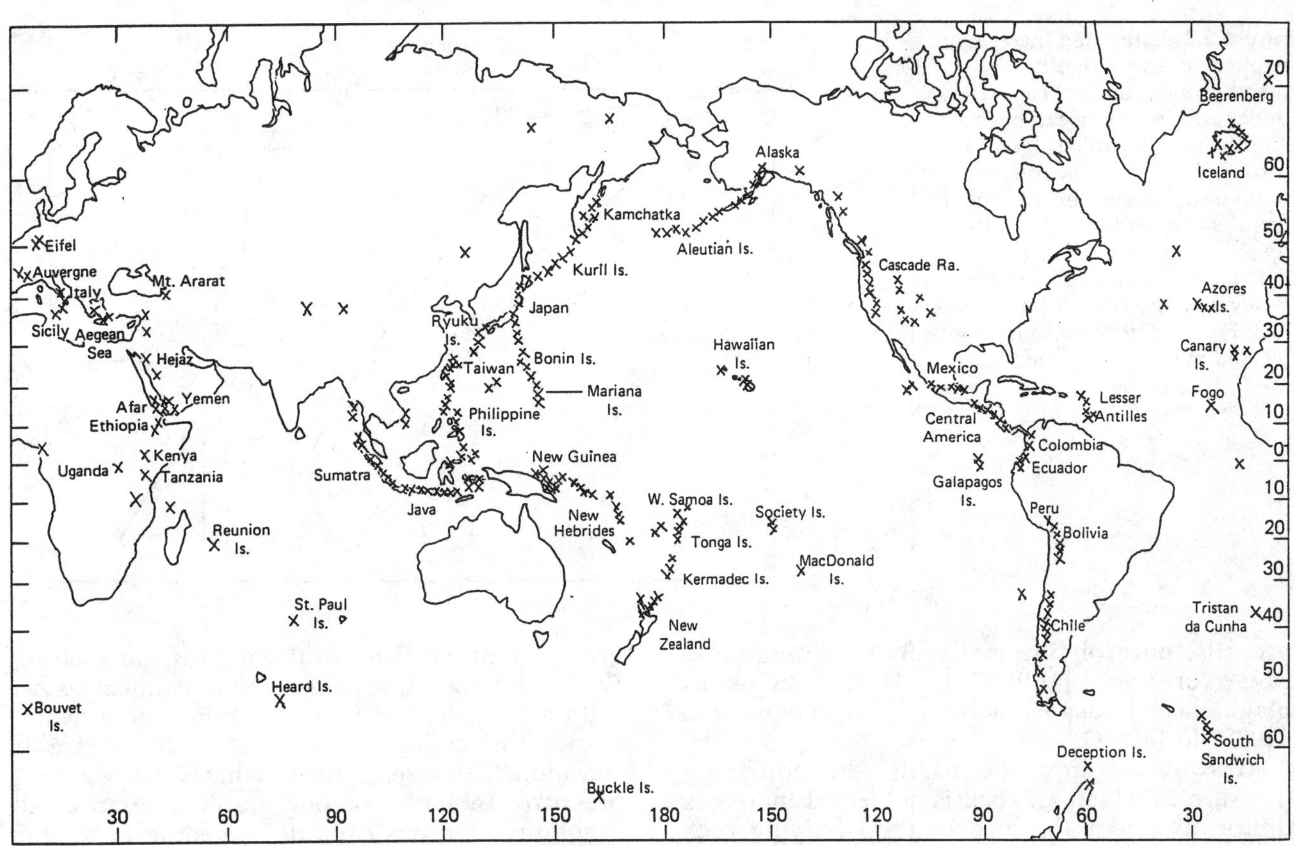

Figure 5.7 Sketch map of the earth showing the locations of volcanoes known or judged to have erupted within the past 12,000 years, as determined by radiocarbon dating, geological evidence, and other techniques. Each "X" shows a single volcano or a cluster of volcanoes. (Data originally compiled by the Smithsonian Institution, Washington, D.C. Based on a map published in 1979 by World Data Center A for Solid Earth Geophysics at the Geophysical and Solar-Terrestrial Data Center, National Oceanic and Atmospheric Administration, Boulder Colorado. Map copyright © by Arthur N. Strahler.)

supposed that the enormous volume of mafic magma continually rising along the spreading plate boundaries collects first in magma chambers near the base of the oceanic crust at a depth of 4 to 6 km below the ocean floor. Magma that rises from a location above a descending lithospheric plate at a subduction (converging) boundary is produced under quite different conditions and depths, as explained later in this chapter. Under the continental crust conditions are generally unfavorable for spontaneous partial melting because of the great lithospheric thickness.

In Chapter 3 we described the composition of the upper mantle as that of peridotite—mostly olivine and pyroxene. Included in this peridotite are minor amounts of calcic plagioclase feldspar, which, together with pyroxene (and sometimes olivine), makes up basalt. Partial melting of the peridotite would free the necessary components to form pryoxene and calcic plagioclase feldspar, which would move slowly upward, accumulating in chambers of basalt magma beneath the spreading plate boundaries. It is important to note that enormous quantities of basaltic magma are continuously required to supply the basaltic rock that must be added to the lithosphere along these spreading boundaries. The hypothesis of partial melting meets this requirement because the bulk of the upper mantle is enormous.

Temperatures can only be estimated downward through the deep crust and into the upper mantle. Figure 5.8 is a graph showing the estimated increase in temperature with depth. Two curves (geotherms) are shown, one typical of conditions under the continents, the other for conditions under the ocean basins. Both curves show that while the temperature increases, the rate at which it does so falls off rapidly with increasing depth. Temperatures within the suboceanic asthenosphere are largely in the range from 900°C to 1200°C. For comparison, the melting point of basalt (peridotite) at the earth's surface is about 1100°C. It might seem like a simple procedure to measure the melting point of a specimen of igneous rock and use the temperature—depth curves in Figure 5.8 to find the depth at which melting is to be expected and magma will be formed.

Unfortunately, the actual relationships are not that simple. The temperature at which silicate minerals will melt depends upon several factors. Each mineral has its own melting point for a given environment. For example, in the surface environment, under the atmospheric pressure that

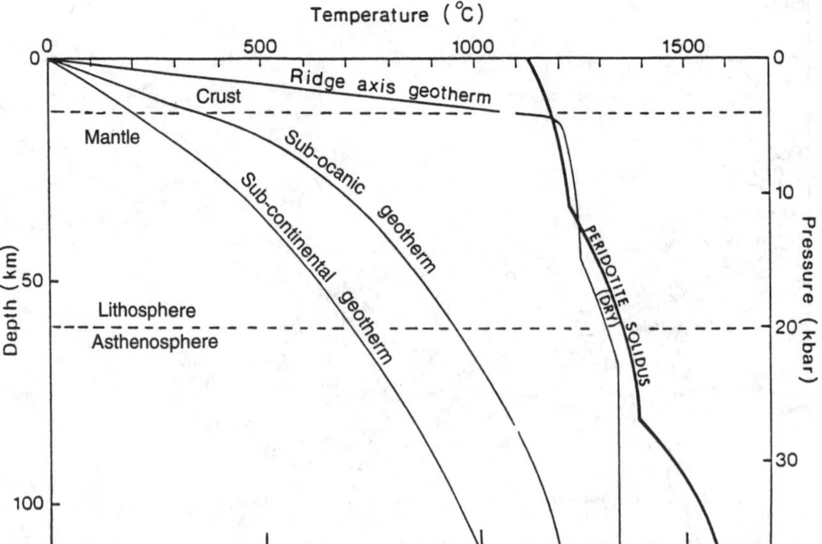

Figure 5.8 Estimated increase in temperature with depth (geothermal gradient) separately under continents, ocean basins, and the mid-oceanic ridges. The broken line shows the melting point of dry peridotite. (Adapted from data of Anthony Hall, 1987, *Igneous Petrology*, Longman Science & Technology and John Wiley & Sons, joint publishers, p. 323, Figure 236. Data sources given by Hall in the figure legend).

prevails, pure olivine melts in the temperature range of about 1600°C to 1800°C, whereas plagioclase feldspar melts in the range from 1200°C to 1400°C.

Downward into the earth, the confining pressure to which all rock is subjected increases uniformly under the load of the overlying rock layer. In other words, confining pressure increases in a direct proportion to depth, assuming the rock to be homogeneous. (See pressure scale on Figure 5.8.) The unit of pressure used by geologists is the *kilobar*, which is equal to one thousand bars, a *bar* being approximately equal to the pressure of the earth's atmosphere at sea level—about 1 kg per sq cm. An increase in pressure causes the temperature of the melting point of a given mineral or rock to increase. For example, the melting point of iron at a depth of about 100 km, under a confining pressure of 40 kb, is about 1650°C, which is 150°C higher than at the surface.

When the conditions shown in Figure 5.8 prevail, the curve of the melting point (the *solidus*) of dry peridotite lies far to the right of the typical temperature curve beneath the deep ocean floors, and no melting is occurring. But when we plot the geotherm directly beneath the spreading axis, it crosses over the dry-peridotite solidus at a depth of about 12 km below sealevel, which is about 6 km below the ocean floor. This juxtaposition of the two curves, which continues down to a depth of about 35 km, calls for melting to be taking place. What physical change in the lithosphere and asthenosphere is required to bring about these conditions favorable to melting?

The answer to our question requires that we apply the principle that a reduction to the confining pressure of the rock will bring it closer to the melting point. If pressure can continue to fall while at the same time there is no appreciable loss of heat contained in the rock, melting becomes inevitable. This process is called *decompression melting*. So our next step is to look for a tectonic process that will lead to decompression melting. For the mid-ocean spreading plate boundaries, we call on a local thinning of the lithosphere, which allows the asthenosphere below it to rise in elevation. This rise, in turn, reduces the confining pressure. In terms of our graph in Figure 5.8, decompression has caused the geotherm to shift far toward the right, so that it crosses over the dry-melt curve.

Besides lithospheric thinning horizontally, there may also be acting a lifting force, or pressure, exerted from below by rising mantle rock. We may want to think of the upward pressure of rising mantle between two symmetrical mantle circulation cells rotating on horizontal axes, as depicted in Figure 3.26B. As the mantle rock moves away from the spreading axis, it sinks to lower depths under a thickening lithosphere, so that the geotherm shifts back toward the left on the graph (Figure 5.8) and stable pressure relationships are restored.

Later in this chapter we will return to the subject of decompression melting under the mid-oceanic ridges, giving more details of how partial melting allows fractionation of the rising mantle rock to take place and to separate the oceanic basalt/gabbro crust from the ultramafic mantle below.

5.6 Igneous and Hydrothermal Activity at Oceanic Spreading Boundaries

Igneous activity in the axial zone of oceanic spreading plate boundaries has come under direct observation by geologists. One of the most remarkable pioneering submarine discovery missions was the probing of the axial rift of the mid-oceanic ridge of the North Atlantic Ocean at a point about 650 km southwest of the Azores Islands. You can find this area on Marie Tharp's topographic Diagram B of Plate 1 in Chapter 4. It lies in the middle of the map, just below the center, in a short length of ridge axis offset between two transform faults. Here, starting in 1971, began the French-American Mid-Ocean Undersea Study known as Project FAMOUS. The project culminated in the summer of 1974 in a series of 42 dives by three submersibles, each carrying a crew of three and capable of reaching the seafloor—here at a depth of 2000 to 3000 m—for direct observation and sampling. Thousands of photographs were taken, and a detailed map was made of a small area of the floor.

As expected from dredged rock samples, the floor of the axial rift zone proved to be underlain with fresh basaltic lava flows taking the form of pillow lavas. As the lava is extruded from narrow cracks and comes in contact with the seawater, it solidifies into strange bulbous and tubelike shapes. Although no volcanic activity was in progress at the time of the explorations, the very high rate of heat flow upward through the ocean floor suggested that a magma chamber is present not more than about 2 km below the surface.

Another feature of great significance is the presence of numerous open fractures, or *fissures*, up to 10 m wide, in the basalt lava floor. More than 400 cracks, some only hairline fractures, were counted in an area of about 6 sq km. Most of the fractures were oriented parallel with the ridge axis, and are regarded as conclusive evidence of a pulling apart of the ocean crust.

Researchers then turned their attention to the spreading boundaries of the eastern Pacific Ocean basin. In the late 1970s, *Alvin*, a manned submersible operated by the Woods Hole Oceanographic Institution, made many dives to permit observation of the floor of these rifts in two localities. (Refer to the world tectonic map, Figure 7.3.) One dive was made along the Galapagos rift, which is the east-west plate boundary between the Cocos and Nazca plates, approximately on the equator and not far from the Galapagos Islands. The second locality was on the East Pacific Rise off the Gulf of California, on the rift boundary between the Pacific plate and the northern end of the Cocos plate. (This part of the Cocos plate is also recognized as a small independent plate, the Rivera plate.) Spreading rates on these plate boundaries are about 6 cm/yr, which is much faster than on the Mid-Atlantic Ridge axis, where the rate is only 2 cm/yr.

Perhaps as a result of faster spreading, the eastern Pacific rifts are low in topographic relief; they lack the mountainous flanks seen in the Mid-Atlantic rift. Fresh lavas on the rift floors also differ in surface appearance. Whereas pillow lavas dominate the Mid-Atlantic rift floor, smooth-surfaced sheet lavas are extensive in the eastern Pacific rift floors. The sheet lavas have flow features somewhat like the pahoehoe (ropy) lava surfaces of the Hawaiian basalt flows. The eastern Pacific rifts also have pillow lavas that form hill-like volcanic masses.

The most newsworthy discovery in the eastern Pacific rift floors was of numerous thermal springs issuing from vents in the pillow lavas. In the Galapagos rift these are warm springs that support unique colonies of sea worms 2.5 m long and large clams, as well as shrimp, crabs, and fish. In the East Pacific Rise were found strong jets of hot water (temperature over 350°C). These jets are densely turbid and appear either white or black; they have been called "smokers." The hot water carries high concentrations of sulfides of copper, iron, and zinc, which are precipitated around the vent, building up a solid stalk-like "chimney" of mineral matter. The hot water jets represent seawater that has penetrated the permeable pillow lavas, become heated by the surrounding rock, heavily mineralized, and returned to the ocean floor under high pressure. Figure 5.9 is a schematic diagram showing the flow paths of cold ground water entering the ocean floor and returning as hot water. This hydrothermal process not only transports a large amount of heat out of the crust beneath the rift, but appears to supply a large quantity of manganese to the ocean, along with other chemical components of seawater.

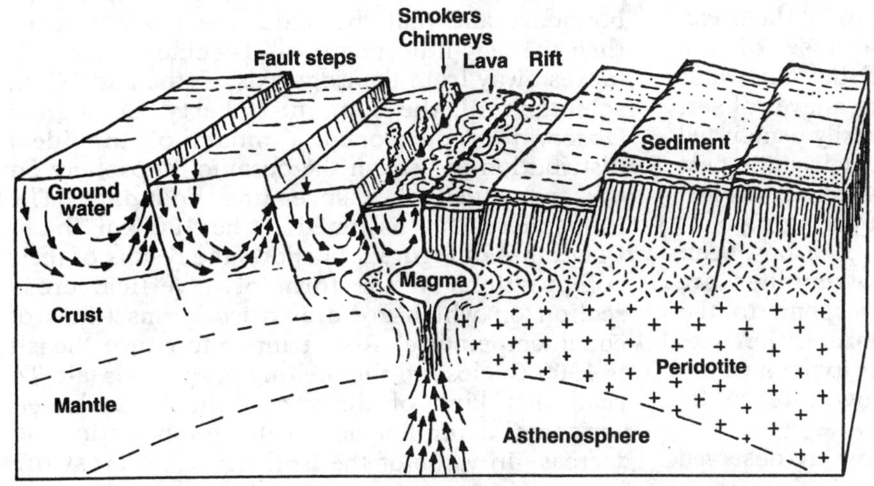

Figure 5.9 Schematic diagram of a spreading plate boundary with axial rift, rising magma, and block faulting. Geology is shown at right; ground-water circulation system at left. Features are not drawn to scale. (Copyright © by Arthur N. Strahler.)

5.7 Heat Flow and Spreading Plates

There is a steady upward flow of heat through the earth's crust. This quantity of heat is extremely small compared with that received by the earth's surface from solar radiation. The total outward heat flow in one year per unit of surface area is only enough to melt an ice layer 6 mm thick. Therefore the earth's heat flow from depth is of no significance in the earth's surface heat balance or in powering the atmospheric and oceanic circulation systems.

The increase in temperature with depth, or *geothermal gradient*, has been well known for many decades from observations in deep mines and bore holes on the continents; it has a value of about 3 C° per 100 m. In SI units, the rate of upward flow of heat within the solid earth is given as Wm^{-2} (watts per square meter). The average rate of heat flow for our planet as a whole is estimated at about 80 mWm^{-2} (Fowler, 1990, p. 234).

Only in the past three decades has the heat flow gradient beneath the ocean floors been widely measured; it ranges around 50 mWm^{-2} for large expanses of the deep ocean basins, but rises to much higher rates along the mid-oceanic ridges. (Sclater et al., 1990a, 1990b). Heat flow for the continents averages about 60 mWm^2, but is about 40 mWm^2 over the Precambrian shields and about 70 mWm^2 in the Mesozoic/Cenozoic orogenic areas (Lee, 1970, as shown in Stacey, 1977, p. 185, Table 7.1). Thus heat flow rate of the continental crust decreases with the rock age, and this must be taken into account in comparing oceanic rates with continental rates. Low values for the Precambrian shields can perhaps be attributed to the long period of erosional removal, the decay of radioactive isotopes, and the great thickness of old lithosphere. (See Fowler, 1990, p. 243-246, for a discussion of this topic.) In contrast, the basaltic ocean floor is very young, and it should be compared to the correspondingly young continental crust. We then have 60 to 80 mWm^{-2} for oceanic crust vs. 70 mWm^{-2} for the Mesozoic/-Cenozoic continental crust.

Measuring heat flow through the deep ocean floors is not as difficult as it might seem, largely because of two facts. The temperature of the ocean floor is extremely uniform because of the enormous layer of overlying cold bottom water that moves very sluggishly. Second, a layer of soft sediment is widely present and is easily penetrated by the piston coring apparatus. To determine heat flow, temperature sensors, called *thermister probes*, are attached to the outside of the coring pipe, as shown in Figure 5.10. After the core has been driven into the sediment, a few minutes are allowed for the thermisters to respond to the temperature of the surrounding ooze. Differences of temperature from one thermister to the next are recorded, allowing the heat flow rate to be calculated.

Some very high rates of heat flow are observed

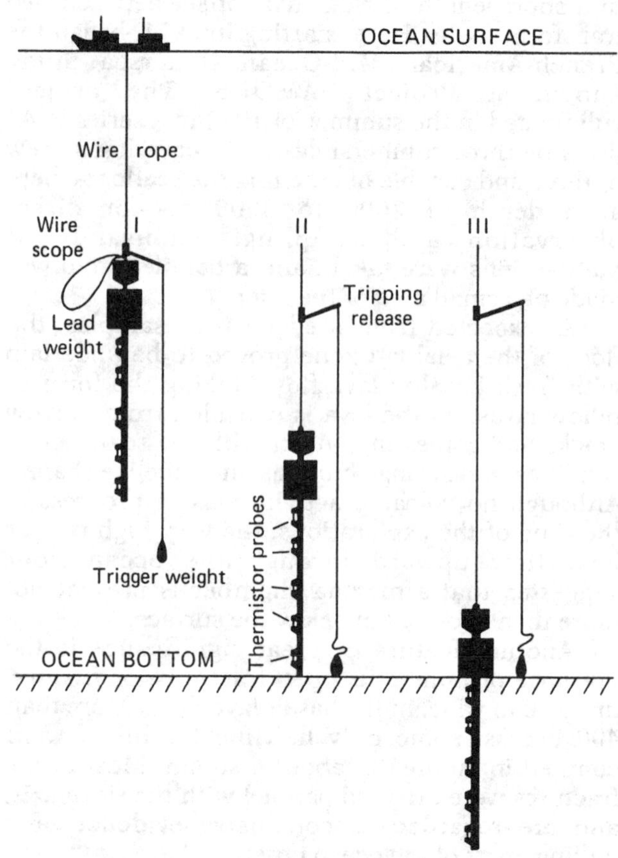

Figure 5.10 The apparatus used to measure heat flow in sediments of the ocean floor consists of thermister probes attached to the pipe used to obtain piston core samples. The instrument for recording the temperature of the probes is located in the lead weight. (Courtesy of Lamont-Doherty Earth Observatory of Columbia Unversity.)

along the active spreading boundaries, represented by the axial rift of the mid-oceanic ridge. Generally, heat flow along the axial rift is over 200 mWm^{-2} and in some spots as high as 300 mWm^{-2}. The high rate of heat flow is just what we would predict for a zone of lava extrusion, with a chain of magma chambers present at shallow depth.

If we accept as assumed that new oceanic lithosphere is being formed along the spreading boundary and that the plates are moving apart, then the new lithosphere will become cooler as it moves away from the ridge axis. In the late 1970s, scientists of the Lamont-Doherty Geological Observatory developed a model of the ideal distribution of heat in the oceanic lithosphere on the two sides of a spreading boundary. The lithosphere was assumed to be 100 km thick. Diagram A of Figure 5.11 shows the results of their computations in the form of a vertical cross section on which are drawn isotherms (lines of equal temperature). Rock temperature near the rift is 1300°C, close to the melting point of basalt. To read this kind of diagram, follow a selected horizontal depth line across the graph, noting the decrease in value of the isotherms that cross the line. As the plate becomes cooler, the volume of the rock contracts and its density increases. The plate then sinks lower into the asthenosphere, with the result that the depth to bedrock seafloor increases away from the spreading axis. Points on Figure 5.11B show the increase in depth with distance actually observed in the northwestern Atlantic Ocean. The theoretical curve of deepening provided by the model is shown as a continuous curve on the same graph. The agreement of the observed depths with the predicted depths is very close.

Because the plate becomes cooler with increasing distance from the spreading axis, the rate of heat flow through the ocean bottom should also decrease with distance. Points on Figure 5.11C show the heat-flow values measured in seafloor sediment in the northwestern Atlantic Ocean.

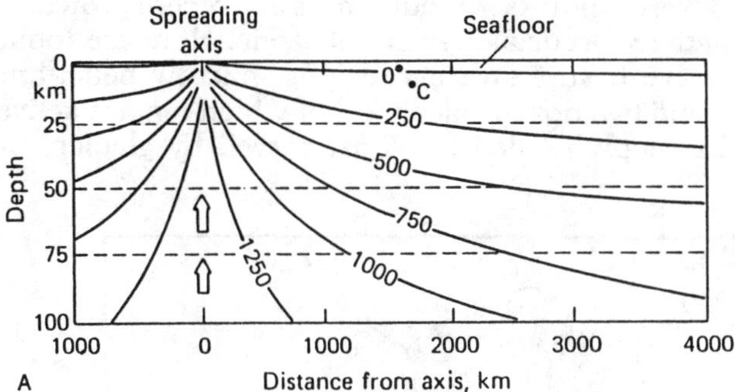

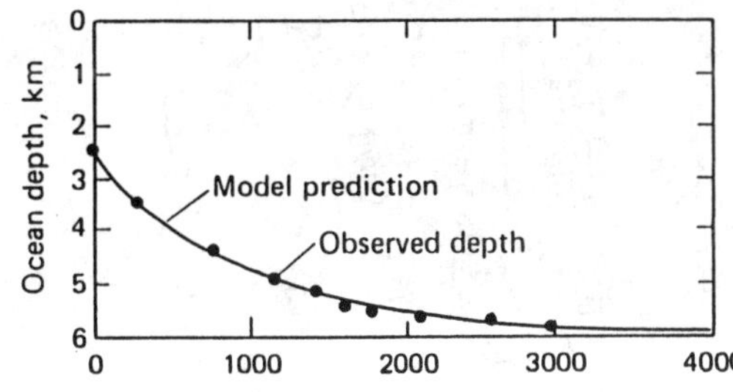

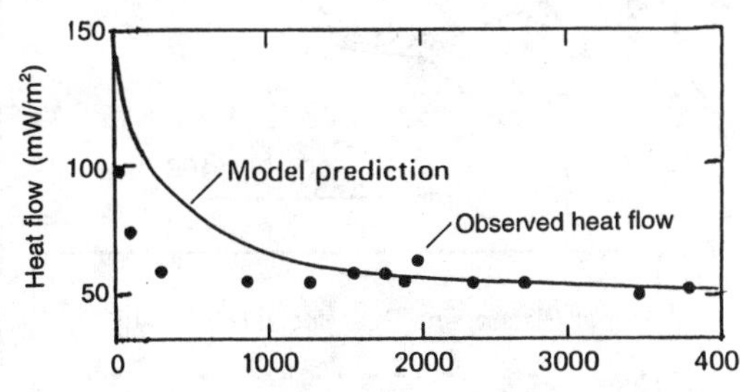

Figure 5.11 Temperature, depth, and heat flow in the vicinity of a spreading plate boundary. (A) Ideal distribution of temperatures in the lithosphere, as computed by model. (B) Observed and predicted depths of the ocean floor. (C) Observed and predicted rates of heat flow through the ocean floor. (Redrawn from M.G. Langseth, Lamont-Doherty Earth Observatory of Columbia University, *Yearbook 1977*, v. 4, p. 42. Used by permission.)

Although the observed values are highest near the axis and decrease with distance, the rates are much lower than predicted by the model in the first 1000 km. Scientists of the Lamont-Doherty Observatory offered the following explanation for the lower observed heat-flow values (Langseth, 1977, p. 42).

Cold ocean water penetrates deep into the crustal rock near the spreading axis, becomes highly heated, and returns to the ocean floor by other flow paths. As illustrated in Figure 5.9, the water emerges in submarine springs located in areas where bedrock is exposed on the seafloor and sediment cover is absent. Thus, by a convection process water circulation effectively carries a great deal of the residual heat out from the crust, and that explains why heat-flow measurements taken by thermister probes in seafloor sediments show values lower than the model predicts. The same relationships between observed and predicted heat-flow values have been found near the spreading plate boundary in the North Pacific Ocean.

According to Henry N. Pollack, an authority on this subject, of the total heat loss at the surface of the earth, "the greater part—nearly three fourths of the total—is exhausted through the creation and subsequent cooling of new oceanic lithosphere at oceanic ridges. The plates of oceanic lithosphere serve as the cooling fins of the Earth's heat engine" (1982, p. 472).

5.8 Magmas of the Spreading Rifts

At this point we need to review some of the basic petrologic data of extrusive mafic magmas of spreading plate boundary rifts, as well as intrusive mafic and ultramafic magmas that solidify in layered zones beneath the extrusive layer. The following table reviews the major mineral components of these magmas:

Intrusive	Extrusive	Typical composition (% by vol)		
		Calcic plagioclase feldspar	Pyroxene	Olivine
Gabbro	Basaalt	43	57	0
Olivine gabbro	Olivine basalt	18	64	18
Peridotite		0	40	60
Dunite		0	0	100

Basalt of the mid-ocean ridges is designated by the acronym MORB (MidOcean Ridge Basalt). The typical basalt of the spreading ridges is *tholeiitic basalt*, or *tholeiite*, a silica-oversaturated basalt characterized by the presence of orthopyroxene, the low-calcium variety of pyroxene. Olivine may be present, but is not necessary to define the rock. The alternative name *subalkaline basalt* is preferred by some petrologists. Magma brought up into hotspots above deep mantle plumes may include tholeiite in the earliest stages of eruption, but this typically gives way to alkaline basalts (alkali-rich basalts) undersaturated in silica.

MORB is thought to originate at shallow depths by fractional crystallization of an ultramafic magma rising from the underlying upper mantle (Ehlers and Blatt, 1982, p. 205; Condie, 1989, p. 224-226). On later pages of this chapter we show different models of this fractionation zone, visualized as located under the axis of the mid-oceanic ridge at depths of 5 to 8 km, just above the Moho.

Through eons of geologic time, depletion of felsic components of the primeval mantle occurred as the incompatible elements were segregated in the subduction-melting process and concentrated in the felsic upper crust. Radiogenic isotopes were also segregated into the upper crustal layer as the continents were formed and enlarged. As a result, MORB has smaller fractions of the products of radioactive decay than we would expect to be found in magmas rising up in plumes from the lower mantle. Thus MORB is described as having been formed from a *depleted mantle*. We will refer to this subject again on later pages. (For in-depth coverage of the petrology of magmas, see Condie, 1989, Chapter 7.)

5.9 Sheeted Dikes of Iceland

The North Atlantic island of Iceland lies across the axis of the mid-oceanic ridge. Here, geologists can see surface exposures of the spreading plate axis and examine the rocks in detail. Figure 5.12 is a geologic map of Iceland showing the rock ages and their distributions along with the principal volcanic centers. The spreading axis is marked by a great troughlike rift running northeast-to-southwest through the central part of the island. Several points of current and recent volcanic activity occur along this rift zone. Here are found active fissure swarms in long, narrow belts, and some two dozen volcanoes, of which ten are active. In deeply eroded canyons, carved by glaciers on

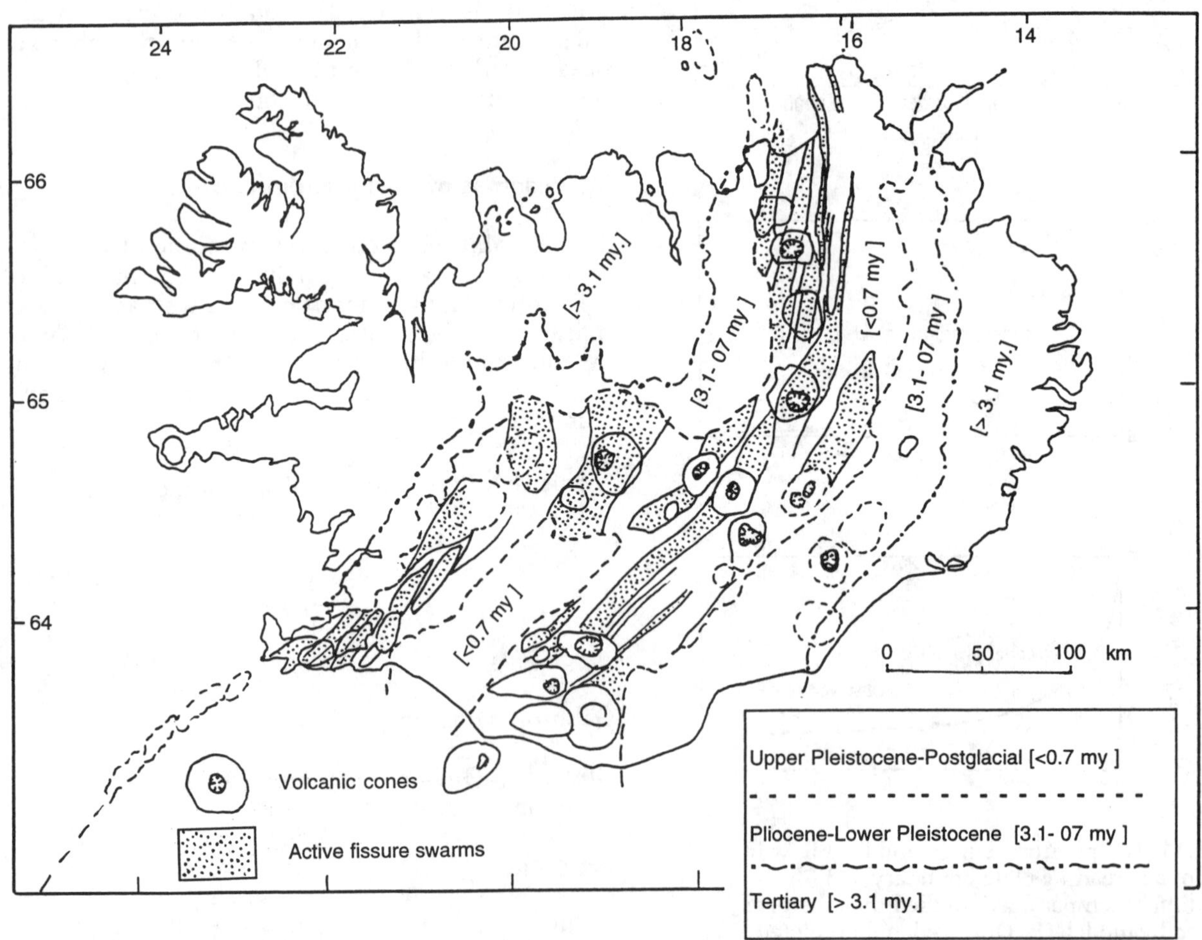

Figure 5.12 Simplified geologic map of Iceland showing volcanic and tectonic features of the Mid-Atlantic Ridge. (Based on original data of Sasemundsson, 1978, as presented by Johann Helgason, 1984, *Geology*, v. 12, p. 213. Reproduced with permission of the publisher, The Geological Society of America, Boulder, Colorado, USA. Copyright © 1984.)

older parts of Iceland, the geologist can examine the bedrock structure of the spreading zone. Particularly striking is the presence of innumerable vertical basalt dikes, stacked side by side like upended decks of cards in an arrangement called *sheeted dikes*.

Combining the seafloor observations of Project FAMOUS, which showed pillow lavas at the surface, with the observations of sheeted dikes on Iceland, it was possible in the 1980s to reconstruct an idealized section of the rock structure in new oceanic crust formed in spreading zones (Figure 5.13). At the top of the igneous rock sequence are pillow lavas, fed by dikes; below that, a zone of sheeted dikes through which the lava had risen in fissures. Still farther down we infer the presence of a layer of gabbro, a plutonic mafic rock of the same composition as basalt. The gabbro would represent magma bodies that cooled very slowly as they moved away from the spreading axis. Mineral crystals settle to the base of the melt layer, forming a layered coarse-textured plutonic rock known as a *cumulate*. The base of the gabbro was assumed to mark the seismic Moho, with a rather abrupt transition into denser ultramafic rock (peridotite) of the upper mantle. Note that this reconstructed section shows the completed crust as it would be found at some distance away from the spreading rift. This location is obvious from the presence of a rather uniform pelagic sediment layer at the top.

5.10 Ophiolite Suites

The layered sequence of mafic and ultramafic rocks we have described has been identified in rock exposures on the continental crust where it is called an *ophiolite suite*, or simply an *ophiolite*. We now realize that these occurrences represent slabs or slices of oceanic crust that became caught up in

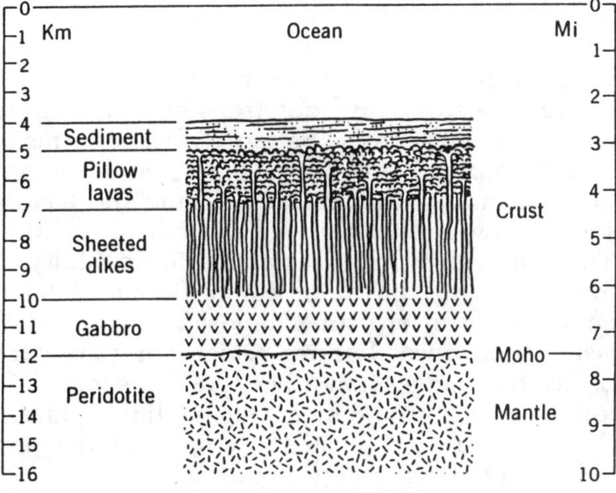

Figure 5.13 A schematic diagram of the composition and structure of oceanic crust, formed at an accreting plate margin in the zone of seafloor spreading. The sediment is deposited later, after the crust has moved away from the spreading zone. (Copyright © by Arthur N. Strahler.)

continental orogens and were carried inland along overthrust faults, eventually becoming part of the continental crust (Chapter 9).

Figure 5.14 shows layered columns for six well known terrestrial ophiolite suites (Lewis, 1983, p. 152). Serpentinization had affected the gabbroic layer and its cumulates, as well as the ultramafic rock in the upper part of the mantle. Serpentine has been sampled from rock of the axial zone of the mid-oceanic ridge. The line of stepped horizontal arrows separates crust from mantle. The crustal thickness ranges from 2 km to 8.5 km. Brian T.R. Lewis explains:

> The wide thickness variation of the basaltic sections indicates significant variations in the quantity of basaltic magma available for the formation of these sections. Since the degree of melting is very sensitive to temperature, one could infer from these data that these sections were formed in areas with different mantle temperatures (1983, p. 152).

While there is good agreement among geologists that ophiolites found today in compressional orogens represent former oceanic crust, there is debate as to the kind of oceanic crust that a particular ophiolite suite represents. In Chapter 8 we describe different locations and circumstances under which spreading boundaries are formed. Besides the great mid-oceanic rift system, described in this chapter, local spreading rifts occur on a smaller scale in backarc basins, and there the new oceanic crust differs in some important respects from what we describe here.

To give an example of the continuing debate about the details of ophiolite origin, the following evidence is relevant. Age determinations have shown that certain ophiolites were added to continental crust very soon after being formed (Roger Mason, 1985, p. 138-139). This relationship seems most unlikely for a spreading boundary located far from continents for several consecutive geologic periods—the Atlantic basin, for example. The spreading rift must have been very close to a subduction zone and would have been thrust up on the continent soon after the ophiolite was formed. How this situation might apply to an arc-continent collision is explained in Chapter 9.(See "Detachment and Delamination," and Figure 9.2.c.) The process is called "obduction" or "supra-subduction." Obduction during the docking of a terrane is also described in Chapter 9. (See Figure 9.34.)

5.11 Slow-Spreading and Fast-Spreading Plate Boundaries

Before turning to cross-sectional models of the igneous activity beneath spreading oceanic rifts, we need to recognize the basic differences in form, dimension, and intensity of igneous activity between typical slow-spreading and fast-spreading

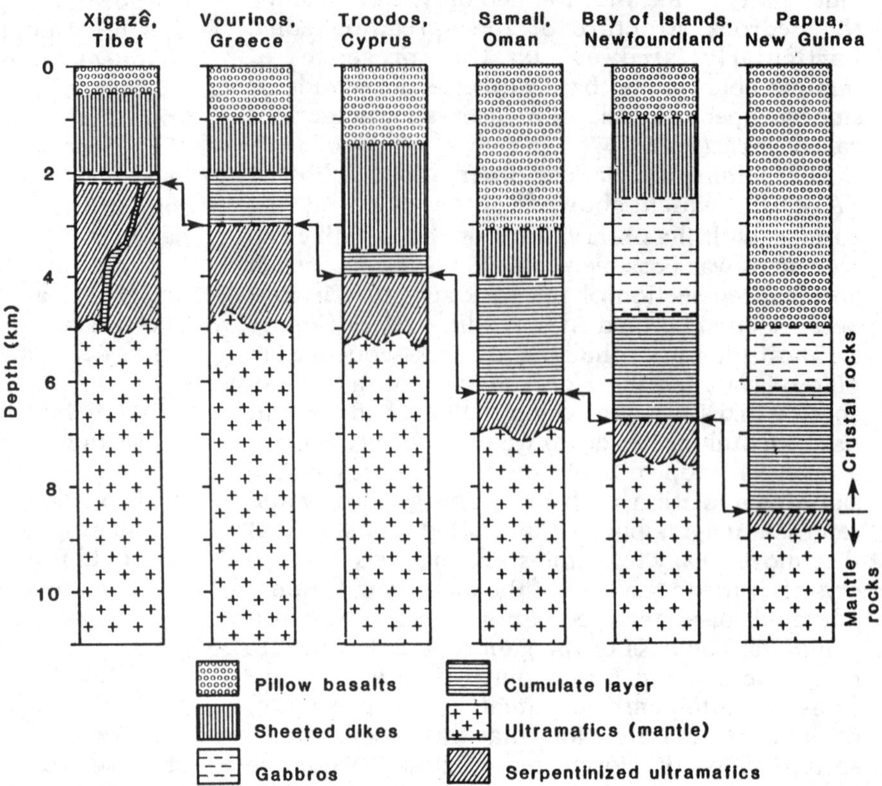

Figure 5.14 Schematic sections of six ophiolites. (From Brian T.R. Lewis, 1983, *Science*, v. 220, p. 152, Figure 1. Copyright © 1983 by the American Association for the Advancement of Science Used by permission.)

rifts. The type examples are the East Pacific Rise (EPR), a fast spreader opening at rates as high as 180 mm/yr, and northern Mid-Atlantic Ridge (MAR), a slow-spreader with rates around 25 mm/yr. Some of these differences are listed in Table 5.3. (See Ken C. Macdonald, 1989, p. 93-100, for a full description of the EPR.)

Figure 5.15 compares typical surface profiles of the two types drawn from a data base of more than 300 transverse profiles obtained by the latest methods of sound scanning (Malinvereno, 1993, p. 640). Both the actual data (dotted line) and a fitted function (solid line) bear out the much greater relief of the MAR as compared with that of the EPR. Especially clear is the deep, wide rift valley and high flanking ridges of the MAR in contrast to the prominent but small, narrow axial ridge of the EPR. The broad, low rise of the EPR with its relatively low relief is also clearly shown. (Note that this pair of profiles spans a horizontal distance of 200 km, which is vastly greater span than in profiles and cross sections in the figures that follow.)

Figure 5.16 is a schematic block diagram showing some landforms of the Mid-Atlantic Ridge (MAR). The vertical exaggeration is about ×3. The depth scale agrees approximately with SeaBeam bathymetry data (Smith and Cann, 1993, p. 708). 1). The *median valley*, shown here as about 6 km wide, is defined by steep *bounding walls*; they are fault scarps. Centered, more or less, in the median valley is the *axial volcanic ridge*. Between the opposed fault scarps is the *inner valley floor*, divided into two corridors by the axial ridge.

Volcanic surface forms of the MAR are shown in plan in Figures 5.17 and 5.18. These maps are sketched from three-dimensional SeaBeam imagery (Smith and Cann, 1993, p. 708). Figure 5.17A shows how the axial volcanic ridge rises as a highly variable lava band lying within the inner valley floor and its bounding walls. Volcanic cones are scattered in a rather irregular distribution over the valley floor. While most cones are within the axial ridge, a few lie close to the base of the bounding wall. The map on the right (B) shows another common tectonic feature of the ridge—its segmentation into sections that overlap in en echelon fashion. The obliquely oriented gaps between sections are not transform offsets. (In Chapter 7, the tectonic patterns of ridge forms are examined on a larger scale.) Figure 5.18 is a more detailed map of the surface volcanic and tectonic forms between the inner valley walls of the MAR. The axial ridge here rises about 500 m above the low points of the inner valley floors. Volcanic cones are densely superimposed on lava flows rising from linear fissures. Older cones are partly buried by younger flows. The lava flows form long, low ridges. On the younger ridges (stipple pattern), the ridge crest is indicated by a line with diverging ticks (not to be interpreted as anticlines).

The fast-spreading East Pacific Rise (EPR) is dominated by volcanic processes. Representative profiles of both MAR and EPR are shown in Figure 5.19. Instead of a median valley, the EPR typically has a prominent, narrow axial ridge, within which there may lie an axial summit graben. Normal faults are of relatively small displacement. They

Table 5.3 Comparison of East Pacific Rise and Mid-Atlantic Ridge

East Pacific Rise (EPR)	Mid-Atlantic Ridge (MAR)
Fast-spreading, 18 cm/yr	Slow-spreading, 2.5 cm/yr
Volcanic processes dominate	Tectonic processes dominate
Broadly arched rise with narrow axial ridge Summit graben 1-2 km wide	Prominent, deeply rifted axial zone 30-45 km wide, 1-2 km deep
Fault scarps are low Faults are listric, shallow	Fault scarps are high Large tectonic relief
No median valley Rise surface built up of highly fluid sheet flows	Median valley 5-12 km wide Floor built up of many coalesced volcanoes built up in piles
Axial ridge is segmented	Rift valley is segmented

Based on data of Smith and Cann, 1993, p. 709-711; Cann, 1991-92, p. 40.

are numerous and form shallow grabens in a broad zone flanking the axis. The relative proportions of tectonic and volcanic forms differ considerably from one part of the ridge to another (Langmuir, et al., 1992, Figure 7, p. 41).

Figure 5.20 has two schematic block diagrams showing many of the tectonic and volcanic details of the EPR. Block A shows the features of the fast spreading rise described above. Block B shows the EPR with typical forms associated with a moderate spreading rate. Here, volcanic activity is a dominant axial feature. Lavas of the EPR include sheet flows, lobate flows, and pillow basalts. Numerous normal faults in parallel sets accommodate the spreading of the ridge as a whole. These are interpreted as parallel faults taking the form of either tilted (listric) faults or horst-and-graben block faults (Macdonald, Fox, Alexander, Pockalny, and Gente, 1996, p. 125). The axial ridge is segmented; individual segments range in length from 15 to 25 km. The gaps between segments are not transform boundaries. Volcanic ridges appear as long, narrow whale-back features with tapering ends.

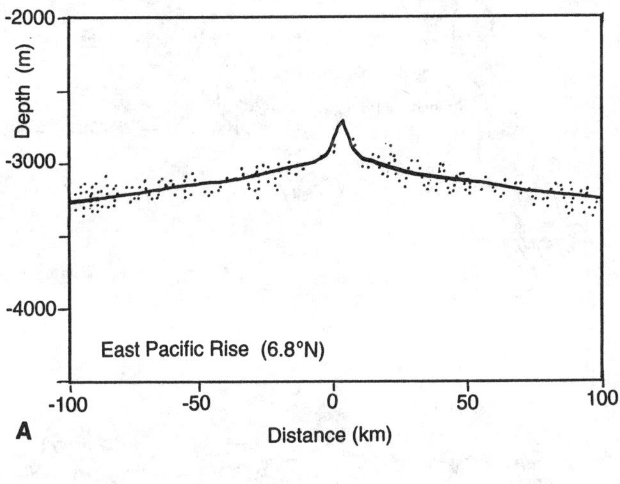

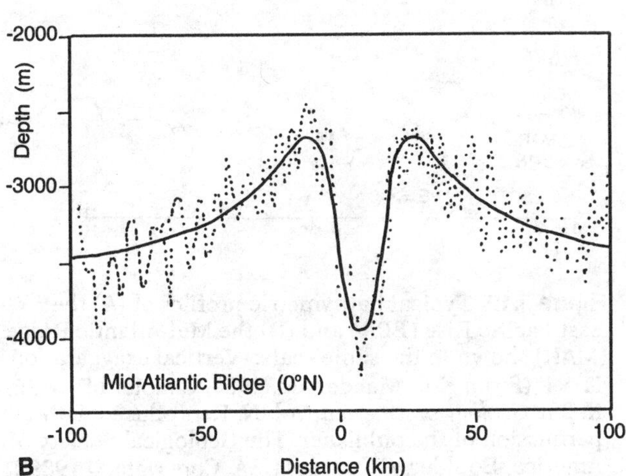

Figure 5.15 Transverse topographic profiles of (A) the Mid-Atlantic Ridge on the equator and (B) the East Pacific Rise at lat. 6.8°N. Dotted line shows actual sonar profile. Bold curve is a mathematical function fitted to the sonar data. (From Alberto Malinverno, 1993, *Geology*, v.12, p. 640, Figure 2. Reproduced with permission of the publisher, The Geological Society of America, Boulder, Colorado, USA. Copyright © 1993.)

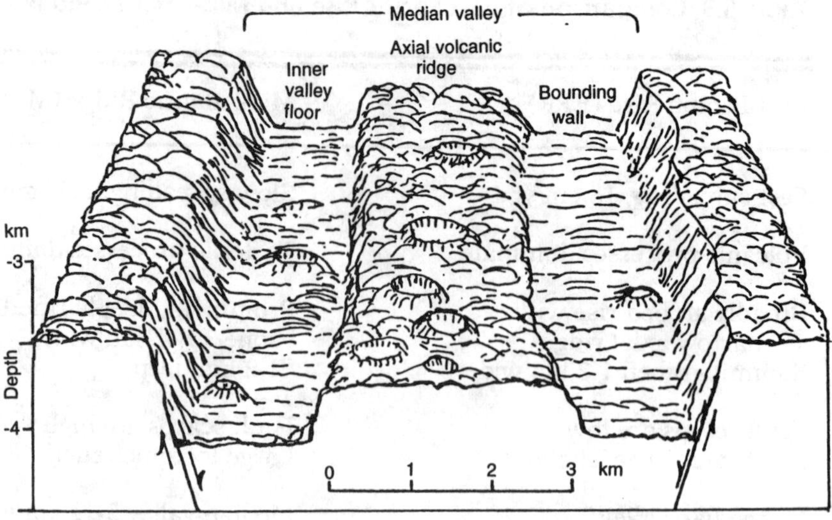

Figure 5.16 A schematic block diagram of a typical median valley of the Mid-Atlantic Ridge, showing the crustal structure and geomorphic features of the inner valley floors and axial volcanic ridge. (Copyright © by Arthur N. Strahler.)

Figure 5.17 Simplified maps of the inner valley floor of the Mid-Atlantic Ridge, drawn from three-dimensional SeaBeam imagery. (A) An unbroken section of a segment of the ridge. (B) Segments of the ridge separated by en echelon gaps. (From D.K. Smith and J.R. Cann, 1993, *Nature*, v. 365, p. 708, Figure 2. Reproduced by permission of Macmillan Magazines Ltd. and the authors.)

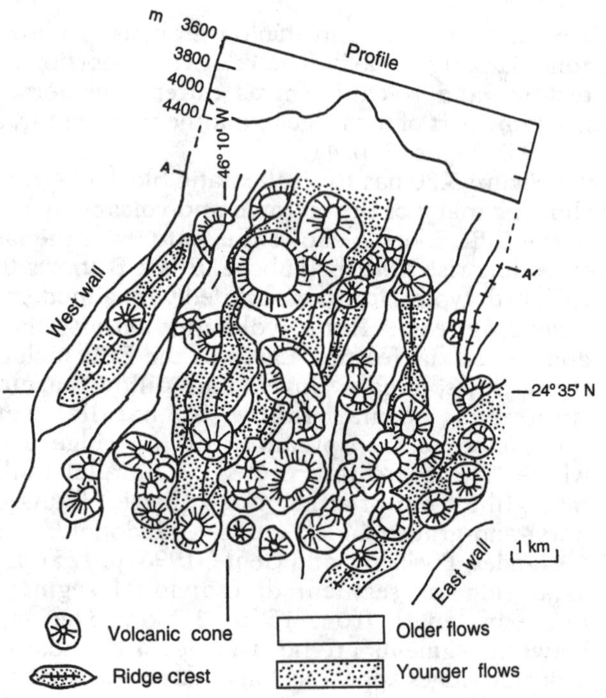

Figure 5.18 Geologic map of a portion of the inner valley floor and axial ridge of the Mid-Atlantic Ridge, drawn from SeaBeam bathymetry. Younger flows are distinguished from older flows. (From D.K. Smith and J.R. Cann, 1993, *Nature*, v. 365, p. 709, Figure 3. Reproduced by permission of Macmillan Magazines Ltd. and the authors.)

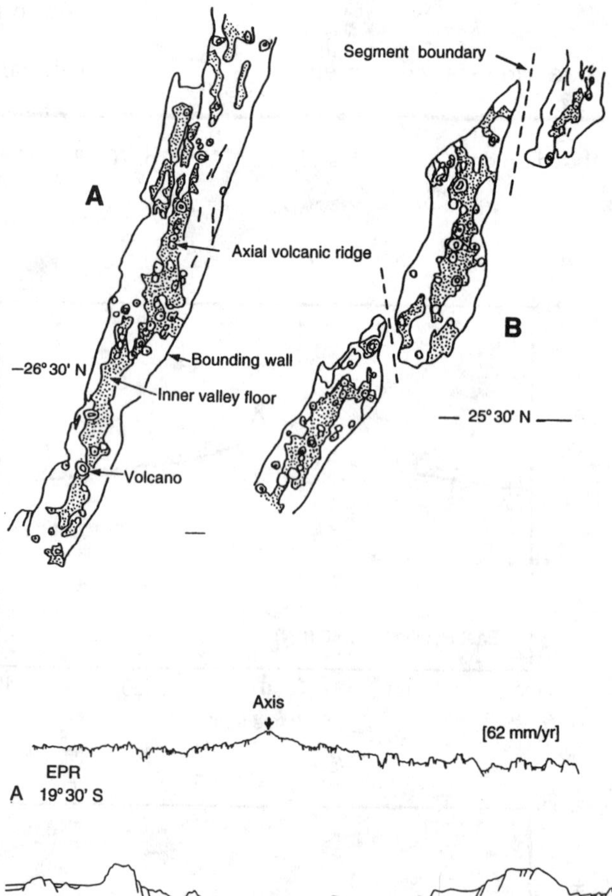

Figure 5.19 Typical bathymetric profiles of (A) the East Pacific Rise (EPR) and (B) the Mid-Atlantic Ridge (MAR) shown to the same scale. Vertical exaggeration is ×4. (From K.C. Macdonald, 1989, Chapter 65, p. 96, in *The Geology of America*, vol. N. Reproduced with permission of the publisher, The Geological Society of America, Boulder, Colorado, USA. Copyright © 1989.)

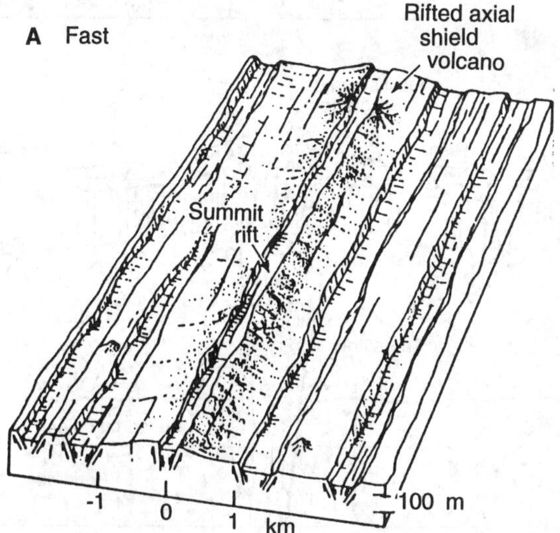

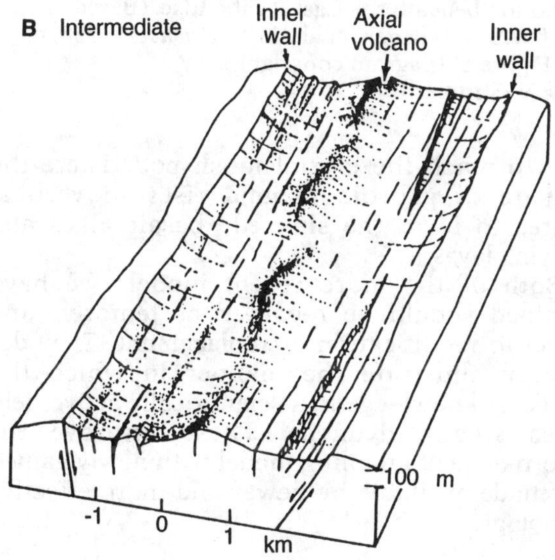

Figure 5.20 Schematic block diagrams showing the tectonic and geomorphic features of two typical sections of the East Pacific Ridge. (From K.C. Macdonald, 1989, Chapter 65, p. 98, in *The Geology of America*, vol. N. Reproduced with permission of the publisher, The Geological Society of America, Boulder, Colorado, USA. Copyright © 1989.)

5.12 Igneous Activity below the Rift Axis

Since the early 1970s, when the submarine discovery voyages of project FAMOUS first allowed the floors of the midocean rifts to be seen, photographed, and sampled, speculation began as to what kind of igneous system lies deep under the rift zone. Various different model cross-sections of this zone soon appeared in print. The interpretation shown in Figure 5.21 was developed in the early 1970s and has continued to be favored by some geologists. This model has been dubbed the "layer cake" model because it generates a continuous set of uniform horizontal layers (Dick, 1992, p. 26-27; Snow, 1995, p. 413). It applies particularly to the slow-spreading Mid-Atlantic Ridge. The model calls for a large magma chamber, some 4 to 5 km high and 4 to 6 km wide at the base, occupying the space that later becomes the entire gabbro zone below the sheeted dike layer. Perhaps the lower part of the chamber contains a mixture of magma and crystals. The magma rises spasmodically from the central ceiling of the chamber through narrow fissures that feed the pillow lava eruptions above it. Magma in these conduits solidifies to construct the layer of sheeted dikes. A cumulate layer is formed at the base of the gabbro layer. The magma chamber is continually fed by rising diapirs of magma originating in the asthenosphere, so that while the magma of the outer chamber wall solidifies into gabbro, the magma chamber retains the same size and shape. This program is one of *steady state*, in which form remains constant while mineral matter continuously moves into and out of the system, changing its physical state as it moves.

The layer cake model was inferred from typical structure of ophiolites, as shown in 5.13 and 5.14, but there had been no way to verify independently the presence of the magma chamber. Seismic tomography was subsequently introduced, but it failed to confirm the presence of large magma chambers beneath the spreading rifts, Consequently, new models of the igneous system had to be constructed. The models had to be treated separately for the two ridge types, EPR and MAR. The newer models are shown in Figures 5.22 and 5.23.

An alternate model for the MAR, put forward more recently by Johnson (Joe) Cann (1991-92), dispenses with a magma chamber; substituting in its place a special horizontal zone in which rising diapirs of magma reach an upper limit of progress

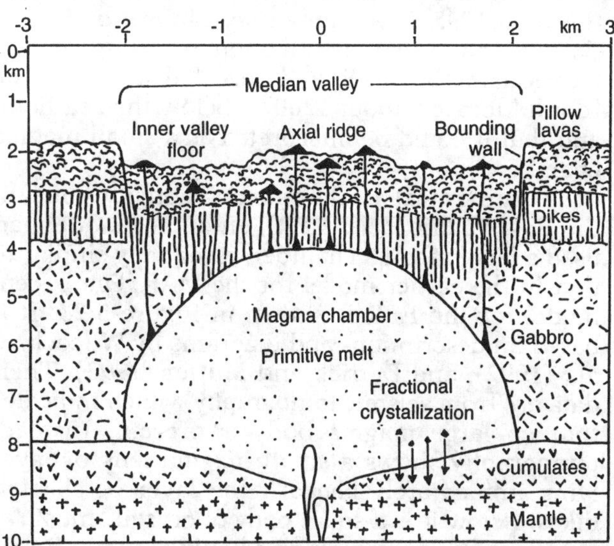

Figure 5.21 This schematic cross section of the slow-spreading Mid-Atlantic Ridge shows the magma-chamber model developed in the 1970s. (Copyright © by Arthur N. Strahler.)

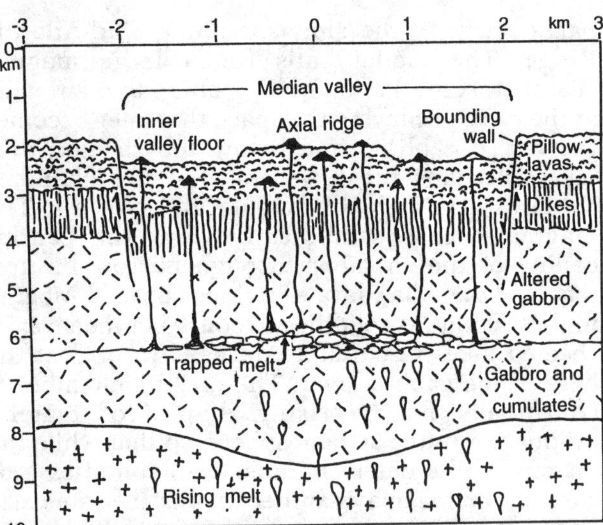

Figure 5.22 A version of magma distribution beneath the Mid-Atlantic Ridge, proposed in the early 1990s. (Based on data of Johnson R. (Joe) Cann, 1991-92, *Oceanus*, v. 34, no. 4, p. 40. Diagram copyright © by Arthur N. Strahler.)

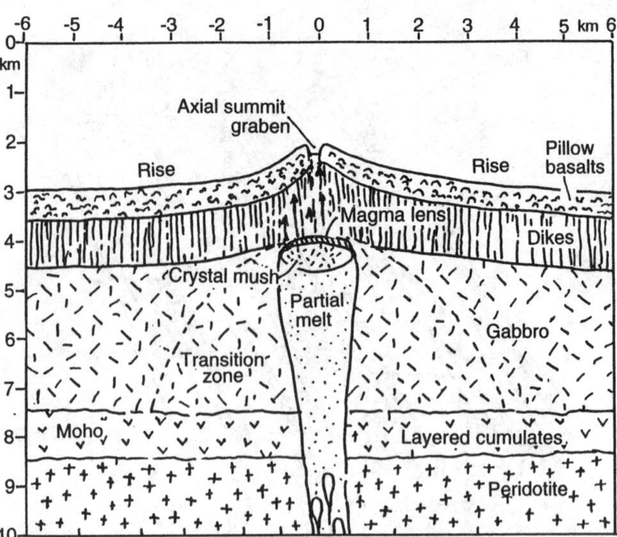

Figure 5.23 A newer interpretation of magma distribution beneath the East Pacific Rise. (Based on data of W.S.D. Wilcock, et al., 1992, *Science*, v. 258, p. 1473, Figure 5. Diagram copyright © by Arthur N. Strahler.)

and accumulate as small pod-like bodies (Figure 5.22). The zone is assigned a depth of about 6 km and lies at the base of the gabbro zone. Some fractionation of the magma occurs in the accumulation layer, and the denser crystals settle out to form a thick cumulate zone extending down to 8 to 9 km depth, which is the base of the crust. Blebs of magma are shown to rise from much deeper in the mantle, and it is these magma diapirs that undergo fractional mineral crystallization at their limit of ascent. Following magma fractionation, another generation of diapirs rises through the lower crust, and these make their way higher through fissures to solidify as sheeted dikes or to reach the surface to form volcanoes and flows. In 1995, it was announced in *Nature* by A.J. Calvert that seismic reflection profiling at one location in the MAR had revealed a 4-km-wide "dome" located about 1200 m below the sea floor, and that it could be interpreted as a small magma chamber.

Turning next to the igneous activity beneath the East Pacific Rise (EPR), an earlier model had used a large magma chamber, essentially similar to that in the earlier model for the MAR. One recent model for the EPR is shown in Figure 5.23. It is based on descriptions and diagrams by Wilcock, et al., (1992), and Detrick and Mutter (1993). Their data are from seismic tomography, which indicates that no large magma body is present. Instead, tomography shows a small magma lens or layer lying immediately beneath the layer of sheeted dikes. Below it is a small body of crystal "mush," a mixture of solid crystals and liquid magma. Below that is a relatively narrow stalk of partially melted gabroic rock, and this stalk is shown to continue down into the mantle below. Diapirs of magma are shown as rising from the mantle and through the stalk, to reach the crystal mush pod. There the distillate of gabroic magma rises in vertical fissures to form the sheeted basalt dikes and overlying lavas.

Both of the more recent models we have examined should be regarded as tentative and subject to modification or replacement. They do, however, illustrate the manner in which the frontier of knowledge in a scientifically active field makes small advances. These improve the conformance of an ailing model with newly gained data made available by newer and more effective technologies.

5.13 Plumes, Hotspots, and Oceanic Island Chains

We have listed among volcanic phenomena related to plate tectonics the inferred rise of a stalklike column of heated mantle rock—a *mantle plume* (Figure 5.2). For many years, the concept was largely hypothetical because we had no way of directly observing or verifying the existence of such a phenomenon. There emerged the hypothesis that plumes rise from near the base of the lower mantle, penetrating the entire mantle as narrow ascending columns that reach to the base of the lithosphere. As explained in Chapter 3, seismic tomography has supported this hypothesis, along with a model of a two-layer mantle. The 670-km discontinuity that separates the upper mantle from the lower mantle is thought to remain largely intact, but with local penetrations by descending subducted plates and by rising magma plumes originating near the core-mantle boundary.

A direct surface manifestation of a mantle plume is a hotspot. It is a relatively small center of past or present volcanic activity, occurring within a lithospheric plate and typically located some distance away from any active plate boundary (Seyfert, 1987, p. 412, 560). Hotspots may be represented by isolated volcanoes or volcano groups on both continental and oceanic crust. They make up long chains of basaltic volcanoes rising from the deep ocean floors within an oceanic lithospheric plate. (See Chapter 4, guyots, coral atolls.) The criterion of identification of a hotspot is that it is fed by a mantle plume that remains relatively fixed in the mantle, while the lithospheric plate moves over the mantle plume (Duncan, 1991, p. 216). This criterion can apply both to oceanic lithosphere and to continental lithosphere. Only the most recently formed volcano or volcano group is active; those that have been moved away from the plume have become inactive. It follows logically that the extinct hotspots of a chain grow older in the direction of plate motion.

The numerous small volcanoes situated in the axial zone of a spreading plate boundary are usually excluded from the hotspot category because they lie on the boundary between two lithospheric plates and are explained by the more-or-less continuous rise of magma from a shallow magma chamber, rather than from a mantle plume. In a few localities, however, a mantle plume lies directly beneath a spreading boundary, causing the growth of large volcanoes and volcano groups and/or large accumulations basaltic flows. Iceland is a fine example and is usually listed as a hotspot (Figure 5.12). Seismic studies have indicated that beneath Iceland there is located a "hot, narrow plume of upwelling mantle" (Wolfe, Bjarhason, VanDecar, and Solomon, 1997, p, 245.) Other examples are a few volcanic islands on or near the Mid-Atlantic Ridge; e.g., Azores, Ascension, Tristan da Cunha. As the plates spread apart, these hotspots are carried off to one side or the other of the ridge, producing two opposing island chains. (See Figure 5.27.)

Also excluded from the category of hotspots are the volcanoes of island and mountain arcs formed over subduction zones of converging plate boundaries. This igneous activity is directly linked to the larger tectonic system and produces volcanic chains parallel with the plate boundary.

The concept of hotspots formed over magma sources deep in the upper mantle was first suggested in 1963 by the Canadian geophysicist J. Tuzo Wilson (1963a, 1963b). Prior to that time, the Hawaiian Islands chain in the North Pacific had been intensively studied and its seafloor topography had been mapped. (See Figure 5.26). Geologists had previously interpreted the Hawaiian volcano chain as rising from a crustal rift or a tear fault that had propagated from northwest to southeast. In this way they explained why the ages of the islands are progressively younger in that direction. But Wilson torpedoed this hypothesis when he pointed out that the line on which the volcanoes lie is *aseismic*, meaning that it is virtually free of earthquakes. Wilson then proposed his own hypothesis of a deeply fixed mantle plume and a moving lithospheric plate above it. About the same time, Wilson was developing his hypothesis of the origin of hotspots in the South Atlantic. These form symmetrical island chains diverging diagonally from the Mid-Atlantic Ridge in the South Atlantic (see Figure 5.27). Wilson called these "lateral ridges." Figure 5.24 reproduces his drawing illustrating these two manifestations of plume activity. Notice that the base of the plume is shown to be just below the asthenosphere, and that he labels this mantle zone a "stagnant region." [Wilson had not used the term "hotspot," but by 1971 it was well established in the literature.] Seven years later, W. Jason Morgan hypothesized that the mantle plumes below hotspots originate far down in the lower mantle and possibly as deep as the base of the lower mantle (Morgan, 1971).

A list of 122 global hotspots, all of which have been active within the past 10 m.y., was compiled by Wilson in 1976. Of these, 53 are on oceanic crust and 69 on continental crust. Of those on oceanic crust, 15 are located on the axial rift of the mid-oceanic ridge and 9 others are not far from the axis. Of the major lithospheric plates, the African plate has more hot spots than any other—43 in all. Of these, 25 are on continental crust and the remaining 18 are on oceanic crust.

Wilson's major contribution to plate tectonics through the interpretation of hot spots was to show how the volcanic chains or lines formed over

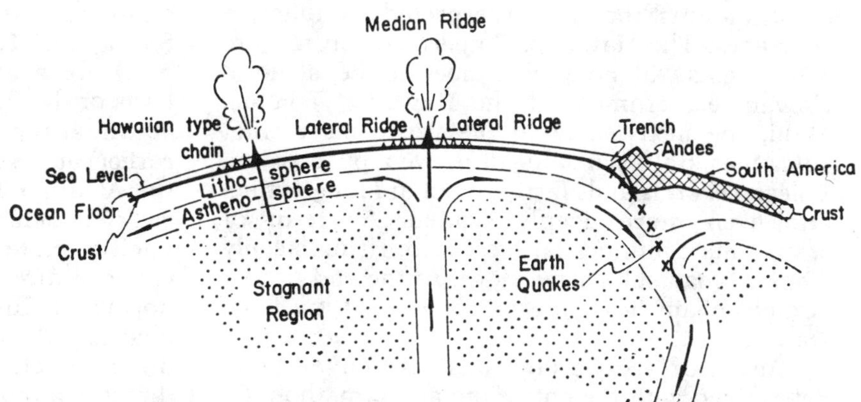

Figure 5.24 "Diagrammatic section showing a type of convection which might explain the origin of pairs of lateral ridges, median ridges, Hawaiian-type chains and mountain building." (Legend and diagram from J. Tuzo Wilson, 1963b, *Nature*, vol. 198, no. 4884, p. 929. Reproduced by permission of Macmillan Magazines Ltd.)

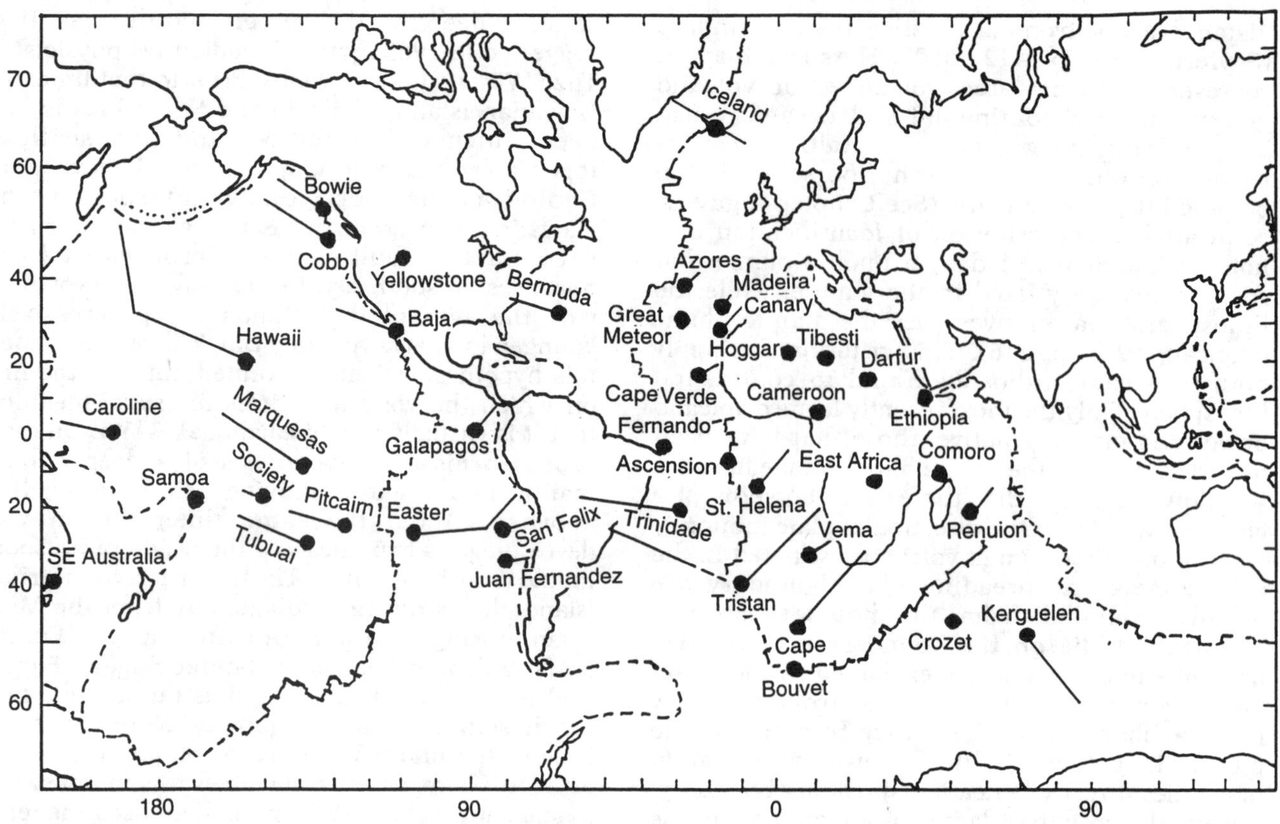

Figure 5.25 A world map of forty-some hotspots (dots) and their hotspot traces (straight line segments) selected by S. Thomas Crough from other sources, including maps by Morgan (1982), Burke and Wilson (1976), and Jarrad and Clague (1977). Plate boundaries shown in broken line.(From S.T. Crough, 1983, *Ann. Rev. Earth Planet Sci.*,vol. 11, p. 196. Adapted by permission from *Annual Reviews, Inc.*,© 1983.)

hot spots and how they can thus be used to determine the direction and rate of motion of plates. We shall return to that subject in Chapter 7.

Figure 5.25 selects a number of important hot spots to illustrate the possible relationships between the spots and plate boundaries (Crough, 1983). Many of them display hotspot traces, and these are in accord with the known directions of plate spreading. Note that hot spots within the African continent are shown to be lacking in traces.

Consider first the hotspots of the Pacific plate. There are three major Pacific volcanic island chains, represented by active volcanoes and lines of seamounts that are interpreted as inactive volcanoes. The Hawaiian-Emperor chain (Figure 5.26) begins with active volcanoes on the island of Hawaii, easternmost of the Hawaiian Islands. Maui, the next island to the west, has extinct volcanoes only partially destroyed by erosion. Volcanoes on islands farther west are long extinct and even more deeply eroded. A chain of seamounts continues far westward, rising steeply from a broad submarine ridge. At the end of this straight chain lies Midway, some 2400 km from Hawaii.

Ages of Hawaiian basalts have been determined with the potassium-argon method. By 1974, G. Brent Dalrymple and colleagues of the U.S. Geological Survey had carried out the radiometric age determination of lavas of the Hawaiian Island chain, finding that the age increases progressively to the northwest, but not in a linear age progression (Dalrymple et al., 1974). In general agreement with Wilson's hypothesis, the ages increase from Hawaii (recent to 0.5 Ma) westward to Kauai (4.5 to 5.6 Ma). The small island of Necker, located much farther west, has a rock age of 11 Ma. Using this evidence we can calculate that the Pacific plate has moved west-northwest at the rate of about 10 cm/year.

At a point west-northwest of Midway, another chain of seamounts begins—the Emperor Seamounts. They trend in a direction just west of north for a distance of about 2400 km. Ages of lavas of the Emperor Seamounts start with about 40 Ma at the southern end and reach 65 Ma (or earlier) at the northern end, where the chain meets the Aleutian Trench. The interpretation seemed clear enough: From about 75 Ma (or earlier), the Pacific plate moved almost due north, then changed direction rather abruptly to move west-northwest. In 1995, this simple explanation was challenged. Briefly, the cause of the sharp direction change has now been attributed to directional control by horizontal motions of the

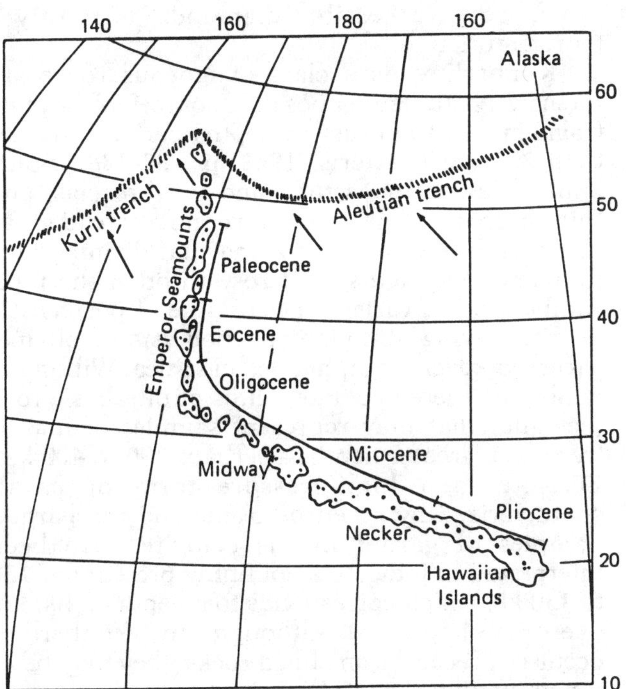

Figure 5.26 Sketch map of the North Pacific Ocean, showing the Hawaiian-Emperor seamount chains. Dots are summits; line around dots marks the base of the volcanic pile. Geologic ages of the volcanic rock of the seamounts are given on the accompanying scale. Present motion of the Pacific plate is indicated by arrows. (Based on data of Geologic Map of the Pacific Ocean, Sheet 20, Geological World Atlas of UNESCO.)

mantle beneath. (See Chapter 7, "Plate Motions Relative to Hotspots.)

Two other seamount and island chains, both in the South Pacific, show the same west-northwest direction of Pacific plate motion as does the Hawaiian chain. One of these, called the Austral group, starts with Macdonald seamount, an active volcano. The other is the Tuamoto group, starting with Pitcairn Island, also volcanically active (Burke and Wilson, 1976, p. 50). The trajectories of these two hotspot chains parallel each other and that of the Hawaiian Island chain.

The Dalrymple research group found evidence from seismic reflection profiling that seamounts of the central Emperor chain at depths now below 1300 m are capped by coral reef structures and shallow-water sediments and that surface features of atolls are clearly recognizable. Rejecting the hypothesis that early Cenozoic ocean temperatures could have been warm enough to permit reef growth, they favored instead the hypothesis that the seamounts must have been formed in more southerly latitudes (Greene, Dalrymple, and Clague, 1978, p. 70-73). This conclusion agrees with the northward plate motion indicated by the orientation of the Emperor chain.

Hotspots of the Atlantic Ocean basin show a different type of behavior from those of the Pacific plate. The Atlantic hot spots seem to have originated on or near the early axial rift that developed when the American plate broke free from contact with the African-Eurasian plate, beginning the opening up of the Atlantic basin. (See Chapter 10 for an explanation.) In the South Atlantic basin, a hotspot exists today in the active volcanic island group of Tristan da Cunha (Figure 5.27). Extending from this point northeast to the African continent is a submarine ridge called Walvis Ridge. Extending northwest to South America is another such topographic feature, the Rio Grande Rise. These submarine ridges have no active volcanoes today and are interpreted as basaltic lava accumulations built originally on or near the same site as the present hotspot, Tristan da Cunha, but gradually transported away from the spreading axis by diverging plate motions. Corroboration comes from a similar pair of diverging tracks extending out from Iceland across the Atlantic Ocean basin northwestward into Greenland and southeastward to the North Sea.

Deepsea core drilling has now penetrated many volcanoes of the hotspot island chains,

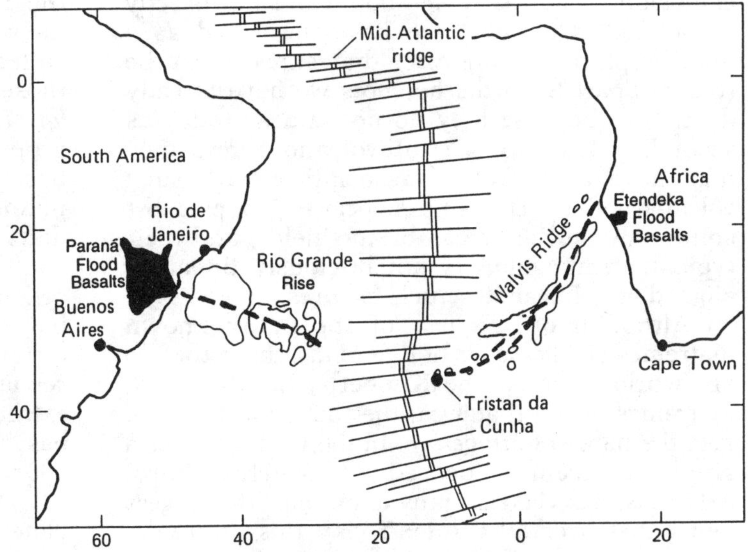

Figure 5.27 Sketch map of the South Atlantic Ocean, showing the paired volcanic submarine ridges that may have originated from a single hot spot now located beneath the active volcano group of Tristan da Cunha. (Copyright © by Arthur N. Strahler.)

giving an opportunity not only to obtain new argon-40/argon-39 age dates for the basalts, but also to allow samples to be analyzed for strontium-87/strontium-86 ratios. As we explained earlier in this chapter, magma of the mid-oceanic ridges (MORB) has a strontium ratio that is uniquely an indicator that it comes from the upper mantle. Samples from the hotspot lavas yield a different ratio, with a higher value (centered about on 0.7050) than the typical ratio for MORB (centered no higher than 0.7042)

Continental lithospheric hotspots, both active and inactive, are abundant on Africa, including Madagascar and adjacent parts of the Arabian Peninsula (see Figure 5.25). Yellowstone is shown on world maps as the one active hotspot in North America, and there are at least two in Antarctica. No active hotspots are shown for Eurasia, South America, and Australia. (Active volcanoes paralleling the plate subduction boundaries are not included.) East Africa would be expected to have numerous hotspots because that region is now strongly affected by large-scale continental rifting. This connection implies that continental rifting leading to the breakup of a continent is accompanied by (or caused by) the rise of large magma plumes from deep in the mantle. (See Chapter 10.)

5.14 Diatremes, Kimberlites, and Xenoliths

A unique volcanic phenomenon, but one seemingly free of any direct physical connection with plate tectonics, is the exposure at the continental surfaces of rock that probably originated deep in the mantle and has been rapidly propelled upward through the crust in a powerful jetlike blast. The presssure of this jet has been attributed to expanding water or possibly to carbon dioxide. The conduit itself is described as a *pipe*. The pipe, along with the rock that has risen in it and remains in place is called a *diatreme*. A broader petrographic definition of a "diatreme" would be: "A breccia-filled volcanic pipe formed by a volcanic explosion." The diatreme should not be directly associated with what we have described as a mantle plume. Moreover, diatremes must be treated apart from the hotspots we have already described, because they do not appear today as secondary features of stratovolcanoes, and they may have been free of association with such volcanic activity. Diatremes appear in groups, most commonly on the Precambrian shields, and their typical arrangement is not obviously linear or aligned with linear structural features.

Although only a few of the many known diatremes yield crystals of diamonds, those that do are world famous—the Kimberly, South Africa, diatremes. From that area, the rock in a diatreme gets the name of *kimberlite*. In the United States a single diatreme, located at Murfreesboro, Arkansas, has yielded many diamonds, the largest being just over 40 carats. Today this diatreme, exhausted of accessible diamonds, is mostly a tourist attraction.

Kimberlites as a class of igneous rocks are intensively studied as possible sources of original fragments of the crust at depths perhaps greater than 200 km (Pasteris, 1983, p. 282-288). Some kimberlites occur as tuffs and tuff-breccias, and this suggests that they were not extruded as magmas, but as rising magma that disintegrated into solid fragments as it rose through the pipe. Kimberlite is a variety of peridotite of porphyritic texture having abundant phenocrysts of olivine, garnet, pyroxene, amphibole, and mica. Within the kimberlite there occur xenoliths of ultrabasic rock (eclogite) that may represent samples of mantle from even greater depths—perhaps 300 to 400 km. Eclogite is a high-pressure form of basalt characterized by green pyroxene and red garnet. Samples of garnet in the eclogite have been interpreted to indicate a confining pressure of 120 to 130 kb, which corresponds to a depth of 400 km (Kerr, 1991, p. 783). Although most kimberlites occur in Precambrian shield rocks, they may be of much younger age. (For in-depth coverage of kimberlites, see Hall, 1987, Chapter 13, p. 454-468.)

In 1996, a small ripple in the popular news media greeted a letter in *Nature* announcing the finding of an inclusion of staurolite in a diamond crystal from the Dokolowayo kimberlite in Swaziland (Daniels, Gurney, and Harte, 1996, p. 153-156). Staurolite is a common metamorphic mineral formed from aluminum-rich sediments, and could have been carried down into the mantle in a subducting continental plate. The staurolite fragment would have served as a nucleus for the growth of the diamond crystal. A number of similar finds have been recorded during past decades (White, 1996, p. 117-118).

5.15 Basalt Plateaus and Flood Basalts

We turn next to very large outpourings of basalt that have taken place in Phanerozoic time on both the deep ocean floors and in the continental interiors. Those built on oceanic crust are usually called *submarine plateaus* or *oceanic plateaus*; those on the continental crust are called *flood basalts* or *plateau basalts*. For simplicity, we shall group both classes under the name of flood basalts. All of them are attributed to mantle plumes that, like the hotspots we have already described, rise from deep in the mantle. Opinion continues to be divided as to whether the plume originates at the base of the upper mantle or at the base of the lower mantle (see Chapter 3). The difference between flood basalts and hotspots seems to lie largely in the volume of magma extruded and the rate of extrusion, that of the flood basalt being greater in volume by a factor of, say, 100 times the volume of a hotspot.

The global distribution of basaltic oceanic plateaus is shown in Figure 5.28. Also included are the tracks of hotspots, shown in Figure 5.25. Figure 5.29 is a graph on which the oceanic plateaus are plotted in terms of two properties: surface relief and depth to Moho. Our interest here is in the crustal thickness of oceanic plateaus as a group. In this respect, they seem to be intermediate between the oceanic and continental crusts. Figure 5.30 compares the crustal makeup, in terms of the seismically defined layers, of oceanic crustal types with three samples of continental crust. Here, again, the oceanic plateaus are intermediate in position, but seem more closely related to the continental crust in terms of compressional wave velocities.

Turning now to the continental flood basalts, Figure 5.31 is a pictorial diagram showing how the highly fluid basalt flows, extruded from fissures, inundate the low-lying valleys and basins of a continental area, leaving prominent hills and mountains to rise as 'islands' in the basalt 'lake'.

The most familiar North American flood basalt province is the Columbia Plateau of Oregon, Washington, and Idaho. Here, the Columbia River basalts today cover about 130,000 km^2, have a thickness ranging from 600 to 1200 m, and a volume of at least 250,000 km^3 (Figure 5.32). Much of the original mass of basalt has been removed by fluvial erosion. Prior to the onset of the flooding, the region had a local relief of some 800 m. Flows first filled in the valleys and eventually rose to cover many summits. The highly fluid basalt flows began to appear in the Early Miocene, about 17 Ma, and continued into the late Miocene, a time span of about 11 m.y. More than 95 percent of the total basalt volume was produced in the first 3.5 m.y. During the period of peak rate of extrusion, about 15 Ma, a unit known as the Grand Ronde Basalt accumulated as a succession of more than 60 flows, averaging about one every 10,000 y, flooded the Columbia Plateau. The Grand Ronde flows accounted for more than 85 percent of the entire volume and were extruded in a period of about 0.5 m.y. (Baksi, 1990, p. 1835). Some of these flows spilled through the rising Cascade volcanic range to reach the Pacific coast (Hooper, 1982, p. 1463-1465).

Even more impressive is the Deccan Plateau Province of peninsular India, with a total basalt thickness of about 3000 m and covering today an area of over 550,000 km^2 (Figure 5.33). The original volume is estimated to have been 1,500,000 km^3. The Deccan Traps, as the flows are called, are of early Paleocene age, about 66 Ma (Table 5.4).

In recent years, the Deccan flood-basalt volcanism has been hypothetically linked to the great worldwide Cretaceous/ Tertiary (K/T) biotic extinction (Officer and Drake, 1985). The main extrusion event of the Deccan Traps has been dated to within plus-or-minus 1 m.y. of the stratigraphic K/T boundary (Baksi and Farrar, 1991). This form of large-scale volcanism was offered as an alternative to the bolide impact scenario of extinction, but just how the basalt

Table 5.4 Major Flood Basalt Provinces

Province	Age (Ma)	Original volume (× 1000 km^3)	Duration (m.y)
Columbia Plateau, U.S.A.	17-13	300	>3.5
North Atlantic Tertiary	60	1000-2000	2-3
Deccan Traps, India	66	1000-2500	0.5-1.5
Parana-Etendeka, S. America, W. Africa	120-125	1000-1500	1-2
Karoo, S. Africa	193-195	1000-2000	2 (?)
Siberian Traps	240	1000+	(?)
Keweenawan Basalts, L. Superior	1095	1300	2-3

Based on data of R.S. White, 1989, *EOS*, v. 70, no. 46, p. 1480, R.A. Duncan, 1991, *GSA Today*, v. 1, no. 10, p. 214, and other sources.

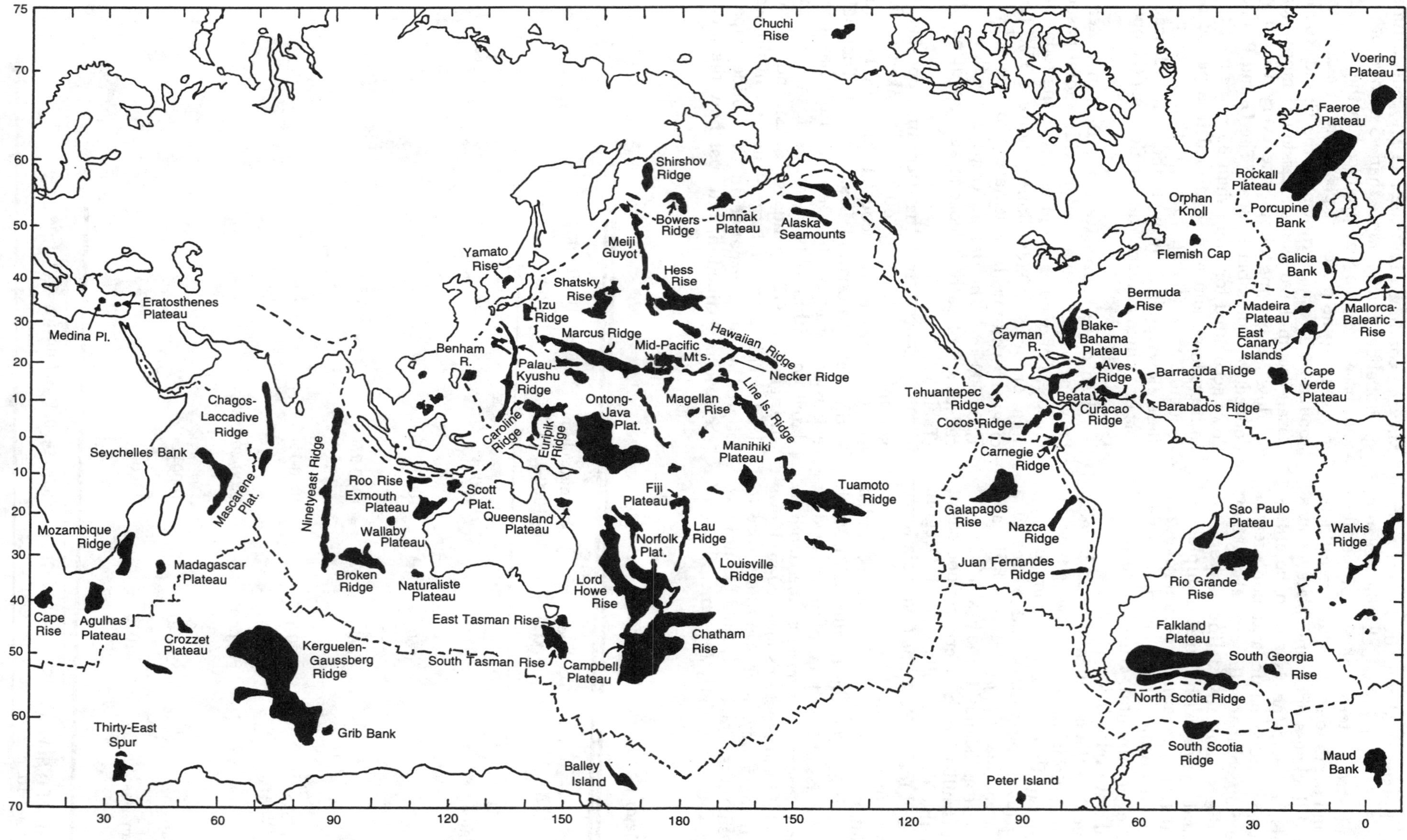

Figure 5.28 World map of oceanic plateaus, most of which are built up of basalt outpourings. (From Ben-Avraham, Nur, Jones, and Cox, 1981, *Science*, v. 213, p. 48, Figure 1. Figure 1. Copyright © 1981 by the American Association for the Advancement of Science. Used by permission.)

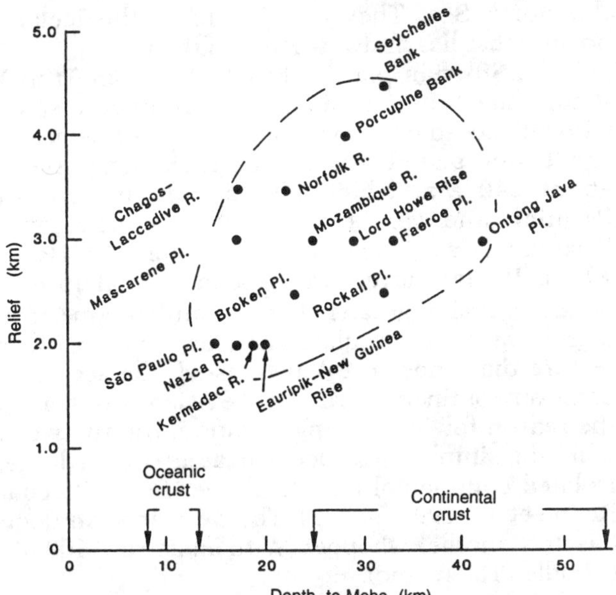

Figure 5.29 Graph of relief versus depth to Moho for several oceanic basalt plateaus. (From Ben-Avraham, Nur, Jones, and Cox, 1981, *Science*, v. 213, p. 49, Figure 2. Figure 1. Copyright © 1981 by the American Association for the Advancement of Science. Used by permission.)

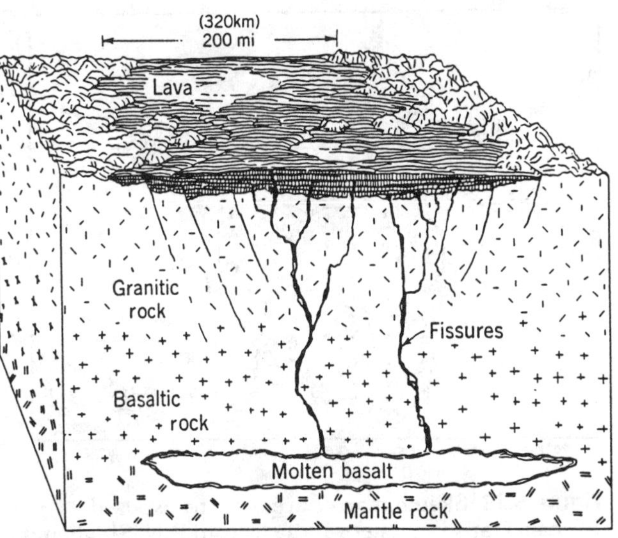

Figure 5.31 This schematic block diagram suggests the inferred relationship between flood basalts and a deep chamber of basalt magma located near the base of the continental crust or in the uppermost mantle. (Copyright © by Arthur N. Strahler.)

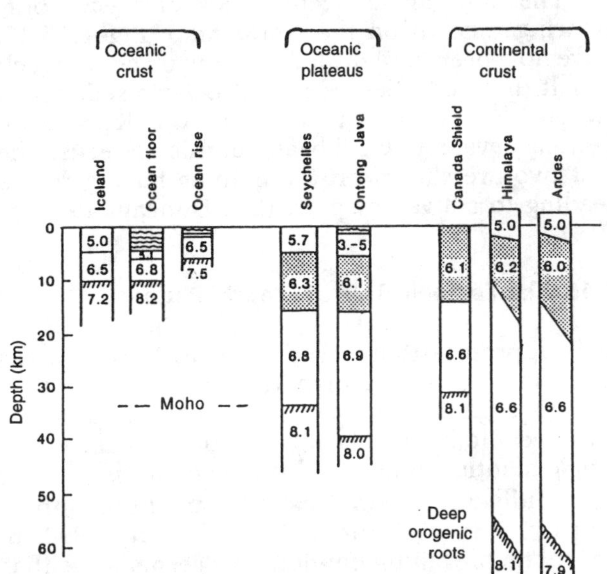

Figure 5.30 Thicknesses and seismic compressional wave speeds of two oceanic basalt plateaus (center) with oceanic crust (left) and continental crust (right). (From Ben-Avraham, Nur, Jones, and Cox, 1981, *Science*, v. 213, p. 49, Figure 3. Figure 1. Copyright © 1981 by the American Association for the Advancement of Science. Used by permission.)

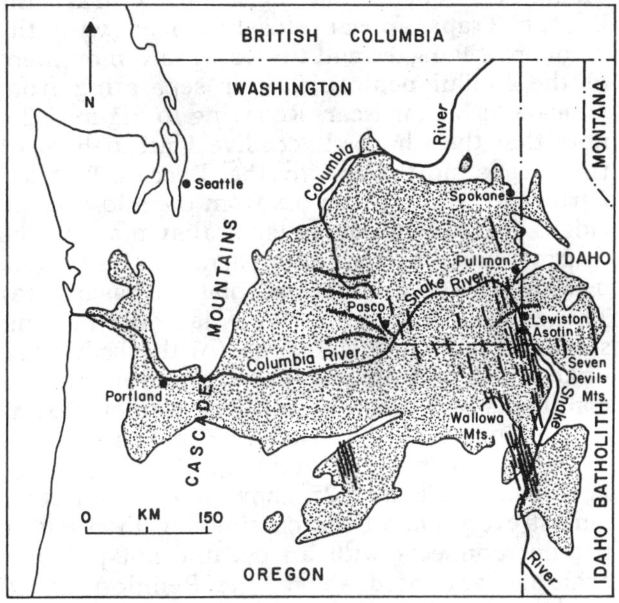

Figure 5.32 Map showing extent of the Columbia River basalts in Washington, Oregon, and Idaho. The bold straight lines show the approximate location of feeder dikes. (From Peter R. Cooper, 1982, *Science*, v. 251, p. 1465, Figure 3.Figure 1. Copyright © 1982 by the American Association for the Advancement of Science. Used by permission.

eruption would act to cause wholesale extinction of species remains speculative. Robert S. White lists as possible effects on the biosphere: a global dust cover and/or massive CO_2 injection, creating a "nuclear winter"; global fires; acid rain; and a heavy ash fallout (1989, p. 1490). Another great basalt emission, the Siberian Traps of early Triassic time, has been tied in causally to the Permian/Triassic boundary extinction. (Bolide impact as the possible cause of continental rifting is appraised in Chapter 10.)

The Columbia Plateau basalts are thought

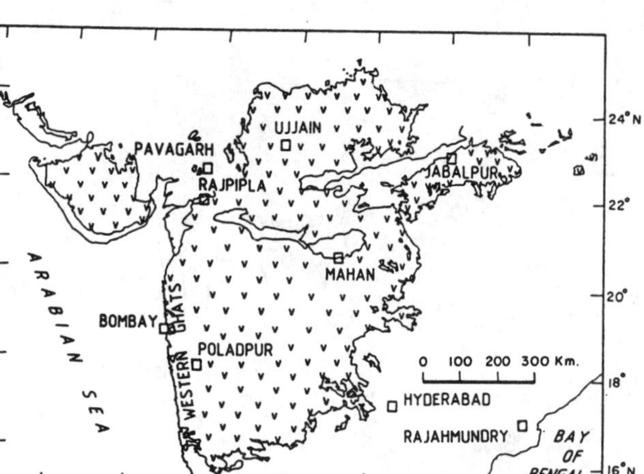

Figure 5.33 Sketch map of areas of the exposed Deccan Traps in western India. (From R.N. Singh and K.R. Gupta, 1994, *EOS*, v. 75, no. 31, p. 365. Data of the National Geophysical Institute, Hyderabad, India. Copyrighted by the American Geophysical Union.)

possibly to be tied in to the deep easterly penetration of a subducting plate on a low inclination beneath the region. In contrast, the Deccan Traps appear closely linked with the breakup of Pangaea and the northward movement of the Indian peninsula after separating from Africa and Madagascar. Referring to Figure 5.25, note that the Chagos-Laccadive Plateau hotspot trail leads northward to the Deccan Plateau. Farther to the south, across from the mid-oceanic ridge, is the Reunion hotspot that may be the "mirror" hotspot. It appears, then, that we may be dealing with two classes of plateau basalts: (a) Those that are linked with laterally-moving shallow subduction slabs and (b) those that are linked with rifting and the separation of new continents and ocean basins. The former class is covered in Chapter 8; the latter in Chapter 10.

Notice further that our map of hotspots and flood basalts, Figure 5.25, shows a line connecting almost every one of the continental flood basalt patches connects with an oceanic hotspot. For example, as stated above, the Reunion Island hotspot in the Indian Ocean is pared to the Deccan Plateau. In another example, The Tristan da Cunha hotspot in the middle of the South Atlantic is paired to both the Parana basalt plateau in Brazil and the Etendeka basalts of southwestern Angola (see Figure 5.25). In Chapter 10, these and other examples will provide convincing evidence of the breakup of Pangaea.

The Karoo basalts of southeastern Africa are also on the list of great basalt floods (Table 5.4). Of Early Jurassic age, they are exposed in several patches and are estimated to have totaled 2 million km^3 in volume with a duration of 2 m.y. Similar in statistics of volume and duration are the North Atlantic Tertiary Province basalts of 60 Ma that now lie in two parts: Greenland coast and off of the North Sea. They are tied in to the Iceland hotspot that lies midway between them.

The Siberian plateau basalt (Siberian Traps), within the Siberian shield, seems unconnected with any oceanic hotspot, and it does not lie near a subduction plate boundary. Its radiometric age is about 240 Ma, which places it in uppermost Permian and very close in time to the great Permian/Triassic extinction (Renne and Basu, 1991). It may have had a mean annual rate of basalt extrusion greater than 1.3 million km^3. You might want to speculate that, as a much older feature than those previously listed, the accretion of newer continental crust to the Asian continent is the reason for its seeming isolation. Alternatively, it might simply have been located over a large, isolated continental mantle plume (Basu, Poreda, Renne et al., 1995, p. 822). The Keweenawan flood basalt is another whopper. With an age of 1100 Ma (Middle Proterozoic).

Another interesting example on our map is Wrangellia, a long, narrow belt of metamorphosed basaltic rock that parallels the Alaska/British Columbia coast. In Chapter 8 we explain this rock body as an accreted terrane that had previously traveled across the Pacific basin from some distant source—probably an ancient submarine basalt plateau.

The submarine occurrences of basalt outpourings shown on the world map, Figure 5.25, have now been core-drilled in many places to reach basalt that underlies a cover of pelagic sediments. Among the largest in area are the Kerguelen, Ontong Java, and Caribbean oceanic plateaus. The last two are shown on the map as having tracks leading to active hotspots. (See Duncan, 1991, p. 214).

5.16 The Tectonic Role of Mantle Plumes

It is appropriate in this chapter to look into the phenomenon of large mantle plumes and how they supply large quantities of magma for continental and oceanic basalt plateaus. With the ability of a single mantle plume to deliver basalt to the surface as rapidly as 22 km^3/year the phenomenon is worthy of special attention (Hill et al., 1992, p. 186). The prevailing opinion now seems to be that the plumes which supply the heat needed to produce basalt plateaus arise at the base of the lower mantle and are able to penetrate the 670-km density discontinuity that separates the mantle into two separate convection systems (Chapter 3). Thus the rising plume operates largely independently of mantle convection as well as of lithospheric plate motion.

Because of its heat content, derived at the core-mantle interface, the plume possesses both lower density and lower viscosity than the mantle surrounding it and above it. It is described as beginning its ascent as a large, bulb-like body, which is trailed by a narrow conduit or "tail." The leading body, or plume head, is envisioned as having at first a more-or-less spherical body, but as it approaches comparatively shallow depths (less than 1000 km) it increases in horizontal diameter, becomes thinner in the vertical direction, and thus becomes a disk, perhaps 200 km in thickness and 1500 km in diameter. This transformation is illustrated in Figure 5.34. As the plume head flattens, it also undergoes decompression because the load above is diminishing as it rises. This change leads to large-scale decompression melting, which can explain the extremely high rates at which enormous volumes of basalt magma can pour out upon the surface through multiple fissures (Duncan, 1991, p. 215). Consider next that dating of points along the tracks of plumes—now represented by oceanic flood basalt accumulations—shows that the same plume must have had an active life span on the order of 120 m.y. (Duncan, 1991, p. 215). This evidence suggests that a plume head can be continually restocked with hot mantle rock from below through a narrow pipelike conduit.

A tectonically important effect of a rising plume head is that it causes the lithosphere to be lifted up into the form of a low dome, or swell, as shown by greatly exaggerated profiles in the upper part of Figure 5.34. This doming stretches and thins the lithosphere. Then, as the lithosphere drifts slowly away from the plume and tens of millions of years elapse, the elevated layer has become cooled, so it subsides to form a crustal basin in which sediments accumulate (see Chapter 12). This total process of thermal and structural reworking above mantle plumes has been termed *plume tectonics* (Hill et al., 1992, p. 187).

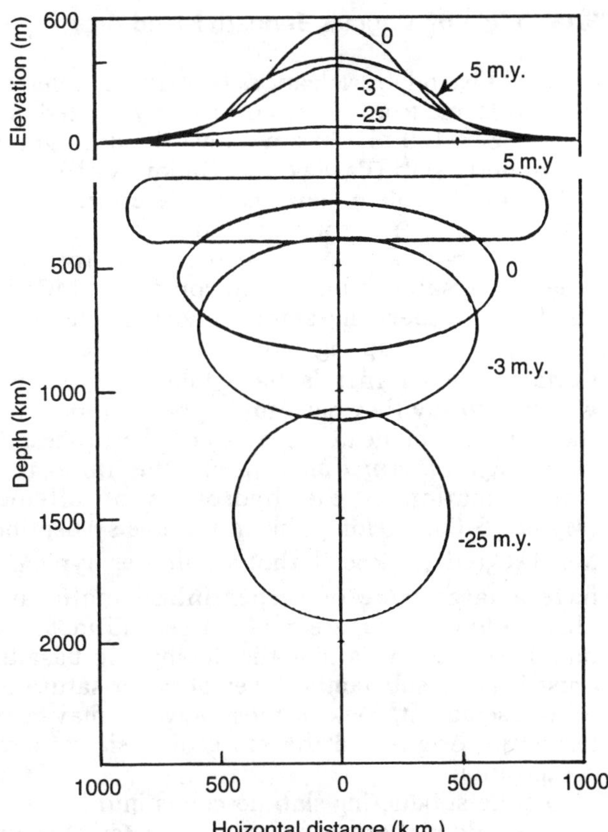

Figure 5.34 Schematic diagram of an idealized rising mantle plume head showing it as flattening and broadening, and at the same time causing a surface uplift of the overlying crust. (From R.I. Hill, E.H. Campbell, G.F. Davies, and R.W. Griffiths, 1992, *Science*, v. 256, p. 185. Figure 1.Copyright © 1992 by the American Association for the Advancement of Science Used by permission.)

5.17 Subduction Boundary Volcanism

Note that on our world maps of lithospheric plates (Figures 1.11 and 7.3) the Pacific, Nazca, and Cocos plates consist almost entirely of oceanic lithosphere. In North and South America, oceanic lithosphere of the Pacific, Nazca, and Cocos plates is being subducted beneath continental lithosphere of the American plate. Arcs of andesitic volcanoes mark these subduction zones in the Aleutian Islands, the Cascade Range, Central America, and the Andes Range. (The word "andesite" is derived from its abundance as a rock type in the Andes Range.) Other arcs of andesitic volcanoes follow the western boundary of the Pacific plate, making several island arcs extending south from the Japanese Islands through the Philippines, and into the southwestern Pacific. Another similar volcanic arc forms the Indonesian crescent, including the islands of Java and Sumatra. Here, the Austral-Indian plate is being subducted beneath the margin of the Eurasian plate. Rhyolite lavas are also present in volcanic eruptions of this "ring of fire," but in smaller volumes than the andesite lavas. Our world maps also show volcanic activity in a subduction boundary that bounds the Caribbean plate on the east, and a quite similar arrangement in the South Atlantic, where the Scotia plate has a small volcanic arc on which lie the South Sandwich Islands. Finally, the Mediterranean Sea has a small subduction plate boundary enclosing the Aegean Sea basin, with a short volcanic arc to the north, linking Greece with Turkey.

A first step is to form two classes of volcanic arcs. One, which we shall call *intra-ocean arcs*, *oceanic arcs*, or *island arcs*, has large expanses of deep ocean, floored by oceanic crust, on both sides of the plate boundary. The other class consists of the *continental margin arcs* (*continental arcs*, for short) in which the volcanoes receive their magma through conduits in the continental crust. The term *arc magmas* can be applied to both classes. The arc magmas arise from locations in or just above the descending lithospheric plate, but there are some important differences in the petrologic changes the magmas of the two classes experience as they penetrate the overlying lithospheric plate.

5.18 Origin of Magmas Beneath Island Arcs

Chains of island arc volcanoes (sometimes referred to as "volcanic fronts") are consistently located in a narrow belt 100 to 150 km above the downgoing lithospheric slab (Pawley and Halloway, 1993, p. 664). Our problem here is to determine why magma formation is concentrated in this zone.

The input of upper oceanic crust into the oceanic-arc subduction system consists of MORB, but it has undergone some important chemical changes after erupting from the mid-ocean rift. Certain of its minerals have taken up water—which is to say they have undergone *hydrolysis* in the presence of heated seawater. The process is called *hydrothermal alteration*. One important transformation is the hydrolysis of olivine, $(Mg,Fe)_2SiO_4$, yielding the very stable serpentine, $Mg_3Si_2O_5(OH_4)$. Recall that ophiolites typically have a large zone of serpentinized mafic and ultramafic rock (Figure 5.14). A second factor to take into account is that the downgoing basaltic crust bears a substantial layer of water-saturated pelagic sediment, some or most of which may be of terrestrial origin and therefore of felsic mineral composition.

As the subducting slab descends into levels of increasingly higher temperature, *dewatering* of the serpentinized basalt and the sediment sets in. This initial water loss can be expected to be complete at a depth of 30 km and a temperature of 500°C (Fryer et al., 1988, p. 774). At this depth the slab is passing under the accretionary prism. As shown in Figure 5.35, the slab descends more steeply to the depth range of 100 to 150 km, which is directly under the volcanic front. Here, dehydration melting of hydrous minerals occurs (Pawley and Halloway, 1993, p. 664). Minerals of basalt and gabbro, which form the oceanic crust, undergo phase transformations to garnet and jadeite pyroxene. Both of these minerals are of greater density than minerals in the parent rock. The transformation thus yields the denser rock *eclogite* (Kirby and Hacker, 1993, p. 70).

The water made free by this transformation may be expected to diffuse upward through the mantle wedge above the plate, causing hydration, and this may result in a substantial lowering of the melting temperature of rock in that mantle zone. The free water "may also allow the slab to melt directly if temperatures are high enough" (Pawley and Holloway, 1993, p. 664). Next, we turn to the problem of how the mantle above the descending slab can be heated enough to allow it to melt. Perhaps this can be solved by hypothesizing a suitable convection system.

5.19 The Building of Oceanic Volcanic Arcs

Details of an asthenospheric convection mechanism operating above a descending lithospheric plate have been worked out on the basis of studies of the volcanic arc that borders the Aleutian Trench on the north and separates the Aleutian Islands from the Bering Sea. The central and western part of the arc, which trends about east-west, consists of a rather simple line of active volcanoes formed of basaltic andesite, intermediate between andesite and basalt. Immediately north of the volcanic arc lies a deep backarc basin floored by the Bering abyssal plain. It is thought to be a comparatively new subduction zone formed in the midst of an area of oceanic lithosphere. In any case, this oceanic volcanic arc seems to be a relatively young feature, as compared with the complex Japan and Kuril arcs, which contain old rocks. The active volcanic centers are quite uniformly spaced along the chain, and it appears that comparatively small bodies of magma are being produced at regular intervals at a position just above the down-going plate and at the base of the stationary oceanic plate that lies above it. The source of enough heat to cause melting has been a scientific problem difficult to solve. The descending slab is relatively cold, and calculations show that friction along the upper boundary of the slab is not a sufficient source of heat to cause melting.

Our hypothesis of the mechanism of mantle heating close to the descending plate was devised in 1979 by Bruce D. Marsh, of The Johns Hopkins University. It became known as the *corner flow*

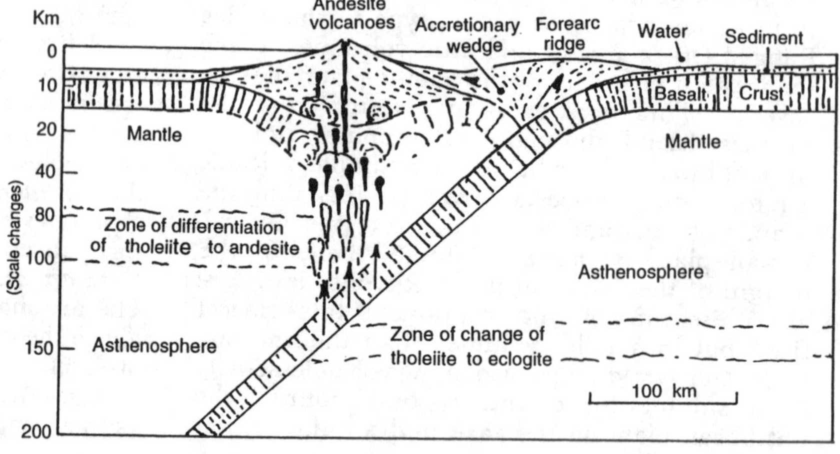

Figure 5.35 Schematic diagram of an island arc showing downgoing oceanic crust and dehydration of tholeiitic basalt, producing eclogite, and the zone of differentiation of rising hydrous tholeiitic magmas. (Based in part on data of A.E. Ringwood, 1974, and others. Diagram copyright © by Arthur N. Strahler.)

model because it postulates a current in the asthenosphere flowing into the tight corner between the two lithospheric plates, as shown in Figure 5.36. From the corner, the descending plate exerts a drag on the soft mantle rock, forcing it back down and perpetuating the inflow into the corner. Melting occurs in the narrow confines of a "pinch zone" (Marsh, 1978, p. 176; see also Wyllie, 1982, p. 475). Returning downward close to the surface of the descending slab, the mantle rock heats the upper surface of the slab, causing melting of a thin upper layer of its crust consisting of basalt and gabbro altered to eclogite. Rising in diapirs, the magma makes its way up through the overlying lithosphere. Fractional crystallization at one or more higher levels yields andesite magma that erupts as a submarine volcano (Wyllie, 1982, p. 496).

The corner flow pattern we have outlined seems to be powered by the down-moving plate, and is the effect of plate motion, rather than the cause. In Chapter 8 we show that the comparatively cold subducting slab will remain denser at all levels than the surrounding asthenosphere through which it descends, so that a gravitational slab-pull force is in play and can be called upon to drive the corner convection system.

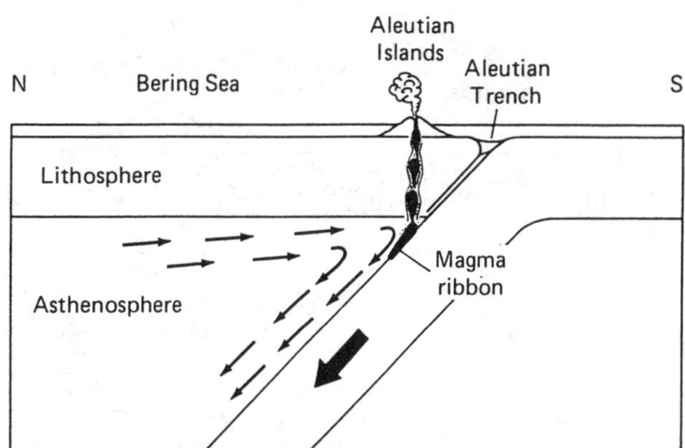

Figure 5.36 Schematic cross section showing the sharp bend in flow lines postulated under the corner-flow model of currents in the asthenosphere. A volcanic arc lies above the line where a magma ribbon is formed. (Copyright © by Arthur N. Strahler.)

5.20 Crustal Growth of an Island Arc

Once a new subduction boundary has come into existence within the oceanic lithosphere, the process of magma accumulation sets in on the seafloor of the upper plate as volcanoes are built. Magma also begins to accumulate beneath that oceanic crust. Thus the growing volcanic arc can be thought of as consisting of three parts, as shown schematically in Figure 5.37. At the top is the volcanic *edifice*. Below the crust is a *root*, or *keel*, that grows downward by accumulation of plutons. The point of this illustration is to show that it is necessary for the young arc to have upward growth of the edifice balanced by compensating downward growth of the root. This compensation keeps the entire structure in a state of isostatic equilibrium such that the edifice continues to protrude higher above sea level. (Isostasy is explained in Chapters 11 and 12.) Figure 5.37 gives density values that will satisfy the equilibrium equation (Gastil and Phillips, 1982, p. 465-466). If no root were formed, the volcanic crust would remain relatively low.

Figure 5.37 is, of course, unrealistic as a model for the actual composition and structure of an oceanic arc because the growth process must include melting of the original crust and its replacement by new igneous structures. A more realistic model is shown in Figure 5.38. It is patterned after the active Lesser Antilles island arc system in the vicinity of the volcanic island of Saint Vincent (Ladd, Westbrook, and Lewis, 1982, p. 17). The root of the arc is shown to be composed of the down-sunken remains of the original mafic crustal mass along with plutonic bodies of ultramafic cumulates and some magma chambers in which magmatic fractionation is occurring. The upper half or so of the arc is shown as made up of andesitic lavas and pyroclastics, with some diorite plutons. Pelagic sediments form a thin cover over the submarine slopes of the edifice.

Whereas the submarine mid-oceanic ridge is constructed of tholeiitic basalt (MORB), the edifice of the island arc is constructed mostly of andesitic magma, which is more silicic than that of the basalt. Andesite can be formed by partial melting of hydrous tholeiite. Lesser amounts of rhyolite may be included. In these respects the magmas of both oceanic and continental volcanic arcs differ as a group from the magmas of both the spreading ridges and the intraplate volcanic island chains.

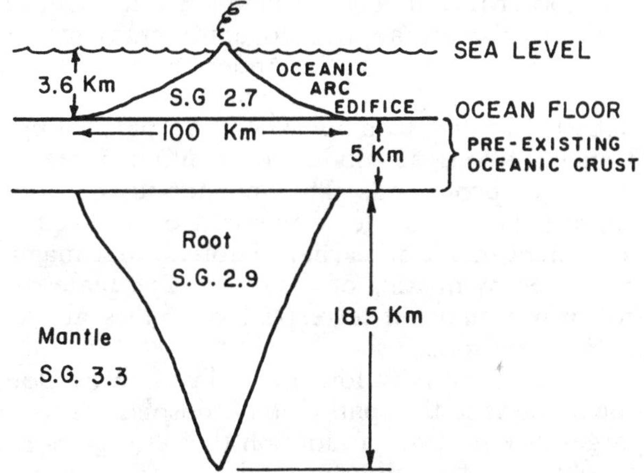

Figure 5.37 Schematic diagram of an island arc to show how the addition of a keel counterbalances the growth of the volcanic edifice to maintain isostatic equilibrium. (From Gordon Gastil amd Richard P. Phillips, 1982, *Bull. Geological Soc. of Amer.*, v. 93, p. 465. Figure 2. Reproduced with permission of the publisher, The Geological Society of America, Boulder, Colorado, USA. Copyright © 1982.)

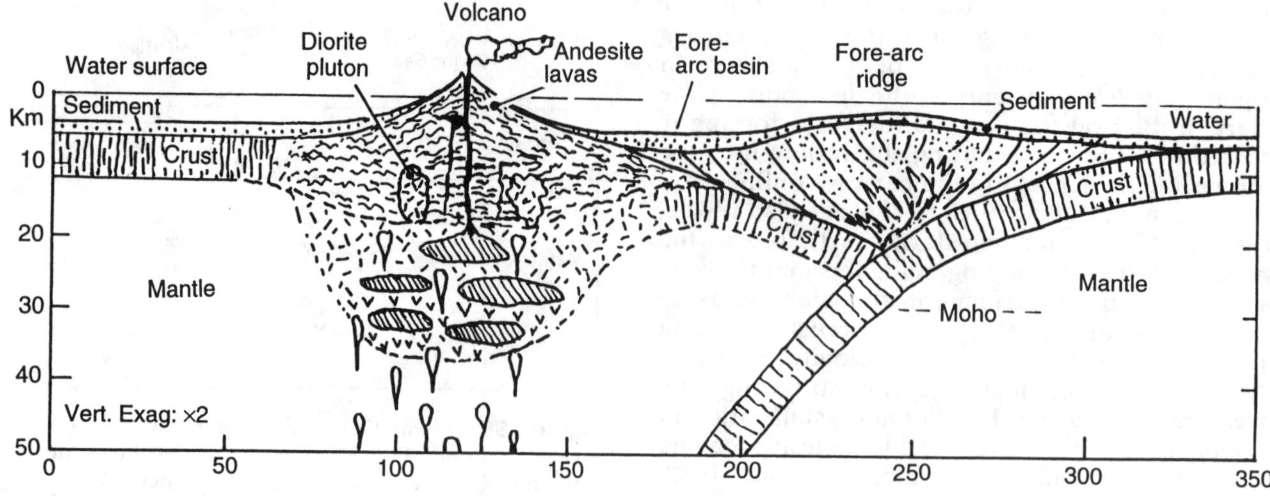

Figure 5.38 An idealized cross section of a mature volcanic island arc, with a well-developed accretionary prism and fore-arc basin. (Copyright © by Arthur N. Strahler.)

The mature island arc with its complex petrology has a bulk (vertical dimension and volume) greater than oceanic crust by a factor of about six; so should we classify it instead as continental crust? With a thickness of 30 to 35 km, as depicted in our figures 5.37 and 5.38, it compares favorably with continental crust, shown in figures 3.2 and 3.5 as ranging from 30 to 35 km as an average thickness, and up to 65 km or greater under high mountains. So perhaps our answer should be yes, it is continental crust. On the other hand, the absence of an upper felsic crust of granitic composition would seem to disqualify it.

5.21 Continental Margin Arcs

The corner-flow model of island-arc volcanism can perhaps also be applied to continental margin volcanic arcs, such as the Andes Range of South America. It explains the continuous volcanic activity limited to a narrow zone paralleling a trench. As long as subduction continues, magma will be produced. The corner-flow model represents a valuable refinement of our general statement, made in earlier chapters, that magma produced by melting of the downgoing plate rises to form a chain of terrestrial volcanoes above a subduction zone.

Igneous activity forming volcanic arcs along the margins of the continental lithosphere involves large-scale magma production that also gives rise to plutons of granite, granodiorite, and diorite. Reaching the surface, these same magmas emerge as lavas of acidic (felsic) and intermediate types, generating lava flows and pyroclastics of rhyolite and andesite. The depth at which this upward migration begins is estimated to commence at about 120 km depth, but the melting then extends down to depths of 200 km or more on the upper surface of the downgoing plate.

5.22 Batholithic Emplacement in Collision Orogens

"The most important role in the emplacement of plutonic igneous rocks is played by gravity. Their mode of intrusion is largely determined by the difference in density between the magma and its country rocks" (Anthony Hall, 1987, p. 66). Over many decades, petrologists have listed possible mechanisms of upward movement of magmas through overlying crustal rock as including the following: ascent by forceful injection, magmatic stoping, replacement, or dike intrusion. There is little evidence favoring large-scale assimilation (Ehlers and Blatt, 1982, p. 37, 217). Most batholiths are composed of granite or closely related felsic rocks, such as quartz monzonite, and granodiorite, but a single batholith may consist in part of another igneous rock, such as diorite and/or gabbro (Hall, 1987, p. 376-377).

While batholiths are usually mapped and named as single units (e.g., "the Idaho batholith exposed over an area of 42,000 km^2"), they are virtually all composites of many intrusions. Take for example the Coastal Batholith of Peru, stretching for some 500 km parallel with the Pacific coast. It was emplaced over a span of perhaps 70 m.y. (between 102 and 34 Ma). It is made up of some 1000 plutons, and no single granitic intrusion exceeds 30 km in diameter (Hall, 1987, p. 93). We can think of a batholith as a large cluster of many small intrusions—called *diapirs*—emplaced over tens of millions of years. The mode of rise of these small intrusives is known as *diapirism*. This is a general term for the upward forcing of a relatively soft, plastic medium of lower density penetrating the rock above it and making room for itself. Most commonly the term applies to the spontaneous rise of salt columns through overlying shale beds. (See Chapter 11.)

Batholithic diapirism is closely linked tectonically with continental subduction zones and with both arc-continent and continent-continent collisions. Although we have been particularly concerned here with the emplacement of batholiths within a continuously operating subduction system along a continental margin, the problems of mechanics of emplacement are common to all three tectonic scenarios.

One of the major problems in postulating a mode of emplacement of granitic batholiths is to explain what happened to the country rock that was displaced by the rising magma diapirs assuming, of course, that the magma was produced from other, deeper sources than the country rock itself. If, instead, we visualize the magma as produced directly by melting and recrystallization of older country rock, the problem of finding room for the batholith largely disappears.

Geologists have an alternative explanation for the emplacement of large plutons, and it relates to plate tectonics. The continental crust above a descending lithospheric plate is in some cases stretched horizontally and tends to become thinner. Thinning allows rising magma diapairs to take advantage of this horizontal mass motion by pushing the older country rock aside, rather than upward. By this mechanism there is almost no limit to the volume of new plutons that can be accommodated in the crust (Hanson and Glazner, 1995).

In Chapter 9, on the subject of arc-continent and continent-continent collisions, we will have more to say about igneous intrusion and the emplacement of batholiths. Those collisions are strongly compressional, greatly thickening the crust, and seemingly making more difficult the process of large-scale pluton emplacement.

5.23 Primary Metalliferous Ores and Plate Tectonics

"It is becoming increasingly clear that few if any of the subdisciplines of earth science will remain unaffected by the power and breadth of plate tectonic theory. The geology of ore deposits is no exception." With that paragraph Frederick J. Sawkins of the University of Minnesota opened his 1972 paper titled "Sulfide Ore Deposits in Relation to Plate Tectonics." He and a coauthor, U. Petersen (a specialist in the ore deposits of South America) had outlined the main points of his published paper in an abstract for the 1969 annual meetings of the Geological Society of America. What we offer here is a brief review of Sawkins's system of classification of metalliferous ore deposits according to inter-plate and intra-plate tectonics (Sawkins, 1972). (See also Hammond, 1975a, 1975b; Sawkins, 1990).

The source of primary metalliferous ore deposits is magma, rising from great depths to penetrate the crust. Hydrothermal deposits and pegmatites illustrate these mineral concentrations from igneous sources. Turning to plate tectonics, we have established in this chapter that igneous activity is largely concentrated in three types of environments or locations: (A) spreading (accreting) plate boundaries, where new oceanic crust is being created; (B) subduction zones, where magma is being produced by deep melting and is giving rise to intrusion and extrusion; and (C) hot spots of rising mantle rock, which may be found at almost any location within a lithospheric plate, far from its boundaries. Over the past two decades many details have been added to document the occurrences of important classes of ore deposits within each of these three tectonic zones of igneous activity.

Our tectonic classification of metallic ore deposits recognizes five basic types (Figure 5.39). We shall give each a tentative name, keeping in mind that we are dealing with an area of scientific exploration in its developing stages.

<u>1. Cyprus-type Ore Deposits</u> On the island of Cyprus in the eastern Mediterranean Sea, a huge deposit of copper sulfide ore occurs in the Troodos Massif, a broad band of mafic igneous rock cutting across the central part of the island. The ore bodies occur within a zone of pillow lavas of basalt composition, near the northern margin of the igneous rock zone. Adjacent to the pillow lava and grading into it is a zone of sheeted basaltic dikes, which in turn gives way to an adjacent zone of coarsely crystalline mafic rock of gabbro composition.

What geologists are seeing on Cyprus is an

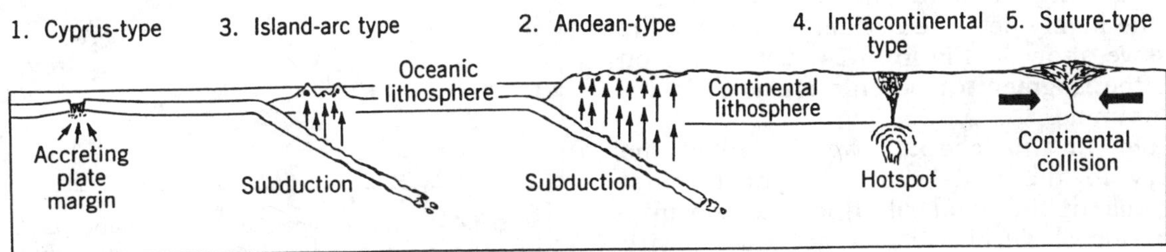

Figure 5.39 Schematic diagram showing five types of ore deposits in the frame of reference of plate tectonics. (Copyright © by Arthur N. Strahler.)

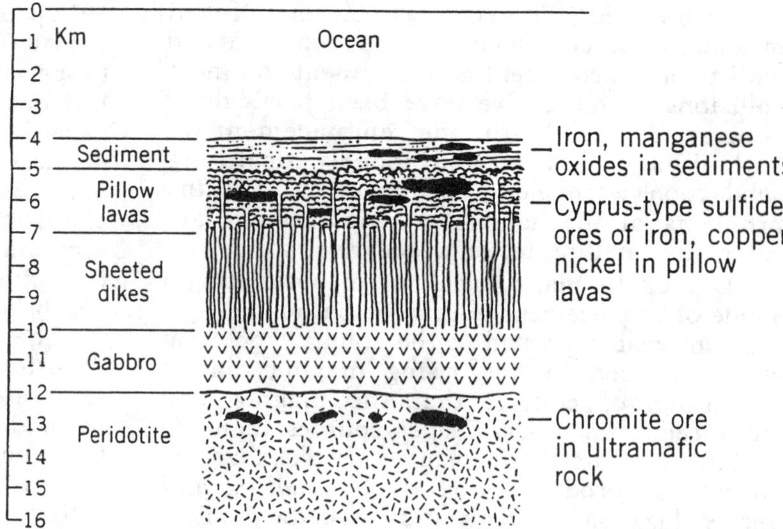

Figure 5.40 Cyprus-type ore deposits occur within an ophiolitic suite of rocks formed at accreting plate margins. The arrangement of rocks is the same as in Figure 5.8. (Copyright © by Arthur N. Strahler.)

ophiolitic suite (Rona, 1973, p. 90-92; Hurley, 1975, p. 16-17). As we explained earlier, ophiolites are thought to have originated as masses of oceanic crust, originally produced along accreting plate margins in the spreading zones of backarc basins and now exposed in continental locations. Figure 5.40, the schematic geologic cross section of ore bodies in the undisturbed oceanic crust, closely resembles that which we showed in Figure 5.13. Figure 5.14 compared the Troodos ophiolite section with five others.

Cyprus-type ore bodies, which are usually sulfides of iron, copper, or nickel, seem to have been deposited in the pillow lava layer by hydrothermal solutions. Sediments deposited upon the pillow lavas also receive hydrothermal deposits, and these are commonly enriched with compounds of iron and manganese (Koski, 1995; Humphris et al., 1995). Bodies of chromite (chromium ore) are sometimes found within the ultramafic rock at the base of the ophiolitic suite, as shown in Figure 5.40. These bodies may have formed by magmatic segregation in deep pockets of ultramafic magma at the same time that the seafloor spreading was in progress.

If the Cyprus ophiolite rocks were indeed formed at accreting plate margins in a spreading zone, how did they come to be elevated and exposed as a mountain range? During continental collision, masses of oceanic crust are broken away from the descending plate and slide up along overthrust faults to take an elevated position among the highly deformed strata of the tectonic belt, as we show in Figure 9.24. Later erosion exposes the fragment of oceanic crust, as in the Cyprus example.

Earlier in this chapter we described the discovery in the mid-1970s of hydrothermal phenomena in the axial rift floors of the mid-oceanic ridges. Turbid jets of hot water, with temperatures over 350°C—"smokers" they are called—were found to be carrying high concentrations of sulfides of copper, iron, and zinc, which precipitated around the vents. We also presented a schematic diagram (Figure 5.9) of the circulation of ocean water in the upper crust in the spreading zone. It soon became apparent that the seawater played a major chemical role in production of the sulfides. It was pointed out that chlorine in the seawater aids in the leaching out of the metals from the mafic rock, and that sulfates in the seawater take part in precipitating the metals as sulfides (Hammond, 1975, p. 869).

2. Andean-type Ore Deposits Our second class of ore deposits related to plate tectonics has been recognized in continental crust lying above a descending plate adjacent to a subduction zone. As shown in Figure 5.41, magma bodies rising from the descending plate reach the upper crust to solidify as plutons or to emerge as volcanic rocks such as andesite and rhyolite. The rising magmas have brought up a supply of metals, which now

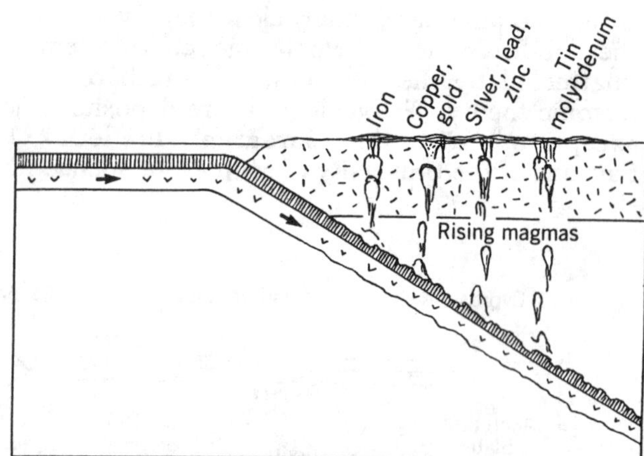

Figure 5.41 Andean-type metallic ore deposits are formed by magmas rising from an oceanic lithospheric plate undergoing subduction. Magma reaches the surface zone of the overlying continental lithosphere. (Copyright © by Arthur N. Strahler.)

occur in ore bodies in the igneous rocks. Because this class of deposits occurs as important tin and copper ores in the Andes Mountains of South America, it is referred to as the Andean-type of ore deposit (Hammond, 1975a, p. 779; Hurley, 1975, p. 18).

Magmas produced at various depths along the descending plate differ in dominant metallic element content. Consequently, the ore deposits show a distinct zoning by dominant metallic elements from continental margin to continental interior, as shown in Figure 5.41. Ores of iron are typical of a belt closest to the plate margin. Then come successive zones: copper and gold; silver, lead, and zinc; tin and molybdenum. This sequence has been recognized in the western United States and has been related to past episodes of subduction of the Farallon plate beneath the North American plate. Porphyry copper deposits are thought to be one of the forms of the Andean-type ore deposits. A possible example would be the porphyry copper at Bingham Canyon, Utah. Porphyry copper also occurs in the Andes and beneath ancient subduction zones in Eurasia. The concept has guided recent searches for new porphyry ore deposits.

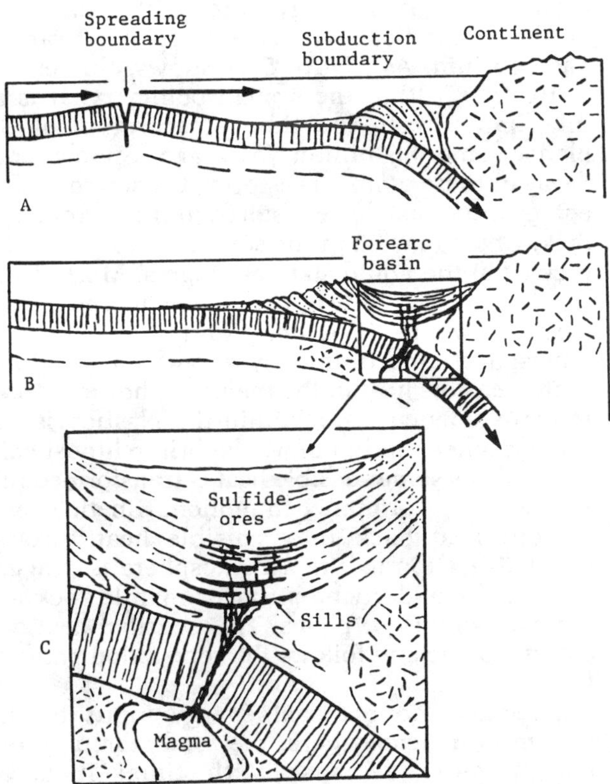

Figure 5.42 Conditions favorable to the accumulation of sulfide ores in forearc basin sediments above a subducted spreading plate boundary. (Copyright © by Arthur N. Strahler.)

3. Island-arc type Ore Deposits A third group of metallic ore deposits occurs within massive accumulations of felsic (acidic) lavas—andesite and rhyolite—within volcanic island arcs. An example often cited is the occurrence in Japan of important copper sulfide ores, one of the few rich mineral resources with which that island nation is endowed. The ore occurs in massive bodies and is usually a mixture of sulfides of copper, zinc, and lead, along with lesser amounts of silver and gold (Hedenquist and Lowenstern, 1994, Figure 1).

A special type of sulfide ore accumulation occurs along a subduction plate boundary when a spreading plate boundary closes in distance with the continent, or the same with a massive island arc. As shown in diagram A of Figure 5.42, the active spreading boundary nears the trench of the subduction zone. Continuing to function, the spreading boundary is carried intact beneath the accretionary prism and arrives at a position below a forearc basin, as shown in diagram B. Here, basaltic magmas carrying ore-bearing hydrothermal solutions rise from the spreading rift in dikes that penetrate the thick, clay-rich terrestrial sediments of the forearc basin. The magma spreads laterally into the sediment layers, forming sills, in which the sulfide ores reside. This scenario seems to explain an important type of sulfide ore, named a Besshi deposit after a well known sulfide ore body found in Japan. The accumulation of sulfides in terrestrial deposits has been identified in the Gulf of California where thick river sediment overlies an active spreading plate boundary (Edmond and Von Damm, 1983, p. 92-93).

4. Intracontinental Ore Deposits Important ore deposits occur far from plate boundaries and lie in the heart of large areas of continental crust. An example is the lead and zinc ore deposits of the Mississippi/Ohio valley region. These ores are found in sedimentary strata of the continental platform. A highly speculative hypothesis can be put forward that ores of this type are formed by hydrothermal solutions rising from a hotspot in the mantle below. Independent evidence of such hotspots is not found, however, in the same area as the occurrence of the ores.

An entirely different hypothesis of lead and zinc mineralization in the U.S. interior continental platform was proposed in 1986 by geophysicist/-seismologist Jack Oliver of Cornell University, mentioned in Chapter 3 for his leadership in COCORP—the Consortium for Continental Reflection Profiling. That program included seismic profiles of the great Appalachian overthrust sheets, and it may be that Oliver's familiarity with these orogenic structures led to the formulation of his explanation. The lead/zinc ores were emplaced about the time of the Allegheny orogeny that occurred in Permian time, causing folding and thrusting of Paleozoic strata in the Central Appalachians and Ouachita Mountains. Overthrusting would have compressed underlying

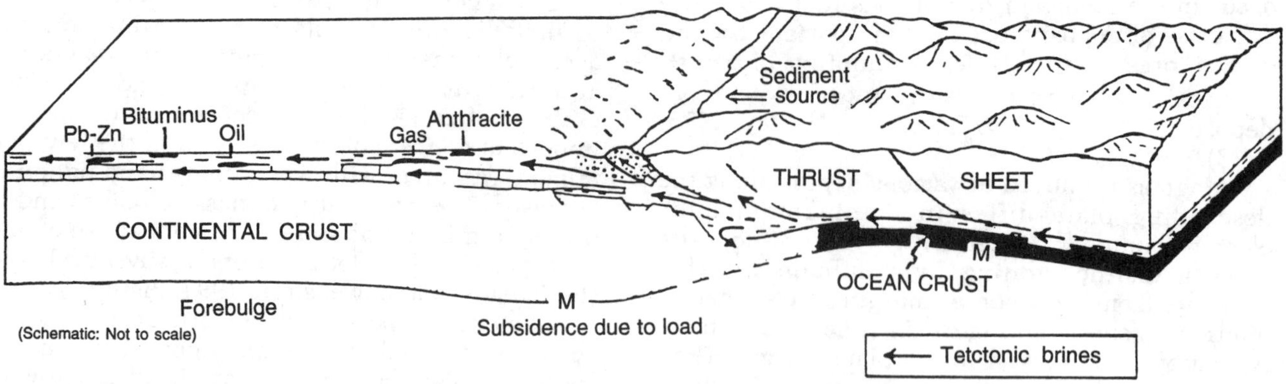

Figure 5.43 A schematic block diagram showing how tectonic brines carrying lead and zinc solutions, might be expelled from beneath an advancing thrust sheet and penetrate far into platform sediments of the continental interior. (From Jack Oliver, 1986, *Geology*, v. 14, p. 99, Figure 2. Reproduced with permission of the publisher, The Geological Society of America, Boulder, Colorado, USA. Copyright © 1986.)

strata saturated with ocean water, expelling the fluid horizontally toward the interior. At the same time, the surface of the orogen itself was brought to a higher topographic position than the interior platform strata. The result would have been to force the mineral-ladened brines to migrate into the interior strata, as schematically illustrated in Figure 5.43. Along with the tectonic brines there would travel liquid and dissolved gaseous petroleum hydrocarbons, explaining the widespread occurrences of petroleum and natural gas in the same interior region (Oliver, 1986, p. 99-102).

5. Suture-type Ore Deposits Any one of the four ore deposit types previously named could, in the geologic past, have become involved in continental collisions. Today the rock types which bear these ores are found crumpled, overthrust, and metamorphosed in sutures within the continental shields. Take the case of the ore deposits of Newfoundland. Throughout the Paleozoic Era, the Appalachian belt, in which Newfoundland lies, suffered repeated continental collisions and terrane dockings alternating with episodes of continental rifting, as the primitive Atlantic Ocean basin opened and closed (Chapters 9 and 10). The final suturing occurred at the close of the Paleozoic Era. Geologists can recognize in the rocks of Newfoundland the typical ophiolitic ore suite of the Cyprus type in the Bay of Islands ophiolite (Figure 5.14). Also found in Newfoundland are island-arc ore deposits in great volcanic rock masses, and even porphyry ores of the Andean type that formerly occurred above subduction zones.

No longer in its early stages, the tie-in of ore deposits with plate tectonics has produced a healthy optimism within the ranks of economic geologists engaged in exploration for new mineral deposits. Now they have a tectonic frame of reference in which to place the major types of ore deposits. Interpretation of a particular rock sequence in terms of plate tectonics allows the geologist to predict what type of ore deposit may occur there. As with any search program, knowing what to look for and where to look for it gives the searcher a great advantage.

5.24 Modeling the Earth's Internal Energy System

Tectonic and volcanic activity represent expenditures of internal energy stored within the nuclei of atoms of radioactive elements, such as uranium and thorium. As Figure 5.44 shows, this energy source lies within the system boundary. It is an inheritance from the time of accretion of the planet some 4.6 billion years ago. Spontaneous decay of these atoms transforms the stored atomic energy into sensible heat stored in the surrounding rock, which may be in the solid state as crystalline rock or in the liquid state as magma. Most of this sensible heat is slowly conducted to the earth's surface, where it is lost to the oceans and atmosphere, and ultimately to outer space. Some of the sensible heat in the mantle is, however, used to drive slow currents within the plasticoviscous asthenosphere and to move the brittle lithospheric plates. Thus some sensible heat is transformed into kinetic energy of matter in motion. Kinetic energy is converted back into sensible heat through internal friction as the asthenosphere is dragged against the underlying stronger mantle rock and the overlying rigid plates. This sensible heat also enters storage and follows the conduction pathway to the surface.

Because no external energy input to this system is indicated here, the total stored system energy must decrease with time; it is an exponential decay system. We have not taken into account the possibility that some energy enters the system through tidal flexing of the earth. There is also the possibility that important new energy inputs have been made from time to time by infall

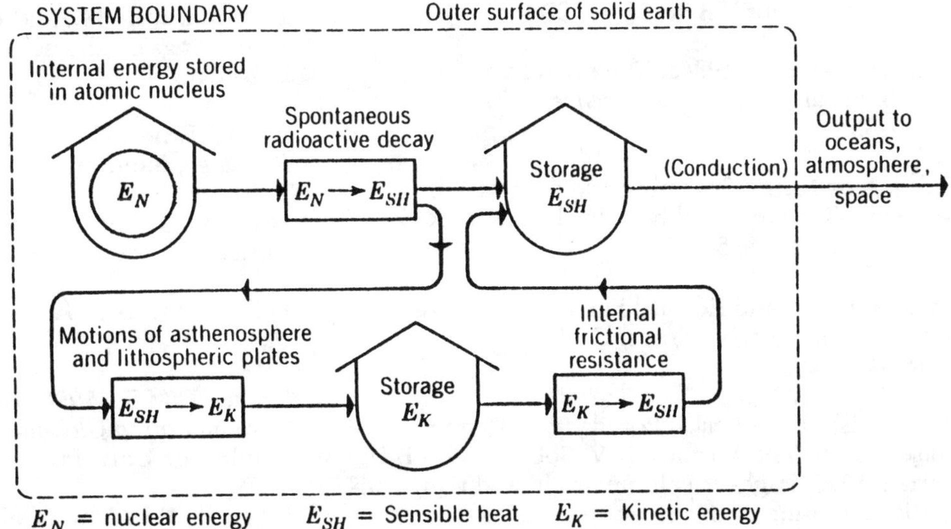

Figure 5.44 Flow diagram of the earth's internal energy system. (Drawn by Arthur N. Strahler. Copyright © 1987 by John Wiley & Sons, New York. Reproduced by permission of the publisher.)

and impact of comets and asteroids. Solar energy also participates in the tectonic system (a) through physical processes of rock decomposition and disintegration and the erosion and transportation of mineral matter, and (b) through biological processes that form organic and biogenic sediment.

Because the earth's initial store of radioactive elements is slowly but steadily diminishing through spontaneous decay, the total energy available to operate the moving plate system must be decreasing. From this conclusion we can speculate that plate motions and tectonic activity will become less vigorous as eons of time pass. Correspondingly, igneous activity will decline in intensity. There will be fewer orogenies, and new mountains will not rise as high above sea level. Perhaps we can speculate that erosion of the continents will ultimately dominate. At that distant eon, the continents will be maintained at a much lower average elevation and will ultimately show only subdued relief features.

REFERENCES CITED

Anderson, Don L., 1984a, The earth as a planet: Paradigms and paradoxes. *Science*, v. 223, p. 347-355.

Baksi, Ajoy K., 1990, Timing and duration of Mesozoic-Tertiary flood basalt volcanism. *EOS*, v. 71, no. 49, p. 1835-1836.

Baksi, Ajoy K., and Edward Farrar, 1991, $^{40}Ar/^{39}Ar$ dating of the Siberian Traps. *Geology*, v. 19, p. 461-464.

Basu, Asish R., Robert J. Poreda, P.R. Renne, F. Teischmann, Y.R. Vasiliev, N.V. Sobolev, and B.D. Turrin, 1995, High-^{3}He plume origin and temporal-spatial evolution of the Siberian flood basalts. *Science*, v. 269, p. 822-825.

Ben-Avraham, A. Nur, D. Jones, and A. Cox, 1981, Continental accretion: From oceanic plateaus to allochthonous terranes. *Science*, v. 213, p. 47-54.

Burke, Kevin C., and J. Tuzo Wilson, 1976, Hot spots on the earth's surface. *Scientific American*, v. 235, no. 2, p. 46-57.

Calvert, A.J., 1995, Seismic evidence for a magma chamber beneath the slow-spreading Mid-Atlantic Ridge. *Nature*, v. 377, p. 410-413.

Cann, Joe, 1991-92. Onions and leaks: Magma at mid-ocean ridges. *Oceanus*, v. 34, p. 36-41.

Conde, Kent C., 1989, *Plate Tectonics & Crustal Evolution*. Oxford, Pergamon Press.

Crough, S. Thomas, 1983, Hotspot swells. *Ann. Rev. Earth Planet Sci.*, v. 11, p. 165-193.

Dalrymple, G.B., M.A. Landphere, and E.D. Jackson, 1974, Contributions to the petrography and geochronology of volcanic rocks from the leeward Hawaiian Islands. *Bull. Geological Soc. Amer.*, v. 85, p. 727-738.

Daniels, Leon R.M., John Gurney, and Ben Harte, 1996, A crustal mineral in a mantle diamond. *Nature*, v. 379, p. 153-156.

DePaolo, Donald J., 1981, Nd isotopic studies: Some new perspectives on earth evolution and structure. *EOS*, v. 62, no. 14, p. 137-140.

Dick, Henry J.B., 1992, A new mandate for deep-ocean drilling. *Oceanus*, v. 35, no. 4, p. 26-30.

Duncan, Robert A., 1991, Ocean drilling and the volcanic record of hotspots. *GSA Today*, v. 1, no. 10, p. 213-216, 219.

Edmond, John M., and Karen Von Damm, 1983, Hot springs on the ocean floor. *Scientific American*, v. 248, no. 4, p. 78-93.

Ehlers, Ernest G., and Harvey Blatt, 1982, *Petrology*, San Francisco, W.H. Freeman and Co.

Ernst, W.G., 1969, *Earth Materials*. Englewood Cliffs, N.J.: Prentice-Hall.

Falloon, Trevor, 1993, Get out your umbrellas. *Nature*, v. 365, p. 298-299.

Fowler, C.M.R., 1990. *The Solid Earth: An Introduction to Global Physics*. Cambridge, UK: Cambridge Univ. Press.

Fryer, P., E.L. Ambos, and D.M. Hussong, 1985, Origin and emplacement of Mariana forearc seamounts. *Geology*, v. 13, p. 774-777.

Gastil, Gordon, 1982, Symposium on subduction of oceanic plates: Summary, *Bull. Geological Soc. Amer.*, v. 93, p. 464-467.

Greene, H.G., G.B. Dalrymple, and D.A. Clague, 1978, Evidence for northward movement of the Emperor Seamounts. *Geology*, v. 6, p. 70-74.

Hall, Anthony, 1987, *Igneous Petrology*, Harlow, Essex, U.K., Longman Scientific & Technical; New York: John Wiley & Sons.

Hammond, Alan H., 1975a, Minerals and plate tectonics: A conceptual revolution, *Science*, v. 189, p. 779-781.

Hammond, Alan H., 1975b, Minerals and plate tectonics II: Seawater and ore formation. *Science*, v. 189, p. 868-869, 915.

Hanson, R. Brooks, and Allen F. Glazner, 1995, Thermal requirements for extensional emplacement of granitoids. *Geology*, v. 23, p. 213-216.

Hedenquist, Jeffrey W., and Jacob B. Lowenstern, 1994, The role of magmas in the formation of hydrothermal ore deposits. *Nature*, v. 370, p. 519-527.

Helgason, Johann, 1984, Frequent shifts of the volcanic zone in Iceland. *Geology*, v. 12, p. 213.

Holmes, Arthur, 1978, Holmes' *Principles of Physical Geology*, 3rd. Ed., New York: John Wiley & Sons.

Hooper, Peter R., 1982, The Columbia River basalts. *Science*, v. 215, p. 1463-1468.

Humphris, Susan E., P.M. Herzig, D.J. Miller et al., 1995, The internal structure of an active sea-floor massive sulphide deposit. *Nature*, v. 377, p. 713-716.

Hunter, Donald M., 1993, Atmospheric evolution of the terrestrial planets. *Science*, v. 259, p. 915-920.

Hurley, Patrick, 1975, Plate tectonics and mineral deposits. *Technology Review*, v. 77, no. 5, 15-21.

Jason, W. Morgan, 1971, Convection plumes in the lower mantle. *Nature*, v. 230. p. 42-43.

Kaula, William M., 1968, *An Introudction to Planetary Physics: The Terrestrial Planets*. New York: John Wiley & Sons.

Kay, S. Mahlburg, and R.W. Kay, 1985, Role of crystal cumulates and the oceanic crust in the formation of the lower crust of the Aleutian arc. *Geology*, v. 13. p. 461-464.

Kerr, Richard A., 1991, Deep rocks stir the mantle pool. *Science*, v. 252, p. 783.

Kirby, Stephen, and Brad Hacker, 1993, Earthquakes at the deep roots of arc volcanoes. *EOS*, v. 74, no. 6, p. 70.

Koski, Randolph A., 1995, The making of metal deposits. Nature, v. 377, p. 679-680.

Ladd, John, Graham Westbrook, and Stephen Lewis, 1982, Subduction tectonics in forearcs: Guatemala vs. Barbados. *Lamont-Doherty Geological Observatory Yearbook 81-82*, v. 8, p. 17-21.

Langmuir, C., J. Reynolds, K. Kastens, B. Ryan, and J. Bender, 1992, Ocean ridges as active volcanoes. *Lamont-Doherty Geological Observatory Report 90-91*, p. 33-34.

Langseth, Marcus, 1977, The seafloor and the earth's heat engine. *Lamont-Doherty Geological Observatory Yearbook 1977*, v. 4, p. 41-44.

Lewis, Brian T.R., 1983, The process of formation of ocean crust. *Science*, v. 220, p. 151-156.

Lewis, John S., 1973, The origin of the planets and satellites, *Technology Review*, v. 76, no. 1, p. 21-35.

Lewis, John S., 1974, The chemistry of the solar system. *Scientific American*, v. 230, no. 3, p. 51-65.

Macdonald, Ken C., 1989, Tectonic and magmatic processes on the East Pacific Rise. Chapter 6, p. 93-110 in *Geology of North America*, vol. N, Boulder Co: Geological Society of America.

Macdonald, Ken C., P.J. Fox, Russ T. Alexander, Robert Pockalny, and Pascal, Gente, 1996, Volcanic growth faults and the origin of Pacific abyssal hills. *Nature* v, 380, p. 125-129.

Malinverno, Alberto, 1993, Transition between a valley and a high at the axis of midocean ridges. *Geology*, v. 21, p. 639-642.

Marsh, Bruce D., 1979, Island-arc volcanism. *American Scientist*, v. 67, March-April, p. 161-172.

Mason, Brian, 1966, *Principles of Geochemistry*, 2nd Ed., New York, John Wiley & Sons.

Mason, Bryan, 1985, Ophiolites. *Geology Today*, Sept.-Oct. 1985, p. 136-140.

Morgan, W. Jason, 1971, Convection plumes in the lower mantle, *Nature*, v. 230, p. 42-43.

Murray, Bruce, Michael C. Malin, and Ronald Greeley, 1981, *Earthlike Planets: The Surfaces of Mercury, Venus, Earth, Moon, Mars*. San Francisco: W.H. Freeman & Co.

Mutter, John C., and Jeffrey A. Karson, 1992, Structural processes at slow-spreading ridges. *Science*, v. 257, p. 627-634.

Newsome, Horton E., and Kenneth W.W. Sims, 1991, Core formation during early accretion of the earth. *Science*, v. 252, p. 926-933.

Officer, C.B., and C.L. Drake, 1985, Terminal Cretaceous environmental effects. *Science*, v. 227, p. 1161-1162

Oliver, Jack, 1986, Fluids expelled tectonically from orogenic belts: Their role in hydrocarbon migration and other geologic phenomena. *Geology*, v. 14, p. 99-102.

Pasteris, Jill Dill, 1983, Kimberlites: A look into the earth's mantle. *American Scientist*, v. 71, p. 282-288.

Pawley, Alison R., and John R. Holloway, 1993, Water sources for subduction zone volcanism: New experimental constraints. *Science*, v. 260, p. 664-666.

Peterson, Ivars, 1993, A rocky start. *Science News*, v. 143, p. 190-191.

Pollack, Henry N., 1982, The heat flow from the continents. *Annual Rev. Earth Planet Sciences*, p. 459-481.

Renne, Paul R., and Asish R. Basu, 1991, Rapid eruption of the Siberian Traps flood basalts at the

Permo-Triassic boundary. *Science*, v. 253, p. 176-179.

Rona, Peter A. 1973, Plate tectonics and mineral resources. *Scientific American*, v. 299, p. 86-95.

Sawkins, Frederick J., 1972, Sulfide ore deposits in relation to plate tectonics. *Jour. of Geology*, v. 80, p. 377-397.

Sawkins, Frederick J., 1990, *Metal Deposits in Relation to Plate Tectonics*, 2nd Ed. New York: Springer-Verlag.

Sclater, J.G., B. Parsons, and C. Jaupart, 1981b, Oceans and continents: similarities and differences in the mechanisms of heat loss. *J. Geophysical Res.*, v. 86, p. 11535-11552.

Sclater, J.G., C. Jaupart, D. Jalson, 1981a, The heat flow through oceanic and continental crust and the heat loss of the earth. *Rev. Geophysics Space Physics*, v.18, 269-311.

Seyfert, Carl K., 1987, Mantle plumes and hotspots. Pages 312-430 in Seyfert, Ed., 1987.

Seyfert, Carl K., Ed., 1987, *Encyclopedia of Structural Geology and Plate Tectonics*. New York: Von Nostrand Reinhold.

Silver, P.G., R.W. Carlson, P. Bell, and P. Olsen, 1985, Mantle structure and dynamics. *EOS*, v. 66, no. 48, p. 1195-1198.

Smith, Deborah K., and Johnson R. Cann, 1993, Building the crust at the Mid-Atlantic Ridge. *Nature*, v. 365, p. 707-715.

Snow, Jonathan E., 1995, Of Hess and layer cake. *Nature*, v. 374, p. 413-414.

Stacey, Frank D., 1977, *Physics of the Earth*, 2nd ed. New York: John Wiley & Sons.

Wetherill, George W., 1991, Occurrence of earth-like bodies in planetary systems. *Science*, v. 253, p. 535-538.

White, Robert S., 1989, Igneous outbursts and mass extinctions. *EOS*, v. 70, no. 46, p. 1480, 1490-1491.

White, Robert S., and Dan P. McKenzie, 1989, Volcanism at rifts, *Scientific American*, July, p. 62.

White, William M., 1996, Best friend hides deep secret. *Nature*, v. 379, p. 117-118.

Wilson, J. Tuzo, 1963a, A possible origin of the Hawaiian Islands. *Canadian Jour. of Physics*, v. 41, p. 863-870.

Wilson, J. Tuzo, 1963b, Hypotheses of Earth's behavior. *Nature*, v. 198, no. 4884, p. 925-929.

Wilson, J. Tuzo, 1963c, Continental drift. *Scientific American*, April, 1963.

Wolfe, Cecily J., Ingi Th. Bjarnason, John C. VanDecar and Sean C. Solomon, 1997, Seismic structure of the Iceland mantle plume. *Nature*, v. 385, p. 245-247.

Wyllie, Peter J., 1982, Subduction products according to experimental prediction. *Bull., Geological Soc. Amer.*, v. 93, p. 468-476.

Chapter: 6 Seismicity and Plate Tectonics

The positive relationship between earthquake activity, or *seismicity*, and lithospheric plate boundaries is remarkably strong and consistent. Relatively few strong earthquakes have occurred in the interiors of continental plates and along passive continental margins. Vast expanses of the ocean floors appear on global maps to be nearly void of seismicity. In this chapter we examine the relationships between seismicity and plate tectonics, and in so doing demonstrate how the geophysical science of seismology provided essential evidence supporting the main concepts of plate tectonics.

6.1 The Global Scope of Seismicity

Figure 6.1 is a set of three world maps showing (A) epicenters of recorded earthquakes over a seven-year period, (B) epicenters of great earthquakes over an 80-year period, and (C) epicenters of deep-focus earthquakes only.

Notice first on Map A the abundance of earthquakes in a ring almost surrounding the Pacific Ocean. Most of this *circum-Pacific belt* is a line of intense volcanic activity as well as seismic activity. Comparison with the global map of lithospheric plates, Figure 1.11, will immediately show that the circum-Pacific belt marks the outer margins of the Pacific, Nazca, and Cocos plates, and that most of this plate boundary is one of active plate subduction.

A second major belt of intense seismic activity shown on Map A stretches from the Mediterranean Sea to the Indonesian region. This belt corresponds to the tectonically active boundary between the Eurasian plate on the north and the African, Arabian, and Austral-Indian plates that border it on the south. Starting at the Atlantic Ocean, a zone of Cenozoic continental collision extends eastward from the Pyrenees range of Iberia, across southern Europe and Asia minor. (A small part of the Mediterranean section is, however, an active plate subduction boundary.) The collision boundary zone continues eastward between the Persian and Arabian plates, and with a sharp offset to the north, follows the Himalayan arc. The seismic belt then turns southward into Burma, Thailand, and Malaysia. The south-easternmost segment is the subduction zone known as the Sumatra/Java arc. Elsewhere on the globe are two short sections of active subduction boundaries: the Antilles arc and Scotia arc, both in the Atlantic ocean basin.

We can conclude from Map A of Figure 6.1, that as a general rule that active subduction and collision boundaries produce the large bulk of the earth's relatively shallow earthquakes. Most of the great earthquakes, shown in Map B, are distributed along the subduction boundaries. An important exception lies in Mongolia and China, where a scattered group of great earthquakes suggest a unique tectonic pattern. Map C, showing only deep-focus earthquakes, can serve quite well as a world map of the active subduction plate boundaries.

Another important belt of consistently high seismicity, showing clearly on Map A, runs down the middle of the Atlantic Ocean basin, through the Indian Ocean, and across the southern Pacific basin. Comparison with our global maps of lithospheric plates (Figures 1.11 and 7.3) shows that this belt coincides with the active mid-oceanic spreading plate boundaries where new oceanic crust is being produced. The numerous earth-quakes that occur along the spreading plate boundaries are for the most part of moderate to low intensity and are of the shallow-focus type. Notice that Maps B and C give no hint of the existence of the mid-oceanic ridges. One feature that will emerge more clearly is that seismicity is found not only in the rift axis, where two oceanic plates are separating by spreading, but also on transform faults that offset those spreading boundaries.

6.2 Seismicity and Plate Tectonics

We begin this investigation of seismicity and plate tectonics with a historical approach in which the pioneering role of seismology in establishing the paradigm of plate tectonics is recounted step by step. In so doing, some of the basic applications of seismology to tectonic analysis are reviewed. We assume that our readers have a knowledge of general descriptive seismology and the mechanisms of earthquakes.

The topical order of our chapter presentation is displayed in Table 6.1, which recognizes four major tectonic classes. Class I: Active plate boundaries lying entirely within oceanic lithosphere and including both spreading (divergent) and transform boundaries. Class II: Active subduction (convergent) boundaries between oceanic and continental lithosphere. The volcanic arcs fall into this category. Class III: Active continent-continent collision boundaries and their orogens, including both compressional thrusts and related strike-slip faults. Class IV: Fault systems entirely within continental lithosphere. This intracontinental class includes four distinct tectonic subclasses. Subclass A: Continental transform systems serving as plate boundaries. Subclass B: Compressional orogenic systems. Subclass C: Intracontinental rift systems. Subclass D: Reactivated cratonal rifts and Paleozoic/Mesozoic orogens.

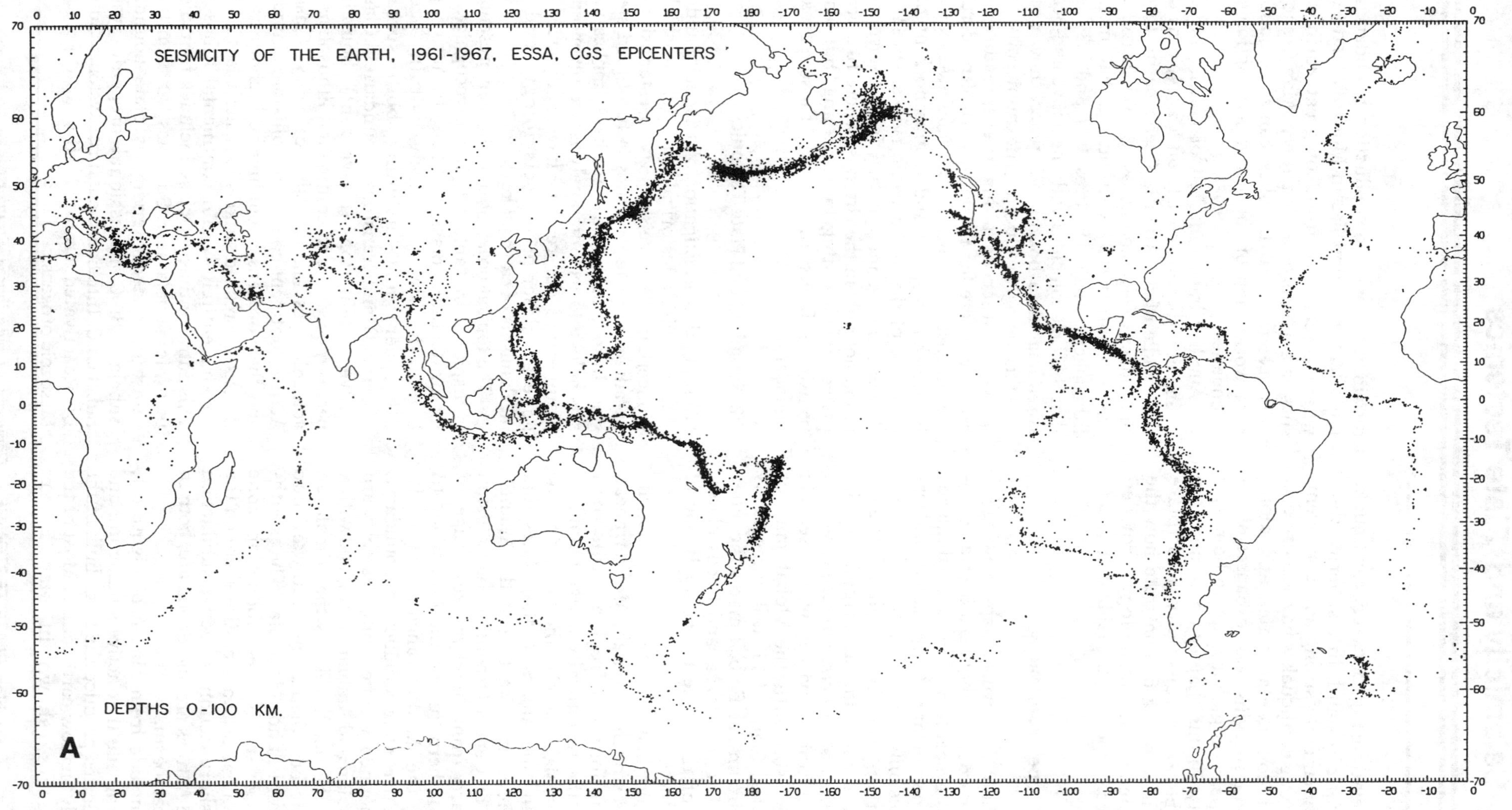

Figure 6.1 World maps of seismicity of the earth. Map A: Epicenters of earthquakes originating at depths from 0 to 100 km (dots) over the period 1961-1967. Each dot represents a single epicenter or a cluster of epicenters. Map B: Epicenters of earthquakes originating at depths from 100 to 700 km, 1961-1967. Each dot represents a single epicenter or a cluster of epicenters. Map C: Epicenters of great earthquakes, Richter magnitude 8.0 and greater, 1897-1985. (Epicenter data in maps A and B compiled

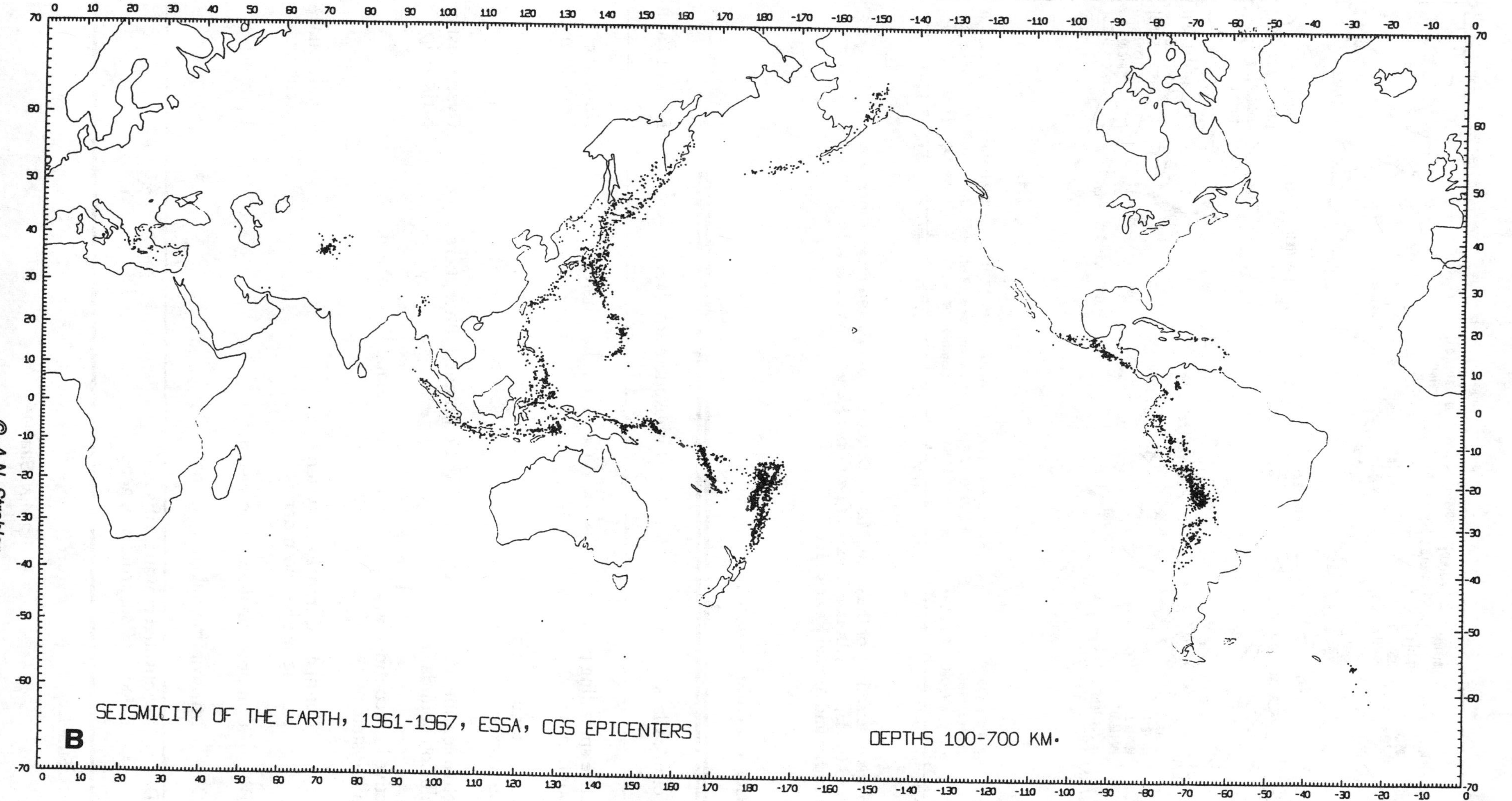

from ESSA, Coast and Geodetic Survey, in J. Dorman and M. Barazangi, 1969, *Seismological Society of America, Bull.*, v. 50, no. 1, Plates 2 and 3. Epicenters of great earthquakes from W. Hamilton, 1979, *Professional Paper 1078,* U.S. Geological Survey. Map C. Data on locations and magnitudes of great earthquakes from Hiroo Uyeda, 1986, *Annual Review of Earth and Planetary Science*, v. 14, p. 294. Used by permission of the author and Annual Reviews Inc.

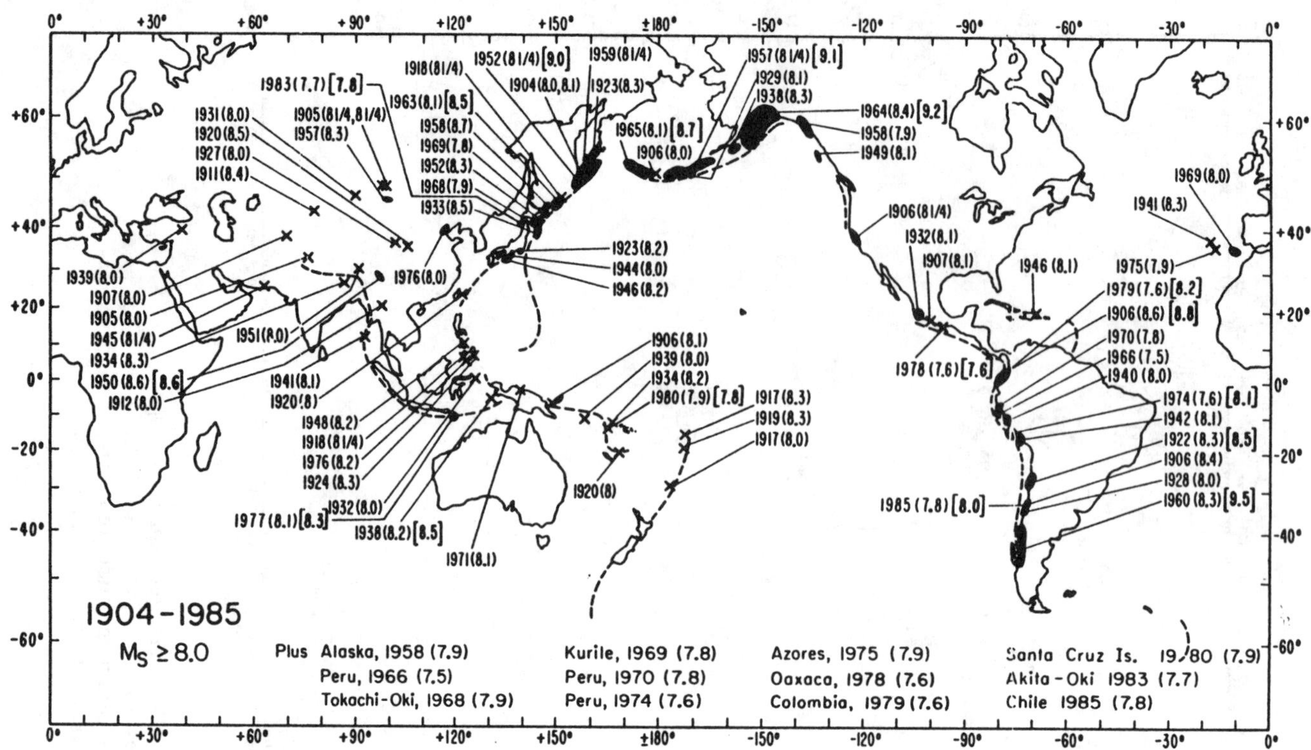

Figure 6.1-C World maps of seismicity of the earth. Map C. Data on locations and magnitudes of great earthquakes from Hiroo Uyeda, 1986, *Annual Review of Earth and Planetary Science,* v. 14, p. 294. Used by permission of the author and Annual Reviews Inc.

Table 6.1 Seismicity and Plate Tectonics

	Tectonic Class	Lithosphere Involved	Kind of Fault
Class I	Active spreading plate boundaries	Oceanic lithosphere	Normal or Transform
Class II	Active subduction plate boundaries	Oceanic and continental lithosphere	Underthrust
Class III	Active continent/continent collision boundaries	Continental lithosphere	Overthrust or Strike-slip
Class IV	Active intracontinental fault systems	Continental lithosphere	
Subclass A	Continental transform systems serving as plate boundaries		Continental transform
Subclass B	Compressional orogenic systems		Upthrust
Subclass C	Intracontinental rift systems		Normal
Subclass D	Reactivated cratonal rifts and Paleozoic/Mesozoic oroggens		

6.3 Oceanic Transform Faults and Seismicity

Under our Class I, two kinds of faults are included—normal and transform. Shallow normal faults produced along the walls of a mid-oceanic spreading rift typically generate shallow earthquakes of low magnitude, and these require no special treatment here. In contrast, the seismic significance of transform faults that offset the midoceanic rift eluded geologists during the early period of discovery. Their correct interpretation finally led to a full-blown theory of plate tectonics. The concept involved may be elusive to some geology students, so we must make a special effort to show how transform faults work. First, however, we need to distinguish between a *transcurrent fault* and a *transform fault*. The two are compared in Figure 6.2. Both are of the structural class of strike-slip faults, meaning, of course, that ideally the fault plane is vertical and the relative motion is horizontal. Here, we shall limit the use of "transform fault" to a segment of strike-slip fault that lies between the offset ends of a spreading boundary in oceanic crust. It is illustrated in Figure 6.2B. It is also shown in our block diagram in Figure 1.8, where Plate *X* and Plate *Y* are shown to be undergoing separation. The transform fault separating the ends of the offset spreading boundaries remains active as a transverse segment of the plate boundary.

Our maps and relief diagrams of the ocean basin floor, such as Diagram B of Plate 1 in Chapter 4, usually show a large number of long, transverse ridge-like features known as *fracture zones*. These lines project out in both directions from the mid-oceanic line almost as far as the continental boundary (see Figures 4.10 and 4.11). Thus, a fracture zone (FZ) may appear to be simply an extension of the transform fault. By casual inspection of a map showing this relationship, many geologists jumped to what seemed an obvious conclusion: "We have here numerous very long transcurrent faults."

Figure 6.2, Diagram A, shows a simple transcurrent (strike-slip) fault imagined to be offsetting a mid-oceanic ridge. The direction of relative movement on the fault is shown by two bold arrows. The entire plate north of the fault, Plate *X*, moves toward the left. The entire plate south of the fault moves as Plate *Y* toward the right. Thus we have here a left-lateral transcurrent fault.

While this simple interpretation of oceanic fracture zones as continuous active faults may have seemed adequate, it had some unacceptable consequences. The FZs were traced across the entire basin floor and found to end just short of adjacent continental crust. What happens at the two ends of this active fault? Do they disappear beneath the continental shelves? Not a likely hypothesis! This problem aroused the curiosity of the Canadian geologist and geophysicist, J. Tuzo Wilson. He reasoned that if the fault movement is continuous along the entire FZ, as it must be between rigid plates, the fracture line cannot simply end abruptly in a point of zero relative movement. You can get the point of Wilson's argument by taking a sheet of paper and cutting a slit across the middle area, but not reaching either edge of the page. If you try to move one part of the sheet parallel with the other along the slit, you will find it impossible to do so without buckling or tearing the paper. Clearly, the simple transcurrent fault model is not workable in the case of the transverse

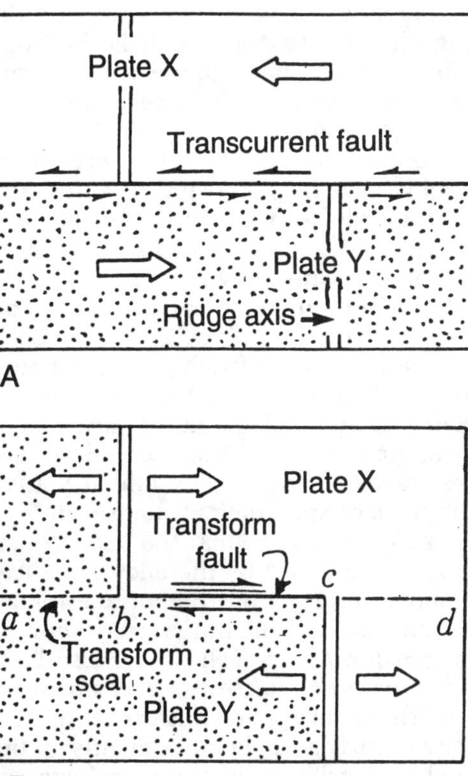

Figure 6.2 Transcurrent and transform faults compared. (A) Simple transcurrent fault in continental crust. (B) Imagined oceanic "fault zone" interpreted as a continuous active transcurrent (strike-slip) fault extending out far to right and left. (C) Transform fault lying between offset ends of a spreading boundary. Transform scars (a-b and c-d) continue outward to left and right. (Copyright © by Arthur N. Strahler.)

In 1965, Professor Wilson found the answer to the puzzle of the transverse fracture zones by postulating a new type of fault, which he named the "transform fault" (Wilson, 1965). Its relative motion is shown in Figure 6.2, Diagram B. First, we postulate that active plate spreading is in progress on the ridge axis both north and south of the fracture zone. A single lithospheric plate (Plate Y, stippled) lies to the left of the ridge axis on both sides of the fault; the other plate (Plate X, blank) occupies the right side. Shearing motion between the two plates occurs only on segment *b-c* of the fracture zone lying between the offset ends of the spreading boundary. As the thin arrows show, motion on the transform fault is the opposite of that in our imaginary simple transcurrent fault. There is no movement along segments *a-b* and *c-d* of the "fracture zones."

Keep in mind that along the spreading boundaries new oceanic lithosphere is continuously being formed by accretion. Motion along the transform fault is necessary to accommodate the plate motion required by plate accretion. But how would Wilson explain what appeared to be the extensions of the fault lines across the ocean floor on both sides of the offset spreading boundaries? These so-called "fracture zones", as they had been officially designated on maps, are conspicuous topographic features of the ocean floor, and some can be traced for over 4,000 km! If you visualize the progress of spreading at point *b* in Figure 6.2, Diagram B, you realize that the line segment *a-b* is a trail, or "scar," left by the end of the transform fault and impressed on the surface of the plate. These extensions of the transverse fractures can be called *transform scars*. (They have also been called *healed transform faults* or *extinct transforms*, but both of these terms are misleading.) They often appear as nearly straight escarpments on the ocean floors. [A description of the transform scar as a topographic feature is given in Chapter 4, in the section on "The Mid-Ocean Ridge System." See also Chapter 5 for information on the formation of transform scars.]

A satisfactory proof of Wilson's transform fault hypothesis would be in seismic activity. Under the older, transcurrent-fault hypothesis, seismic activity should be observed along the entire length of the fracture zone. Under the transform-fault hypothesis, seismic activity should be limited to the transform segment only, and of course, to the axial rift of the spreading boundary segments. In contrast, the transform scars should prove to be, for the most part, lacking in seismic activity; i.e., they are *aseismic* features. (Note that their pattern is not revealed by the world earthquake map, Figure 6.1A.)

If the offsets of the spreading boundary between two plates are indeed transform faults, active slip movement must be limited to the fault line between the offset ends. If so, seismic maps should show that shallow earthquake epicenters are limited to those active portions. The task of carrying out this crucial seismic test was undertaken by Lynn R. Sykes, who in 1959 had joined the staff of the Lamont-Doherty Geological Observatory of Columbia University as a graduate student. He began his research by greatly improving the accuracy of positioning of hypocenters of shallow earthquakes, including those of the ocean floors (Oliver, 1996, p. 54, 55, 56). A colleague suggested to Sykes that he test Wilson's hypothesis of transform faulting. Professor Jack Oliver, his mentor writes: "To make a short story of a long and challenging task, Lynn made that effort and Wilson's transform fault model was suported in timely fashion (1996,p, 57).

Sykes was able to report in 1966 that the first motion along the transverse segment is just what would be expected of a transform fault, as J. Tuzo Wilson had envisioned.(Figure 6.3). In contrast, first motions of the faults with epicenters along the axial rift showed them to be normal faults, such as we would expect of movement on crustal blocks breaking off on the two sides of the widening rift and settling down into the bottom of the trough (Sykes, 1967).

It was at this point that crustal spreading and the existence of transform faults won the full acceptance of nearly all members of the scientific community actively carrying on research on tectonics of the oceanic lithosphere.

[For a full account of the growth of the Lamont institution, its research staff, and their acheivements see Jack Oliver's 1996 book titled *Shocks and Rocks: Seismology in the Plate Tectonics Revolution.*]

To understand how seismology is used to verify the motions of tectonic plates we need to look deeper into the interpretation of the seismic data. Figure 6.3 is Lynn Sykes's map of a portion of the

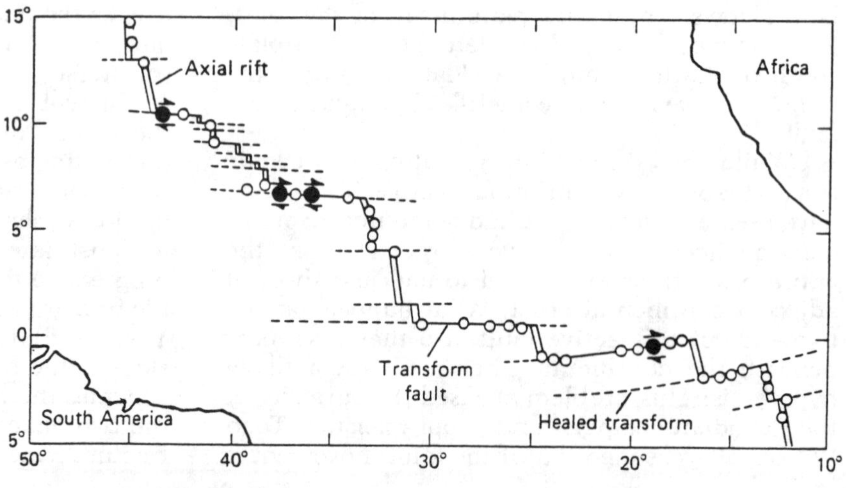

Figure 6.3 Sketch map of the Atlantic Ocean basin between Africa and South America showing the locations of earthquake epicenters (open circles) with respect to the axial rift of the Mid-Atlantic Ridge and its offsets on transform faults. The solid circles with arrows are epicenters for which direction of first motion was determined, establishing that they lie on transform faults. (Simplified and stylized from L.R. Sykes, 1967, *Journal of Geophysical Res.*, v. 72, p. 2137, Figure 4. Copyrighted by The American Geophysical Union.)

Mid-Atlantic Ridge. There are many closely spaced offsets of the ridge axis in this region. Small circles show the epicenters. Nearly all the shallow-focus earthquake epicenters lie along either the ridge axis or the connecting portion of the transverse fracture zones. Few, if any, epicenters lie on extensions of the fracture zones beyond the ridge axis. Many other examples of the same seismic pattern could be offered.

While the evidence of the limited positioning of epicenters might seem strong proof that the transform segments are active faults, we need more precise evidence in the form of the relative direction of the fault movement. This evidence comes from analysis of seismograms of earthquakes originating along a supposed transform fault. The principles involved in this analysis are illustrated in Figure 6.4. Diagram A is an oblique birdseye view of a rectangular plot of the land surface, across which runs a right-lateral strike slip fault. We assume the fault plane to be vertical. The focus of the earthquake lies directly beneath the epicenter. We first draw a circle around the epicenter to create a field for radial analysis. Diagram B shows the ground viewed straight down upon the epicenter. Let's suppose the circle is some 200 km in radius. We have divided the circular zone into four quadrants by adding a line at right angles to the fault trace. We have given the quadrants Roman numerals in clockwise order, starting with the upper-right quadrant. Within each quadrant are some seismic observation stations, scattered more or less at random. Radial arrows are drawn from each

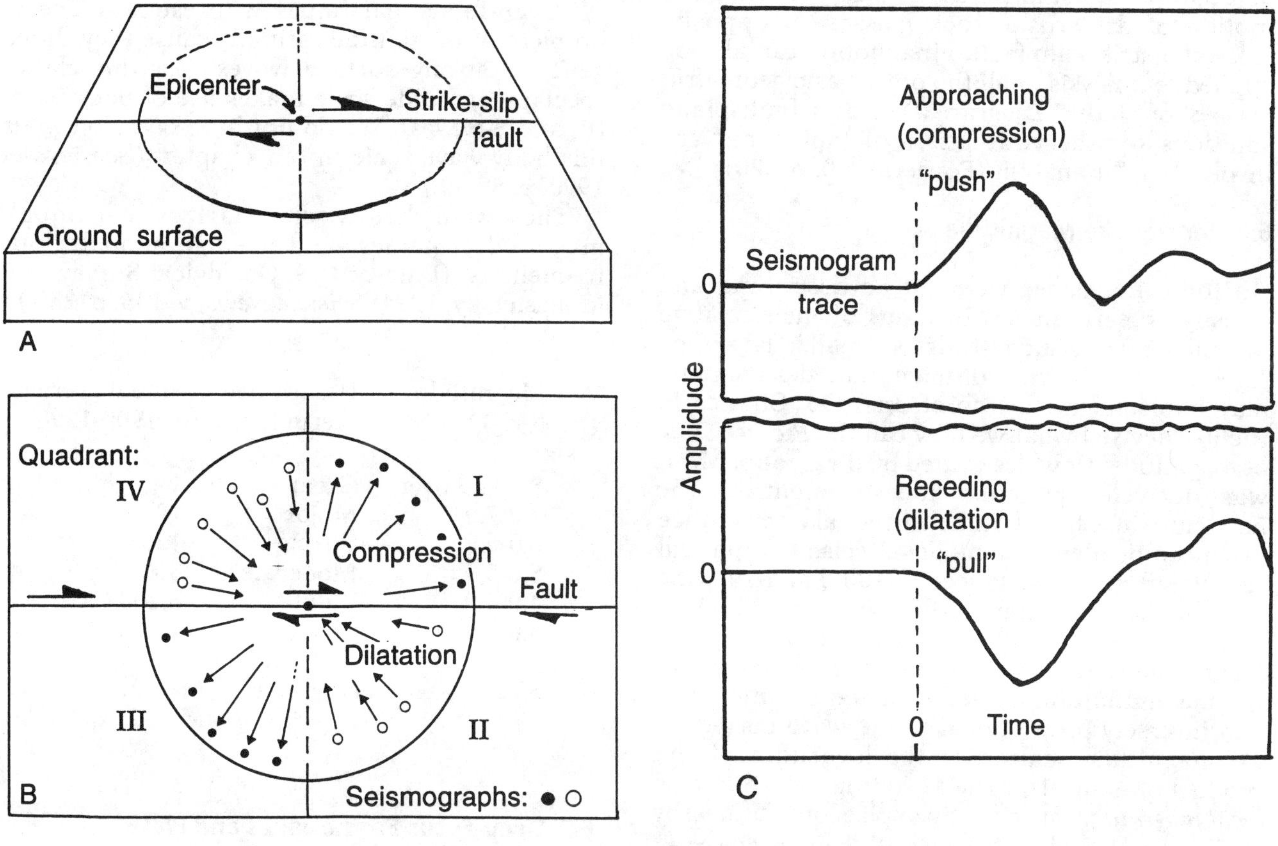

A

Epicenter
Strike-slip fault
Ground surface

B

Quadrant:
I
II
III
IV
Compression
Dilatation
Fault
Seismographs: ● ○

C

Approaching (compression)
"push"
Seismogram trace
Receding (dilatation
"pull"
Amplidude
0
Time

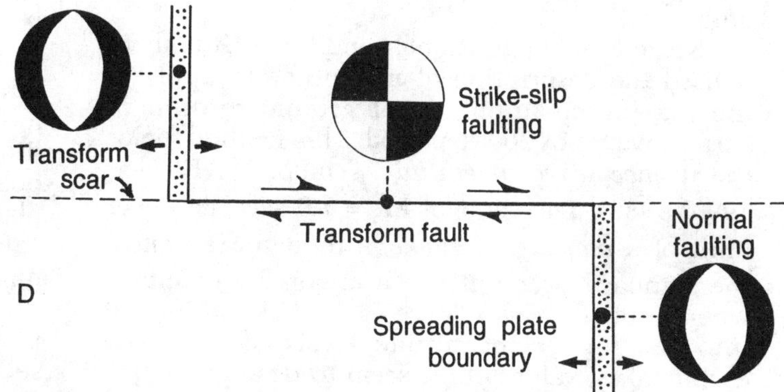

Figure 6.4 Schematic diagrams showing how the first motion detected at a seismograph station reveals the sense of motion on a right-lateral strike-slip fault. (Copyright © by A.N. Strahler.)

seismograph, and they point either to the epicenter or to the seismograph.

Stop now and think about the force that will be exerted by the initial wave, a P-wave, that starts to move out from the focus at the instant of fault rupture. You know that the P-wave is a compressional wave, in which the rock motion is alternately forward and backward in the line of wave motion, i.e., it alternately "pushes" and "pulls" in that direction. Thus, all waves moving out in quadrants I and III "push" outward from the epicenter at the instant of rupture, whereas those in quadrants II and IV "pull" inward toward the focus. Quadrants I and II are quadrants of *compression*; quadrants II and IV are quadrants of *dilatation*, a fancy word for "stretching." Diagram C is a schematic graph to show in concept how the seismogram trace of the first P-wave would look. So here we have a capability to use the record of *first motion* to establish the relative directions of motion of the crustal rock masses on opposite sides of a strike-slip fault. First motion can also be applied to analysis of all the other basic geometric classes of faults. Diagram D shows fault-plane solutions for the two classes of faults that are involved in our analysis (Fowler, 1990, p. 320).

6.4 Earthquake Magnitude Scales

On following pages we shall be describing and classifying earthquakes in terms of their relative magnitude using such words as "small," "large," or "great." A brief review of magnitude designations may be useful at this point. In 1935, Charles F. Richter devised what we now call the *Richter scale* of magnitude. Now designated by the symbol M_L, it was derived by actual measurement of the maximum amplitude of the earthquake wave trace produced by a specific model of seismograph and calculated for a distance of 100 km from the earthquake epicenter (Bolt, 1978, p. 104-105; Strahler, 1981, p. 198-200, Figures 8.24, 8.25). Magnitude value is always directly proportional to the maximum amplitude, A, of the seismic wave and inversely proportional to the wave period, T. All magnitude scales use the logarithm of the product of A and 1/T. The M_L rating, referred to as *local magnitude*, specifically applies only to nearby shallow earthquakes. Because all magnitude scales are logarithmic, in theory they have no finite upper limit.

Some years later, Richter and Beno Gutenberg revised the description of magnitude to apply to the maximum amplitude of ground motion of surface waves of 20-sec period. This method yields the *surface wave magnitude*, symbol M_S (Fowler, 1990, p. 88). The value of $M_S = 7.0$ sets the lower limit of a *major earthquake*. Although M_S is now the standard usage, it has a major disadvantage when applied to very large earthquakes. Upward into the higher magnitude levels of observed earthquakes, values of M_S seem to be approaching a finite limit, thus underestimating the actual magnitudes (see Bullen and Bolt, 1985, p. 375-377.)

In 1977, Japanese seismologist H. Kanamori published a new magnitude scale making use of the *seismic moment* of an earthquake. Seismic moment, M_0, is defined as the product of the shear modulus, μ, the area of the fault surface, A, and the displacement of the fault, u. Using the logarithm of the seismic moment, the *moment magnitude*, M_W, is derived. Kanamori's new measure provided a uniform scale upwards for the maximum recorded earthquakes. For example, for the great Alaskan earthquake of 1964 (described below), $M_S = 8.4$ whereas $M_W = 9.2$. The rating of the great Chilean earthquake of 1960, calculated at $M_S = 8.3$, was raised to a world's record value of $M_W = 9.5$. On the other hand, ratings of moderate to small earthquakes differ very little between the two scales.

Deep-focus earthquakes present a special problem of magnitude rating because they do not generate strong surface waves. For this class a special magnitude scale makes use of body waves (P- and S-waves). We do not have occasion to use this body-wave scale in our chapter. (See Fowler, 1990, p. 89-90.)

The table below summarizes earthquake magnitudes, names, and average annual global frequencies. (Data of U.S. Geological Survey in R. Monastersky, 1994, *Science News*, v. 146, p. 250.)

Magnitude (M_S)	Descriptive term	Annual average 1900-1990
8.0 and over	Great	1
7.0-7.9	Major	18
6.0-6.9	Strong	120
5.0-5.9	Moderate	800
4.0-4.9	Light	6,200 (est.)
3.0-3.9	Minor	49,000 (est.)
>3.0	Very Minor	M=2-3: 1000/day M=1-2: 8000/day

6.5 Deep-Focus Earthquakes and Plate Subduction

If we accept the petrological and geophysical evidence of continued accretion of oceanic lithosphere at spreading plate boundaries, we must look for equally strong evidence that oceanic lithosphere is being consumed at converging plate boundaries. Otherwise, the material flow cycle of plate tectonics could not form a complete circuit capable of being sustained for hundreds of millions of years.

The task of establishing beyond doubt the phenomenon of plate subduction fell to the seismologists, and they put on a brilliant scientific performance. Proof that lithospheric plates do, indeed, exist and that they plunge deeply into the asthenosphere came slowly at first, as the locations and depths of earthquake foci were plotted on the map in increasing numbers and the points began to fall into significant global patterns. Finally, modern seismology applied its sharpest tools to a great fund of new data and revealed remarkable details of plate subduction and of the forces acting within a descending plate.

To understand the nature of the seismic evidence of plate subduction, consider the case of the island arcs made up of northern Japan and the Kuril Islands (Figure 6.5). Adjoining these arcs on the east is the Japan Trench, and to the west lie the Sea of Japan and the Sea of Okhotsk, which are backarc basins. Earthquakes are frequent in this region, and their epicenters have been plotted in great numbers. Shallow quakes are abundant in a zone immediately adjacent to the trench on the landward (western) side; those of intermediate depth occur under the island belt and under the eastern side of the Sea of Japan. Those of deep focus, however, are centered close to the margin of the Asiatic mainland. When these foci, or hypocenters, are plotted on a vertical cross section, as is done on the face of the block diagram in Figure 6.5, it is obvious that they define a slanting zone within which fracturing has been occurring.

A hint as to the possible geologic significance of the depth relationship of deep earthquakes to horizontal distance from trenches goes back at least as far as 1930, which we usually think of as being well within the "Wegener era" (Chapter 2). In that year a Japanese seismologist, K. Sagisaka, "showed that seismographs of deep-focus earthquakes exhibit the same pattern of first motions as shallow shocks and must, therefore, be produced by essentially the same mechanisms" (Shea, 1985, p. 274). (In that decade and continuing into the 1960s, "mechanism" of earthquake might have referred to a theory then popular with the Japanese scientists, namely, that an earthquake is the result of a sudden forced intrusion of magma (Aki, 1988, p. 267.)

Establishment of the depth-distance relationship of deep-focus earthquakes and a hypothesis to go with it can be credited to the Japanese seismologist K. Wadati. His 1928 paper on this subject included maps of the significant differences in behavior of P and S waves between shallow-focus earthquakes and those of deep focus (see Richter, 1958, p. 302-303). Reproduced here as Figure 6.6 are comparison maps of two earthquakes with foci very close together, one with

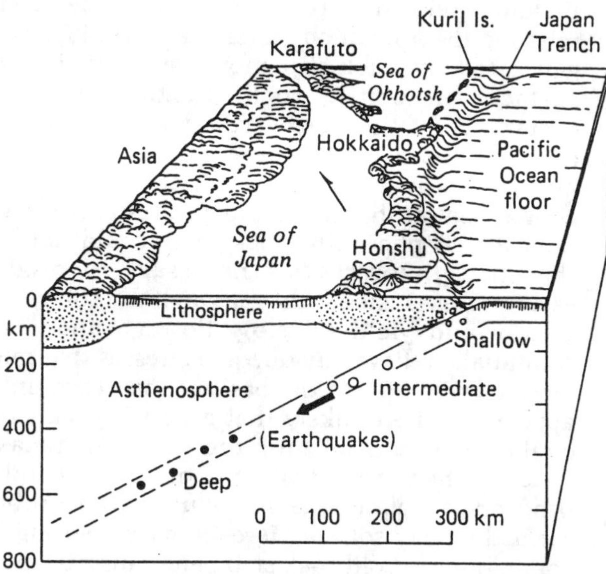

Figure 6.5 Block diagram of the Japan-Kuril arc showing how earthquake foci are distributed in the crust and mantle beneath. (Based on data of B. Gutenberg and C.F. Richter, 1949. *Seismicity of the Earth,* Princeton, Univ. Press, Princeton, N.J. Diagram copyright © by Arthur N. Strahler.)

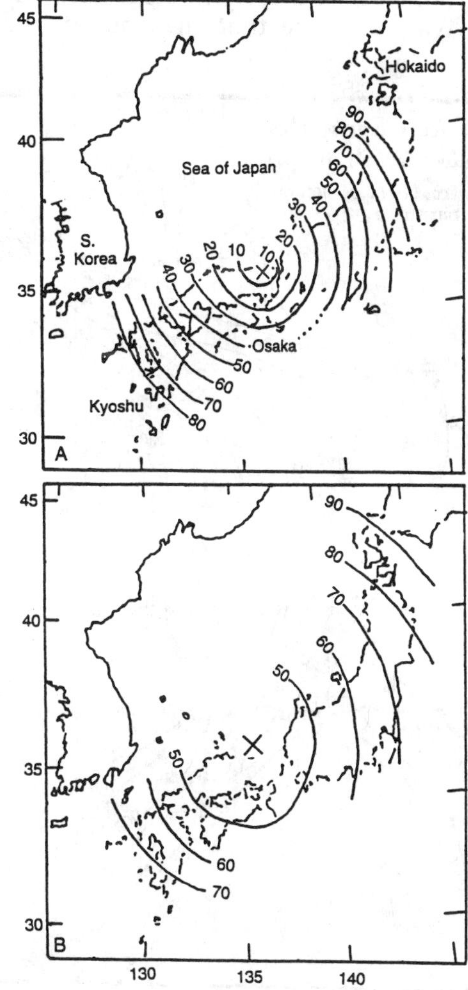

Figure 6.6 Maps made by K. Wadati in 1928, to show the time difference in arrival times of P and S waves for (A) a shallow-focus earthquake and (B) a deep-focus earthquake. Contours show the time difference, S-P. From Richter, 1958, p. 302, Figure 19-1, credited to K. Wadati, 1928.

shallow focus, the other with deep focus. The contours are lines of equal values of the difference in time in seconds of the arrival of P-wave and S-wave at surrounding seismological stations.

In 1935, Wadati published a landmark paper in the *Geophysical Magazine*; its title: "On the activity of deep-focus earthquakes in the Japan Islands and neighbourhoods" (Reprinted in Shea, 1935, p. 61). Wadati proposed the following definitions of focal depths: *shallow focus*, d < 100 km; *intermediate-focus*, 100 < d < 200 km; *deep-focus*, d > 200 km (1935 p. 61). Most of the shallow-focus earthquakes originate in depths less than 60 km. Wadati plotted the positions of large numbers of both shallow-focus and deep-focus quakes over Japan and the adjacent ocean bodies; his map is reproduced here as Figure 6.7. Particularly important was Wadati's drawing of depth contours over the general belt of deep-focus earthquakes. The contours show a considerable range in the steepness of decline, and today we would interpret this variability as meaning that the subducted plate plunges much more steeply in some areas than in others. Wadati wrote that the contour surface "suggests that there exists in the crust something like a weak surface at where the earthquake outburst is liable to occur" (p. 324). Wadati gave credit to seismologists H. Honda and M. Takehana for having shown "that almost all deep-focus earthquakes occurring near Japan are caused in like manner by a certain state of stress stored in the crust" (p. 324).

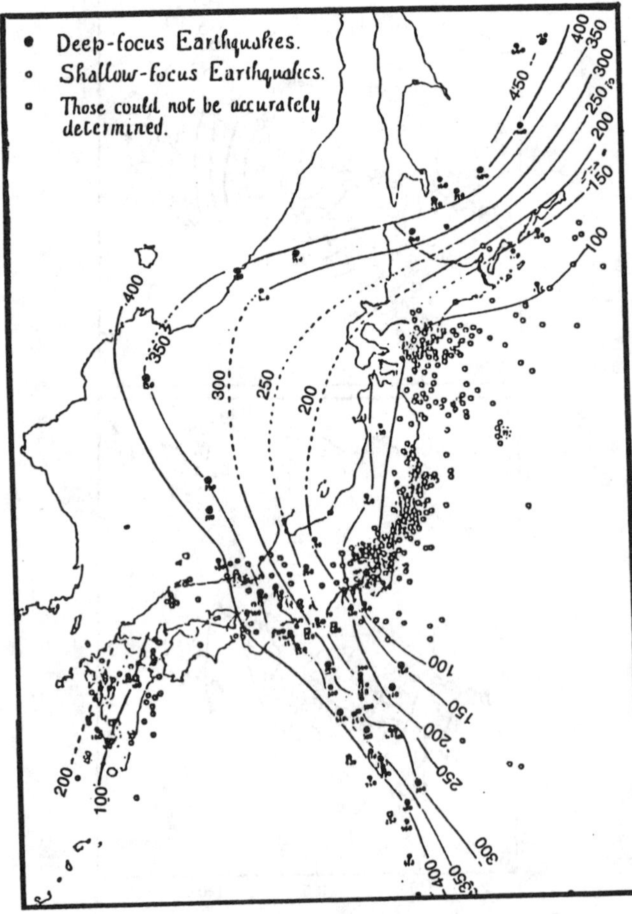

Figure 6.7 Map made by K. Wadati in 1935 showing shallow-focus and deep-focus epicenters for central and northern Japan. Depth contours in km reveal the location and extent of a subducting plate.(Depth numerals have been clarified.) (From K. Wadati, 1935, *Geographical Magazine*, v. 8, p. 321, Figure 4.)

Wadati also pointed out that the Japanese volcanoes seemed to occur over the foci of intermediate depth earthquakes. (The locations of the volcanic arcs are shown in Figure 5.7.) From what is now known of volcanic island arcs, this relationship is to be expected. Recall from Chapter 5 that the corner-flow model calls for magma formation at depths around 100 km. Wadati's interpretation was enigmatic: "Thus we can probably say that the volcanic and seismic activities are of the same phenomenon" (p. 324).

American seismologist Hugo Benioff is also credited with recognizing the significance of the distribution of deep-focus earthquakes, but his first publication on this subject appeared over a decade later (in 1949) with the title "Seismic evidence for the fault origin of oceanic deeps." Another paper of his, published in 1954, provided additional seismological evidence. As a result, in the scientific publications of western seismologists, the down-slanting seismic feature became known as the *Benioff zone*, but it is now considered proper to refer to it as the *Wadati-Benioff zone (WZB)*.

The existence of the Wadati-Benioff zone posed some very difficult scientific problems. By the early 1960s, seismologists as a group had achieved a final acceptance of the theory of earthquake mechanism presented by Harry Fielding Reid in 1910. It was called the elastic-rebound theory, which states that earthquakes are generated by stick-slip movements on fracture surfaces in brittle rock. In that light, the occurrence of the deep earthquakes with foci far down in the asthenosphere seemed particularly puzzling. The seismologists were assuming, of course, that at the high temperatures prevailing in the asthenosphere, the rock there could not have the strength properties necessary to produce earthquakes. Instead, they argued, the soft mantle rock would yield by slow flowage and would continually relieve any unequal stresses that might tend to build up. On the basis of this reasoning, it appeared quite unlikely that a slanting fault zone could be responsible for the deep earthquakes. Later, when the concept of a descending lithospheric plate was introduced, the problem seemed largely solved: Here we have a strong and comparatively cold rock slab penetrating deep into the asthenosphere and providing the right kind of material to yield by the stick-slip mechanism that generates earthquakes. But there remained an unanswered question.

As the descending plate moves into the hot asthenosphere, will it not be rapidly heated and become too soft to produce earthquakes? The answer to this question seems to lie in the rapid rate of descent of the cold slab. If it moves down rapidly enough, it will remain cool and strong, at least in the inner part of the plate. Cracking of this cool zone could then continue, even when the plate has reached a depth as great as 600 to 700 km.

In his 1996 retrospective book, *Shocks and Rocks; Seismology in the Plate Teconics Revolution*, Jack Oliver has given us a fascinating account of Bryan Isacks's seismological test designed to show the existence of a deeply descending plate. Their game plan was as follows: Find a deep ocean area across which there lies an island arc bounded by a deep trench leading down to great depth in a Wadati-Benioff zone (WBZ). Then find also a distant island to serve as a second receptor of seismic waves emanating from the same WBZ. Seismic receiving stations are set up at both of these locations. When an earthquake occurs at a point in the WBZ, its waves will move outward in widening concentric circles, reaching each of the receiving stations. Since we have chosen receiving sites that lie about the same distance from the source, the travel time should be about the same for both.

It is fair to say that the first clear statement of the modern concept of a descending lithospheric plate was published in 1967 by Oliver and Isacks of the Lamont Geological Observatory of Columbia University. Published in the *Journal of Geophysical Research*, its title was "Deep earthquake zones, anomalous structures in the upper mantle, and the lithosphere." For the Tonga-Kermadic arc (between lat. 15° and 35°S) the authors defined an "anomalous zone" with a thickness on the order of 100 km (Figure 6.8 C,D). The upper surface of the anomalous zone "is approximately defined by the highly active seismic zone that dips to the west beneath the island arc and extends to depths of about 700 km" (1967, p. 4259). What was most significant in the findings of Oliver and Isacks was that the S waves emanating from foci in the "anomalous zone" and propagating up that zone are "much less subject to attenuation than are waves of the same type propagating in parts of the mantle at similar depths elsewhere" (p. 4259).

Recognition of the seismic characteristic of deep-focus earthquakes had also appeared in 1960 in a paper by the Japanese seismologist, M. Katsumata. From studies of a small group of earthquakes at a depth of about 350 km, he had concluded that "...the seismic waves in the media in which earthquakes occur frequently have larger velocities and attenuate more slowly than ones in the other media" (as quoted by Oliver and Isacks, 1967, p. 4274). Oliver and Isacks did not, however, know of Katsumata's 1960 paper until after their own paper had been submitted for journal publication.

The uniqueness and importance of the "anomalous" zone behavior of the S-waves lies in relating the phenomenon to the physical state of that zone and the tectonic process that could be inferred from it. Oliver and Isacks go on to state:

> If low attenuation of seismic waves correlates with strength, this structure suggests that the lithosphere has been thrust or dragged down beneath the Tonga arc and hence implies a certain mobility for the lithosphere elsewhere. (1967, p. 4259)

Notice that the authors were cautiouslly separating their seismic data from, their geological hypothesis. For this reason they presented two separate diagrams (A and B in Figure 6.8). Oliver states that for months after the Tonga seismic data were in hand he and Isacks puzzled over its geologic and tectonic meaning until a moment of insight arrived (1996, p. 69). He writes

> We sensed immediately that we had the answer and that it was a big one. The rocks that underlay the normal deep sea floor to the depth of about 100 km or so were descending as a layer into the interior in the vicinity of the trench-island arc system. Furthermore, they could be traced to, and hence must have moved to, at least a depth of 700 km. It was underthrusting on a huge scale! (p. 69)

To understand the physical principles behind these geologic and tectonics inferences, we need to expand somewhat on the concept of attenuation of seismic waves. As in the case of electromagnetic radiation emanating from a point source, the outgoing waves lose energy as they travel outward in all directions. Quite aside from the geometric factor of energy reduction inversely as the square of increasing radius, some additional loss of energy occurs from friction with the medium through which the waves are traveling. This lost elastic energy has been converted into sensible heat (heat of molecular motion). In the equation for magnitude of wave amplitude decrease by attenuation, a constant q is entered as a negative exponential variable with radius to represent the frictional factor. Seismologists use the reciprocal of q, designated as Q, in describing their findings on attenuation of the deep-focus shocks. For the Fiji-Tonga arc, Oliver and Isacks found that Q is roughly 1000 for a ray following a path within the anomalous zone, but only about 150 for a path largely in the surrounding mantle, which we would think of as the asthenosphere. The low Q value of 150 agrees rather well with values assigned to the crust and upper mantle, i.e., to lithosphere (1967, p. 4267). The authors illustrated their findings with two simple diagrams, reproduced here as Figure 6.8, A and B. They scrupulously kept separate the seismological zones from the corresponding tectonic zones, the former being the presentation of the observed data, the latter being their tentative geologic interpretation. With what now seems a gross understatement, they concluded: "The new feature of this paper is the evidence that suggests a

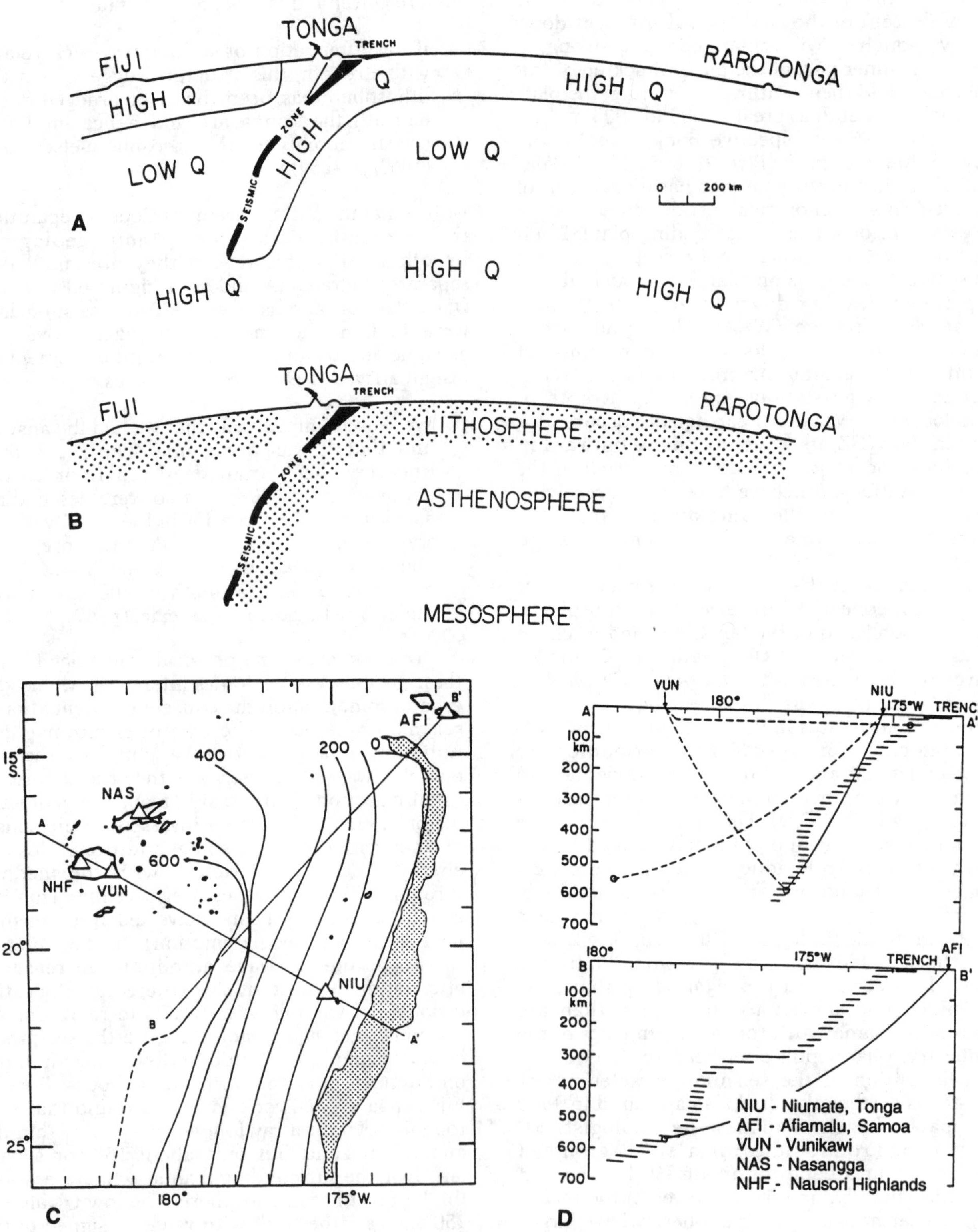

Figure 6.8 (A and B): Two diagrams published by Oliver and Isacks in 1967, showing a hypothetical cross-section through Fiji, Tonga, and Rarotonga. Section A shows boundaries between high-Q and low-Q zones. Section B interprets the Q data in terms of lithosphere and asthenosphere. C and D:(left) Index map of seismograph locations; (right) cross sections of the seismic zone and wave paths. Solid lines are paths of less-attenuated waves; dashed lines show low frequency waves.(From Jack Oliver and Bryan Isacks, 1967, *Jour. of Geophysical Research*, v. 72, pp. 30, 33, 42, 43. Used by permission of the authors and The American Geophysical Union.)

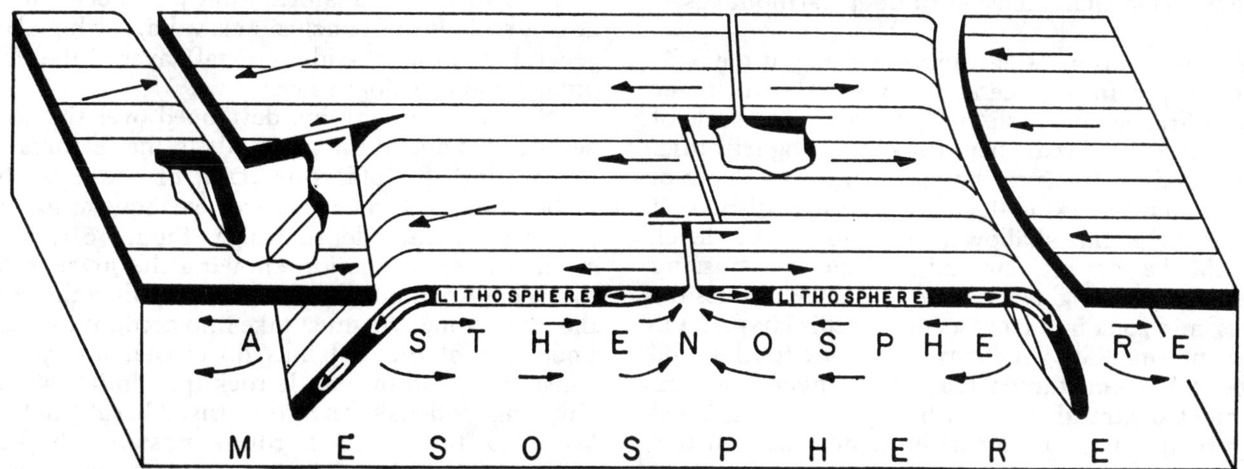

Figure 6.9 This block diagram was published in 1968 by Isacks, Oliver, and Sykes, who described it as "illustrating schematically the configurations and roles of the lithosphere, asthenosphere, and mesosphere in a version of the new global tectonics." (From Bryan Isacks, Jack Oliver, and Lynn R. Sykes, 1968, *Journal of Geophysical Research*, v. 73, no. 18, p. 5857. Reproduced by permission of the authors and the American Geophysical Union.)

new configuration for, and perhaps the extent of the mobility of, the lithosphere" (p. 4273).

It was to be only a year later that these two authors, jointly with Lynn R. Sykes, published their historic synthesis of "the new global tectonics," illustrated by cross sections showing solid slabs of lithosphere plunging deep into the asthenosphere (Isacks, Oliver, and Sykes, 1968). In that landmark paper, they included a block diagram showing the essential features of plate tectonics. We reproduce it here as Figure 6.9.

Figure 6.10 is a cross section of a descending lithospheric plate showing by means of isotherms (lines of equal temperature) the temperature conditions postulated for a plate descending at a rate of 8 cm/yr after subduction has been in progress for about 6.5 m.y. The plate is outlined and the foci of earthquakes are shown schematically. This idealized model seems to fit conditions known to exist under Japan and in the subduction zone of the Tonga Trench in the southwestern Pacific basin.

Some further support for the hypothesis of a cold lithospheric slab descending into the asthenosphere is found in observations of heat flow at the surface. Generally, heat flow is lower than average in the floors of the trenches, the value being less than one heat-flow unit. [One heat-flow unit is: 1 $\mu cal/cm^2$ sec.] This is what we would expect, because the cool mass of the oceanic lithospheric plate has been carried to a greater depth. Heat flow is greater than average (more than two units) in the surface belt that lies directly above the middle and lower part of the descending slab. These conditions are shown by the upper profile line in Figure 6.10. The higher rate of heat flow over the deeper part of the slab does not seem to be expected by this hypothesis and requires some further explanation. The same conditions of rates of heat flow apply also to the Peru Trench, in which the rate is low, and the adjacent Andes volcanic range, where the rate is high. The presence of chains of active volcanoes adjacent to a trench seems to account for the high rate of heat flow because magma is rising from depth. The puzzling part was that a cold descending slab should furnish the surplus heat needed for the formation of magmas. That problem seems to have been solved by the corner-flow model in which heat is derived from flowage in the asthenosphere (Chapter 5).

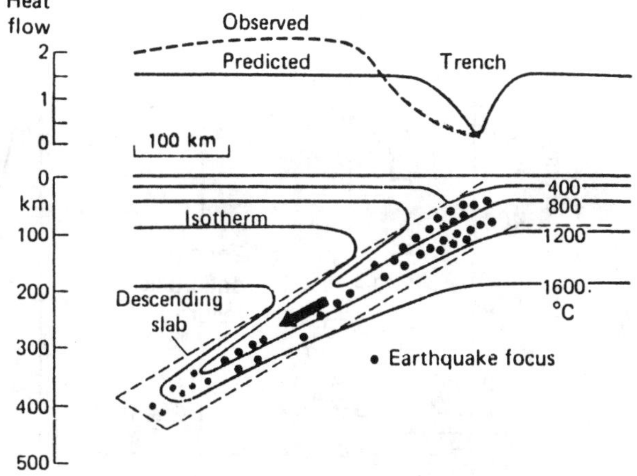

Figure 6.10 Schematic cross section of a descending lithospheric plate. Isotherms are drawn for each 400 C°. A profile of heat flow is shown above. (From M. Nafi Toksöz, *Technology Review*, v. 75, no. 2, p. 28. Copyright © 1972 by The Alumni Association of the Massachusetts Institute of Technology. Reproduced by permission.)

6.6 Seismic Characteristics of Deep Earthquakes

The distribution of earthquakes (magnitude > 5) with depth in a descending slab is shown in the depth/frequency graph in Figure 6.11. The scale of numbers per year per 10 km is logarithmic. Intermediate focus earthquakes set in at a depth of 40 to 60 m, marking the top of the Wadati-Benioff zone. In a thin shallower zone above this level, earthqake foci are few and in some ares missing entirely, defining an *aseismic zone*. (We discuss the aseismic zone in a later section of this chapter.) In the intermediate zone between about 100 km and about 300 km, the decrease in numbers plots as almost a straight line, which indicates a good approximation to a logarithmic decrease. In this depth range the earthquakes are within the same depth zone as the asthenosphere.

In the intermediate zone, which in many cases lies below a typical down-bend in the slab, earthquake foci are concentrated in a layer identified with the oceanic crust of the slab, i.e., in a top layer of the slab (Pennington, 1983, p. 1045). In Chapter 5, we noted that this depth zone lies directly under the arc volcanoes, and we gave an explanation of this linkage based in part on dehydration melting of hydrous minerals of the crust, continuing down to depths of 150 km. We also explained that the minerals which largely make up oceanic crustal basalt and gabbro undergo phase transformations to garnet and jadeite pyroxene. Both of these minerals are of greater density than the minerals in the parent rock, so that the transformation yields eclogite, a denser rock. If this conclusion is valid, earthquakes generated in the top-side (crustal) layer of the slab originate in an eclogite layer.

Seismic tomography, developed over the past decade, has added many details to the features of the Wadati-Benioff zone. One of these is the recognition of a lower zone of earthquake foci in the intermediate depth range. Figure 6.12 is a schematic cross section showing the lower-zone foci. They are much fewer in number than those of the upper zone. We must take into account that the underside of the slab has no crustal layer, and consists instead of mantle rock (peridotite) which has a higher density than the crustal basalt/gabbro. We also take into account possibly higher temperature of the adjacent mantle on the top side because of the corner-flow effect. These factors would perhaps tend to produce fewer earthquakes on the bottom side. Notice also, that the upper and lower zones seem to converge with depth, and this change might be the result of warming penetrating more deeply into the slab with depth. The lower zone of foci disappears short of the 200-km depth, and is not found in the deep-focus zone below.

We turn next to the deep-focus zone. Figure 6.11 shows that between 300 and 450 km, the numbers of earthquakes are low, then sharply increase to a peak near 600 km before falling off sharply at 660 km. The deepest earthquake recorded as of 1995 occurred in June of that year. It was located at a depth of 637 km beneath Bolivia (American Geophysical Union, 1995, p. 3-4;

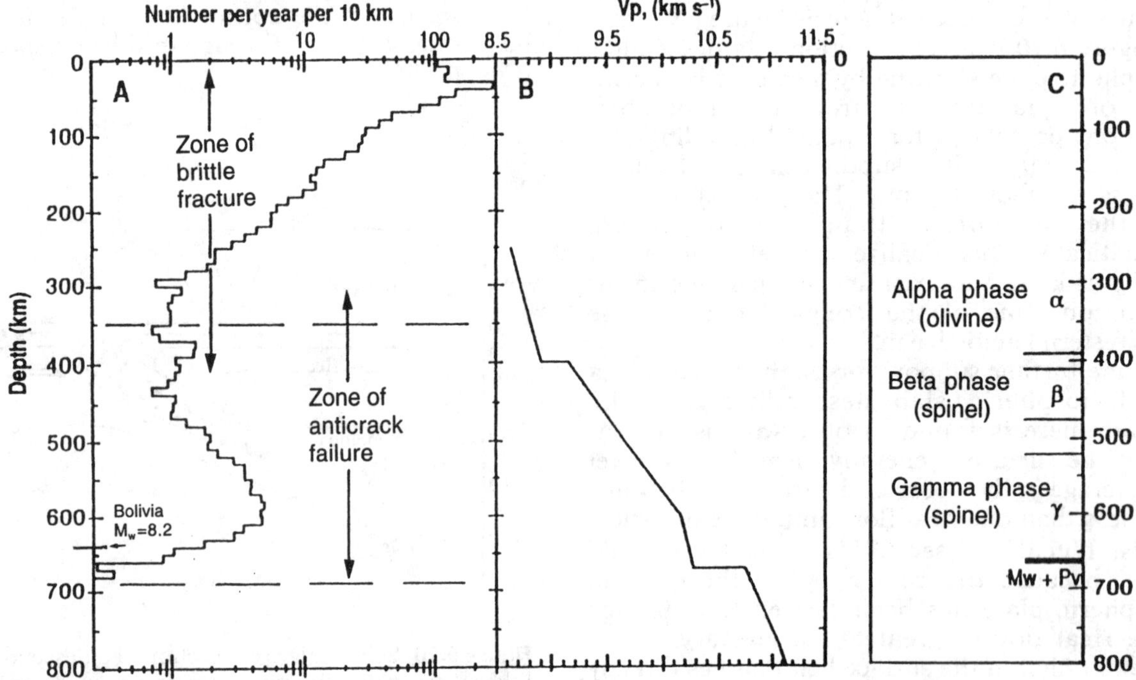

Figure 6.11 (A) Histogram showing the number per year per 10-km depth of earthquakes, M_S > 5. (B) Variation of P-wave velocity with depth. (C) Olivine/spinel phase transition zones. (From Kirby, Durham, and Stern, 1991, *Science*, v. 252, p. 217, Figure 1. Used by permission of the Amer. Assoc. for the Advancement of Science and the authors.)

Frolich, 1995,p. 43.) No epicenter has thus far been registered below 670 km, which is the strongly marked level of the jump in P-wave velocity.

One interesting characteristic of the deep group of earthquakes is that very few aftershocks have until recently been recorded. Even some very large deep quakes had no aftershocks. For the small deep earthquakes, aftershocks that do occur appear at distances 30 or more kilometers from the initial focus. In contrast, shallow-zone aftershocks of small earthquakes cluster much closer to the initial focus (Frolich, 1989, p. 53). These characteristics suggest that the mechanism of the deep group is quite different from that of earthquakes above the 300 km level. In 1994 a series of aftershocks was observed following an earthquake, magnitude M_w = 7.6, depth 564 km, off the Tonga arc in the southwest Pacific (Wiens et al., 1994). The aftershocks originated within a steeply dipping plane. This was an unprecedented event and perhaps may be explained by the greatly improved seismic observation network.

6.7 A New Theory of Deep Earthquakes

For over seven decades—since the 1920s—seismologists pondered a serious problem about the deep-focus earthquakes. It was known that about 20 percent of all earthquakes occur in the deep-focus range of from 300 to about 670 km, but from everything that could be safely surmised about the physical properties of the mantle in this depth range, the occurrence of earthquakes through the stick-slip mechanism is next to impossible, taking into account the existing combination of extremely high pressure and high temperature at those depths. The downward increase in confining pressure sharply raises both fracture strength and resistance to frictional sliding (Kirby, Durham, and Stern, 1991, p. 216.)

A number of theories were offered for the large number of deep earthquakes below the 350 km depth. Theories making use of phase transformations had been proposed as early as 1945 by Percy W. Bridgman and in 1967 by A. McGee (see reference citations in Pennington, 1983, p. 1046). One early theory made use of a sudden phase change to a denser state sufficiently powerful to produce a localized implosion. This explanation was quickly rejected because the seismograms do not show the requisite implosion pattern of strong dilatational first motion from all four quadrants. Instead, the seismograms show basically the same arrival characteristics as those of shallow focus, indicating that a stick-slip mechanism of some sort is the cause.

A modern earthquake hypothesis that gained strength rapidly in the early 1990s has been based upon the principle of phase change, or *phase transformation*, in atomic structure of silicate minerals that accompanies increasing temperature and confining pressure. In Chapter 3 we attributed a sharp increase in P-wave velocity at the depth level of about 390 to 400 km to a phase transformation in the mantle rock, which is of peridotite composition, with olivine the major mineral component. Above this level the olivine is in the *alpha phase* (Figure 6.11). With the phase transition it changes to the spinel crystal structure, which is in the isometric system. We stated that this phase transition had been demonstrated in laboratory experiments, and that it amounts to a density increase of about 10 percent. This spinel state is called the *beta phase*. Downward from this transition, P-wave velocity and rock density increase gradually and quite uniformly. The next phase change in the olivine, occurring at a depth of about 550 km, is to the *gamma phase*, but no change of rate of velocity increase is detectable. These phase transformations are marked off and

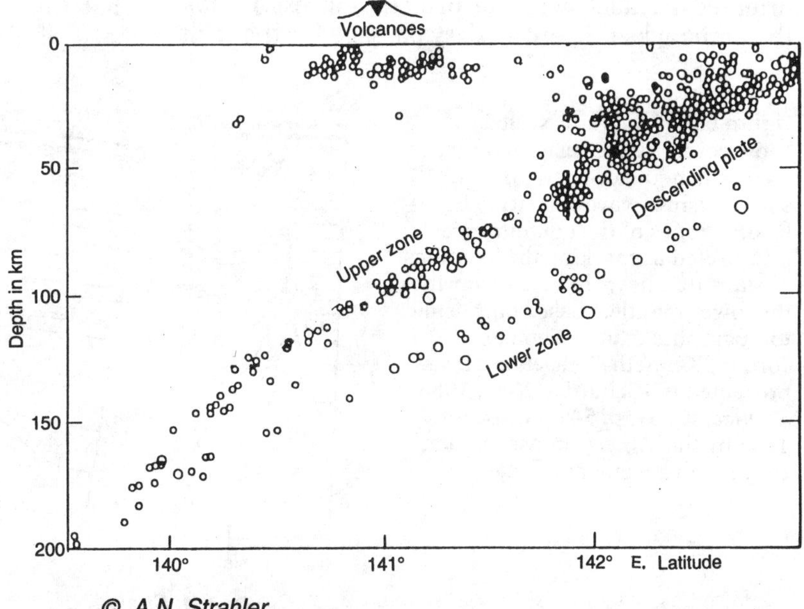

Figure 6.12 A vertical cross-section showing by numerous plottted hypocenters the image of the upper and lower zones of seismicity in a descending lithospheric plate. (Adapted from Keiiti Aki, 1988, *Bull., Geological Society of America,* v. 100, p. 628, Figure 2. Reproduced with permission of the publisher, The Geological Society of America, Boulder, Colorado, USA. Copyright 1988.

labeled in part C of Figure 6.11. At about the 660-km level another phase transformation takes place, forming a combination of two other minerals (one of them perovskite) for which the temperature and density are too great to permit earthquakes to be generated (Kirby, Durham, and Stern, 1991, p. 26).

The basic hypothesis we are developing proposes that as a descending slab passes down through the upper mantle it will undergo the above phase transformations, but the hypothesis takes into account that the interior region of the slab remains colder than the surrounding mantle. Thus the phase transformations would be delayed and would take place at greater depths (Kirby et al., 1991, p. 216). The delay would probably cause an unstable olivine state to develop within the slab, so that when the transformation occurs it is extremely rapid, releasing in a single package the energy sufficient to generate an earthquake. The mechanism would need to be one of slip on a new fracture surface. The seismic signature of such a slip would resemble that of a shallow-zone fault slip following a buildup of elastic strain in the rock. There remained to be developed a specific model for the development of a slip fracture under the existing unfavorable conditions of high pressure and temperature.

Laboratory experiments conducted by Harry W. Green II, and colleagues in the 1980s and early 1990s led to discovery of a viable localized mechanism that could precede the final slip failure (Green, 1993; 1994). Green and a graduate student, Pamela C. Burnley, began to experiment with the effects of high compressive stress levels on samples of a synthetic rock of spinel composition. The crystal lattice of this rock sheared into thin lamellae, or "lenses" of the denser spinel phase, creating a much weaker bulk structure. It was then found that these new microstructures, named *anticracks*, allowed shear faults to develop. (The prefix *anti* was used because the tensile lamellae are oriented normal to the axis of compressive stress, whereas in brittle failure the cracks are oriented parallel with the principal stress.) Thus the anticracks prepare an easy passage for the fault surface, so to speak. The anticrack fault mechanism is entirely different from the brittle failure mechanism, yet both generate the same kinds of seismic waves.

6.8 Slab Penetration into the Lower Mantle?

Although the lower limit of occurence of deep-focus earthquakes has held at the 670-km P-wave discontinuity, some strong evidence suggests that this density barrier is penetrated by downgoing slabs. We discussed this topic in Chapter 3, reviewing the way in which seismic tomography detects anomalies in the mantle. To repeat some of that text here, we explained that seismic tomography requires computer analysis of enormous volumes of collected arrival times of seismic waves from many different sources at many receiving points over the globe. These wave paths crisscross one another and can thus reveal velocity anomalies and locate their positions within the mantle. Within a given anomaly zone, the wave speed may be either increased or slowed, depending upon the nature of the physical anomaly present. For example, in the upper mantle, masses of cold, downsinking subducted lithosphere are revealed by a cluster of fast wave speeds. Speed anomalies can also reveal horizontal currents in the mantle and indicate their directions of flow.

One of the greatest impacts of seismic tomography has been to strengthen evidence for the existence of vertical components of mantle flow that are capable of exchanging substantial amounts of mineral matter between the lithosphere and the deep mantle, and even extending to the very floor of the lower mantle. Science writer Richard A. Kerr, in a 1988 review of developments aired by geochemists and geophysicists, reported that seismic tomography has shown that slabs of subducted lithosphere can actually pierce the 670-km density barrier to enter the lower mantle, and that the possibility exists that this same slab material can descend to the base of the lower mantle. Tomographic images

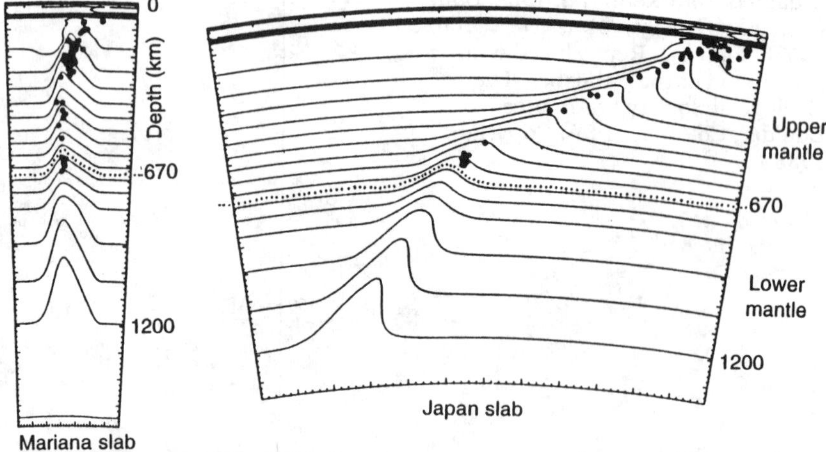

Figure 6.13 Diagrams scaled to show correctly the relation of deep-focus earthquakes to contours of equal seismic-wave velocity. The flexure zones of the contours are interpreted as marking the locations of slabs that have descended far into the lower mantle. (Based on seismic tomographic data of Thomas Jordan, Kenneth Creager, et al., as presented in Richard A. Kerr, 1986, *Science*, v. 231, p. 549. Copyright © 1986 by the American Association for the Advancement of Science.)

obtained by seismologist Thomas Jordan of the Massachusetts Institute of Technology and his student, K.C. Creager, in the early 1980s published diagrams showing slabs beneath the western Pacific as having descended several hundred kilometers below the 670-km barrier (Kerr, 1986a, p. 549). Figure 6.13 reproduces two of these diagrams, which show contours of seismic wave velocity on cross sections of two slabs: one descends gently; the other very steeply. Because no earthquakes have so far been recorded below the 670-km level, the downward continuation of the slab is inferred from the trail of nested contour flexures.

Independent confirmation of these observations was obtained in 1991 by Yoshio Fukao and colleagues of Nagoya University in Japan (Kerr, 1991, p. 1096; Fukao, 1992). Their seismic tomography revealed that whereas some slabs in the western Pacific flatten out and move horizontally above the discontinuity, other slabs were observed to have pierced the barrier and descended to a depth of 1200 km; in so doing, the masses had become deformed. (See also Monastersky, 1992, p. 132.) In 1993, Paul J. Tackley of the California Institute of Technology found that in creating computer model simulations of slab descent into the mantle, the slab material tended to pile up above the 670-km barrier, and only occasionally was the scenario punctuated by a "flushing" of great masses of rock down through the boundary (Monastersky, 1993, p. 133).

In 1993, a strikingly clear seismic tomography image revealed a columnar, fast-velocity lower-mantle zone, interpreted as possibly extending down from the Middle America Trench to the core-mantle boundary at 2700 km and spreading horizontally along that boundary (Vidale and Lay, 1993, p. 1401). More recently, seismic tomography cross sections of p-waves and s-waves showed what appears to be a continuous stream of mantle pouring downward from the surface to a depth of 2700 km. It has been interpreted as the descending Farallon slab (S.P. Grand, R.D. vander Hilst, and S. Widiyantoro, 1997).

6.9 Stress Axes and Faulting

Seismology has more to offer on the subject of subduction of lithospheric plates. To present this additional material, we need to look into the geometry of the stresses that produce an earthquake. Beyond that we need first to go back even one step further to review the stresses that come into play when brittle rock is fractured in different ways and on different scales that include the processes of faulting and joint fracturing.

For many decades geologists have known that when a smoothly dressed block of homogeneous rock (sandstone or marble, for example) is put in a powerful press that squeezes the block from top to bottom, failure typically occurs on a diagonal surface (Figure 6.14). The angle between the fracture plane and the *compressional axis* is always less than 45° and typically about 30° (Hobbs, Means, and Williams, 1976, p. 325-330: Twiss and Moores, 1992, p. 165-168). The fault plane here is perpendicular to the book page. In yielding by fault rupture, the block is shortened in length. As shown here, the fault rupture surface is oriented at a 30-degree angle to the compressional axis, which is indicated by the vertical broken line. As shown in B, the entire block is free to move horizontally (on roller bearings), so that shortening of the vertical dimension by faulting can be accommodated by a corresponding widening of the block without requiring a distortion of the shape of the block. Thus the apparatus simulates the formation of a new fault surface and its continued slip.

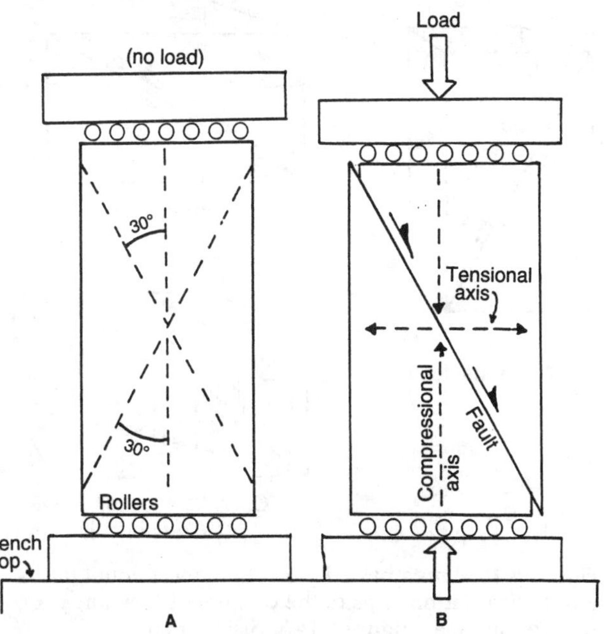

Figure 6.14 Simplified diagram of a laboratory device to apply compression stress on a stone block, causing it to rupture. (A: Adapted from Hobbs, Means, and Williams, 1976, *An Outline of Structural Geology*, p. 340, Figure 7.41a. Copyright © 1976. Reprinted by permission of John Wiley & Sons, Inc. B: Copyright © by Arthur N. Strahler.)

We can now use these same geometrical relationships to illustrate a normal fault, a reverse fault, and a strike-slip fault. We need only change the viewing angle, by turning the block, but keeping the ground surface on top, as shown in perspective in Figure 6.15: (A) With the compressional axis vertical, a normal fault is shown. (B) Flip the block on its side with the compressional stress axis horizontal and with the fault trace on the front panel, and we are modeling the vertical cross-section of a reverse fault. (C) Rotate the block B away from you 90° on its compressional axis so that the fault trace is now on the ground surface, demonstrating a strike-slip

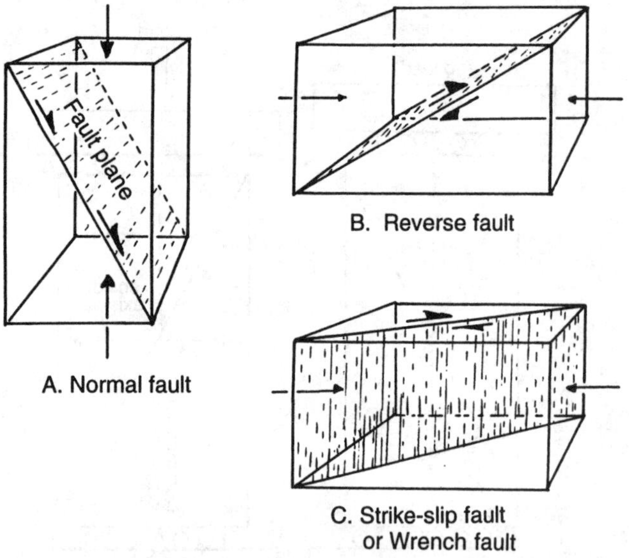

Fault plane

A. Normal fault

B. Reverse fault

C. Strike-slip fault or Wrench fault

Figure 6.15 Three basic kinds of compressional faults and their relationships to the compressional axis. (Same source as Figure 6.14A, p. 329. Figure 7.34. Used by permission of John Wiley & Sons, Inc.)

fault (also called a *wrench fault*). This completes our basic analysis of *compressional faulting*.

So far, mention of a tensional stress has been missing from the analysis. The *tensional axis* is shown in Figure 6.14B by arrows pointing outward from the center. It is oriented at right angles to the compressional axis. Tension, or "pulling apart," can cause *extensional faulting*, but the orientation of the fault plane is quite different than in compressional faulting. Let us imagine that we can design the apparatus needed to exert tensional stress on the same block of rock used in the compressional experiment. As shown in Figure 6.16, a powerful pull is exerted on the block, tending to stretch it to greater length. Being a brittle solid, it yields suddenly with a fracture, which lies in a plane approximately perpendicular to the tensional axis. This kind of "cracking" of rock is accompanied by an explosive energy release, generating an earthquake. Of course, once the initial fracture has spread across the entire test block, the two parts are no longer physically connected, so that the tensional stress has collapsed to zero. What follows here is the *translation* of two independent blocks, resulting in a widening gap, or fissure (Figure 6.16B).

Figure 6.17 illustrates an experimental demonstration of the two different forms of fracturing of rock under compressional and tensional forces, applied in that order. It was performed by Professor Winthrop Means at the State University of New York–Albany. First, loading was applied, shortening the limestone block by about one percent of its original length, and producing the diagonal shear fractures seen on the vertical front face of the block. After removal of the load, spontaneous upward

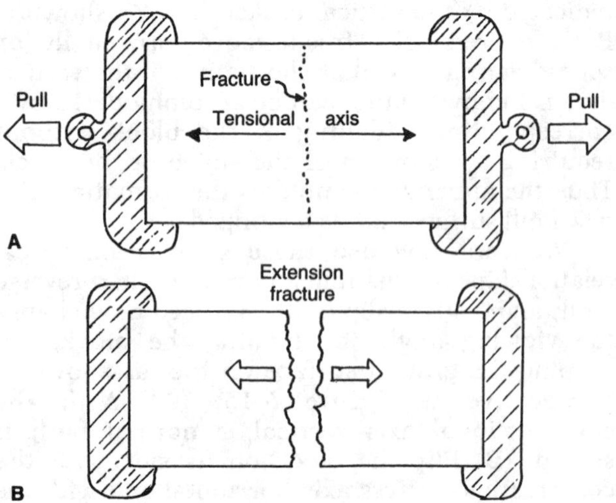

Figure 6.16 An imagined mechanical device to apply tensional stress to a block of sandstone or marble, causing it to yield by brittle freacture. (Copyright © by Arthur N. Strahler.)

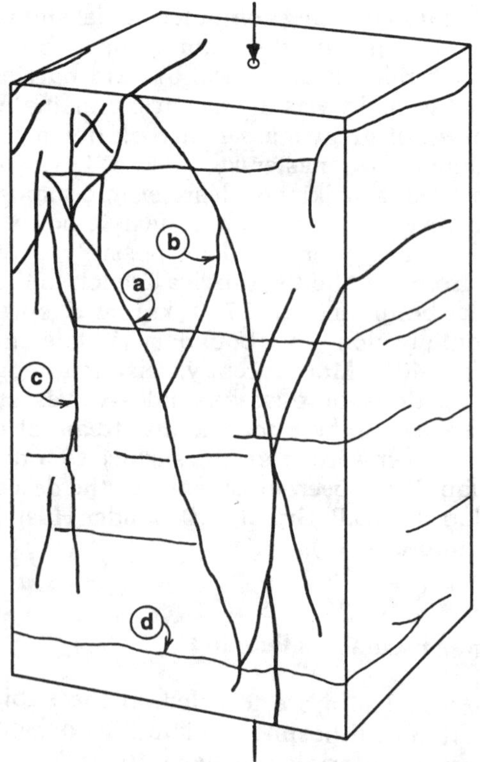

Figure 6.17 Drawing of fractures showing on the surface of an experimental block of Solenhofen limestone fractured by compressional stress. Cracks labeled (a) and (b) are conjugate shear fractures; the vertical crack labeled (c) is an extensional fracture produced during loading. The horizontal cracks labeled (d) were developed after pressure was removed, allowing the rock to expand slightly along the vertical axis. (From Hobbs, Means, and Williams, 1976, p. 326, Figure 7.31. Reprinted by permission of John Wiley & Sons, Inc.)

expansion of the rock took place, producing the horizontal extensional fractures seen on the front and side of the block, as well as a vertical extensional fracture. Note that all these fractures are joints, rather than faults, the distinction being that in a joint there is no observable displacement parallel with the plane of the joint, whereas in a fault, measurable parallel displacement has occurred. A secondary distinction would lie in the vastly greater dimensions possible in the extent of a single continuous fault surface.

6.10 Stress Directions within a Descending Plate

To distinguish whether an earthquake has been generated by compressional or tensional stress requires study of the first motion of S-waves. This operation had proved to be very difficult, but a method was finally perfected. H. Honda and other Japanese seismologists began to determine the type of stress and its direction for intermediate and deep earthquake foci beneath the Japanese islands (Honda, 1934; S. Uyeda, 1978, p. 135-140). They found that the axis of compressional stress, when plotted on a map, is consistently at right angles to the trend of the trench and volcanic arc associated with it (Figure 6.18A). This applies to earthquake foci below 200 km, but not necessarily to intermediate-depth foci, and not to shallow earthquakes. Seen in cross section, as in Figure 6.18B, the stress-axis symbols are consistently tilted down-dip so as to be parallel with the plane of the earthquake foci. This evidence strongly supported the hypothesis of a lithospheric plate being forced to descend, but it also showed that the earthquake-producing force acts parallel with the sloping plate and is not a horizontal force. Why is the stress axis parallel with the plate? The answer seems to lie in the resistance offered by the surrounding mantle to the downward motion of the relatively cool rigid slab. As the leading edge of the slab passes through the asthenosphere and begins to penetrate the stronger mantle that lies deeper, resistance to further penetration begins to build. The force of resistance is thus passed back up the rigid slab as a compressional stress.

Later, the same kind of seismic analysis revealed that in many subduction zones, stresses causing intermediate-depth earthquakes near the top of the downplunging slab are of the tensional type (Figure 6.19). Apparently, in some cases the upper part of the slab is under tensional stress at the same time that the deep portion is under compressional stress. Why is the slab being "stretched" in its upper part? The answer offered to this question is that the slab is sinking under the force of gravity. As it moves into the low-strength zone of the asthenosphere, resistance to down-sinking is diminished, and the plate tends to sink faster, causing a stretching force in the plate in this upper region. Simultaneously, the leading edge of the same plate may be under compressional stress because it is penetrating stronger mantle material.

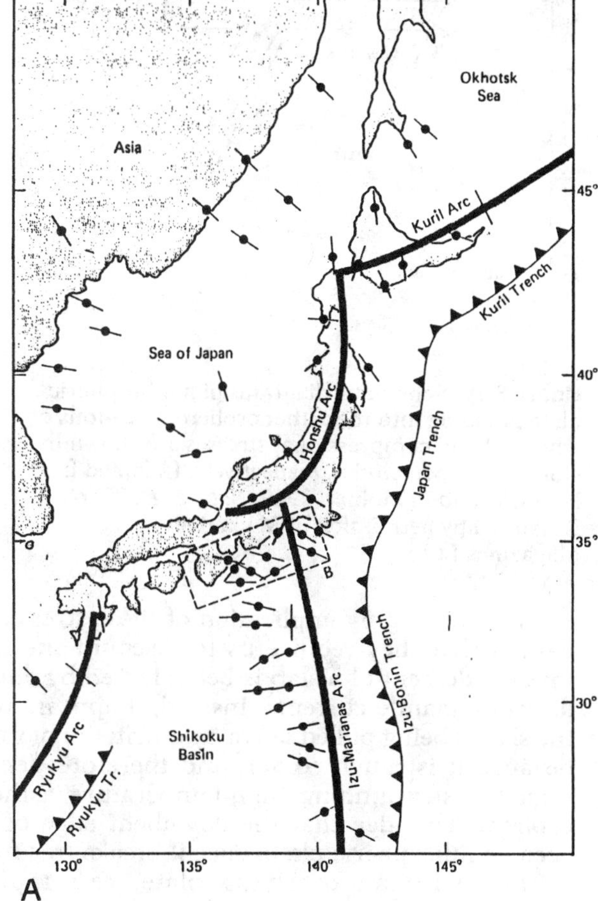

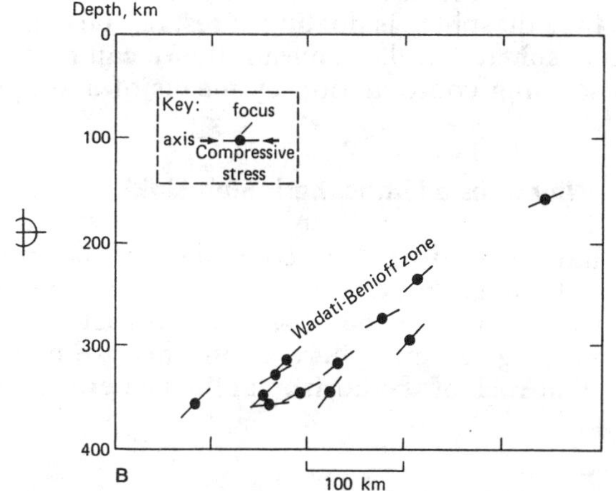

Figure 6.18 Stress directions within a descending plate. (A) Short lines on the map show the directions of greatest horizontal compressional stress at the foci of intermediate and deep earthquakes beneath the Japanese islands and the Sea of Japan. (B) Cross sectional diagram showing the axes of compressional stress in the outlined map zone. (Data of H. Honda and M. Ichikawa. Adapted from S. Uyeda, 1978, *The New View of the Earth*, pp. 139 and 140. Figures 5-8 and 5-9. Copyright © 1978 by W.H. Freeman and Company. Used by permission of author and publisher.)

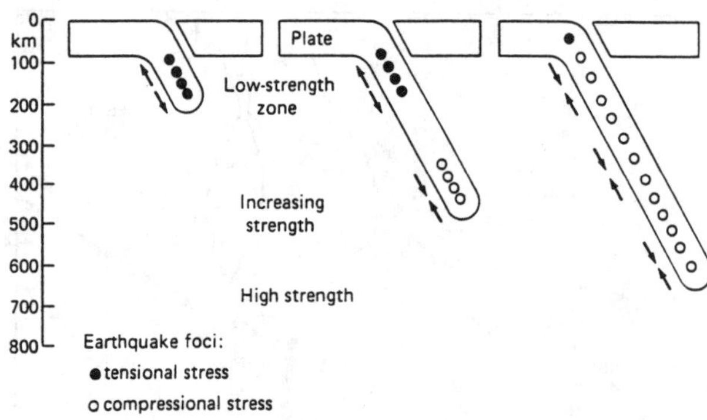

Figure 6.19 Schematic diagrams of a lithospheric plate plunging into the asthenosphere. Locations of tensional and compressional stresses are shown by closed and open circles, respectively. (Adapted from B. Isacks and P. Molnar, 1969, *Nature*, v. 223, p. 1121. Reprinted by permission of Macmillan Magazines Ltd.)

The interesting implication of these stress-axis data is that they require us to discount the idea that the descent of a slab is being forced by down-dragging mantle currents. Instead, it appears that the slab is being pulled down by gravitational force because it is much colder, and therefore denser than the surrounding high-temperature asthenosphere. The idea that the downbent edge of an oceanic lithospheric plate, once it breaks free from contact with an overlying plate, can rapidly "founder of its own weight" seems at first thought to contradict the doctrine of isostasy, which holds that the lithosphere is floating at rest on the denser asthenosphere that lies beneath it. We can resolve this seeming contradiction by means of a simple model.

6.11 Why Does a Lithospheric Slab Sink?

We have stated that a cold slab of oceanic lithosphere sinks through the asthenosphere because it is denser than the soft, hot rock of the surrounding asthenosphere. From this, we might infer that rock of the horizontal lithosphere of the ocean basins is also denser than rock of the asthenosphere below it. Evidence from seismology seems to confirm this inference.

In 1970, Professor Frank Press, a leading American seismologist, published the results of an elaborate investigation in which a computer was programmed to generate a large number of models of the possible change of rock density with depth in the earth. The results, in which densities and s-wave velocities were in good general agreement, are shown in a simplified version in Figure 6.20 (Press, 1970). Density increases rapidly in the first 100 km but levels off in the depth range of 100 to 200 km. Then, below about 200 km, density begins to decrease. In the general depth range of 200 to 400 km, we see a zone of reduced density values. Below about 400 km, density increases rapidly into the mantle. Figure 6.20 also shows the results of this computer study with respect to the S-wave velocities. The low-velocity zone of the asthenosphere appears very distinctly on the graph with a minimum value in the depth range of about 150 to 200 km. This depth zone is the "softest" part of the asthenosphere.

The important message from Frank Press's results comes from the reversal of the density curve within the asthenosphere. The reversal indicates a condition of potential instability favoring the possibility that a lithospheric plate will sink of its own weight once it begins to descend into the asthenosphere. Now, a new physical principle needs to be taken into account. When a dipping slab of oceanic lithosphere begins to enter the asthenosphere, density conditions change because the slab is continually moving into a region of increasing confining pressure. The slab contracts slightly in volume under this confining pressure and becomes denser than it was at the surface. Under this principle, at any given level in the asthenosphere, rock of the cold slab must be denser than mantle rock of the surrounding asthenosphere. Remember that most of the oceanic lithosphere is composed of ultramafic rock, probably of peridotite composition, and that it is probably of the same chemical composition as

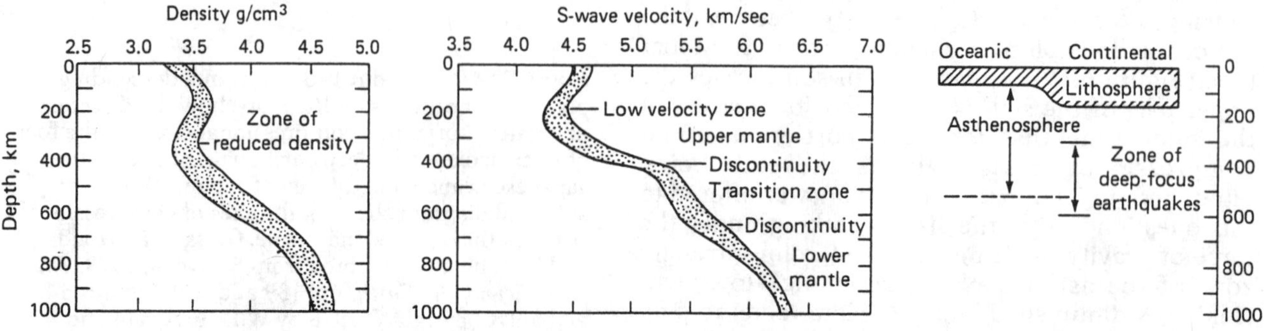

Figure 6.20 Graphs showing computer-derived changes of density and S-wave velocity with depth. The descending band in each graph shows the limits within which numerous model curves fell. (Data of F. Press, 1970. Used by permission.)

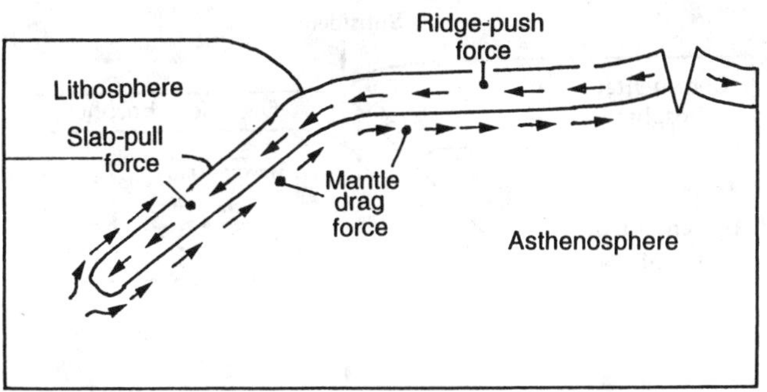

Figure 6.21 Schematic block diagram showing forces postulated to be important in the motions of lithospheric plates. (Copyright © by Arthur N. Strahler.)

the asthenosphere. Because the chemical compositions of the two materials are alike, differences in temperature are very important in causing density differences where the two materials are under the same confining pressure. We can also postulate that, as oceanic crust is subducted and enters a region of higher pressure, the basalt and gabbro of which it is composed undergo a phase change and turn into eclogite, which has a density about equal to that of peridotite. In any case, the oceanic crust is only a very thin layer (about 5 km thick) in comparison with the oceanic lithosphere, which is on the order of 50 to 70 km thick over large areas. Because the oceanic crust is so thin, it could have little buoyant effect on a subducting slab.

At this point, it will be helpful to introduce a partial analysis of forces that act upon a subducting slab. Figure 6.21 shows schematically a single plate of oceanic lithosphere diving beneath a continental plate. Starting at the right, the oceanic plate is shown as being elevated along the flank of the spreading rift, so as to slope down toward the subduction boundary. This gradient sets up a small component of the vertical gravitational force directed parallel with the plate; it is called the *ridge-push force*. Within the descending slab, a large component of the gravitational force is directed parallel with the slab; this is the *slab-pull force*. These two forces allow the entire oceanic plate to move spontaneously as a unit. Opposing this movement is a *mantle-drag force*, countering the motion of the plate. [A complete statement of these and other forces acting on moving plates is given in Chapter 7. See Figure 7.34.]

If our argument favoring spontaneous sinking of a subducting lithospheric plate is sound, it must have an answer for the following problem: In order for subduction to start along some particular line within an expanse of continuous horizontal oceanic lithosphere requires an initial rupturing force that is obviously not the slab-pull force. The initiating force must be capable of breaking the lithospheric plate and forcing one edge down into the asthenosphere. The ridge-push force is one possible candidate for causing the initial plate rupture. We may imagine that if the plate is lifted high enough by rising mantle rock along an existing spreading axis, the ridge-push force will be transmitted to distant points on the plate. Then, at some place where a structural weakness exists, the plate ruptures along a descending shear plane in a reverse-fault movement. The shear plane then spreads rapidly in both directions and a new subduction boundary comes into existence.

6.12 Shallow-Depth Seismic Activity at Convergent Plate Boundaries

An idealized cross-section through the uppermost 50 km of the subduction zone of a volcanic arc is shown in Figure 6.22. It was compiled by seismologists of the Lamont-Doherty Geological Observatory of Columbia University, including Dan Byrne, Dan Davis and Lynn Sykes (Lamont-Doherty, 1988). The major parts of the system include: subducting oceanic crust, trench, accretionary wedge (or prism), forearc basin, outer-arc high, backstop. (These features are

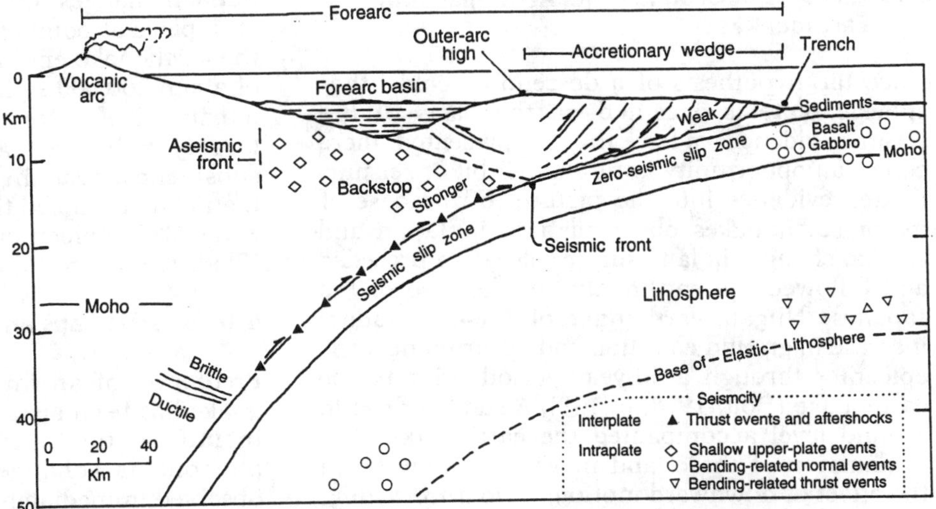

Figure 6.22 Idealized cross-section through the subduction zone adjacent to a volcanic island arc. (Adapted from *Lamont Log*, Winter 1988, p. 1-2, Lamont-Doherty Geological Observatory of Columbia University. Used by permission.)

described and explained in detail in Chapter 8.) Seismicity is of two classes: (a) Interplate seismicity is generated on the surface between the two plates; (b) Intraplate seismicity, within the outer boundaries of either plate.

Starting at the right, shallow earthquakes on normal faults are numerous in the oceanic crust as it begins to bend downward under the trench. These are classified on the map as "intraplate bending-related normal events." The crust then passes beneath the accretionary wedge, within which relatively minor overthrusting is occurring. On the plate beneath, a soft upper layer of pelagic sediments allows aseismic slip. This *aseismic slip zone* ends at a depth of about 12 km beneath the outer-arc high. At this point the *backstop* is encountered; it consists of volcanic rock of high strength, in which shallow intraplate earthquakes are numerous. The point where the upper surface of the descending plate first encounters the backstop is called the *seismic front*. At this point, much or all of the pelagic sediment will have been offscraped from the slab surface. Down-slope from the seismic front, the slab is thrust directly against the volcanic/metamorphic crustal backstop, generating strong earthquakes along a continuous overthrust fault zone that marks the plate boundary. This is the *interplate seismic slip zone*. It persists down to a depth of about 40 km, where the behavior of the mantle changes from that of brittle rock to that of ductile rock. In the latter zone, the earthquakes are "bending-related thrust slips" occurring within the slab. Near the base of the elastic lithosphere, "intraplate bending-related thrust events" occur directly below the trench, starting at a depth of about 35 km. Some bending-related intraplate normal events occur between 40 and 50 km in the lower part of the descending slab.

Not all of the components listed above will always be present. A very young subduction boundary might lack the accretionary wedge and forearc basin. The aseismic slip segment may be absent because an accretionary prism has not yet been constructed beyond the seismic slip zone.

6.13 Changes of Ground Level Accompanying Earthquakes

Once the hypothesis of a descending cold lithospheric plate is accepted on the basis of the seismic evidence we have thus far presented, there comes an opportunity to fit another bit of seismic-related evidence into the picture. In the case of major earthquakes observed both in Japan and Alaska, changes in land surface elevation preceded and followed the earthquake. In the case of the Japanese Niigata earthquake of 1964, a gradual increase in ground elevation had occurred near the epicenter through a 60-year period prior to the earthquake (Bolt, 1978, p. 138). A sudden drop in ground level accompanied the earthquake. The explanation of these land movements may lie in the effect of downward motion, or *underthrusting*,

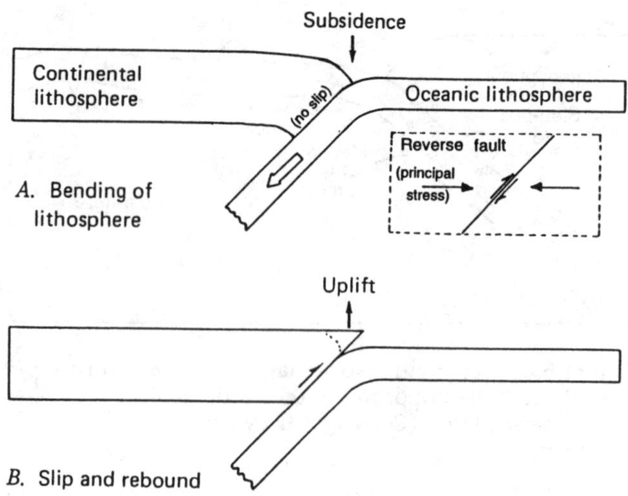

Figure 6.23 A greatly exaggerated cross section of alternate elastic bending and rebound of the edge of the continental plate at a subduction boundary. The actual amount of deformation is much too small to be shown to true scale here. (Copyright © by Arthur N. Strahler.)

upon the continental lithospheric plate. As shown in Figure 6.23A, the steadily plunging plate tends to pull down with it the edge of the overlying continental plate. This down-flexing occurs over a long time period prior to the earthquake; it represents elastic strain being stored in the bent continental plate. When the earthquake occurs, the flexed plate rebounds upward. The mechanism of elastic rebound thus seems to hold for shallow earthquakes in subduction zones. In a simplified analysis, the interplate compressional stress axis is horizontal and generates the reverse-fault form of shear, as illustrated in Figure 6.15B.

In our second example, the Good Friday Earthquake of March 27, 1964, the epicenter lay between the Alaskan cities of Anchorage and Valdez (Figure 6.24). Depth of the focus was about 35 km. The shock had a magnitude of $M_S = 8.4$ ($M_W = 9.2$), which is close to the maximum known. Sudden changes of land level, both up and down, took place at points as far distant as 500 km from the earthquake epicenter and covered a total area of about 200,000 sq km. A belt of uplift reaching a maximum of 10 m paralleled the coast and was largely offshore. A broad zone of shallow subsidence, reaching amounts somewhat more than -2 m, occupied the landward side of the uplift zone. The epicenter lay between these zones (Plafker, 1965, p. 1677).

6.14 Seismic Gaps and Earthquake Prediction

Prediction of an immediately impending earthquake has been approached in a number of ways, including the study of various precursory phenomena—changes in physical phenomena observed immediately prior to a large earthquake.

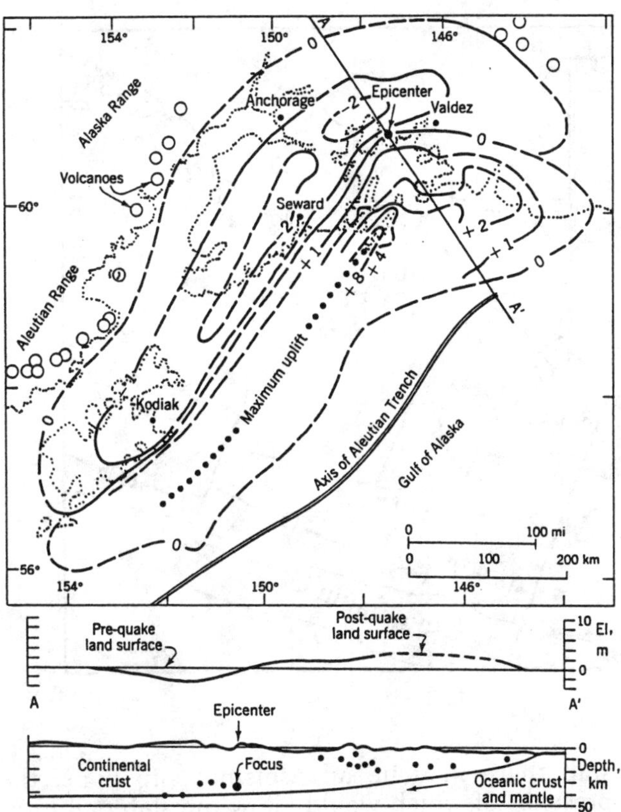

Figure 6.24 Map of south-central Alaska showing crustal uplift and subsidence associated with the Good Friday earthquake of March 27, 1964. Contours in meters. Profile and structure section below are drawn through the epicenter along a NW-SE line (AA'). (Data of the U.S. Geological Survey. Redrawn and simplified from G. Plafker, 1964, *Science*, v. 148, p. 1677, Figure 2, and p. 1681, Figure 6.)

In contrast is the historical method of forecasting into future decades or centuries the occurrence of a major earthquake. Such forecasts are often based on an assessment of the time that has elapsed since a major earthquake caused a release of strain along a given section of a known active fault. It is a method well suited to the circum-Pacific subduction plate boundaries.

When a careful study is made of the epicenter locations and times of occurrence of major quakes in this belt, there emerges a pattern in which certain sections of the subduction boundary have had no major activity for several decades. These sections are designated *seismic gaps* when no major seismic activity has occurred within the past 30 or more years (McNally, 1983). Seismic gaps were identified as early as the 1920s in Japan. [The same term was also applied to the "locked" sections of major continental strike-slip plate boundaries, such as the San Andreas Fault of California, but this text section is limited to the subduction boundaries.]

Before going further, we must note the fact that subduction of the oceanic lithosphere is continuing quite steadily at a known long-term average rate as great as several centimeters per year along the island and continental arcs. The average rate does differ, however, from one region to another. Within that constraint, two basic lines of explanation need to be considered. First, elastic strain has been building up steadily in the locked contact surface between the two plates, and this cannot continue indefinitely. Sooner or later, a great earthquake will release that strain energy. Second, it may be that aseismic slip (slow creep) is going on steadily, keeping pace with the rate of subduction, and that no significant strain is accumulating. Although that process continues indefinitely, no large earthquake will occur. When one reads about the *gap theory*, the first explanation (locked plates) is usually implicit as the hypothesis being defended. By 1980, several examples of seismic gaps with potentiality of generating great earthquakes were identified and studied.

The Aleutian Islands arc is shown in Figure 6.25. It shows three gaps: Alaska/British Columbia (AK/BC) gap, Shumagin gap, and Yakataga gap. Within the AK/BC gap, there occurred in 1979 a large earthquake (M_S = 7+), named the St. Elias

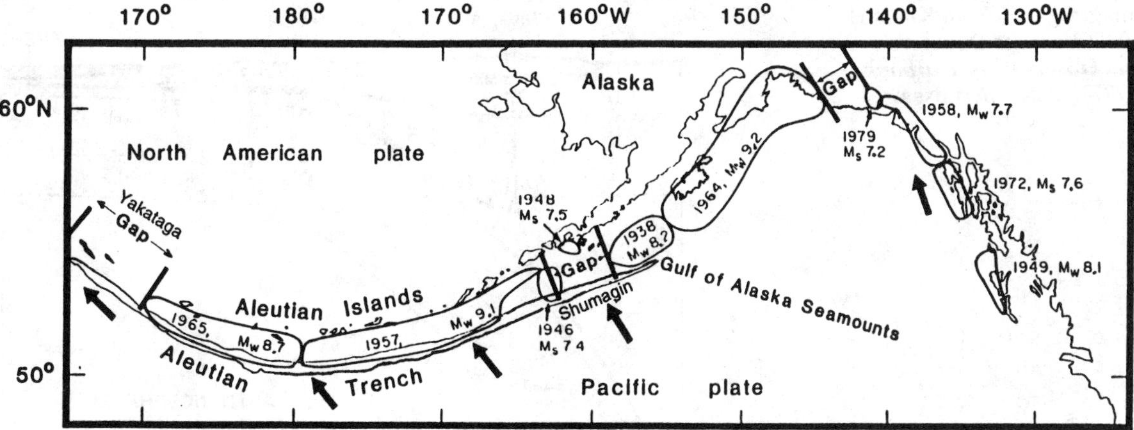

Figure 6.25 General seismic map of the Aleutian volcanic arc, showing seismic gaps. (From McCann, Peréz, and Sykes, 1980, *Science*, v. 207, p. 1310. Copyright © 1980 by the American Association for the Advancement of Science.)

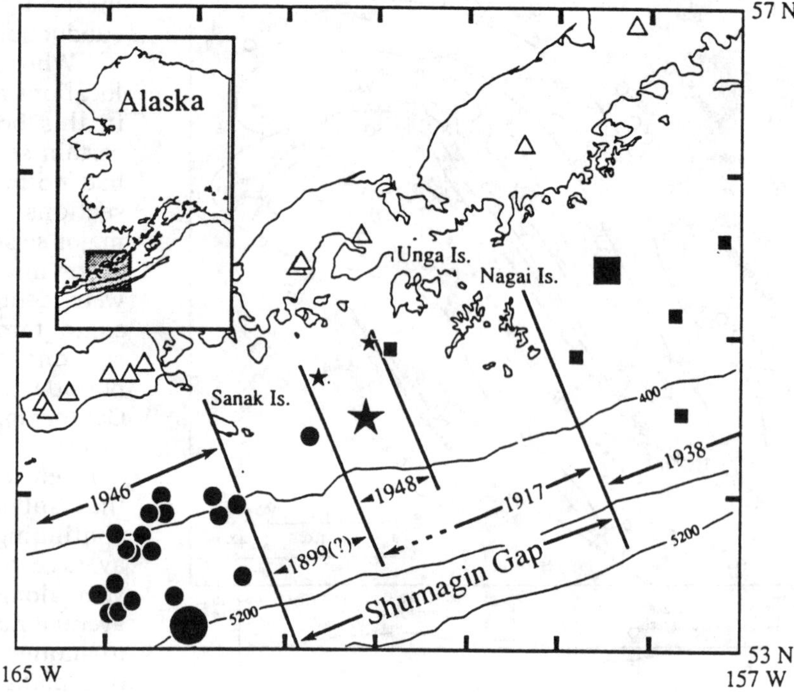

Figure 6.26 Seismic map of the Shumagin map and environs. Black circles: 1946 quakes. Black squares: 1939 quakes. Stars: 1948 quake. Extent of rupture shown by black parallel straight lines. (Courtesy of Thomas Boyd, Lamont-Doherty Earth Observatory. From Boyd, et al., *Geophysical Research Letters*, 1988, v. 15, p. 201-204. Used by permission.)

earthquake. While this slip released some of the elastic strain, the entire accumulated strain remaining in the gap, estimated at 3.8 m, has a potential of producing an earthquake as large as $M_S = 8$ (Lahr and Plafker, 1980, p. 483). Near the middle of the arc is the Shumagin gap. At the far western end of the arc lies the Yakataga gap, which has experienced no great earthquake since 1899. A large amount of strain has accumulated in the gap and a great earthquake is to be anticipated. Note that the plate motion at this gap is nearly parallel with the strike of the arc, so that the displacement may be in large part a strike-slip motion.

Figure 6.26 is a detailed map of the Shumagin gap. Figure 6.27 is a schematic cross section of the Shumagin gap, showing the locked thrust zone beneath the Shumagin Islands. Down-dip on the slab there may lie an aseismic slip zone, the presence of which would allow the slab-pull force to exert a tensional stress directly upon the slab in the locked zone, causing it to slip and generate a great earthquake.

In 1917 the Shumagin gap experienced a strong earthquake, estimated at $M_S = 7.6\text{-}7.9$, but the exact location of the epicenter cannot be determined. Our local map, Figure 6.26, shows by the two outer pairs of parallel black lines the estimated width of the 1917 rupture zone. A lesser quake in 1948 ruptured only a narrow central segment of the fault. Also shown in the gap is one aftershock epicenter from the 1946 quake (to the west) and one from the 1938 quake (to the east). What this all adds up to is that no rupture across the full width of the gap has occurred within the

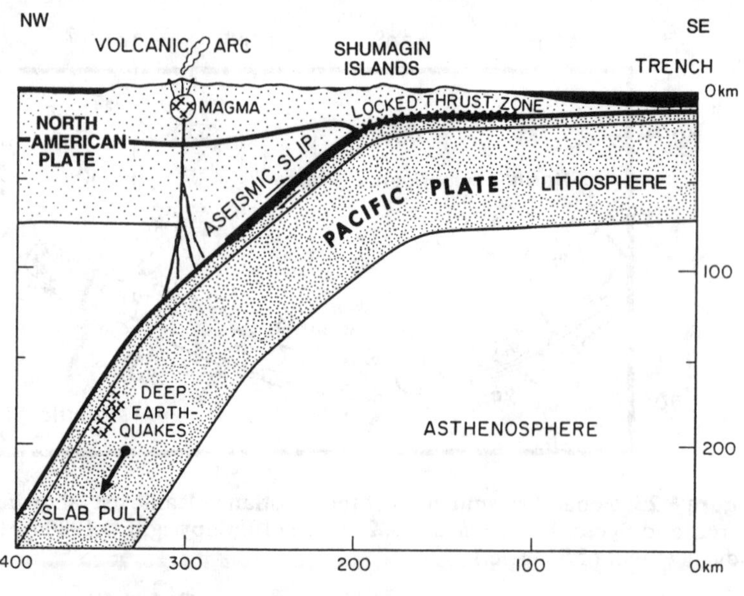

Figure 6.27 Stylized cross section of the Shumagin gap. (From Klaus H. Jacob, 1987, Lamont-Doherty Geological Observatory *Yearbook 1987*, p. 77. Used by permission.)

past 70 years (Sykes et al., 1980, p. 1344).

Besides the Aleutian gaps, good examples have been found in Japan, Mexico, Nicaragua, Chile, Colombia, and New Zealand. In southern Honshu Island, between Tokyo and Nagoya, is a seismic gap being watched with much apprehension; already it has received a name: The Great Tokai Earthquake (Douglas, 1978, p. 282).

Another interesting example of a seismic gap lies along the southern coast of Mexico in the region of Oaxaca. It had been identified as early as 1973. About 150 km long, this gap had shown no seismic activity for about 50 years. In 1976, a team of three seismologists at the University of Texas at Galveston focused their attention upon this gap. (Two of the team members were Japanese seismologists.) They knew that the gap had been in a precursory phase in which little or no seismic activity had been occurring, and that this stage had been followed by a second phase in which a series of minor quakes originated in the gap. On the hunch that a large earthquake, perhaps as great as $M_S = 8$, was in the offing, the Texas team published a forecast to that effect. Their urgent requests to Mexican and U.S. government agencies to install seismic monitoring equipment in the gap were denied. Then, on November 29, 1978, an earthquake of $M_S = 7.8$ occurred in the gap. Fortunately, a research team from the California Institute of Technology, with strong cooperation from the University of Mexico, had been able to set up portable seismographs in the gap area shortly before the earthquake occurred, and was able to monitor the minor shocks that immediately preceded the major energy release (Kerr, 1979, p. 860-862).

6.15 The Gap Theory Challenged

The gap theory as a means of predicting where large, devastating earthquakes are most likely to occur enjoyed considerable support over the two decades, or so, during which it could point to having successfully tagged a few likely gaps and even narrowed down the times of earthquake occurrence on the basis of a logical set of premonitory seismic signals. Support had come from prestigious seismic research institutions, both academic and governmental. But science as it is actually practiced includes open and vigorous dissent and debate within the peer group. And debate, though perhaps delayed, arrived with a bang in the 1990s.

Two geophysicists of the University of California–Los Angeles, David Jackson and Yan Kagan, decided to test the gap theory. They used as their target data a world map of subduction-boundary earthquakes prepared by Columbia University seismologists of the Lamont-Doherty Geological Observatory. Published in 1979, the map divided the seismically active zones into segments of three classes: high risk, intermediate risk, and low risk (Monastersky, 1992). Jackson and Kagan superimposed dots on the Lamont map to show the locations of all earthquake foci of magnitude $M_S = 7$ and higher for the period 1979 through 1988. A substantial share of the dots fell into zones of low risk and intermediate risk. The number of quakes in the low-risk zones was five times greater than in the high risk zones. In one case, a gap that had been "filled" by a $M_S = 8.4$ quake in 1964 had subsequently experienced two quakes of $M_S = 7$ or higher. A heated debate between seismologists of the opposed groups was held in 1993 at the annual meeting of the American Geophysical Union (Science Reporter, 1993, p. 1724). It led to recognition of the need to distinguish between two intensity classes of quakes: moderate quakes over $M_S = 7$ but well under $M_S = 8$, and those great quakes of $M_S = 8$ and over, ranging up to $M_S = 8.5$. It was pointed out that in terms of energy released, a quake of $M_S = 8$ is 32 times greater than one of $M_S = 7$; that of a quake of $M_S = 9$, nearly 1000 times greater than $M_S = 7$ (see Strahler, 1981, p. 200 and Figure 8.25). This means that an $M_S = 7$ quake is trivial in terms of relieving the large amount of elastic strain built up after many decades of quiet in a gap. These moderate quakes can occur in a gap either before or after a great quake occurs. We see in the gap debate an example of how hypotheses are modified and refined to accommodate closer scrutiny of raw data and in some cases will emerge stronger as a result.

6.16 Seismicity of Young Continent-Continent Collision Orogens

The great continent-continent and arc-continent collisions of the geologic past are today located for the most part in low-seismic parts of the continents, their sutures and thrust boundaries lying mute. We can only conjecture about the vast numbers of great seismic events that accompanied the crustal telescoping those continental masses underwent. The most recent sequence of great collisional events was that in which continental fragments of Gondwana closed with the northern continents of Laurentia and the more recently accreted continental masses that had formed a single Eurasian plate.

Collisional events that formed the European Alps were largely completed by the end of the Miocene Epoch, and these orogens today produce large numbers of lesser earthquakes of $M_S \leq 7$. We will pass over the Aegean Sea region of presently active plate subduction, already noted earlier in this chapter. By Late Miocene, the Arabian plate had begun to impinge strongly on Eurasia, producing collision sutures and a major reverse-fault boundary between it and the adjacent Zagros subplate. The Zagros region, while seismically active, has produced no large earthquakes in historic time. However, aseismic

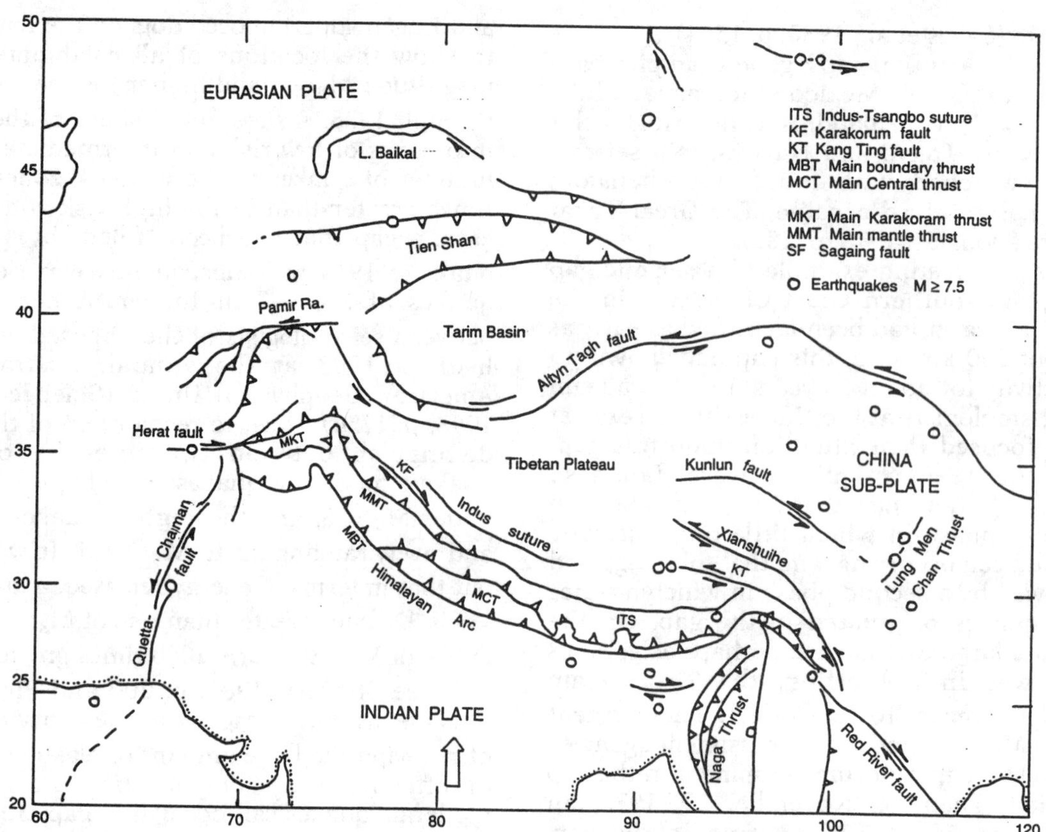

Figure 6.28 Sketch map of the major tectonic features of the Himalayan/Tibetan/Siberian region of southern Asia. (Based on data of Gupta and Singh, 1986, Molnar, Burchfiel, et al., 1987, Harrison, et al., 1992, and other sources. Map copyright © by Arthur N. Strahler.)

deformation may be playing an important role in active development of folds and thrusts.

We now focus on the collision zone between the Indian fragment of Gondwana and Asia, an orogeny that was in progress in the Late Miocene. Compressional tectonics continued through the Pliocene, forming the Himalayan Range and elevating the Tibetan Plateau. The process is continuing today, with a closing rate of about 1.7 cm/yr. As a result, seismic activity is intense and includes many large earthquakes recorded in historic time. [The India/Asia collision history is described in detail in Chapter 9.]

Figure 6.28 is a sketch map of the Himalayan/Tibetan region showing the major underthrust faults, collision sutures, and transcurrent faults (Harrison et al., 1992, p. 1664). Located close to the topographic boundary between the Indo-Gangetic alluvial plain and the Himalayan foothills lies the Main Boundary thrust (MBT). It descends only to shallow depth and becomes almost horizontal. Paralleling it on the north but with an irregular trace and widely variable separation distance is the Main Central thrust (MCT). During the past two centuries many great earthquakes ($M_W \geq 8$) have occurred along these fault surfaces within a zone 10 to 50 km wide, north-south, and over 1000 km long. Depths of foci have been 15 and 20 km below sea level. Numerous earthquakes have occurred in scattered locations over the vast surface of the Tibetan Plateau, but these are of small to moderate size.

Traced northeastward to the India-Burma region, the boundary fault arc bends sharply southwest in a 500-km multiple thrust zone known as the Eastern Syntaxis (Gupta and Singh, 1988). On one of these faults lies the epicenter of the great 1950 earthquake, $M_W = 8.7$. To the south of the Eastern Syntaxis lies another arc of multiple thrusts, but these trend north-south and are concentrically curved concave toward the east, as the map shows. One of these is the Naga thrust. Farther east, in the Eastern Highlands of Burma, lies a curving arc of four large earthquake epicenters, all of these shocks occurring between 1908 and 1946.

Turning our attention now to the western end of the Himalayan arc, we observe a sharp bend from northwest to west. Here a third underthrust zone, The Main Karakorum thrust, lies to the north of the Main Central thrust. This northernmost indentation of the Himalayas is a region of intense seismic activity. Farther north lies the Pamir thrust arc, the fault-plane dip being southward and opposite to that of the Karakorum thrust. The Pamir arc is also a zone of intense

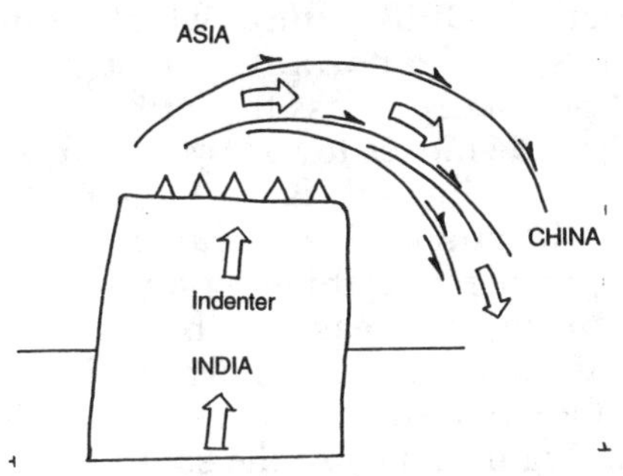

Figure 6.29 Cartoon map of Indian continent indenting Asia. (Copyright © by Arthur N. Strahler.)

seismic activity.

A major feature of the tectonics of Himalayan-Tibetan Plateau region and adjacent areas of China and Siberia is the presence of great transcurrent faults (strike-slip faults) along which large earthquakes have been occurring. These are conspicuously displayed on our map, Figure 6.28. The Karakorum strike slip fault, for example, trends parallel with the Main mantle thrust and the Main boundary thrust. Traced northwest, this fault becomes the Main Karakorum thrust, but this transition occurs where the strike changes abruptly from NW to ESE. This observed relationship is to be expected because both kinds of faults are products of the same compressional stress. The longest of the transcurrent faults in this region is the Altyn Tagh fault, which follows the southern boundary of the Tarim Basin. The epicenters of three large earthquakes lie close to the fault. Movement on this fault has been estimated to have an average rate of about 3 cm/yr (Molnar et al., 1987, p. 250). Lying to the south of the Altyn Tagh fault are three shorter transcurrent faults: Kunlun, Xianshuihe, and Kang Ting. They are parallel in strike with the Altyn Tagh and have the same left lateral displacement. One major earthquake epicenter lies close to the Kunlun fault, while two epicenters lie near the western end of the Kang Ting fault. Note that the southeastern end of the Kunlun fault abuts the Lung Men Chan thrust fault, on which two epicenters of large earthquakes are located.

Another major transcurrent fault shown on the map is the Quetta-Chaman fault in Pakistan. On it lies the epicenter of a large earthquake that occurred in 1892. Called the Baluchistan earthquake, it had a left-lateral (sinistral) motion with a displacement of about one meter (Richter, 1958, p. 608-609). Look next on our map to the eastern boundary of the India plate, which lies in Burma. East of the Naga thrust is shown the north-south trending transcurrent Sagaing fault (Zaw, 1989, p. 94; Acharyya, p. 95). It is a right-lateral fault and lies close to major earthquakes. It offers a mirror image of the Quetta-Chaman fault, and we can visualize the Indian plate to be moving northward between these two side-boundaries as it indents the Asian continent.

It is generally agreed that the Indian plate continues to 'indent its way' northward into the Eurasian plate, so to speak. The total convergence is thought to be absorbed, not only by the thrust faults (reverse faults) of the Himalayan arc, but also by the east-west trending transcurrent faults we have described, i.e., Karakoram, Altyn Tagh, Kunlun, Xianshuihe, and Kang Ting. Their overall regional effect is visualized as 'pushing aside' or 'squeezing out' great sections (segments) of lithosphere toward the east (Figure 6.29). The name *extrusion tectonics* has been given to this process. Adding all of these together, Peter Molnar and his associates estimated the convergence to amount to about 5.3 cm/yr (Molnar et al., 1987, p. 250). This estimate approaches the total plate convergence figure of 5.8 cm/yr published by Minster and Jordan in 1978. We have here an excellent example of the role of seismic data in revealing the existence of active faults, determining the directions and amounts of their displacements, and thus improving our understanding of large-scale plate motions.

6.17 Seismicity of Continental Transform Plate Boundaries

In terms of our classification system of seismicity and plate tectonics, presented in Table 6.1, we have completed overviews of the first three classes: Class I, Active spreading plate boundaries, Class II, Active subduction plate boundaries, and Class III, Active continent/continent collision boundaries. Here, we turn to Class IV, Active intracontinental fault systems. The first of the four subclasses is Subclass A, Continental transform fault systems that serve as plate boundaries lying within continental lithosphere.

Transform plate boundaries within continental lithosphere are distinguished from Class I transform plate boundaries that lie entirely within the oceanic lithosphere. Many geologists broaden the definition of "transform fault" to read: any plate boundary that is a pure strike-slip displacement (Bates and Jackson, 1987, p. 695; Dennis and Atwater, 1974, p. 1034). Our criteria of distinction here are (a) the class of lithosphere in which the boundary lies and (b) the kind of crust it bears. A continental transform boundary may form at least one segment of the complete set of boundaries enclosing a single plate, and thus it may join end-to-end with a subduction boundary, a continental suture, or a spreading boundary in adjacent oceanic lithosphere. (Keep in mind that a single plate, such as the North American plate, may consist of both continental and oceanic lithosphere.)

Our first example of a transform plate boundary in continental crust is the western

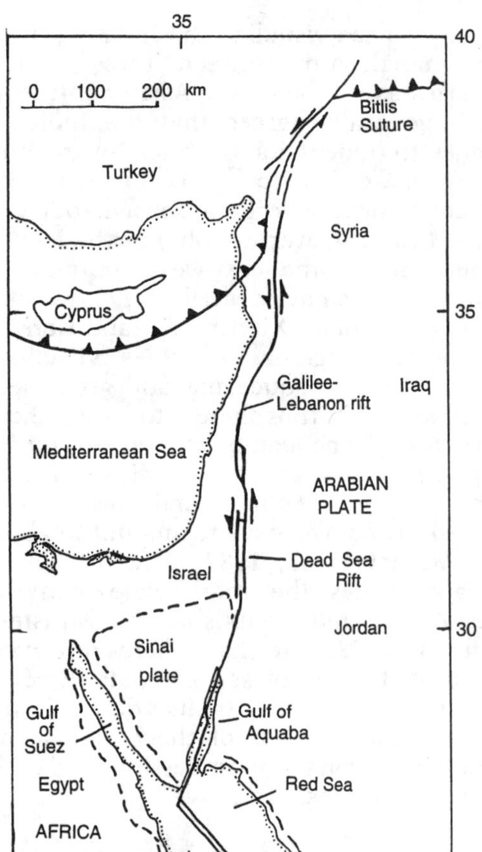

Figure 6.30 Sketch map of the western transform fault boundary of the Arabian plate. (Based on data of Zvi Ben-Avraham and V. Lyakhovsky, 1992, *Geology*, v. 20, p. 1140; Garfunkel, 1981; and other sources. Map copyright by Arthur N. Strahler.)

boundary of the Arabian plate, delineated and labeled on the world plate tectonic map, Figure 7.4. Some details of this boundary are shown in Figure 6.30. Starting at the south, where it is joined to the Red Sea spreading plate boundary, this 1000-km transcurrent fault runs north through the Gulf of Aqaba into the Dead Sea rift, then into the Galilee-Lebanon rift. It continues north to terminate at the Bitlis suture, which bounds the Arabian plate on the north. If you stand close to this fault line, facing across the fault, the block on the opposite side moves toward your left, so this is a left-lateral (or sinistral) fault. Pull-apart troughs (Dead Sea Rift and Galilee-Lebanon rift) complicate the fault zone in its mid-section.

Constituting the eastern boundary of the Arabian plate is another transform fault, called the Owen fault zone, also with right-lateral slip. (See world map, Figure 7.11.) At the south end, it starts from a transform fault on the Carlsbad Ridge, which is a spreading plate boundary in the Arabian Gulf, and trends northeast to terminate at the Zagros suture along the Makran coastline. As to seismicity, these two transform boundaries are only weakly active. A few epicenters of small earthquakes lie on or close to these boundaries.

Our second example features intense seismic activity on a major intracontinental transcurrent fault found in Asia Minor farther to the northwest of the Arabian plate. The locality is northern Anatolia, Turkey (Figure 6.31). Called the North Anatolian fault, it lies some 50 to 100 km south of the shore of the Black Sea and trends almost due east-west for a distance of 800 km with right-lateral slip. In December 1939 a quake of $M_S = 8$ epicentered near Erzincan, at the eastern end of the fault, brought death to upwards of 20,000 persons and destruction of some 30,000 dwellings. The displacement extended for a distance of 340 km along the fault. There followed within the next five years four quakes $M_S = 7.3$ to 7.6, occurring in succession on epicenters located farther to the west on the same fault. In 1953 a similar large quake occurred on the same fault some 200 km farther to the west (Richter, 1958, p. 612-616; Allen, 1975, p. 1042). Then, in 1992 a strong quake, $M_S = 6.8$, epicentered near the eastern end, devastated Erzincan. The North Anatolian fault serves to bound the Anatolian microplate (or Anatolian Block) within the Eurasian plate. Extensions of this fault can be traced westward across the northern floor of the Aegean Sea, where it is interpreted as an oceanic spreading boundary.

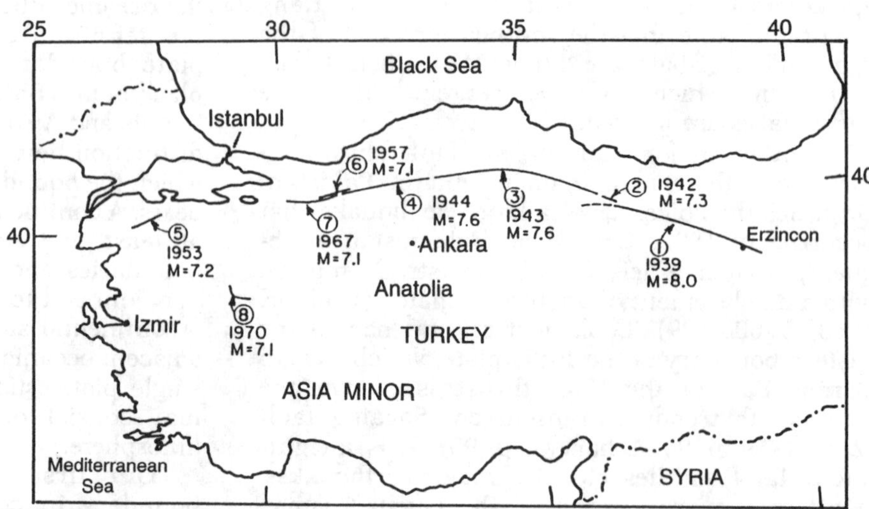

Figure 6.31 Sketch map of the North Anatolian fault and earthquake epicenters. (Adapted from Clarence Allen, 1975, *Bull., Geol. Soc. Amer.*, v. 86, p. 1042, Figure 2. Reproduced by permission of the author and The Geological Society of America, Boulder, Colorado, USA © 1975.)

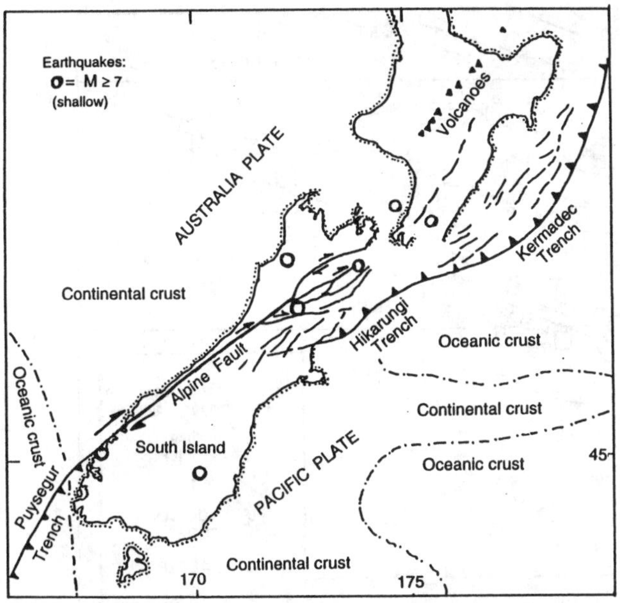

Figure 6.32 Sketch map of New Zealand showing the Alpine fault and it relationship to connecting trench systems. (Based on data of Camp and Nelson, 1987, and other sources.)

For that reason the fault has been called the Anatolian Transform (Dewey and Sengor, 1979, p. 85-88).

Our third example, the Alpine fault of the South Island of New Zealand, is a dextral transcurrent fault (Figure 6.32). It originates offshore as a continuation of the Puysegur subduction plate boundary, along which the Australia plate is diving beneath the Pacific plate. However, continental crust surrounds the islands of New Zealand, so that, where the Alpine fault intersects the western coast of the South Island, it is a true continental transform boundary. The fault trends northeast for some 400 km, then seems to subdivide into a splay of smaller strike-slip faults. To the east, offshore of the North Island, there lies the Hikarungi trench, a subduction boundary that extends northeastward to become the Kermadic trench. On that plate boundary, the Pacific oceanic lithosphere dives northwestward under the North Island. Thus the Alpine fault has served as a transitional link across continental crust between two opposed subduction zones. The main section of Alpine fault is only weakly seismic, whereas the subduction boundary zones to both south and north are highly seismic, with a substantial number of large shallow quakes, $M_S \leq 7$.

It is important to know that the Alpine fault combines strike-slip motion with a reverse-fault component of motion. Thus the fault is also engaging in a convergence of the two plates that is responsible for the rise of the Southern Alps (Cooper and Norris, 1994). So here we also have an active continent-continent collision! This combination of two motions is called *transpression*, a phenomenon described in detail in Chapter 9.

A fourth example of a transform fault in continental crust comes from Guatemala in Central America, where a transform boundary cuts across that nation from east to west, defining the northern boundary of the Caribbean plate. Figure 6.33 shows the regional relationships. The northern boundary of the Caribbean Plate is a great east-west transform fault, mostly in oceanic crust. It stems from the Lesser Antilles volcanic arc, which is an active subduction boundary, then runs west along the floor of the Puerto Rico trench, offsets to the south near the Cayman rise, and becomes the Swan FZ (a misnomer, since it is an active transform fault!). The fault zone penetrates the American continental margin at the head of the Gulf of Honduras (Figure 6.34). A short distance inland, the plate boundary is represented by three parallel strike-slip faults, all left-lateral. The southernmost of these is the Motagua fault, along which occurred the 1976 Guatemalan earthquake, $M_S = 7.5$. It claimed nearly 23,000 lives and injured more than 76,000 persons. Maximum strike slippage was 3.25 m at a point north of nearby Guatemala City, where the damage level was rated at IX on the Modified Mercalli scale. Several large earthquakes had occurred on this fault zone inhistoric time. One of those, that of

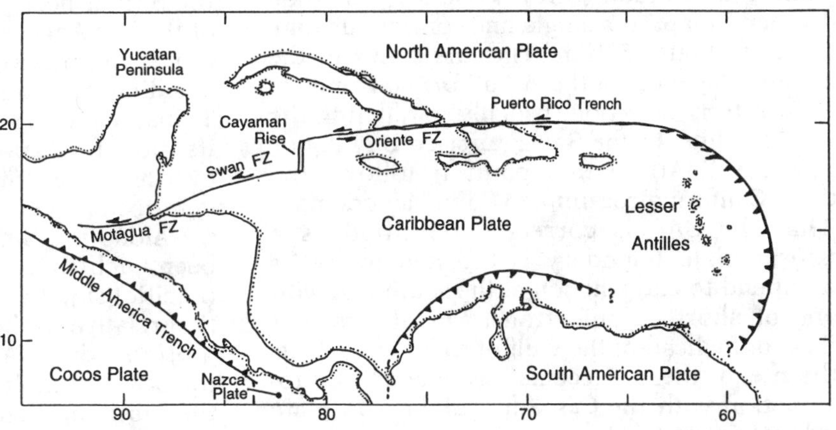

Figure 6.33 Tectonic sketch map of the Caribbean plate. (Adapted from data of the U.S. Geological Survey, Espanosa, 1976, and other sources.)

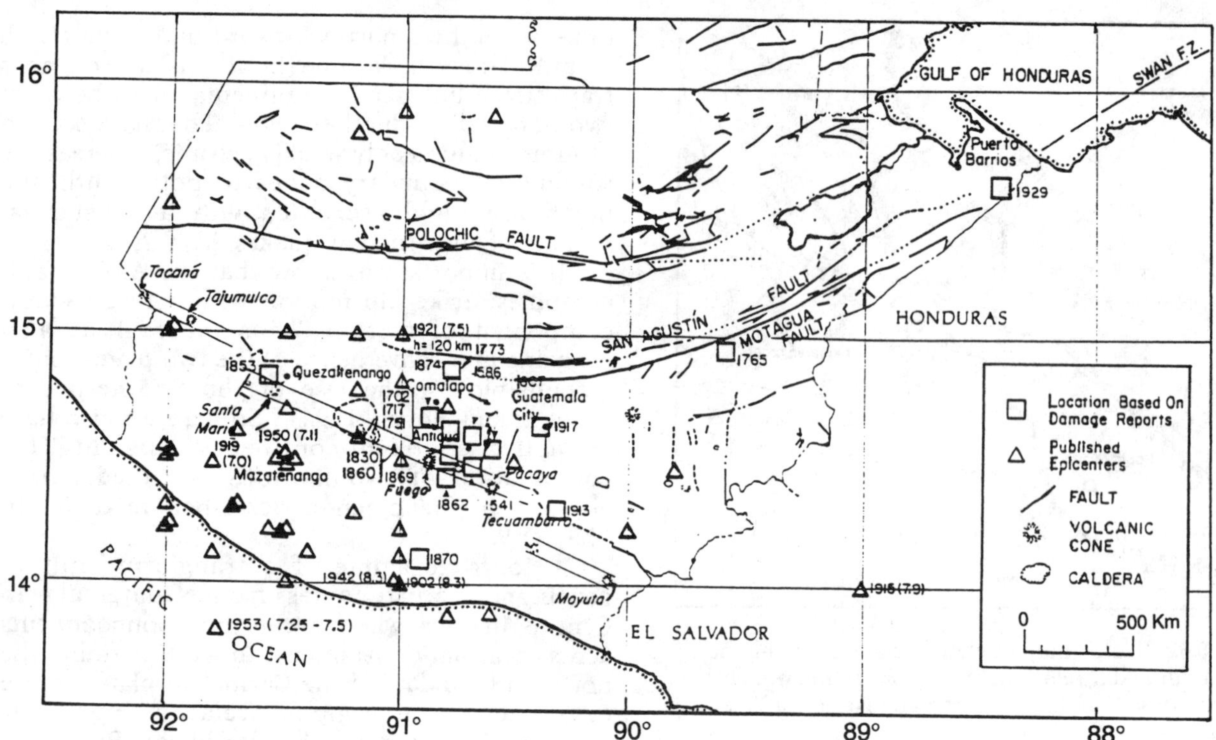

Figure 6.34 Seismicity map of Guatemala showing the transform fault zone. (From the U.S. Geological Survey, Espanosa, Prof. Paper 1002, 1976.)

1921, was also $M_S = 7.5$ (Espinosa, 1976). The plate boundary zone represented by the three parallel transform faults terminates just short of the line of active volcanoes paralleling the Pacific continental margin, where the subduction boundary of the Cocos Plate (the Middle America trench) is extremely active. Thus we have a triple junction of North American, Cocos, and Caribbean plates. (This junction is given the code number 11 on the world map, Figure 7.3.)

6.18 The San Andreas Fault System

The San Andreas fault of California, an active right-lateral transcurrent (strike-slip) fault, is interpreted by geologists as forming a major plate boundary—that between the Pacific plate and the North American plate (see Figures 1.11 and 7.3). The San Andreas fault (SAF) is usually drawn on most general maps as a single line continuous for a distance of about 950 km. The line starts in the Salton Sea Basin of southern California, trends in a northwesterly direction, roughly paralleling the Pacific coastline, to the San Francisco Bay region (Figure 6.35). Above this point it follows the northern California coastline to Cape Mendocino.

That the SAF is correctly identified as a transform plate boundary is attested to by its apparent end-to-end junction at the south end with a zone of short oceanic transform offsets that reaches to the head of the Gulf of California. At its northern end, the SAF seems to make an end-to-end junction with the Cascadia subduction plate boundary (Figure 6.35).

On either side of the SAF are several other major active faults, as our map shows. Some of these strike roughly parallel with the SAF, and in some cases branch from it. This complex aggregation is recognized as the San Andreas fault system. By their individual strike displacements, members of the system contribute to meeting 60 to 70 percent of the overall steady relative motion between the North American plate and the Pacific plate (Hill et al., 1990, p. 137). This "sharing role" is nicely displayed in the southernmost section of the SAF system, where the Banning and Elsinor faults run almost parallel with the SAF.

In strange tectonic contrast, in a belt between Santa Barbara and Los Angeles, several major faults trend at various obtuse angles to the principal SAF trend. A prominent example is the Garlock fault, crossing the Mojave Desert to meet the SAF at nearly right angles. Starting just north of the Los Angeles Basin is a chain of long, narrow block mountains, paralleled by major faults trending east–west (Figure 6.35). Known as the Transverse Ranges, many of the active faults along its mountain and valley segments are high-angle overthrusts. Seismicity of the Transverse Ranges is described in a later section of this chapter.

Along the SAF, plate motion has consistently been such that the crustal mass on the western (Pacific) side has moved in a northwesterly direction relative to the eastern mass. With this type of motion, the SAF is a right-lateral (dextral) transcurrent fault. The same holds true for most of the subsidiary faults branching from or parallel to the SAF. Movement along the SAF has been going

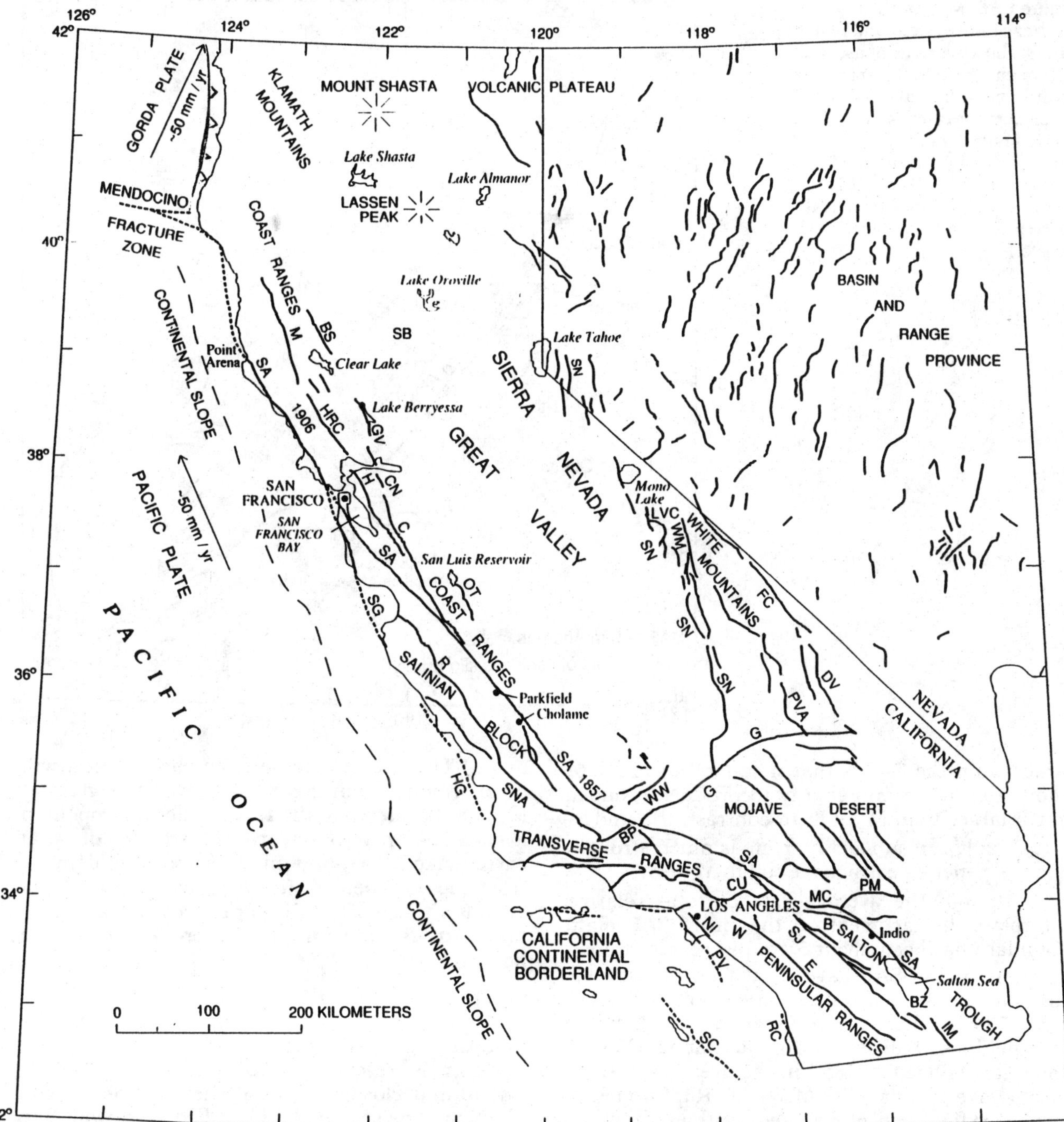

Figure 6.35 Map of the San Andreas Fault system and associated major faults of California. Faults are shown by solid lines; dotted where concealed. (From R.E. Wallace, 1990, U.S. Geological Survey Professional Paper 1515, p. 118.)

on for many millions of years. Matching of rock masses in terms of their lithology and age as displaced along the two sides of the fault shows a total lateral movement of about 500 km over the past 150 million years. In Chapter 7, that history is covered in some detail.

Among seismologists, the SAF is said to be a "weak fault," and that this property is true of other faults like it. In other terms, the SAF is said to have "low shear strength" (Lockner and Byerlee, 1993, p. 250). One possible cause for this low strength is the presence in the surrounding rock of excessive fluid pressure in the saturated zone below the water table. It has also been proposed that a layer of soft rock flour or powder (fault gouge), formed along the vertical fault surfaces, causes the weakness. As a third possibility, it is suggested that the maximum shear stress becomes turned to lie parallel with the fault plane, so that the coefficient of friction is minimized. One consequence of low

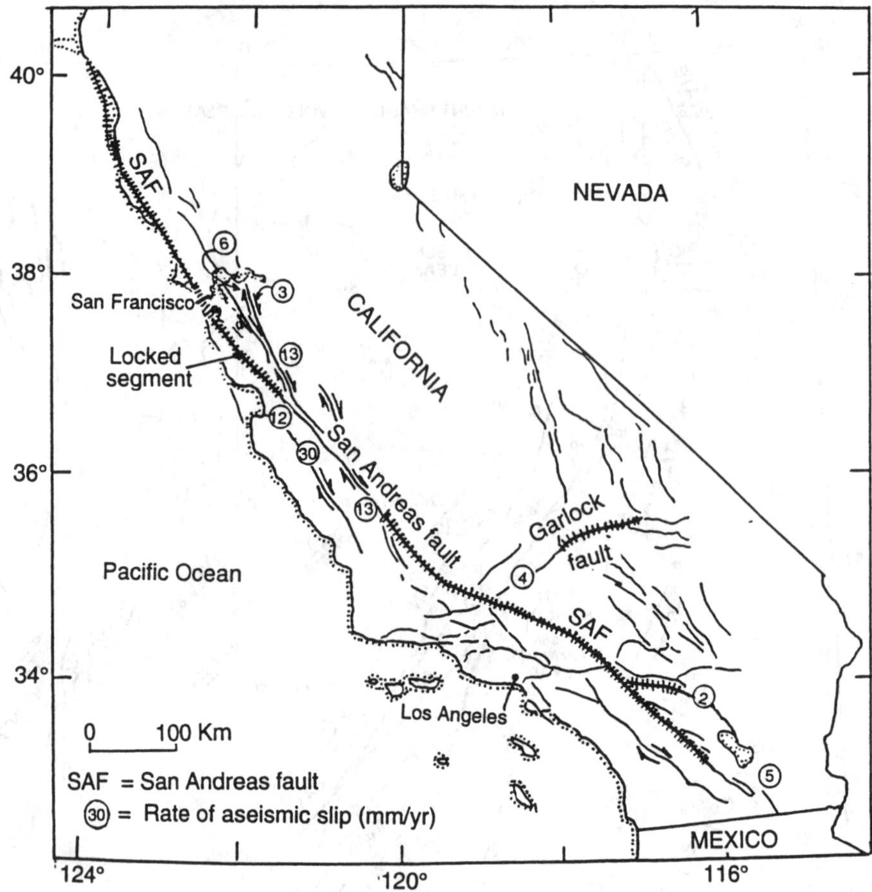

Figure 6.36 Map of the San Andreas fault system and related faults, showing rates of aseismic slip in cm/yr (bold numbers), and relative right-lateral displacement rates in cm/yr (boxed numbers next to double-pointed arrows) for active sections of fault. (From R.E. Wallace, 1990, U.S. Geological Survey Professional Paper 1515, p. 196.)

strength on the SAF is that it cannot accumulate enough elastic strain energy to produce a quake much larger than M_W = 8. In contrast, the underthrust fault of a subducting plate is much stronger and can generate earthquakes up to M_W = 9.

Although the average rate of total relative interplate displacement on the entire SAF plate boundary has been about 5 cm per year, two long sections of the SAF have shown no measurable movement for a nearly a century or longer (Figure 6.36). The southern one of these sections, between Parkfield and San Bernardino and about 350 km long, last slipped in 1857 in the great Fort Tejon earthquake, estimated as M_W = 7.8. Rupture began near Parkfield and propagated southward, with a 9-m offset in the Carrizo Plain stretch, and diminishing southward to 3 to 4 m at its end near Tejon Pass. The northern locked section runs from near Hollister to Cape Mendocino. There has been no significant fault motion in this section since the great San Francisco earthquake of 1906, estimated as M_W = 8.2. These two seismically inactive sections are referred to as being *locked*; each has a great potential for generating a major earthquake within several decades from now. Applying the average interplate motion of 5 m per century, the anticipated single horizontal displacement in the locked sections comes to roughly 7 m for the southern section and 5 m for the northern. (This calculation does not, of course, take into account other contributions to the total plate displacement.) The energy release from each section will be enormous when it comes—perhaps as great as M_W = 8. Residents of the Los Angeles metropolitan area can anticipate strong effects of that earthquake at a point in time that could range from the very near future to a few decades from now. For those of the San Francisco Bay area, the prognosis is for rupture over one century from now.

In contrast to the locked sections, there are other sections of the SAF along which a very slow, almost continuous movement is occurring. This motion is referred to as *fault creep* and is monitored closely. In an earlier section on subduction-zone seismicity, we called it aseismic slip. Where creep is steadily occurring, there may also be generated many earthquakes of very small magnitudes. Figure 6.36 shows the zones of creep and seismic activity along the San Andreas Fault and related branch faults.

Figure 6.37 is a seismic map of the SAF system and other seismic areas beyond both northern and southern ends of the SAF. Seismicity important in contributing to relative motion between the two plates extends far inland to the eastern flank of the Sierra Nevada and the western Basin and Range Province in Nevada. Earthquake epicenters in this inland region are shown in Figure 6.37. Fault motions in this group include both strike-slip and normal displacements, the latter representing crustal extension. Here, four quakes of $M_W \geq 7$,

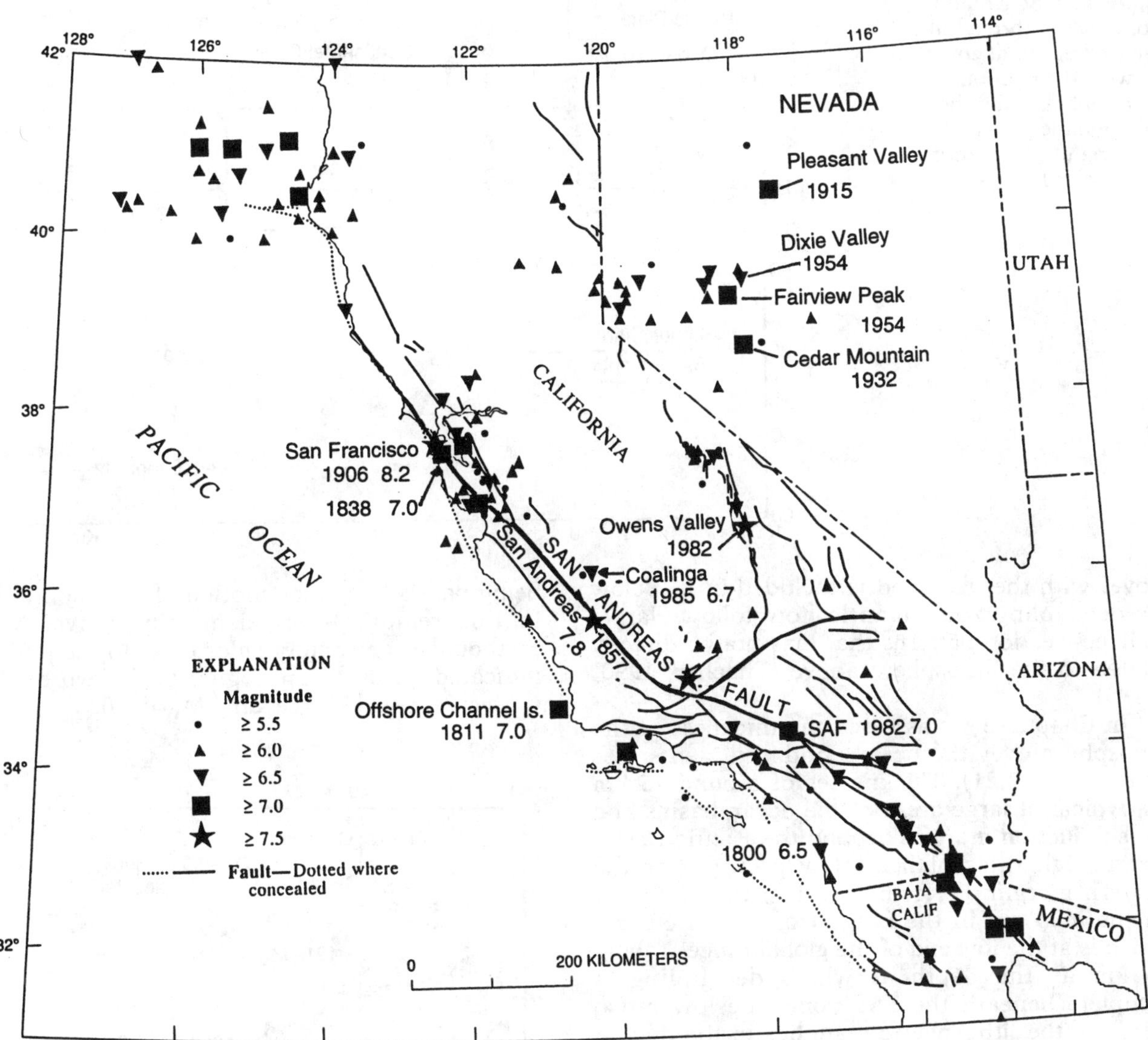

Figure 6.37 Map of seismicity of California and adjacent areas. Epicenters shown are for the period 1769-1989. (From R.E. Wallace, 1990, U.S. Geological Survey Professional Paper 1515, p. 154.)

lined up south to north in order of occurrence, are labeled on the map. Southernmost of the group is the Owens Valley quake of 1872, now estimated as M_W = 7.6. It was a right-lateral slip with displacement of 6 m. The northernmost two quakes of the group were generated along normal faults, as typical of faults in the Basin and Range Province to the east.

We turn next to the mechanics of faulting as applied to the SAF system. The strike-slip faults are essentially vertical, or presented that way in diagrams and cross sections. Plots of large numbers of very small earthquakes on cross sections made at right angles to the faults show the foci to form narrow vertical bands extending down to depths of at least 10 km but rarely more than 20 km. Plots of this kind are typical of the aseismic (creep) sections of the SAF and its branches. For locked sections of the SAF, foci are rare or scattered (Hill et al., 1990, p. 129-134).

The fault plane of the SAF lies within the upper brittle layer of the continental crust. Below it is the zone of ductile yielding in which elastic strain cannot (in principle) accumulate. Figure 6.38 is a schematic diagram to illustrate these relationships. The brittle/ductile transition has been placed at a depth of about 20 km below the SAF in central California (Fuis and Mooney, 1990, p. 214-215). Where, then, is the base of the lithosphere? Throughout this book our cartoon-like cross sections of plates and plate boundaries show the base of the lithosphere as a thin solid line—commonly drawn parallel with the upper surface of the plate. To be realistic, the base of the lithosphere lies somewhere in a transition zone of downward-diminishing strength within the asthenosphere (see Chapter 3 and Figure 3.18). At some level in this transition zone, called a *decoupling zone*, mantle rock ceases to move along with the plate. Above that zone, a layer of mantle

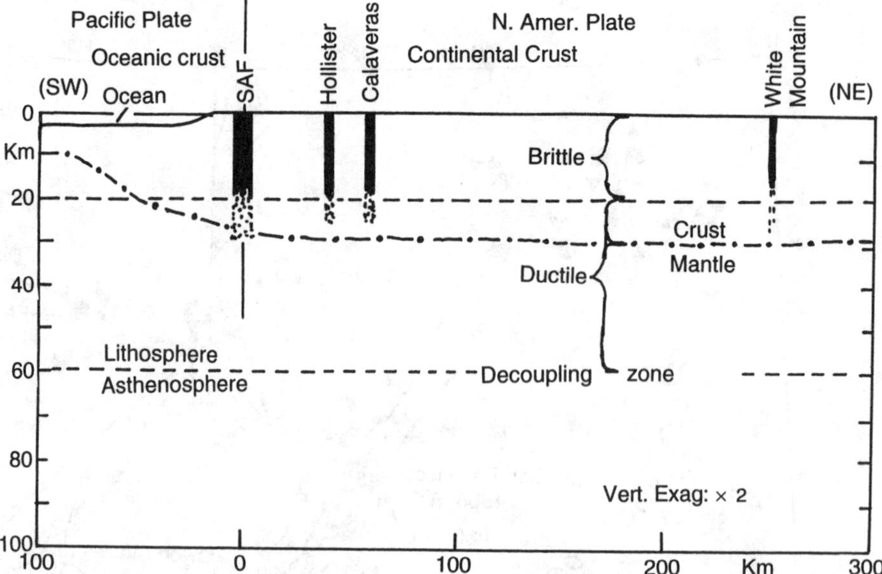

Figure 6.38 Schematic cross-section through the San Andreas fault zone showing the relationships between faults and the crust-mantle zones. (Copyright © by Arthur N. Strahler.)

moves with the plate and is included in it. Below the decoupling zone, mantle flow follows large-scale convection patterns that may not be directly related to the lithosphere above (Thacher, 1990, p. 199).

In Chapter 3 we assessed the thickness of the lithosphere over the oceans and continents (see map, Figure 3.21). Thicknesses of around 75 km are typical of large areas of the ocean basins and the subduction margins around the Pacific Basin, where high rates of heat flow prevail. For the western margin of North America, values shown on the map are in the range from 45 to 60 km, which is at the low end of the global range. Taking 60 km as the depth at which decoupling is complete beneath the SAF zone, the lower two thirds of the lithospheric plate lies in the ductile zone (Figure 6.38). Here, a broad and deep layer of slow mantle flowage, perhaps as wide as 500 km, moves as a part of the plate. The occurrence of plate boundary transform faults 'inserted' (so to speak) into what would otherwise be a great continuous subduction plate boundary along the entire western edge of North America, can be looked at as a special tectonic phenomenon.

Another example worthy of brief attention is the Queen Charlotte fault (QCF) off the British Columbia/Alaska coast. It extends just offshore of the British Columbia-Alaska shoreline for a distance of nearly 1000 km (Figure 6.39). This is a coastline of submergence, deeply embayed with fiords and islands. The fault line, though drawn over ocean water, lies within the limit of the continental crust. At its southern end, the QCF seems to be joined to the northern end of the trench line of the Cascadia subduction zone (Riddihough and Hyndman, 1989, p. 404-405). At its northern end, the QCF penetrates the mainland and merges with faults that delimit the Yakutat block, an actively accreting terrane of Alaska (Bruns, 1983, p. 718). The QCF is a dextral transcurrent fault and its strike is very close to being parallel with the motion of the Pacific plate in this region. It is seismically active. Major earthquakes epicenters on or close to the fault are indicated on our map, Figure 6.39. Two of these were great shocks, exceeding $M_W = 8.0$.

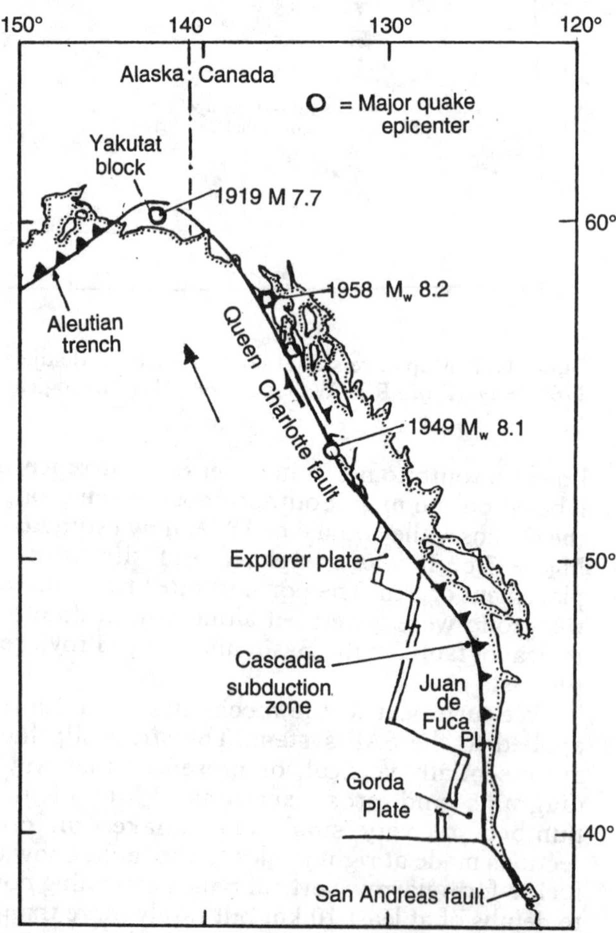

Figure 6.39 Sketch map of the North American Pacific coast, showing the Queen Charlotte fault and related tectonic features. (Copyright © by Arthur N. Strahler.)

6.19 Seismicity of Intracontinental Compressional Orogenic Systems

Horizontal crustal compression that consists of folding and reverse thrust faulting—often called "telescoping"—can occur entirely within continental lithosphere. Strong seismicity is associated with this form of orogeny. These occurrences fall into our Class IV, Subclass B, Compressional orogenic systems (Table 6.1). This category is not to be confused with tectonic classes II and III, which are plate boundary related and derive their energy from plate subduction or plate collisions. We concentrate on a single example of this subclass.

Mentioned earlier in this chapter, the Transverse Ranges of south central California trend east-west, more-or-less diagonal to the trend of the San Andreas fault (Figure 6.35). Figure 6.40 shows more details of the fault patterns and gives locations of the larger earthquakes of historical record. The entire tectonic pattern in this region is extremely complex geologically. Several of the major transverse faults strike east-west, whereas other faults in this area have trends intermediate between E-W and the NW-SE trend of the San Andreas system. Some of the faults lie along the bases of the mountain ranges. Others lie within the range itself, and some are located in sedimentary basins well away from a mountain base and underlain by thick alluvium. The typical thrusts are of the high-angle type, with steep dips where they emerge at the surface. With increasing depth, the thrust fault plane dip may diminish (i.e., is listric), and possibly merge with a general detachment fault, or décollement, at a depth of several kilometers. Some of thrust fault planes dip to the north, others to the south. Most of these thrusts do not emerge at the ground surface and are known as *blind faults*. Anticlines have formed along the same strike as local thrust faults, and may contain the high-angle reverse faults. Figure 6.41 is a detailed map of faults in the northwestern part of the Los Angeles basin. Notice that none of these faults strike due E-W. Two anticlines are shown. One fault (Benedict Canyon) is labeled as transcurrent.

The total or generalized picture of the transverse belt is one of a shortening, or telescoping, of the crust along the north-south direction. (The term "convergence" is also applied to this form of tectonics, although that term usually connotes a subduction plate boundary.) The telescoping action began in late Pliocene time (2-3 Ma), and has thus far resulted in crustal shortening of an estimated 53 km, with an average

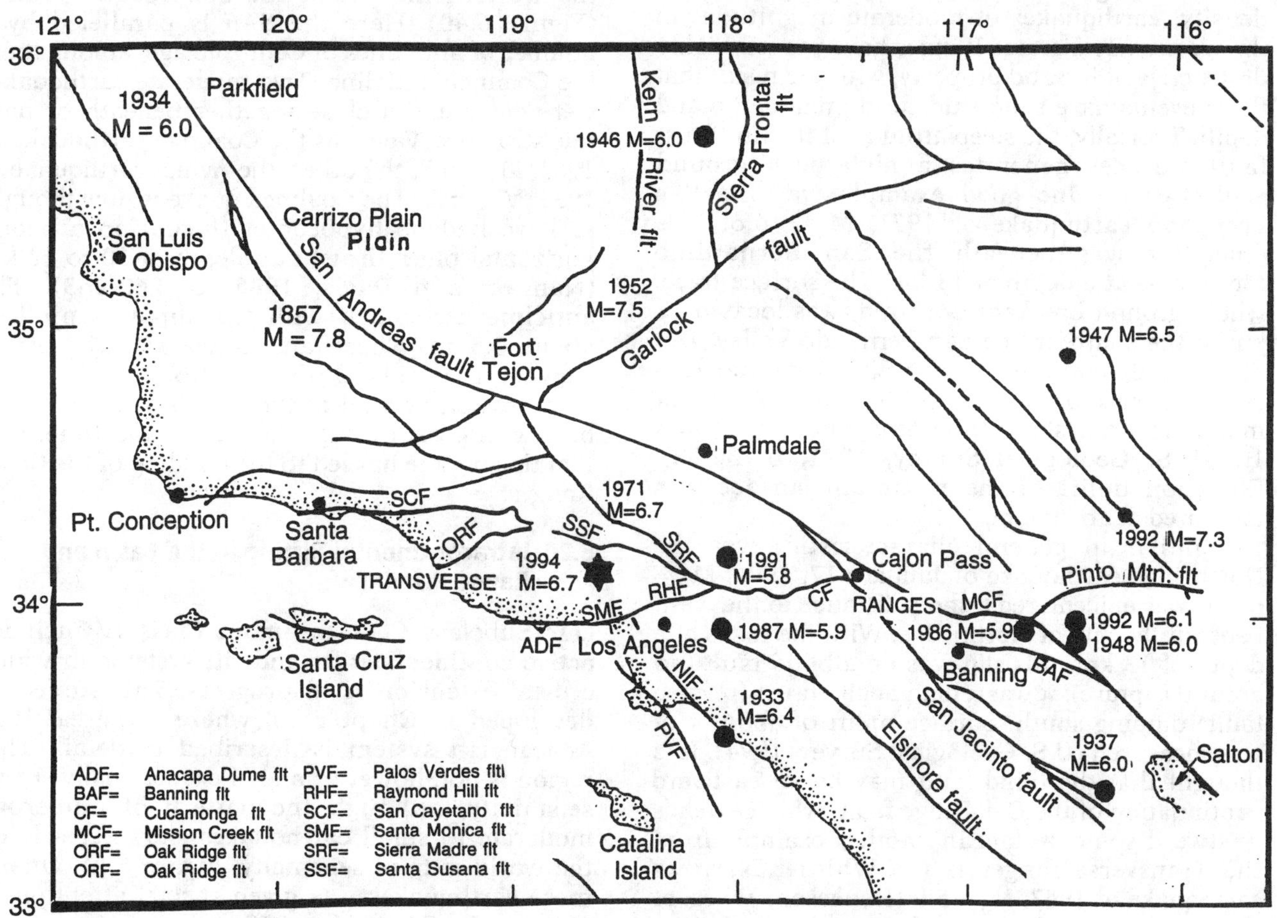

Figure 6.40 Map of major faults and earthquakes of the Transverse Ranges of south-central California. (Adapted from the U.S. Geological Survey and the Southern California Earthquake Center, 1994, *Science*, v. 266, p. 391.)

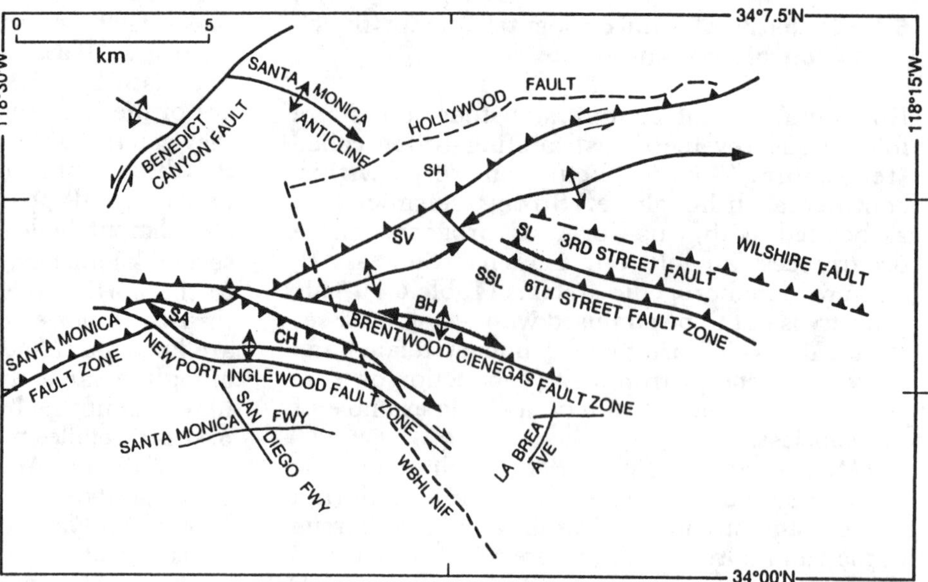

Figure 6.41 Map of subsurface faults and anticlines of the northwest Los Angeles basin. (Data from H.R. Lang and R.S. Dresser, 1975, *Calif. Division of Oil & Gas Tech. Papers*, TP01, p. 15-2 as used in *Geology*, v. 22. p. 959. Used by permission.)

rate on the order of 2 cm/yr (Namson and Davis, 1988, p. 675). Resulting increase in crustal thickness is responsible for the elevation of the ranges.

Occurring in a region of high population density, earthquakes of moderate magnitudes in the western Transverse Ranges have proved highly destructive of life and property, with the result that these events have been studied in great detail and depth. Typically, the steep attitude of the up-thrust fault surfaces generates a high peak ground acceleration. One good example was the San Fernando earthquake of 1971, M_s = 6.6. The epicenter was beneath the San Bernardino Mountains at a depth of 13 km. The surface trace, where ground breakage occurred, was located 12 km to the south, in the San Fernando Valley. Dip of the fault plane was 52° NE. Substantial left-lateral strike slip also occurred; the ratio of vertical motion to strike-slip motion being between 1.5 and 1.0 (U.S. Geological Survey, 1971, p. 30-32). Elevation uplift of the mountain surface was measured at about 2 m.

Similar in general characteristics was the Northridge earthquake of January 17, 1994, M_S = 6.7; it was epicentered a short distance to the west, beneath the city of Northridge. With the focus at a depth of 13 km, this slip was on a blind fault (no ground rupture); it was a high-angle thrust (reverse fault) dipping south. Surface uplift of about 1 m was measured (U.S. Geological Survey, 1994). It is thought that the blind fault may be an eastward continuation of the Oak Ridge fault, which extends westward some 40 km. In another example from the Transverse ranges is the Whittier Narrows earthquake of 1987, M_S = 5.9 (Hauksson, Jones, et al., 1988). Rupture occurred on a north-dipping thrust fault lying beneath a growing anticline of the same strike. The anticline is deeply buried and is one of a class called an *antiform*.

Quite different in terms of compass orientation, but nevertheless to be included in the region of active telescoping of California crust, is an area on the northeast side of the SAF and on the western margin of the San Joaquin Valley (Figure 6.40). Here the SAF is paralleled by a number of anticlines of Cenozoic age, among them the Coalinga anticline. Two moderate earthquakes were epicentered close together beneath or near this structure. One was the Coalinga earthquake of 1983, M_S = 6.7, the other, the Avinal earthquake of 1985, M_S = 5.5. The Coalinga quake is now thought to have had its hypocenter (focus) on a nearly horizontal blind thrust at a depth of 10 to 12 km (Namson and Davis, 1988, p. 262-263). The anticline associated with the slip was uplifted about 0.5 m. These and other seismic events suggest that, along this section of the SAF, compression normal to the SAF is active and has been going on through late Cenozoic time, and that this regime has led to the building of the Coast Ranges.

6.20 Intracontinental Rifting in the Basin and Range Province

Our Subclass C of the main Class IV includes active continental rifts and rift systems in which crustal extension is in progress. This subject is developed in Chapter 10, where the great East African rift system is described in detail. That region is not, however, one of exceptionally strong seismicity, although the pattern of numerous moderate to small earthquakes shows clearly on the world map of seismicity, Figure 6.1A. One of these earthquakes was given special attention in Charles F. Richter's 1958 volume, *Elementary Seismology* (p. 621-623, 716-717). Located just north of the equator, the Subikia earthquake produced a fresh scarp some 25 km long at the base of the steep escarpment of a large uplifted fault block.

We shall concentrate here on the seismicity of the Basin and Range Province (BRP). (See maps, Figures 10.35 and 10.36). It represents a broad area of Neogene crustal stretching, expressed in the crust by normal faulting. The faults are comparatively shallow, with upwardly-concave fault planes that rapidly approach horizontality with depth and merge with broad detachment surfaces. Nested sets of such parallel faults produce tilted fault blocks, now expressed as roughly parallel mountain ranges separated by open alluvial valleys.

In describing the San Andreas fault system, seismicity of the western border zone of the Basin and Range Province (BRP) was briefly mentioned. In west-central Nevada and eastern central California, we recognized a string of large-earthquake epicenters arranged in a north-south line (see Figure 6.37). Of these epicenters, the two at the northern end, both just over $M_S = 7$, belong in the BRP and were generated within the past few decades on normal faults. Traveling east, we find that much of the central BRP in Nevada and Utah shows only weak seismic activity. Along the eastern margin of the province in Idaho and Utah are more than 15 normal faults that have shown activity within the Cenozoic Era (Figure 6.42). At least a half-dozen of these have ruptured in historic time (Simpson and Anders, 1992, p. 120). Along many of these normal faults there is included a strike-slip component. Scarps of prehistoric slips on these faults are in many cases clearly evidenced by fault scarps and other geomorphic features. Taken altogether, these faults demonstrate the extensional tectonics that characterizes the entire BRP.

Worthy of special note are two examples of recent major earthquakes in this northeastern part of the BRP. One is the Borah Peak earthquake of 1983, $M_S = 7.3$, occurring on the Lost River fault in central Idaho, just north of the Snake River plain (Figure 6.42). The 34-km-long rupture on this normal fault averaged a left-lateral displacement of 17 cm for each 100 cm of dip slip (Crone and Machette, 1984). The net extensional movement is in conformity with the direction of motion of the North American plate, which is about S60°W.

The second example shows noteworthy differences from the typical BRP faults. It is the Hebgen Lake, Montana, earthquake of 1959, $M_S = 7.3$, well known for having set off the great Madison landslide that dammed the Madison River. It occurred on the Hegben Lake fault, which trends roughly northwest-southeast, and combines normal dip-slip with a right-lateral slip. Moreover, is lies close to the north-south Madison fault and the east-west Centennial fault. These three faults are also adjacent to the Yellowstone volcanic area, interpreted as the remains of a hotspot produced over a mantle plume that later migrated west and north into the Columbia Plateau. To explain this

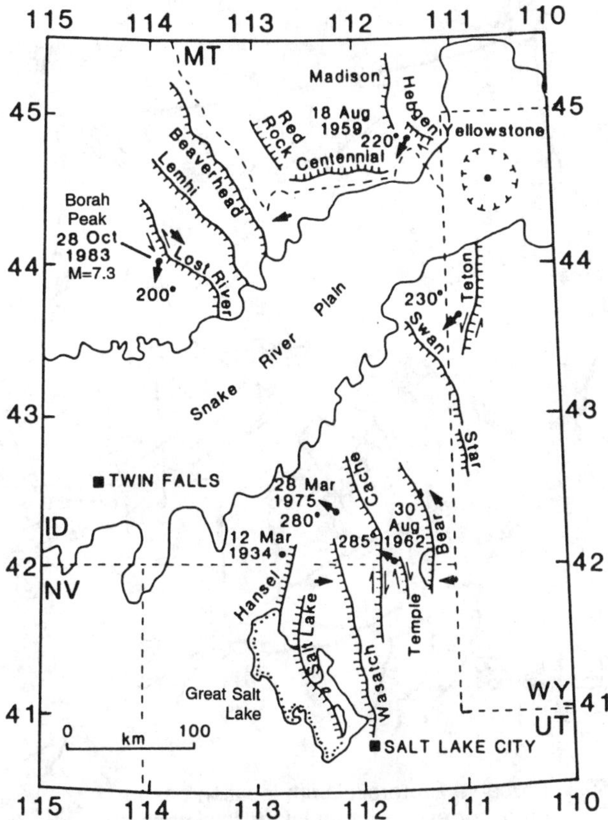

Figure 6.42 Sketch map of normal faults of the northeastern part of the Basin and Range province. Arrows show slip vector azimuths. (From Rob Westaway, 1989, *Geology*, v. 17, p. 780, Figure 1a. Reproduced by permission of the publisher, The Geological Society of America. Boulder, Colorado, USA. Copyright © 1989.)

curious arrangement of fault orientations it has been proposed that their individual fault blocks have been rotated clockwise on vertical axes, and that this rotation resulted from magma intrusions in the Yellowstone hotspot (Westaway, 1989).

6.21 Seismicity within the North American Craton

Earthquakes, mostly small but including a few large ones, originate in the stable continental crust at locations far from active plate boundaries and apparently free of large-scale compressional or extensional tectonic activity. These we have relegated to Subclass D of Class IV: Reactivated cratonal rifts and Paleozoic/Mesozoic orogens (Table 6.1). Of course, earthquakes signify fault slippage in the brittle crust (ruling out local faulting connected with localized magma movements) and are responses to either compressional or tensional forces. Left open for speculation is the possibility that faults responsible for this intracontinental seismicity are deep down in the crust, where ancient fault surfaces are being reactivated in response to regional compression or extension.

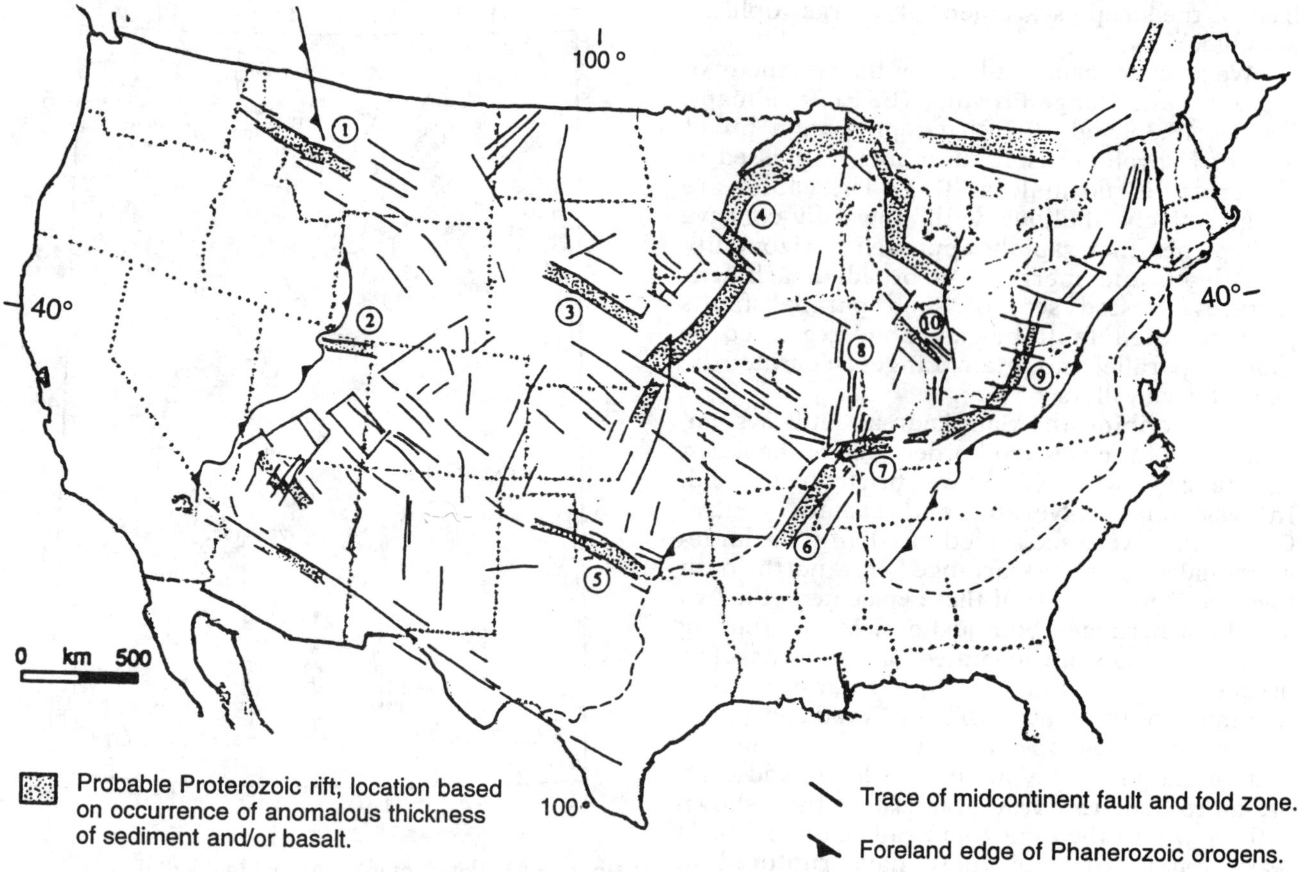

100°

40°

40°

0 km 500

100°

Probable Proterozoic rift; location based on occurrence of anomalous thickness of sediment and/or basalt.

Trace of midcontinent fault and fold zone.

Foreland edge of Phanerozoic orogens.

1— Helena embayment, 2—Uinta trough, 3—Nebraska sag, 4—Midcontinent rift 5—Southern Oklahoma aulacogen, 6—Reelfoot rift, 7—Rough Creek graben, 8—La Salle deformation belt, 9—Rome trough, 10—Fort Wayne rift.

Figure 6.43 Regional map showing interepreted traces of fault and fold zones in the United States mid-continent region. (From Stephen Marshak and Timothy Paulsen, 1996, *Geology*, v. 2, p. 151, Figure 1. Reproduced by permission of the publisher, the Geological Society of America, Boulder, Colorado, USA. Copyrighht © 1996.)

As background information, turn to Chapter 13 and examine Figure 13.2, a geologic map of North America showing crustal provinces and giving their ages. Each province is separated from its neighbors by sutures. We turn first to the mid-continent platform region of North America where flat-lying Paleozoic strata blanket the Precambrian crust that had been reduced by erosion to a undulating surface—a peneplane of comparatively low relief. Low domes and shallow basins characterize the overlying strata. Typically, the basins show thickening of strata toward the basin centers, and this suggests deposition in subsiding areas of the Precambrian crust (Chapter 11). An example is the Michigan Basin.

Seismic studies and seismic refraction profiling are revealing ancient fault basins that lie beneath the cover of Paleozoic strata. Figure 6.43 is a map showing zones of revealed or suspected fault and fold structures. Ten such zones are listed. In these zones, fault slippages are thought to be recurring along the old structural lines of weakness. Otherwise, this continental crust has, in general, been tectonically stable through the entire Cenozoic Era. With this theme in mind, we look for exceptions in the form of large earthquakes. Table 6.2 lists a number of large earthquakes that have occurred in the last three centuries in stable continental crust in this and other continental locations. Our map, Figure 6.44, shows the locations of quakes in the North American mid-continent region.

In 1811 and 1812, three great earthquakes occurred in close succession in the Mississippi River alluvial floodplain not far from the town of New Madrid, Missouri. Because these events occurred several decades before modern seismographs were invented, estimates of the magnitudes of these shocks were sought in historical accounts of persons living in the area as well as observations of ground shaking that was felt in surrounding states. The tremors were said to have cracked plaster walls in Richmond, VA, and to have rung church bells in the District of

Table 6.2 Some Large Earthquakes Recorded in Stable Continental Crust

	M_S	Crustal class
Lisbon, Portugal, 1858	8.5?	II-B
New Madrid, MO, 1812	8.3?	II-A
New Madrid, MO, 1811	8.2?	II-A
New Madrid, MO, 1812	8.1?	II-A
Rann of Kutch, India, 1819	7.8?	II-A
Baffin Bay, 1933	7.7	II-B
Charleston, SC 1886	7.6	II-B
Grand Banks, Newfoundland,1929	7.4	II-B
Exmouth Plateau, Australia, 1906	7.2	II-B
Libya, 1935	7.1	II-B

Based on data of Richter, 1958; Johnston and Kanter, 1990; and others.

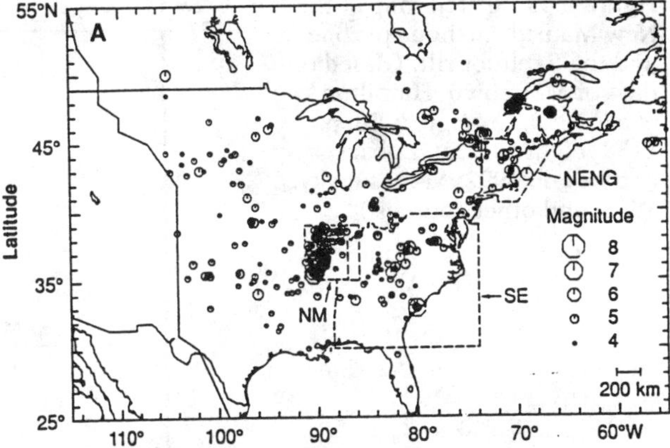

A. Epicenters of earthquakes with $M_b \geq 4$ from 1638 to 1972. NM—New Madrid cluster NENG—New England SE—Southeast U.S.

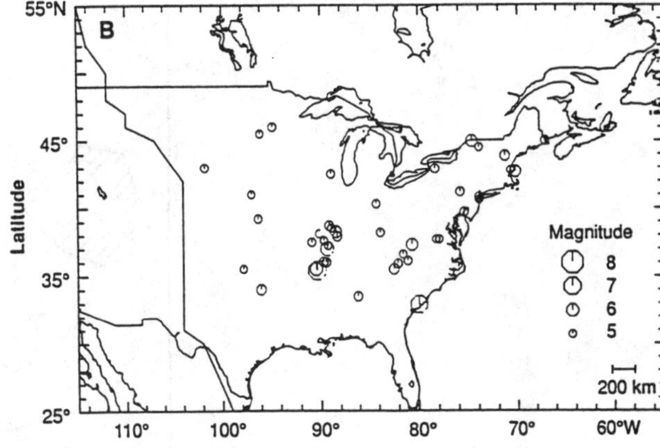

B. Epicenters with $M_b \geq 5$ from 1727 to 1980.

Figure 6.44 Seismic maps of the central and eastern U.S. and northeastern Canada. (From Nishenko and Bollinger, 1990, *Science*, v. 247, p. 1413, Figure 1. Reproduced by permission of the Amer. Assoc for the Advancement of Science.)

Columbia. Seismologists have since come to the realization that the waves of an intracontinental earthquake travel exceptionally far with relatively low energy loss, as compared with, say, those from the San Andreas fault.

Seismic reflection profiling and aeromagnetic data have revealed the presence at depth of a rift zone originally formed in late Precambrian time and/or early in the Paleozoic Era (Figure 6.45). Named the Reelfoot rift, its parallel boundaries, 60 km apart, trend about due NE-SW, diagonally crossing the Mississippi floodplain (Liu, Zoback, and Segall, 1992). The great New Madrid shocks originated along the northwestern rift margin. It is possible that the rift was a downfaulted trough (graben) in the Precambrian crust, and was filled with early Paleozoic sediments. Right-lateral strike-slip displacement parallels the rift boundaries, and there is also a dip-slip component in the movement. High rates of strain and strong compressive crustal stresses have been measured, with the principal stress axis oriented due east-west. It has also been found that heat flow from the rift zone is higher by about 20 percent than in adjacent areas. This finding suggests that the lithosphere beneath is warmer and softer than elsewhere, and thus capable of yielding to permit the fault slippage (Monastersky, 1993, p. 342). Some evidence has suggested that magma intrusion from a hot spot may have occurred here about 40 Ma. A low ridge that runs along the center of the rift zone is interpreted as an arching effect caused by magma diapirs rising at great depth below (McKeown et al., 1990).

Seismicity in the southern and central Appalachian mountain zone (Piedmont, Blue Ridge, Ridge-and-Valley) is represented by numerous epicenters of comparatively small earthquakes (Figure 6.46). As a rule, these smaller earthquakes do not break the surface, and it is difficult to relate each to a specific local structure. Roughly defined belts seem to parallel the strike of folds and thrusts. For example, some epicenters seem to follow the Brevard thrust fault along the eastern foot of the Blue Ridge, and another along the western margin of the Blue Ridge. Two other groups seem to form zones transverse to these same belts. The epicenters that lie near the northwestern limit of Appalachian folds (shown by broken line in Figure 6.46) have been identified by Russell Wheeler of the U.S. Geological Survey as normal faults of the Iapetan suture that was formed during the Caledonian collision that closed the Iapetan Ocean (1995, p. 105-107). (See Chapter

Figure 6.45 Sketch map of the New Madrid earthquake zone and the Reelfoot rift. (Based on data of McKeown, Hamilton, et al., 1990, *Geology*, v. 18, p. 1158. Figure 1; Liu, Zoback and Segall, 1992; Monastersky, 1993; and other sources.)

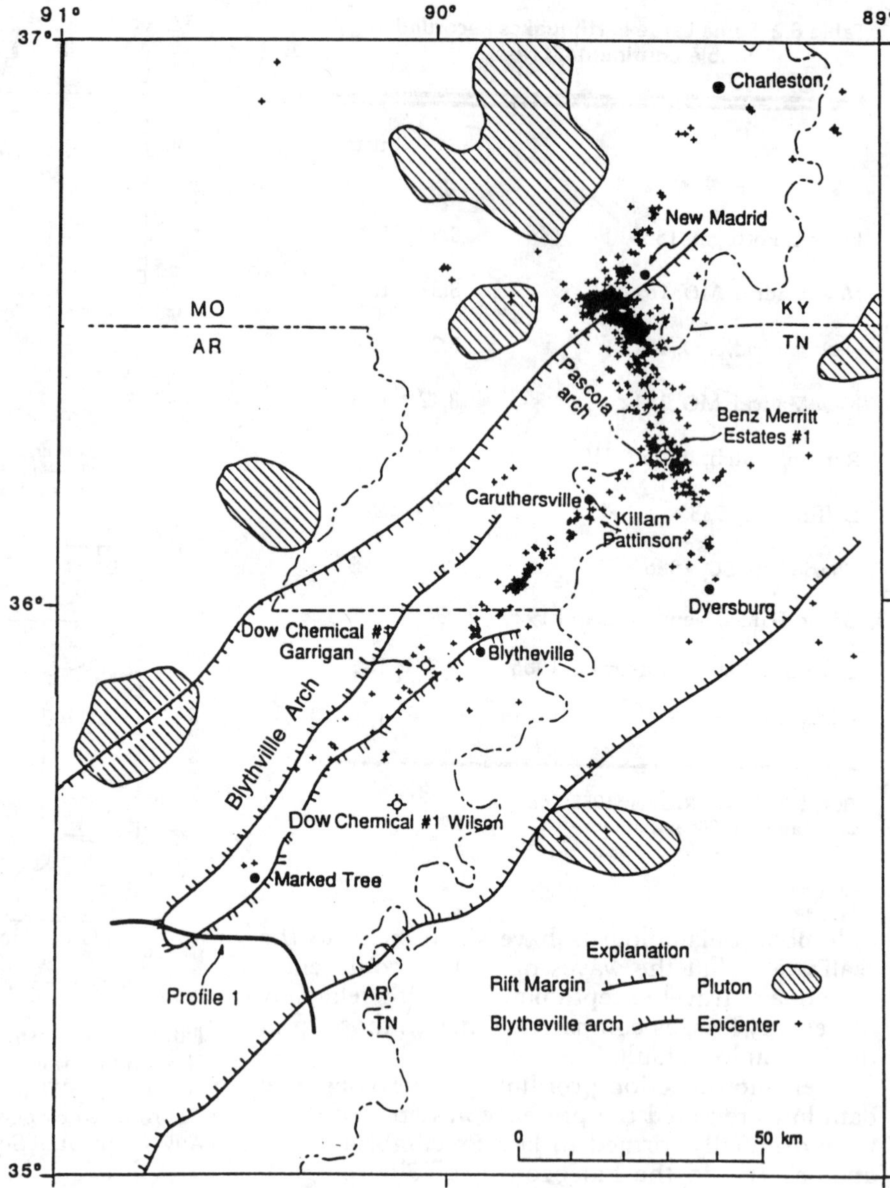

13 and Figures 13.30 and 13.31.) Wheeler states: "Earthquakes at five localities in the Iapetan margin have been attributed to compressional reactivation of Iapetian normal faults" (p. 105). Reactivation of Appalachian Paleozoic faults, including deep, almost horizontal basal detachment faults, is a general explanation awaiting substantiating evidence.

Seismicity also extends northeastward into southern New England and farther northeast into the Maritime Provinces. The Cape Ann, Massachusetts, earthquake of 1755, estimated M_S = 6, was one of the larger New England earthquakes of historic record.

6.22 Other Eastern North American Seismic Localities

Yet another distinctive seismic area in eastern North America consists of the Adirondack province and a large area of southern Canada lying to the north of it (Figure 6.44). The Precambrian shield crust here is inland of the limits of the Appalachian system. The epicenters seem rather randomly distributed, with a number of small groups. In all of this area relationships to structural lineaments remain to be established. A maverick in this group was the 1989 quake, M_S = 6, on the Ungava Peninsula at a latitude of about 60°N. Its surface break was found, extending NE-SW for 8 km.

An important earthquake group lies in the St. Lawrence River estuary in the Province of Quebec at a latitude of about 70°. Here, in 1925, occurred a widely felt quake of M_S = 7.0. Two other earthquakes had occurred close by; one in 1870, M_S = 6.5; the other in 1663, estimated M_S = 7. This strong group lies on the boundary between the Appalachian and Laurentian provinces, with Precambrian crust on the north and Paleozoic crust on the south.

The Charleston, South Carolina, earthquake of

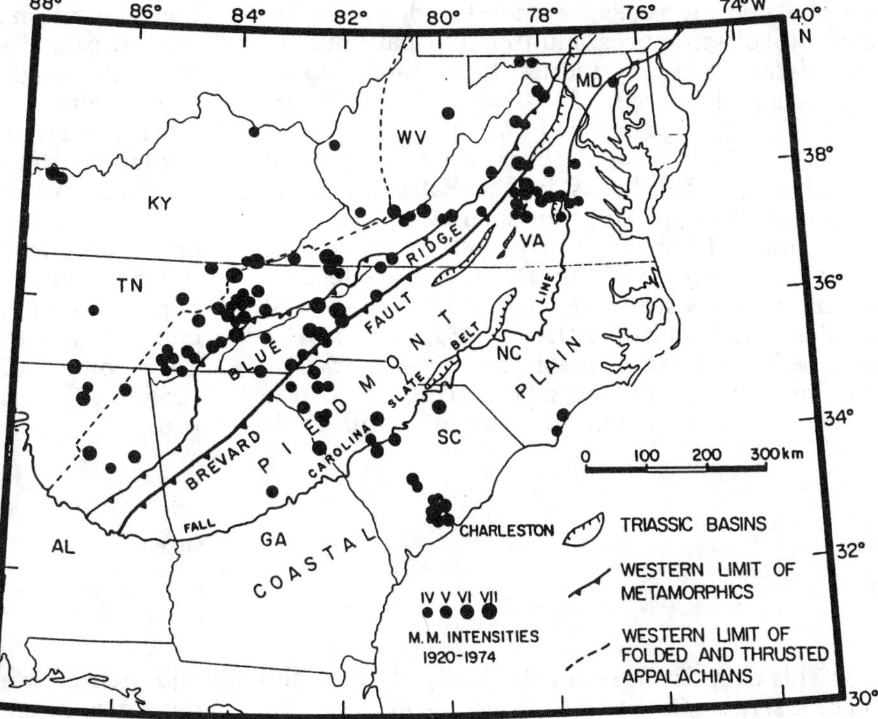

Figure 6.46 Seismic map of the Southern Appalachians and Coastal Plain. Epicenters are for the period 1920-1974; they are plotted only in states identified by initials. (From Seeber, Armbruster, and Ballinger, 1982, *Geology*, v. 10, p. 382, Figure 1. Reproduced with permission of the publisher, The Geological Society of America, Boulder, Colorado, USA. Copyright 1982.)

1886, estimated M_s = 6.6-7.1, resulted in the death of about 60 persons and destruction of 90 percent of building structures in the city. A rating of X on the modified-Mercalli scale has been given to small coastal areas just northeast of the city, and of IX to the city area. As Figure 6.47 shows, the rating zone II-III extended inland as far distant as 1600 km. This damage area is rated as probably second only to those of the New Madrid quakes for all of the central and eastern U.S. These areas are much larger than those of the San Andreas fault. "For a hypothetical 7.2 earthquake, the areas of peak horizontal ground acceleration in the East are estimated to be up to ten times as large as those in the west" (Nishenko and Bollinger, 1990, p. 1415). These data suggest that some fundamental differences exist in the properties of the crust in the two regions.

Neotectonic studies in the Charleston area have resulted in the finding of geomorphic features—sand boils, for example—that identify earlier earthquakes in the Charleston area. These liquefaction episodes have been dated and found to be separated by a mean time interval on the order of 1000 years, with variation as short as 500 to as long as 2000 years (Amick and Gelinas, 1991, p. 657). The implication of the figures is that a repeat of the 1885 Charleston quake may be several centuries in the future.

Located on the Atlantic shoreline, the Charleston earthquake epicenter lies on the passive continental margin, beneath which strata of Mesozoic age lie concealed by a thick cover of Cenozoic sediments. As the proto-Atlantic ocean basin began to widen, the continental crust, made

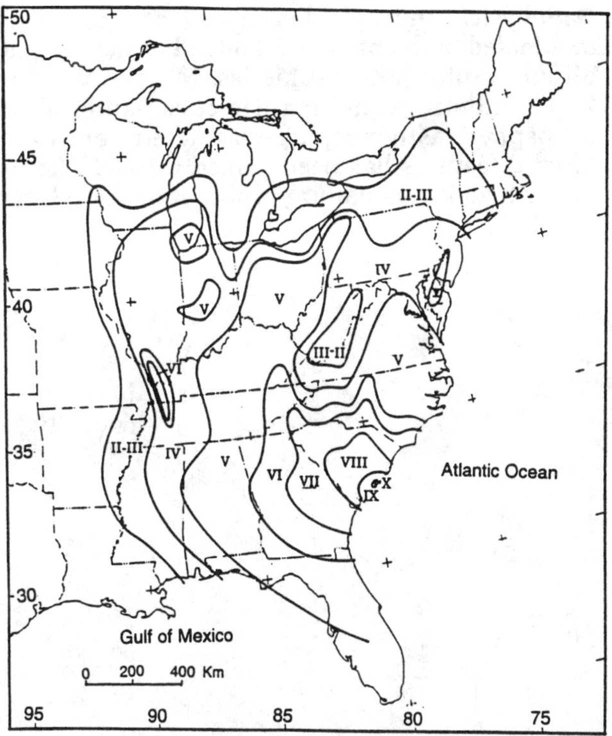

Figure 6.47 Damage estimate map for the 1886 Charleston, SC, earthquake. Isoseismal lines give intensity on the Modified Mercalli scale. (From G.A. Bollinger, 1977, U.S. Geological Survey Professional Paper 1028, p. 25.

up of Paleozoic rocks, was stretched, producing extensional structures: multiple normal faults of the listric type, bounding block-fault basins paralleling the margin. (See Chapter 11 and Figure 11.22.) It is hypothesized that these Mesozoic faults—of Triassic and Jurassic age—represent reactivated older faults in the Paleozoic crust (Swanson, 1986, p. 419). One such Mesozoic basin, the South Georgia basin, lies beneath the Charleston area. COCORP seismic reflection profiling shows structures that can be interpreted as Mesozoic fault basins (Heck, 1989, p. 711). With this evidence, it seems possible that the Charleston earthquakes represent a reactivation of the Mesozoic faults. On the other hand, this continental margin is subject to present-day compressional stress within the North American plate, the axial direction of which is ENE-WSW. This compressive stress would tend to produce reverse and transcurrent faults, rather than normal faults. One interesting bit of evidence of crustal displacement in the Charleston area is that bent railroad rails in one place showed that 5 m of crustal shortening had occurred. This evidence and the aftershock distribution pattern reinforce a hypothesis that links the Charleston slip to a deep, compressional low-angle thrust detachment in Paleozoic rocks below the Mesozoic rocks (Lamont-Doherty Geological Observatory, 1983, p. 6).

* * * * * *

This chapter on seismicity and plate tectonics ends a series—Chapters 3 through 6—that has laid a foundation for the systematic description of how plate tectonics works and what tectonic structures it produces. That foundation lies largely in geochemistry and geophysics, including respectively the chemistry of the solid earth and the physics of the solid earth. Geochemistry figured heavily in our Chapter 3 on the earth's layered zones and in Chapter 5 on igneous activity. Geophysics, through the subject of seismology, dominated both chapters 3 and 6, but in two quite different informational modes. Most of what we know about crust/mantle/core and about lithosphere/asthenosphere as fixed, or static, layered features has been gained through the use of earthquakes as natural probes into these layers and their interfaces. Most of what we know about dynamics of entire plates and of mantle flowage below them has been interpreted from the behavior of natural earthquake waves that yield information on directions and rates of relative motions. Other fields of geophysics—terrestrial magnetism, gravity, geodesy, and heat flow—have also contributed to basic knowledge of the solid earth and to plate tectonics.

Our next four chapters are devoted to systematic plate tectonics, using as a theme the main elements of the Wilson cycle, presented in outline in Chapter 1. Seismology will again enter the picture; this time through artificially generated seismic waves used as probes that go far below the deepest bore holes yet drilled.

References Cited

Acharyya, S.K., 1989. Pages 95-98 in Zaw, 1989.

Aki, Keiiti, 1988, Impact of earthquake seismology on the geological community since the Benioff zone. *Bull. Geol. Soc. Amer.*, v. 100, p. 625-629.

Allen, Clarence R., 1975, Geological criteria for evaluating seismicity. *Bull., Geol. Soc. Amer.*, v. 86, p. 1041-1057.

American Geophysical Union, 1995, Geophysical briefs. *Earth in Space*, v. 8, no. 8, p. 3-4.

Amick, David, and Robert Gelinas, 1991, The search for evidence of large prehistoric earthquakes along the Atlantic seaboard. *Science*, v. 251, p. 655-658.

Bates, Robert L., and Julia A. Jackson, Eds., 1987, *Glossary of Geology*, 3rd ed. Alexandria, VA: American Geological Institute.

Benioff, Hugo, 1949, Seismic evidence for the fault origin of oceanic deeps. *Bull. Geol. Soc. Amer.*, v. 60, p. 1837-1856.

Benioff, Hugo, 1954, Orogenesis and deep crustal structure—additional evidence from seismology. *Bull., Geol. Soc. Amer.*, v. 65, p. 385-400.

Bolt, Bruce A., 1978, *Earthquakes: A Primer*. San Francisco: W.H. Freeman & Co.

Bruns, Terry R., 1983, Model for the origin of the Yakutat block, an accreting terrane in the northern Gulf of Alaska. *Geology*, v. 11, p. 718-721.

Bullen, K.E., and Bruce A. Bolt, l985, *An Introduction to the Theory of Seismology*, 4th Ed., Cambridge, U.K: Cambridge University Press.

Camp, Peter J.J. and Campbell S. Nelson, 1987, Tectonic and sea-level controls on nontropical Neogene limestones in New Zealand. *Geology*, v. 15, p. 610-613.

Cooper, Alan F., and Richard J. Norris, 1994, Anatomy, structural evolution, and slip rate of a plate-boundary thrust: The Alpine fault at Gaunt Creek, Westland, New Zealand. *Bull., Geol. Soc. Amer.*, v. 106, p. 627-633.

Crone, Anthony J., and Michael N. Machette, 1984, Surface faulting accompanying the Borah Peak Earthquake, Central Idaho. *Geology*, v. 12, p. 664-667.

Dennis, J.G., and T.M. Atwater, 1974, Terminology of Geodynamics. *Bull. Am. Assoc. of Petroleum Geologists*, v. 58, p. 1030-1036.

Dewey, J.F., and A.M.C. Sengor, 1979, Aegean and Surrounding areas. *Bull. Geol. Soc. Amer.* v. 90, p. 84-92.

Douglas, John H., 1978, Waiting for the "Great Tokai Quake." *Science News*, v. 113, no. 17, p. 282-286.

Ellsworth, William L., 1990, Earthquake History, 1769-1989. Pages 153-181 in Wallace, Ed., 1990.

Engeln,J.F., D.A. Wiens, and S. Stein, 1986, Mechanisms and depths of Mid-Atlantic Ridge transform faults. *Jour. Geophysical Res.*, v. 91, p. 548-578.

Espinosa, A.F., Ed., 1976, The Guatemalan earthquake of February 6, 1976, a preliminary report. *U.S. Geological Survey Professional Paper 1002*. Washington, D.C.: U.S. Government Printing Office.

Fowler, C.M.R., 19909, *The Solid Earth: An Introduction to Global Physics*. New York: Cambridge Univ. Press.

Frolich, Cliff, 1989, Deep earthquakes. *Scientific American*, v. 260, no. 1, p. 48-55.

Frolich, Cliff, 1995, Shaken to the core. *New Scientist*, v. 148, no. 2007, p. 43-46.

Fuis, Gary S., and Walter D. Mooney, 1990, Lithospheric structure and tetonics from seismic-refraction and other data. Pages 207-236 in Wallace, Ed.,1990.

Fukao, Yoshio, 1992, Seismic tomography of the earth's mantle: geodynamic implications. *Science*, v. 258, p. 1069.

Gordon, Richard G., 1991, Plate motion. Reviews of *Geophysics; Supplement*, p. 748-758. U.S. National Report to International Union of Geodesy and Geophysics 1987-1990.

Grand, Stephen P., Rob D. van der Hilst, and Sri Widiyarntoro, 1979, *GSA Today*, v. 7, no.4, p. 1-6.

Green, Harry W., Jr., 1993, The mechanism of deep earthquakes. *EOS*, v. 72, no. 2, p. 23.

Green, Harry W., II, 1994, Solving the paradox of deep earthquakes. *Scientific American*, v. 27, no. 3, p. 64-71.

Gupta, H.K., and H.N. Singh, 1986, Seismicity of the north-east India region, *Jour. Geological Soc. of India*, v. 28, p. 367.

Harrison, T. Mark, Peter Copeland, W.S.F. Kidd, and An Yin, 1992, Raising Tibet, *Science*, v. 255, p. 1663-1670.

Hauksson, E., Lucile M. Jones, et al., 1988, The 1987 Whittier Narrows earthquake in the Los Angeles metropolitan area, California. *Science*, v. 239, p. 1409-1412.

Heck, Frederick R., 1989, Mesozoic extension in the Southern Appalachians. *Geology*, v. 17, p. 711-714.

Hill, David P., Jerry P. Eaton, and Lucile N. Jones, 1990, Seismicity, 1980-86. Pages 115-151 in Wallace, Ed., 1990.

Hobbs, Bruce E., Winthrop D. Means, and Paul F. Williams, 1976, *An Outline of Structural Geology*. New York: John Wiley & Sons.

Honda, H., 1934, On the mechanism of deep earthquakes and the stress in the deep layer of the earth crust. *Geophysical Magazine*, Japan Meteorological Agency, v. 8, p. 179.

Isacks, Bryan, Jack Oliver, and Lynn R. Sykes, 1968, Seismology and the new global tectonics. *Jour. of Geophysical Res.*, v. 73, no. 18 p. 5855-5899.

Jacob, Klaus H., 1987, Hunting the great earthquake. *Yearbook*, Lamont-Doherty Geological Observatory, p. 73-78.

Johnston, Arch C., and Lisa R. Kanter, 1990, Earthquakes in stable continental crust. *Scientific American*, v. 262, no. 3, pp. 68-75.

Kanamori, Hiroo, 1977, The energy release in great earthquakes. *Jour. Geophysical Res.*, v. 82, p. 2981-2987.

Kerr, Richard A. 1991, New hints of deep slabs. *Science*, v. 252, p. 1069.

Kerr, Richard A., 1979, Earthquake prediction: Mexican quake shows one way to look for the big ones. *Science*, v. 203, p. 860-862.

Kerr, Richard A., 1986a, Sinking slabs puncture layered model. *Science*, v. 271, p. 548-549.

Kerr, Richard A., 1988. The mantle's structure—having it both ways, *Science*, v. 240 p. 175.

Kirby, Stephen, and Brad Hacker, 1993, Earthquakes at the deep roots of arc volcanoes. *EOS*, v. 74, no. 6, p. 70.

Kirby, Stephen, William B. Durham, and Laura A. Stern, 1991, Mantle phase changes and deep-earthquake faulting in subducting lithosphere. *Science*, v. 252, p. 216-225.

Lahr, John C. and George Plafker, 1980, Holocene Pacific-North American plate interaction in southern Alaska. *Geology*, v. 8, p. 483-486.

Lamont-Doherty Geologic Observatory, 1983, New Constraints on the 1886 Charleston Earthquake from contemporary newspaper reports. *Lamont Newsletter*, Spring 1983, p. 6.

Lamont-Doherty Geological Observatory, 1988, Model for estimating maximum size of major earthquakes at subduction zones. *Lamont*, Winter/88, p. 1-2.

Liu, Lanbo, Mark D. Zoback, and Paul Segall, 1992. Rapid intraplate strain accumulation in the New Madrid seismic zone. *Science*, v. 257, p. 1666-1669.

Lockner, David A., and James D. Byerlee, 1993, How geometrical constraints contribute to the weakness of mature faults. *Nature*, v. 363, p. 250-252.

Marshak, Stephen, and Timothy Paulsen, 1996, Midcontinent U.S. fault and fold zones: A legacy of Proterozoic intracratonic extensional tectonism? *Geology*, v. 24, p. 151-154.

McCann, William R., Omar J. Perez, and Lynn R. Sykes, 1980, Yakataga gap, Alaska: Seismic history and earthquake potential, *Science*, v. 207, p. 1309-1314.

McKeown, F.A., R.M. Hamilton, S.F. Diehl, and E.E. Glick, 1990, Diaperic origin of the Blytheville and Pascola arches in the Reelfoot rift. *Geology*, v. 18, p. 1158-1162.

McNally, Karen C., 1983, Seismic gaps in space and time, *Ann. Review Earth & Planetary Sciences*, v. 11, p. 359-369.

Minster, J.B., and T.H. Jordan, 1978, Present-day plate motions. *Jour. of Geophysical Research*, v. 83, p. 5321-5354.

Molnar, Peter, B. Clark Burchfiel, Liang K'uangyi, and Zhao Ziyun, 1987, Geomorphic evidence for active faulting in the Altyn and northern Tibet., *Geology*, v. 15, p. 249-253.

Monastersky, R., 1993, Midcontinent heat may explain great quakes. *Science News*, v. 143, p. 342.

Monastersky, Richard, 1992, Hitting a deep barrier within the planet. *Science News*, v. 141, p. 132-133.

Monastersky, Richard, 1992, Shaking up seismic theory: Are you any better off after an earthquake? *Science News*, v. 141, p. 136-137.

Monastersky, Richard, 1993, Mixing earth's mantle with a delayed flush. *Science News*, v. 143, p. 133.

Monastersky, Richard, 1994, Abandoning Richter. *Science News*, v. 146, p. 250-252.

Namson, J.S. and T.L. Davis, 1988, Seismically active fold and thrust belt in the San Joaquin Valley, Central California. *Bull. Geol. Soc. Amer.*, v. 100, p. 257-273.

Namson, Jay, and Thom Davis, 1988, Structural transport of the western Transverse Ranges. *Geology*, v. 16, p. 675-679.

Nishenko, S.P., and G.A. Bollinger, 1990, Forecasting damaging earthquakes in the central and eastern United States. *Science*, v. 249, p. 1412-1416.

Oliver, Jack, and Bryan Isacks, 1967, Deep earthquake zones, anomalous structures in the upper mantle, and the lithosphere. *Jour. of Geophysical Res.*, v. 72, p. 4259-4275.

Pennington, Wayne D., 1983, Role of shallow phase changes in the subduction of oceanic crust. *Science*, v. 220, p. 1045-1048.

Plafker, George, 1965, Tectonic deformation associated with the 1964 Alaska earthquake. *Science*, v. 148, p. 1675-1678.

Press, Frank, 1970, Regionalized earth models. *Jour. of Geophysical Research*, v. 75, p. 6575.

Reid, Harry Fielding, 1910, The mechanism of the earthquake, in the California earthquake of April 18, 1906. *Report of the State Investigation Commission*, vol. 2. Washington, DC: Carnegie Institution of Washington.

Richter, Charles F., 1958, *Elementary Seismology*. San Francisco: W. H. Freeman.

Riddihough, Robin, and Roy D. Hyndman, 1989, Queen Charlotte Islands margin. Pages 403-411 in *Geology of North America*, vol. N. Boulder, Co: Geological Society of America.

Savage, J.C., M. Lisowski, and W.H. Prescott, 1986, Strain accumulation in the Shumagin and Yakataga seismic gaps, Alaska. *Science*, v. 231, p. 585-587.

Science Reporter, 1993, Getting at the heart of the seismic gap debate. *Science*, v. 260, p. 1724.

Seeber, L., J.G. Armbruster, and G.A. Bollinger, 1982, Large-scale patterns of seismicity before and after the 1886 South Carolina earthquake. *Geology*, v. 10, p. 383-386.

Seeber, Leonardo, 1986, Eastern mysteries of intraplate Earthquakes: United States and China. Lamont-Doherty Geological Observatory *Yearbook* 1985-86, p. 34-42.

Shea, James H., Ed., 1985. *Continental Drift*. New York: Van Nostrand Reinhold Co.

Simpson, David W., and Mark H. Anders, 1992, Tectonics and topography of the Western United States. *GSA Today*, v. 2, no. 6, p. 117-121.

Strahler, Arthur N., 1981, *Physical Geology*. New York: Harper & Row, Publishers.

Sykes, L., J.B. Kisslinger, L. House, J. Davies, and K.H. Jacob, 1980, Rupture zones of great earthquakes in the Alaskan-Aleutian arc, 1784-1980. *Science*, 210, p. 1343-1345.

Sykes, Lynn R., 1967, Mechanism of earthquakes and nature of faulting on the mid-oceanic ridges. *Jour. of Geophysical Res.*, v. 72, p. 2131.

Thatcher, Wayne, 1990, Present-day crustal movements and the mechanics of cyclic deformation. Pages 189-205 in Wallace, Ed., 1990.

Twiss, Robert J., and Eldridge M. Moores, 1992, *Structural Geology*. New York: W.H. Freeman & Co.

U.S. Geological Survey, 1971, *The San Fernando, California, Earthquake of February 9, 1971*. Washington, D.C.: U.S. Government Printing Office.

U.S. Geological Survey and Southern California Earthquake Center, 1994, The magnitude 6.7 Northridge, California, earthquake of 17 January 1994. *Science*, v. 266, p. 389-397.

Uyeda, Seiya, 1978, *The New View of the Earth*, San Francisco: W.H. Freeman. (Original edition in Japanese, 1971. Tokyo: Iwanami Shoten Publishers.)

Vidale, J.E., and T. Lay, 1993, Phase boundaries and mantle convection. *Science*, v. 261, p. 1401-1402.

Wadati, K., 1935, On the activity of deep-focus earthquakes in the Japan Islands and neighborhoods. *Geophysical Magazine*, v. 8, p. 305-325.

Wadati, Kiyoo, 1928, Shallow and deep earthquakes. *Geophysical Magazine* (Tokyo), v. 1, p. 161-202. (continued in vol. 2 (1929) and vol. 3 (1930).

Wallace, Robert E., Ed., 1990, *The San Andreas Fault System*, U.S. Geol. Survey, Prof. Paper 1515, Washington, D.C.: U.S. Govt. Printing Office.

Westaway, Rob, 1989, Northeast Basin and Range province active tetonics: An alternative view. *Geology*, v. 17, p. 779-783.

Wheeler, Russell, 1995, Earthquakes in the cratonward limit of Iapetan faulting in eastern North America. *Geology*, v. 23, p. 105-108.

Wiens, D.A., J.J. McGuire et al., 1994, A deep earthquake aftershock sequence and implications for the rupture mechanism of deep earthquakes. *Nature*, v. 372, p. 540-543.

Wilson, J. Tuzo, 1965, A new class of faults and their bearing on continental drift. *Nature*, v. 207, p. 343.

Zaw, Khin, 1989, Comments and Reply on "Transcurrent Movements in the Burma-Andaman Sea region. *Geology*, v. 21, p. 93-95.

Chapter: 7 Tectonics of the Oceanic Lithosphere

This chapter title begins with "Tectonics," appropriate because it is the first chapter that tackles plate tectonics as its main theme. At this point, a few words about terminology may be appropriate, but you may chose to skip them. The adjective *tectonic* derives from the Greek *tektonikos*, in reference to a skilled builder—a carpenter, for example. The inference here is that "structure" and "structural" are strongly involved. The same root is obvious in "architecture." The noun *tectonics*, with the same Greek root, became a French word. Recall from Chapter 2 that geologist Emile Argand in the 1920s was a leader in unfolding alpine structure. Alfred Wegener in 1929 referred to Argand's interpretations in *La Tectonique de l'Asie* (1924). In those times, another noun, *tectonism*, was used as synonymous with "diastrophism."

We need to give attention here to the academic distinction in meaning and scope between "tectonics" and "structural geology." This distinction grew to require attention in the 1960s as plate tectonics entered geoscience with a staggering impact. Structural geology, as the then-entrenched academic subject, while continuing its essential role in basic geology, needed definition *vis-á-vis* plate tectonics. The authors of one widely used textbook of structural geology, published in 1975, inserted a special chapter labeled "Tectonics" (Hobbs, Means and Williams, 1976). It was explained that tectonics "in the broad sense includes study of earth structures on every scale," whereas "in the narrower sense...tectonics deals specifically with very big structures" (p. 433). They added that for this reason tectonics "is sometimes called 'geotectonics' to emphasize its global aspect." Under this distinction, "tectonics and structural geology are both concerned with relative movements of parts of the earth" (p. 433). The distinction here is largely one of scale of magnitude of recognizable individual features. This distinction is upheld in the *Glossary of Geology*, Third Edition (Bates and Jackson, 1987, p. 653).

By the early 1990s, the newcomer had grown to full stature, as we find in two state-of-the-art textbooks: one is *Structural Geology* (1993), the other *Tectonics* (1996). They are by the same pair of authors: Robert J. Twiss and Eldridige M. Moores (and vice versa). They too, imply scale as the criterion of distinction and perhaps for that reason can feel free to delete the word "Plate" from their book title "Tectonics." They state that both tectonics and structural geology "deal with motion and deformation of the Earth's crust (1995, p. 3-4), but they point to another and perhaps more significant distinction:

> They differ in that tectonics is predominantly the study of the history of motion and deformation on a regional to global scale, whereas structural geology is predominantly the study the study of deformation in rocks at a scale ranging from submicroscopic to regional. (1995, p. 4)

These authors consider the two realms as being interdependent, as well as being overlapping at the regional scale.

Recognition of the large content of historical geology in plate tectonics is important. A very large proportion of what is written on plate tectonics is an appraisal of what happened in the distant past. We do, however, also attempt to discern and describe the basic recurring forms and cycles—such as the Wilson cycle—that can be thought of as "timeless knowledge." This form of knowledge verges on the formulation of a set of laws of geoscience. On the other hand, modern laboratory and computer modeling of tectonic processes can be virtually free of the historical element.

To avoid confusion terms of scale, we use throughout this book the full term "plate tectonics," easily abbreviated to "PT." In so doing, we avoid the ambiguity of implying a tectonics that applies to small-scale deformations. It is hard to resist a final but gratuitous suggestion that PT is clearly recognized by the intense excitement it generates among the laity as well as among geoscientists!

A study of the oceanic lithosphere is largely a study in present-day processes of geology; it is a study of new features of the solid earth in the process of being formed. In contrast, a study of rocks and structures of the continental lithosphere is largely a study of what has already happened through the activity of plate tectonics during all of recorded geologic time.

Geologists have long been influenced by the uniformitarian concept that "the present is the key to the past." In keeping with this concept, we can say that the present-day tectonic and igneous activities of the oceanic lithosphere and its plate boundaries supply us with the keys to the geologic past—that past being largely represented by the continental lithosphere. Many crustal features of the continents that puzzled geologists for decades

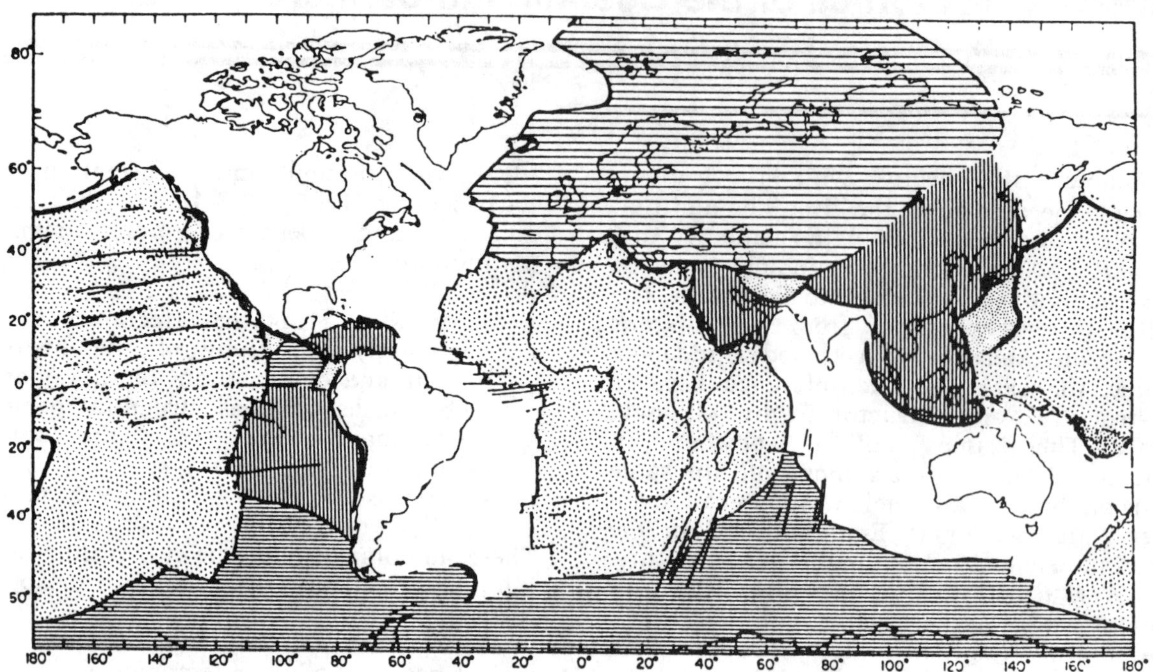

Figure 7.1 Published in March, 1968, this map by Princeton geophysicist W. Jason Morgan bore the following legend: "The crust is divided into units that move as rigid blocks. The boundaries between blocks are rises, trenches (or young fold mountains), and faults. The boundaries drawn in Asia are tentative, and additional sub-blocks may be required." (From W.J. Morgan, 1968, *Jour. of Geophysical Res.*, v. 73, no. 6. Reproduced by permission of the Amer. Geophysical Union.)

have been solved by the key of the present. For example, ancient turbidites and ophiolites found on the continents defied explanation until geologic research on the ocean basins revealed the conditions under which turbidites are now being deposited and new oceanic crust is being generated.

7.1 Plate Boundaries and Their Junctions

As outlined in Chapter 1, the boundaries of lithospheric plates fall into three types: (1) spreading plate boundaries, (2) convergent boundaries where subduction is in progress, and (3) transform-fault boundaries. Each plate is an independent fragment of a spherical earth shell, completely surrounded by other plates. Apparently, the nature of the forces that drive plates is such that several major plates are required to be present on the globe simultaneously. Their sizes and outlines are quite varied, and they change in both size and shape as time passes. Entire plates can disappear by subduction and new plates can form by rifting processes.

The first global maps of lithospheric plates appeared in published form in 1968. Shown here in Figure 7.1 is a reproduction of one of the two earliest versions of such a map. It appeared in March 1968 in a paper authored by W. Jason Morgan of Princeton University and was based on a map of the oceanic ridge system published in the same year by Lynn Sykes. This map also included additional features from a tectonic map published in 1965 by Bruce C. Heezen and Marie Tharp (Morgan, 1968, p. 1960). Morgan showed 20 "blocks," or plates. Only three months later in the same year, a global plate map was published by Xavier Le Pichon of the Lamont-Doherty Geological Observatory of Columbia University (L-DGO). We reproduce it here as Figure 7.2. Notice that it distinguished between spreading and converging boundaries and in an accompanying table gave figures of the relative rates of extension and compression at many locations (Le Pichon, 1968, p. 3675).

There have since been many minor changes and revisions in these early maps. Some boundaries have been relocated and new plates identified. Differences have appeared in the naming of plates, as well. Today, however, a fairly good consensus exists in the geologic community as to the numbers and names of the major plates, the nature of their boundaries, and their relative motions. Differences of interpretation persist in many boundary details. Also, a few sections of plate boundaries continue to be of uncertain classification or location. As we progress, make use of our world map of plates, Figure 7.3.

To familiarize yourself with the geometry of spherical plate systems on a globe, get a half-dozen well-worn tennis balls. With a very soft lead pencil, experiment with drawing various shapes and numbers of plates that might conceivably exist on a hypothetical globe. One rule you must follow is that every boundary shared by two plates (a plate-boundary segment) terminates in a common triple junction with two other boundary segments. On grounds of extreme improbability, a quadruple or

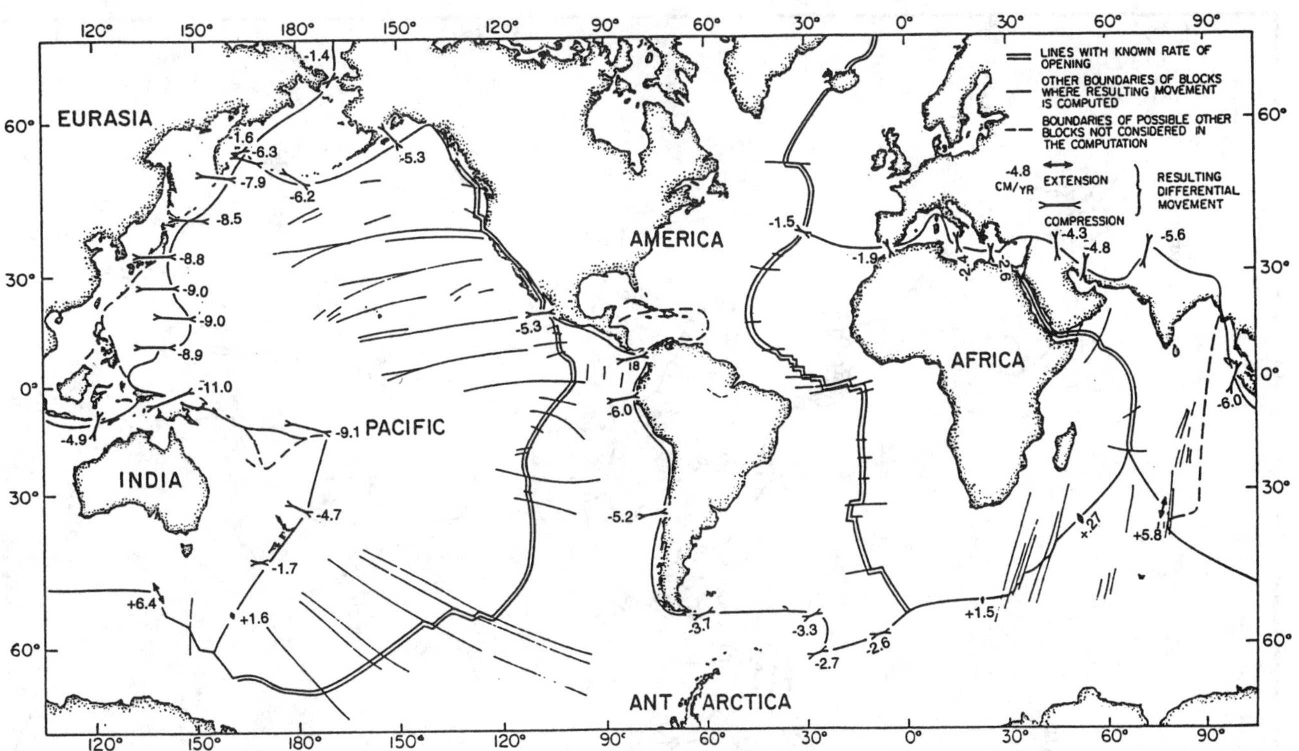

Figure 7.2 Published in June 1968, in the same journal as Morgan's map, this map by Columbia Unversity geophysicist Xavier Le Pichon included symbols showing both the directions and relative motions of the plates along their boundaries. The numbers beside the symbols give the actual rates in cm/yr. (From X. LePichon, 1968, *Jour. of Geophysical Res.*, v. 73, no. 12, p. 3661. Reproduced by permission.)

quintuple junction is not allowed. Initially, draw all plate boundaries as single lines, without any distinction as to the type of boundary each represents. Later, after you have become acquainted with the possible kinds of boundary junctions, you may wish to mark the boundaries as to their types.

Figure 7.4 illustrates some results. As you can see from these samples, models with as few as two, three, and four symmetrical plates can be imagined. The four-plate model is analogous with the geometry of a tetrahedron, while the six-plate model consisting of four-sided plates is analogous with the geometry of the cube or rhombohedron. The 12-plate system with pentagonal plates is based on a common crystal form known as a pyritohedron (commonly seen in the mineral pyrite).

7.2 The Global Plate System

For a particular lithospheric plate to be identified and named, its boundaries should all be active. In other words, there must be good evidence of present or recent relative motion between the plate and all its contiguous (adjoining) plates. A plate is uniquely defined, or set apart, by its boundary segments and triple junctions. A *plate boundary segment* is the continuous line of separation between two plates and is terminated at both ends by a triple junction. A *triple junction* is the common point of meeting of three boundary segments, or the common point at which three plates are in contact. It follows that for a given plate the number of boundary segments must equal the number of triple junctions. Figure 7.5 shows six forms of plates in order of increasing numbers of boundary segments and triple junctions, from the simplest, or lenticular type, with only two boundary segments, to the complex type, combining one or more lenticular forms with a simple polyhedral form.

While the lenticular type, with its two boundary segments, sets the lower limit of simplicity, there seems to be no upper limit to the number of boundary segments. The two largest plates (Pacific, American) each have 10 boundary segments and 10 triple junctions. The median number of triple junctions is five, and this might lead us to guess that there is a tendency for an "ideal" plate to be a pentagon, or pentalateral. This speculation would seem to favor a simple global model of 12 pentalateral plates, as shown in Figure 7.4. Table 7.1 lists 15 global plates with the numbers of boundary segments and triple junctions.

Another requirement of an active lithospheric plate is that it must move as a unit; the surface track of its motion over the spherical globe must be an arc of a circle. This is a subject we will elaborate upon later in the chapter.

A given boundary segment need not consist of

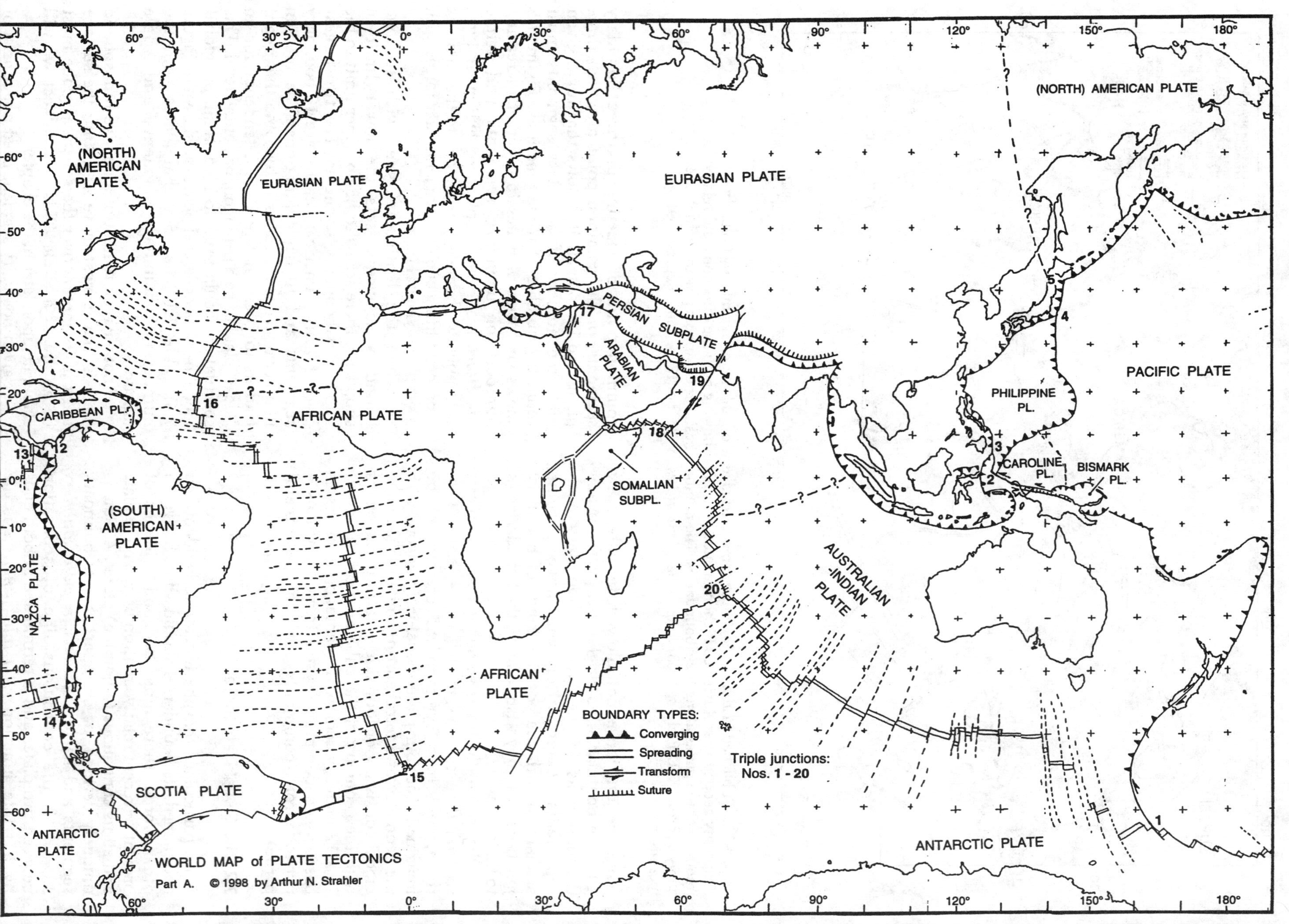

WORLD MAP of PLATE TECTONICS

Part A. © 1998 by Arthur N. Strahler

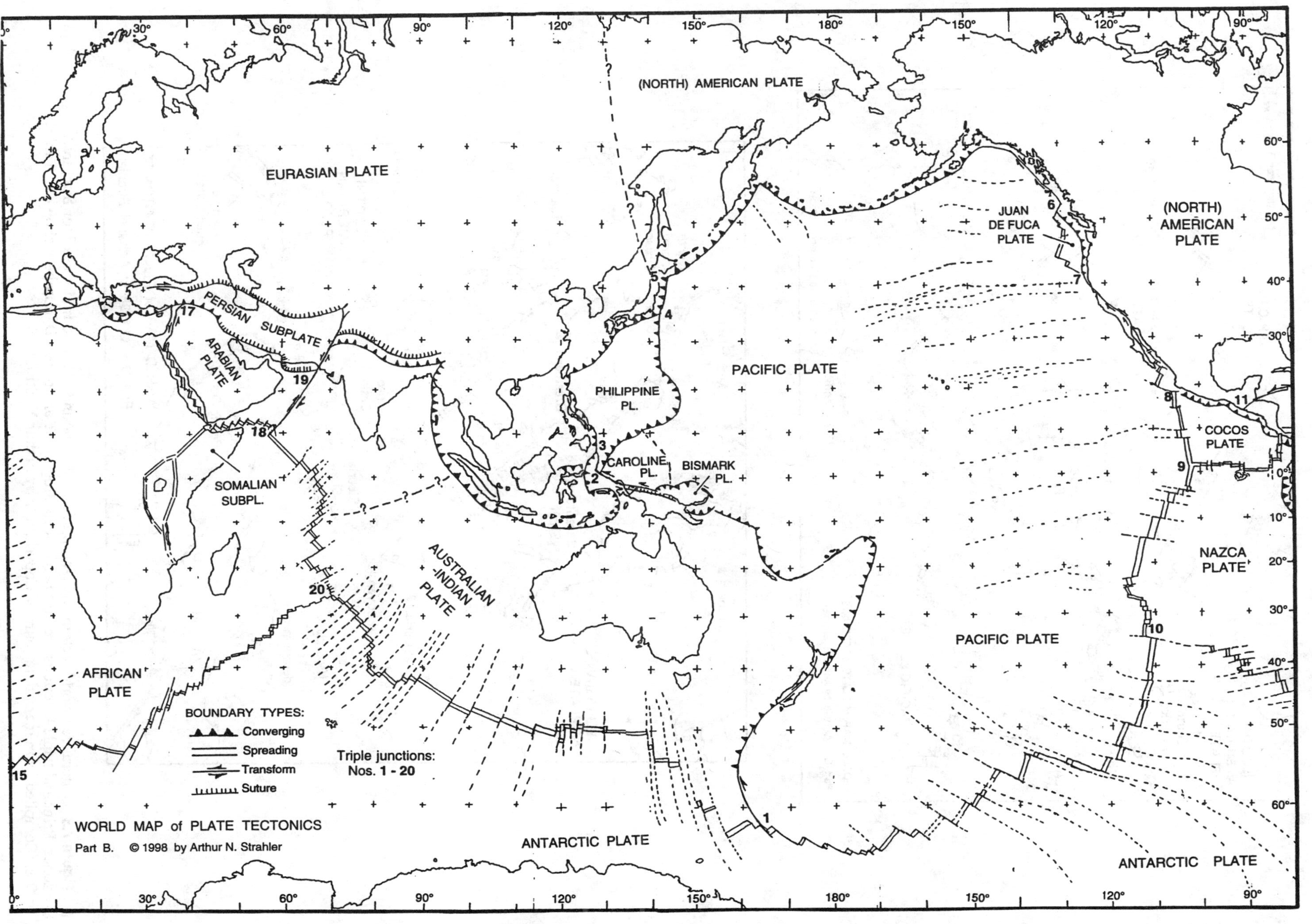
EURASIAN PLATE
(NORTH) AMERICAN PLATE
(NORTH) AMERICAN PLATE
JUAN DE FUCA PLATE
PACIFIC PLATE
PHILIPPINE PL.
CAROLINE PL.
BISMARK PL.
COCOS PLATE
NAZCA PLATE
PACIFIC PLATE
PERSIAN SUBPLATE
ARABIAN PLATE
SOMALIAN SUBPL.
AUSTRALIAN -INDIAN PLATE
AFRICAN PLATE
BOUNDARY TYPES:
Converging
Spreading
Transform
Suture
Triple junctions: Nos. 1 - 20
WORLD MAP of PLATE TECTONICS
Part B. © 1998 by Arthur N. Strahler
ANTARCTIC PLATE
ANTARCTIC PLATE

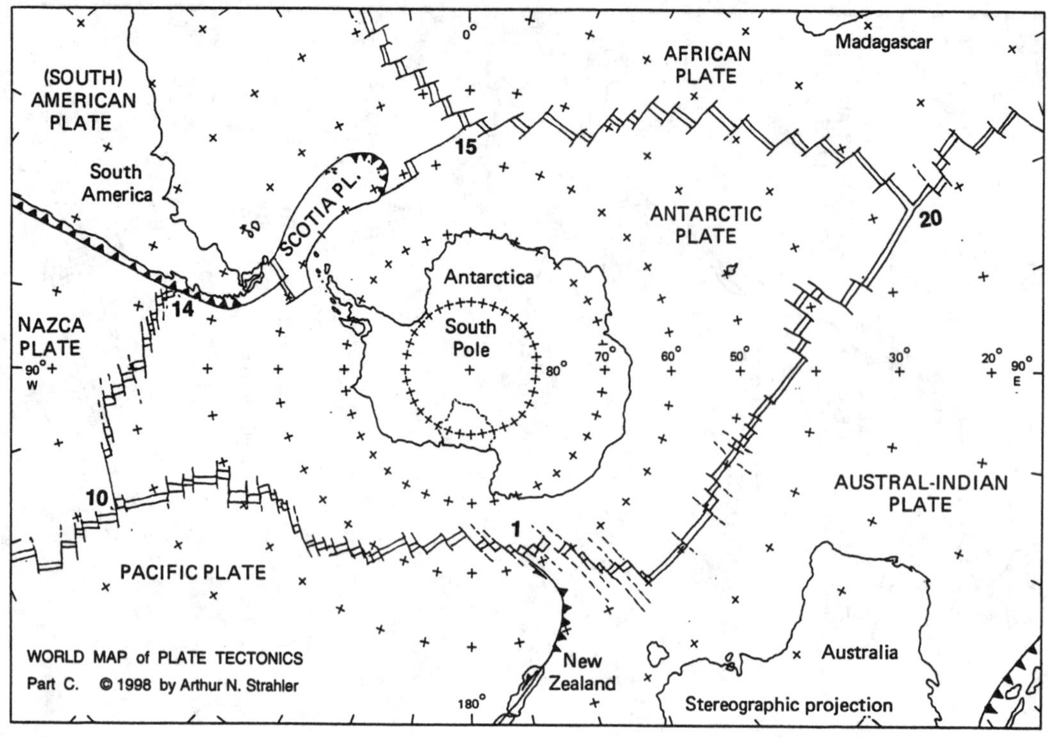

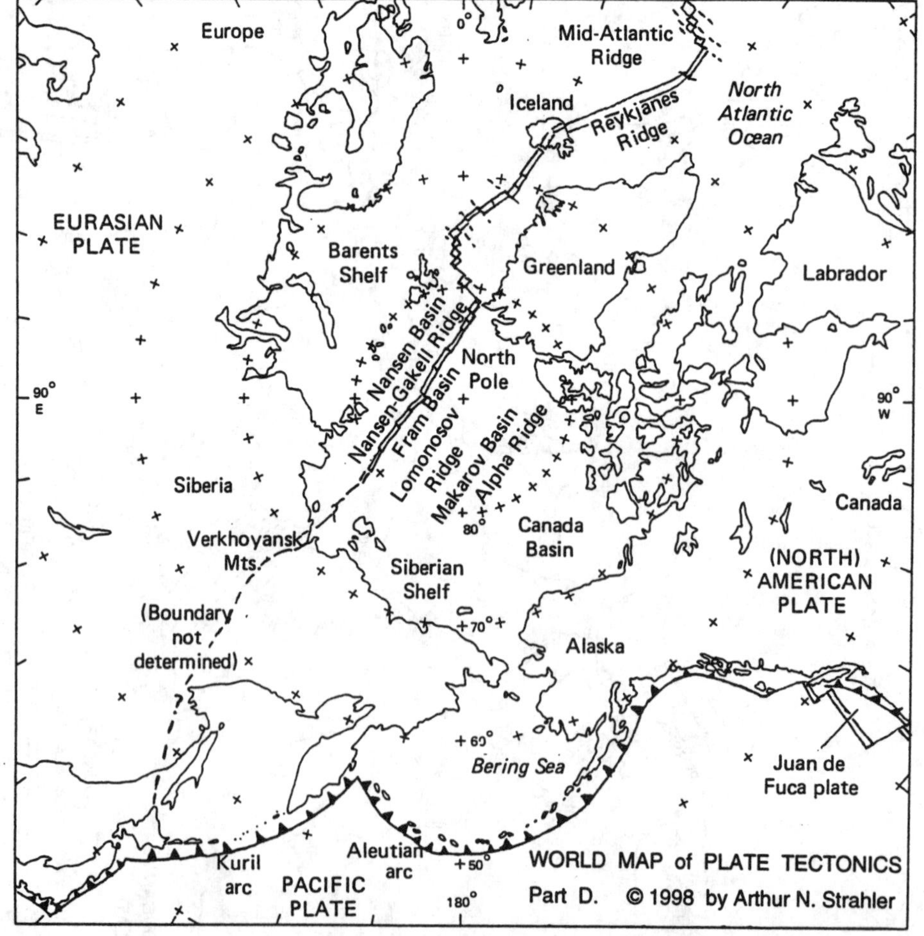

Figure 7.3 Generalized world tectonic map emphasing plate boundaries and major seafloor fracture zones. Principal triple junctions are numbered according to the arbitrary I.D. numbers shown in Table 7.2. (Compiled from many data sources. Copyright © by Arthur N. Strahler.)

only one boundary type (spreading, converging, transform). Instead, the segment may be made up of two boundary types joined in sequence. Many plate boundaries consist of alternating short sections of spreading and transform boundary meeting at about right angles, and this pattern is the rule rather than the exception for the mid-oceanic ridge system. Converging boundaries are often strongly curved in plan-form (map trace) and may show winding bends.

Recognition is given by some authors to the separate existence of a North American plate and a South American plate, the boundary of which can be arbitrarily drawn between the Antilles arc (Caribbean plate) and the Mid-Atlantic Ridge (DeMets et al., 1990). However, no active faults appear in this area, so triple junctions cannot be established. Our plate tectonic map, Figure 7.3, recognizes the two plates by parenthetical "North" or "South" with each "American" plate label. We do not, however, count or number the possible additional plate junctions that would be required by a subdivision.

Table 7.1 The Lithospheric Plates

Plate name	Number of boundary segments and triple junctions
The Major Plates:	
Pacific	10
American	10
(North American)	
(South American)	
Eurasian	7
Persian subplate	
African	5
Somalian subplate	
Australian+Indian	5
Antarctic	5
Nazca	4
Cocos	5
Philippine	2
Caribbean	2
Arabian	4
Juan de Fuca	2
	Total: 61
Other plates:	
Scotia	
Caroline	
Bismark	

7.3 Triple Junctions

Given all possible combinations of three boundary types, irrespective of the order in which they are listed, triple junctions are limited to nine basic stable varieties, shown in Figure 7.6. The three boundary types are assigned a letter: R (Rift)—spreading boundary; T (Trench)—converging, subduction, or consuming boundary; F (Fault)—transform-fault boundary. Thus a three-letter code suffices for a given triple junction. Of the 10 geometrically possible combinations, one must be ruled out because the nature of transform faulting requires that plates must move in the same direction as the fault line. Thus, combination FFF is eliminated, leaving the nine possible triple junctions shown in Figure 7.6. Note that a triple junction can take the form of either a "Y" or a "T", since the only requirement is that three plates meet at a common point. The "T" form is the more common of the two. Six examples are shown in Figure 7.7.

Triple junctions, like the plates that form them, can move over the asthenosphere and disappear by subduction beneath adjacent lithospheric plates. New triple junctions come into existence by rifting or by the formation of a new subduction boundary. A triple junction of one type may evolve into a triple junction of another type.

Table 7.2 lists the 20 triple junctions that form the common corners of the first 12 major plates we recognized in Table 7.1 and on our plate map, Figure 7.3. For convenience, each junction is assigned a circled reference number, which appears on these world maps. The code numbers have no significance except to help you keep track of the junctions and correlate one map with another. Three of the junctions (1, 10, and 16) are listed as "RRF or RFF." Choice of one of these two possibilities depends on how much importance is given to the possible presence of a short transform fault offsetting a spreading boundary. Junction 5 is described as "undetermined"; it cannot be identified by code because one of the three boundaries is of uncertain position and classification. The uncertain boundary, which separates the Eurasian and American plates, may cut through eastern Siberia, but there is no clear, strong line of seismic activity by which it can be located. As we shall explain, active plate boundaries are located and defined by their seismic activity, indicating stick-slip movement between adjoining plates.

Note in Tables 7.1 and 7.2 that we have identified as a single plate what is listed as the "Australian+Indian plate." In the early 1990s, evidence began to be accumulated to indicate that these are two separate plates (Gordon and Stein, 1992, p. 335-336; White, 1995, p. 337, 343). On our global plate map, Figure 7.3, we have drawn a dashed area across the Indian Ocean lying between longitude 70°E and 95°E and elongated N-S. It measures about 900 km in length. In this area no magnetic lineations are found. The area

Table 7.2 The Triple Junctions

I.D. No.	Variety	Plates meeting at common junction of three plates
1	RRF or FFR	Pacific, Antarctic, Australian+Indian
2	FFR(?)	Pacific, Philippine, Australian+Indian
3	FFT(?)	Eurasian, Philippine, Australian+Indian
4	TTT	Pacific, Eurasian, Philippine
5	Undetermined	Pacific, Eurasian, American
6	RTF	Pacific, American, Juan de Fuca
7	FFT	Pacific, American, Juan de Fuca
8	RTF	Pacific, American, Cocos
9	RRR	Pacific, Cocos Nazca
10	RRF or FFR	Pacific, Nazca, Antarctic
11	TTF	American, Cocos, Caribbean
12	TTF(?)	American, Nazca, Caribbean
13	TTF	Cocos, Nazca, Caribbean
14	TTR	American, Nazca, Antarctic
15	FFR	American, African, Antarctic
16	RRF or FFR	American, African, Eurasian
17	FFT	African, Eurasian, Arabian
18	FFR	African, Arabian, Australian+Indian
19	FFT	Arabian, Eurasian, Australian+Indian
20	RRR	African, Antarctic, Australian+Indian

contains epicenters of a large number of small earthquakes and is interpreted as a broad zone of crustal deformation containing a very large number of small fault lines. Accumulated crustal shortening across the zone has been documented as between 10 and 30 km. This evidence points to an anticlockwise rotational motion of the Australian plate that is bringing the rigid Indian and Australian parts closer together. This scenario is something that we have not accommodated as a kind of plate boundary, since there seems to be no plate subduction boundary present. However, crustal shortening could be understood as a product of multiple strike-slip faults. To take notice of this remarkably strange tectonic process as signifying an active boundary between the two plates, we have placed a "plus" symbol between the two names in our tables. So far no mapable triple juctions have been established to justify inserting a conventional geometric relationship. Besides, the estimated rate of relative motion between the two plates is extremely small, amounting to only a few millimeters per year (White, 1995, p. 343). Deforming zones have been identified in several other plates (Gordon and Stein, 1992, p. 334).

7.4 Stability of Triple Junctions

To endure for long periods, a triple junction must meet certain geometrical requirements. It must be capable of moving laterally, or migrating, in the direction of one of the three boundaries that comprise it. During the early years of rapid formation of the hypothesis of plate tectonics D.P. McKenzie and W.J. Morgan, along with other investigators, presented the geometrical criteria for testing the stability of a triple junction (McKenzie and Morgan, 1969. See also Dewey, 1972, p. 61-63;

A. Two hemispherical plates

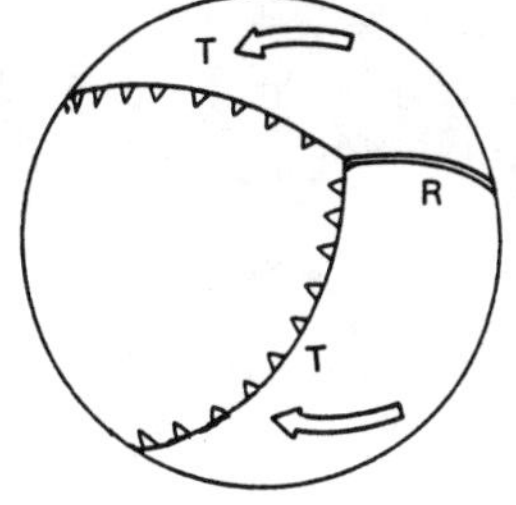

B. Three trilateral plates

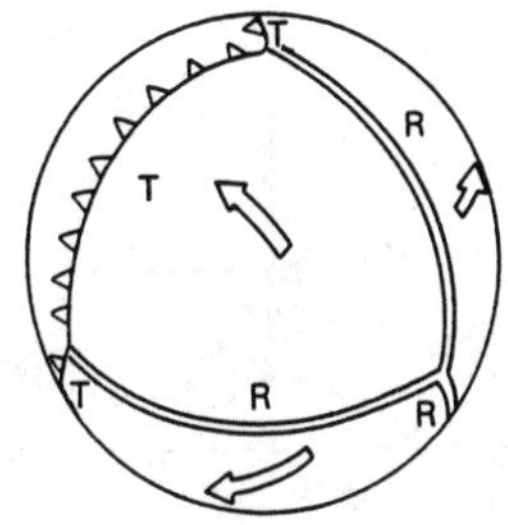

C. Four trilateral plates (tetrahedron)

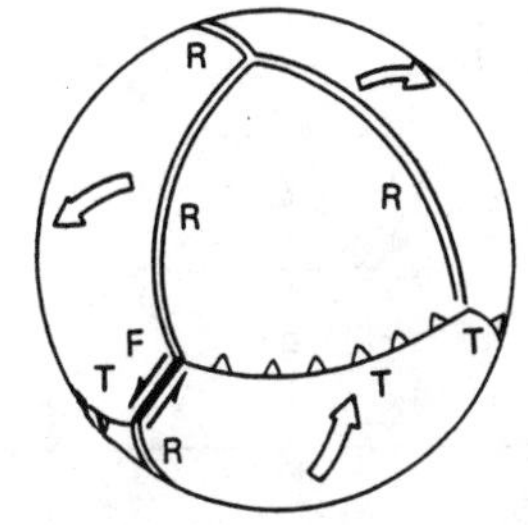

D. Five plates: two trilateral, three quadrilateral (pentahedron)

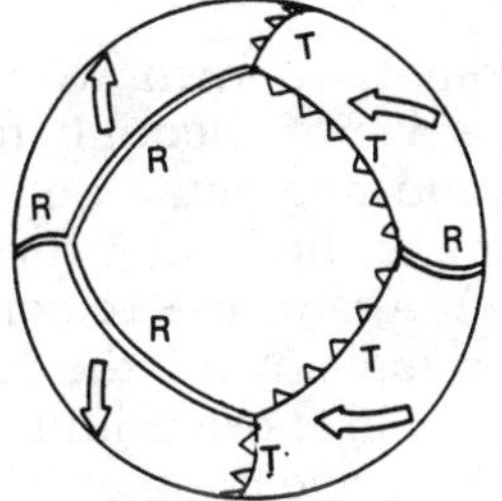

E. Six quadrilateral plates (cube, rhombohedron)

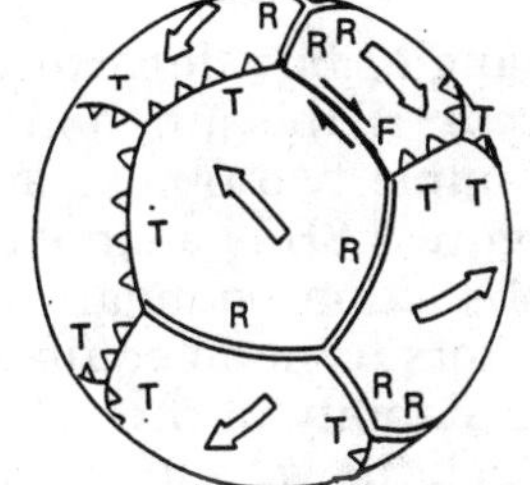

F. Twelve pentalateral plates (pyritohedron)

Figure 7.4 Six ideal symmetrical plate systems inscribed on a sphere. Reference to crystal forms is a fanciful analogy. (Copyright © by Arthur N. Strahler.)

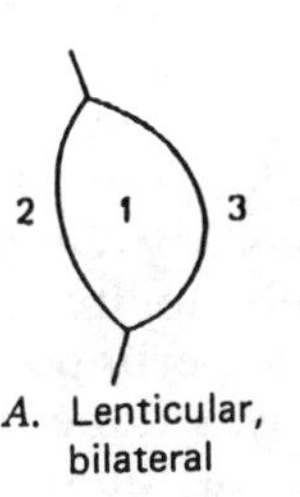

A. Lenticular, bilateral

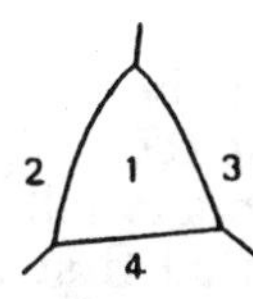

B. Trilateral

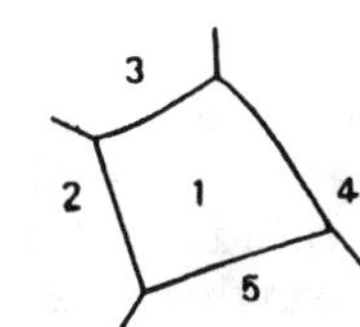

C. Quadrilateral

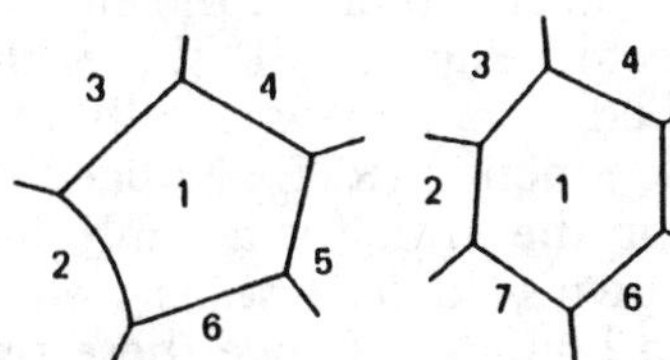

D. Pentalateral

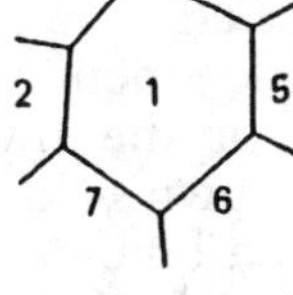

E. Hexalateral

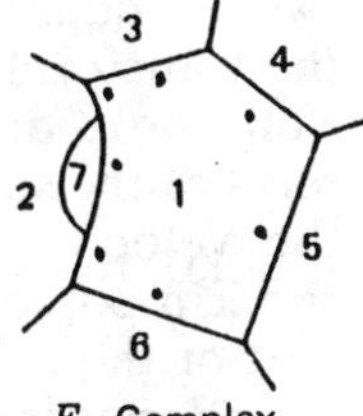

F. Complex

Figure 7.5 Six plate outlines with their triple junctions. The number of triple junctions is equal to the number of plate boundary segments. (Copyright © by Arthur N. Strahler.)

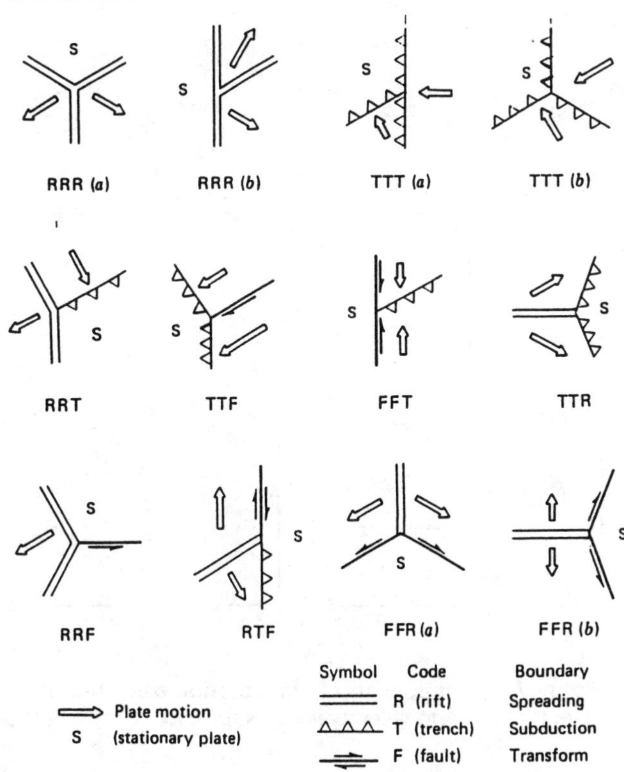

Figure 7.6 The triple junctions. Alternate forms, (a) and (b), are given for two of the types. (Copyright © by Arthur N. Strahler.)

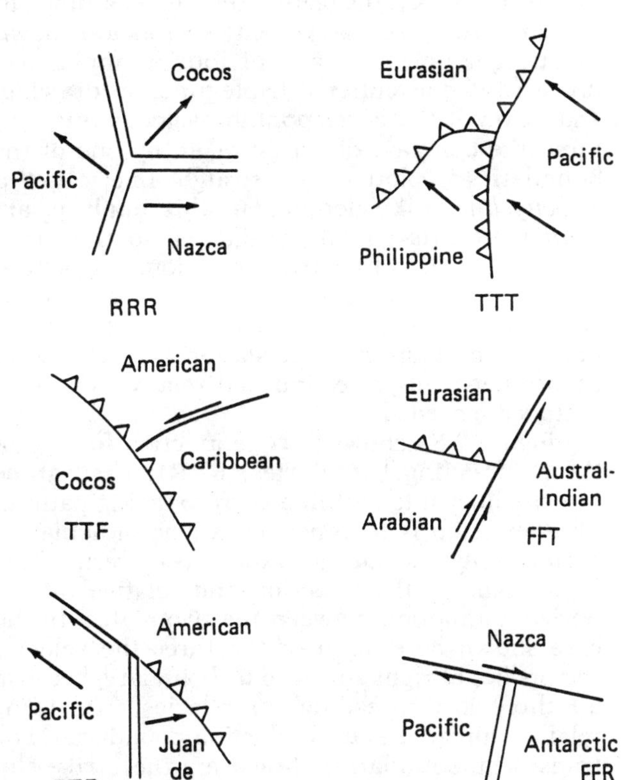

Figure 7.7 Examples of triple junctions. See Figure 7.5 for explanation of symbols. (Copyright © by Arthur N. Strahler.)

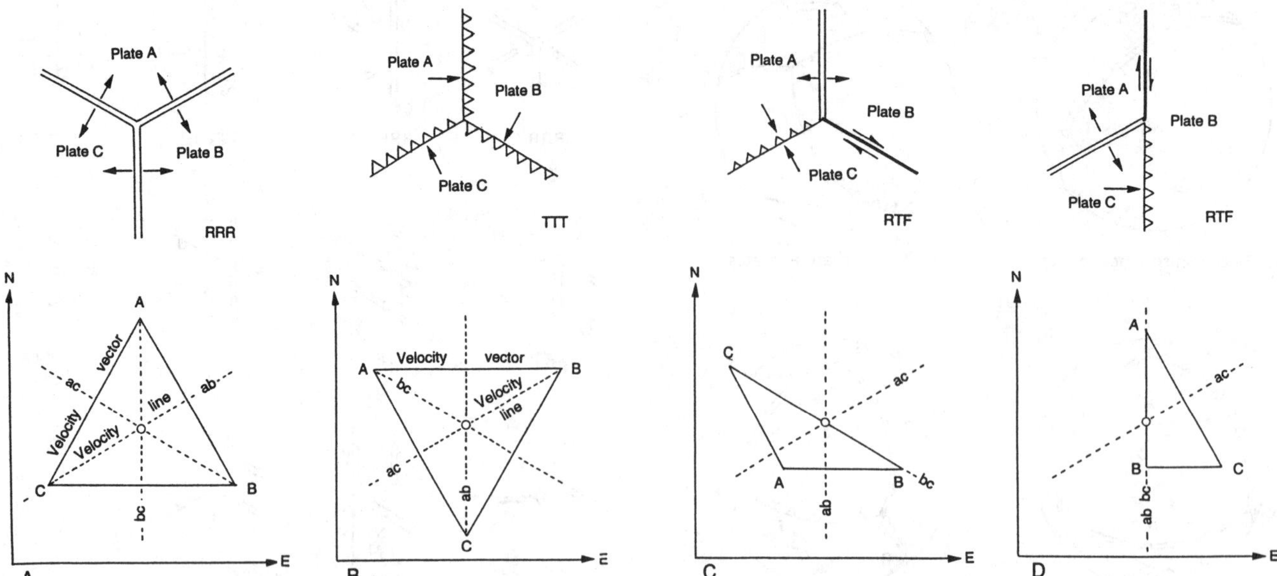

Figure 7.8 Components of plate motion contributing to four kinds of triple plate junctions, with velocity lines and velocity vectors for each. (Copyright © by Arthur N. Strahler.)

Cox and Hart, 1986, p. 51-84; Seyfert, 1987, p. 810-816; Kearey and Vine, 1990, p. 129-137; Moores and Twiss, 1995, p. 64-67).

Figure 7.8 shows the geometrical analysis used to determine the three components of plate motion contributing to the triple plate junction. For the sake of simplicity, the plate assembly is assumed to be planar (flat), so that velocity vectors are shown by straight lines. In each of four examples, we furnish the conventional triple-junction drawing, and below it the corresponding velocity analysis. First, the compass direction taken by one of the boundaries is plotted as a straight line, called a *velocity line*. All velocities in this analysis are *relative velocities*; relative, that is, to the other plates of the trio of the triple junction. In practice, one of the three plates can be designated as stationary, while the other two are considered as moving with respect to the stationary plate and to each other. Only direction and relative length of vectors are needed.

Figure 7.8A shows a triple junction formed of three spreading boundaries (RRR). Their three velocity lines intersect in a corresponding pattern. The next step is to construct a perpendicular to each velocity line, giving us the *velocity vector*. This vector tells us the direction and relative rate of horizontal motion between the two plates. In the case shown here, each of the three the velocity vectors lies at right angles to its boundary, because all three are spreading boundaries. The same relationship applies to subduction boundaries. For transform boundaries, however, the strike-slip motion requires that the velocity vector be drawn parallel with the boundary.

The three velocity vectors are now formed into a triangle, also shown in the lower part of Figure of 7.8A. In this case it turns out to be an equilateral triangle, but departures from that form would occur if the junction angles were unequal; for example two obtuse angles and one acute angle. Figure 7.8B is a similar example, but using three subduction boundaries (TTT). Again, the velocity vectors form an equilateral triangle. Now, the test for stability of the junction lies in those points at which the velocity lines intersect one another. For complete stability, all three velocity lines (ac, ab, bc) should cross one another at a common point. This condition is met for our first two examples.

However, a further provision needs to be added: For triple junctions containing one or more transform boundaries, keep in mind that on a transform boundary, the plates on either side move parallel with the boundary. Therefore the velocity line and the velocity vector lie on one and the same line, not at right angles (as in the case of the spreading and subduction boundaries. Figure 7.8C shows as an example the RTF triple junction. The arrows beside each boundary tell the story. On the lower drawing, we plotted first the velocity line (bc) of the transform fault, and then superimposed on it the velocity vector. After this was done, we plotted the velocity vectors for each of the other two boundaries and connected them to the ends of the transform-fault vector. Figure 7.8D shows the same procedure applied in a somewhat different form of the same triple junction (RTF). Notice that the velocity vector of the transform fault lies superimposed on its own velocity line as well as that of the subduction boundary (since these two boundaries form a straight line).

7.5 Varieties of Transform Faults

In 1965, J. Tuzo Wilson recognized six classes of transform faults, defined according to the kind of

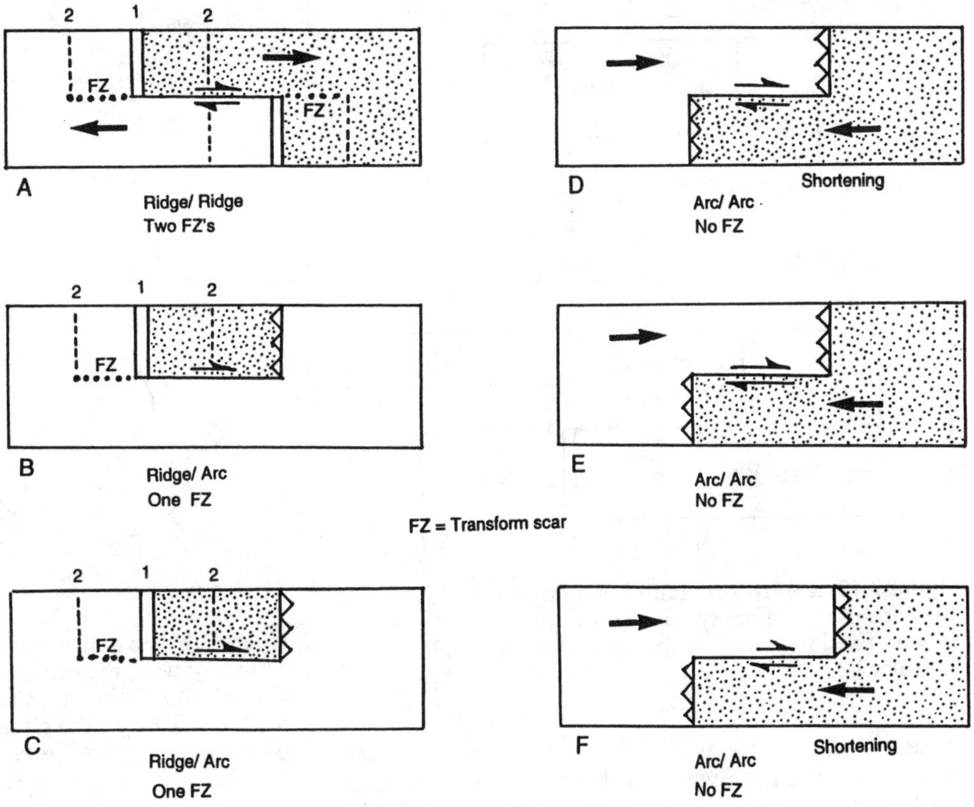

Figure 7.9 Six possible kinds of dextral transform faults entirely within oceanic lithosphere. (Based on data of J. Tuzo Wilson, 1965. Drawing copyright © by Arthur N. Strahler.)

plate boundary to which the transform fault segment is connected at either end. Figure 7.9 shows the six; all being dextral (right lateral) faults (Wilson, 1965). (An equal number of matching classes can be set up for sinistral, or left-lateral, faults.) In Class A, the transform fault connects at both ends with a spreading boundary. This is the typical class for boundaries between two plates of oceanic crust, as found in the mid-oceanic ridge system. On the eastern boundary of the Pacific plate, no less than 60 offsets can be counted, each with an active transform fault. In Class B. the transform fault connects with a spreading boundary at one end and with a subduction boundary at the other. If we should insert at the top of the drawing another dextral transform fault to connect the open ends of the other two boundaries, forming a rectangular plate, it would easily be recognized as the sliding "sunroof" plate model shown in Figure 1.10. Class C pairs with Class B in having the subduction boundary switched to point right. Classes D, E, and F link the transform fault to two subduction boundaries: Class D, opposed and pointing inward; Class E, both pointing left; and Class F, pointing opposite and outward. An example of Class F would be the Alpine fault of the South Island of New Zealand, described in Chapter 6 and illustrated in Figure 6.29. We need only rotate the two subduction boundaries of Figure 7.8D so as to form a continuous line with the transform fault.

Wilson also pointed out that among the six classes of transforms, with the passage of time, two of them (A and E) remain unchanged in length, another (F) grows in length, and one (D) becomes shorter. The consequences of these length restrictions lie in the possibility that transform scars can be formed with the passage of time. First, eliminate the classes for which no transform scar can be formed (D, E, and F); none is possible for these last three, because no spreading boundary is included. As Figure 7.10 shows, Class A will produce two transforms scars simultaneously. Classes B and C can generate a scar in one direction only.

7.6 Plate Rotation on a Sphere

A lithospheric plate is a fragment of a spherical shell that moves as a unit over a complete spherical surface. If you cut apart an old tennis ball, making small pieces of it, you can slide these pieces over the surface of a second ball. In so doing, you will observe that the center point of each small piece follows a circular path as it moves (Figure 7.11). You might then attach a thread to a point near the center of the small piece and anchor the other end of the thread to a pin driven into the complete ball. As you move the small piece, the taut thread serves as a radius controlling the circular track of the small piece. The pin in this model represents the *pole of rotation* of the plate. Note that the "pole" described here is in no way related to the pole of earth rotation, although the two might by barest chance happen to coincide.

The correct scientific term for the pole of

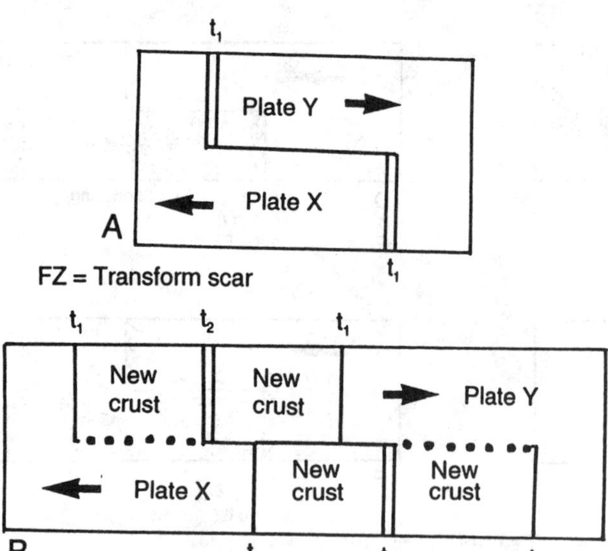

Figure 7.10 A transform fault boundary connecting the ends of two offset spreading boundaries tends to remain fixed in length. (Copyright © by Arthur N. Strahler.)

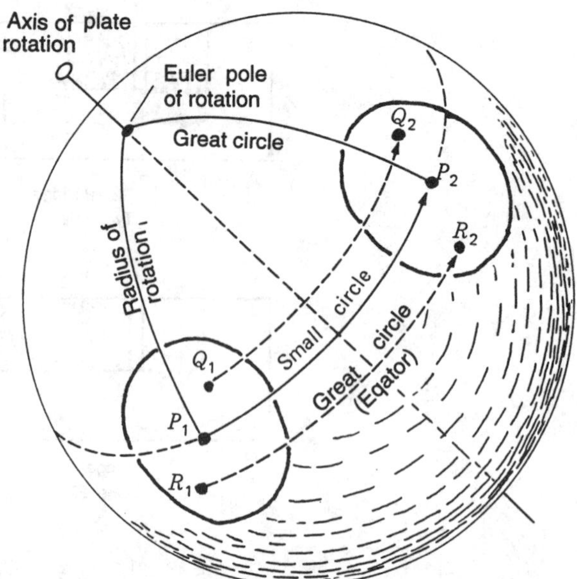

Figure 7.11 As a lithospheric plate moves over the asthenosphere, the radius of rotation with respect to the pole of rotation is an arc of a great circle. Any point (P, Q, R) on the plate follows a small circle. (Copyright © by Arthur N. Strahler.)

rotation of a plate is the *Euler pole*, named after the 18th century Swiss mathematician Leonhard Euler. What we have described above with a pin and a thread is based on Euler's Theorem: The motion of a portion of a sphere over its own surface is uniquely defined by a single angular rotation about a pole of rotation.

To make our model more nearly complete, we should use a pin long enough to pass completely through the ball along its true diameter. The point of emergence is the *antipode*. When this is done, the entire pin represents the *axis of rotation* of the lithospheric plate. When we give (a) the exact global latitude and longitude of the Euler pole of rotation of a given plate and (b) the angular distance, or arc, through which it turns per time unit, we have exactly described its motion. As shown in diagram A of Figure 7.12, the radius of plate motion is always an arc of a *great circle*, whereas the point of reference on the plate produces a track or path that is a *small circle*, as shown in diagram B (see also Figure 7.11). Other points of reference on the same plate produce other small circles, but all of the small circles are parallel and concentric; they share the same pole and axis (Figure 7.11).

A point lying 90° from the pole of rotation would produce a great circle, but this is a special case. We can visualize that points on the plate that are closer to the pole of rotation move shorter distances than those farther from the pole, although all points cover the same arc (degrees) in the same unit of time. This is the same principle that applies to the grooves of a rotating phonograph record or to persons riding on a carousel: Points nearer the outer edge move with greater speed and cover more distance per unit time.

Next, consider a transform fault between two lithospheric plates. Figure 7.13 uses as a background a conventional global grid of meridians of longitude and parallels of latitude (broken lines). On it we have superimposed a tectonic plate with its Euler pole coinciding with the earth's north geographic pole. Its southern boundary is shown as an alternation of north-south segments of oceanic spreading boundary offset by east-west transform faults. Meshed perfectly with this boundary is the opposing boundary of Plate B. (You have probably deduced that Plate B has its Euler pole at the other end of the axis of rotation.) In order for one plate to slide past the other without any gap opening up and without one plate overriding the other, each transform fault must itself be an arc of a small circle conforming to the common pole of rotation. Along the "equator" the transform is a great circle, and it is on this circle that relative plate motion is the fastest. Taking the equatorial value as 100%, we have shown the declining percentages northward. These values will be recognized as the cosines of the respective latitudes in degrees.

It was recognized by D.P. McKenzie and R.L. Parker in 1967 and by W.J. Morgan in 1968 that the geometric relationships described above can be used to locate the Euler pole of a plate, given a good map of the transform faults. Fitting an arc of a small circle to the fault line, a great circle arc can then be projected at a spherical right angle. A common intersection of several such great circle plots should determine approximately the pole position.

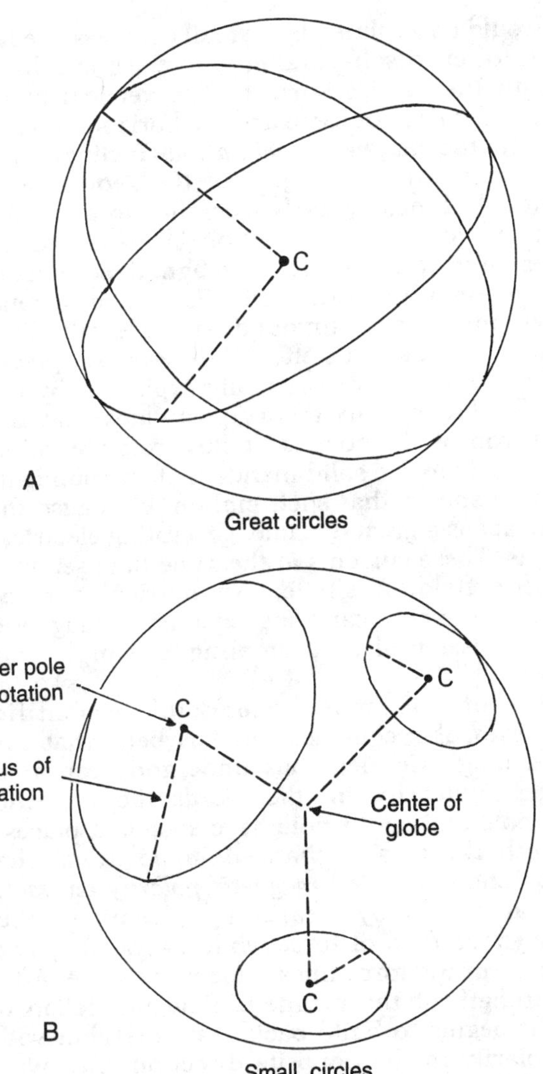

Figure 7.12 A. Great circles are formed by planes slicing through the center of a sphere; circle diameter is the same as sphere diameter. B. Small circles are formed when planes slice through a sphere without passing through the center. (Copyright © by Arthur N. Strahler.)

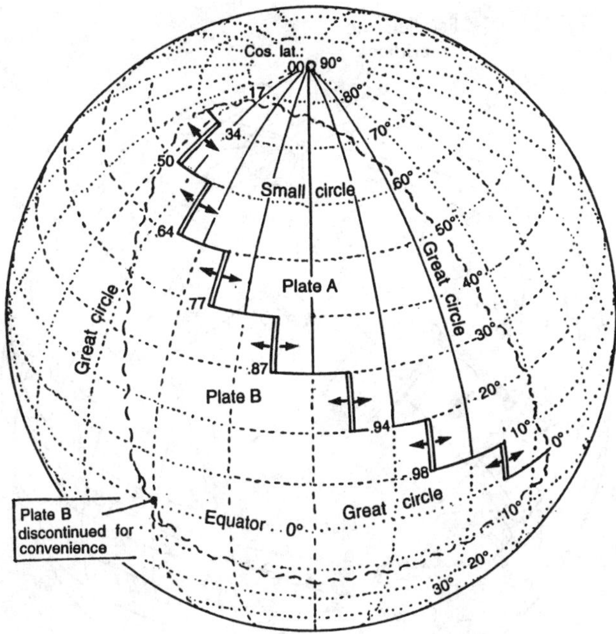

Figure 7.13 Two plates (A, B) joined along a spreading boundary offset by transform faults. Their common Euler pole of rotation is shown to be placed at the North Pole of an ordinary Earth globe with meridians and parallels. (Copyright © by Arthur N. Strahler.)

In Figure 7.14 we have introduced a third plate (Plate C), sharing a plate boundary with Plate B, another Euler pole of relative rotation (Pole B-C) must be plotted. Pole B-C describes the relative motions between Plates B and C. Keep in mind that when we speak of plate motion, we usually mean only the motion of one plate relative to another. Looking at the broad arrows placed at the two plate boundaries in Figure 7.14, it may seem to you that Plate B is moving in a different direction at the spreading boundary with Plate A than at the converging boundary with Plate C. How can a single plate be moving in two different directions at the same time? To resolve this difficulty, imagine that Plate B is not moving at all, but that Plate A is moving away from it in a westward direction while at the same time Plate C is plunging beneath it from the southeast.

The actual motion, or absolute plate motion, would be its motion with respect to the earth's entire inner mantle and core. Absolute motion is very difficult, if not impossible, to measure. We will have more to say about this subject later in the chapter.

The segments of the spreading boundary shown in Figure 7.14 are shown as parts of great circles and lie on radii connecting the boundary segments with the pole of rotation. The segments of spreading boundaries are offset by transform faults. As distance from the pole increases (i.e., as radius of rotation increases), (a) the rate of plate spreading increases. Therefore, new oceanic lithosphere will be produced more rapidly at a greater distance from the pole of relative rotation. For the same reasons, for Plates B and C, sharing the same pole but joined along a subduction boundary, the rate of plate consumption must increase with increasing distance from the pole of relative rotation.

One task that geologists have performed is to calculate the pole of relative rotation of each pair of adjoining lithospheric plates. Of course, the pole of relative rotation between two given plates can change its position through time. When such a change occurs, the track of a reference point undergoes an abrupt change in direction, following a new small-circle track required by the new pole position. Changes in pole positions play an important role in the geologic history of the earth's crust.

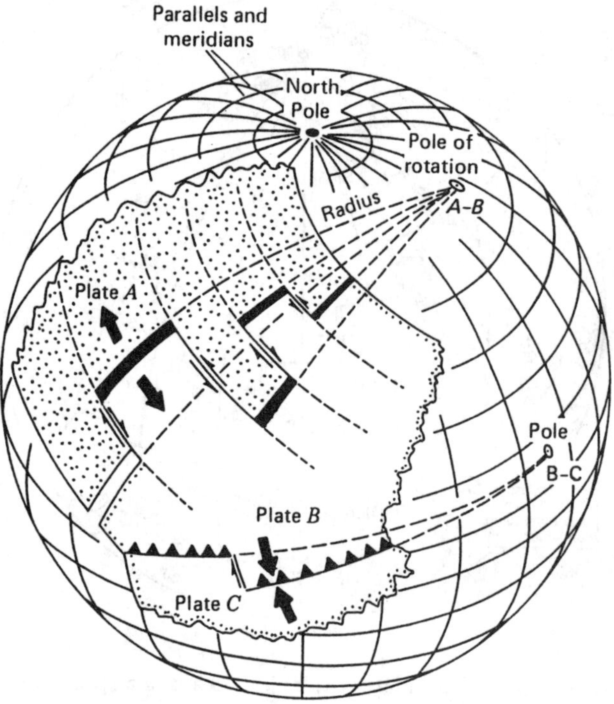

Figure 7.14 The relative motion of two plates in contact along a spreading boundary with transform faults is described by a common pole of relative rotation. The rate of spreading increases with distance from the pole. (Copyright © by Arthur N. Strahler.)

7.7 Geomagnetism

As essential background information, we briefly review the subject of the earth's magnetism, which is called *geomagnetism* (Merrill and McElhinny, 1983). In its simplest aspect, the earth's magnetic field resembles that of a bar magnet located at the earth's center (Figure 7.15). The axis of the imaginary bar magnet coincides roughly with the earth's geographic axis. At the points where the projected line of the magnetic axis, or *geomagnetic axis*, emerges from the earth's surface are the *magnetic poles*. Note that the earth's magnetic axis presently forms an angle of about 15° with respect to the geographic axis. (The angle is exaggerated in the figure for the sake of clarity.) As a result, the magnetic poles do not coincide with the geographic poles.

Figure 7.15 shows lines of force of the earth's magnetic field in relation to the earth's core. The force lines pass through a common point close to the earth's center. The magnetic axis is oriented vertically in this diagram. There exists a *magnetic equator*, lying in a plane at right angles to the geomagnetic axis and encircling the earth's surface approximately in the region of the geographic equator. Visualized in three dimensions, the lines of force of the earth's magnetic field form a succession of doughnutlike rings, suggested in Figure 7.15. The small arrows show the attitude that would be assumed by a small compass needle, free to orient itself parallel with the force lines close to the earth's surface. The vertical angle between the lines of force and the horizontal plane is called the *magnetic inclination*. Inclination is nearly zero over the region of the geomagnetic equator but nearly 90° over the area of the geomagnetic poles. Inclination is measured by means of a *dip needle*, a magnetized needle mounted on a horizontal axis. Force lines extend far out into space surrounding the earth. This entire field of magnetic effect is the *magnetosphere*.

Earth magnetism is usually explained by the *dynamo theory*. This theory postulates that the liquid iron of the core is in slow rotary motion with respect to the solid mantle that surrounds it. It can be shown that such motion will cause the core to act as a great dynamo, generating electrical currents. These currents at the same time set up a magnetic field. A single, symmetrical current system in the core can thus explain the magnetic field as essentially resembling a simple bar magnet.

One of the most remarkable scientific discoveries of recent decades has been that the earth's magnetic field has undergone repeated changes in polarity. In other words, the magnetic north pole and south pole have switched places, but with the axis unchanged in position. The phenomenon is called *magnetic polarity reversal*. Reversal begins by weakening (decay) of the geomagnetic field of force while the polarity and direction of the force lines remain the same. After the strength of the magnetic field has fallen to zero, it begins to build back to normal, but with the polarity in the opposite direction—i.e., with reversed polarity. The time intervals between polarity reversals seem to be irregular in length; the sequence does not follow a cyclic or rhythmic pattern.

7.8 Paleomagnetism

Basaltic lavas as well as lavas of other compositions contain, in addition to the abundant silicate minerals, minor amounts of oxides of iron and titanium. These oxides typically occur as magnetite (Fe_3O_4) intergrown in a solid solution with titanium oxide ($FeTiO_4$ or $FeTiO_3$). Magnetite and other iron minerals susceptible to becoming magnetized are called *magnetic minerals*.

At the high temperatures of a magma, the magnetic minerals have no natural magnetism. As cooling sets in, however, each crystallized magnetic mineral passes a critical temperature known as the *Curie point*, below which the mineral becomes magnetized. The Curie point is reached between 600°C and 400°C. Because the magma crystallizes within the influence of the earth's magnetic field, the magnetism of the mineral particles assumes a direction parallel with the lines of force of the earth's field. With further cooling, this *thermal remnant magnetism* becomes

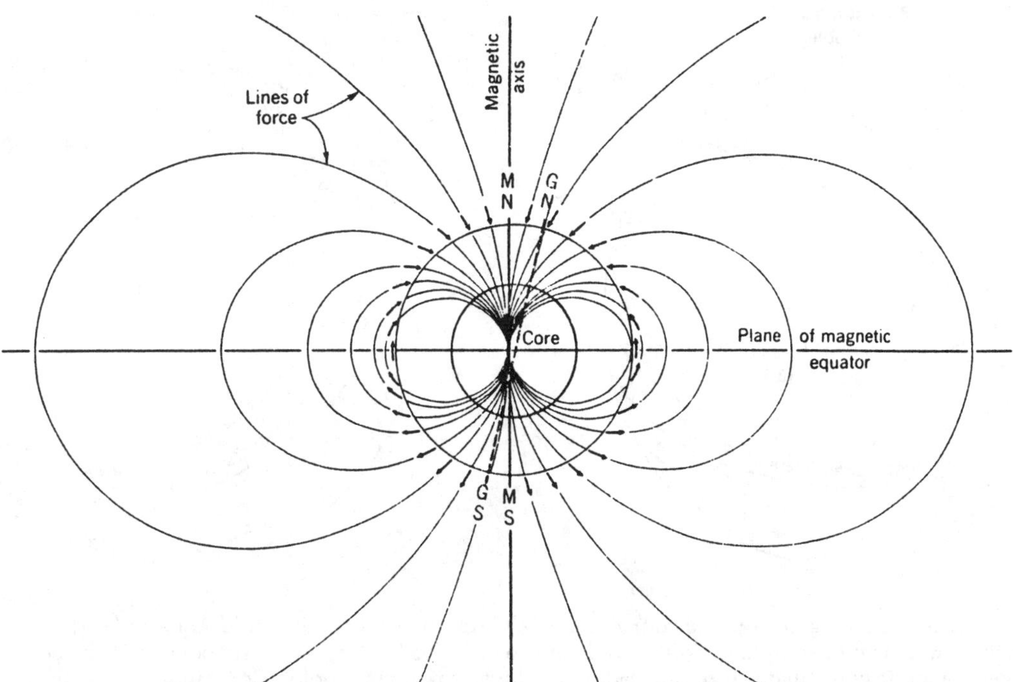

Figure 7.15 Lines of force in the earth's magnetic field are shown here in a cross section passing through the magnetic axis. Letter *M* designates *magnetic*; *G*, *geographic*. Arrows at the surface of the earth show the orientation of a magnetized needle. (Copyright © by Arthur N. Strahler.)

permanently locked within the solidified rock and thereafter serves as an enduring record of the earth's magnetic field at the time the magma cooled. The permanent magnetism that is acquired at various points in geologic time is called *paleomagnetism*.

In the study of igneous rock magnetism, a sample of rock is removed from the surrounding bedrock. Orientation of the specimen core is carefully documented in terms of geographic north and horizontality. The specimen is then placed in a *magnetometer*, a sensitive instrument that measures the direction and intensity of the permanent magnetism within the rock. Measurement is also made of the inclination of the magnetic axis of the specimen. After a number of samples have been obtained from a single lava flow, the magnetic readings are compared for consistency, and then averaged. The average direction and inclination of the paleomagnetism can be compared with present conditions and with the magnetic field at other locations and at different times in the geologic past. Two other forms of paleomagnetism are useful in working out past geologic events. One is a permanent magnetism acquired by a hydrogenic mineral as it grows by chemical precipitation. Hematite, an oxide of iron (Fe_2O_3), is one such mineral that acquires permanent magnetism as it forms from weathering processes involving the oxidation of magnetite. More important, however, is *detrital remnant magnetism*, which is found in detrital sediments laid down in quiet water of lakes or the oceans. Particles of magnetic minerals, previously magnetized, come to rest in a position of orientation in which their magnetic axes are parallel with the earth's magnetic force lines. In other words, the particles act like compass needles that swing into line with the force field surrounding them. Detrital magnetism can also be acquired during diagenesis after sedimentation. Needless to say, detrital remnant magnetism is of great value in determining the paleomagnetic history of layers of pelagic-detrital sediment that have accumulated on the deep ocean floor.

Rock samples that retain permanent magnetism acquired at the time of their origin yield two kinds of information. One is the compass direction of the lines of force; it tells the direction one would follow on a great circle to reach the former north (or south) magnetic pole (Figure 7.16A). The other item of information is the inclination of the former magnetic lines of force at the point where the sample is taken. Looking back to Figure 7.15, it is obvious that the magnetic inclination, as registered by the angle of a dip needle at the earth's surface, will vary according to the magnetic latitude. Thus, the amount of inclination read from the sample tells the distance to the former magnetic north pole. "Distance" in this case is the number of degrees of arc along the great circle to the former pole (Figure 7.16A). The paleomagnetic data tell us the position of the former north magnetic pole in terms of present latitude and longitude, stated in our conventional system of geographic coordinates. But, as you can

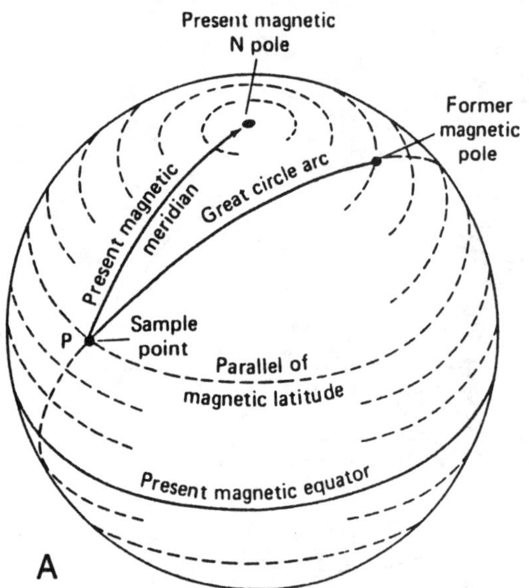

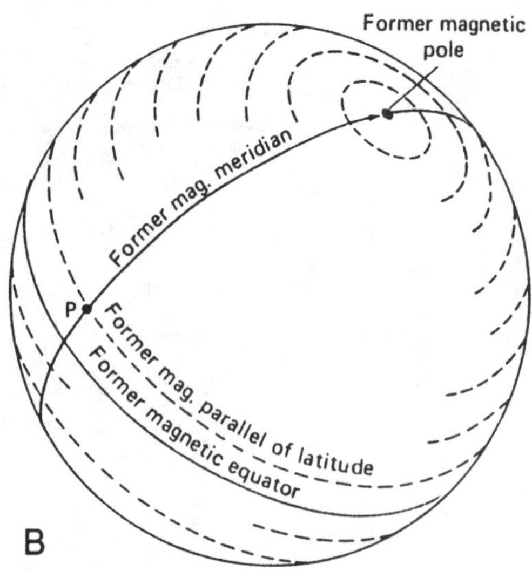

Figure 7.16 Present and past geomagnetic coordinates. (A) Present geomagnetic pole, equator, and meridian. Paleomagnetism of sample at Point P indicates where the former magnetic pole was located. (B) Former geomagnetic coordinate system based on the former magnetic pole. (Copyright © by Arthur N. Strahler.)

see from Figure 7.16B, the sample point could have been located anywhere on the former geomagnetic parallel of latitude. In other words, while we know the former geomagnetic latitude of the sample, we do not know the former geomagnetic longitude. [The subject of paleomagnetism is continued in Chapter 13.]

7.9 Geomagnetic Polarity Reversals

As early as 1906, Bernard Brunhes, a French physicist, had observed that the magnetic polarity of some samples of lavas is exactly the reverse of present conditions. He concluded that the earth's magnetic poles must have been reversed at the time the lava solidified. You might wish to propose as an alternative hypothesis that through the passage of time the rock magnetism itself has spontaneously undergone a change in polarity, and this possibility has been given careful study, along with other possible alternatives. In the 1920s, a Japanese geophysicist, Motonari Matuyama, made extensive studies of the magnetism of samples of young volcanic rocks. He found that while one group of samples showed magnetic inclination close to that of the present geomagnetic field, a second group showed polarity roughly opposite to that of the first group. He also estimated the ages of his rock samples, finding that rocks of his second group were all of early Pleistocene age or older. The observations of Brunhes and Matuyama remained 'on the shelf' for the next three decades. During that period advances were made in the dynamo theory of terrestrial magnetism, and some consensus was reached that polarity reversal was a possibility (Cox, 1973, p. 138-139).

Three lines of evidence favor the hypothesis that the earth's magnetic poles have switched directions at time intervals as short as 50,000 y (0.05 m.y.) and over much longer intervals. The first is a necessary geological field relationship, such as that shown schematically in Figure 7.17, in which an intruding dike has formed an adjacent baked zone in the older country rock. Intense heating of the country rock has caused its remnant magnetism to be reformed to match that of the cooling intrusive mass. A second line of evidence needed to reinforce the first is the finding of a geological field relationship in which a continuous change from one polarity to the other is demonstrated. This requirement is illustrated in Figure 7.18, showing detrital remnant magnetism in sedimentary strata laid down on the floor of the ocean or a deep lake. Through successively younger layers the inclination has rotated through 180 degrees. The third line of evidence is required of all polarities observed in the stratigraphic record: All rock samples of a given geologic age the world over must be of the same polarity. This requires that the duration of the single period of polarity, whether it be normal or reversed, is long enough to encompass the probable error of measurement of the geologic age. In recent years, there has been general agreement among members of the scientific community that these requirements have been met, and that rock magnetism is a permanent and reliable indicator of the former states of the earth's magnetic field.

Intensive research on magnetic polar reversals set in during the late 1950s. Pioneering geophysicists in this field included former graduate students at the University of California-Berkeley: Richard Doell, Brent Dalrymple, and Allan Cox.

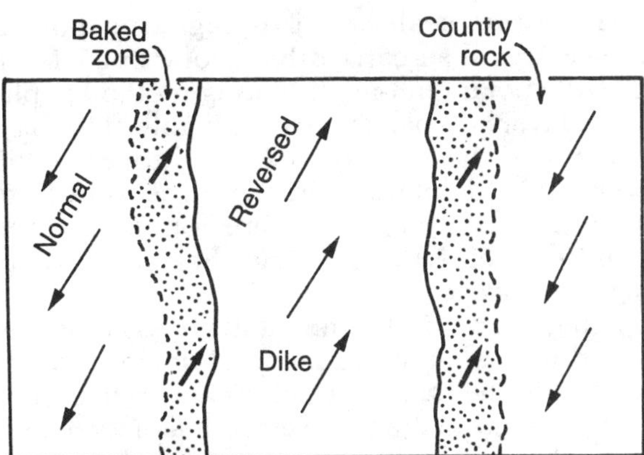

Figure 7.17 Sketch of an outcrop of a vertical dike showing the baked zone which its intense heat has caused in the enclosing country rock. Arrows show magnetic polarity. (Copyright © by Arthur N. Strahler.)

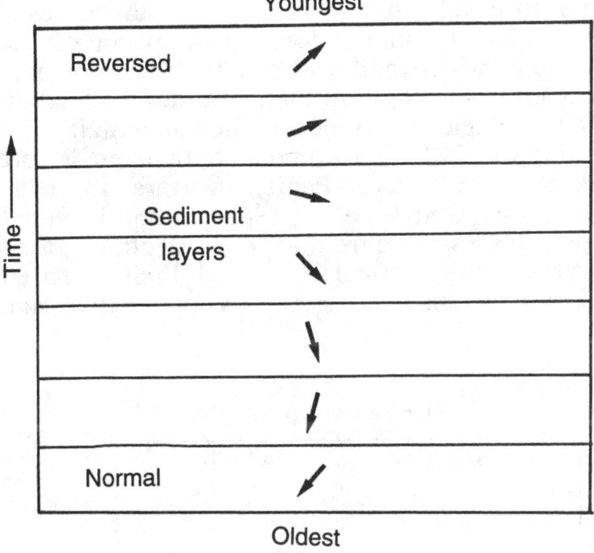

Figure 7.18 Schematic vertical cross-section through a deep-sea core showing the change in magnetic inclination in successive sediment layers as the polarity is completely reversed. (Copyright © by Arthur N. Strahler.)

Carrying on their research on the staff of the U.S. Geological Survey, their group produced several major papers between 1960 and 1964 (see Cox and Doell, 1960; Cox, 1961, Cox, Doell, and Dalrymple, 1964), and more in later years of the 1960s that also included other co-authors. (See also Cox, Dalrymple, and Doell, 1967.) In the late 1950s Allan Cox undertook a study of reversed polarity in basalt samples of the Snake River Plain. His initial conservative hypothesis was that those reversals are controlled by differences the mineralogy of the samples. After several years of work on this project, he came to the conclusion that polarity depended, instead, on the age of the sample (Cox, 1973, p. 140-141).

7.10 Polarity Reversals and the Geologic Time scale

The geologic age of a rock specimen is available through radiometric methods. We assume our readers to be familiar with these methods (see Dalrymple, 1991; Eicher, 1976). By the late 1950s, potassium-argon dating was made sufficiently accurate to allow dating of Pleistocene samples, and by the late 1960s permitted dating to a limit of about 4.5 Ma, which includes most of the Pliocene Epoch. Extensive determinations of both magnetic data and rock ages soon revealed that there have been at least seven *geomagnetic polarity reversals* of the earth's magnetic field in the last 4 m.y. Figure 7.19 shows the time scale of these magnetic events, as determined in 1964. Polarity matching that which exists today is referred to as a *normal epoch*, opposite polarity as a *reversed epoch*. Each epoch was named for an individual or a locality. For example, the pioneer work of Bernard Brunhes is recognized in assigning his name to the present *Brunhes normal epoch,* which began about 700,000 years ago (0.7 Ma). An epoch of reversal, honoring the early contributions of Motonori Matuyama, extends to 2.4 Ma. This *Matuyama reversed epoch* contains two shorter periods of normal polarity classified as *events.* They are the Jarmillo and Olduvai normal events. Still older is the *Gauss normal epoch,* named in honor of the mathematician Karl Gauss (1777-1855). It carries back the paleomagnetic record to about 3.3 Ma, and

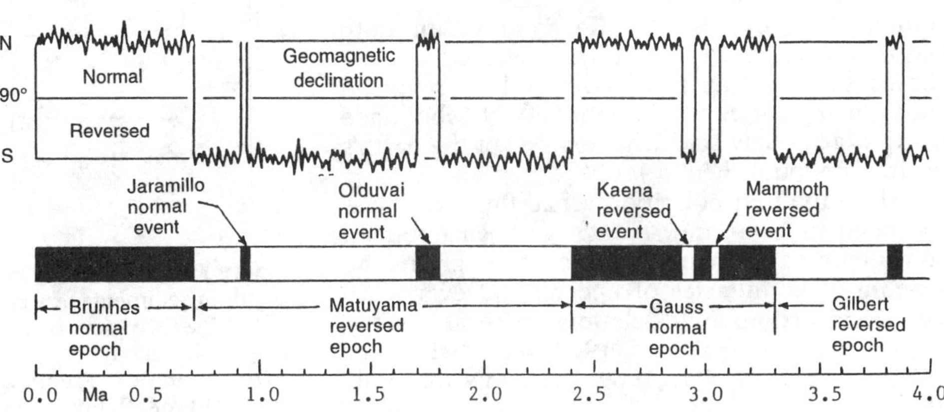

Figure 7.19 Time scale of magnetic polarity reversals over the past 4 m.y. The graph of geomagnetic declination fluctuations is schematic. (Adapted from data of E.A. Mankinen and G.B. Dalrymple, 1979, *Jour. of Geophysical Res.*, v. 84, p. 615-626. Used by permission of the American Geophysical Union.)

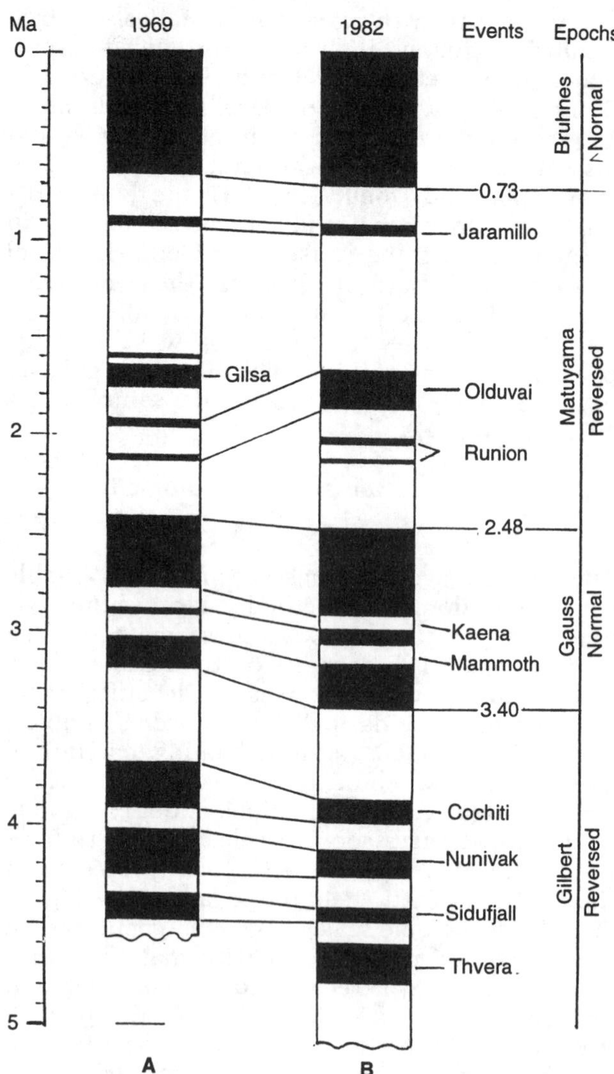

Figure 7.20 A comparison between two magnetic reversal schedules. At the left (A) is a 1969 version extending to 4.5 Ma. At right (B), a 1992 version, with events and epochs labeled. (A. From Allan Cox, 1969, *Science*, v. 163, p. 240. Copyright © 1969 by the American Association for the Advancement of Science. Used by permission. B. From W.B. Harland, A.V. Cox, et al., *A Geologic Time Scale*, p. 66. Copyright 1982 by the the Cambridge University Press. Used by permission.)

contains two reversals, the Kaena and Mammoth reversed events. Oldest of the reversed epochs shown on the diagram is the Gilbert reversed epoch, named after Sir William Gilbert, who made the first genuinely scientific analysis of the earth's magnetism, published in 1600.

Since the first polarity reversal time scale was compiled in 1964, new data have been obtained and minor adjustments made accordingly in the spacing of boundaries of epochs and events, as well as insertions and deletions of some events. Figure 7.20 compares a 1969 scale with one published in 1982 (Cox, 1969; Harland, Cox, et al., 1982).

The time scale of geomagnetic polarity reversals was then carried back to about 7 Ma by use of the potassium-argon dating method applied to lava layers. A particularly valuable find was a succession of lava layers in Iceland totaling 3500 meters in thickness. There, three additional magnetic polarity epochs were found to extend beyond the Gilbert epoch, and these were simply designated as epochs 5, 6, and 7.

Using the detrital remnant magnetism of deep-sea sediments, it became possible in 1966 for scientists of the Lamont Geological Observatory to identify the normal and reversed magnetic epochs in samples of soft sediment obtained from the ocean floor by piston-coring (Opdyke, Glass, Hayes, and Foster, 1966). On the sea floor, epochs are encountered in age sequence from top to bottom within the core. Core orientation is not known in terms of north and south, since the cores are turned frequently during extraction and handling, but top and bottom are known. Therefore paleomagnetic analysis can be based upon magnetic inclination. Small specimens are cut from the core and subjected to measurement of magnetic inclination. At high latitudes, inclination is a high angle with respect to the horizontal.

Figure 7.21 shows actual data from a core taken from North Pacific waters in 1968 (Ninkovich, Opdyke, et al., 1966, p. 486). Each dot represents a sample from the core. Depth in core is given on the vertical axis, and inclination in degrees on the horizontal axis. A negative sign

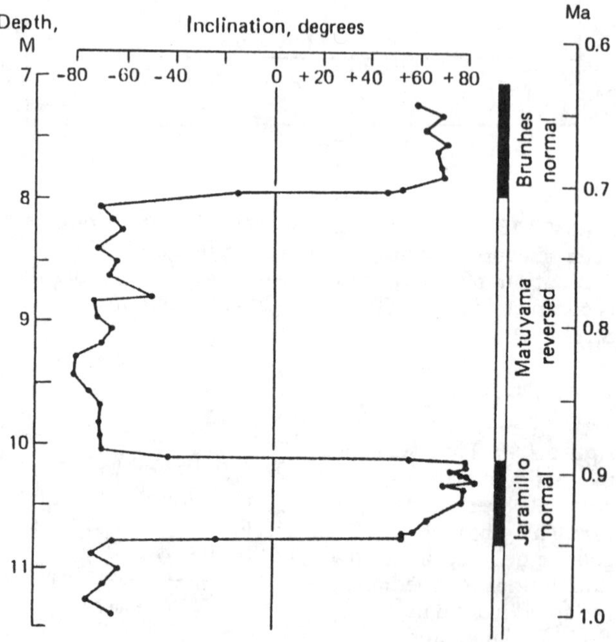

Figure 7.21 Changes in magnetic inclination with depth in sediments of a core taken at about lat. 45°N in the Pacific Ocean by the Research Vessel *Vema*. (From N.D. Opdyke, p. 64 in *History of Earth's Crust: Symposium*, R.A. Phinney, Ed., Princeton University Press © 1968. Reproduced by permission.)

means that the north-seeking end of a dip needle would point down (normal field); a positive sign means that the same end of the needle would point upward (reversed field). Along the right of the graph is the history of polarity reversals, as in Figure 7.19.

Because of the established time scale of polarity reversals, it was possible to establish the rate of accumulation of deep-sea sediment at the locations sampled by the cores. For North Pacific cores, this rate was found to differ from core to core and ranged between 0.3 and 1.1 cm per year. Sediment cores reveal older epochs of polarity reversals dating back tens of millions of years.

7.11 Sea-Floor Spreading as the Discovery Key to Plate Tectonics

We are now prepared to return to the subject of the tectonics of sea-floor spreading along the mid-oceanic ridge, making use of magnetic polarity reversals as evidence of plate spreading and the rates at which it occurs. First, however, it is appropriate to review the related historical events that were taking place during the decades 1950-1970 in the formulation of plate tectonics as a scientific theory. Our account in Chapter 2, covering earlier historical events, took a close look at Arthur Holmes's 1933 diagram (republished in 1944) of continental rifting to form a new ocean with an axial island, or "swell" (see Figure 2.23). While his model was clearly one of a pulling apart and rupturing of a continent to open up an ocean basin, it lacked any hint of a rising and diverging current of hot mantle situated beneath a fixed spreading axis. As we noted, Arthur A. Meyerhoff in 1968 nominated Holmes as "originator of (the) spreading ocean floor hypothesis." We added that, in response, Robert S. Dietz had observed that "Holmes' concept is not really sea-floor spreading," while Harry H. Hess had commented that Holmes' model and that of modern sea-floor spreading "have very little in common" (see Chapter 2 for references).

As explained in Chapter 4, during the 1950's our knowledge of topography of the ocean floors began to unfold rapidly as profiles generated by the precision depth recorder transected entire ocean basins in many parts of the globe. Collecting and plotting these profiles at the Lamont-Doherty Geologic Observatory (L-DGO) of Columbia University, Bruce C. Heezen and Marie Tharp made detailed topographic diagrams of the mid-oceanic ridges, and they were led to make a fundamental interpretation that seemed inescapable: seafloor spreading must be in progress. Heezen presented his interpretation in this author's graduate seminar, and the argument seemed highly plausible, but the hypothesis attracted no support from Maurice Ewing, who headed the Lamont observatory. (Ewing at that time was a stalwart member of the "fixist" group and held to the theory that the ocean basins were geologically ancient crustal areas.)

Unhappily, acceptance of sea-floor spreading forced Heezen into a serious theoretical dilemma, because the Atlantic and Indian ocean basins were flanked by passive margins with no mechanism to "dispose" of the expanding oceanic crust. Moreover, the trenches of the circum-Pacific margins were still an enigma, and the Lamont geophysicists had recently shown the falsity of a popular theory that a deep crustal downfold was active along the continental marginal deeps (Ewing and Worzel, 1954; Worzel and Ewing, 1954). Keep in mind that seismic proof was yet to come that oceanic crust was continually subducting beneath continental crust. This information vacuum left Heezen with no alternative but to adopt an expanding-earth theory, which he did in 1958. Independently, geophysicist Laszlo Egyed had published in 1956 a paper proposing that earth expansion was necessary to account for the wide separation of the fragments of Pangaea. Heezen also gained as a fellow advocate Samuel W. Carey, an Australian geologist who had been expounding since 1953 his own special theory of an expanding earth.

In December 1959, Heezen presented a paper at a symposium held at Columbia University. The symposium title was "Concepts of the expanding earth and continental drift. The paper title: "The tectonic evolution of the oceans." We reproduce here as Figure 7.22 a hastily drawn manuscript figure from the unpublished text of that paper; it

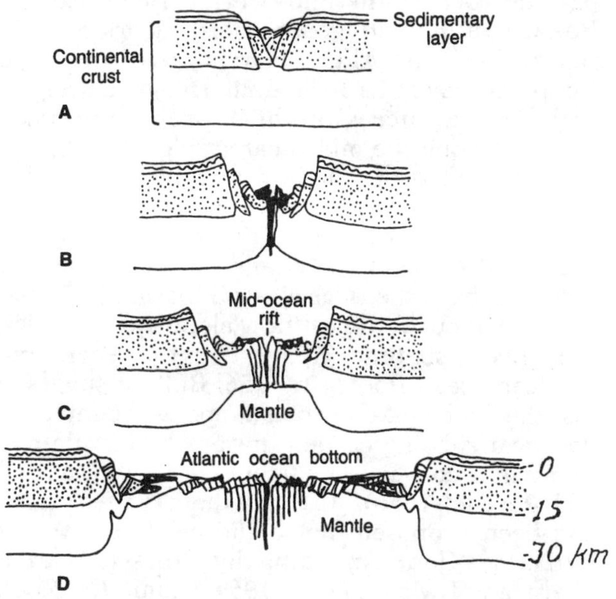

Figure 7.22 This rough sketch of stages in rifting apart of a continent and the formation of a widening ocean basin was drawn by Bruce Heezen for presentation in a 1959 symposium. It was intended to illustrate his views on the sequence of oceanic crustal development. Labels are taken from legend of Heezen, 1960. See our text for full description. (Used by permission of Marie Tharp.)

bore the legend: "Schematic sequence of oceanic crustal development." The diagram traces the evolution of a new ocean basin from the initial stage of continental rifting to a full-blown but narrow ocean basin. Two layers of continental crust are shown—felsic above, mafic below. A strong vertical center line gives the impression of a feeder dike rising vertically beneath the axial rift, and that as the rift valley widens, vertical dikes fill in the available space. Clearly, this was a scenario of sea-floor spreading as a process of generating a new ocean floor. However, no hint is given of convection currents in the mantle. The four stages shown are stated to be modeled after the following topographic profiles: A. African Rift Valley, passing through Lake Tanganyika; B. Red Sea, between Somalia and Aden; C. North Atlantic, between Greenland and Spitzbergen; D. Mid-Atlantic Ridge between Flemish Cap and England. (A finished version of Figure 7.22 was published in Heezen's widely distributed popular paper in the *Scientific American*, October, 1960.) Thus we can credit Heezen with the first graphic description of sea-floor spreading in its modern form. It was to be adopted some years later by J. Tuzo Wilson as a model for the early stages of his cycle of the opening and closing of ocean basins (Jacobs, Russell, and Wilson, 1974, Chapters 15-16).

At this time Heezen and others of the Lamont research staff had at their disposal some important information about heat flow along the mid-oceanic ridge axis. In the early 1950s geophysicists had been successful in making accurate measurements of heat flow in the sediment layer overlying the basaltic rock of the mid-oceanic ridge. Edward Bullard, a British geophysicist, working with researchers of the Scripps Institution of Oceanography at La Jolla, California, had designed and built a successful heat probe and taken readings along the mid-oceanic ridge. [In Chapter 5 we described the modern method of heat-flow measurement by means of thermister probes attached to piston cores (Figure 5.10), and we presented data on the change in heat flow rate outwards from the ridge axis.] Bullard's group had shown that outward heat flow along the ridges was some five to six times greater than the general rate for deep ocean floors. In 1956, Bullard suggested that this high heat-flow rate supports the inference that heat is being carried upward by mantle rock rising in a convection current (Bullard, Maxwell, and Revelle, 1956). Already, then, a mechanism had been proposed that could easily be worked into a sea-floor spreading hypothesis. Heezen, Tharp, and Ewing, in their 1959 volume *The Floors of the Ocean*, had already cited Bullard's findings on heat flow and recognized them as important in understanding the dynamics of the mid-oceanic ridges, but their text falls short of suggesting any specific use of that information (1959, p. 103).

Strong support soon came to Heezen's 1959 seafloor spreading model in a paper by Robert S. Dietz, published in June 1961 in *Nature*, then (as now) a prestigious British science journal. Its title: Continent and ocean basin evolution by spreading of the sea floor. Dietz was then on the staff of the U.S. Navy Electronics Laboratory in San Diego and was a veteran contributor to the science of the ocean floors. He made use of the strong distinction between continental and oceanic lithosphere, stressing the petrologic, seismologic, and density differences between continental and oceanic lithosphere and crust, and the way in which isostatic equilibrium assured that the continents would rise high above the level of the sea floor. A description of his "sea floor theory" followed:

> Thus the oceanic 'crust' (the gabbroic layer) is almost wholly coupled with the convective overturn of the mantle creeping at a rate of a few cm./yr. So the sea floor marks the tops of the convection cells and slowly spreads from zones of divergence to those of convergence. The gross structures of the sea floor are direct expressions of this convection. The median rises mark the up-welling sites or divergences; the trenches are associated with the convergences or down-welling sites; and the fracture zones mark shears between regions of slow and fast creep. (p. 855)

Dietz called attention to the median position of the rises (axial rifts) as a strong point of evidence that the spreading had controlled the opening and widening of the Atlantic basin. He recognized that "the role of the continents is passive":

> It also follows that the clastic detritus swept into the deep sea from the continents is not permanently lost. Rather it is carried slowly towards, and then beneath, the continents, where it is granitized and added anew to the sialic blocks. (p. 856)

Perhaps the most significant new contribution Dietz made in this paper was to visualize the entire plate tectonic cycle from uprising, divergence, and lateral spreading to its final destination in convergence and descent at the foot of the continents. In short, he put together an entire flow system of mass from beginning to end, i.e., from source to sink.

Closely following Dietz's contribution was a 1962 paper by Harry H. Hess of Princeton University, whose pioneering oceanographic studies we noted in Chapter 2 in connection with his discovery and naming of guyots. Hess had specialized in the petrology of the crust and mantle with special attention to the serpentization of the crust. In this paper, Hess endorsed the mechanism of a mantle convection system in which a rising current divides its flow near the surface into two laterally-flowing currents. His cross-section showing this system is reproduced here as Figure 7.23. He described the process as including "actual movement of the earth's surface passively riding on

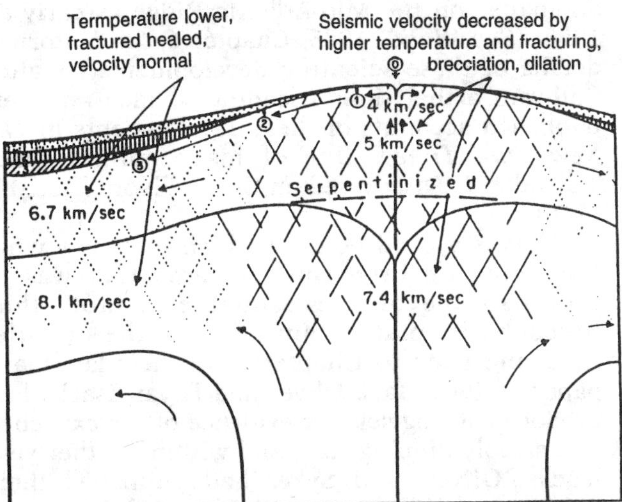

Figure 7.23 Harry H. Hess's 1962 diagram showing how pelagic sediments accumulating on the sea floor would be carried away from the axial ridge crest ridge by convective flow of mantle rock rising and spreading laterally. (From H.H. Hess, 1962,in *Petrological Studies*, a volume in honor of A.F. Buddington; Engel, James, and Leonard, Eds., Reproduced with permissionn of the publisher, the Geological Society of America, Boulder, Colorado, USA. Copyright © 1962.)

the upper part of the convection cell" (Hess, 1962, p. 30). The line of separation into two diverging crustal layers he placed exactly on the axial rift of the mid-oceanic ridge. He accepted Heezen's estimate of a widening rate. Hess's amplification of this concept includes a clear statement that the moving crust is finally carried downward close to the active continental margins:

> On the system here suggested any sediment upon the sea floor ultimately gets incorporated in the continents. New mantle material with no sedimentary cover on it rises and moves outward from the ridge. The cover of young sediments it acquires in the course of time will move to the axis of a downward-moving limb of a convection current, be metamorphosed, and probably eventually be welded onto a continent. (1962, p. 31)

Although Hess makes no mention *per se* of subducting slabs of lithosphere, his last sentence (above) comes very close describing our present concept of what takes place along subduction boundaries. His closing paragraph summarizes the entire main theme of plate tectonics, and is well worth quoting in full:

> The Atlantic, Indian, and Arctic oceans are surrounded by the trailing edges of continents moving away from them, whereas the Pacific Ocean is faced by the leading edges of continents moving toward the island arcs and representing the downward-flowing limbs of mantle convection cells or, as in the case of the eastern Pacific margin, they have plunged into and in part overriden the zone of strong deformation over the downward-flowing limbs. (1962, p. 37)

Unfortunately, Hess's diagram does not include the continental margins, so his picture of that part of the mantle convection cell remains obscure. His figure does, however, show how successive layers of sediment accumulate during spreading. From zero thickness at the axial rift, each layer thickens with increasing distance, a relationship that has since been fully documented over large areas. He also shows that the crust and mantle subside as they move away, causing deepening of the ocean floor. This relationship we have described in Chapter 4 (Figure 4.25). Hess also pointed out that the consistent central location of the mid-oceanic ridge as it is traced through the North and South Atlantic ocean basins is a telling argument in favor of sea-floor spreading. He did not, however, use the term "sea-floor spreading." From what Hess put forward in this paper, it is understandable that he has been credited by many geologists with having been the first to present a satisfactory basic statement of sea-floor spreading coupled with crustal descent into the asthenosphere. His statement (like Dietz's) remains largely valid to the present. In the question of priority of these two key papers we have compared, judgment should not be made on the basis of date of publication, for Hess had completed his paper early in 1960 and it had been widely circulated for nearly two years before being published (Menard, 1986, p. 152-153). Rather, we should appreciate the expression of two quite different and independently derived perspectives: Hess's, from classic petrology; Dietz's from marine geology. Taken in combination, we can consider these two documents to be the first announcement of a theory soon to be given the name "plate tectonics."

7.12 Paleomagnetism and Sea-Floor Spreading

If the axial rift valley is indeed a line of upwelling basaltic lavas, and if crustal spreading is a steady, continuous process, the lava flows that have poured out in the vicinity of the axial rift will be slowly moved away from the rift. [See Chapter 5 for coverage of igneous activity on and beneath oceanic spreading plate boundaries and descriptions of the igneous surface features of the rift zones.] The solid lava, being brittle, is easily fractured by extensional stress. Fissures form continuously in the floor of the axial rift. The newly formed ribbon of lava is continuously divided more-or-less into two halves, one half adhering to the crust on one side of the rift and the other half adhering to the opposite side. A similar process of division takes place in the underlying gabbroic and ultramafic rock of the newly formed crust and upper mantle. Thus the lithospheric

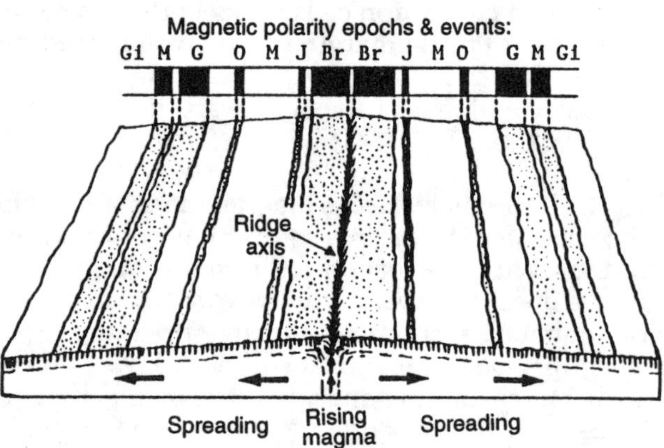

Figure 7.24 Schematic diagram of development of a symmetrical pattern of magnetic polarity stripes in ocean-floor basalts during sea-floor spreading. See Figure 7.19 for time scale. (Copyright © by Arthur N. Strahler.)

plates on the two sides of the spreading boundary undergo accretion at about equal rates. (Inequality in rate of accretion on the two sides does occur in some cases.) As a result of this continuous process, the oceanic crust produced in a given interval of time—say one million years—forms two parallel bands or stripes of equal width, one on each side of the rift. As time passes, stripes of the same age-span will increase in distance of separation, as shown in Figure 7.24. The lava zones, dubbed 'zebra stripes,' can be identified in terms of the epochs of normal and reversed magnetic polarity. In our figure, these epochs will be represented by symmetrical striped patterns on either side of the rift. In the history of plate tectonics, this explanation is now known as the *Vine-Matthews hypothesis*, named for the two scientists who published it in *Nature* in 1963: F.J. Vine and D.H. Matthews.

Actually, Lawrence Morley, a student of J. Tuzo Wilson, had also been carrying out research on magnetic anomalies of the North Atlantic sea floor, using data from traverses made by Canadian aircraft as well as ships. A manuscript of his paper, explaining how magnetic anomalies could reveal polarity reversals and thus measure the rate of sea-floor spreading, was submitted to *Nature* early in 1963, but was rejected, as was a letter then submitted to the *Journal of Geophysical Research*. Meantime, the Vine-Matthews manuscript was published later that same year (R.M. Wood, 1985, p. 151-152). Thus it would seem only fair to use the name "Morley-Vine-Matthews hypothesis."

In 1965, Wilson joined Vine in supporting the new hypothesis with data from off the coast of Vancouver. In 1966, Vine published in *Science* more evidence that included magnetic anomaly stripes from the Rejykanes Ridge south of Iceland, obtained by J.R. Heirtzler, X. Le Pichon, and J.G. Baron of the Columbia's Lamont Geological Observatory. That group had described magnetic anomalies on the Mid-Atlantic Ridge as early as 1953. (See Wood, 1985, Chapter 6, for historical details of these scientific developments.) Walter Sullivan, a that time a leading science reporter, published accounts of these developments in *The New York Times*. One of his headlines read: 'Calendar' Is Discovered on Ocean Floors (Dec. 10, 1966).

This is a good point at which to review what was going on in seismic research that was to establish beyond reasonable doubt that lithospheric plates plunge into the mantle. Referring back to Chapter 6, in their landmark paper of 1967, Jack Oliver and Bryan Isacks had produced strong seismic evidence of the existence of a steeply dipping slab, and within another year Isacks, Oliver, and Sykes had published their summary 1968 paper with the now-legendary schematic block diagram showing both sea-floor spreading and lithospheric subduction as comprising a working tectonic system (see Figure 6.9).

We turn now to some of the technical details of the recording and analysis of the magnetic anomaly patterns. By the early 1950s the use of magnetometers towed by oceanographic research vessels had already begun. An improved model of fluxgate magnetometer developed by Maurice Ewing at Lamont came into use to carry out east-west traverses across the mid-oceanic ridge in both Atlantic and Pacific oceans. It was quickly found that there are small variations in the strength of the magnetic field. These departures from a constant normal value are referred to as *magnetic anomalies*.

An improved model of the magnetometer made it capable of accurate calibration and was put in use by 1954 by the Scripps Institution of Oceanography. Ronald G. Mason of Scripps was fortunate enough to have been invited by the U.S. Navy to use the improved model on a detailed hydrographic survey cruise covering a 500 km wide band of sea floor extending from south to north off the U.S. and British Columbia coast. The parallel traverses were spaced 8 km apart so that, as with topographic profiles across a set of parallel mountain ridges, contours of the magnetic "terrain" could be drawn.

Much to everyone's surprise, there emerged a persistent pattern of parallel magnetic "ridges" and "valleys." If one were to apply a dark color only to the ridges, there would emerge a map pattern of narrow bands or stripes, extending for long distances. The stripes of normal polarity (positive anomalies) were referred to as "highs"; those of reversed polarity (negative anomalies) as "lows." Figures 7.25 and 7.26 show magnetic field anomaly maps of two widely separated expanses of the ocean floor. Figure 7.25 shows the mapped region off the Pacific west coast; Figure 7.26, a smaller area southwest of Iceland in the North Atlantic, centered on a section of the Mid-Atlantic Ridge known as the Rekjyanes Ridge. Notice the mirror

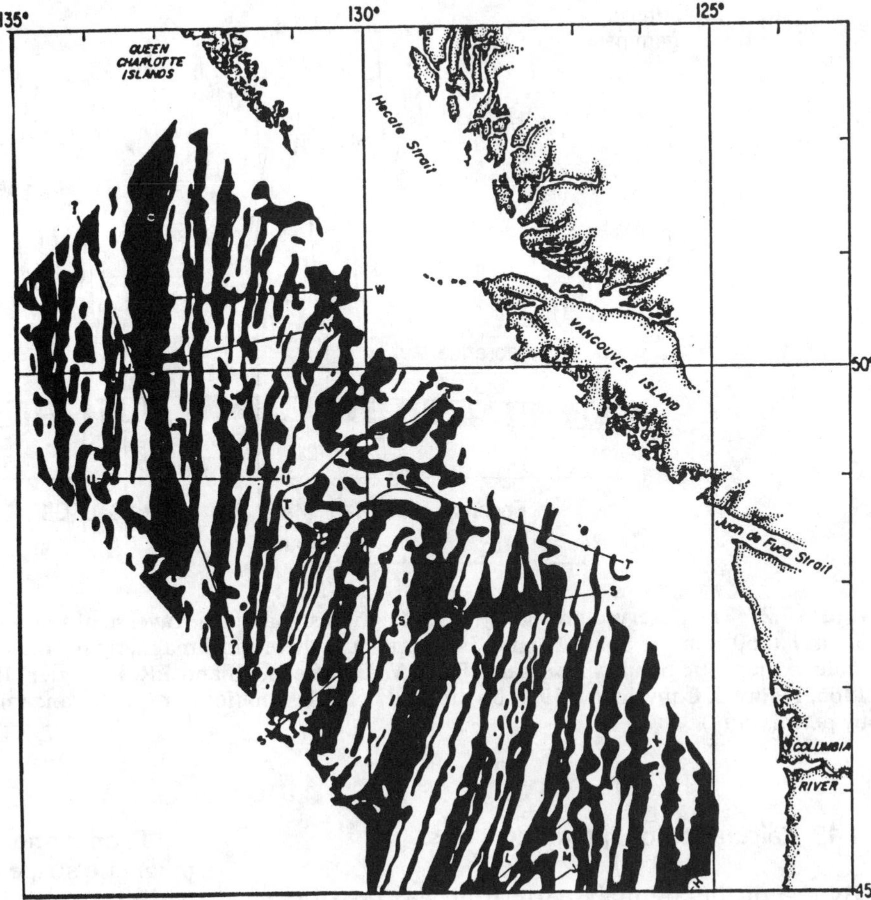

Figure 7.25 Map of magnetic anomaly patterns on the floor of the Pacific Ocean west and south of Vancouver Island. Compare with Figure 7.37. (From F.J. Vine and D.H. Matthews, 1963, *Nature*. v. 199, p. 947-949.)

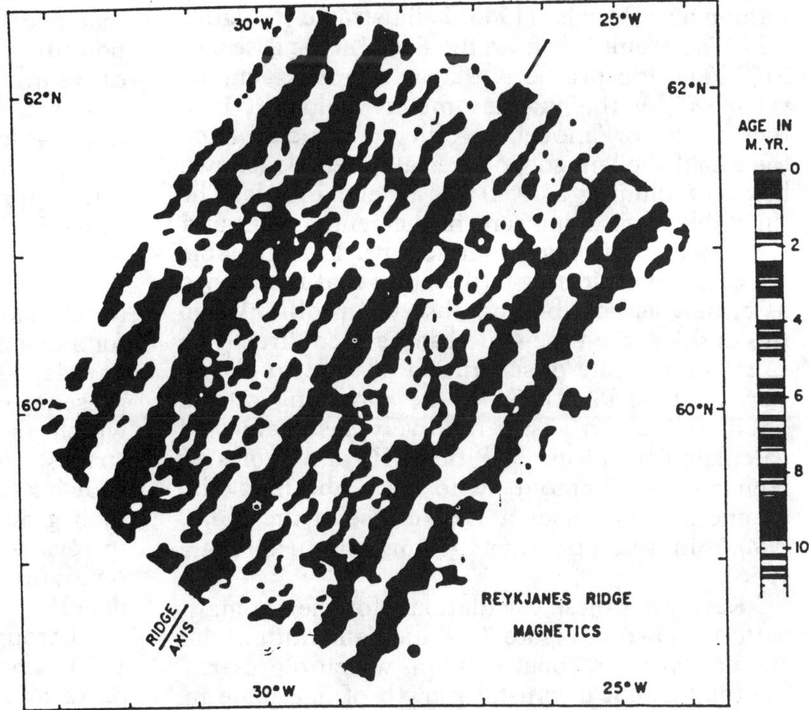

Figure 7.26 Magnetic anomaly pattern for the Reykjanes Ridge, located on the Mid-Atlantic Ridge southwest of Iceland, with approximate rock ages in millions of years. (From F.J. Vine, *Science*, v. 154. Copyright © 1966 by the American Association for the Advancement of Science. Used by permission.)

symmetry of the striped pattern on either side of the axis of the Rekjyanes Ridge.

Finding the magnetic stripes on the ocean floor proved to be the key to the scientific revolution in geology. There followed rapidly a series of magnetic surveys along many sections of the mid-oceanic ridge, all revealing similar striped patterns in mirror image.

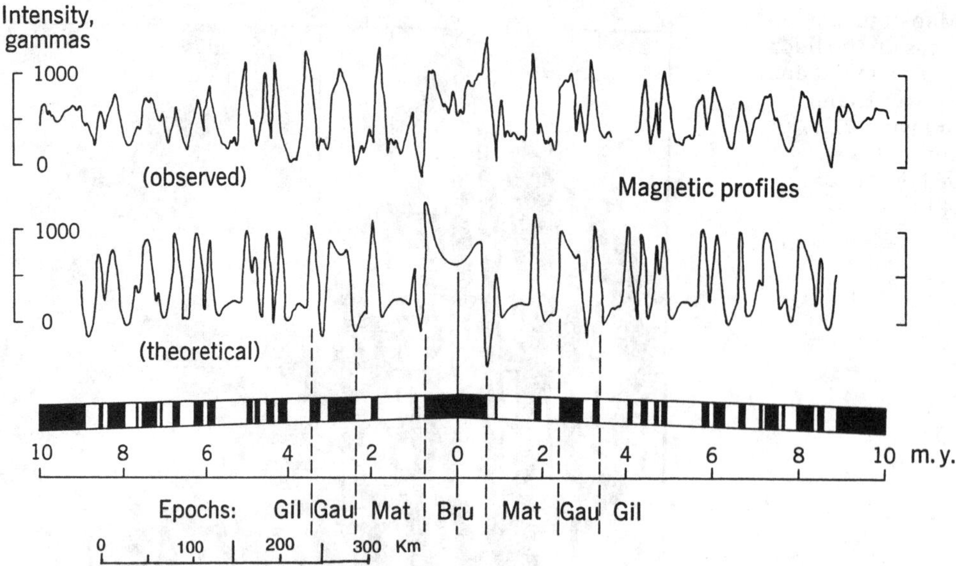

Figure 7.27 The observed profile of magnetic intensity along a traverse of the mid-oceanic ridge at about lat. 60°S in the South Pacific. Below it is the theoretical magnetic profile correlated with the time scale of magnetic polarity reversals. (From W.C. Pitman, III and J.R. Heirtzler, 1966, *Science*, v. 154, p. 1166, Figure 3. Copyright © 1966 by the American Association for the Advancement of Science. Used by permission.)

7.13 Calculation of Spreading Rates

By use of the anomaly pattern, it was possible to identify the normal and reversed epochs, as we have done in Figure 7.24. The procedure used by Pitman and Hertzler (1966) is illustrated in Figure 7.27. The example is from the East Pacific Rise, lat. 51°S. The top profile is that which was actually recorded by the magnetometer. Below it is a theoretical, or "model," profile constructed from the established magnetic reversal timetable (shown below) including as well the briefer events. The timetable starts from zero in the center point and is duplicated in opposite directions. The timetable is expanded uniformly to the point that it matches as closely as possible the observed profile. When this is done, the time scale can be used directly to calculate the rate of separation of the two plates. For the East Pacific Rise, the spreading rate is about 4.4 cm/yr. This relatively fast rate was calculated by Walter J. Pitman III and James R. Heirtzler of Lamont, who had obtained the magnetic data during a 1965 cruise of the *U.S.S. Eltanin* in Antarctic waters (Pitman and Heirtzler, 1966).

Reviewing these calculations, for the anomaly pattern shown in Figure 7.27, the half-width of the anomaly zone is about 450 km, which represents the total extent of crustal growth of one plate in about 10 m.y. Thus the average rate of horizontal motion of one entire plate (called the *half spreading rate*) during this time has averaged about 4.5 cm/yr, which means that the *full separation rate* of the two plates (rate of rift-widening) is double this value, or 9 cm/yr.

From one ocean region to another, the magnetic stripe of a given epoch can have different widths, and this can only mean that the rate of spreading of plates has been different in one place than another. Figure 7.28 is a graph on which the distance from the axial rift to the line of each polarity reversal is plotted against time in millions of years, using the time scale established by radiometric methods. The scale extends only to 4 Ma., which is about halfway into the Pliocene Epoch. The steeper the plotted line, the faster the rate of spreading. The highest observed separation rate—9 cm/yr—is along the East Pacific Rise, which is the spreading boundary between the Pacific plate and Nazca plate. The separation rate for the North Atlantic basin is the lowest observed for a major plate boundary, about 2 cm/yr.

Magnetic anomaly patterns clearly reveal the presence of transform faults and transform scars, which show as abrupt offsets of the magnetic stripes. Figure 7.29 is a set of map-like diagrams showing how the stripes can become offset during their growth. (Refer back to figures 7.13 and 7.14 to review the concept of increasing rate of plate separation with increasing distance from the Euler pole.)

Throughout the late 1960s and well into the 1970s, anomaly patterns were mapped over large parts of all the ocean basins. As the magnetic anomaly pattern was being mapped in a particular area, the magnetic reversals were being dated on the basis of ages of fossils in sediment resting on the rock floor. These samples were obtained by seafloor drilling. Cores obtained by the *Glomar Challenger* were used in this way. Cores that

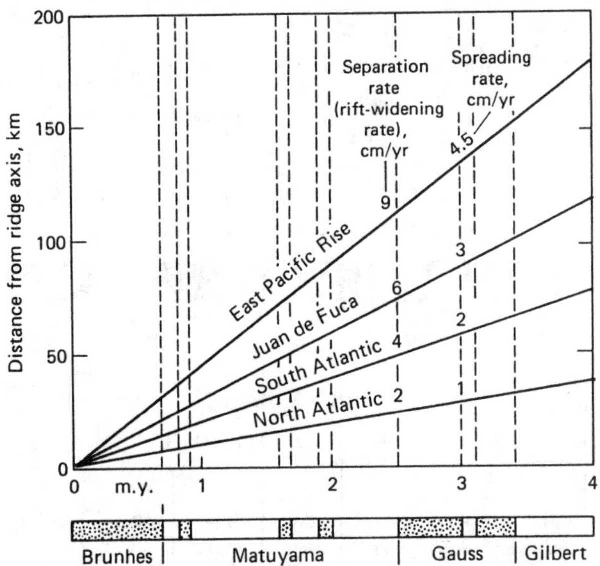

Figure 7.28 As the rate of plate spreading increases, the distance between the ridge axis and a given magnetic stripe increases in direct proportion. The half-spreading rate refers to the rate at which one plate moves away from the axis. Full-spreading rate of plate separation by rift widening is double the half-spreading rate. (Based on data of F.J. Vine, J.R. Heirtzler, and others.)

penetrated the basalt were dated by the radiometric method, establishing the point in time at which a reversal occurred. The result was a full chronology of magnetic polarity reversals dating back into the Jurassic. Figure 7.30 is a modern version of the polarity time scale prepared by the research staffs of the Lamont-Doherty Geological Observatory and the Graduate School of Oceanography of the University of Rhode Island (Cande et al., 1989).

Starting about 84 Ma and continuing to about 110 Ma there was a long interval within the Cretaceous Period when normal polarity seems to have persisted without reversal. This blank period in the reversal record is referred to as a *magnetic quiet interval*. Then, in the early Cretaceous time, about 110 Ma, polarity reversals again appear, and these extend into the Upper Jurassic Period, as far back as about 150 Ma. Altogether, 22 polarity reversals were documented in this activity group, called the *Mesozoic polarity reversals*.

Magnetic anomaly patterns have allowed geophysicists to make bedrock geologic maps of the ocean-basin floors. Our copy of selected samples of the map (originally published in color) is shown in Figure 7.31. A preliminary edition, with large areas incomplete, was published in 1974. It was complied by Walter C. Pitman III, Roger L. Larson, and Ellen M. Herron of the Lamont group. The task was completed in 1983 by

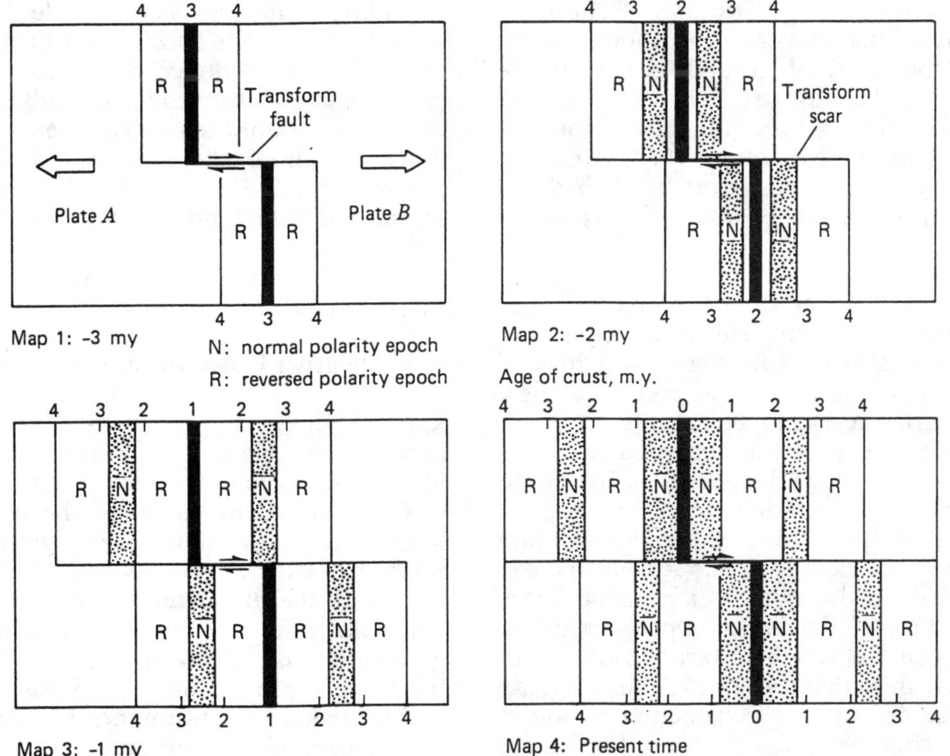

Figure 7.29 This set of schematic map-diagrams shows how the offsetting of magnetic stripes can take place during continued movement on a transform fault. The maps are drawn at intervals of one million years. We have assumed that the spreading rate holds constant. The offset in the magnetic polarity stripes is propagated as a lengthening transform scar. (Copyright © by Arthur N. Strahler.)

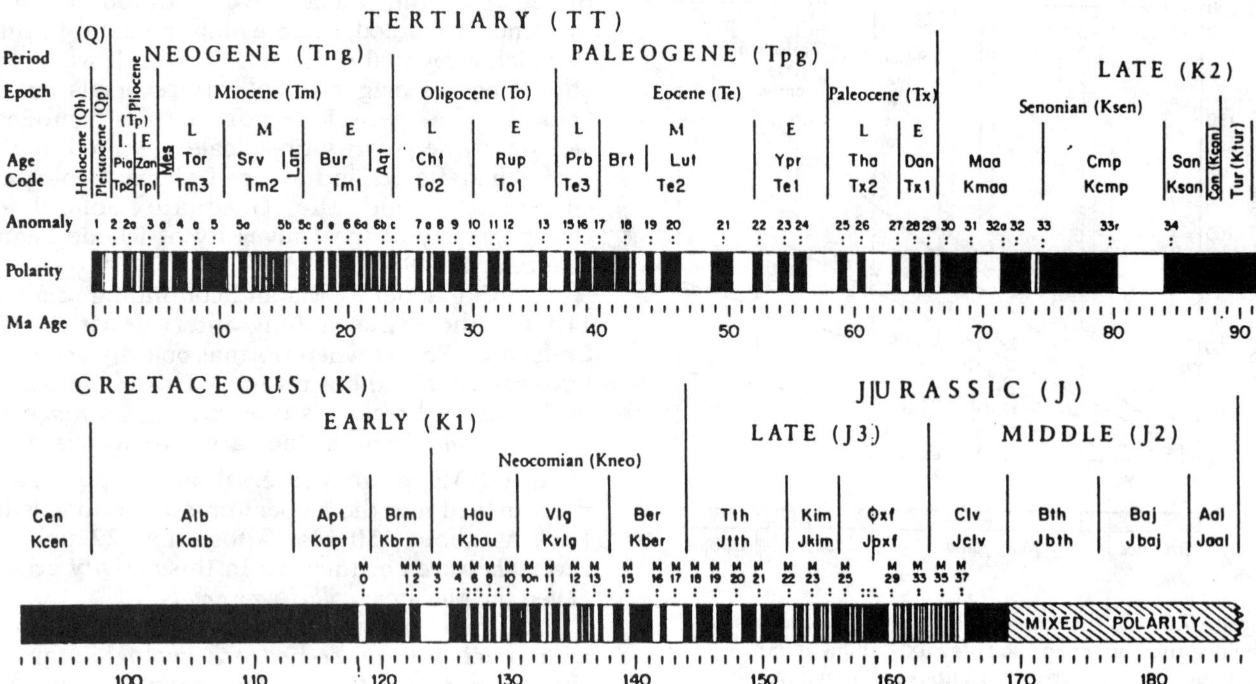

Figure 7.30 A magnetic polarity time scale extending back into the late Cretaceous Period. (From S.C. Cande, J.L. LaBreque, W.C. Pitman, III, et al., 1989, *Magnetic Lineations of the World's Ocean Basins* (Map). Tulsa OK, Amer. Assoc. of Petroleum Geologists. Used by permission.)

an expanded group of seven scientists whose affiliations included the Graduate School of Oceanography of the University of Rhode Island, the Lamont-Doherty Geological Observatory, the Department of Geological Sciences of the University of Durham, and the Marathon Oil Company (Pitman, Larson, et al., 1983). Geologic ages on the map are the ages of the basalt bedrock that lies immediately below the pelagic sedimentary layer. Of course, the ages of sediment layers lying above the bedrock floor will include all geologic periods younger than the bedrock age, right through to the present. Thus, the map shows the age of the oceanic rock floor as it was formed by sea-floor spreading and the accretion of new oceanic crust along spreading boundaries.

This geologic map of the ocean basin floors tells us a great deal about the history of the ocean basins. For example, the oldest rock floor mapped in the North Atlantic basin is of Jurassic age and occurs in two bands close to the continents. One is off the U.S.-Canada coast extending from Newfoundland to the Caribbean. Opposing it is a band off the coast of northwestern Africa. From this pattern, we infer that the North Atlantic Ocean basin began to open up by continental rifting at some point during the Jurassic Period. Looking at the Pacific plate, we note that there is a large area of Jurassic bedrock in the western part of the plate. This area terminates abruptly along the trenches, since it is on this line that the plate is being consumed in a subduction boundary. Notice on the eastern margin of the Pacific plate that the spreading boundary has two triple junctions; these mark corners of the Nazca and Cocos plates.

While the evidence of the magnetic polarity reversals might seem to have validated beyond any reasonable doubt the reality of sea-floor spreading, there remained skeptics within the geological community. We must, therefore, continue our search for independent evidence of an entirely different sort to confirm on-going as well as past plate motion along spreading boundaries and transform faults.

7.14 Relative Plate Motions

Relative direction and rate of motion of one lithospheric plate with respect to an adjacent plate are, as shown earlier in this chapter, formally stated in terms of the angular motion with respect to their Euler poles of relative rotation (Minster and Jordan, 1978). We can also state the direction and rate of motion of a particular reference point on a plate in terms of its compass direction in degrees with respect to the earth's geographic meridians and parallels and its speed in centimeters per year relative to an adjacent plate. An arrow on the map will display this information. Note that the map grid used must be the equatorial Mercator projection, so that the arrow will be correct in terms of true angle as measured with a protractor relative to a vertical line representing north. For showing

Figure 7.31 Portions of a world geologic map of the ocean floor, showing ages of the basaltic oceanic crust. (Sketched from *The Bedrock Geology of the World*, compiled by R.L. Larson, W.C. Pitman, et al. Copyright © 1985 by R.L. Larson and W.C. Pitman III. Published by W.H. Freeman and Co. Reproduced by permission of Larson and Pitman.)

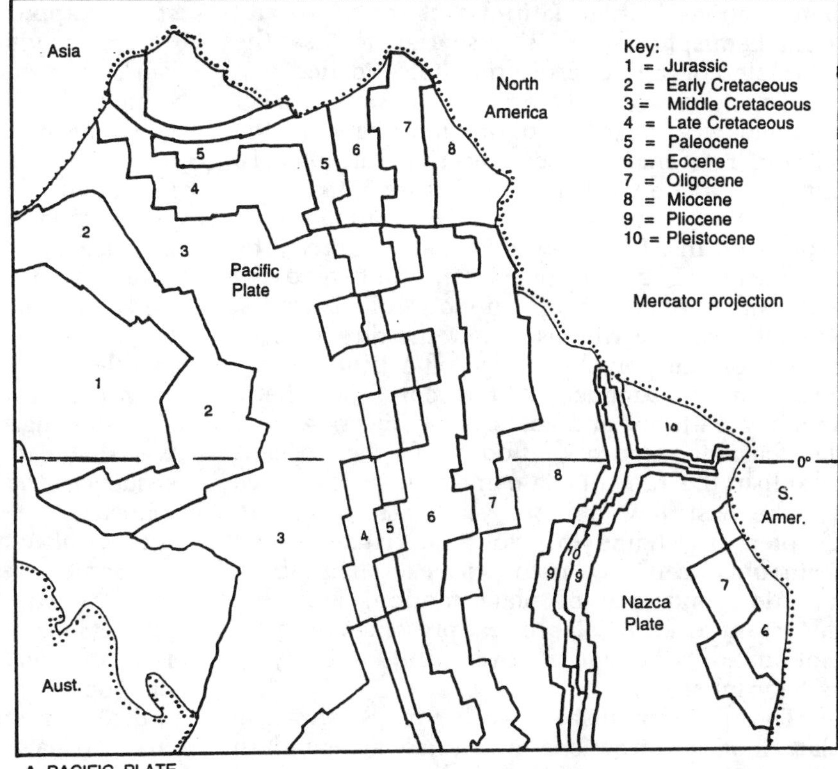

A PACIFIC PLATE

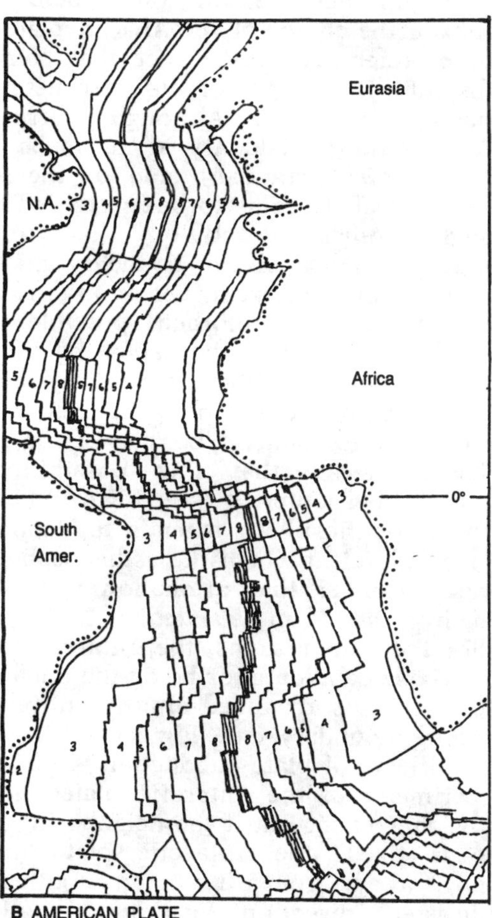

B AMERICAN PLATE

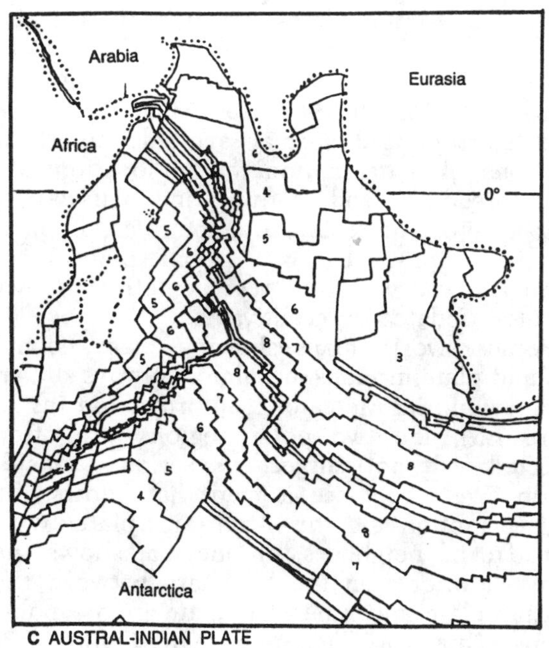

C AUSTRAL-INDIAN PLATE

plate motions in high latitudes of the north and south hemispheres, it is essential to use the polar stereographic projection (also called the Wulff net), on which the arrow is always correct in angle with respect to the meridian of the point of reference. These projections are used in our global plate tectonic map, Figure 7.3.

Relative plate motion can be estimated by various means. Direction is indicated directly by movement on transform faults, confirmed by determination of first motion of P-waves. Seismic evidence will also show the direction of motion of the downbent edge of a lithospheric plate in a subduction boundary. Magnetic anomaly patterns and accessory data on age of the basaltic bedrock floor of the oceans establish the rate of plate motion, as averaged for the past few million years. As stated in Chapter 5, chains of volcanic islands and seamounts can be used to establish both direction and rate of plate motion, and this information also establishes present and past motion of the plate over the underlying asthenosphere.

The first published world maps showing plate motion directions and rates appeared in 1968. Both were produced by a group of geophysicists of the Lamont-Doherty Geological Observatory (L-DGO). The earlier map, appearing in March 1968, used calculations from the available magnetic anomaly data (Heirtzler, Dickson, Herron, Pitman, and Le Pichon, 1968). The second map, reproduced here as Figure 7.2, appeared three months later in a paper authored solely by Xavier Le Pichon, a young French geophysicist conducting research at the L-DGO (Le Pichon, 1968). (He was a junior member of the same group that produced the earlier map.) Le Pichon's map showed plate boundaries and gave names to the plates, so it may well be recognized as the second modern global plate map—the first being that of W. Jason Morgan published in March 1968 (see Figure 7.1). Le Pichon's map used special symbols to show directions of plate motion for 37 locations on both spreading and converging boundaries. Numbers show his calculation of rates of plate motion in cm/yr. On our global plate map, Figure 7.3, you will find representative arrows and rates, updated to recent values.

Because world maps showing plate boundaries and plate motions are almost always drawn on the equatorial Mercator map projection (as in Figure 7.3), the two polar regions are often neglected and not subject to serious consideration. We rarely see a map that shows the relative motion of the Antarctic plate with respect to its neighbors, or one that shows the relative motions on the boundary between the Eurasian plate and American plate in the polar regions. Our world tectonic map, Figure 7.3, includes special polar-centered maps of both arctic and antarctic regions. These use the stereographic projection.

In showing plate motions by arrows on a world map, such as that of Figures 7.2 and 7.35, we are establishing only the relative motion of one plate with respect to another that adjoins it on a plate boundary segment, or the relative motions of three plates with respect to one another where they meet in a triple junction. For practical purposes, one of the three plates is assumed to be fixed in position (see Figure 7.14), but this does not imply the meaning that it has no motion with respect to the underlying mantle. Expanding the relative-plate system from plate to plate to encompass all the plates is a frustrating exercise, but worth attempting. So we shall try to tie together in chainlike sequences the relative motions of all contiguous plates with respect to one fixed plate, until we "come full circle."

Some investigators have selected the African plate as a fixed plate of reference because some of the hot spots on the African shield contain lavas of a wide range of geologic ages stacked up one upon the other in correct chronological order in a small area. This evidence suggests that Africa's continental lithosphere has been fixed for a long time with respect to the assumed source of magma (a mantle plume) in the upper mantle. Another reason one could almost anticipate the choice of the African plate as the plate of reference is the fact that some five-sixths of the length of its perimeter is a spreading boundary. Although there is a collision suture boundary along much of the northern (Mediterranean) side of the African plate, most of it seems to be inactive. The only strongly seismic activity that indicates subduction or transform boundary motion in progress is in the Aegean Sea and the Near East (see Chapter 6). Another possible reason favoring this choice is that, speaking in general terms, continental lithosphere may be much slower to move laterally over the asthenosphere than oceanic lithosphere, because of the greater thickness. Recall that this possibility was discussed in Chapter 3 (see Figure 3.2). The continental lithosphere extends to depths over 300 km, a level at which the asthenosphere may be much stronger than at shallower depths—or so the hypothesis can be stated.

For the same reasons, the Antarctic plate is also a viable candidate for being the single fixed plate, as it is surrounded almost entirely by a spreading boundary (see Figure 7.3C). Only a very short arc of plate subduction is included in the perimeter of the Antarctic plate: the South Sandwich Trench. But if the neighboring African plate is fixed, the Antarctic plate must be moving away from it in a southerly or southeasterly direction. Furthermore, all other plates that bound the Antarctic plate must be moving away from it at a rate sufficient to accommodate its growth on all spreading boundaries. (We are assuming, of course, that along a spreading boundary both plates are growing at about the same rate, and this assumption seems to be generally accepted as a requirement of plate tectonics, discarded only when the anomaly pattern requires asymmetry.) Actually, the spreading rate of the mid-oceanic ridge between southern Africa and Antarctica is very low (2 cm/yr) in comparison with spreading rates between the Antarctic plate and the Australian-Indian and Pacific plates (7 to 9 cm/yr).

Suppose, then, that we designate the Antarctic and African plates as jointly serving as the "fixed" core for a global system. This premise then calls for the American plate(s) to be moving westward, a motion readily accommodated by the active subduction boundary along almost the entire western side of the American plate(s). Correspondingly, the Pacific plate is freely moving westward to disappear beneath the Eurasian plate. So it looks as if the subduction boundaries that enclose the Pacific plate serve as the terminal sink of our imagined global system.

In a section to follow, we will return to the problem of arriving at a global system of plate motions. We will deal specifically with the physical relationships between the plates and the asthenosphere, including evidence from tracks of hotspots. First, however, it is important to examine newer geophysical and astronomical methods for measuring relative plate motions.

17.15 Geodetic Measurements of Plate Motions

A totally new means of measuring relative rates of plate motion emerged in 1976, when NASA launched its Lageos satellite into orbit. LAGEOS is the acronym for Laser Geodynamics Satellite. The satellite serves as a reflector for laser pulses sent up to it from ground stations, which also receive the reflected returning pulses. Using two or more ground stations as a triangular system, the Lageos serves as a highly accurate triangulation instrument for geodetic measurements (Spencer, 1977; Gordon and Stein, 1992, p. 337-338). This system goes by the name of Satellite Laser Ranging (SLR). In 1979, NASA set up its Crustal Dynamics Project to study the dynamic behavior of the earth, which in turn was to generate an improved understanding of earthquake mechanisms and motions of the crust. This project made use not only of the Lageos satellite SLR system, but also a very different technique called Very Long Baseline Interferometry (VLBI). It makes use of the random radio noise emitted by quasars and other compact celestial objects. These signals are recorded by radio telescopes spaced large distances apart. The two systems operate from two different sets of base stations. At the outset, VLBI was capable of measuring ground distances with a precision of about 3 cm (*Geotimes*, 1981, p. 17-18, Flinn, 1981). Observatories participating in the Crustal Dynamics Project are located in such diverse places as Australia, North America, South America, and Europe.

A third system, GPS (Global Positioning System), uses a set of stationary satellites orbiting over the earth's equator at a height of about 20,000 km. Each of these broadcasts a message telling the time and an estimate of its position. Signals from a group of these satellites, collected at ground stations, are used to calculate within a few centimeters the distances between pairs of ground stations. The GPS system will in future years provide most of the data on current relative plate motions (Gordon and Stein, 1992, p. 337; Herring, 1996).

It was soon realized that both the laser ranging SLR system and the VLBI system could be used to measure lateral crustal movements as small as one centimeter per year between widely separated ground stations. The slowest-moving plates move at about that speed, while the fastest move at rates on the order of 10 cm/yr. By 1985 it could be safely announced that the continents are actually observed to be moving relative to each other at rates of a few centimeters per year. By 1986 a set of VLBI rates was announced that correlated well with the corresponding geophysical/geological rates. Figure 7.32 is a world map showing end points of great circle arcs connecting pairs of VLBI observatories. Labels on the lines show the VLBI rates along with the corresponding rates based on geophysical/-geological data (Carter and Robinson, 1986, p. 54).

By way of discussion of the rates shown on this map, notice that Australia seems to be moving toward North America at a rate of 7 cm/yr. Note that the connecting arc—a great circle—between Australia and California crosses a subduction boundary, the New Hebrides trench, so the observed closing of distance between the two continents is to be expected. On the other hand, we see that Australia seems to be moving away from South America at a rate of 2.3 cm/yr. A connecting great circle drawn from southeastern Australia to Nazca, Peru, where the geodetic station is located, crosses not only two spreading plate boundaries, but also a subduction boundary (the Peru-Chile trench). Thus both lengthening by spreading and shortening by subduction are in progress on this trajectory and it could be difficult to calcuate the net value of the separation between.

In the early 1990s, a new and highly complex system of determining relative plate motions was put into use. Called NUVEL-1, it is a global model for describing the geologically current motions between twelve plates, assumed to be rigid (DeMets, Gordon, Argus, and Stein, 1990; Gordon, 1991). NUVEL-1 builds upon a similar model successfully put into use by Chase in 1978

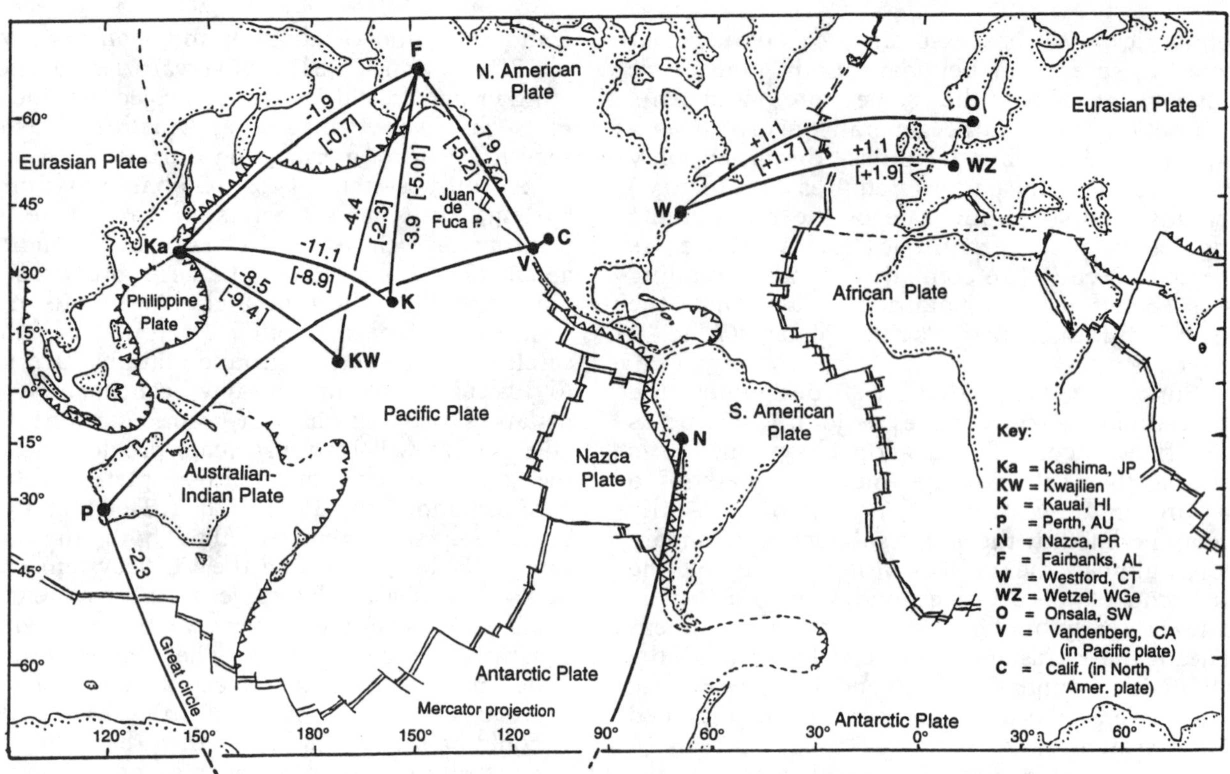

Figure 7.32 A world map showing 11 VLBI ground stations with connecting great-circle arcs. Net spreading rate is given for each arc. A minus sign denotes a closing rate; a plus sign, separating rate. Number above the line is the VLBI measurement; number in box below the line is the corresponding geophysical/geologic estimated rate. (VLBI data from H.V. Frey, NASA Crustal Dynamics Project, 1989. Map copyright © by Arthur N. Strahler.)

and Minster and Gordon in 1978. NUVEL-1 uses over 1000 data items, including 277 plate-spreading rates from magnetic anomaly data, 121 transform-fault azimuths, and 724 earthquake slip vectors.

For a complex global model such as NUVEL-1 it is necessary to define an arbitrary global network of plates based on decisions as to which plates to include and which to omit or combine. Having done this, data are combined and the motions are computed and listed for all possible pairs of shared boundaries. A twelve-plate system is used. Figure 7.33 is a topological presentation of the network made up of "nodes" and "arcs" (connecting lines). Information categories are given by the arc line symbols. Africa with 7 arcs has the most shared boundaries. Eurasia with 6 arcs comes next, while Arabia with 3 arcs has the fewest. The Philippine and Juan de Fuca plates were omitted from the network, but data are computed for them as well. India and Australia are treated as two separate plates.

As a summary comment on this section, we can safely say that plate motions are remarkably steady over long time spans. Relative plate motion rates averaged over a few years by geodetic methods are generally very closely matched with those averaged over several million years, based on paleomagnetic data (Gordon, 1991; Gordon and Stein, 1992, p. 338-339).

7.16 Forces Involved in Plate Motion

From thinking only in terms of plate motions relative to adjacent plates along plate boundaries, we will be turning to the task of estimating the direction and speed of each plate relative to the asthenosphere that lies beneath it. To think this way, it is necessary to analyze the forces that are involved in the motion of a plate over the asthenosphere, as well as between two plates along a subduction boundary or along a transform fault boundary.

Our summary of the various possible forces that may affect plate motion follows closely a system presented by Seiya Uyeda (1978, p. 190-193), Alan Cox and Robert B. Hart (1986, p. 343-346), and Philip Keary and Frederick J. Vine (1990, p. 89). Those authors, in turn credit the analysis and terminology to D. Forsyth and S. Uyeda (1975). There are minor differences in the terminology and notation in each of these references, but the basic principles are agreed upon.

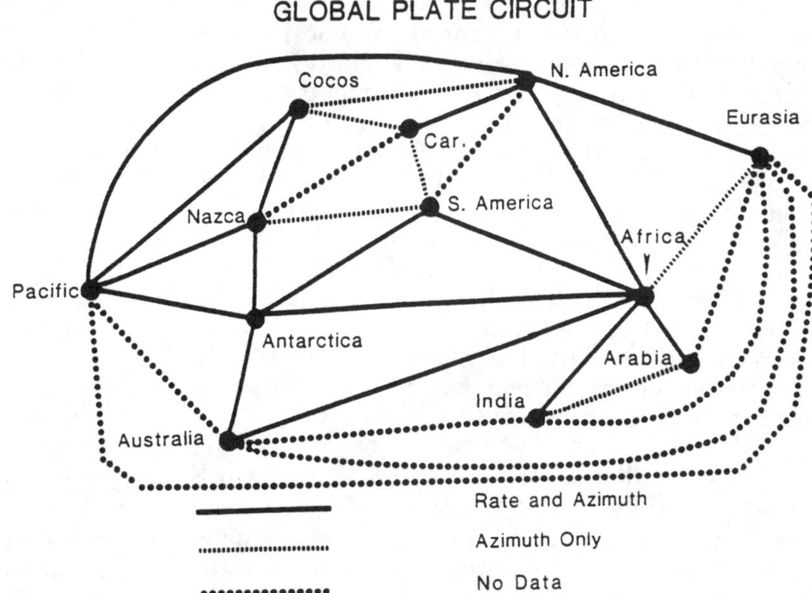

Figure 7.33 The NUVEL-1 network for plate motion analysis. (A) Map of plates as adapted for use in NUVEL-1. Two large areas of diffuse plate boundaries are shown, each with an arbitrary line of plate separation. (B) The global network of "plate circuit closures." (From C. DeMets, R.G. Gordon, D.F. Argus, and S. Stein, 1990, *Geophysical Jour. International*, p. 438, Figure 4, and p. 439, Figure 5. Reproduced by permission.)

All forces involved in plate motion fall into two main categories, or classes. First are the *driving forces*; they are the forces that tend to produce plate motion relative to the asthenosphere, or of one plate relative to another along a common fault boundary. Gravitational force (as gravity) is the common agent behind the driving forces and works essentially as the expenditure of the stored potential energy of elevation in lithosphere lifted by tectonic processes powered by the earth's internal heat. Second are the *resisting forces* that are set up by the action of the driving forces. These forces tend to build up an equal resistance or opposition to the motion. This concept is stated more formally by Keary and Vine as follows: "Since the present velocities of plates appear to be constant, each plate must be in dynamic equilibrium, with the driving forces being balanced by inhibiting forces" (1990, p. 89). In systems language, a moving plate tends to achieve and maintain a steady state of operation in terms of mass transport and energy flow. A simple analogy is seen in the terminal velocity of a sand grain falling through still water.

In Chapter 3, under the heading of "Convection Systems in the Asthenosphere," we compared two models relating oceanic lithospheric plate motion to the viscous motion that takes place in the underlying soft, hot asthenosphere (see Figure 3.31). An older model called for a mantle current to drag with it the overlying oceanic crust, whereas a newer model called for the moving plate to drag with it the underlying mantle. We reviewed the objections that were urged against the older "current-drags-plate" model, causing it to be abandoned. Brief mention was made of the plate-driving forces we are setting forth here.

Figure 7.34 is a schematic block diagram showing the force system. The major forces involved are of two main classes: Class F, Plate-driving forces; Class R, Resisting forces. In a table accompany the diagram we have made two columns for these classes, placing the corresponding resisting force opposite to each driving force.

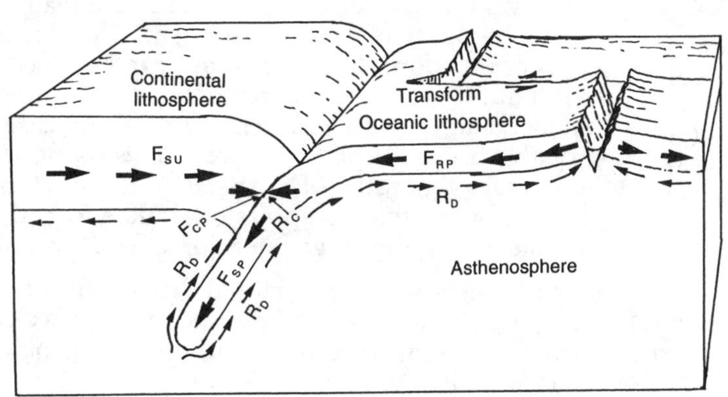

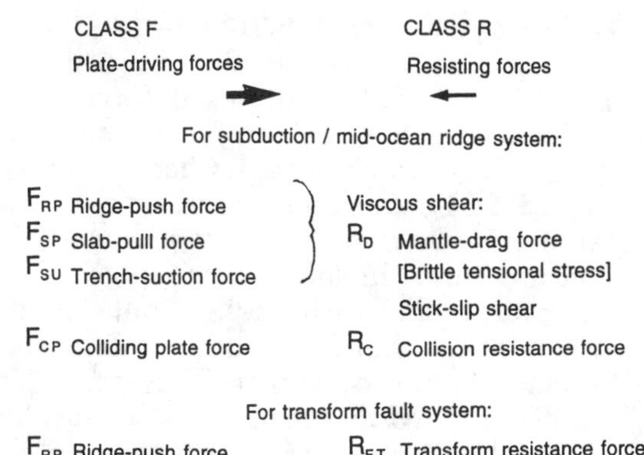

Figure 7.34 Schematic diagram of the system of plate-driving forces and resisting forces. (Based on data of Seiya Uyeda, 1978, Cox and Hart, 1986, and Kearey and Vine, 1990. Diagram copyright © by Arthur N. Strahler.)

Within Class R we need to recognize subclasses to represent two different forms of energy dissipation. Dissipation between a plate and the asthenosphere occurs in a layer throughout which viscous shearing occurs. The *viscous shear* generates sensible heat (kinetic energy of molecular motion) throughout this layer of the mantle. Resistance occurring between two brittle plates in direct contact is dissipated through localized friction, in which the motion is of the stick-slip type, which we have labeled as *stick-slip shear*. The heat of friction is conducted away through the adjacent plate masses. Of course, this process generates earthquakes, widely dissipating energy as the seismic waves travel outward.

Starting with the oceanic lithospheric plate, which is "in charge" of the entire system, a *ridge-push force* (F_{RP}) is present as gravitational body force in the oceanic plate. It starts at the spreading ridge, where the slope of the plate away from the ridge is steepest, but continues to act over the expanse of deepening abyssal floor. This driving force is counteracted by the *mantle-drag force* (R_D). Within the descending slab, the gravitational body force is named the *slab-pull force* (F_{SP}). It, too, is resisted on both lower and upper surfaces by mantle-drag force. At its lower edge, the slab is forcing its way into mantle rock. Uyeda (1978, p. 192) has identified at this location a special "slab-resistance force," but for simplicity we are including it with the mantle-drag force.

We turn next to the continental plate, which is being impacted by the oceanic plate, and is thus in a relatively passive role. Geophysicists studying the subduction zones bounding the Pacific plate discovered that the continental plate is moving slowly toward the subduction boundary, while at the same time, the oceanic plate has been correspondingly narrowing in total width. This gives the impression that the trenches have been "retreating" away from their respective continents (Cox and Hart, 1986, p. 346), or conversely, that the trenches are "migrating" oceanward (Uyeda, 1978, p. 192). Thus it might seem inescapable that the Pacific plate is shrinking in area. To account for this relative motion, the geophysicists have recognized a *trench-suction force* (F_{SU}) that is 'pulling' the continental plate toward the trench. The nature of this supposed force is not well understood. One explanation is that the mantle corner flow, which we described in Chapter 5 (see Figure 5.31), or some other similar rising and falling mantle current, exerts a down-drag on the continental lithosphere, causing it to buckle downward and causing a horizontal pulling force on the plate. Another hypothesis states that, as the trench migrates oceanward, the entire downgoing slab is required to force its way broadside through the asthenosphere, tending to create a great "potential vacuum" behind it. This potential deficiency of mass exerts a "suction" on the continental plate, which in turn sets up a lateral trenchward motion of the entire continental plate (Cox and Hart, 1986, p. 346).

Convergence of the two plates causes the continental plate to press strongly against the upper surface of the down-sinking oceanic plate, and that pressure will be present whether or not a trench-suction force is in operation. We recognize this pressure as a *plate-colliding force* (F_{CP}). The force builds up stored strain energy, relieved by stick-slip shear that generates earthquakes, both great and small, and by continuous fault creep (see Chapter 6). The counteracting resistance is of the frictional class, and is named the *collision-resistance force* (R_C).

Finally, we come to motion along transform faults that are serving as plate boundaries. Figure 7.34 shows this case in an inset diagram toward the back of the block. The basic plate-driving force is ridge-push force, localized at the fault plane by the difference in speed of the adjacent plates. Here, friction is present between fault surfaces, and stored strain energy is released when stick-slip shear occurs, or by continuous creep.

Since the above analysis of plate-driving forces was laid out, further study of the subject has brought forward some refinements in the relative values given to the forces (Gordon, 1991, p. 356; Harper, 1989). Ridge-push force and slab-pull force continue to be rated as dominant forces. Newtonian viscous shear continues to be regarded as the major resisting force under a plate surface (Kerr, 1995).

We can next apply this information about plate-driving and resisting forces to explain the global scheme of relative rates of motion of lithospheric plates, described in our earlier section. Continual motion of two oceanic plates away from each other along a spreading boundary is satisfactorily explained by the ridge-push force, energized by the continual lifting of the lithosphere by a rising current of hot mantle rock. Ridge-push force continues to act, although with diminishing strength, as the plate moves farther away from the rift. The surface gradient diminishes, but partial compensation is developed by the thickening that the plate undergoes at it cools—increasing its mass—and to a lesser extent by the added load of a thickening layer of pelagic sediment. The slowing effect of transform fault resistance can be expected to maintain a drag on the plate, but this is largely independent of plate gradient, and in any case is probably a very weak drag force (as is thought to hold true generally of transcurrent faults not affected by oblique compressional plate forces). A diminishing of the ridge-push force tends to build up and sustain compressional stress within the plate, which may explain how such thin plates can travel such long distances without being pulled apart and rotated.

In the case of the Atlantic Ocean basin we ask: What happens to the driving force where the oceanic lithosphere merges with continental lithosphere along passive margins, such as those of the eastern coastlines of the American continents, and all within the American plates? The ridge-push force must continue to be transmitted entirely across the American continental masses to the convergent boundaries on the western side, where the Pacific, Cocos, Nazca, and Antarctic plates are subducting. Here is where the trench-suction force can perhaps assist by exerting its pulling force and making room for the westward moving plate.

By 1995, an alternate hypothesis had appeared to explain how room could be made available for westward motion of South America. Geophysicists Raymond M. Russo and Paul G. Silver of the Carnegie Institute of Washington, in a paper presented at the American Geophysical Union in May, 1995, revealed that seismic tomography shows deep mantle flow parallel to the western continental boundary. From a central point, one mantle current is directed northward, the other southward. Together these currents are directing the mantle flow around the north and south ends of the South American continent (see Monastersky, 1995).

Turning next to the Pacific Ocean basin, consider the East Pacific Rise and its adjacent plates: Pacific plate on the west; Cocos, Nazca and Antarctic plates on the east. For both sets of plates, the ridge-push force delivers the plates to subduction boundaries, where slab-pull force takes over to carry them far down into the mantle. Now our question should be: of the two spreading ridges—Atlantic and Pacific—which can we expect to have the higher rate of plate spreading? The obvious answer is the Pacific ridge. At about latitude 20°S, the rates are faster for the Pacific ridge by a factor of about four. In Chapter 5, Table 5.3, the fast-spreading East Pacific Rise (EPR) was compared with the slow-spreading Mid-Atlantic Ridge (MAR) in terms of spreading rate, geologic processes at work, axial zone topography, and fault-scarp characteristics. Figure 5.15 contrasts the topographic profiles of these two classes of ridges. Whereas that of the EPR is broad and has low flanking slopes; that of the MAR is steep-sided and has much greater local vertical relief. The MAR would thus develop a much stronger ridge-push force, and this may be a response to the high resistance put up by the great masses of continental lithosphere forming a major part of each of the bounding plates. In contrast, the bounding plates of the EPR, experiencing much lower resistance, move away more rapidly from the axis and tend to maintain a low profile.

7.17 Plate Motions Relative to Hot Spots

Assuming, as we have, that each plate is a rigid fragment of a sphere, the rotational center of which is its own Euler pole, every point on that plate describes a small circle upon the asthenosphere beneath it as the plate moves (see Figures 7.12 and 7.14). As we explained earlier, these small circles are concentric and parallel, but the linear speeds of motion of points on them differ in relationship to the arc distance from the Euler pole. These are all speeds of lithospheric plates relative to an ideal asthenosphere, which we imagine to be fixed in place on the solid earth sphere beneath. That being our specified condition, the linear speed of each point on the plate can be said to be the *absolute motion*. Next, we introduce a second case, in which the asthenosphere itself has its own independent set of internal motions with respect to an imagined solid global shell of rock below it. Recall from Chapter 3 that this third shell has been named the *mesosphere*— a term rarely used. We shall stipulate that the mesosphere rotates at the astronomical speed we observe for the planet as a whole, but here we shall subtract that planetary rotation and assign to the mesosphere a zero rotation speed. So now we visualize three global shells: lithosphere, asthenosphere, and mesosphere.

The next step is to recognize that the asthenosphere can be moving independently over the mesosphere, while at the same time, the lithosphere is moving independently over the asthenosphere. That being the case, absolute direction of plate motion with respect to the mesosphere must be the vector sum of those two motions, in terms of both their directions and their speeds. In Chapter 3 we described very slow convectional motions of the upper and lower mantle that included vertical (rising and sinking) currents as well as horizontal motions. These convection currents are active within what we have called here the "mesosphere," as well as in the asthenosphere, so it seems foolish and futile to assume the mesosphere to be a rigid ball. Our present lack of even a partial global map of the horizontal motions of the asthenosphere, driven by the mantle convection system, makes it impossible to take those motions into consideration. However, it is reasonable to postulate that motions affecting the asthenosphere must be one or more orders of speed lower than the relative motions between plates, so the only practical course is arbitrarily to define *absolute plate motion* as motion with respect to existing hotspots assumed to be formed by mantle plumes rising from great depth, and these plumes in turn assumed to remain fixed in position relative to each other.

In Chapter 5 we described hotspot chains, showing hotspot tracks in Figure 5.25. Following the first presentations of hotspots and their motions by J. Tuzo Wilson in 1963, the use of hotspot tracks to indicate direction and speed of plate motion was put forward by W. Jason Morgan of Princeton University (1971). His map showed sixteen hotspots with directional arrows. Most are within the ocean floors, both along the mid-oceanic ridge and in intraplate locations. Within a decade, the number of hotspots, including both active and recently active volcanic clusters, had risen to about two dozen, most of the added ones being in interior Africa. Definitions of what constitutes a hotspot differ from one author to another. A global map showing a complete set of absolute motion vectors for the entire expanse of each plate was published in 1990 by Alice E. Gripp and Richard G. Gordon. It is reproduced here as Figure 7.35.

In recent years, the assumption that hotspots have held their positions over very long time spans has been challenged. Increasingly accurate calculations have led to the conclusion that there has been relative motion between certain hotspot pairs on the order of 1.5 to 2.0 cm/yr (Kearey and Vine, 1990, p. 82). P. Molnar and J. Stock in 1987 concluded that hotspots do not define a fixed reference frame. Gordon (1991, p. 755, p. 755; Gordon and Stein, 1992) points out that this conclusion can be challenged by introducing the alternative hypothesis that diffuse horizontal deformation of the lithosphere can occur within the boundary zone of a plate, giving the effect of altering the relative position of a hotspot with respect to hotspots on other plates. Whatever may be the ultimate outcome of these disagreements of interpretation, the rates involved are small compared with the speeds of the faster-moving plates, and they do not seriously affect the hotspot determinations of absolute rates and directions within the past few million years.

7.18 Tectonic Geometry of Rifts and Transforms

Perfect patterns of transform offsets of mid-ocean spreading rifts, such as that in Figure 7.3, developed by two plates in motion about a common Euler pole of rotation, are rarely continued over long time spans. Realistically, we can expect this steady motion to be interrupted by rather sudden changes in the position of the pole of rotation.

Figure 7.36 shows what might be expected when the pole "jumps" to a new location. We have shown a blank earth-globe as it would look in visual perspective (i.e., as if it had been photographed). We start with an arbitrary zero-time, at which a transform fault is slipping along a small-circle arc oriented at 90° (spherical) with respect to its Euler pole of rotation (P_1). This transform is, of

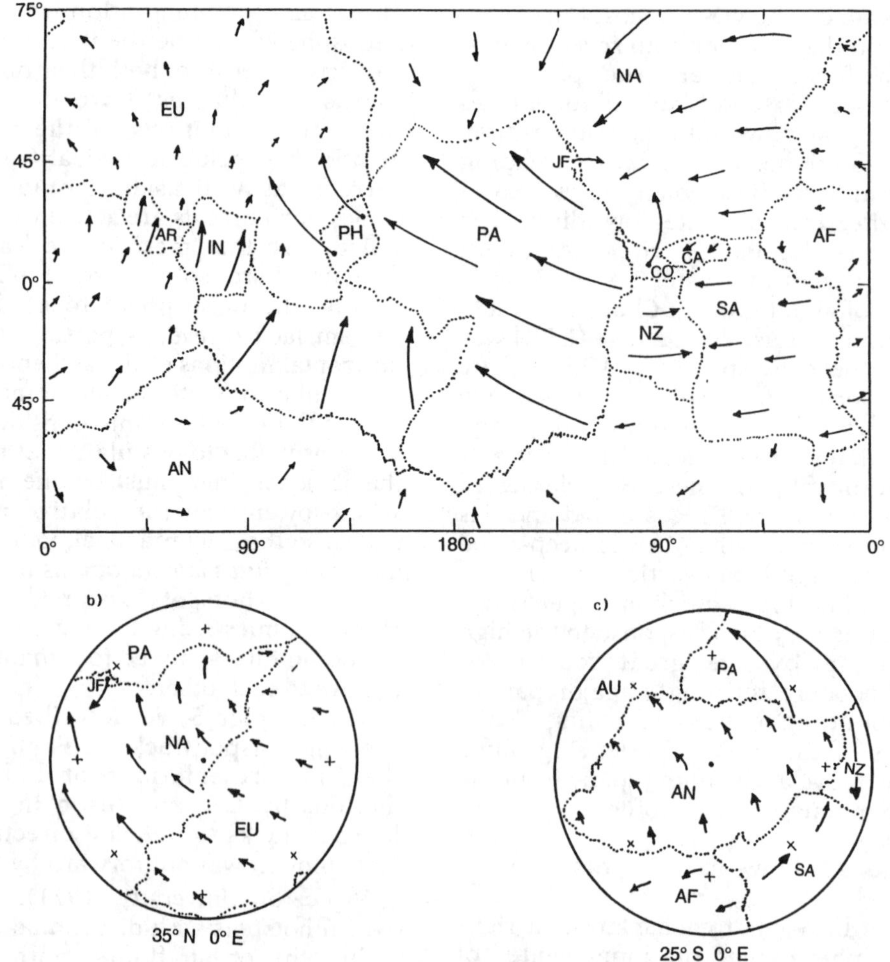

Figure 7.35 World map of plate velocity vectors, based on evidence of plate motion relative to hot spots. (Adapted from I.B.Minster and T.H. Gordon, 1987, Present-day plate motions., *J. Geophys, Res.*, v. 83. Used with permission of the American Geophysical Union and the authors.)

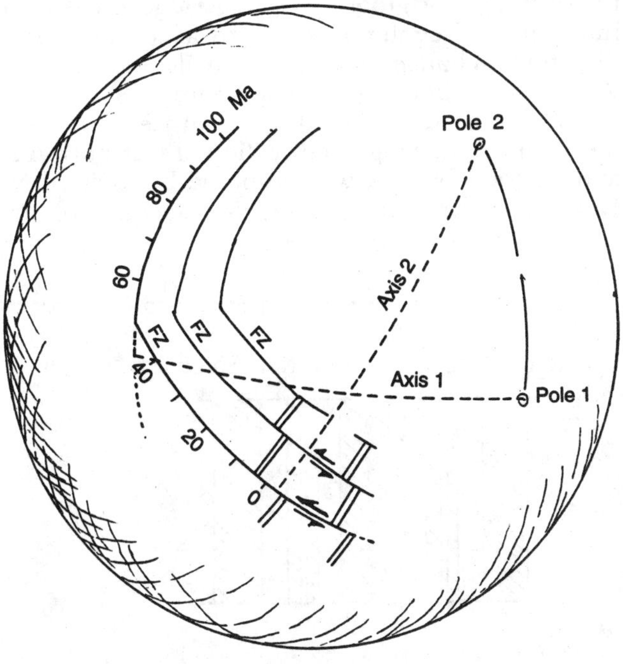

Figure 7.36 Drawn on a sphere seen in perspective, a jump in the Euler pole of rotation of a plate from position 1 to position 2 results in an abrupt change of direction of the small-circle track of a transform plate boundary. (Copyright © by Arthur N. Strahler.)

course, a plate boundary between two plates—one on the north, the other on the south—but these are not indicated. The transform fault is generating a transform scar (i.e., a "fracture zone," or FZ) that is lengthening in extent along the same small circle. Suppose that the pole of rotation suddenly jumps to a position 45 degrees of arc distant from the Pole 1. The pole position is now shown at Pole 2. As a result, the transform and its scars will abruptly change direction to follow a different small circle. Some tens of millions of years later, the transform scar, now grown much longer, looks as shown in the diagram. We have added an imagined time scale along the track. Of course, it may take some time—perhaps a few million years—for the pole to complete its jump, so the track may make a curving change in direction, rather than abruptly turn a corner.

Notice the general resemblance between Figure 7.36 and Figure 5.26, showing the Hawaiian-Emperor island chain, which has long been interpreted as revealing an abrupt 60-degree change in direction of motion of the Pacific plate occurring 43 Ma. Other Pacific island chains show parallelism with the Hawaiian chain, but the Emperor leg is strikingly anomalous. In a paper published in 1995 in *Tectonics,* Ian O. Norton documented in great detail the anomalous nature of the Emperor chain. It appears not to have been accompanied by any plate reorganization, and this leaves open the hypothesis that the hotspot forming the older leg was moving independently of the plate above it. Perhaps it was being guided in part by a horizontal mantle flow diagonal to the plate motion. At 43 Ma, the hotspot became fixed in the overlying lithosphere, requiring it to follow closely thereafter the motion of the Pacific plate.

Most genuine direction changes of a plate are of relatively small amounts, but the principle is the same: Any abrupt shift in the position of the Euler pole of a pair of contiguous plates will cause the pattern of spreading ridges and transforms to change directions.

During the late 1960s, H.W. Menard, a pioneering marine geologist on the staff of Scripps Institution of Oceanography at La Jolla, had been mapping fracture zones and magnetic anomalies of the northeast Pacific Ocean basin. Data were also obtained from the National Geophysical Data Center, which in turn received data from many cooperating sources, one of which was the Lamont-Doherty Geological Observatory (L-DGO) of Columbia University. Although these accumulating data were under scrutiny by Menard and his co-workers, it was not until 1989 that a set of tectonic maps of the northeast Pacific, based on the Scripps data, was prepared by Tanya Atwater and Jeff Severinghaus. The map set was published in 1989 by the Geological Society of America in honor and memory of Menard. In the meantime, a world map titled *Magnetic Lineations of the Oceans*, compiled by W.C. Pitman III, R.L. Larson, and E.M. Herron of the L-DGO, had been published in 1974 by the Geological Society of America. An updated successor to this map was compiled by S.C. Cande, J.L. LaBrecque, R.L. Larson, W.C. Pitman III, X. Golovchenko, and W.F. Haxby, representing the L-DGO and the Graduate School of Oceanography of the University of Rhode Island; it was published in 1989. We have reproduced here selected portions of this map in Figures 7.37, 7.42, and 7.47.

Examples of magnetic anomaly patterns and transform scars showing rather abrupt shifts in direction began to be noticed in the late 1960s as seafloor charting rapidly increased in volume of incoming data. Figure 7.37 shows an area off the Alaska/British Columbia/Washington coast of North America, with FZs and magnetic anomaly boundaries in the Gulf of Alaska. Whereas the pattern appears as a highly orderly NS–EW grid westward of anomaly 5, the trend shifts quite suddenly to an oblique trend (N17°E) in a younger area to the southeast, where the present spreading plate boundaries with the Juan de Fuca, Gorda, and Explorer plates are located. The age of anomaly 5 is given as about 10 Ma, so the direction change may have set in as recently as about 5 Ma.

Geologists were intrigued with the phenomenon of change in direction of plate motion and they immediately began to speculate about how the spreading ridge rotates to accommodate the polar jump. In an article published in *Nature* (1968), Menard and a graduate student, Tanya Atwater, focused their attention on the changes in direction indicated by bends in the FZs of the

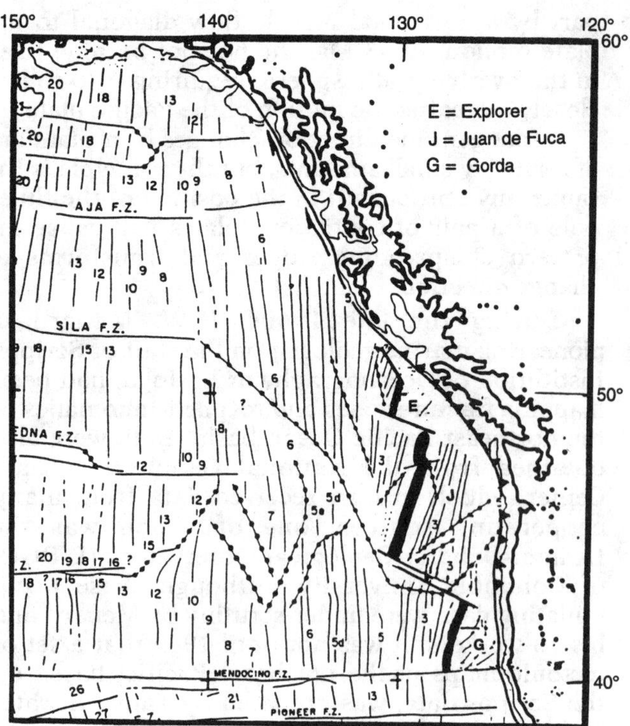

Figure 7.37 Map of a portion of the eastern Pacific ocean floor off the western coast of North America, showing magnetic anomalies, spreading ridges, transform faults, and transform scars (FZs). (From S.C. Cande, J.L. LaBreque, W.C. Pitman, III, et al., 1989, *Magnetic Lineations of the World's Ocean Basins* (Map). Tulsa OK, Amer. Assoc. of Petroleum Geologists. Used by permission.)

central North Pacific and the Gulf of Alaska (Menard and Atwater, 1968). You will notice that on the western two-thirds of our map, Figure 7.37, the anomaly stripes, indicated by more-or-less straight lines, trend about due N-S. However, in the vicinity of the Explorer and Juan de Fuca plates, there occur a succession of small rotations toward a more northeast orientation. Menard and Atwater used this geometry to devise a simple model of direction change, shown in our Figure 7.38. Diagram A shows a normal set of paired anomaly stripes. Diagram B shows that newer stripes are inclined at an acute angle and that each stripe narrows from one end to the other, giving it a wedgelike form. This form is generated by the horizontal rotation of the spreading rift, which sweeps over a larger area at one end than the other. At the same time, these stripes are being generated on the opposite side of the rift, but in an inverted position. Diagram C shows the resumption of normal anomaly stripes in the new direction. In applying this diagram to the map, Figure 7.37, keep in mind that the Gorda, Juan de Fuca, and Explorer plates at the right have been largely subducted under the North American continent, hiding from view much of the earlier anomaly pattern in that direction. Menard and Atwater added a modification to the above model in which the original spreading ridge breaks up into shorter segments, so as to accomplish the directional change much more easily and quickly. We show this in Diagram D of Figure 7.38.

About a decade later, a quite different mechanism of change in direction of transform/FZ and magnetic stripes was proposed by Richard N. Hey, Frederick Duennebier, and Jason Morgan

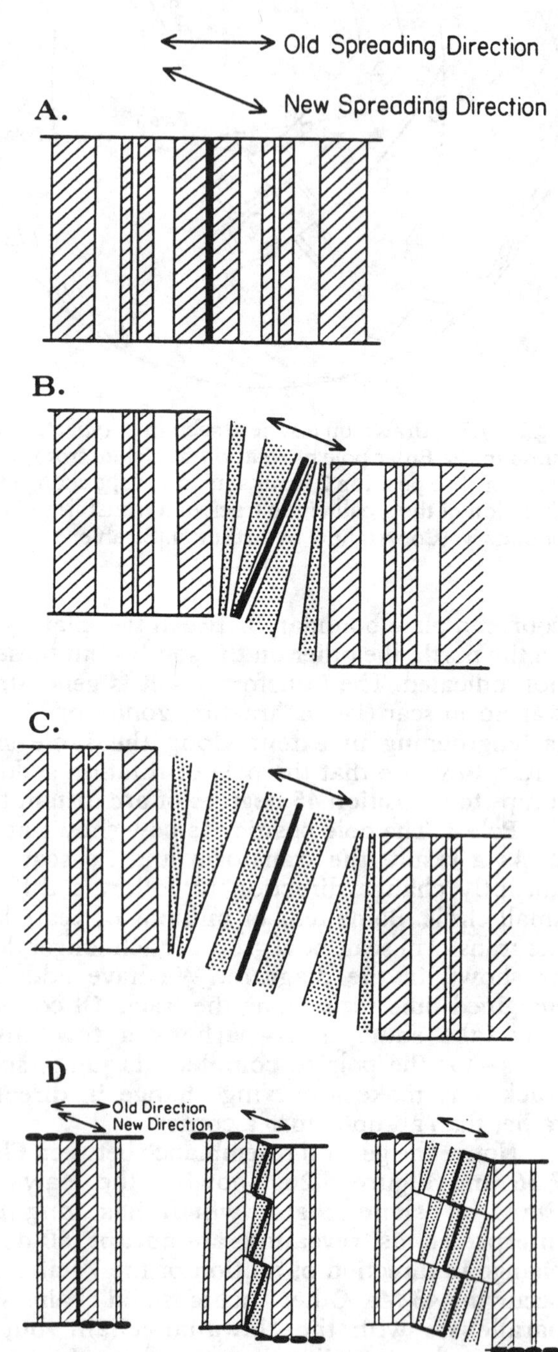

Figure 7.38 (A, B, C) Diagrams of stages in change of plate spreading direction. (D) The spreading ridge may break up into smaller segments, reducing the time required to complete the change in direction. (From Menard and Atwater, 1968, *Nature*, v. 219, Figures 3 and 5. Reproduced by permission of Macmillan Magazines, Ltd.)

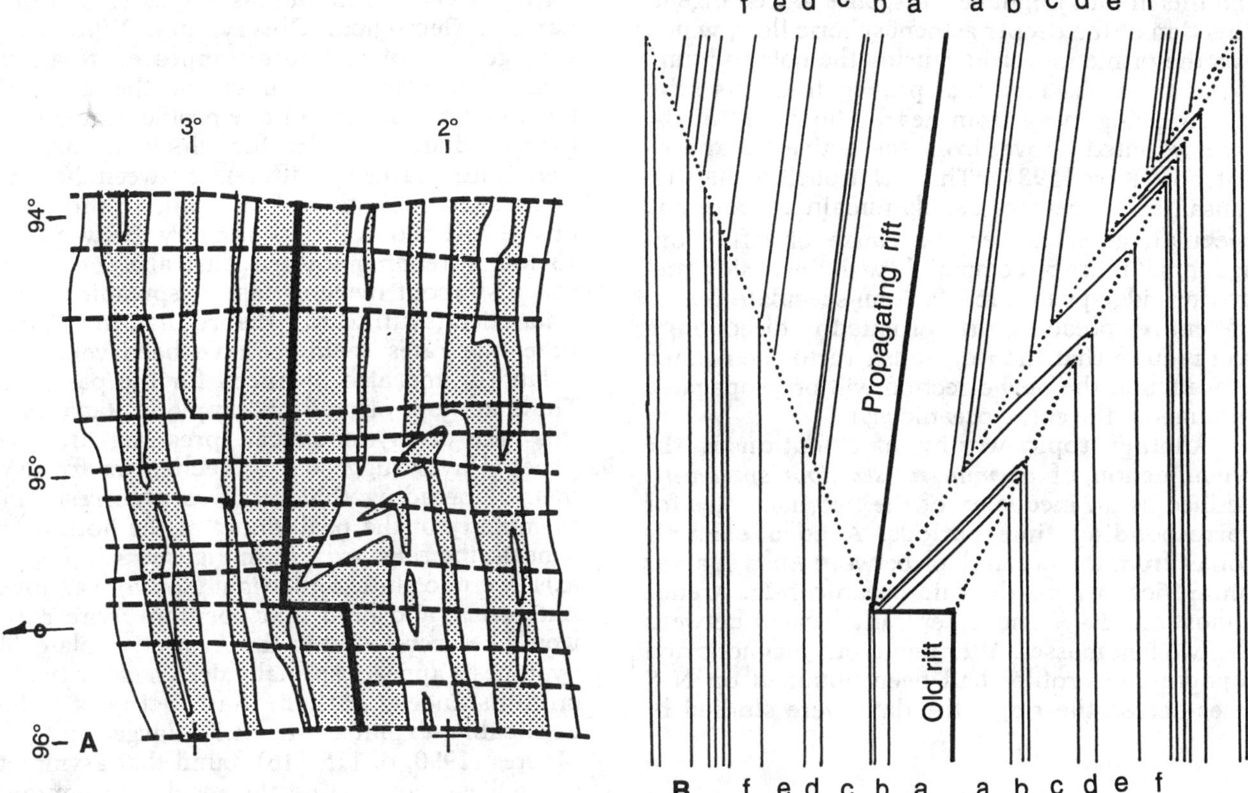

Figure 7.39 A propagating rift. (A) The observed anomaly pattern. (B) Schematic interpretation. (Fropm Hey, Duennebier, and Morgan, 1980, *Jour. of Geophysical Res.*, v. 85. Reproduced by permission of the authors and the American Geophysical Union.)

(Hey et al., 1980; Kerr, 1981). It was interpreted from a strange anomaly pattern found west of the Galapagos Islands, on the Cocos plate. Our Figure 7.39 shows this area and the interpreted tectonic pattern. (Here, the Cocos/Nazca plate boundary runs E–W, but we have rotated the diagrams 90° to match our earlier figures.) What seems to happen is that one segment of spreading ridge extending between two transform faults breaks through that separating transform and, by growing longer, penetrates the domain of the adjoining ridge segment. Of course, this new addition takes the new direction required by the Euler pole jump. As this *propagating rift* grows, it substitutes itself for the adjacent rift, which becomes weakened and ultimately dysfunctional; i.e., it becomes a *failed rift*, These developments are shown in Figure 7.40. The task of the propagating rift is accomplished when it has reached the far side of the zone marked by the next transform fault. Obviously, propagating rifts must develop simultaneously in a chain along the entire plate boundary to answer fully the command given by the jumped Euler pole. Once the changeover is completed, the plate as a whole moves in its new direction, generating a new pattern of orthogonal stripes between FZs. A propagating rift requires a source of rising magma, and this requirement suggests the possibility that a new rift forms first at the base of the lithosphere,

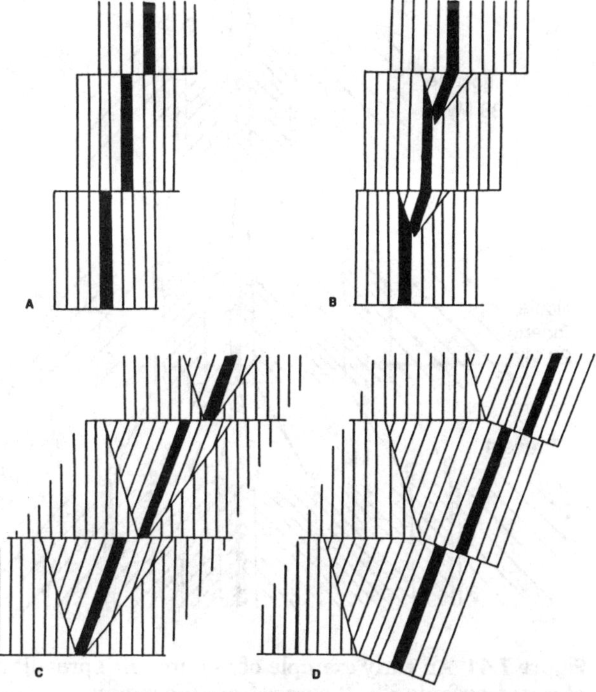

Figure 7.40 Simplified and stylized drawing of stages in the growth of a series of propagating rifts. In the final stage a new set of rift segments and transforms has been completed with reorientation of the transform faults. (Copyright © by Arthur N. Strahler.)

and this in turn might be a response to a change in direction of the deeper asthenospheric flow, which was the prime mover in causing the pole to jump. It has been observed that propagating rifts have been moving away from nearby hotspots; in the case we cited above, from the active Galapagos hotspot (Kerr, 1981). This relationship may be causal, but necessary details remain obscure and speculative. Whatever the cause of rift propagation, it must be compatible with the basic plate-driving ridge-push force. We can speculate that as the entire spreading rift is rotated in direction, it will require that the ridge-push vector be rotated as well, and the new direction will be propagated throughout the entire oceanic plate.

Another topic worthy of attention is the phenomenon of *asymmetric sea-floor spreading*, defined as an inequality of the two half-rates for corresponding time periods. A good example comes from the ocean floor between Australia and Antarctica, where the mid-oceanic ridge trends almost due E–W and is centrally located between the two landmasses. After numerous magnetic and topographic profiles had been obtained on N–S lines across the ridge, the data were studied by

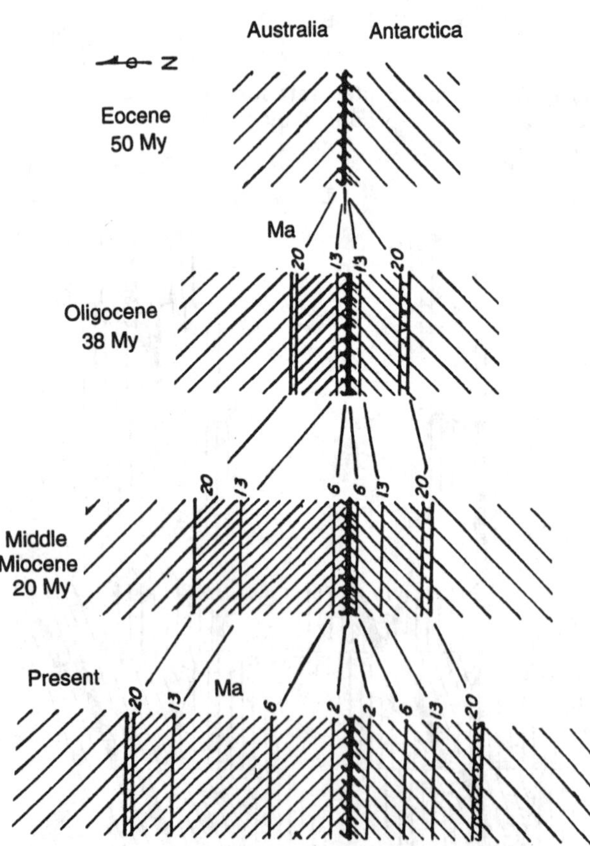

Figure 7.41 An early example of asymmetric spreading of a mid-oceanic rift. It comes from the region between Australia and Antarctica. The diagram has been rotated with north to the left. (Adapted from Weissel and Hayes, 1971, *Nature*, v. 231, p. 437. Copyright © by Macmillan Magazines, Ltd. Reproduced by permission of the publisher.)

Jeffrey Weissel and Dennis Hayes (1971) of the Lamont Geological Observatory. Whereas the average rate of spreading appeared to be very nearly uniform over much of the area, they identified one section of one profile, located along the meridian of 132°E, for which the half-rates were quite markedly different between 20 and 40 Ma, a span consisting of anomalies 6 through 13. Figure 7.41 shows this asymmetry. Between 2 and 13 Ma, spreading toward Australia (northward) was just about twice as fast as spreading toward Antarctica (southward). Before that, in Oligocene time, the rates seem to have been very evenly balanced, and also balanced for the past 2 m.y. These authors offered no simple explanation for this case of asymmetrical spreading. In a 1976 paper, Hayes suggested a mechanism for asymmetric spreading that requires a corresponding asymmetry of the positioning of the hottest zone beneath the ridge axis. If, in Figure 7.41, this "heat axis" were to shift to the right (south), i.e., toward Antarctica, and hold that position, more magma would be accreted onto the Australian plate. This hypothesis appears specially designed for the local circumstances, rather than being a widely applicable explanation. R.J. Varga and E.M. Moores (1990, p. 115-116) found that asymmetric anomalies may also be the result of asymmetric multiple simple shear caused by detachment faulting at ridge crests. Listric normal faulting on only one side of the rift extends the crust on that side of the axis.

7.19 Magnetic Puzzles of the Pacific Plate

In the 1960s, scientists studying the Pacific plate were treated to two mysterious features that required explanation. One is a curious, abrupt bend in the trend of magnetic stripes in the Gulf of Alaska, shown in Figure 7.42 at about lat. 50°N, long. 160°W. First documented in 1967 during ocean surveys by the U.S. Coast and Geodetic Survey, this feature was named the Great Magnetic Bight (Elvers et al., 1967). The rather abrupt change in trend of magnetic stripes can be interpreted in terms of what happens at a triple junction of the RRR type: Rift-Rift-Rift (see Figure 7.5). Figure 7.43 is a schematic map of an RRR triple junction with the magnetic anomaly patterns it would generate, allowing the Great Magnetic Bight to fit into a portion of the Pacific plate. If this explanation is valid, there should have been two other plates (Plate "X" and Plate "Y") to complete the triple junction. Just where these other two plates were located or where they are now was the mystery.

An answer was proposed in 1968 by Walter C. Pitman III and Dennis E. Hayes of the Lamont-Doherty Geological Observatory. Their schematic reconstruction of the tectonic history of the North Pacific region is shown in Figure 7.44. The predicted triple junction existed during the late Cretaceous Period (75 Ma). One of the two

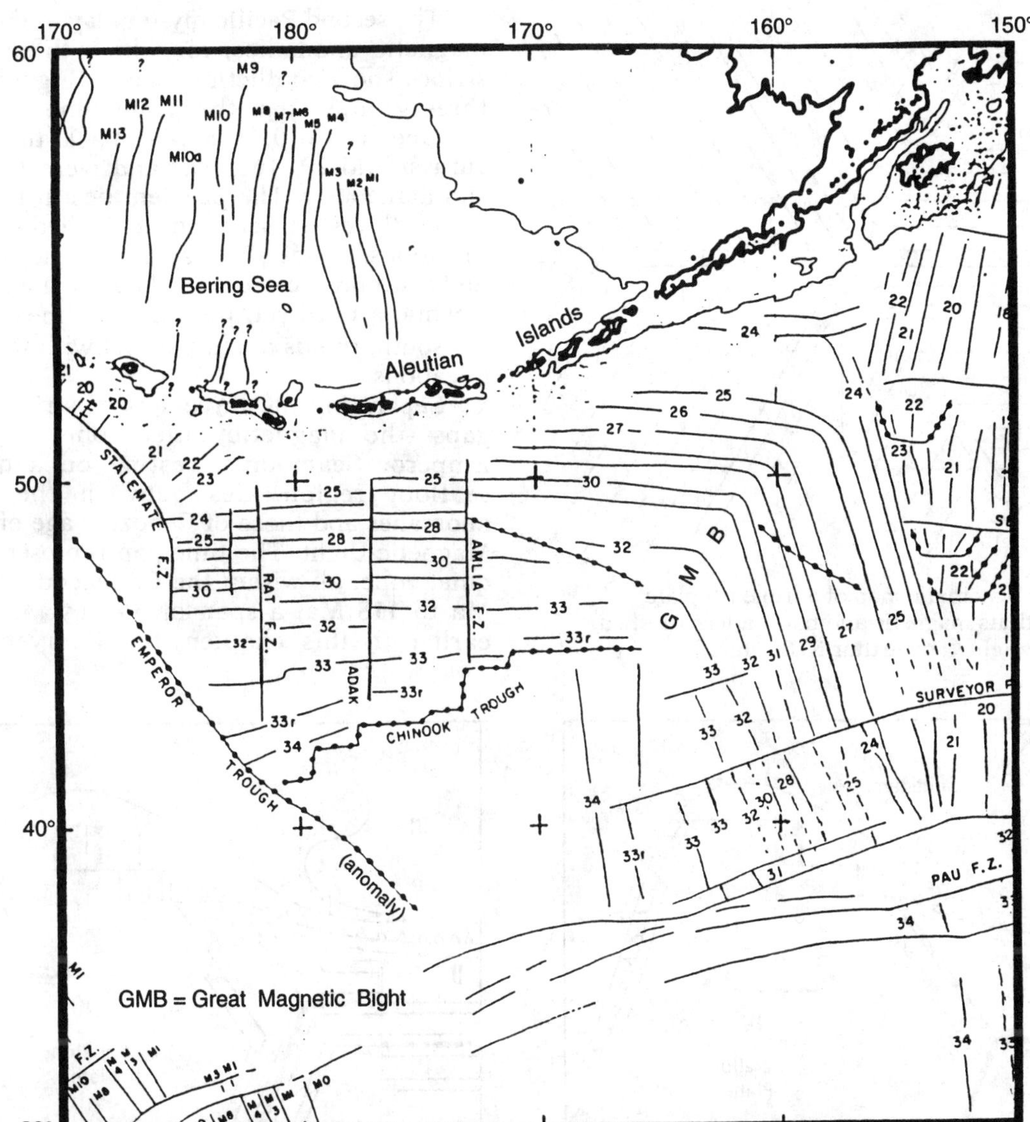

Figure 7.42 Magnetic anomaly map of the northeastern Pacific Ocean. Magnetic anomalies are represented by dotted lines. The numbered anomalies are approximately on the time boundaries separating Cenozoic epochs and the Cretaceous Period. Transform scars (FZs) offset the anomaly pattern. (From S.C. Cande, J.L. LaBreque, W.C. Pitman, III, et al., 1989, *Magnetic Lineations of the World's Ocean Basins* (Map). Tulsa OK, Amer. Assoc. of Petroleum Geologists. Used by permission.)

presently missing plates was named the Kula plate, the other, the Farallon plate. The triple junction migrated northeastward, producing the pattern of stripes we see today in the Great Magnetic Bight. When the western branch of the triple junction reached the subduction zone of the Aleutian Trench, the entire Kula plate simply disappeared—"down the drain" so to speak—and the spreading boundary disappeared with it. The east-moving Farallon plate headed toward a subduction boundary along the western margin of the American plate where it, too, was largely consumed, but small portions of it remain today: Gorda, Juan de Fuca, and Explorer to the north; Cocos and Rivera to the south.

Figure 7.45 is a set of four paleotectonic maps showing this northeastern region from 65 Ma (Paleocene) to the present. Notice that bold dots show the positions of the Hawaiian (H) and Yellowstone (Y) hotspots. Their positions do not shift with reference to the border of the map, whereas the plate boundaries and continental coastlines shift from one frame to the next. (Use of the Mercator projection requires that the north-pointing arrows in high latitudes lengthen and splay outward, but this pattern does not imply any real area spreading within in the plates.)

Figure 7.46 is a set of six paleotectonic maps also showing the history of the Pacific, Kula, and Farallon plates from Paleocene to the present (Grigg, 1988), and including the entire Pacific plate. Arrows showing the directions of motion of the plates are particularly helpful in visualizing the succession of changes we have described.

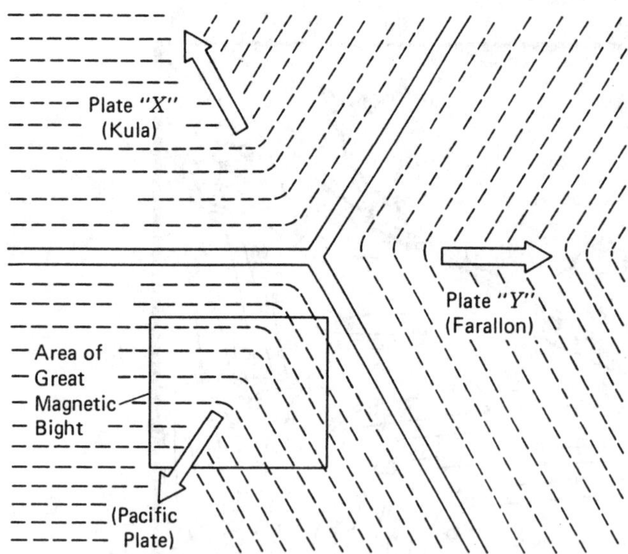

Figure 7.43 Schematic map of a triple rift plate junction with its magnetic anomaly pattern (dashed lines). (Copyright © by Arthur N. Strahler.)

The second Pacific mystery lay in the Mesozoic magnetic anomalies, for which three groups of stripes show conflicting trends (Figure 7.47). All three groups span the same time range: Early Cretaceous (M-0, 118 Ma) back through Late Jurassic (M-29, 160 Ma) and were thus formed simultaneously. The problem lies in the fact that the northwestern set of stripes, called the Japanese lineations, trends about at right angles to a second and centrally located set—the Hawaiian lineations—while a third set, the Phoenix lineations far to the south, trends about parallel with the Japanese lineations.

Separating the three sets of stripes are wide gaps—the magnetic quiet zone. The line of Emperor Seamounts, resting on a quiet zone seafloor region, lies between the Mesozoic anomalies and those of Cenozoic age of the Great Magnetic Bight. The time gap represented by the quiet zone, all within the Cretaceous, is from 84 Ma to 118 Ma, a span of 34 m.y. As explained earlier in this chapter, the intervening areas

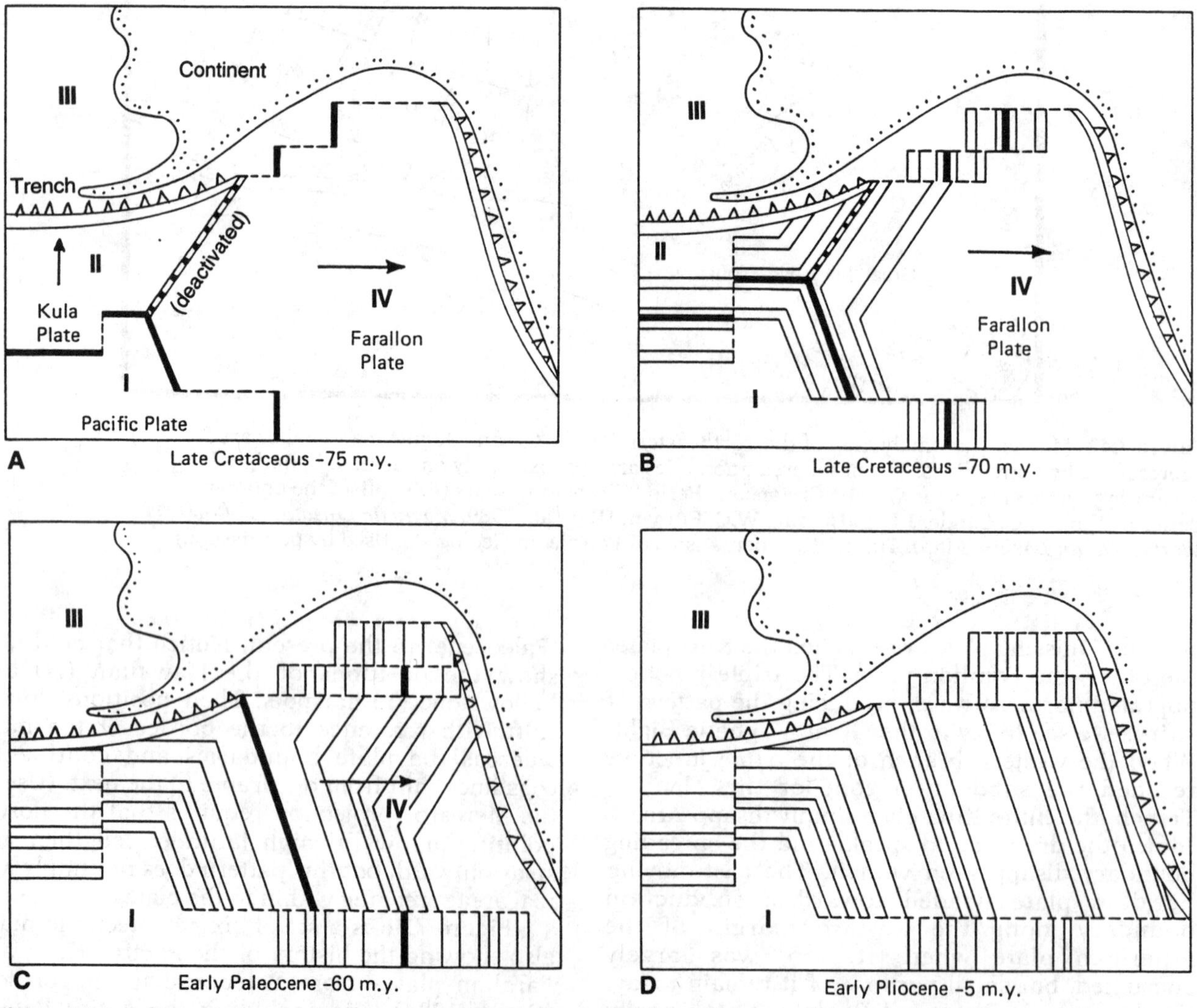

Figure 7.44 Schematic maps of the northeastern Pacific Ocean basin showing the migrations of spreading plate boundaries and the disappearance of the Kula plate. (From W.C. Pitman III and D.E. Hayes, 1968, *Jour. Geophysical Res.*, v. 73, p. 6577, Figure 4. Copyrighted by the American Geophysical Union. Used by permission.)

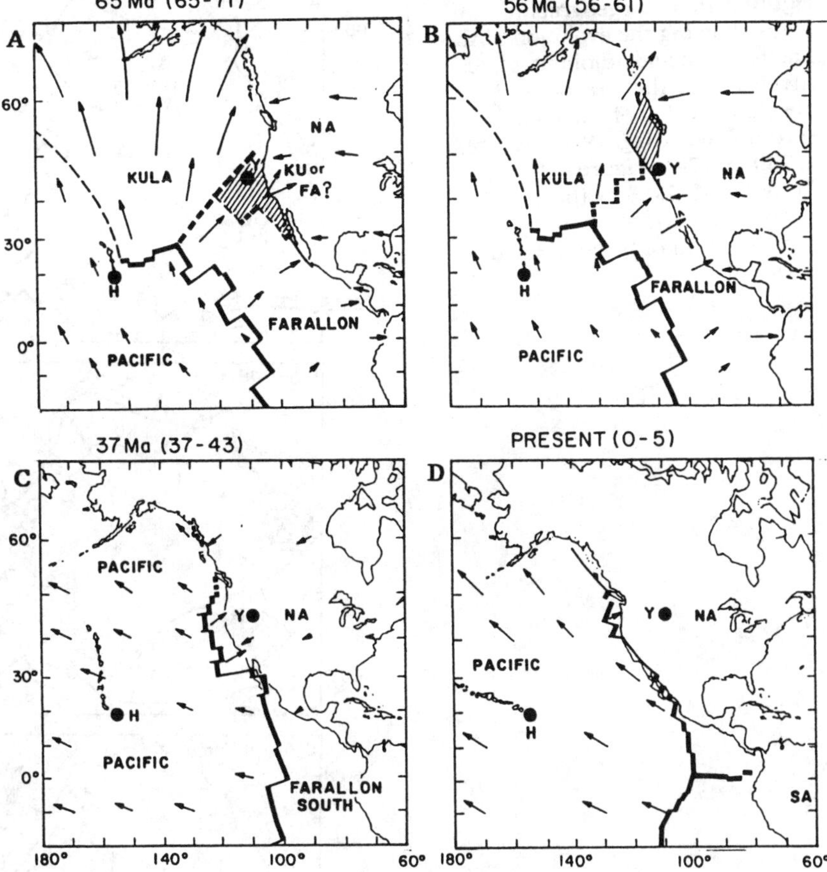

Figure 7.45 Paleogeographic maps of the northeast Pacific Ocean showing evolution of the Kula, Farallon, and Pacific plates. Black circles show locations of the Hawaiian (H) and Yellowstone (Y) hotspots. (From T. Atwater, 1989, Plate tectonic history of the northeast Pacific and western North America. Chapter 4, p. 42, Figure 14, in *The Geology of North America*, Volume N, the Geological Society of America, Boulder, Colorado, USA. Reproduced by permission of the publisher.)

without stripes represent periods during which crust was being produced by seafloor spreading, but no reversals were taking place by means of which to produce any record of anomalies.

A full account of the events that produced these Mesozoic anomalies would be long, involved, and perhaps difficult to follow. We do, however, show how a pattern of stripes such as those observed could have come about by seafloor spreading and plate accretion. Figure 7.48 is a schematic diagram making use of two triple junctions of the RRR type. One of these (that at the top of the figure) is the same RRR junction shown in Figures 7.43 and 7.44, except that we have now regressed in time another 40 m.y. to a tectonic geography as it might have been earlier in the Cretaceous Period, at about 110 Ma. The second triple junction lay to the southeast and involved another plate, the Phoenix plate, which formed a triple junction with the ancestral Pacific plate and the Farallon plate. We can consider the Pacific plate to be stationary with reference to the other three plates, so the threefold pattern of stripes that emerges resembles the Mesozoic anomaly pattern. We have outlined the relative position of groups of stripes, from which you can see that the Japanese and Phoenix groups have stripes about parallel in direction but arranged in opposite order of appearance from north to south. The intermediate Hawaiian group of stripes is oriented about at right angles to the other two.

7.20 Evolution of the San Andreas Fault as a Plate Boundary

Returning to the history of the Farallon plate, let us look into the events that may have led to the development of the San Andreas Fault as a transform plate boundary. Geologists agree that the San Andreas fault (a right-lateral strike-slip fault) forms the main boundary between the Pacific plate and the American plate from the head of the Gulf of California to a point on the northern California coast near Cape Mendocino. In certain areas the fault line is difficult to establish, and other neighboring strike-slip faults are thought to take part in the displacement of the two plates. (The San Andreas Fault system is described in Chapter 6; see Figures 6.31-6.33.)

The history of the San Andreas plate boundary which we present here was determined by Tanya Atwater, at that time a graduate student at the Scripps Institution of Oceanography. Her report was published in *Science* in 1970. During the early Cenozoic, the northeast-moving Farallon plate had been undergoing subduction along the North American plate boundary from as far north as British Columbia to as far south as central Mexico (see Figures 7.45 and 7.46). As subduction continued, the North American plate and the spreading boundary between the Farallon and Pacific plates were coming closer together. Thus,

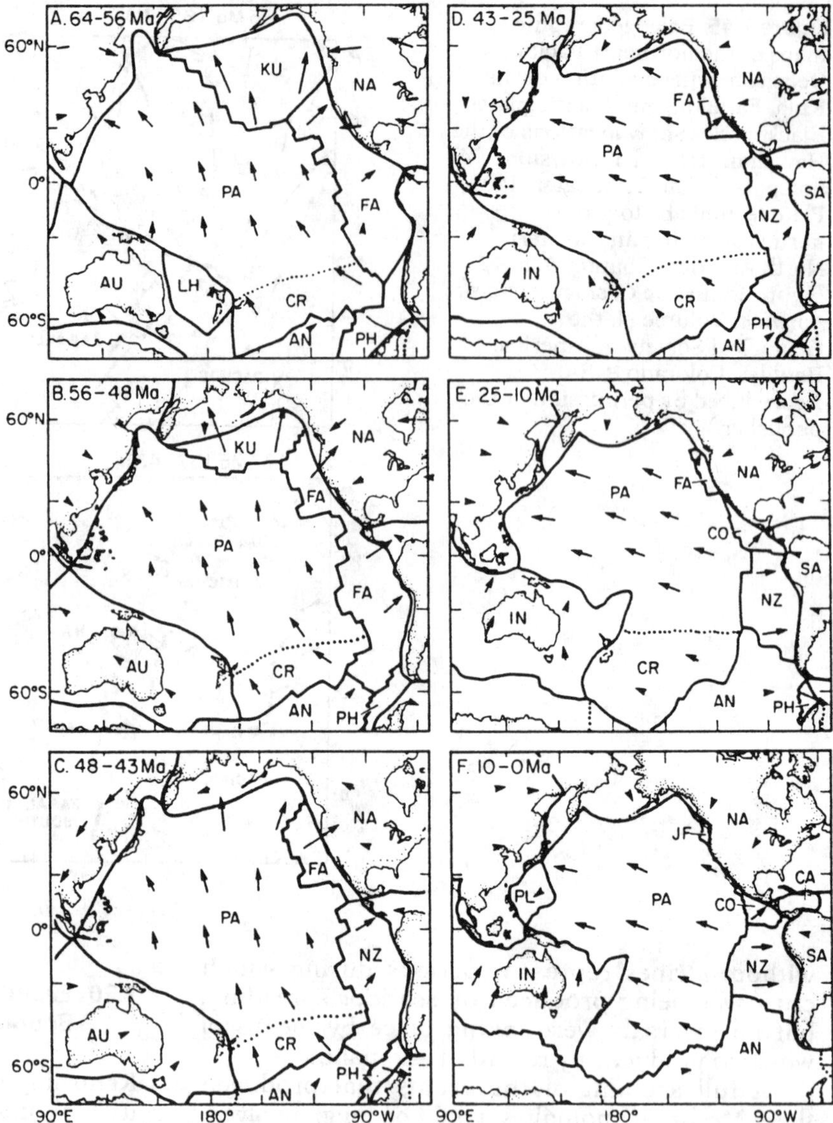

Figure 7.46 Paleogeographic maps showing the evolution of the Pacific plate and adjoining plates. Arrows show the directions of absolute motion of each plate. (From R.W. Grigg, 1988, *Science*, v. 240, p. 1741, Figure 4. Copyright © 1988 by the American Association for the Advancement of Science. Used by permission.)

the exposed surface area of the Farallon plate was shrinking in width.

Figure 7.49 is a series of schematic maps adapted from the original series presented by Atwater (1970, Figures 5 and 8), showing the subduction of the Farallon plate beneath the American plate, starting with conditions in the late Eocene, about 40 Ma. The American continental margin is depicted as a straight line at a 45-degree angle to the page. The rate of relative motion between the American plate and the Pacific plate is taken to be 6 cm/yr. The position of the Pacific plate is fixed on our book page, so that the American plate seems to move obliquely toward the lower right. Relative motions of the three plates are shown by a closed vector triangle.

Notice first in Map A that the spreading boundary between the Pacific and Farallon plates was offset by a long transform fault, with the result that a salient (a promontory) of the Pacific plate first made contact with the American plate at a single point, shown in Map B to be located not far from the present-day position of Guyamas on the Mexican mainland. It would seem obvious that immediately thereafter subduction of the Pacific and Farallon plates would have begun. As to the Farallon plate, for which the relative motion (F/A) is to the northeast, normal to subduction boundary, subduction would easily begin. But subduction was not to be continued for the Pacific plate, because it had a northwesterly motion relative to the American plate (P/A). As a result, the plate boundary here became a transform fault (Map C), and further subduction ceased along that stretch of transform boundary. As subduction of the Farallon plate continued both to the north and to the south, the intervening new transform boundary increased in length (Map D).

When we refer to the locations of Los Angeles and San Francisco on the American plate and observe their locations on successive maps, we see that the northern tip of the transform boundary is extending in a northwesterly direction, passing by Los Angeles first, then San Francisco. In Map E, showing what should be "Present" conditions, two remnants of the Farallon plate persist today. The

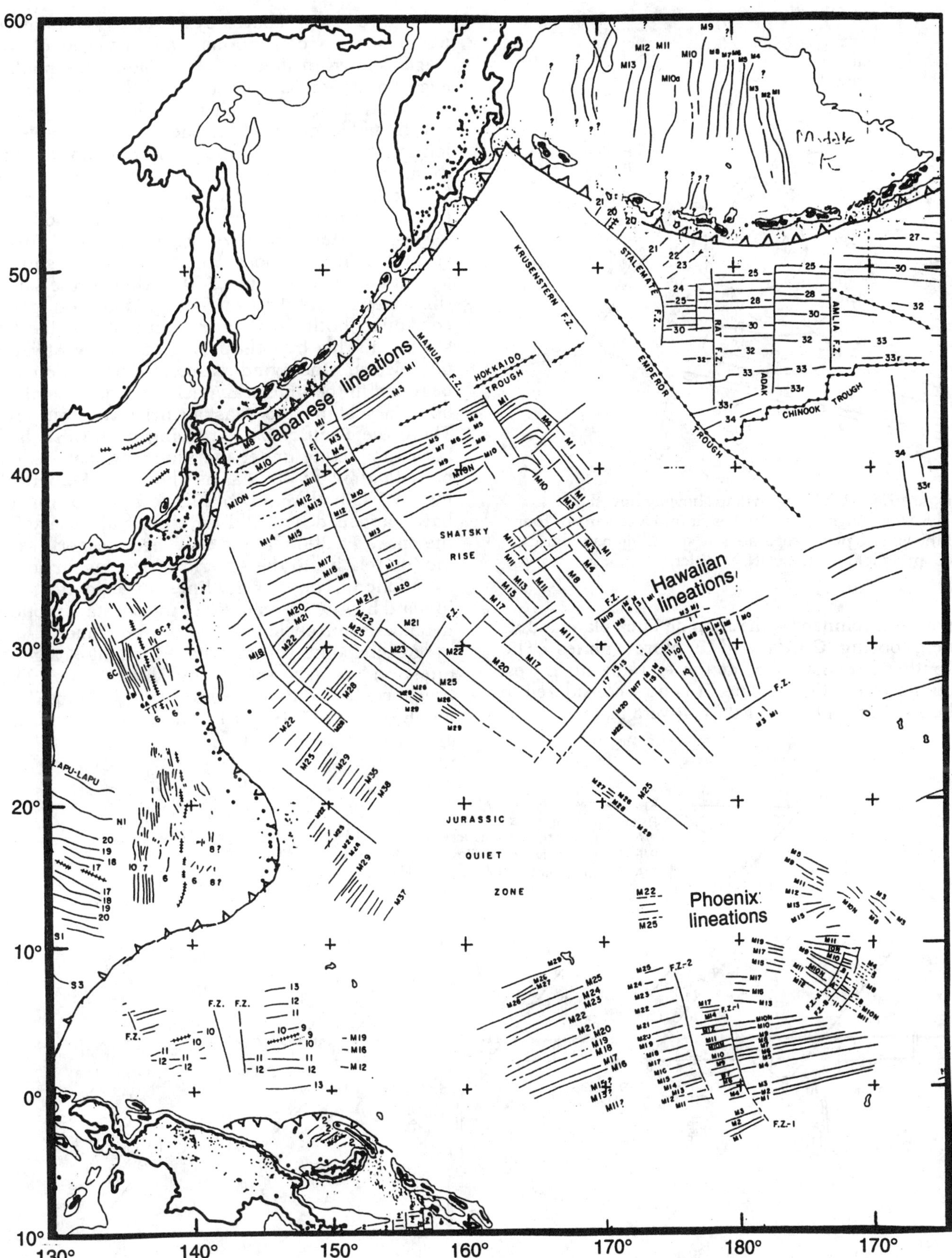

Figure 7.47 Map of the western Pacific Ocean basin showing the Mesozoic magnetic anomalies. (From S.C. Cande, J.L. LaBreque, W.C. Pitman, III, et al., 1989, *Magnetic Lineations of the World's Ocean Basins* (Map). Tulsa OK, Amer. Assoc. of Petroleum Geologists. Used by permission of the AAPG.)

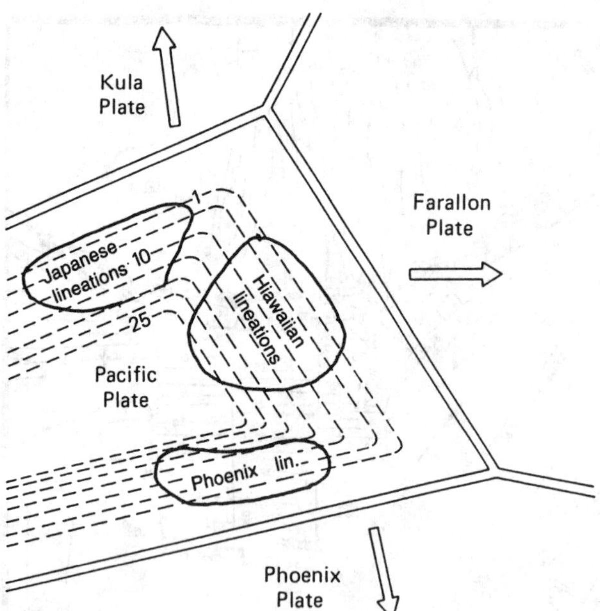

Figure 7.48 A schematic map showing how the Mesozoic magnetic anomalies fit into a scheme of four lithospheric plates separated by spreading boundaries. (Copyright © by Arthur N. Strahler.)

northern remnant is the Juan de Fuca plate and its neighboring Gorda and Explorer plates. The southern remnant lies at the extreme northwest corner of the Cocos plate. It is now considered to be a separate plate, called the Rivera plate.

Figure 7.50, prepared by Atwater (1970, Figure 6), presents a continuous time scenario of the stages shown in Figure 7.49. Holding a straightedge horizontal and uncovering the graph from bottom to top, we watch the strike-slip segment appear and lengthen as the Pacific plate occupies a lengthening sector of the plate boundary. This diagram illustrates what Atwater called the "constant motion model." An alternative model (not shown here) proposed by Morgan in 1968 and Vine and Hess in 1970 called for the American/Pacific plate boundary to have been solidly locked and inactive until 5 Ma, while at the same time trench subduction of the Farallon plate continued both north and south of the locked sediment. This hypothesis was tested by Atwater but rejected. One sound reason for its rejection can be found in the American/Pacific subduction plate boundary along the Alaska/Kurile volcanic arc. There the Pacific Plate, moving northwest, had been subducting under the American plate as far back in time as 40 Ma, as shown in Map C of Figure 7.45 and Map D of Figure 7.46. For this to have happened it would have been necessary for the entire Pacific plate to have been in northwest motion relative to the American plate as far south as Mexico. The strong lines of evidence put forward by Atwater in favor of the constant motion hypothesis quickly led to its wide acceptance.

At this point, you may have thought of a good question to ask about this hypothesis. The transform boundary shown to evolve in Maps C, D, and E of Figure 7.49 must have coincided with the

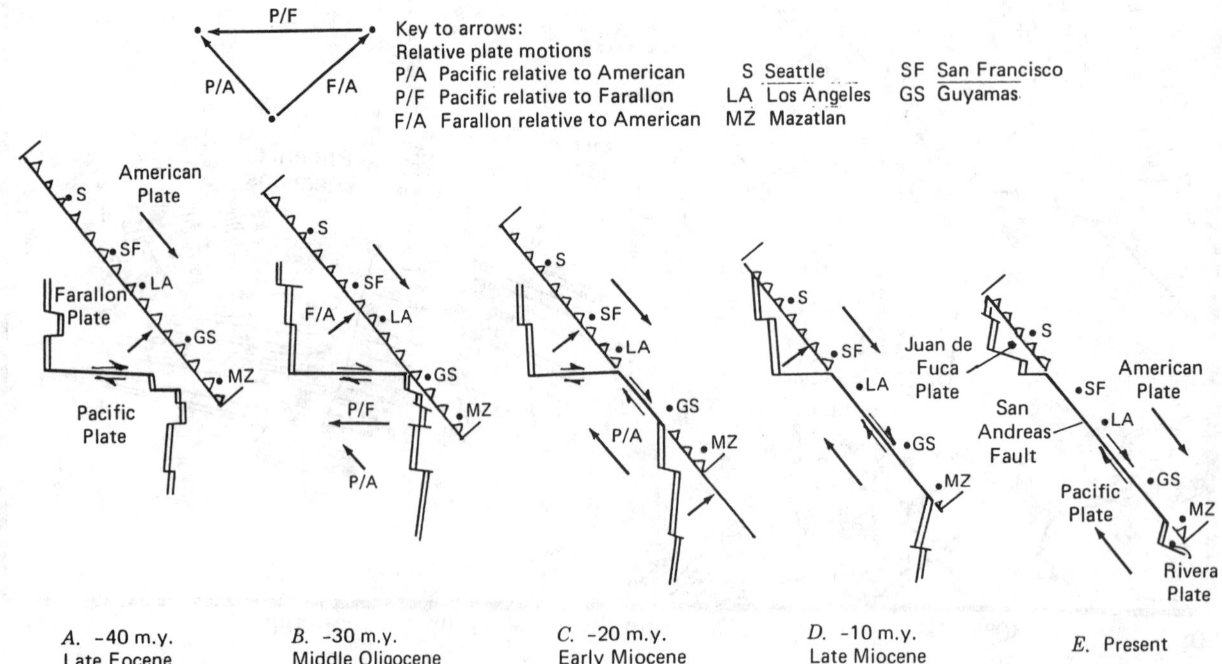

Figure 7.49 Stylized sketch maps showing the consumption of the Farallon plate and the formation of the San Andreas transcurrent fault. (Adapted from T. Atwater, 1970, *Bull., Geol. Soc. Amer.*, v. 81, p. 3513, Figure 5. Used by permission of the author and the Geological Society of America.)

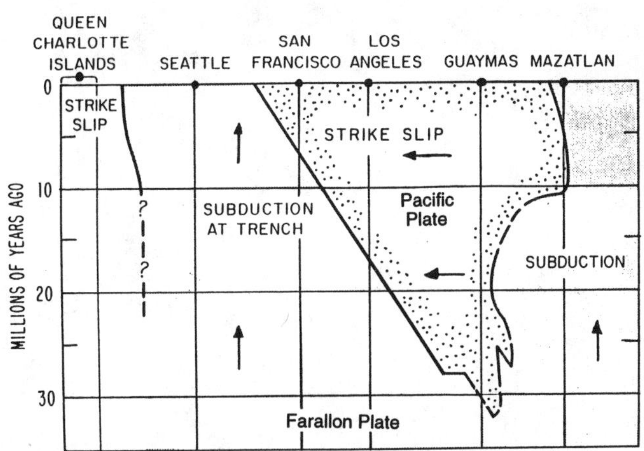

Figure 7.50 A time-versus-distance chart showing the initiation and lengthening of the strike-slip plate boundary accompanying the subduction of the Farallon plate. (From T. Atwater, 1970, *Bull., Geol. Soc. Amer.*, v. 81, p. 351, Figure 6. Used by permission of the author and the Geological Society of America.)

contact between oceanic lithosphere and continental lithosphere. Instead, the San Andreas Fault system, which is the present-day plate boundary, cuts through continental lithosphere from the head of the Gulf of California to a point north of San Francisco. How do geologists explain this intracontinental location? The answer proposed by Atwater is to postulate that the transform boundary made a sudden "jump" from the oceanic/continental boundary to a new position entirely within the continental lithosphere. Figure 7.51 is Atwater's illustration using schematic cross sections corresponding to map stages A,B,C, and E of Figure 7.49. Sections A and B show the oblique subduction of the Farallon plate, giving rise to a volcanic arc in the American plate. Section C shows the active Pacific/Farallon plate boundary to have collided with the American plate, i.e., a *ridge-trench collision* has occurred. Because the Pacific plate is moving parallel with this new Pacific/America boundary, subduction has ceased and a strike-slip boundary (a transform plate boundary) has been established.

What could have caused the inland jump shown to have occurred between sections C and D of Figure 7.51? The suggestion has been made that continental lithosphere is weaker than lithosphere of the contact zone between continental and oceanic lithosphere, so that the transform boundary would not remain for long in its original location. [See Chapter 6 for a discussion of the mechanisms of the San Andreas fault and the lithosphere beneath it.]

The evolution of the Gulf of California is thought to be closely tied to the establishment of the San Andreas fault. In Chapter 10, under the heading of The Gulf of California, we state that the Gulf and the San Andreas fault had a closely

Figure 7.51 Schematic cross sections of the Pacific, Farallon, and American plates showing the formation of the San Andreas Fault as a transform plate boundary. (Adapted from T. Atwater, 1970, *Bull., Geol. Soc. Amer.*, v. 81, p. 351, Figure 15. Reproduced with the permission of the publisher, the Geological Society of America, Boulder, Colorado, USA. Copyright © 1970.)

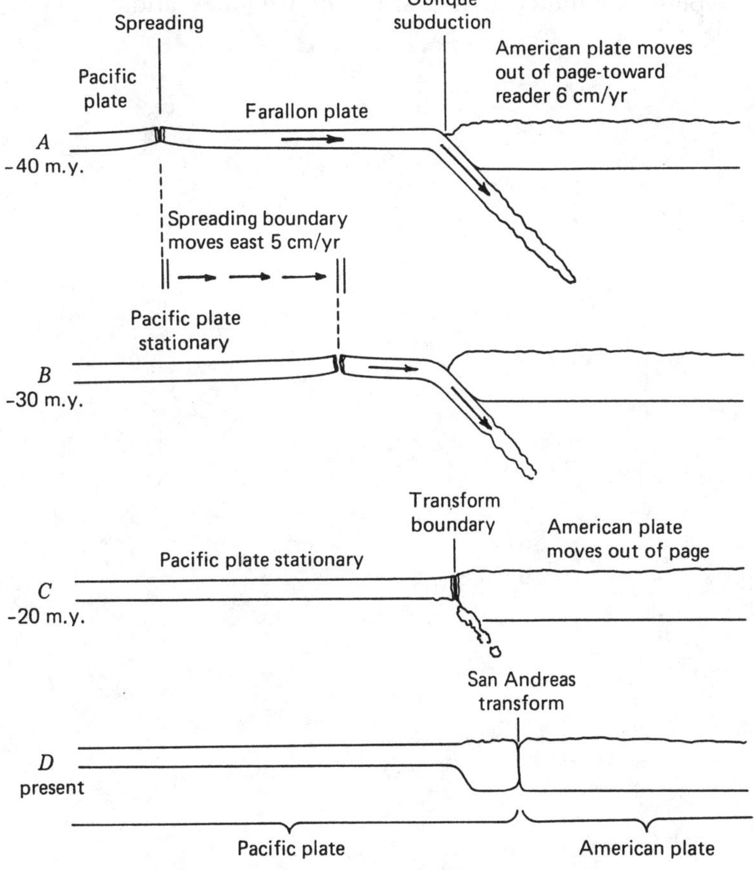

related history. Prior to about 12 Ma, an active subduction boundary existed offshore of what is now the Baja Peninsula. At that time a new plate boundary parallel with the subduction boundary began to develop along a line of strike-slip faulting located some 300 km inland. The East Pacific Rise extended itself inland and intercepted this shear zone, allowing the plate boundary to jump to the new shear zone and leaving behind an outer "fossil trench." The oceanic rift then penetrated northwestward in the form of a series of short oceanic rift segments connected by transforms. These are shown in Figure 10.62. Penetration continued into what is now the Salton basin (Chapter 11), and thence northwestward as the new San Andreas Fault.

* * * * * * * * *

The break between this chapter and Chapter 8 is somewhat arbitrary. We have not completed our study of the oceanic lithosphere because the consumption of that kind of lithosphere in subduction boundaries remains to be considered. Viewed from a different perspective, however, subduction plate boundaries are also those lines along which continental lithosphere meets oceanic lithosphere. New continental lithosphere is being formed along these same boundaries, both by the rise of magma that penetrates the continental crust and by addition of new belts of metamorphic rock which form above a down-moving plate margin or by collision. In Chapter 8 we will resume the topic of plate tectonics with a study of trenches and island arcs.

References Cited

Atwater, Tanya, 1970, Implications of plate tectonics for the Cenozoic tectonic evolution of western North America, *Bull., Geol. Soc. Amer.*, v. 81, p. 3513-3536. Reprinted in A. Cox, Ed., 1973, p. 583-609.

Atwater, Tanya, 1989, Plate tectonic history of the northeast Pacific and western North America. Chapter 4, p. 21-72 in *The Geology of North America*, Volume N, Boulder Co, The Geological Society of America.

Atwater, Tanya, and Jeff Severinghaus, 1989, Tectonic maps of the northeast Pacific. Chapter 3, p. 15-20 in *The Geology of North America*, Volume N, Boulder Co, The Geological Society of America.

Bates, Robert L., and Julia A. Jackson, Eds., 1987, *Glossary of Geology*. Alexamdria, VA: American Geological Institute.

Bott, M.P.H., 1982, *The Interior of the Earth, its Structure, Constitution and Evolution*, 2nd ed., London, Edward Arnold.

Bullard, E.C., A.E. Maxwell, and R. Revelle, 1956, Heat flow through the deep sea floor. *Advances in Geophysics*, v. 3, p. 153-181.

Cande, S.C., J.L. LaBrecque, R.L. Larson, W.C. Pitman III, et al., 1989, *Magnetic Lineations of the World's Ocean Basins* (Map). Tulsa OK, Amer. Assoc. of Petroleum Geologists.

Carter, William E., and Douglas S. Robertson, 1986, Studying the earth by Very-Long-Baseline Interferometry. *Scientific American*, v. 255, no. 5, p. 46-54.

Chase, Clement, 1978, Plate kinematics: The Americas, East Africa, and the rest of the world. *Earth and Planetary Science Letters*, v. 37, p. 355-368.

Cox, A., R.R. Doell, G.B. Dalrymple, 1963, Geomagnetic polarity epochs and Pleistocene geochronology. *Nature*, v. 198, p. 1049-1051.

Cox, Allan, 1961, *Bull.* 1083-E. *U.S. Geological Survey*.

Cox, Allan, 1969, Geomagnetic reversals. *Science*, v. 163, p. 237-245.

Cox, Allan, and R.R. Doell, 1060, Review of Pedeomagnetism. *Bull. Geol. Soc. of Amer.*, v. 71, p. 645, 786.

Cox, Allan, and Robert Brian Hart, 1986, *Plate Tectonics: How It Works*. Boston, Blackwell Scientific Publications.

Cox, Allan, Ed., 1973, *Plate Tectonics and Geomagnetic Reversals*. San Francisco, W.H. Freeman amd Company.

Cox, Allan, G. Brent Dalrymple, and Richard R. Doell, 1967, Reversals of the earth's magnetic field. *Scientific American*, v. 216, no. 2, pp. 44-54.

Cox, Allan, Richard R. Doell, and G. Brent Dalrymple, 1964, Reversals of the earth's magnetic field. *Science*, v. 144, p. 1537-1543.

Dalrymple, G. Brent, 1991, *The Age of the Earth*. Stanford, Stanford Univ. Press.

DeMets, C., R.G. Gordon, D.F. Argus, amd S. Stein, 1990, Current plate motions. *Geophysical Journal International*, v. 101, p. 425.

Dewey, John F., 1972, Plate tectonics. *Scientific American*, p. 56-68.

Dewey, John F., and John M. Bird, 1970, Mountain belts and the new global tectonics. *Jour. of Geophysical Res.*, v. 75, no. 14, p. 2625-2647.

Dietz, Robert S., 1961, Continent and ocean basin evolution by spreading of the sea-floor. *Nature*, v. 190, p. 854-857.

Egyed, T., 1956, The change of earth dimensions determined from paleogeographical data. *Pure Applied Geophysics*, v. 33, p. 42-48.

Eicher, Don L., 1976, *Geologic Time*, 2nd ed. Englewood Cliffs, NJ., Prentice-Hall.

Elvers, D.J., C.C. Matheuson, R.E. Kohler, and R.L. Moses 1967, Systematic ocean surveys by the U.S.C. and G.S.S. Pioneer, 1961-1963. U.S. Coast and Geodetic Survey, Oper. Data Rept. C. GSDR-1, 19 p.

Ewing, M., and J.L. Worzel, 1954, Gravity anomalies and structure of the West Indes, Part I. *Bull., Geol. Soc. Amer.*, v. 65, p. 165-174.

Flinn, Edward A., 1981, Application of space technology to geodynamics, *Science*, v. 213, p. 89-96.

Forsyth, D.W., and S. Uyeda, 1975, On the relative importance of driving forces of plate motion. *Geophysical Jour. Royal Astronomical Soc.*, v. 43, p. 163-200.

Frey, Herbert V., and Bosworth, J.M., 1989, Measuring contemporary crustal motions: NASA's Crustal Dynamics Project. *Earthquakes and Volcanoes*, v. 20, p. 96-113.

Gordon, Richard G., 1991, Plate motion. *Reviews of Geophysics, Supplement*, p. 748-758.

Gordon, Richard G., 1991, Plate motions are steady. *EOS*, v. 72, no. 10.

Gordon, Richard, and Seth Stein, 1992, Global tectonics and space geology. *Science*, v. 256, p. 333-342.

Grigg, Richard W., 1988, Paleoceanography of coral reefs in the Hawaiian-Emperor chain. *Science*, v. 240, p. 1737-1743.

Gripp, Alice E., and Richard G. Gordon, 1990, Current plate velocities relative to hotspots incorporating NUVEL-1 global plate motion model. *Geophysical Research Letters*, v. 17, no. 8, p. 1109-1112.

Harland, W.B., A.V. Cox, P.G. Llewellyn, C.A.G. Pickton, A.G. Smith, and R. Walters, 1982, *A Geologic Time Scale*. Cambridge. UK, Cambridge Univ. Press.

Harper, J.F., 1989, Forces driving plate tectonics: The use of simple dynamical models. *Reviews in Aquatic Sciences*, v. 1. p. 319-336.

Hayes, Dennis E., 1976, Nature and implications of asymmetric sea-floor spreading—"Different rates for different plates." *Bull., Geol. Soc. of Amer.*, v. 87, p. 994-1002.

Heezen, Bruce C., 1960, The rift in the ocean floor. *Scientific American*, October, 1960.

Heezen, Bruce C., Marie Tharp, and Maurice Ewing, 1959, *The Floors of the Oceans*. Geol. Soc. of America, Special Paper 65.

Heirtzler, J.R., G.O. Dickson, E.M. Herron, W.C. Pitman III, and X. Le Pichon, 1968, Marine magnetic anomalies, geomagnetic field reversals, and motions of the ocean floor and continents. *Jour. of Geophysical Res.*, v. 73, no. 6, p. 2119-2136.

Heirtzler, J.R., X. Le Pichon, J.G. Baron, 1966, Magnetic anomalies over the Reykjanes Ridge. *Deep-Sea Research*, v. 13, pp. 427-443.

Herring, Thomas, 1996, The global positioning system. *Scientific Americian*, v. 274, no. 2, p. 44-50.

Hess, Harry H., 1962, History of ocean basins. Pages 23-38 in Cox, Ed., 1973. Pages 599-620 in A.E.J. Engel, Ed., 1962, *Petrological Studies*, New York, The Geological Society of America.

Hey, R.N., H.W. Menard, T.M. Atwater, and D.W. Caress, 1988. Changes in direction of seafloor spreading revisited. *Jour. of Geophysical Res.*, v. 93, no. B4, p. 2803-2811.

Hey, Richard, Frederick Duennebier, and Jason Morgan, 1980, Propagating rifts on midocean ridges. *Jour. of Geophysical Res.*, v. 85 p. 3647-3658.

Hobbs, Bruce E., Winthrop D. Means, and Paul F. Williams, 1976, *An Outline of Structural Geology*. New York: John Wiley & Sons.

Isacks, Bryan, Jack Oliver, and Lynn R. Sykes, 1968, Seismology and the new global tectonics. *Jour. of Geophysical Res.* v. 73, no. 18, p. 5855-5899.

Jacobs, J.A., R.D. Russell, and J. Tuzo Wilson, 1974, *Physics and Geology*, 2nd. ed., New York, McGraw-Hill Book Co.

Kearey, Philip, and Frederick J. Vine, 1990, *Global Tectonics*. Oxford, Blackwell Scientific Publications.

Kerr, Richard, 1981, Rifts propagating in the Pacific. *Science*, v. 212, p. 529.

Kerr, Richard, 1995, Earth's surface may move itself. *Science*, v. 269, p. 1214-1215.

Larson, R.L., W.C. Pitman III, X. Golovchenko, S.S. Cande, J.F. Dewey, W.F. Haxby, and J.L. La Brecque, 1985, *The Bedrock Geology of the World* (World Map), New York, W.H. Freeman and Co.

Le Pichon, Xavier, 1968, Seafloor spreading and continental drift. *Jour. of Geophysical Res.*, v. 73, no. 2, p. 3361-3704.

McKenzie, D.P. and W.J. Morgan, 1969, Evolution of triple junctions. *Nature*, v. 224, p. 125-133.

McKenzie, D.P., and R.L. Parker, 1967, The North Pacific: an example of tectonics on a sphere. *Nature*, v. 216, 1276-1280.

Menard, H. William, and Tanya M. Atwater, 1968, Changes in direction of seafloor spreading. *Nature*, v. 219, p. 463-467. See also pages 412-419 in Cox, 1973.

Merrill, Ronald T., and Michael W. McElhinny, 1983. *The Earth's Magnetic Field*. London, Academic Press.

Meyerhoff, Arthur A., 1968, Arthur Holmes: Originator of spreading ocean floor hypothesis. *Jour. of Geophysical Res.*, v. 73, no. 20, p. 6563-6565.

Minster, J.B., and Thomas Jordan, 1978, Classic determination of motions of plates related to each other and to hotspots. *Jour. of Geophysical Res.*, v. 83, p. 5331-5354.

Molnar, P., and J. Stock, 1987, Relative motions of hotspots in the Pacific, Atlantic, and Indian Oceans since late Cretaceous time. *Nature*, v. 327, no. 6123, p. 587-591.

Monastersky, Richard, 1995, Raising the Andes, *Science News*, v. 148, p. 124-125.

Moores, Eldridge, and Robert J. Twiss, 1995, *Tectonics*. New York: W.H. Freeman & Co.

Morgan, W. Jason, 1968, Rises, trenches, great faults, and crustal blocks, *Jour. of Geophysical Res.*, v. 73, no. 6, p. 1959-1982.

Morgan, W. Jason, 1971, Convection plumes in the lower mantle. *Nature*, v. 230, p. 42-43.

Morgan, W.J., 1968, Rises, trenches, great faults and crustal blocks. *Jour. of Geophysical Res.*, v. 73, p. 1959-1982.

Ninkovich, D., N. Opdyke, B.C. Heezen, and J.H. Foster, 1966, Paleomagnetic stratigraphy, rates of desposition and tephrochronology in North American deep-sea sediments. *Earth and Planetary Science Letters*, v. 1, p. 476-492.

Norton, Ian O., 1995, Plate motions in the North Pacific: The 43 Ma nonevent. *Tectonics*, v. 114, no. 5, p. 1080-1094.

Oliver, Jack, and Bryan Isacks, 1967, Deep earthquake zones, anomalous structures in the upper mantle, and the lithosphere. *Jour. of Geophysical Res.*, v. 72, p. 4295.

Opdyke, Neil D., 1968, The paleomagnetism of oceanic cores. Pages 61-72 in Phinney, 1968.

Opdyke, N.D., B. Glass, J.D. Hayes, and J. Foster, 1966, Paleomagnetic study of Antarctic deep-sea cores, *Science*, v. 154, p. 349-357.

Phinney, Robert A. Ed., 1968. *The History of the Earth's Crust; A Symposium*. Princeton, NJ, Princeton University Press.

Pitman III, Walter C., and J.R. Heirtzler, 1966. Magnetic anomalies over the Pacific Antarctic Ridge. *Science*, v. 154, p. 1164-1171.

Pitman III, Walter C., and Dennis E. Hayes, 1968, Sea-floor spreading in the Gulf of Alaska. *Jour. of Geophysical Res.*, v. 73, p. 6571-6580. Reprinted in A. Cox, Ed., 1973, p. 420-424.

Pitman III, Walter C., Roger L. Larson, and Ellen M. Herron, 1974, *Magnetic Lineations of the Oceans* (Map). Boulder, CO, The Geological Society of America.

Raff, A.D., and R.G. Mason, 1961, Magnetic survey of the west coast of N. America, 40°-52°N Latitude. *Bull, Geol. Soc. Amer.*, v. 72, p. 1267-1270.

Seyfert, Carl K., 1987. Pages 810-816 in Carl K. Seyfert, Ed. 1987.

Seyfert, Carl K., Ed., 1987, *Encyclopedia of Structural Geology and Plate Tectonics*. New York, Van Nostrand Reinhold.

Shea, James H., 1989, A new test of plate tectonics. *Jour. of Geologic Education*, v. 25, p. 38-42.

Spencer, Robert L., 1977, Lageos—A geodynamics tool in the making. *Jour. of Geological Education*, v. 25, p. 38-42.

Talwani, Manik, Xavier Le Pichon, and James R. Heirtzler, 1965, East Pacific Rise: The magnetic pattern and the fracture zones. *Science*, v. 150, p. 1109-1115.

Talwani, Manik, Xavier Le Pichon, and James R. Heirtzler, 1965, East Pacific Rise: The magnetic pattern and the fracture zones. *Science*, v. 150, p. 1109-1115.

Uyeda, Seiya, 1978, *The New View of the Earth*. San Francisco, W.H. Freeman and Co.

Varga, R.J., and E.M. Moores, 1990, Intermittent magmatic spreading and tectonic extension in the Trodos ophiolite: Implications for exploration for black smoker-type ore deposits. Pages 53-64 in J. Malpas, E. Moores, et al, Eds. *Ophiolites: Oceanic Crustal Analogues*. Nicosia: Geological Survey of Cyprus.

Vine, F.J., 1966, Spreading of the ocean floor. *Science*, v. 154, p. 1405-1415.

Vine, F.J., 1968, Magnetic anomalies associated with mid-oceanic ridges. Pages 73-89 in Phinney, 1968.

Vine, F.J., and D.H. Matthews, 1963, Magnetic anomalies over oceanic ridges. *Nature*, v. 199, p. 947-949.

Vine, F.J., and J.T. Wilson, 1965, Magnetic anomalies over a young oceanic ridge, off Vancouver Island. *Science*, v. 150, p. 485-489.

Weissel, Jeffrey K., and Dennis E. Hayes, 1971, Asymmetric sea-floor spreading south of Australia. *Nature*, v. 231, p. 518-521.

White, M. Catherine, 1995, Finding documents split of Indo-Australian plate. *EOS*, v. 76, no. 34, p. 337, 343.

Wilson, J. Tuzo, 1963, A possible origin of the Hawaiian Islands. *Nature*, v. 198, no. 4884, p. 925-929.

Wilson, J. Tuzo, 1965a, A new class of faults and their bearing on continental drift. *Nature*, v. 207, p. 334-347.

Wilson, J. Tuzo, 1965b. Transform faults, oceanic ridges, and magnetic anomalies southwest of Vancouver Island. *Science*, v. 150, p. 482-485.

Wood, Robert Muir, 1985, *The Dark Side of the Earth*. London, Allen & Urwin.

Worzel, J.L., and M. Ewing, 1954, Gravity anomalies and structure of the West Indes, Part II. *Bull., Geol. Soc. Amer.*, v. 65, p. 195-200.

Chapter: 8 Subduction Tectonics

The previous chapter on tectonics of the oceanic lithosphere feeds easily into this one on subduction tectonics, since we will be examining the contact relationships between oceanic lithosphere and continental lithospere. The igneous factory that works ceaselessly in the mid-oceans to produce new oceanic lithosphere is the relentless driver of global tectonism, there being no feedback mechanism to serve as a governor to regulate its production. So there must be a sink that terminates this material flow system. Like that endless conveyor—the pedestrian escalator or airport walkway—what gets on must get off, even if sometimes there is a big pileup to deal with.

8.1 Passive and Active Continental Margins

The *continental margins*, broadly defined, are those long, narrow zones where oceanic lithosphere meets continental lithosphere. Continental margins fall largely into two great classes. First are the *passive margins*, where the meeting line of continental and oceanic lithosphere falls within a single lithospheric plate. This inactive type of margin was illustrated in Figure 1.14; it will be the subject of our detailed investigation in Chapter 11. A passive margin is formed by the rifting apart of a continental lithospheric plate and the growth of new oceanic lithosphere between the two separating continental plates. (See Stages 1 through 3 of the Wilson cycle, Figure 1.13). At present, because the greatest extent of the world's passive continental margins is along the borders of the Atlantic Ocean basin on both western and eastern sides, the passive margins are sometimes called *Atlantic-type* margins. They are also found on other margins of the continental plates that moved apart following the breakup of Pangaea, so they also border the Indian Ocean and Arctic Ocean basins, and they surround Antarctica and much of Australia.

Our concern in this chapter is with the second major class of continental margins, the *active margins*, associated with plate boundaries that are presently or recently tectonically active. According to this definition, then, the active continental margins can be located along either of the two basic kinds of plate boundaries—*convergent boundaries* (or *subduction boundaries*), and *transform boundaries*.

Convergent boundaries bound much of the Pacific Ocean basin on three sides, so this class has been labeled the *Pacific type* of continental margin. It is the major subject of this chapter.

The convergent plate boundaries fall into two broad classes. One consists of mountain arcs, or *continental arcs*, located mostly along borders of the large continents. For these, the trench that marks the locus of subduction lies a short distance off the coast, with only a narrow shelf zone. Major examples are the eastern half of the Aleutian arc bordering Alaska, the Central American arc, and the Peru-Chile arc of South America. A second class consists of *island arcs* separated from the major continents by relatively small ocean basins called *backarc basins* (mentioned in Chapter 4). Typically, these basins have floors at abyssal depths and are underlain by oceanic crust. The island arcs are usually bowed convexly outward from the continents toward the central ocean basin. One important task that faces us in this chapter is to explain the island arcs and their backarc basins.

The active continental margins as a general class also include some important major transform plate boundaries that lie close to the contacts of oceanic with continental lithosphere. These we examined in Chapter 6, including as examples the San Andreas and Queen Charlotte faults (North America), and the Alpine fault (New Zealand).

Passive margins include very young zones of continental rifting where a new spreading boundary lies in the axis of a narrow gulf, such as the Red Sea and the Gulf of California. This rifted type of margin will be a subject of special investigation in Chapter 10.

Our treatment of the subject of convergent plate boundaries began in Chapter 6, in which the seismicity of this class of boundaries was treated in some detail. In that context we were able to introduce the discovery of the existence of subducted lithospheric slabs. It is essential that you be familiar with this seismic information before continuing here. We recommend that you review the structural and seismic details of a typical convergent boundary, shown in cross-section in Figure 6.22. In Chapter 7 we analyzed the forces involved in plate motion. You should be familiar with the driving forces and resisting forces acting on a subducting slab.

8.2 The Structure of a Great Tectonic Arc

Before starting in on many technical details of subduction boundaries, it will be helpful to examine a great tectonic/volcanic arc as a whole system. We want to grasp the big picture of its geographic and topographic configuration, as well as its internal structure. An excellent example is the Java-Sumatra Arc of the Indonesian region, where sediment accumulations were intensively investigated by seismic reflection profiling at a

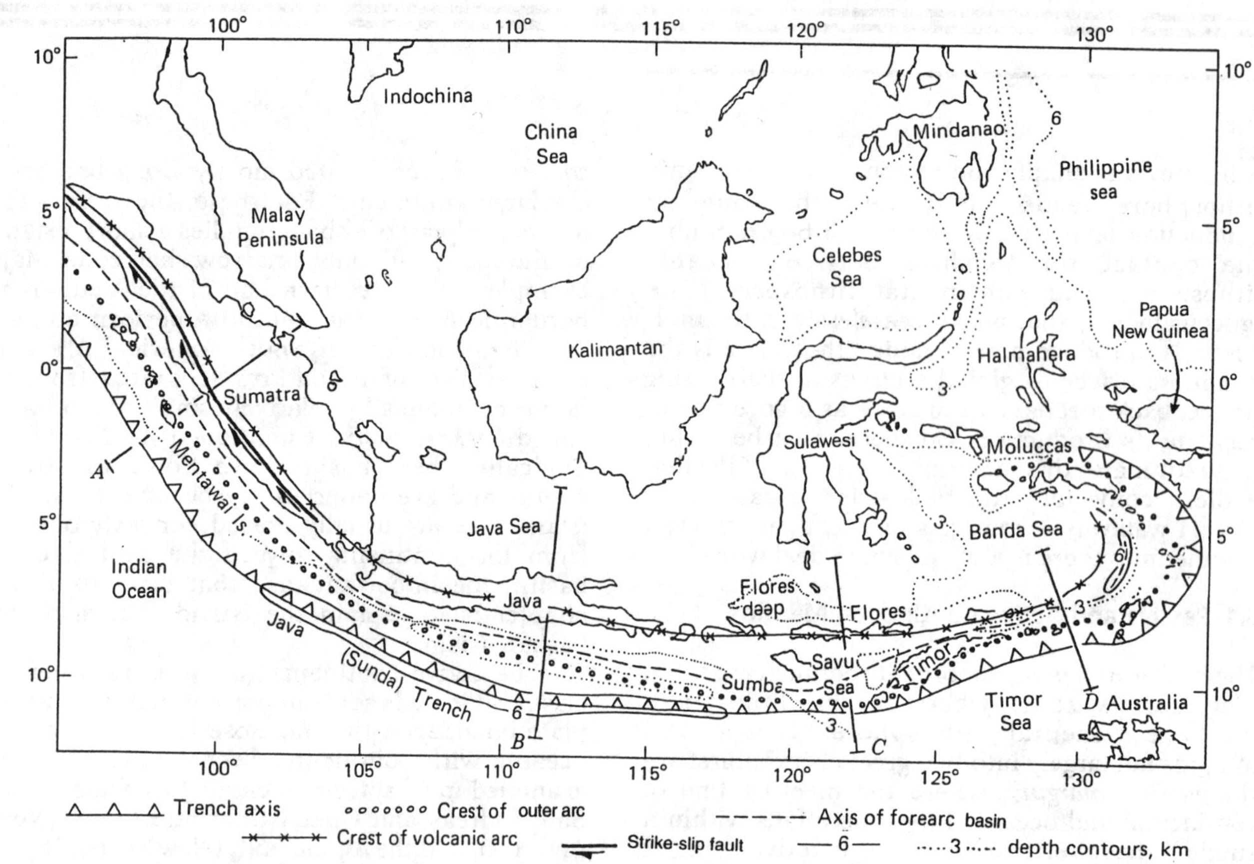

Figure 8.1 Map of the Sumatra-Java tectonic-volcanic arc. (Based on data of Warren Hamilton, 1979, *Professional Paper 1078*, U.S. Geological Survey, and other sources. Map Copyright © by Arthur N. Strahler.)

rather early period in plate tectonics. This is also the arc that had received a great deal of scientific attention in the 1950s because of the previous gravity studies by the Dutch geophysicist, F.A. Vening Meinesz. During the 1920s, he had spent many months in the cramped quarters of a small submarine of the Royal Dutch Navy mapping the gravity field of this trench zone, using a gravimeter of his own design. For a man of unusually great height, it was prolonged torture! What he found—a strong negative anomaly over the trench—led to the speculation that beneath this arc was a narrow zone of down-buckling of the crust into a U-shaped feature called a *tectogene*. After that inference had been bashed into oblivion in 1954 by seismologists Maurice Ewing and J. Lamar Worzel of the Lamont-Doherty Geological Observatory (L-DGO), the completion of a working theory of plate tectonics had to wait some years until seismologists of the same group interpreted the deep-focus earthquakes of Pacific arcs (such as the Indonesian Arc) and could demonstrate the downsinking of lithospheric slabs (see Chapter 6). A monumental treatise on the geology of this area, written by Warren Hamilton of the U.S. Geological Survey, was published in 1979. It contains numerous excellent maps and a large number of seismic reflection images of the sedimentary bodies. Published a year earlier, there had appeared a geophysical atlas of this region, compiled under the direction of Dennis E. Hayes of the L-DGO. Drawing on many sources, it contains six large, detailed charts, including maps of tectonics, sediment thicknesses, crustal structure, and magnetic anomalies (Hayes, 1978).

Figure 8.1 is a map of the Sumatra-Java arc, bordered on the south by the deep Java (Sunda) Trench. Our world map of plates, Figure 7.3, shows that the Austral-Indian plate, moving northward at a rate of about 6 cm/yr, is being subducted beneath the Asian plate. Because of the large arc curvature, the angle of attack changes from direct, where the boundary is east-west, to oblique attack in the west, along the Sumatra coast. This results in the development of a major strike-slip fault through the length of that island.

From the intense seismic and volcanic activity found here, we can be sure that subduction is also an active process. Figure 8.2 shows four transverse cross sections of the basins of contemporary sediment deposition and two intervening mountain arcs. The first feature that can be classified as a major class of accumulation of sediments is beneath the trench floor. This *trench wedge* (TW)

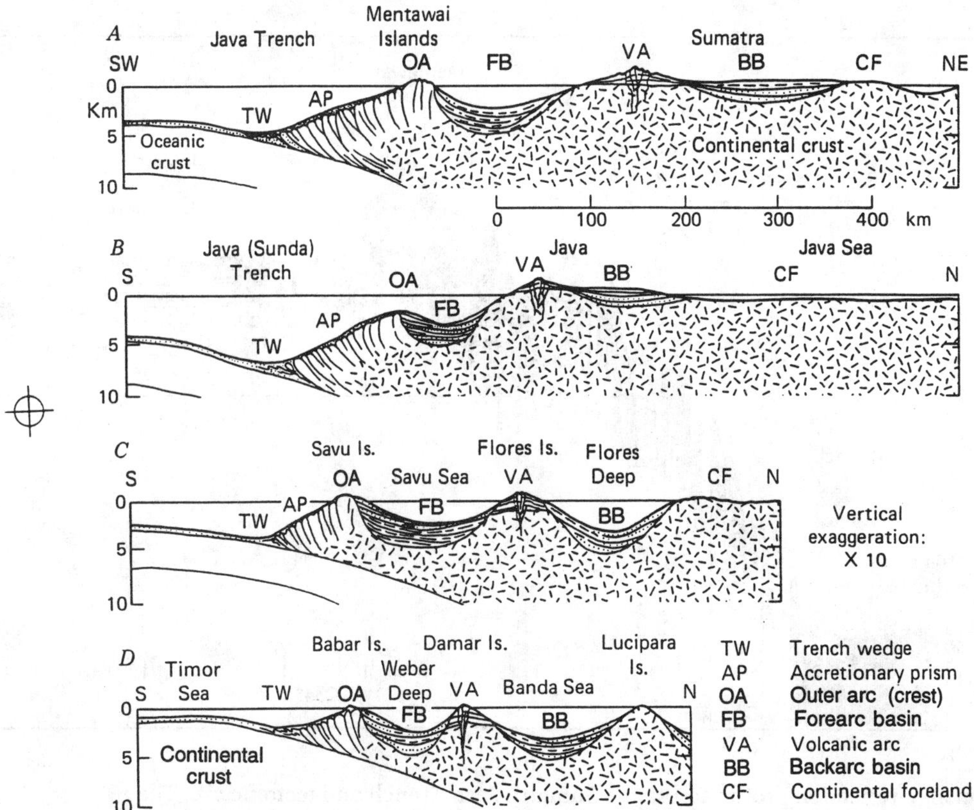

Figure 8.2 Cross sections to accompany Figure 8.1. (Interpreted from data in reference cited in Figure 8.1. Copyright © by Arthur N. Strahler.)

represents sediments that have yet to be scraped off the moving plate. The floor of the Java Trench lies at a depth of about 6000 m. Turbidites and pelagic sediments making up the wedge are severely deformed, starting along a sharply defined line. Here, under compression, a succession of imbricate thrusts develops in the soft sediments, producing an *accretionary prism* (AP), also called an *accretionary wedge*. The wedge is slowly forced upward to form an elevated zone—a low tectonic ridge—described as a "structural high." Here we designate it the *outer arc* (OA). In the Java region, the outer arc lies submerged at a depth of about 1000 to 2000 m for much of its length, but to the northwest, off the coast of Sumatra, it rises above sea level as a chain of islands, the Mentawai Islands (Cross section A). (See Hamilton, 1979, p. 19-25.)

Adjacent to the outer arc is a shallow *forearc basin* (FB)—a long, narrow trough that receives sediment from the volcanic arc of the islands of Java and Sumatra. Sediments of the forearc basin are over 4000 m thick off Sumatra (Section A and Figure 8.3). These sediments are largely clays, muds, and lithic sands eroded from the steep slopes of the volcanic mountain range and transported to the floor of the basin by currents. Because the forearc basin acts as a catchment basin or trap for sediment from the volcanic arc, the trench may become deprived of much of its sediment supply. Later, however, the outer arc may rise above sea level to form a narrow land ridge. When this happens, a new sediment supply becomes available. This seems to have happened off Sumatra, where the Mentawai Islands now furnish sediment to the adjacent trench.

A narrow axial mountain chain on Sumatra and Java represents the *volcanic arc* (VA) of the system. Because Mesozoic and older basement rocks lie beneath the volcanic rocks along this arc, we have here continental crust through which the magmas have risen. Northward of the volcanic arc lies a *backarc basin* (BB) 100 to 200 km wide, representing a second type of sedimentary basin. In Sumatra, this basin lies above sea level and is a low coastal plain, underlain by Cenozoic sediments previously deposited in the basin (Section A). Traced eastward to the region of the Flores Islands, the backarc basin deepens to become the Flores Deep, with bottom depths over 5000 m (Section C).

Still farther to the east, the volcanic arc descends below sea level with only a few small volcanic islands showing above sea level (Section

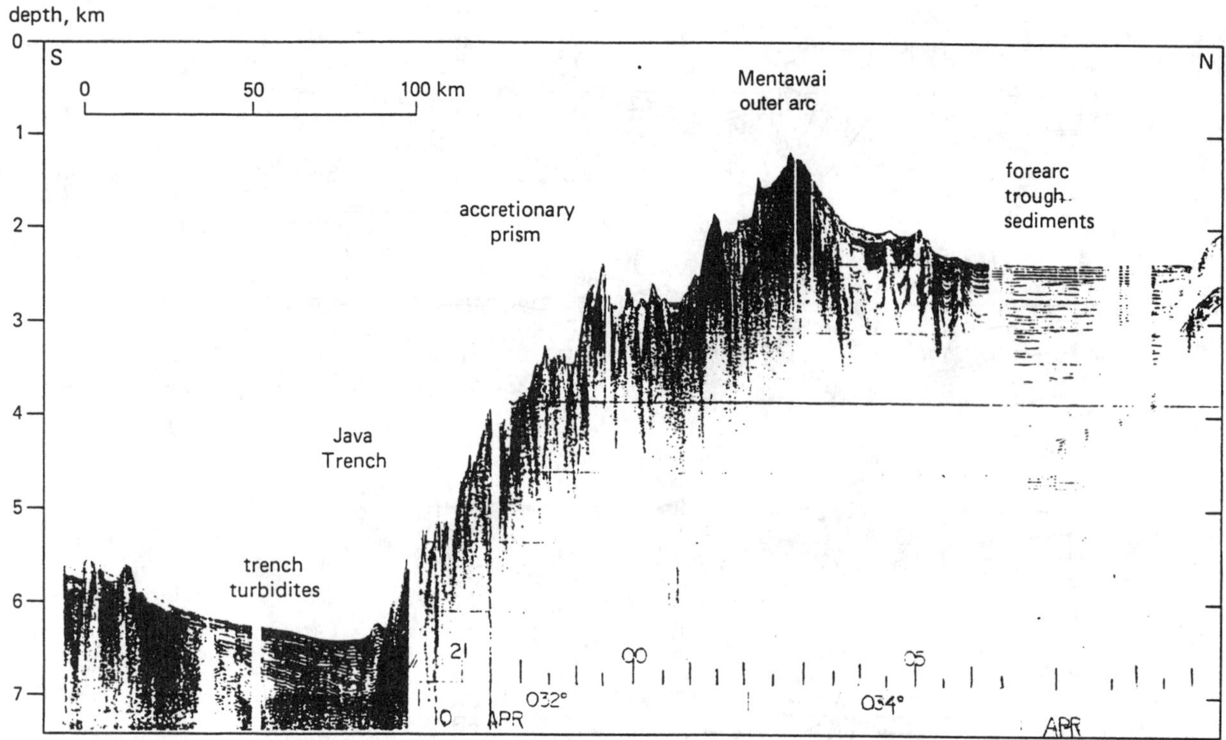

Figure 8.3 An early seismic-reflection profile across the Sumatra-Java Trench and tectonic arc. The profile was obtained by scientists of the Lamont-Doherty Earth Observatory of Columbia University during a cruise of the research vessel *Robert Conrad.* This profile is located off the southern coast of Sumatra, and its approximately equivalent to Section A of Figure 8.2. Vertical exaggeration is about x 25. Layers of sediment are clearly visible in the trench floor at the left and in the forearc basin at the right. Imbricate wedges of the accretionary prism appear to be vertical because of the great vertical exaggeration. (Courtesy of Warren Hamilton, U.S. Geological Survey.)

D). Here, the forearc and backarc basins form a more or less continuous single basin with only a median dividing ridge. Clastic sediments accumulating close to the volcano chain may perhaps be interbedded with volcanic rocks—volcanic ash beds and lavas. Note that in Section D, the continental crust of Australia is shown as forming the down-going plate.

North of the backarc basin lies continental crust with rocks of Paleozoic and Late Triassic age exposed in many places. Thus, the Malay Peninsula and the island of Borneo represent exposures of the *continental foreland* (CF). We use the term "foreland" to refer to any part of the stable continental crust located adjacent to an active plate boundary.

8.3 Initiation of a Subduction Boundary

How does a subduction plate boundary come into existence? What configuration of the crust and lithosphere was present to begin with? We need to recognize two basically different locations for this initiation of a new subduction boundary: Type A, forming along a passive continental margin, later to become a continental volcanic arc; Type B, forming in an oceanic location, far from any continent, and leading to the evolution of an oceanic volcanic arc, or island arc (Figure 8.4). Using the Pacific basin as the model ocean, subduction boundaries of Type A came into existence along the western margin of the American continents, whereas island arcs of Type B came into existence in the western part of the Pacific basin. This is a very important basic generalization, and we will speculate on how it happened that way.

What determines the line along which the oceanic crust will actually fracture to initiate subduction of the Type B model? We must assume that compressive horizontal stress exists throughout the unbroken initial plate and is directed from ocean basin toward continent, and that the continent offers resistance to this stress. A theory proposed in 1992 by Robert J. Stern and Sherman H. Bloomer is that new subduction in a mid-ocean location results through the change of an active transform boundary into a subduction boundary. Figure 8.5 is a schematic diagram to illustrate this transformation. Assumed with the hypothesis is that plate X lies lower than plate Y, a condition commonly found in the Pacific region and present along certain of the major fracture zones. A change in the direction of motion of plate X is then required, with a strong diagonal vector

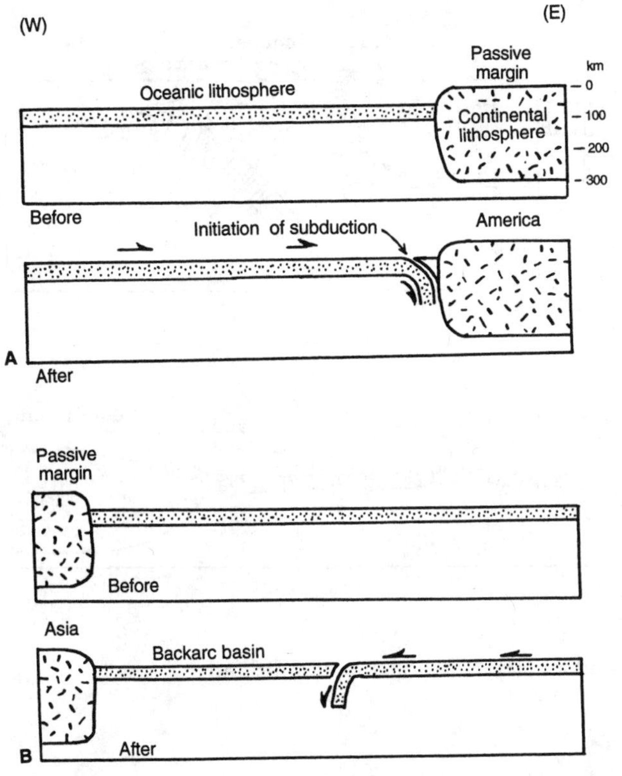

Figure 8.4 Schematic diagram showing initiation of a subduction boundary (A) in ocean floor far distant from continent and (B) at a passive continental margin. (Copyright © by Arthur N. Strahler.)

now directed toward the adjacent plate Y. With this new stress direction, the lower plate is able to force its way beneath the higher plate (Stern and Bloomer, 1992, p. 1627-1629). This breakthrough may be only for a short horizontal distance, but it

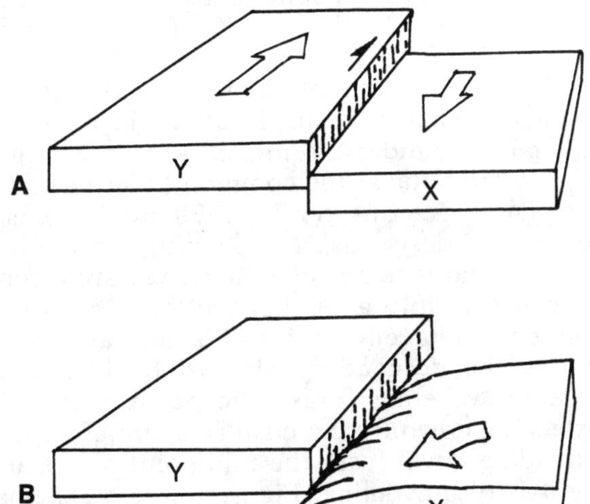

Figure 8.5 Schematic diagram of transformation of a transform plate boundary into a subduction boundary, resulting from a change in direction of Plate X. (Copyright © by Arthur N. Strahler.)

can then be propagated in both directions to become a long subduction boundary. Of course, this hypotheses requires a previously existing oceanic plate boundary, and this may have been the original mid-ocean spreading boundary of the Wilson cycle (see Figure 1.13, Stages 1-3.

We turn now to the initiation of a Type A subduction boundary along a continental passive boundary. The existing mid-ocean spreading ridge cannot close with the passive continental margin until a subduction boundary develops between them. Turning then to the cross-section of a mature passive boundary (Figure 1.15A), we notice the thick wedges of sediment that have accumulated over the passive contact between continental crust and oceanic crust, forcing it to subside. Perhaps a normal fault might develop spontaneously along this contact, dropping the oceanic plate margin and allowing it to penetrate the asthenosphere and begin its nose-dive. Such speculation is permissible, but an example or two would be most welcome. We do know that the crustal extension which occurred in early stages of the rifting of a continent gave rise to numerous major faults in the borderland continental crust, and perhaps these relict structures served as planes of structural weakness that were reactivated when ocean-basin closing began in Stage 4 of the Wilson cycle (see Figure 1.13, Stage 4c).

We turn next to a closer examination of Type B subduction boundaries far advanced in age—aptly described as "mature" forms. Abundant examples of these volcanic island arcs are available and have been probed by seismic techniques and directly sampled by deep drilling. The development and structure of the volcanic island arcs requires special attention. (In a later section, we will concentrate on the structural details of the subduction boundaries of the continental margins.)

8.4 The Building of Volcanic Island Arcs

In Chapter 5, we examined island arcs from the viewpoint of igneous activity, citing as an example the Lesser Antilles arc of the Caribbean region, which contains the volcanic chain of the Windward Islands. Figure 5.33 shows details of the internal igneous structure of that arc, which you may wish to review.

Volcanic island arcs, situated far out from the continental margins, are typical of the western Pacific Ocean basin. A good example is the Mariana arc lying far east of the Philippine Islands. The island arcs originate within the oceanic crust and lithosphere. Figure 8.6 shows stages in the development of a volcanic island arc. The initiation is shown as a new break in the oceanic lithosphere (Diagram A). The broken plate edge sags down into the asthenosphere, creating a new subduction plate boundary. Once the down-plunging plate has reached well into the asthenosphere, magma begins to rise beneath the stationary plate some

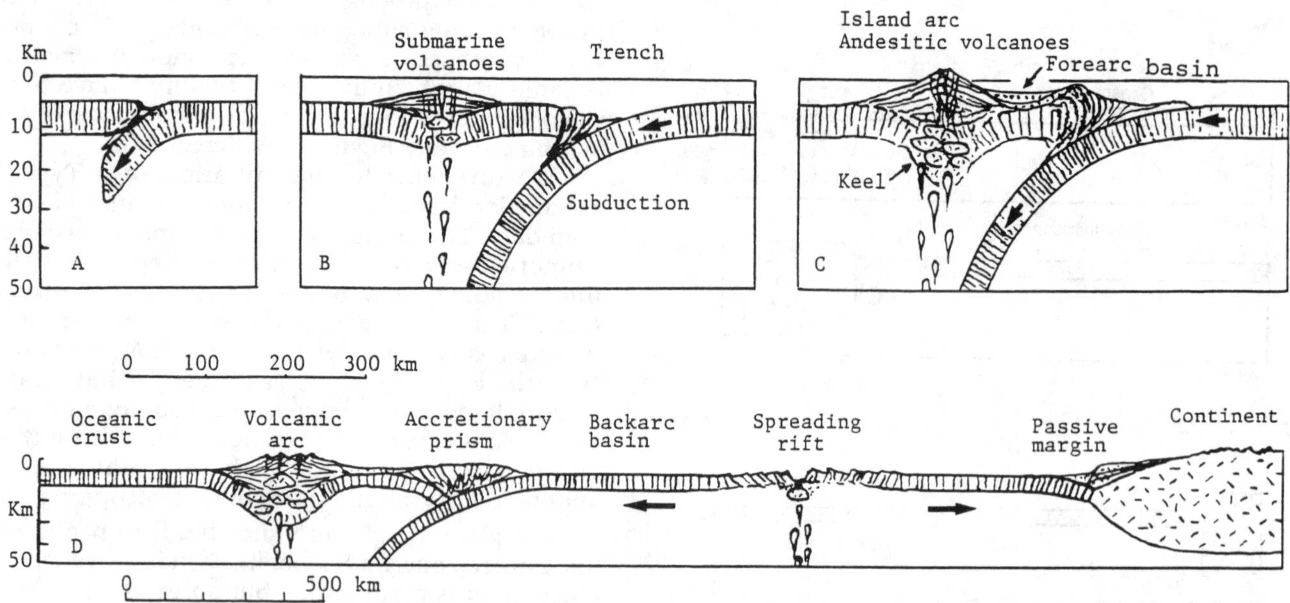

Figure 8.6 (A, B, C) Stages in the development of a volcanic island arc. (D) Relationship of an island arc to a passive continental margin. (Copyright © by Arthur N. Strahler.)

150 to 200 km from the plate boundary. Some of the magma—that of andesitic composition—rises through the oceanic crust and begins to build submarine volcanoes (Diagram B). As these accumulate, the crust sags beneath the load, but eventually volcanoes reach the surface as islands (Diagram C). Rising magma of mafic composition forms plutons in the lower part of the crust, which is thickened, creating a *keel* beneath the volcanic arc. The entire structure is maintained in isostatic equilibrium. Diagram D shows the broader relationship of the volcanic arc to a distant spreading rift and beyond that a passive continental margin.

8.5 Island Arc Curvature and Cusps

Examine the western Pacific basin on our world tectonic map, Figure 7.3. Starting about at the equator and traveling north, we find a string of curved arcs: Palau, Mariana, Izu-Bonin, Japan (Honshu), Kuril, and Aleutian. These arcs are joined in sharp points, or *cusps*. The arc curvature is concave toward the west or north, i.e., toward the Asiatic continental mainland. The concavity of each arc opens toward the down-slope of the plate surface. Other similarly curved arcs found farther south include the Sumatra-Java, Philippine, Bismark, New Hebrides, and Kermadic-Tonga arcs. (There are obvious exceptions to this curvature, with the boundary segment being straight or wavy, or convex with respect to the direction of dip of the downsinking plate.) Two isolated volcanic arcs that conform in curvature with the first-named group are the Lesser Antilles arc and the Scotia arc, both located in the western side of the Atlantic basin.

An important feature of these arcs is that the Wadati-Benioff (W-B) zone of each is correspondingly curved (concave-up), and joins the W-B zone of each adjacent arc in a broadly rounded steeply descending ridge. The W-B zone delineates the descending plate down to a maximum depth of some 600 km. Figure 8.7 is an idealized three-dimensional representation of two adjacent concave arcs, each with its descending slab, warped into a curved surface of sinusoidal waves. This geometric principle was stated in 1968 by F.C. Frank, adopted by C.H. Scholz and R. Page in 1970, and applied by Brian Bayly in 1982. Using theory of buckling of spherical shells, the concept was developed further by K. Yamaoka and Y. Fukao in 1987.

At the time of initiation of a Type B subduction boundary in a midoceanic location, the trace of the new plate boundary is ideally an arc of a great circle originating at the common Euler pole of the two plates. (See Chapter 7 and Figure 7.14.) As the new plate descends, the leading edge of the segment that is to become the curved arc is forced to "squeeze" into a smaller width, as are the arc segments adjacent to it. This lateral pressure causes the descending slab to buckle; i.e., to develop wavelike folds, shown in Figure 8.7. Extending down from a cusp is an anticlinal crest. Extending down from the mid-point of the arc is the axis of a syncline. Figure 8.8 is a schematic contour map of the buckled slab, with dip symbols applied. Notice that the dip must be steepest along the axis of the synclines and least along the anticlinal crest. "At a depth of 500 km, the amplitude of buckling could be as much as one-tenth the wavelength, and dip angles for a plate descending at 45° on average could range from 35°

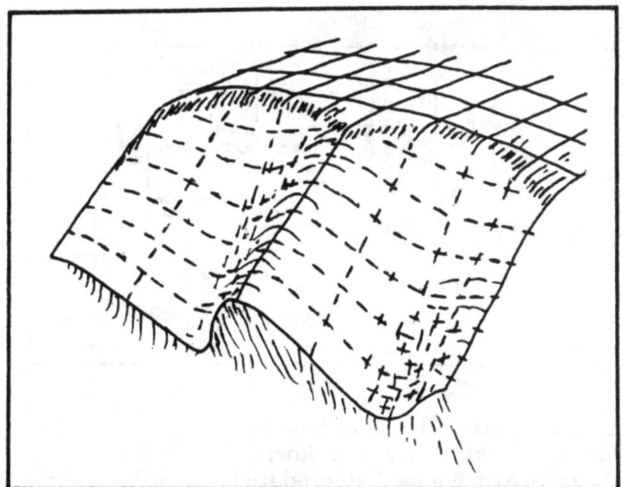

Figure 8.7 Idealized diagram of two arcs and their descending slabs, warped into sinusoidal folds. (From Brian Bayly, 1982, *Geology*, v. 10, p. 629, Figure 1. Reproduced with the permission of the publisher, the Geological Society of America, Boulder, Colorado, USA.Copyright © 1982.)

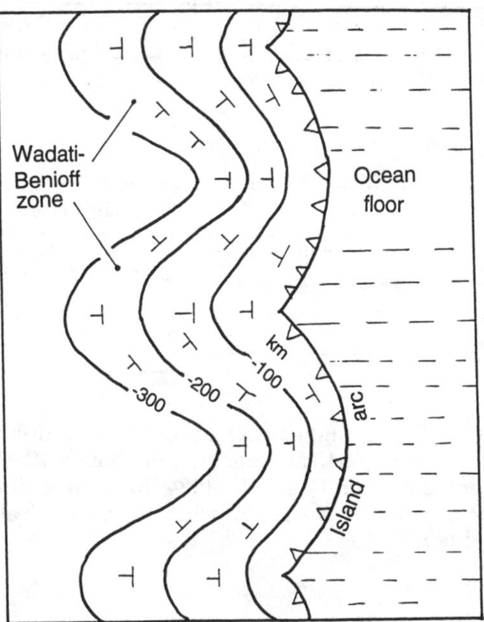

Figure 8.8 Schematic contour map of the surface of a steeply subducting slab adjacent to concave island arcs. Dip symbols are shown on surface of slab. Distance between cusps is on the order of 1500 km. (Copyright © by Arthur N. Strahler.)

to 55°" (Bayly, 1982, p. 629). This relationship is clearly shown in contour maps of the depth of the Wadati-Benioff zone beneath the Japanese Islands (see Figure 6.7). (See also Yamaoka and Fukao, 1987, p. 35, Figure 2.)

You may have noticed that when a thin hollow shell of a sphere—a table-tennis ball, for example—is pushed inward under pressure applied at a single point, the shell (if not brittle) yields with a sudden "pop," forming a concave depression with a circular rim and the form of an element of a sphere; i.e., a reversal of its initial form. A similar event, called a "pop-through," is imagined to occur for our subducting plate. It may take place when the leading edge of the plate has reached a depth of about 100 km (Bayly, 1982, p. 629). At this critical point, the uniform planar form of the slab is quickly replaced by the buckled form with arcs and cusps. The interesting part of this pop-through is that the subduction boundary between each pair of cusps is caused to retreat from its original line. The distance of this retreat may be on the order of 150 km (Bayly, 1982, p. 629). This conclusion will bear on the problem of the origin of backarc basins, discussed in our next section.

8.6 Backarc Basins

The area lying between the a Type B volcanic island arc and the distant continental margin is a *backarc basin*, floored by oceanic crust. Earlier in this chapter, we took note of the characteristic arrangement of island arcs and backarc basins in the western Pacific Ocean. Actually not every one of the named arcs is of Type B, with a deep ocean basin on the Asiatic side of it. One needs to examine closely the bathymetry of each small ocean basin separated from the Pacific Ocean by an arc. Depths of the backarc basins underlain by oceanic crust range from 2 km to over 6 km. The deep Aleutian Basin, lying north of the western part of the Aleutian volcanic arc, has much of its depth over 4 km, and is a good example of a backarc basin with oceanic crust (see Figure 8.12). Another good example is the large Philippine Basin, much of it more than 6 km deep. This basin is essentially equivalent to the entire Philippine plate and is bounded on the east by the Izu-Bonin, Marianas, Yap, and Palau arcs. Another example is the South Fiji Basin lying west of the Tonga-Kermadic arc. Yet another important example is the deep Caribbean Sea basin lying west of the Antilles Arc. Besides abyssal plains, the deeper basins contain many topographic irregularities, and these take varied forms such as rises, abyssal hills, and submarine ridges.

When examining a map showing only plate boundaries and coastlines, you might suppose that the Okhotsk Basin, lying north of the Kuril Islands, qualifies as an ideal Type B backarc basin, but most of it has a shallow floor that is classed as continental crust. A very shallow depth condition (under 200 m deep) applies to the western part of the South China Sea. It lies north of the Sumatra-Java volcanic arc, which should be classified as Type A.

The deep backarc oceanic basins were a real puzzle to geologists who sought to apply the theory of plate tectonics to all major crustal features. They asked: What kind of crust lies beneath these deep basins? Is it oceanic or continental crust?

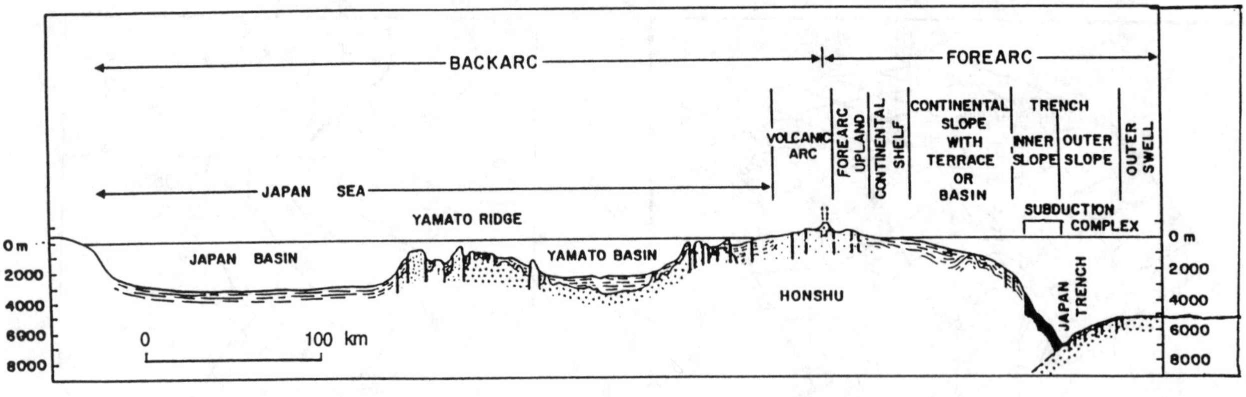

Figure 8.9 Profile and geological structure section across the northern part of Honshu Island and the Japan Basin. Vertical exaggeration about x 10. (Based on data of Tamaki, Honza, and others, as presented by Sam Boggs, Jr. 1984, *Bull., Geol. Soc. of Amer.*, v. 95, p. 670, Figure 2. Reproduced with the permission of the publisher, the Geological Society of America, Boulder, Colorado, USA. Copyright © 1984.)

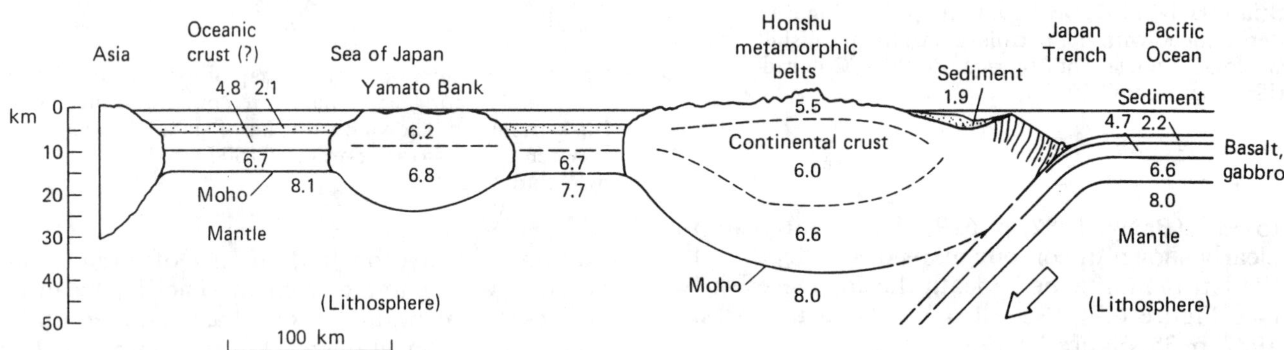

Figure 8.10 Details of the continental and oceanic crust in a cross section through Japan and the Sea of Japan. Vertical exaggeration about x 2.5. (Based on data of A. Miyashiro, Y. Matsuda, and S. Uyeda, as shown in J.F. Dewey and J.M. Bird, 1970, *Journal of Geophysical Res.*, v. 75, p. 2634, Figure 7. Reproduced by permission of the American Geophysical Union.)

How did these basins come into existence? Despite their enigmatic nature, the backarc basins have yielded scientific data on which to base some firm statements and at least two strong hypotheses of origin.

We have chosen first to examine the Japan Basin, which offers some difficult problems of origin. Figure 8.9 is a profile and shallow geologic structure section from the Japan trench to the Asiatic mainland. It includes Yamato Ridge, which elsewhere rises almost to the sea surface as Yamato Bank. The basin floor is presently at a depth of about 3 km, but has a thick sediment layer that has been accumulating through much of Cenozoic time. The island of Honshu is an old volcanic arc that began its growth in Late Cretaceous or Oligocene time (Boggs, 1984, p. 670). Honshu is composed in large part of volcanic rock, but also contains large masses of folded and faulted sedimentary rocks on the Pacific side of the volcanic arc. The profile descends steeply into the Japan Trench, 7 km in depth, then rises to the abyssal Pacific floor 5 to 7 km in depth.

Figure 8.10 is a deep cross-section of the crust along a similar line drawn from northwest to southeast across the Japan Basin. This construction was presented in 1970 by John F. Dewey of Cambridge University and John M. Bird of the State University of New York at Albany, two of the scientists active in the early phases of expansion of principles of plate tectonics. Their paper was titled "Mountain belts and the New Global Tectonics," Using many fine maps and diagrams, they summarized the important findings of the first full decade of plate tectonics as a unified system. The data for this cross section had been gathered and presented by Japanese seismologists S. Murachi and M. Yasui in 1968.

Under the Japan Basin, seismic wave evidence reveals a thin crust, with the Moho situated at a depth of about 15 km (Figure 8.10). Seismic velocity layers within this portion of crust match rather closely those of the Pacific oceanic crust east of the Japan Trench. The island of Honshu is classified as continental-type crust, because it is thick and the seismic P-wave velocities suggest an upper felsic and a lower mafic zone. Thick continental crust is encountered on the Asiatic mainland. There seems to be general agreement that this backarc basin is underlain by oceanic crust and oceanic lithosphere. (The Yamoto Bank may be a small continental fragment detached during the separation of Honshu from the mainland.) The question is how the oceanic crust came to be located in a backarc basin. Two very different mechanisms have been proposed to answer this question.

The *entrapment hypothesis* explains backarc basins as areas of oceanic lithosphere that have been cut off from a large oceanic lithospheric plate by the formation of a new subduction zone. Figure 8.11 is a schematic diagram illustrating this hypothesis. In Diagram A, continental and oceanic lithosphere meet in a passive margin and comprise a single plate. In Diagram B, a new Type B subduction zone has formed within the oceanic lithosphere. Much later, as shown in Diagram C, an island arc of continental crust has been formed adjacent to the subduction zone. The backarc basin now lies between the island arc and the continental mainland. Note that our hypothesis of the initiation of a volcanic island arc, illustrated by Figures 8.4 and 8.5, applies here to the entrapment of a backarc basin.

A good test of the entrapment hypothesis would be to look for magnetic anomaly patterns in the trapped portion of oceanic crust. If no median spreading center is present, and if there exists a distinct ocean floor anomaly pattern matching one of corresponding age on the oceanward side of the island arc, the hypothesis might be acceptable. But this configuration would probably be limited to a very young subduction zone. In the case of the Aleutian Basin of the Bering Sea, a magnetic anomaly pattern has been mapped as a part of the Pacific system of Mesozoic magnetic anomalies,

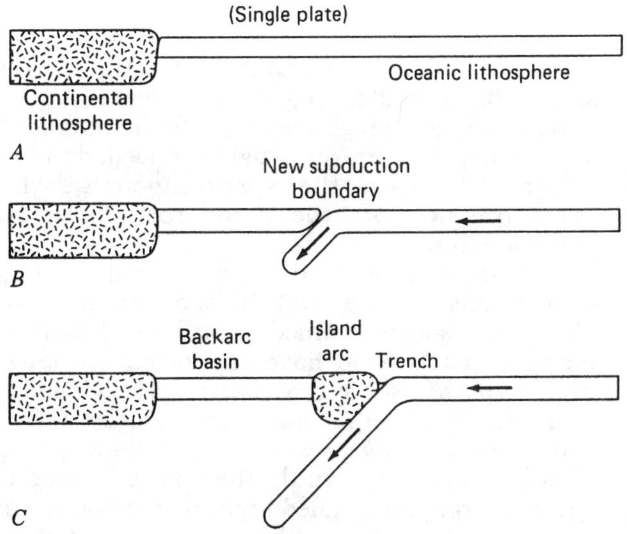

Figure 8.11 Three stages in the formation of a backarc basin according to the entrapment hypothesis. (Copyright © by Arthur N. Strahler.)

which we described in Chapter 7. Anomalies 1 through 13, of Early Cretaceous age, are arranged in stripes trending due N-S. Figure 8.12 shows these anomalies. No fossil spreading ridge is shown. You might argue that the Aleutian volcanic chain is composed mostly of rocks of Cenozoic age and is therefore a younger feature than the backarc basin floor, but these younger volcanics probably conceal a much older core. In total, the evidence seems to favor strongly the entrapment hypothesis for the Bering backarc basin. The anomaly pattern south of the Aleutian arc consists of stripes M21 through M34, ranging in age from Paleocene through Late Cretaceous and trending E-W. This age contrast came about by the subduction of almost the entire Kula plate beneath the Aleutian, as we described in Chapter 7, and illustrated with four paleomaps in Figure 7.44.

An objection to the entrapment hypothesis applied to the Japan Basin is that, had it been entrapped at an early date, it would contain a large thickness of marginal terrestrial sediments derived from the mainland. Instead, the marginal sediment accumulation of the Japan Basin is no more than about 2 km thick, and this is considered much too thin for a very old basin. Thus, in the case of the Japan Basin, the entrapment hypothesis has been rejected.

This brings us to the second hypothesis of backarc basin origin: *lateral drift* of the island arc, illustrated in Figure 8.13. There first exists a subduction boundary between an oceanic plate and a continental plate (Diagram A). A narrow segment of continental plate then rifts apart from the main continental plate (Diagram B). New oceanic crust forms in the widening rift, which becomes a backarc basin (Diagram C). In this scenario, the oceanic crust of the backarc basin is quite young—perhaps much younger than the continental-type crust of the island arc. Note that a new lithospheric plate has come into existence during the process of backarc basin formation. It is bounded by the new spreading plate boundary and the old subduction boundary. This plate, which will usually be narrow in width and of limited or uncertain length, is called a *microplate*. In many cases, the spreading rift becomes inactivated after a few million years, so that the microplate is no longer distinguishable. In a later section we will give examples of microplates.

Supporters of the lateral drift hypothesis have used the strongly curved plan of the island arc and trench as a feature favoring this origin of the backarc basin. As the island arc retreats from the continental plate, the arc becomes increasingly curved or bowed out. We have already shown that arc curvature is a necessary development for reasons of plate geometry and mechanics, and thus is not a factor in distinguishing between the two mechanisms of basin origin. The most obvious evidence favoring lateral drift is the presence of a spreading rift located on the median line of the basin (Figure 8.13). Even when this rift is no

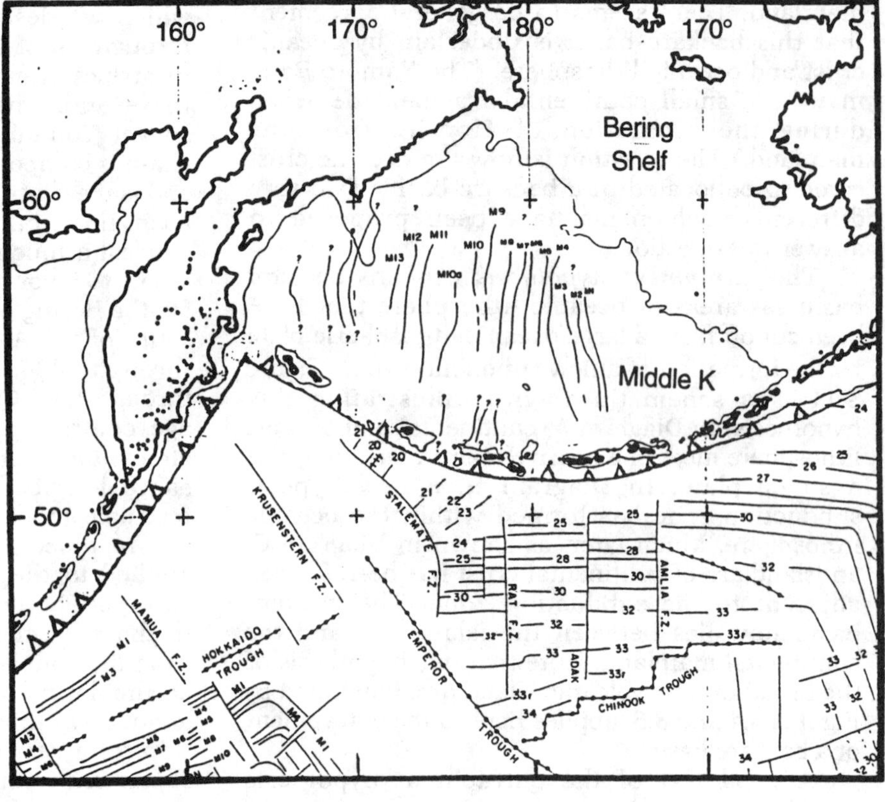

Figure 8.12 Magnetic lineations of the Aleutian Basin. (Adapted from Cande et al., *Map of Magnetic Lineations of the World's Ocean Basins*. Copyright © 1989 by the American. Association of Petroleum Geologists. Used by permission.)

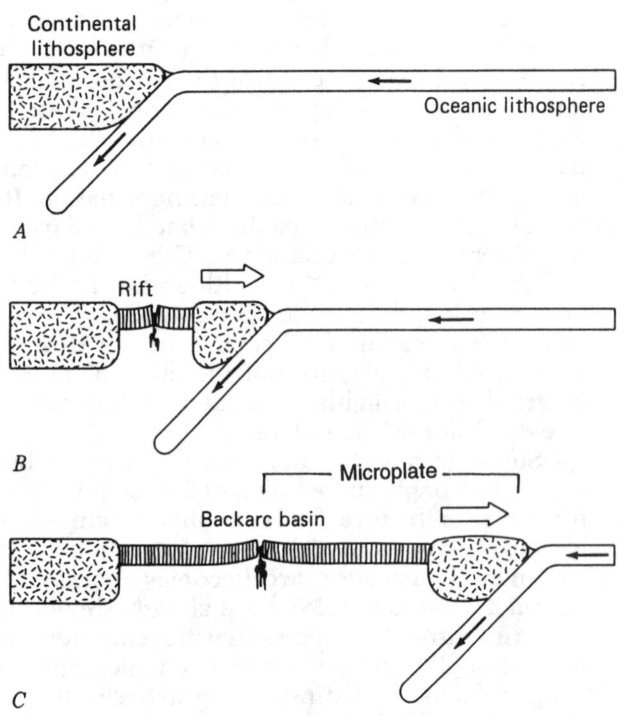

Figure 8.13 Stages in the formation of a backarc basin according to the hypothesis of lateral drift of an island arc. (Copyright © by Arthur N. Strahler.)

longer active, and referred to as a "fossil" rift, the mirror symmetry of the magnetic anomnalies will reveal its location. The characteristic mirror-image pattern of anomaly stripes clearly shows in three backarc basins: the Shikoku Basin of the eastern Philippine Sea, the Lau Basin west of Tonga-Kermadec arc, and the North Fiji Basin east of the New Hebrides arc (Figure 8.14). This evidence strongly supports the lateral drift hypothesis as applied to at least those basins.

As shown in Figure 8.15, hypothetical lateral drift sets in motion a mantle convection-current system in the underlying asthenosphere. A rising current brings up high-temperature mantle rock to shallow depths, furnishing the heat needed to form magmas beneath the spreading rift, while decompression of the rising rock lowers its melting point.

No clear pattern of symmetrical anomaly stripes has been found in the Japan Basin, although a vaguely defined linear pattern has been mapped. Those who have supported the lateral drift hypothesis for that basin have visualized multiple rifts, so that new oceanic crust formed simultaneously along several roughly parallel lines. This mechanism would, they argue, produce irregular, roughly aligned topographic features on the ocean floor but with no clear symmetrical magnetic anomaly pattern. It seems that the Japan Basin is no longer expanding, and if so, no active rift zones are to be expected.

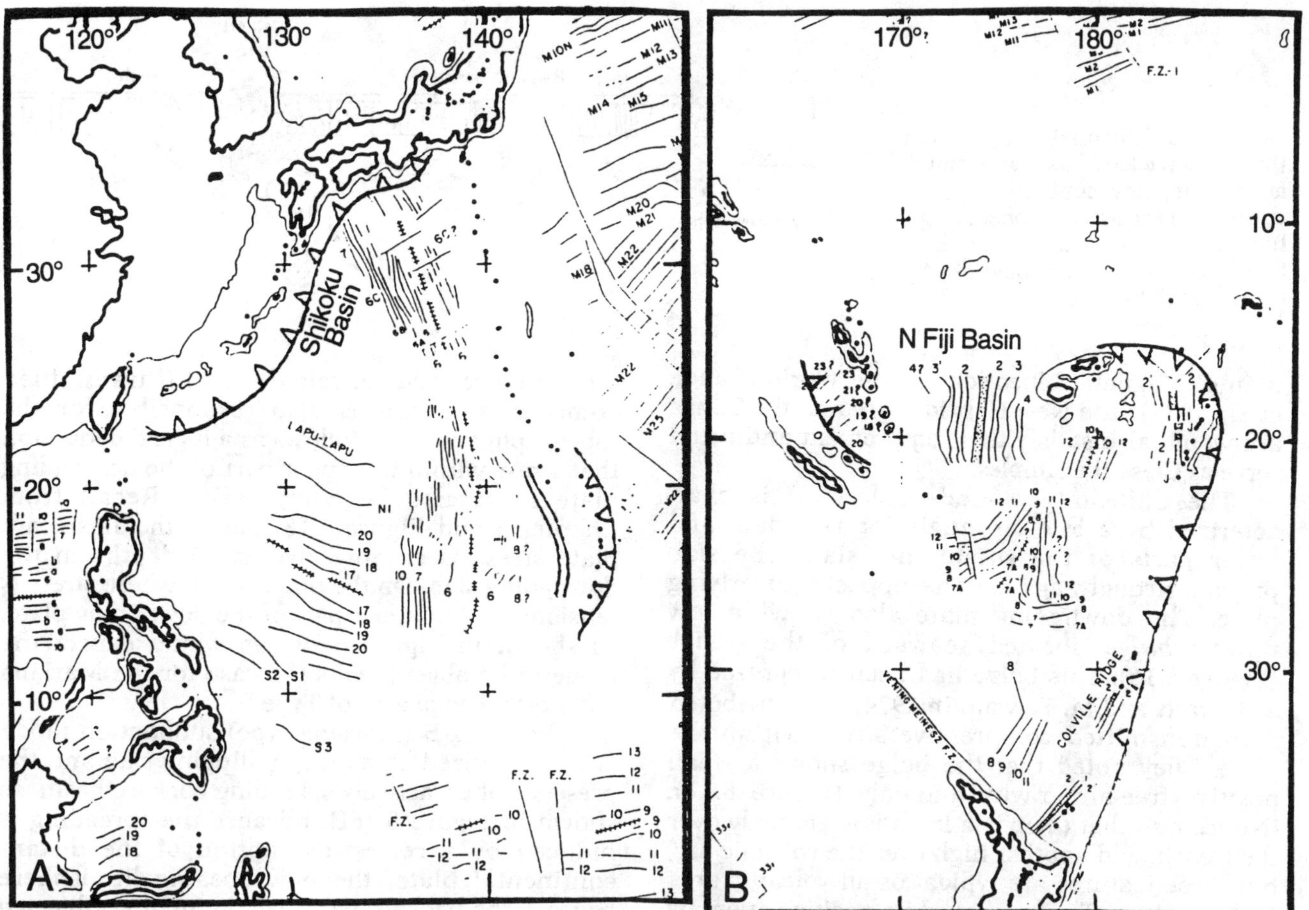

Figure 8.14 Magnetic lineations of (A) the Shikoku Basin and (B) the Lau Basin, both in the Western Pacific region. (Adapted from Cande et al., *Map of Magnetic Lineations of the World's Ocean Basins*. Copyright © 1989 by the American. Association of Petroleum Geologists. Used by permission.)

8.7 Basic Modes of Plate Subduction

From a global study of seismic activity, gravity anomalies, and tectonic structure of subduction zones—most of which bound the Pacific Ocean basin—we may conclude that at least two basically different styles or modes of subduction are taking place. [See Chapter 6 for background information on seismic activity.] The modes were described and analyzed in 1979 by Japanese seismologists Seiya Uyeda and Hiroo Kanamori. They studied the distribution of great earthquakes along subduction zones and uncovered a rather striking fact. Over 90% of seismic energy release on a global basis is from subduction zones lacking an active backarc basin. By "active" we mean that the backarc basin has an active spreading plate boundary between the subduction zone and the continent toward which the subducting slab is dipping, as shown in Figure 8.13C. Great earthquakes, those substantially larger than magnitude 8.5 on the Kanamori scale (designed by Kanamori especially for very large earthquakes), have occurred almost entirely along subduction zones that lack an active backarc basin. Uyeda and Kanamori reasoned that the explanation for the presence or absence of great earthquakes must be tied in with the mechanics of plate subduction (Uyeda and Kanamori, 1979; Uyeda, 1983).

Before going further with this account, we review the major varieties of subduction segments, or arcs, and place them in one of three classes: Class A. Continental subduction arcs having no oceanic backarc; Class B. Mid-ocean subduction boundaries with active backarc basins on oceanic crust. Class C. Active subduction arcs with inactive oceanic backarc basins. Examples are listed in Table 8.1.

Uyeda and Kanamori found that subduction boundaries of Class A reveal a different mode of subduction from those of Class B. The principal differences are shown schematically in Figure 8.16. They applied the name *Chilean* to the mode of subduction associated with arcs of Class A; *Mariana* for the mode associated with Class B. The active spreading basin of the Marianas arc is assumed to be the West Marianas Basin, and that feature is shown on some maps as having a spreading boundary along its axis. However, no spreading axis is shown at that location on the

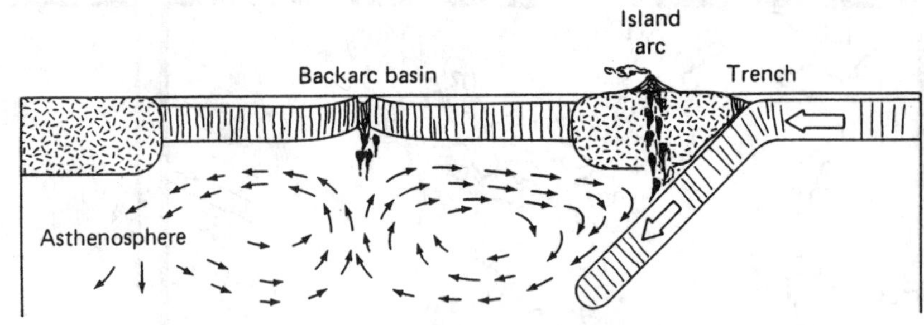

Figure 8.15 Schematic cross section through a backarc basin and island arc showing how convection currents in the asthenosphere might furnish a relatively high rate of heat flow beneath the arc. (Copyright © by Arthur N. Strahler.)

map of Magnetic Lineations of the World (Cande et al., 1989). The New Hebrides arc and the Tonga arc would also satisfy this requirement and could serve as Class B examples.

The Chilean-type mode (Class A) is characterized by a low dip angle for the main and lower parts of the subducting slab. The slab presses strongly against the opposing overlying plate. The downgoing plate also shows a low upward *bulge*, located seaward of the trench (Figure 8.16). This bulge had been recognized by A.B. Watts and M. Talwani in 1974, who attributed it to transmitted compressive stress within the plate. They noted that the bulge shows a small positive free-air gravity anomaly (Figure 8.17). (Notice also that there is a large low anomaly over the trench, and another high over the volcanic arc, but these features are typical of all volcanic arcs and trenches.) The bulge and its positive anomaly were found to be well-developed in most of the Class A arcs, and absent in three out of our four examples of arcs of Class B.

Strong compressive stress is responsible for the occurrence of great shallow earthquakes in subduction zones. (See Chapter 6 and Figure 6.27 for structural and seismic details.) If transmitted compressive stress is also responsible for the topographic bulge, it follows as a logical deduction that stress within the upper part of the descending plate must also be compressive. Recall from Chapter 6 and Figure 6.18 that in the Japan arc plate stress is compressive at all depths in the downgoing slab. On the other hand, where stress is tensional in the upper part of the downgoing plate, as shown in Figure 6.19, we would expect the bulge to be absent, as is the case for the Mariana and north Tonga arcs of Type B.

The Class B (Mariana type) subduction mode is characterized by a steeply dipping slab and the presence of an actively spreading backarc basin, as shown in Figure 8.16B. Because the spreading is induced by a retreating motion of the distant continental plate, the new oceanic lithosphere beneath the backarc basin is continually subjected to tension. Thus, the subduction zone is relieved of compression and great earthquakes do not occur. Lacking strong compression, the arc is not strongly uplifted above sea level and furnishes little sediment to the trench. Typically, the visible arc consists of a chain of volcanic islands. It is also

Table 8.1 Classes of Subduction Arcs

Class	Arc	Backarc basin
Class A. Continental volcanic arcs (Chilean type)	Peru-Chile Alaska Central America Sumatra-Java Kamchatka	
Class B. Subduction arcs with active spreading backarc basins (Mariana type)	Mariana Scotia Tonga New Hebrides	W. Mariana Basin E. Scotia Basin N. Fiji Basin N. Fiji Basin
Class C. Subduction arcs with inactive backarc basins	Kuril Japan (Honshu) Ryukyu Aleutian	Okhotsk Basin Japan Basin East China Sea Aleutian Basin

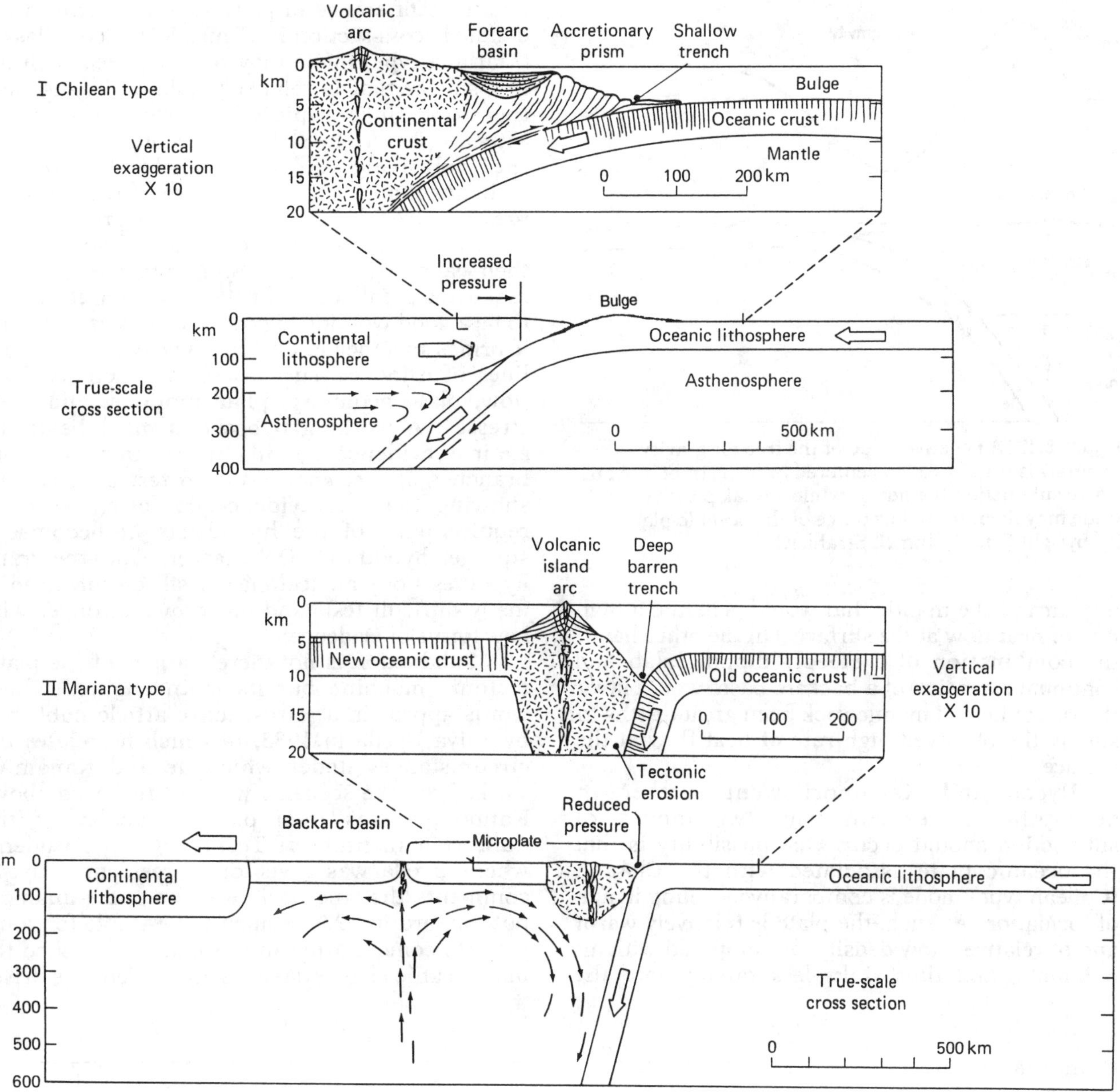

Figure 8.16 Two modes of plate subduction. (I) The Chilean-type subduction zone is one of strong compression, causing great earthquakes. (II) The Mariana-type subduction zone is associated with plate extension, and is subject to little or no compressional stress. It is associated with an active backarc basin. (Based on data of S. Uyeda, 1979, *Oceanus*, v. 22, no. 3, p. 53-62. Drawing copyright © by Arthur N. Strahler.)

possible that slices of the edge of the upper plate can be broken off and carried down with the subducting slab, a process called *tectonic erosion*.

Uyeda and Kanamori showed that their interpretation of the two subduction modes fits rather well with measured rates of plate motions. For the Class A (Chilean type) arcs, the upper (continental) plate has an absolute motion of about 2 cm/yr toward the line of downbending of the subducting plate, generating strong compressive stress. For the Class B (Mariana type) arcs, the upper plate has a relatively rapid absolute speed (6 to 8 cm/yr), but it is in a direction away from the line of downbending. Vector arrows in Figure 8.18 show these contrasting types. Compare, for example, the Peru-Chilean vectors in South America with those of the Mariana and New Hebrides arcs on the western side of the ocean. This fast upper-plate motion of the western arcs allows the retreat of the backarc basin—away from the subduction boundary—and tends to relieve the subduction zone of compressive stress.

In both subduction modes (Classes A and B), we can introduce convection within the asthenosphere, following the corner-flow model shown in Figure 5.31. However, in the case of the Class A (Chilean type) mode with the low-dipping slab, conditions would not be as favorable for deep

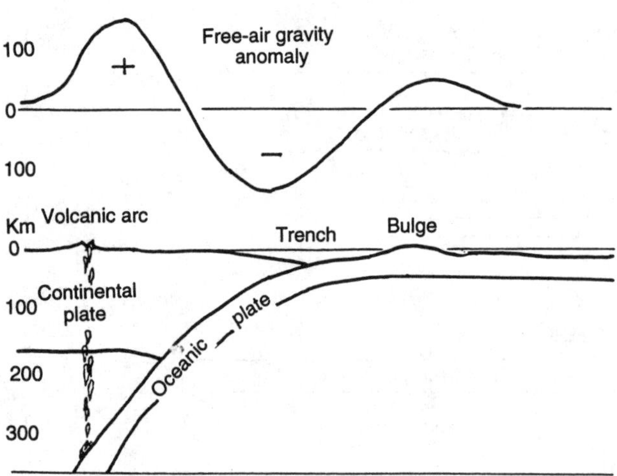

Figure 8.17 A negative value of the free-air gravity anomaly is usually found centered over the trench of an active subduction boundary, while a weak positive value may lie over the low bulge of the oceanic plate. (Copyright © by Arthur N. Strahler.)

overturn of the mantle that would generate a high rate of heat flow at the surface. On the other hand, the combination of a steeply dipping slab and continual extension of a backarc basin would favor the rise of heated mantle rock from great depths to supply the observed high rate of heat flow at the surface.

Uyeda and Kanamori went further in attempting to explain why two modes of subduction should occur. One possibility is that the oceanic plate associated with the Class A (Chilean type) mode is comparatively young in age of formation. As such, the plate is relatively warm and of relatively low density, as compared with an old plate, and thus sinks less rapidly into the mantle. (Difference in plate level is shown in the detailed cross-section in Figure 8.16.) The Class B (Mariana type) mode may be associated with old lithosphere that is relatively cold and dense and therefore sinks rapidly and steeply into the asthenosphere. The slab may become anchored to the relatively strong mantle below the asthenosphere, a factor in preventing it from pressing strongly against the overlying plate.

This analysis of modes of plate subduction and their causes is only a working hypothesis, and it requires a great deal of further research. It appears to be a good working hypothesis, however, because it brings together in an orderly way some diverse lines of evidence, such as seismic activity, heat flow, plate geometry, plate motions, and plate stresses. A working hypothesis must be tested against evidence coming from many different branches of a science. As each test is passed by showing that the evidence conforms with the requirements of the hypothesis, it becomes a stronger hypothesis. On a larger scale, the grand hypothesis of plate tectonics has been subjected to many difficult tests and has grown stronger with new forms of evidence.

"Subduction is not merely a part of the plate-tectonic machine but its main engine." These words appear in a retrospective article published by Seiya Uyeda in 1983, in which he relates the circumstances under which he and Kanamori worked out the scenario we have reviewed above. Kamamori was then on the faculty of the California Institute of Technology in Pasadena, where Uyeda was a visitor in residence. Uyeda comments that the basic idea he and Kanamori put forward in 1979 seemed to be viable for some years to come. Earlier in this chapter we cited the mid-oceanic ridge system as the "relentless driver

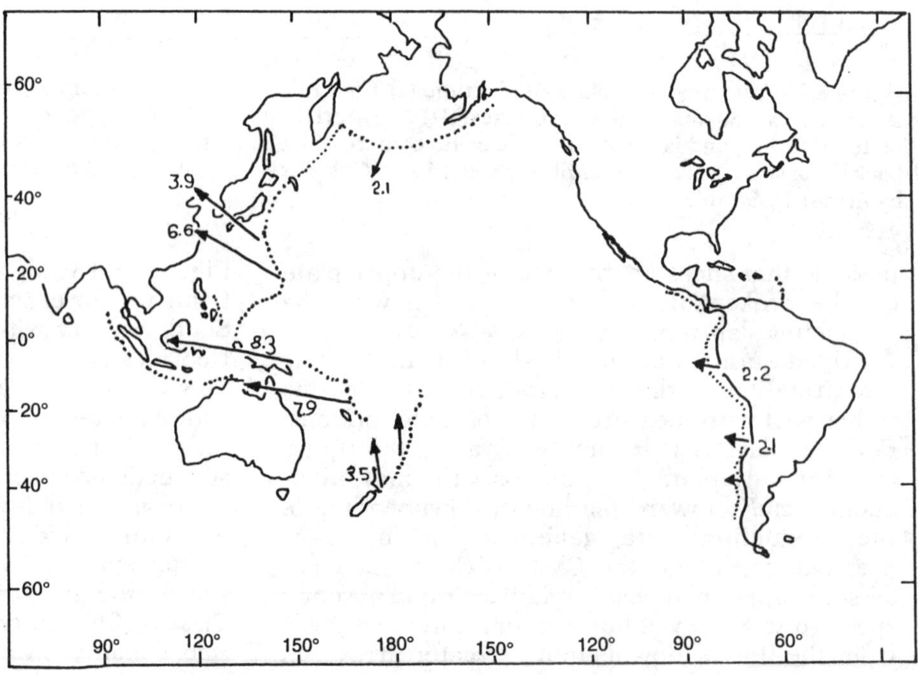

Figure 8.18 Sketch map showing absolute vectors of motion of the upper (overriding) plate on active subduction boundaries. Values are cm/yr. Arrows indicate direction of convergence. (Data of Minster, 1974, and Fitch, 1972, as presented by S. Uyeda and H. Kanamori, 1979.

of plate tectonism." Perhaps a more fair and realistic appraisal is that spreading and subduction act in concert as the driving engine of the plate-tectonic system.

In 1982, Timothy Cross and Rex Pilger, Jr., summarized what they judged to be four independent factors responsible for two different modes of subduction. The two modes are designated as fast convergence and slow convergence, corresponding more-or-less with what we have already distinguished as Class A and Class B, respectively. These authors included points we have already covered, and added other factors. Two of these factors are absolute rate of upper-plate motion toward the trench and rapid relative rate of convergence, much as we have already presented. As a third factor they cite the subduction of seamount chains, aseismic ridges (FZs), and oceanic plateaus. These structures tend to increase the relative buoyancy of the subducting plate, causing it to have a lower angle of dip. A fourth factor, age of the descending plate, acts as we previously explained.

In 1985, A. Hynes and J. Mott assembled data of absolute plate motions to show that both the Tonga-Kermadic and Mariana microplates are moving eastward—toward the Pacific Basin—a relative motion often referred to as "retreating." The subduction boundaries are also retreating eastward. These interpretations support the earlier findings.

In the mid-1990s the basic Class A/Class B classification of subduction boundary types and the explanations for their differences continued to be generally accepted, although with some changes in terminology. In 1993, Leigh H. Royden of the Massachusetts Institute of Technology published a paper in which a distinction is made between *advancing* and *retreating* subduction boundaries; corresponding respectively with our Class A and Class B. His objective was to relate the two classes of subduction boundaries to two different modes of orogeny during continental collision. This is a subject we will take up in Chapter 9.

Mark Cloos and Ronald Shreve (1966, p. 1071) have attributed the numerous large earthquakes along the Chilean type (Class A) margins to their having thick trench fills that allow subducted seamounts to be carried to great depths before jamming against the roof and setting off large thrust-type earthquakes. In contrast, Marianas type (Class B) margins with thin trench fills cause seamounts to be truncated at shallow depth, generating only small earthquakes.

8.8 Sediment Accumulation and Deformation in Subduction Zones

In Chapter 1, we described the trenches of subduction zones as sites where large quantities of terrestrial sediment can accumulate. A high-standing volcanic arc can supply large amounts of detrital sediment to the coastline, from which it is swept across the narrow continental shelf by currents. At the same time, deep-sea pelagic sediment of the ocean floor is carried toward the trench axis on the moving plate. Thus the ptwo classes of sediment—terrestrial and oceanic—meet at the subduction zone, where they are mixed together and restructured in what is to end up as new continental crust.

The accumulations and tectonic modifications of sediments are indicated in Figure 8.19, a cross-section emphasizing three basic zones and structures. The upper diagram (A) has a strong vertical exaggeration (× 3.8), which is typical of diagrams in published reports. The lower diagram (B) has a much smaller vertical exaggeration (× 1.7). The total depth shown in B (300 km) is ten times that shown in A (30 km). The diagram illustrates the Class A (Chilean type) continental subduction arc, typical of the eastern margin of the Pacific Basin, hence the continent is at the right. (For a volcanic island arc of Class B (Mariana type) typical of the western side of the ocean basin, we would place the volcanic islands at the left.)

The basic plan in Figure 8.19 is that of a highly deformed central body of sediment—the *accretionary wedge*, or *accretionary prism.* (Another alternate term is *subduction complex*.) Undisturbed sediment accumulations lie on both sides of it. In the flat floor of the trench are undisturbed, flat-lying soft sediments. The presence of these trench-floor sediments in various localities is well-known and fully documented. The sediments are typically turbidites, the deposits of turbidity currents racing down the *trench slope* and spreading far out over the *trench floor.* The presence of severely deformed soft sediments immediately adjacent to the trench floor on the continentward side is also well-known and fully documented in numerous cases. The two contrasting types of sediment bodies are clearly revealed by seismic reflection profiling. Figure 8.20 is a drawing made from seismic reflection data. The locality is the Middle America Trench off the coast of Mexico, not far from Acapulco (Moore et al., 1982). The triangles show locations of drill holes on Leg 66 of the Deep-sea Drilling Project. Notice that reflections under the deepest part of the trench show the sediment layers to be essentially horizontal, whereas reflectors on the landward rising slope are steeply inclined, indicating thrust faults within the accretionary wedge.

Sediments of the trench floor, both terrestrial and pelagic, are subjected to intensely disruptive tectonic activity. The fixed edge of the solid continental plate, called the *backstop,* acts as a gigantic scraper for sediments dragged against it by the downgoing plate. The activity is often described as *offscraping* and is pictured as a process somewhat like the action of the blade of a snowplow. Although some of the snow at the bottom of the layer passes beneath the blade, most is pushed along in front of the blade, where it piles

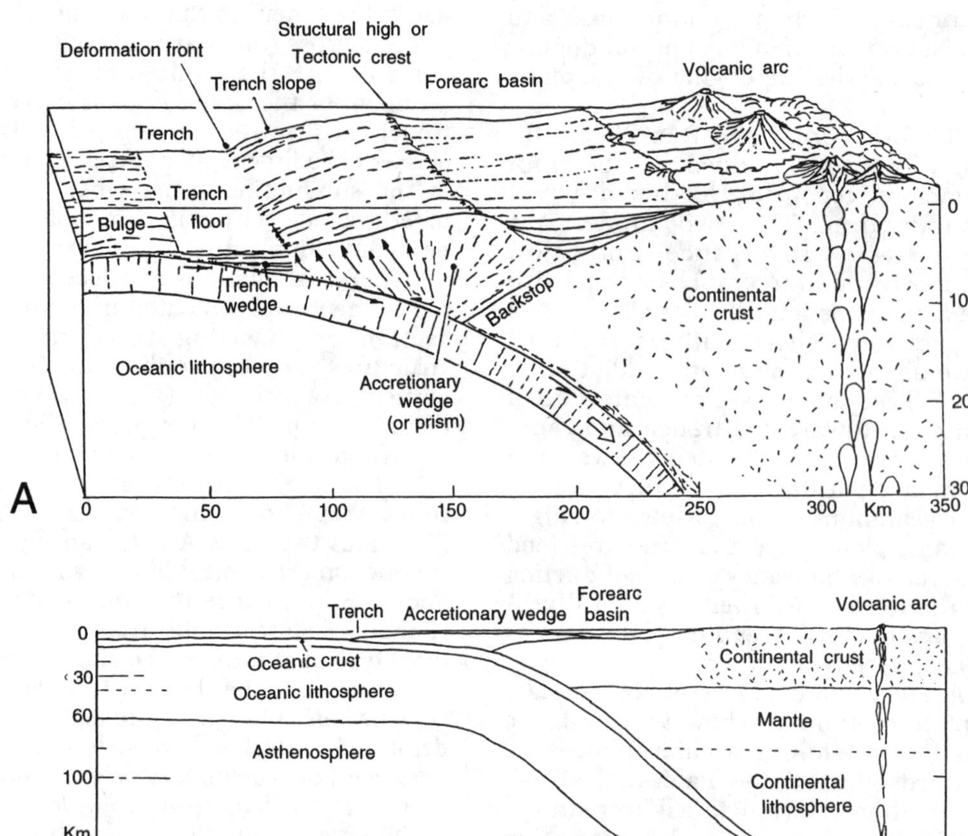

Figure 8.19 Some typical features of a active subduction zone shown in cross section. (A) Large vertical exaggeration (x 3.3) is used to show surface and crustal details. Sediments scraped off the descending plate form an accretionary wedge that grows both longer and higher. Between the tectonic crest and the mainland is a shallow forearc basin in which sediment brought from the land is accumulating and subsiding. Sediment brought down the trench slope by turbidity currents forms a horizontally layered deposit that is continually pushed up into folds by the advancing front of the wedge. Magma rising from the upper layer of the descending plate reaches the surface to build a chain of volcanoes. (B) Cross section of low exaggeration (× 1.7) shows the entire thickness of the lithospheric plates. (Copyright © by Arthur N. Strahler.)

up in a succession of crumpled wedges.

Figure 8.21 is a cartoonlike drawing showing the general interpretation of commonly observed relationships in trenches (Helwig and Hall, 1974, p. 311). The undeformed strata out front are being deformed and piled up in front of the backstop to make the accretionary wedge. At a certain point, called the *deformation front*, the compressional effect of the continental plate manifests itself, like the blade of the snowplow pictured in the lower diagram. Sediment crumpled into the accretionary prism is described as having been *obducted*, as distinguished from subducted sediment dragged far down on the upper side of the descending plate. Every now and then, the snow-plow blade may strike a bump in the pavement beneath, breaking loose fragments of the pavement, and these become mixed in with the snow. The "pavement bumps" in this model might be represented in reality by features such as submarine volcanoes or transform scars (FZs) rising above the basaltic oceanic crust.

Figure 8.22 is a series of schematic cross sections showing the growth of a succession of thrust slices of crumpled trench sediments to form a rising pile. The process has been called *understuffing*. The imbricate thrusts are formed at a low angle, but are pushed upward by newer

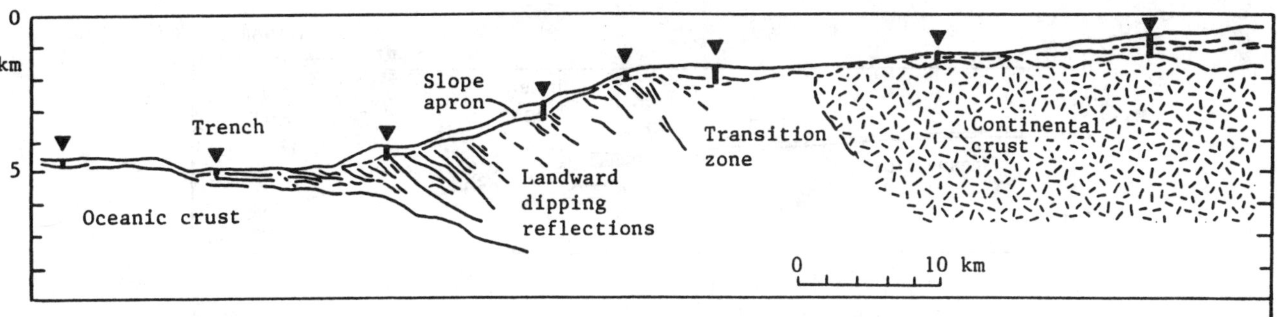

Figure 8.20 A composite cross section along the line of deep-sea drill cores (triangles), obtained on Leg 66 of the DSDP off the coast of southern Mexico. (From J. Casey Moore at al., 1982, *Bull., Geological Society of America*, v. 93, p. 849, Figure 2. Reproduced with the permission of the publisher, the Geological Society of America, Boulder, Colorado, USA. Copyright © 1982.)

wedges and steepen in dip. Figure 8.23 is a cross-section showing the imbricate structure in detail, obtained by seismic reflection profiling. Notice that as the wedges are pushed upward, they are also being buried by newer sediment layers. The newer sediments in turn become folded between the upper edges of the wedges. In this way, numerous small catchment basins are formed and partly filled with sediment on the inner trench slope. Sediment in one catchment basin may overflow, pouring into another farther down the slope. In some trench slopes, however, submarine canyons make a continuous erosion channel from top to bottom, as shown in Figure 8.24. The relatively coarser sediment issuing from the mouth of the canyon accumulates as a small undersea fan. The presence of such submarine canyons has been documented along the Middle America Trench (Underwood and Karig, 1980). In other trenches,

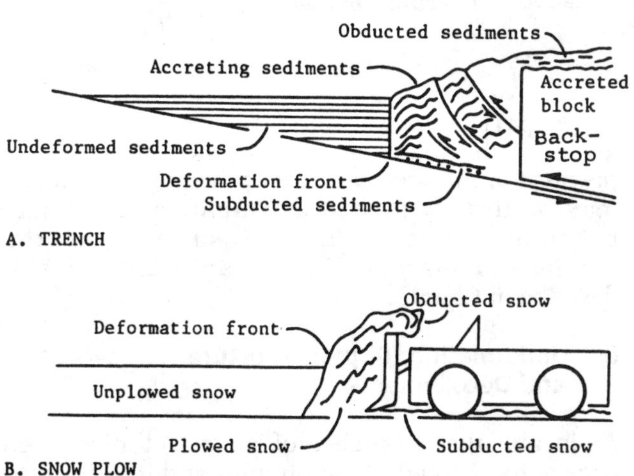

Figure 8.21 Schematic diagram of undeformed and deformed sediments of a trench and subduction zone. The process is analogous to that of a snow plow. (From J. Helwig and G.A. Hall, 1974, *Geology*, v. 2, p. 311, Figure 3. Reproduced with the permission of the publisher, the Geological Society of America, Boulder, Colorado, USA. Copyright © 1974.)

tectonic oversteepening of the trench slope can lead to slumping off of a large mass of sediment that moves downslope rapidly as a debris flow. This moving mass comes to rest at the foot of the slope as a deposit thoroughly mixed and churned.

The density of the material in the accretionary prism is quite low, and it tends to rise as a mass in response to isostasy. In time, there develops a distinct *structural high* (or *structural crest*); it forms a threshold for the widening forearc basin (Figure 8.22). The structural high, an outer arc, then serves as a barrier to terrestrial sediment arriving from the coastline, trapping part of it in a shallow depression, which is called the *forearc basin* (Diagram D of Figure 8.22). Here, sediment layers accumulate and the base of the deposit subsides because the combined load of the accretionary prism and the forearc trough sediments causes the continental plate to sink somewhat lower. At the same time, the accretionary prism grows in width, extending farther and farther out upon the moving plate. The process of growth of the accretionary prism and forearc trough can continue more or less interruptedly for tens of millions of years. In some cases, it continues as long as 100 million years, or about the duration of a major geologic period such as the Cretaceous.

In some subduction complexes of island arcs, the accretionary wedge grows not only trenchward, but also in the direction away from the trench. Figure 8.25 is an example from the Lesser Antilles island arc system. The prism takes the form of a low-angle overthust mass, overriding the oncoming ocean floor, and developing overturned folds and listric thrusts. Notice that the surface gradient of the floor is gently lower in the direction of relative motion of the mass. Does this feature resemble the structure of orogenic overthrusts formed in arc-continent collisions? Superficially, it does, and some authors actually refer to this overthrusting as an "orogenic" phenomenon. But since the word "orogenic" is correctly defined as "relating to continental mountain making," we should not apply it to an accretionary prism in process of its formation. In other words, the accretionary wedge is not to be called an "orogen." (Of course, the

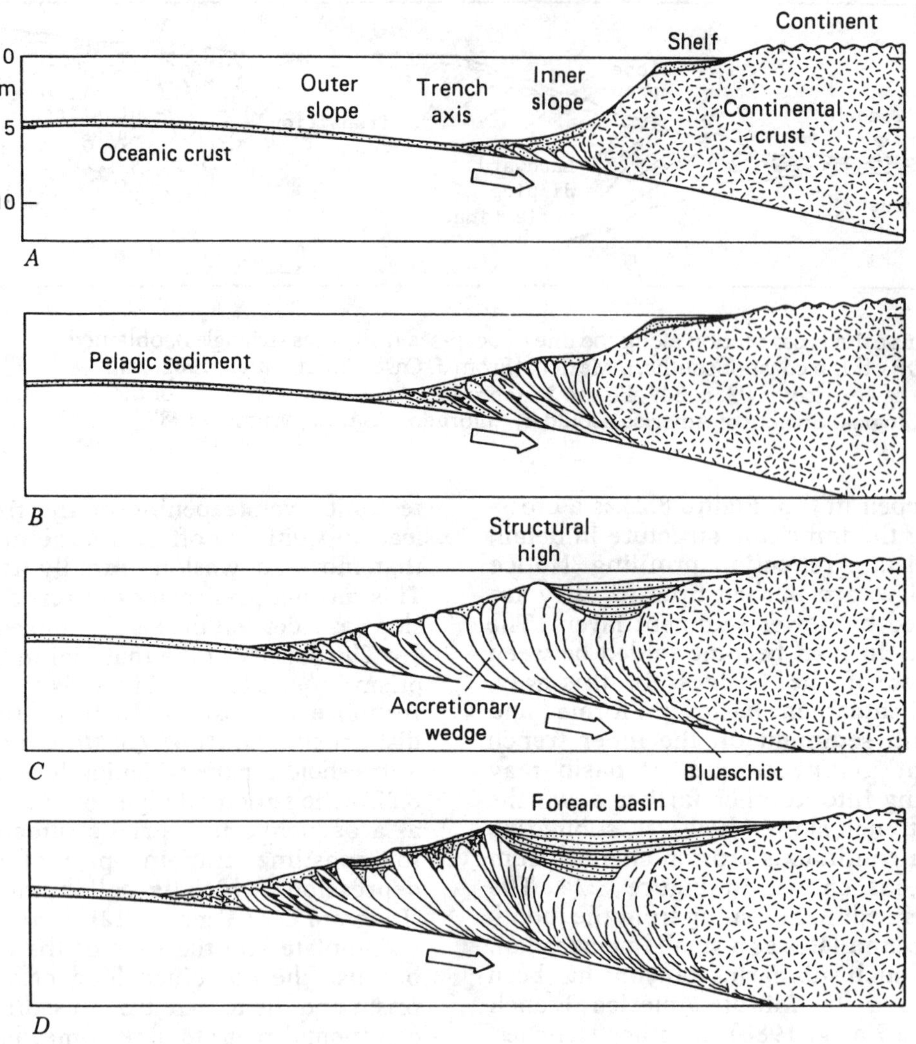

Figure 8.22 Stages in the construction of an accretional wedge by offscraping and understuffing. (Based on data of W.R. Dickinson and D.R. Seely, 1979, *Bull., Amer. Assn. of Petroleum Geologists,* v. 63, no. 1 p. 2-31. Drawing Copyright © by Arthur N. Strahler.)

downbending of the crust and mantle beneath the wedge is a tectonic process.)

A somewhat different mode of evolution of the forearc basin and accretionary wedge occurs when a new subduction boundary forms by breakage within the oceanic plate some distance out from the margin of the continental plate, as shown earlier in Figures 8.4B and 8.5. Figure 8.26 shows additional details of stages in this form of evolution. The lithosphere breaks along a low-dipping fault (A) and subduction begins (B). Understuffing then takes place beneath the tapered edge of the broken crustal segment, forcing it upward (C). The upturned edge of the crust serves as a structural high, forming a forearc basin which receives sediment. As the stack of imbricate wedges rises higher, the crustal wedge and perhaps some of the peridotite mantle below it is elevated further. At the same time, the accumulation of sediments in the forearc basin thickens. So far as the surface forms are concerned, the end result is much the same as shown in Figure 8.22.

A particularly interesting feature of this scenario is that during an ensuing orogeny, portions of the oceanic crust of the upraised wedge may be further faulted and uplifted, eventually becoming exposed at the surface on the continental margin. This is an event we will describe in Chapter 9.

8.9 Underplating, Duplex Structure, and Décollements

As in all other branches of plate tectonics, each decade has brought new findings and insights into the workings of plate subduction. Some of the interesting advances of the early 1980s were summarized in a 1985 Penrose Conference titled: "Structural styles and deformational fabrics of accretionary complexes" (Moore, Cowan, and Karig, 1985). Figure 8.27, appearing in the conference report, summarizes the topics we examine. Refer to the circled letters on the diagram as we review the topics in that order.

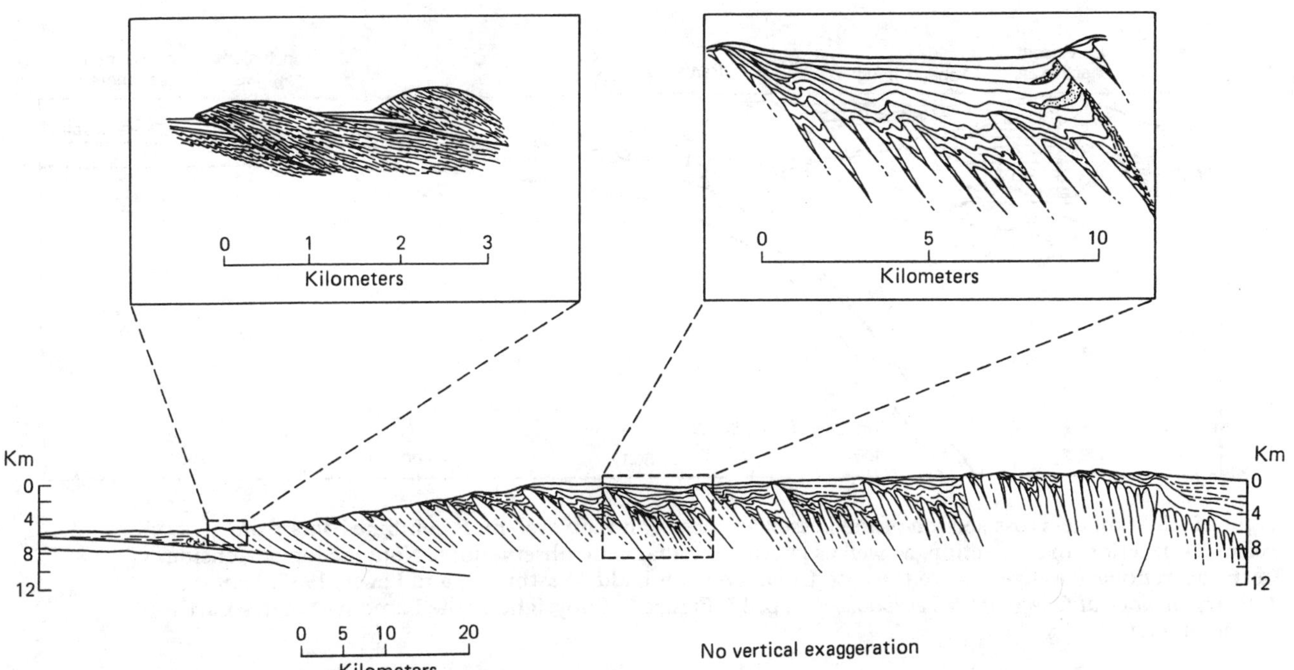

Figure 8.23 Structure sections of imbricate thrusts and sediment accumulation of an accretionary wedge on the lower trench slope of the Sunda arc, Indonesia. This interpretation is based on a seismic reflection profile. Horizontal and vertical scales are the same. (From G.F. Moore and D.E. Karig, 1976, *Geology*, v. 4, p. 696, Figure 5. Reproduced with the permission of the publisher, the Geological Society of America, Boulder, Colorado, USA. Copyright © 1976.)

(A) At the leading zone of imbricate thrusting, a prominent overthrust fault raises a mass of trench sediment to form a *thrust ridge*. Figure 8.28 is an interpretive drawing from a seismic image showing the thrust and the characteristic topographic "hump" it has produced. In three dimensions, the hump is a ridge at the base of the trench slope.

(B) Under the forward-moving wedge is a slip surface—a low-angle underthrust fault—that has been given the name of "décollement," used in an analogous sense with the same term in collision tectonics. The décollement separates the wedge from a layer of fragmental material being carried down, or subducted, on top of the descending oceanic crust. At greater depth, this material

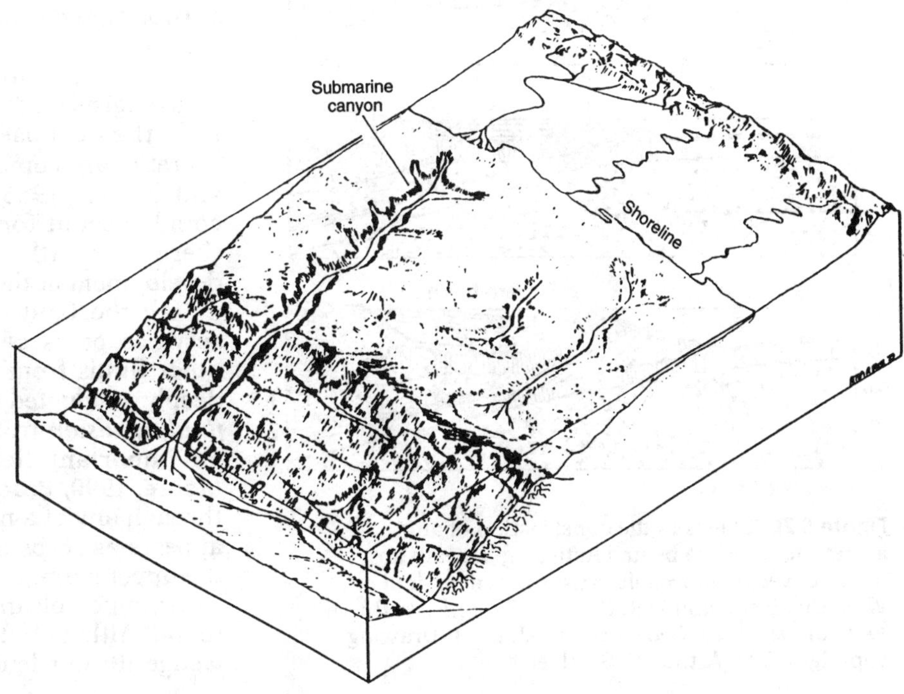

Figure 8.24 Composite drawing of surface features of the trench slope and trench floor, typical of the Middle America Trench. Vertical exaggeration about x 5. (From M.B. Underwood and Daniel E. Karig, 1980, *Geology*, v. 8, p. 435, Figure 3. Reproduced with the permission of the publisher, the Geological Society of America, Boulder, Colorado, USA. Copyright © 1980.)

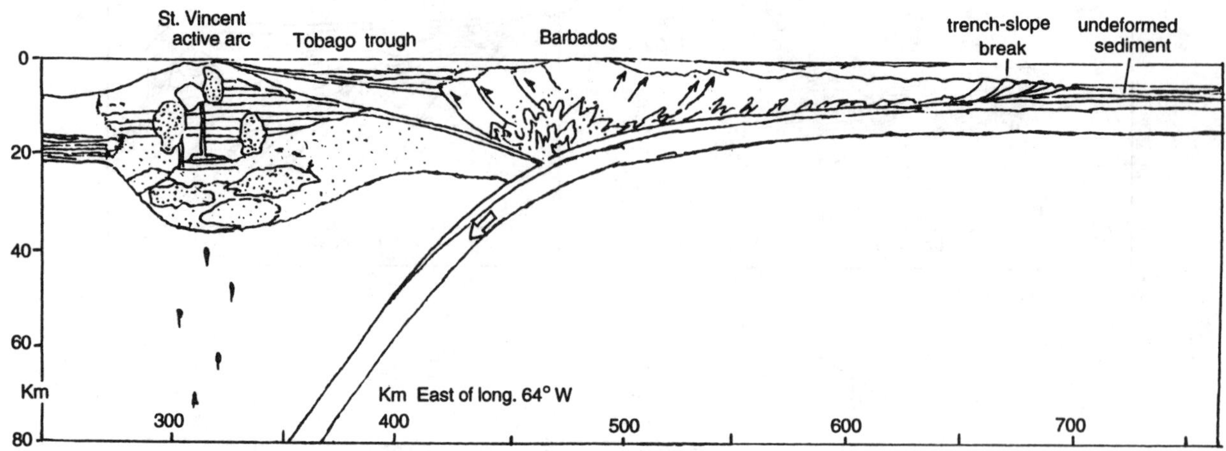

Figure 8.25 A model cross section of the Lesser Antilles island-arc system. It combines data from seismic refraction and reflection, as well as gravity and magnetic observations. Note the long extension of the accretionary wedge toward the east. (Adapted from Ladd, Westbrook, and Lewis, 1982, *Lamont-Doherty Geological Observatory Yearbook*, v. 8, p. 17, Figure 1. Copyright by the Lamont-Doherty Earth Observatory.)

becomes permanently attached to the bottom of the overlying plate in the process of *underplating*, or *subcretion* (Kimura, and Ludden, 1995, p. 219; Kimura, Maruyama, Iozaki, and Terabayasha, 1996, p. 77.)

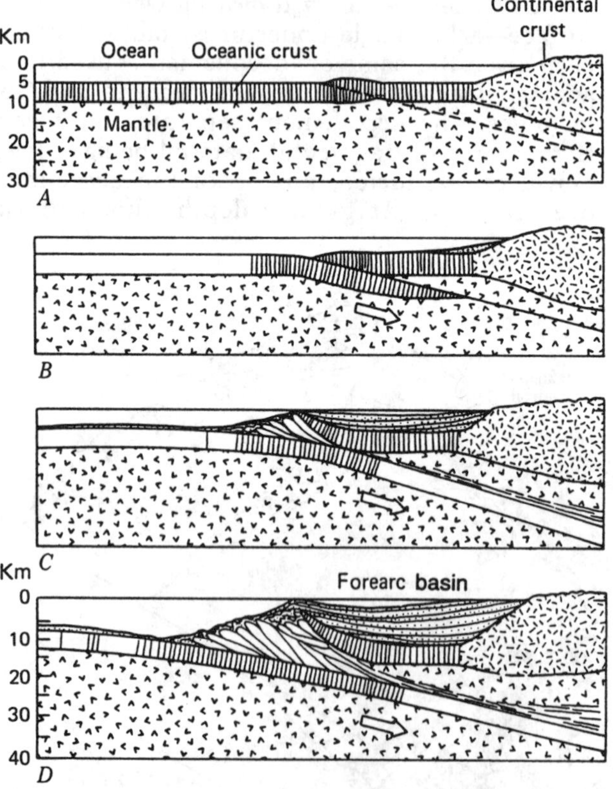

Figure 8.26 Stages in the construction of an accretionary prism by understuffing beneath an uplifted wedge of oceanic crust. (Based on data of W.R. Dickinson and D.R. Seely, 1979, *Bull., Amer. Assn. of Petroleum Geologists*, v. 63, no. 1. Drawing copyright © by Arthur N. Strahler.)

(C) From the décollement a number of listric up-thrusts may develop, and these may reach to the surface of the wedge, as shown in Figure 8.29. This faulting divides the wedge into a number of independent blocks. Note in this cross-section that topographic features on the seafloor produced by normal faulting, including a horst, remain intact during subduction below the décollement.

(D) By duplex geometry, the décollement can be stepped down into a lower level in the subducting oceanic plate, and thus transfer mass from the downgoing plate to the underside of the overriding plate. Figure 8.30 shows the deformation of a duplex. Because the duplex is bounded over the entire roof surface by thrust faults, and also on the bottom surface, it inserts itself into the accretionary wedge without disrupting the overlying rock. The insertion of the duplex will thicken the wedge. The duplexing hypothesis was strongly endorsed in 1985 and 1986 by geologists studying the active Costa Rica Trench and the exposed ancient Alaskan Kodiak accretionary complex (Silver et al., 1985; Samples and Fisher, 1986). They argued that duplexing could account for the growth of the wedge when there was little evidence for imbricate thrust development at the leading edge of the wedge.

All the fault structures described above also serve as paths of rise and outflow of water and other fluids from the accretionary prism and the deeply subducted sediment below it. The study of *fluid expulsion* from subduction zones has become an important field of research (Langseth and Moore, 1990; Peacock, 1990). Expulsion can occur through any of a number of pathways. Some water appears as seeps in the floor of the trench and on the upper surface of the accretionary wedge, where seeps, mud volcanoes, and mud diapirs have been found. Although fault surfaces in the accretionary wedge do not lend themselves naturally to fluid

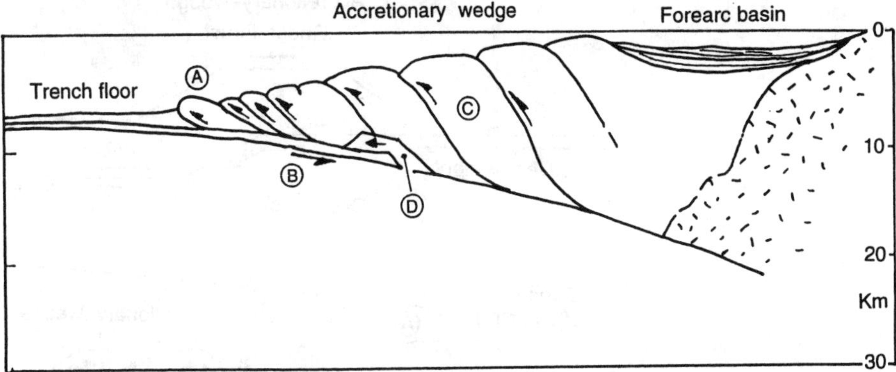

Figure 8.27 Schematic cross section of an accretionary wedge showing the locations of structural styles referred to under A, B, C, and D in the text and shown in Figures 8.28, 8.29. and 8.30. (Based on data of Moore, Cowan, and Karig, 1985. Drawing copyright © by Arthur N. Strahler.)

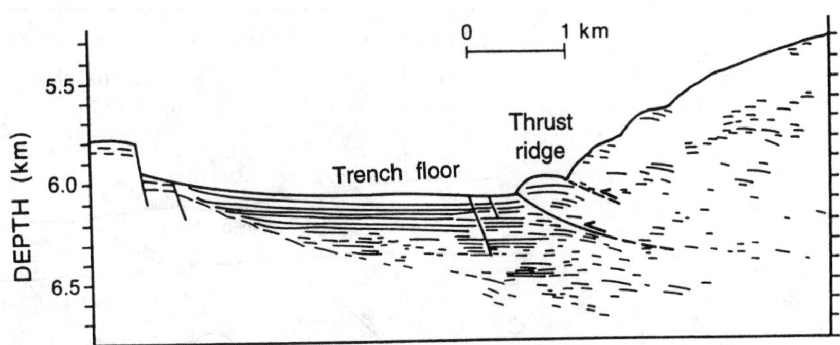

Figure 8.28 Cross section of trench floor and leading edge of an accretionary wedge bearing a thrust ridge. (From G.F. Moore, T.H. Shipley, and P.F. Lonsdale, 1986, *Tectonics*, v. 5, p. 519, Figure 7. Reproduced by permission of the authors and the American Geophysical Union.)

flow, it can occur along fault surfaces that have a mud composition ("muddy faults"). In such faults, *hydrofracture* occurs, forcing a widening of the fault and permitting fluid passage (Brown et al., 1994).

Water and other fluids carried down to greater depths by the subducting plate play an important role in igneous and metamorphic processes. In Chapter 5, in our section on Subduction Boundary Volcanism, we described how the hydrolysis of mafic crustal rock generates large amounts of serpentine. This serpentinized basalt is carried far down into the mantle with the subducting plate. The water present there plays an important role in the melting of the descending plate and the formation of rising magma.

8.10 Accreting and Non-accreting Subduction Boundaries

We have pointed out in an earlier section that subduction boundaries of the Class A (Chilean type) are characterized by strong compressive

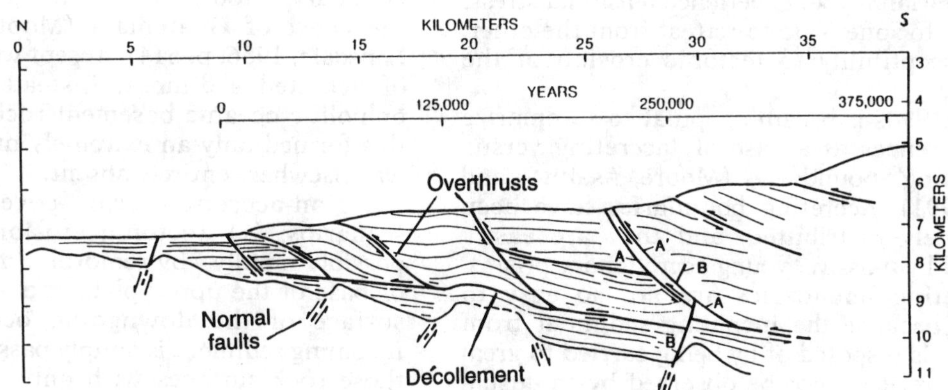

Figure 8.29 Idealized cross section of the central Aleutian Trench and its subduction wedge. Several forms of faults are shown, dividing the wedge into discrete blocks. (From Jill McCarthy and David W. Scholl, 1985, *Bull., Geol. Soc. of America*, v. 96, p. 698, Figure 9. Reproduced with the permission of the publisher, the Geological Society of America, Boulder, Colorado, USA. Copyright © 1985.)

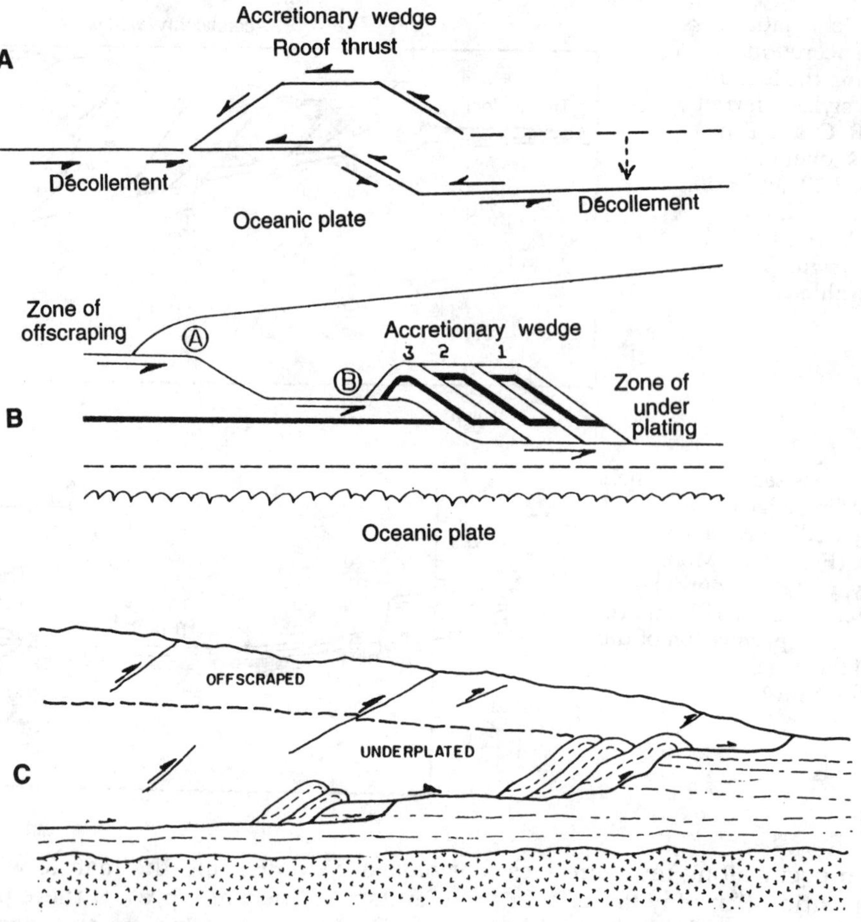

Figure 8.30 Features of duplex geometry. (A) Schematic diagram of a duplex bounded by fault surfaces and generating a new décollement within the down-going slab. (B) Multiple duplex structure and stepping-down of décollement. (C) A more realistic drawing of the above, based on field studies. (Diagram A by A.N. Strahler. Diagram B from J.C. Sample and D.M. Fisher, 1986, *Geology*, v. 14, p. 160, Figure 1; diagram C from J.C. Sample and J. Casey Moore, 1987, *Bull., Geol. Soc. of Amer.*, v. 99, p. 17, Figure 15. Reproduced with the permission of the publisher, the Geological Society of America, Boulder, Colorado, USA. Copyright © 1986, 1987.)

stress and plate convergence, whereas those of Class B (Mariana type) experience tensional stress, a tendency for one plate to retreat from the other, and a susceptibility to tectonic erosion of the upper plate.

In the 1990s is became popular to summarize these differences as a case of "accreting versus non-accreting" boundaries (Moore, Asahito, and Moore, 1991). Accreting boundaries have been found widely distributed, and they are easily recognized by massive, young accretionary prisms. Non-accreting boundaries are not so easy to establish, because the incoming sediment from both plates is disposed of by being carried to great depth, where it cannot be observed by the usual sonic and seismic methods. One criterion would be that the trench slope of the upper plate would have little or no soft, young sediment on it, but instead would yield samples of exposed continental-type metamorphic and igneous rock of relatively great age.

An example of a possible non-accreting boundary is found in the Middle America Arc off the coast of Guatemala (Moore, Shipley, and Lonsdale, 1986, p. 514). Absent were large volumes of accreted sediment; instead, some accreted ophiolitic oceanic basement rock was found, but this formed only an extremely narrow deposit, or was elsewhere entirely absent.

"Non-accretion" can cover two possible scenarios: (1) Tectonic erosion is occurring—possibly rapidly—by removal of rock from the top or base of the upper plate and/or from the upper surface of the downgoing oceanic plate: (2) Incoming sediment is simply passing over or under those rock surfaces with only minimal bedrock erosion.

Tectonic erosion has been visualized as resulting from the physical impact of objects that protrude sharply above the abyssal seafloor, e.g., seamounts, fracture-zone ridges, or horsts. For example, a subducting seamount might uplift the front edge of the trench slope, causing oversteepening of that slope and resulting in a slope failure. The resulting submarine landslide mass would then be rapidly subducted, leaving a deep recess in the trench slope. This model is now considered more realistic than the "buzz-saw" scenario of the seamount being knocked off its base. Also recognized is the possible occurrence of erosion on the underside of the upper plate, and this process would leave evidence of its action through subsidence of the margin of the upper plate, a rise in the upper surface of the subducting plate, and a retreat of the trench axis (von Huene and Lallemand, 1990).

8.11 Metamorphism within the Subduction Complex

Whatever may be the details of development of the accretionary prism, it gives an opportunity for the formation of metamorphic rocks (Ehlers and Blatt, 1982, p. 683-688; Kearey and Vine, 1990, p. 155-161). Deep in the subduction zone (deeper than 20 km), confining pressures are very high (greater than 6 kb). Temperatures close to the descending plate are comparatively low (200°C to 400°C) at this depth because the plate itself is cool in comparison to the surrounding mantle. Here the environment is favorable for the formation of *blueschist*. Blueschist requires high pressure combined with relatively low temperature. A characteristic mineral of blueschist is glaucophane, blue-black in color; another is jadeite. Most blueschist connected with subduction complexes shows the same chemical composition as the oceanic tholeolitic basalts. Thus we can expect to find blueschist being formed deep in the subducting oceanic plate. At still greater depth, with increased pressure, conditions may be favorable for the formation of *eclogite*. A second class of metamorphic rock associated with subduction boundaries is derived from the volcanic rocks—typically andesitic—of the volcanic arc lying directly above the subducting plate. Here, the environment is one of high temperatures and low pressures.

The metamorphic rock produced in active subduction boundaries is normally added later to the continental crust, and thus the continental lithosphere is gradually extended. Denudation of the continental margin is accompanied by a rise of the continental crust, so that eventually the deep-seated metamorphic rocks may appear at the surface. For example, on the Japanese island of Honshu, a narrow belt of blueschist-type rocks lies exposed along the southeastern coastal zone, paralleling the Japan Trench. This rock is of Jurassic and Cretaceous age, it may have formed in the lower part of a subduction complex generated in the Mesozoic Era, well before the backarc basin between Japan and the mainland of Asia was opened. Farther inland on Honshu lies a belt of the low-pressure/high-temperature metamorphic rock. (See Figures 8.9 and 8.10.) Between these two belts, metamorphic rock is absent. In the early 1970s, the Japanese geologist A. Miyasharo noted that this paired arrangement of metamorphic belts was widely present throughout the circum-Pacific arc system and occurs in both the island-arcs and along the active continental margins. It can also be recognized in some older terranes farther inland; for example, in California, where a marginal zone of high-pressure blueschist metamorphics (the Franciscan series) is separated from the low-pressure metamorphics of the Sierra Nevada by a sedimentary belt (the Great Valley sequence). In other cases, the two inland metamorphic belts have been brought into contact with each other, for example, by oblique strike-slip displacement (Ehlers and Blatt, 1982, p. 686).

8.12 Mélange

The intense tectonic activity that goes on within a growing subduction complex affects a wide variety of sediment types as well as fragmented oceanic crust. These diverse ingredients become mixed together in a remarkable kind of rock called *mélange*, a French word refers for "incongruous mixture." Here and there, among the deformed rocks of continental orogenic belts, occur exposures of rock that one might describe as a very coarse breccia. What is remarkable about this breccia is not only the great size of some of the blocks, but also the diversity of their composition and origin. Some of the blocks, consisting of basaltic oceanic crust, appear to have been torn off the subducting plate; these are called *exotic blocks*. Other blocks are fragments of brittle layers, such as sandstone, formed from disrupted trench sediments; they are called *native blocks*. Enclosing the blocks is the *matrix*, consisting of intensely deformed once-plastic (ductile) sediments—a complex mixture of turbidites and pelagic sediments. The adjective "chaotic" is often applied to the structure of the deformed mass. One subclass of mélanges is composed of submarine debris slides, called *olistostromes*, accumulated at the foot of the trench slope. If the mélange should be carried down to great depths in the subduction zone, it may be subjected to high pressure, transforming the mélange into a schist.

Mélanges were first examined and mapped in continental exposures as end products of compressional orogeny, particularly the arc-continent collisions that thrust accretional wedges against a continental margin. In such exposures, the effects of collision orogeny have added many new thrust and fold structures as well as causing additional metamorphism. Mélanges have also been identified in suture zones produced by continent-continent collisions. These orogenic effects are treated in Chapter 9.

Among those geologists who first described mélanges of California in terms of plate tectonics was K.J. Hsü (1967). In the 1960s, Warren

Hamilton of the U.S. Geological Survey made an intensive study of mélanges of the Indonesian region. He reported the exposures of mélanges in the Mentawai Islands, which are emerged summits along the crest of the outer arc of the now-active accretionary wedge off Sumatra (see Figures 8.1 and 8.2). This observation led him to hypothesize that the formation of mélange is an on-going process occurring by intense shearing of the wedge on listric thrusts (Hamilton, 1979, p. 28-31). Hamilton's explanation was endorsed by J. Casey Moore and Tim Byrne in 1987. They stressed the role of dewatering in this tectonic process.

It appears, then, that there are two basic components to many mélanges: The body of the accretionary wedge, formed of terrestrial and pelagic sediments, and the contribution to that prism of fragments derived from the upper surface of the down-going basaltic/gabbroic oceanic crust. Darrel S. Cowan (1985) recognized four basic types of mélange, each of which forms in a typical location within the subuction system. His schematic diagram, reproduced here as Figure 8.31, shows where these types are located. Type I consists of what were originally interbedded sandstone and mudstone that have been disrupted and fragmented by extension parallel with the original bedding planes. Three locations are shown. Type II consists of originally "thin layers of green tuff, radiolarian ribbon chert, and minor sandstone originally interbedded with black mudstone." Both of these types were formed during shearing and imbricate faulting of the wedge. Type III consists of "inclusions of diverse shapes, sizes, and compositions enveloped in a locally scaly pelitic [clay-size] matrix." The materials for this type may have come from olistostromes or mud diapirs. Type IV "consists of lenticular inclusions bounded by an anastomosing network of subparallel faults." This structure indicates a slicing action in brittle fault zones, as shown in Figure 8.32. Notice that the block diagram includes lenses of pillow lavas that are derived from the uppermost layer of the oceanic crust. Thus mélange is not limited in composition to sediments accumulated in the accretionary prism. Large masses of basaltic pillow lavas and sheeted dikes may also be present. (For other and more complex classification systems of mélanges, see Loren A. Raymond, 1984.)

8.13 The Franciscan Complex—An Ancient Mélange

Underlying much of northern California is a unique bedrock belt that reaches some 100 km from the Pacific shores to the Great Valley (and continuing east beneath the younger Valley sediments). It is a remarkable assemblage of rocks that was long a mystery to geologists. This assemblage is roughly in two halves: a western half consisting of the metamorphic *Franciscan Complex*; an eastern half consisting of sedimentary strata of the Great Valley sequence (see Figure 8.33D). The rocks of both halves have an age span of about 100 m.y., the oldest being Late Jurassic (150 Ma) and the youngest Eocene (40 Ma). It appears that the rocks in both halves were formed at the same time and more or less continuously throughout this 100 m.y. time period, which includes all of the Cretaceous Period (duration 70 m.y.). Otherwise, in terms of kind of rock that was formed, the two halves are "as different as day and night."

From the standpoint of making a geologic interpretation, "day" applies to the Great Valley sequence. Any college geology major would immediately identify it as a succession of clastic

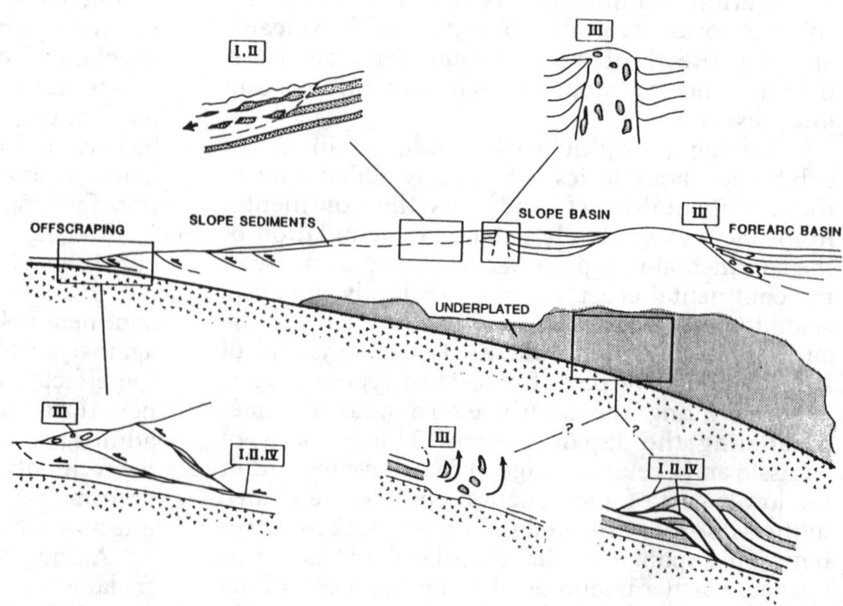

Figure 8.31 Schematic cross section showing the typical locations of occurrence of five basic types of mélange within an accretionary wedge. (From Darrel S. Cowan, 1985, *Bull. Geol. Soc., Amer.*, v. 96, p. 461, Figure 10. Reproduced with the permission of the publisher, the Geological Society of America, Boulder, Colorado, USA. Copyright © 1985.)

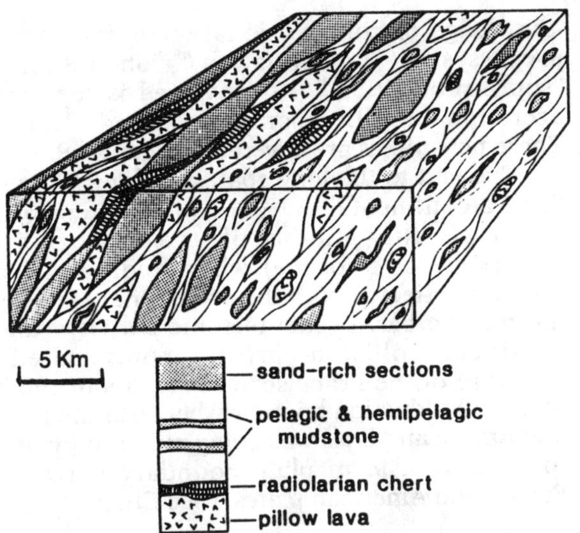

Figure 8.32 Three-dimensional drawing of mélange structure formed by brittle faulting from layers of sand and mudstone overlying chert and pillow lava of oceanic crust. (From Darrel S. Cowan, 1985, *Bull. Geol. Soc., Amer.*, v. 96, p. 460, Figure 9. Reproduced with the permission of the publisher, the Geological Society of America, Boulder, Colorado, USA. Copyright © 1985.)

sedimentary rocks—sandstones, and shales of marine origin—with a basin-like (synclinal) shape. To label the Franciscan Complex as the "night" side is quite appropriate. Much of the Franciscan Complex is an incredibly mixed-up assemblage of small bodies of such rocks as schist (blueschist, glaucophane schist, amphibolite, and eclogite), pillow-lava basalt, peridotite, serpentinite, and sedimentary rock that includes turbidites, dark shales, and thin-bedded cherts. The entire mass is strongly sheared, and the various rock types usually occur in lenslike masses separated by steeply dipping thrust faults. This incongruous mixture of rock types and structures is now generally accepted as being an ancient mélange.

In the light of what is now known of the geology of the tectonic arcs and forearc basins of the Indonesian region and of other subduction zones of the same type, geologists can now say with considerable confidence that the Franciscan Complex is what remains of a massive accretionary wedge, formed more or less continuously through nearly 100 m.y. The Great Valley sequence fits neatly into the picture as the sedimentary accumulation within a forearc basin that persisted at the same time, lying between a structural high—

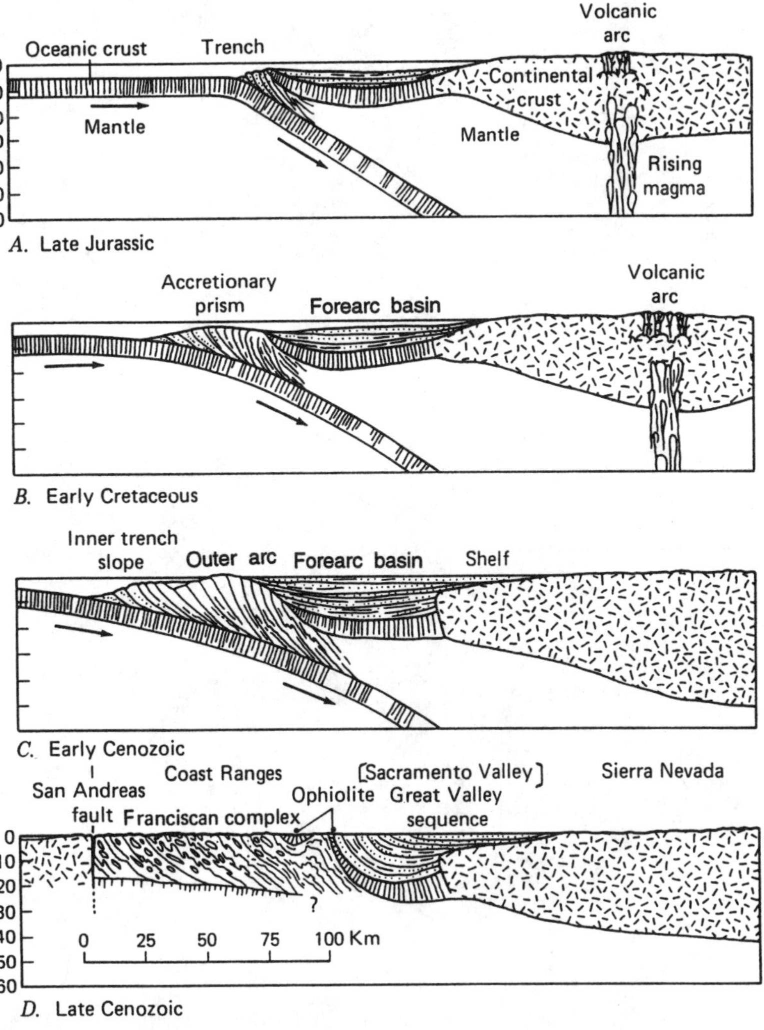

Figure 8.33 Evolution of the Franciscan Complex and Great Valley Sequence in northern California. Horizontal and vertical scales are the same. (Redrawn and simplified from W.R. Dickinson and D.R. Seely, 1979, *Bull., Amer. Assn. of Petroleum Geologists*, v. 63 p. 25, Figure 11. Copright @ 1979. Reproduced by permission of The American Association of Petroleum Geologists.)

the crestline of an outer arc—and a volcanic arc that lay to the east. Figure 8.33 shows by a series of cross sections one possible reconstruction of the development of this continental margin. It makes use of the subduction model shown in Figure 8.26, in which a wedge of oceanic crust is lifted by understuffing and is bent upward to form a forearc basin (Dickinson and Seely, 1979; Ingersoll, 1979, p. 823-824). As the accretionary prism was growing and rising, the forearc basin was receiving sediment and slowly subsiding. Returning to Figure 8.33, notice that structure section D, for the Late Cenozoic (representing the present structure), shows ophiolites within the Franciscan complex. The manner in which this inclusion may have occurred is clear from the preceding three cross sections, i.e., by the formation of a forearc basin over a stretch of oceanic lithosphere that was part of a passive continental margin.

Newer scenarios of the origins of ophiolites have since been proposed. Three of these were compared in a 1996 review published in *GSA Today* under the authorship of William R. Dickinson, Clifford A. Hopson, and Jason B. Saleeby. To pursue the subject further requires knowledge of compressional tectonics, including processes of "delamination," "obduction" and "supra-subduction." Also involved is the topic of accretion of "microcontinents" and "terranes." These new topics are covered in Chapter 9.

The end to the long span of subduction on the Pacific continental margin came rather abruptly about in the middle of the Cenozoic Era (Oligocene or Miocene) when folding and overthrusting affected both the accretionary wedge and the forearc basin. This tectonic activity—an arc-continent collision—greatly complicated the structure of the Franciscan rocks. About this time too, the subduction boundary between the Farallon and American plates was being replaced by the San Andreas transform plate boundary between the Pacific and American plates. (See Chapter 7).

* * * * * *

With this brief venture into the subject of arc-continent collisions, we are providing a smooth transition into Chapter 9: Collision Tectonics and Continental Growth.

References Cited

Bayly, Brian, 1982, Geometry of subducted plates and island arcs viewed as a buckling problem. *Geology*, v. 10, p. 629-632.

Boggs, Sam, Jr., 1984, Quarternary sedimentation in the Japan arc-trench system. *Bull., Geol. Soc. Amer.*, v. 95, p. 669-685.

Brown, Kevin M., Barbara Bekins, B. Clennell, D. Dewhurst, and G. Westbrook, 1994, Heterogeneous hydrofracture development and accretionary fault dynamics. *Geology*, v. 22, p. 259-262.

Cande et al., 1989, *Magnetic Lineations of the World's Ocean Basins* (Map). Tulsa, OK: Amer. Assoc. of Petroleum Geologists.

Cloos, Mark, and Ronald L. Shreve, 1996, Shear-zone thickness and seismicity of Chilean- and Marianas-type subduction zones. *Geology*, v. 24, p. 107-110.

Cowan, Darrel S., 1985, Structural styles in Mesozoic and Cenozoic mélanges in the western Cordillera of North America. *Bull., Geol. Soc. Amer.*, v. 96, p. 451-462.

Cross, Timothy A., and Rex H. Pilger, Jr., Controls of subduction geometry, location of magnatic arcs, and tectonics of arc and back-arc regions. *Bull., Geol. Soc. of Amer.*, v. 93, p. 545-562.

Dewey, John F., and John M. Bird, 1970, Mountain belts and the new global tectonics. *Jour. of Geophysical Res.*, v. 75, no. 14, p. 2625-2647.

Dickinson, W.R., and D.R. Seely, 1979, Structure and stratigraphy of forearc regions. *Bull., Amer. Assoc. of Petroleum Geologists*, v. 63.

Dickinson, William R., 1977, Tectonic-stratigraphic evolution of subduction-controlled sedimentary assemblages. Pages 33-40 in *Island Arcs, Deep Sea Trenches and Back-Arc Basins*, Maurice Ewing Series, vol. I. Washington, DC: American Geophysical Union.

Dickinson, William R., Clifford A. Hopson, and Jason B. Saleeby, 1996, Alternate origins of the Coast Ophiolite (California): Introduction and implications. *GSA Today*, v. 6, no. 2, p. 1-12.

Ehlers, Ernest G., and Harvey Blatt, 1982, *Petrology*. San Francisco: W.H. Freeman and Co.

Ewing, Maurice, and J. Worzel, 1954, Gravity anomalies and structure of the West Indes, Part I. *Bull., Geol. Soc. Amer.*, v. 65 p. 165-174.

Frank, F.C., 1968, Curvature of island arcs. *Nature*, v. 220, p. 363.

Hamilton, Warren, 1979, *Tectonics of the Indonesian Region*. U.S. Geological Survey Professional Paper 1078. Washington, DC: U.S. Government Printing office.

Hayes, Dennis, 1978, *Geophysical Atlas of East and Southeast Asian Seas* MC-25. Boulder, CO, Geological Society of America.

Helwig, James, and Gerald A. Hall, 1974, Steady-state trenches? *Geology*, v. 2, p. 309-316.

Hsü, K.J., 1968, Principles of melanges and their bearing on the Franciscan-Knoxville paradox. *Bull., Geol. Soc. Amer.*, v. 79, p. 1063-1074.

Hsü, K.J., 1987, Melange. Pages 430-434 in Seyfert, 1987.

Hynes, A., and J. Mott, 1985, On the causes of backarc spreading. *Geology*, v. 13, p. 387-389.

Kearey, Philip, and Frederick J. Vine, 1990, *Global Tectonics*. Oxford, U.K., Blackwell Scientific Publications.

Kimura, Gaku, and John Ludden, 1995, Peeling oceanic crust in subduction zones. *Geology*, v. 23, p. 216-220.

Kimura, G., S. Maruyama, Y. Isozaki, and M.Terabayashi, 1996, Well-preserved underplating structure of the jadeitized Francisco complex, Pacheko Pass, California. *Geology*, v. 24, p. 75-78

Ladd, John, Graham Westbrook, and Stephen Lewis, 1981-82. Subduction tectonics in forearcs: Guatemala vs. Barbados. *Lamont-Doherty Yearbook*, 81-82, v. 8, 17-22.

Langseth, M.G., and J. Casey Moore, 1990, Fluids in Accretionary prisons. *EOS*, v. 71, no. 5, p. 245-246.

McCarthy, Jill, and David W. Scholl, 1985, Mechanisms of subduction accretion along the central Aleutian Trench. *Bull., Geol. Soc. Amer.*, v. 96, p. 691-701.

Miyashiro, A., 1973, Paired and unpaired metamorphic belts. *Tectonophysics*, v. 17, p. 241-254.

Moore, C. Casey, Asahiko Taira, and Greg Moore, 1991, Ocean drilling and accretionary processes. *GSA Today*, v. 1, no. 12, p. 265-270.

Moore, Gregory F., and Daniel E. Karig, 1976, Development of sedimentary basins on the lower trench slope. *Geology*, v. 4, p. 693-697.

Moore, Gregory F., Thomas H. Shipley, and Peter F. Lonsdale, 1986, Subduction versus sediment offscraping at the toe of the Middle America Trench off Guatemala. *Tectonics*, v. 5, p. 513-523.

Moore, J. Casey, and Tim Byrne, 1987, Thickening of fault zones: A mechanism of mélange formation in accreting sediments. *Geology*, v. 15, p. 1040-1043.

Moore, J. Casey, Darrel S. Cowan, and Daniel E. Karig, 1985, Structural styles and deformation fabrics of accretionary complexes. *Geology*, v. 13, p. 77-79.

Moore, J. Casey et al., 1982, Geology and tectonic evolution of a juvenile accretionary terrane along a truncated convergent margin. *Bull., Geol. Soc. Amer.*, v. 93, p. 847-861.

Murauchi, S. and M. Yasui, 1968, Geophysical investigations in the seas around Japan. *Kagaku*, v. 38, p. 196.

Peacock, Simon M., 1990, Fluid processes in subduction zones. *Science*, v. 248, p. 329-336.

Raymond, Loren A., 1984, Classification of mélanges. Pages 7-20 in Loren A. Raymond, Ed., 1984, *Mélanges: Their Nature, Origin and Significance*, Special Paper 198. Boulder, CO: Geological Society of America.

Royden, Leigh H., 1993, The expression of slab pull at continent convergent boundaries. *Tectonics*, v. 12, p. 303-325.

Sample, J.C., and D.M. Fisher, 1986, Duplex accretion and underplating in an ancient accretionary complex, Kodiak Islands, Alaska. *Geology*, v. 14, p. 160-163.

Sample, James C., and J. Casey Moore, 1987, Structural style and kinematics of an underplated slate belt, Kodiak and adjacent islands, Alaska. *Bull., Geol. Soc. of Amer.*, v. 99, p. 7-20.

Scholz, C.H., and R. Page, 1970, Buckling in island arcs (Abstract). *EOS*, v. 51, p. 429.

Seyfert, Carl K., Ed., 1987, *Encyclopedia of Structural Geology and Plate Tectonics*. New York: Van Nostrand Reinhold Co.

Silver, Eli A., Martha J. Ellis, Nancy Breen, and Thomas J. Shipley, 1985, Comments on the growth of accretionary wedges. *Geology*, v. 13, p. 6-9.

Stern, Robert J., and Sherman H. Bloomer, 1992, Subduction zone infancy: Examples from the Eocene Izu-Bonin-Mariana and Jurassic California arcs. 1992, *Bull., Geol. Soc. Amer.*, v. 104, p. 1612-1613

Underwood, Michael B., and Daniel E. Karig, 1980, Role of submarine canyons in trench and trench-slope sedimentation. *Geology*, v. 8, p. 432-436.

Uyeda, Seiya, and Hiroo Kanamori, 1979, Back-arc opening and the mode of subduction. *Jour. Geophysical Res.*, v. 84, p. 1049-1061.

Uyeda, Seiya, 1983, Plate motion in convergent plate boundaries. *Geology*, v. 11, p. 681-682.

Von Huene, R., and S. Lallemand, 1990, Tectonic erosion along Japan and Peru convergent margins. *Bull., Geol. Soc. Amer.*, v. 102, p. 704-720.

Watts, A.B., and M. Talwani, 1974, Gravity anomalies seaward of deep-sea trenches and their tectonic implications. *Geophysical Jour. of the Royal Astronomical Society*, v. 36, p. 57-90.

Yamaoka, Koshun, and Yashio Fukao, 1987, Why do island arcs form cusps at their junctions? *Geology*, V. 15, p. 34-36.

Chapter: 9 Collision Tectonics and Continental Accretion

While tectonic activity has been continuous through Cenozoic time in the trench of a subduction zone such as the Sumatra-Java arc, we do not consider this activity as orogenic. Orogeny typically involves intense compressional deformation of sedimentary basins, resulting in great overthrusting and folding, and usually the intrusion of magma to produce plutons. Deformation limited to turbidites and ocean-floor sediments of a trench wedge and accretionary wedge would not fall within this definition of an orogeny. Instead, orogeny of the compressional type requires a massive impact, or collision, between two bodies of continental lithosphere.

The Wilson cycle of opening and closing of an ocean basin, briefly described in Chapter 1, can involve two quite different kinds of collisions. First, while the ocean basin is still wide open, a volcanic island arc can form within the oceanic lithosphere, as explained in Chapter 8 and illustrated in Figure 8.6. The growth of a volcanic arc was described in Chapter 5 and illustrated in Figures 5.32 and 5.33. A mature volcanic arc has a crustal structure and composition resembling that of typical continental crust, with both felsic and mafic layers and a total thickness of over 30 km. The arc may then move toward one of the passive margins of the basin, colliding with it to produce an orogen. This event is an *arc-continent collision* and the resulting orogen is often called a *Cordilleran-type orogen.*

Second, final closing of the ocean basin in the Wilson cycle leads to its terminal event: *continent-continent collision* and suturing of two masses of continental lithosphere into a single continent. To address these major topics, we need information on the structural forms and styles of compressional tectonics. First, however, we present a brief historical review of some of the early geological studies of orogens.

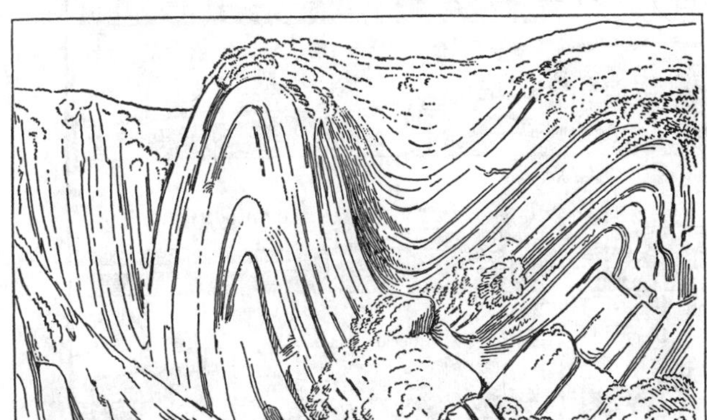

Figure 9.1 Contorted strata on the coast of Berwickshire, Scotland. (After Sir James Hall, Bart., 1812.)

9.1 Early Studies of Alpine Structure

Tectonics as a serious scientific study dates back to the early 1800s, with the recognition by Scottish geologist James Hall of the significance of a series of open folds exposed along the coast of Berwickshire, Scotland (Figure 9.1). His hypothesis—that the strata had once been flat and more or less horizontal but in some manner had been folded—was a first step in tectonics. A prominent American geologist, Bailey Willis, a professor at Stanford University in early decades of this century, wrote:

> Sir James was logical, not only in reasoning from what he saw but also in explaining the process according to his experience. His experience told him that rock cannot be bent. Since he observed it to be bent, the layers could not have been rock but must have been soft mud when the bending occurred. In that conclusion he was mistaken. Three-quarters of a century after him the Swiss geologist, Albert Heim, showed that rocks must have been hard and might have been crystalline as marble when folded. Heim lived, climbed, and thought among the Alps. Inspired rather than awed by their grandeur, he reasoned in terms of their magnitude. (Willis and Willis, 1934, p. 2.)

It was in the high, heavily glaciated European Alps of Switzerland, France, Italy, and Austria that a great effort by many field geologists produced detailed knowledge of the complex structures of compressional tectonics—"telescoping," we now call it. "After the pioneers Bernard Studer and Arnold Escher von der Linth, came their disciple, Albert Heim, whose *Mechanismus der Gebirgsbildung* [Mechanisms of Mountain Building], published in 1876, laid down the basic principles of structural geology" (Willis, 1934, p. 73). Almost a half-century later Heim summed up the state of alpine tectonic geology in a great work, *Der Geologie der Schweitz*, published in three volumes, 1919-1922. Many others contributed to this information, among them Maurice Lugeon, recognized as the founder of a school of structural interpretation that sought to explain the complicated alpine folding and overthrusting—structures that became known as *decken* or *nappes de recouvrement*. Figure 9.2 shows a cross section of nappes of the central Alps as interpreted by Heim.

During this early period, intensive field studies were also being made of the Jura Mountains of France and Switzerland, an arc of open *foreland folds* peripheral to the high Alps (Figure 9.3). By "foreland" we mean a zone representing the outer

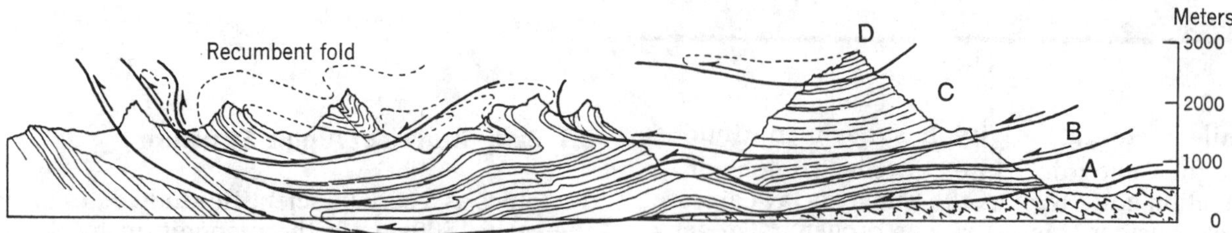

Figure 9.2 Structure section through a portion of the Helvetian Alps, Switzerland. Nappes are labeled A, B, C, and D, in order of age of emplacement. Horizontal and vertical scales are the same. (Simplified from drawings of A. Heim, 1922, *Geologie der Schweiz*, vol. II-1, Leipzig, Tauschnitz.)

region and limit of a compressional orogen. Here the structural relationships were found to be unique, requiring that at a shallow depth below the folds there lies a vast nearly-horizontal surface of overthrusting. The analogy of a table cloth being thrown into folds as the cloth is pushed horizontally against a fixed obstacle was then invoked, and accounts for the term *nappe*, meaning in French a "cover sheet" or "table cloth." Then, as now, the problem of how such sheet-thrusting could occur on so low an angle from the horizontal was a subject of much thought and discussion.

A similar structural configuration in the open folds of the Newer Appalachian Province was recognized and described by Bailey Willis in his 1893 report for the U.S. Geological Survey, titled "Mechanisms of Appalachian Structure." Folds in this belt involved strata that were originally deposited to total thicknesses on the order of 3 to 6 km.

Grove Karl Gilbert, often considered today as the leading physical geologist of that period, had stated in 1880 that under so great a load as would exist in fold belts, such as the Alpine nappes and the foreland folds, the deeper strata would be in a state of high internal friction and high strength, a condition making folding most unlikely (as opposed to brittle fracturing). Reinforcing this opinion were pioneer laboratory experiments on rock deformation under high confining pressure, carried out by Frank D. Adams. He was able to show that rock is many times stronger when greatly compressed from all directions (under hydrostatic pressure). But, on the other hand, he also found that the rock under that confining stress was capable of a sort of plastic deformation; that it could "flow," so to speak, under additional distortional stresses acting more or less horizontally. Today we use the adjective *ductile* for this property of flowage under great confining stress. There remained the central geophysical problem of how a relatively thin sheet of rock could be made to slide or slip bodily over a low-angle fault surface.

In the early period of study of thrusts of the European Alps, before 1880 or so, it was assumed

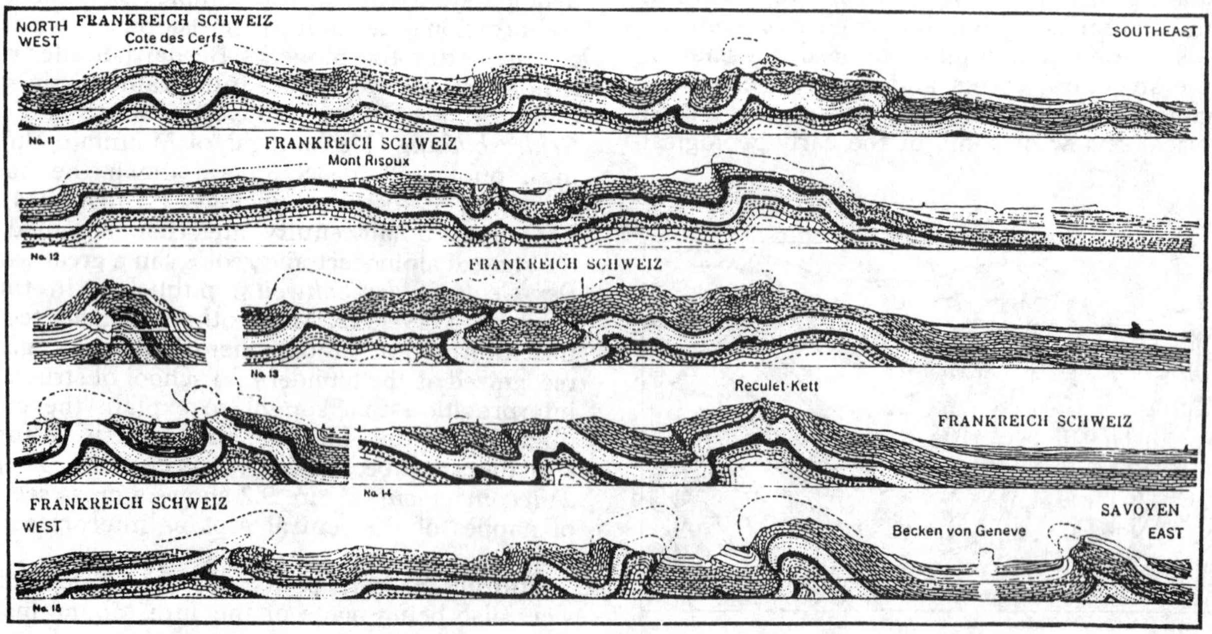

Figure 9.3 Two cross section through the Jura Mountains. (From A. Heim, 1922, *Geologie der Schweiz*, vol. II-1, Leipzig, Tauschnitz.)

that the nappe structures lie today more or less in the same region in which the strata were deposited in a sedimentary basin. The thrust pile was therefore designated as being *autochthonous*. The concept here is that a sedimentary basin was greatly compressed from both directions but remained in its original location over the crust. Toward the end of the century, however, it became obvious to geologists that the strata within essentially flat horizontal thrust sheets had originated great distances away, traveling many tens of kilometers into a region far from the origin. Such foreign masses were then referred to as being *allochthonous* (Hobbs, Means, and Williams, 1976, p. 409-411). These two bulky terms became widely used in subsequent decades, and you may come across them. With plate tectonics now developed to span the entire life history of an orogen, the terms are unnecessary in most cases.

9.2 Development of Overturned and Overthrust Strata

Figure 9.4 shows Heim's 1922 reconstruction of the typical stages in development of an overturned recumbent fold and its transformation into an overthrust sheet. Only in the final drawing do we see a topographic profile, telling us that a large proportion of the nappe has been removed by fluvial and glacial erosion. All of the other diagrams are "dangling in space," with no attempt having been made to show a topographic surface, or to fill in the structures beneath the evolving fold. First, an open and slightly asymmetric anticlinal fold is formed. The axial surface is then rotated forward and results in an overturned anticline, which flattens down upon itself to become a *recumbent fold*. Notice that the strata of the underside of the recumbent fold are upside down as compared with the way they were deposited. At this point, an overthrust fault may develop by rupture at the base of the recumbent fold, after which the upper portion of the fold is carried along as a *thrust sheet*.

Figure 9.2, one of Heim's cross-sections of a complex nappe structure he mapped in the Alps, shows that one nappe lies above another. It was assumed that the nappes formed one above the other, with the first nappe lying at the base of the pile, and successive nappes overriding in the vertical order found. Later, the entire nappe series was folded as a group so the thrust planes are now quite different in dip than when they were first produced. Much of the upper part of the total structure was then removed by erosion. What we see today is the structure exposed in the steep walls of alpine peaks and deep glacial troughs. In varying degrees, strata that have been subject to this form of intense folding and overthrusting have also been altered to metamorphic rocks, which may include slates, schists, gneisses, quartzites, and marble.

Figure 9.5 is a cross-section of a recumbent fold exposed on a steep face of a mountain, the Grand Morgon, in the French Alps. The European names of the Triassic and Jurassic units reappear in reverse order in the higher part of the slope.

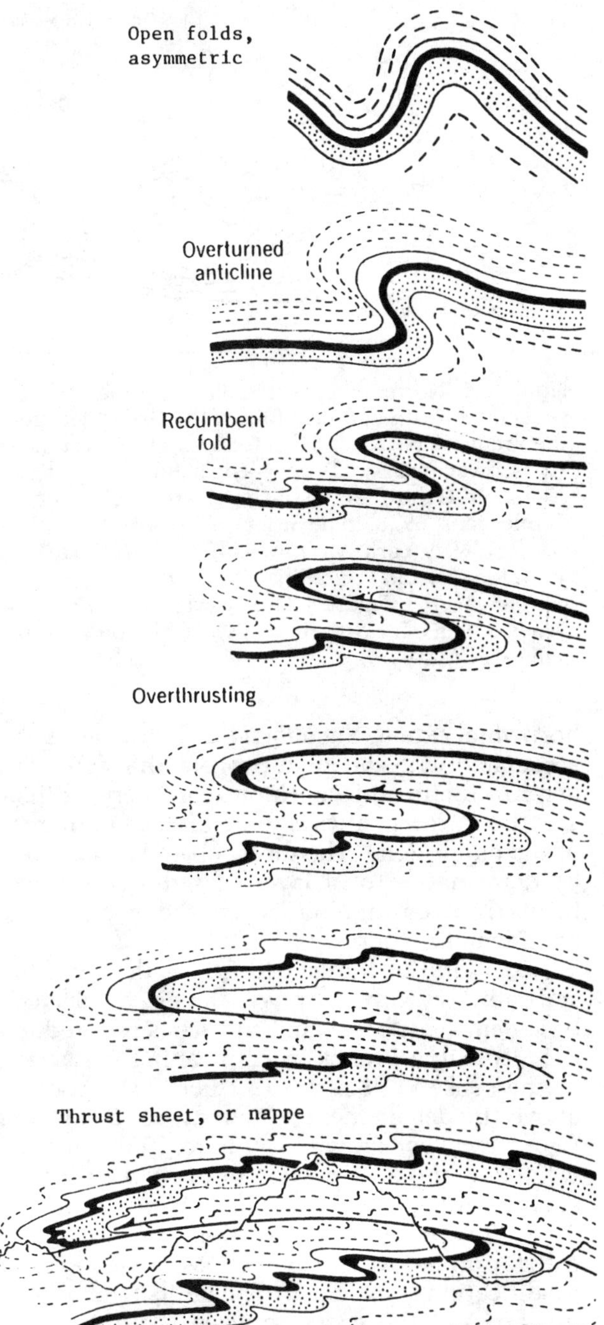

Figure 9.4 Development of overturned and recumbent folds and an overthrust sheet, or nappe. (Adapted from drawings of A. Heim, 1922, *Geologie der Schweiz*, vol. II-1, Leipzig, Tauschnitz.)

In the foreland region we are interpreting overthrust faults in which the attitude of the main fault underlying the thrust approaches the horizontal. The upper layer now assumes the nature of a vast sheet, often several tens of kilometers in

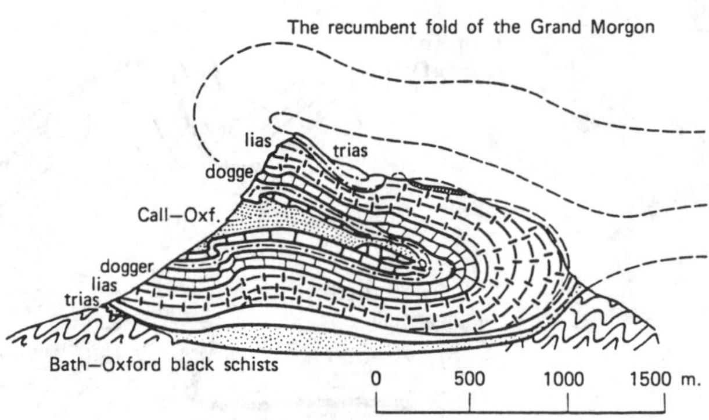

Figure 9.5 Normal and reversed stratigraphic sequences in a recumbent fold of the Grand Morgon in the French Alps. Ages are as follows: Trias-Triassic; Lias-Lower Jurassic; Dogger-Upper Jurassic; Callovian (Cal.) and Oxfordian (Oxf.)-Upper Jurassic. (After Schneegans, 1938, in de Sitter, 1956, *Structural Geology*, New York, McGraw-Hill. From B.E. Hobbs, W.D. Means, and P.F. Williams, *An Outline of Structural Geology*, p. 416, Figure 9.23a. Copyright © 1976 by John Wiley & Sons, Inc. Reprinted by permission of John Wiley & Sons, Inc.)

horizontal extent. Such *foreland thrusts* are strongly associated with the great orogens that form during arc-continent and continent-continent collisions. The thrusts seem always to lie on the continent side of the nappe zone. The thrust sheet is characterized by deformation of a layer of sediments that was formerly a continental-shelf wedge of a passive continental margin.

One kind of foreland thrust is that in which a sedimentary layer moves over a crystalline basement. This basal fault surface is referred to as a *décollement*, a French word meaning "detachment" in the sense of "coming unstuck." The rock sheet above the décollement zone may deform in one of two ways, as shown in Figure 9.6. One is by wrinkling into a succession of open, wavelike folds, such as we found in the Jura Mountains (Figure 9.6A). The other is by breaking up into a set of overlapping overthrust slices. (No erosional modification is included.) The faults tend to steepen upward and the slices between them are stacked like shingles on a roof (Figure 9.6B). Faults of this kind are usually referred to as listric faults. The arrangement is called *imbricate structure*. Both folding and thrust faulting may occur at the same time, giving an extremely complex structure to the moving rock sheet as a whole.

In the case of relatively thin, low-dipping foreland thrust sheets, two quite different kinds are found (Figure 9.7. Here we find that the thrust sheet characteristically coincides with a stratigraphic horizon, which may be (A) the upper surface of the basement of ancient crystalline rocks (metamorphic and igneous), or (B) a bedding surface between two sedimentary formations. In diagram B the fault plane closely follows a bedding plane for a long diatance and is known as a *bedding thrust* or a *bedding slip*. Apparently, the resistance to shearing was least along that particular stratigraphic horizon, which may consist of a weak clay or shale formation between two more massive formations of limestone or sandstone. The figure shows that a cross-cutting thrust fault (left) merges with the upper surface of formation b. Now sequence a-b is repeated. A bedding thrust may be difficult to identify in the field, but its presence must be inferred when an older group of strata overlies a younger group, as shown by their respective fossil contents.

9.3 Overthrusts of the Northern Rockies

To close our introduction to great overthrust sheets, we turn for examples to the Northern Rockies of Montana, Alberta and British Columbia. Here the thrusting occurred at the close of the Cretaceous Period (66 Ma), and continued into Early Cenozoic (Paleocene) time. This was the Laramide Orogeny, which we describe in more detail later in this chapter.

First we will examine the Lewis Overthrust, a prominent geologic and scenic feature in Glacier National Park, Montana. This gives us an opportunity to get a close look at the structural style of the entire thrust belt lying to the north in Canada. This overthrust is exposed for some 200 km along the eastern front of the northern Rocky

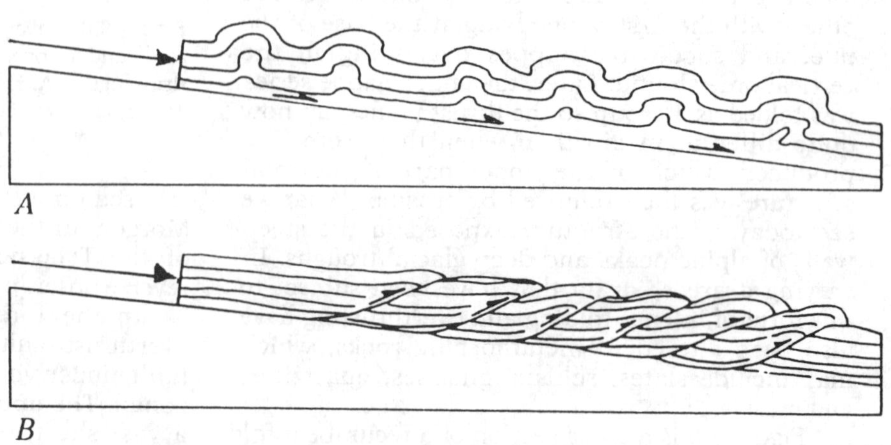

Figure 9.6 Schematic cross sections of tectonic features produced by gravity gliding. A. Open folds, such as those of the Jura Mountains. B. Imbricate thrusts within a thrust sheet. No erosional removal is shown. (Copyright © by Arthur N. Strahler.)

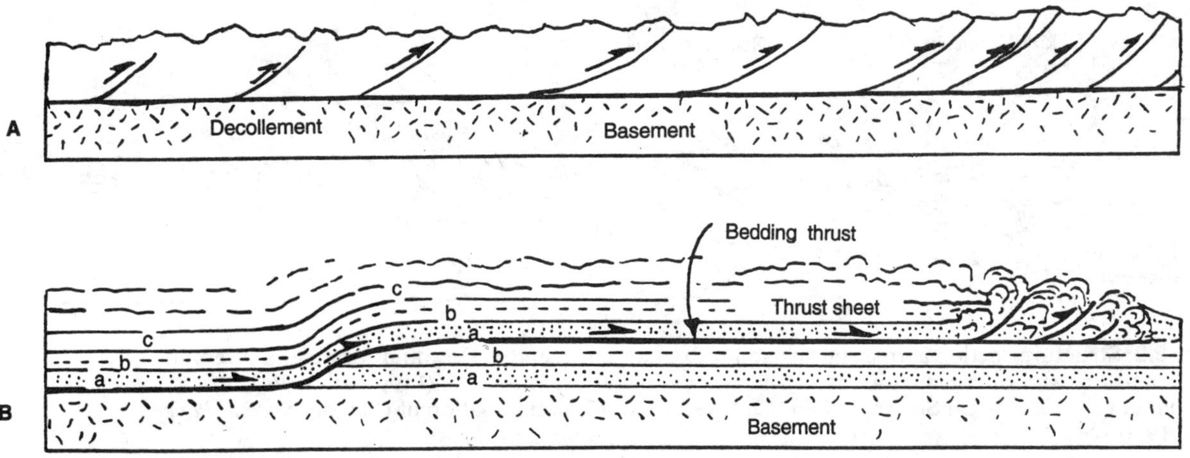

Figure 9.7 Schematic cross sections of (A) Décollement with splay thrusts branching upward, and (B) bedding thrust in horizontal strata. (Copyright © by Arthur N. Strahler.)

Mountains from northern Montana into Alberta. Here, thick, massive Precambrian sedimentary formations form the bulk of the mountain mass. Known as the Belt Series, its formations total from 3 to 7 km in thickness. Prominent as cliff makers in the area of the Lewis Overthrust are two great massive limestone formations, the lower one about 600 m thick; the upper one twice that thickness. Also present are quartzite and shale beds. During the Laramide Orogeny, collision impact from an island arc approaching from the west caused the Precambrian strata, which may have been little deformed up to that time, to be folded and thrust eastward over Cretaceous strata.

Figure 9.8, a diagram published many decades ago, is a greatly simplified version of the tectonic changes that took place. The Lewis Overthrust is shown as originating in a recumbent fold that broke along a low-angle thrust fault, carrying the Belt Series over the Cretaceous strata. Keep in mind that the upper part of the overthrust that seems to hang out over "thin air" would have been undergoing rapid erosion from the time of the first folding and for as long as the fault motion continued and, of course, long after the motion ceased. Horizontal displacement on the Lewis Overthrust is estimated to have been 55 to 65 km. The fault surface is gently inclined to the southwest at a dip angle of about three degrees, more or less. Because the Cretaceous strata lying below the thrust plane are weak and easily eroded by running water, their rapid removal has tended to undermine the overlying massive limestone formations of the Belt Series, producing clifflike mountain walls and a sharp break in slope along the line of exposure of the fault plane.

A very large proportion of the eastern part of the thrust sheet disappeared entirely by erosion through Cenozoic time. At the same time the mountain front became ragged in plan (as seen from the air or on a map), with many promontories projecting eastward into the plains country. Here and there an isolated, islandlike mass of the Belt rocks can be seen as an erosional outlier, completely surrounded by Cretaceous rocks.

Figure 9.9 gives a much more detailed rendition of the details of overthrusting and folding in the Canadian Cordilleran thrust belt, at a point some 500 km north of the U.S.-Canadian boundary, between Banff and Jasper national

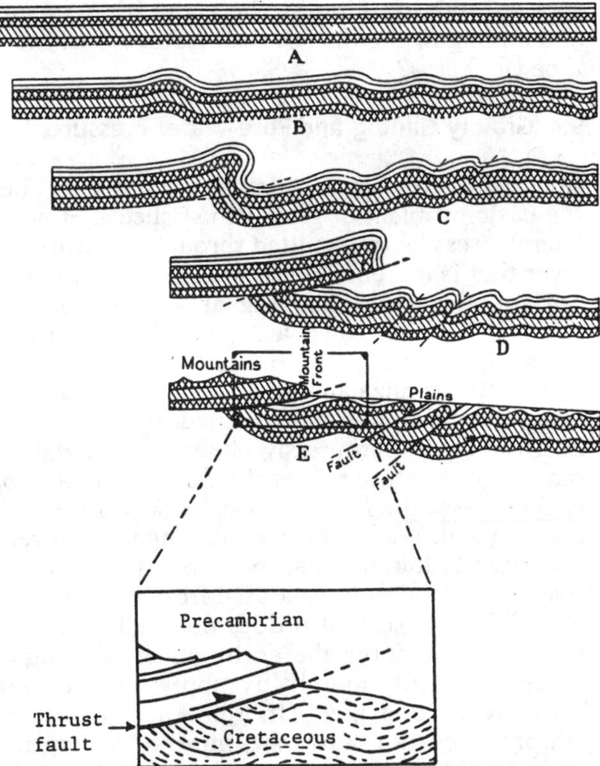

Figure 9.8 Simplified cross sections showing folding and overthrusting leading to production of the Lewis Overthrust in the region of Glacier National Park. Folding is shown to precede the formation of a basal thrust, or décollement. (From National Park Service, 1937, *Glacier National Park*, U.S. Government Printing Office, Washington, D.C., p. 32.

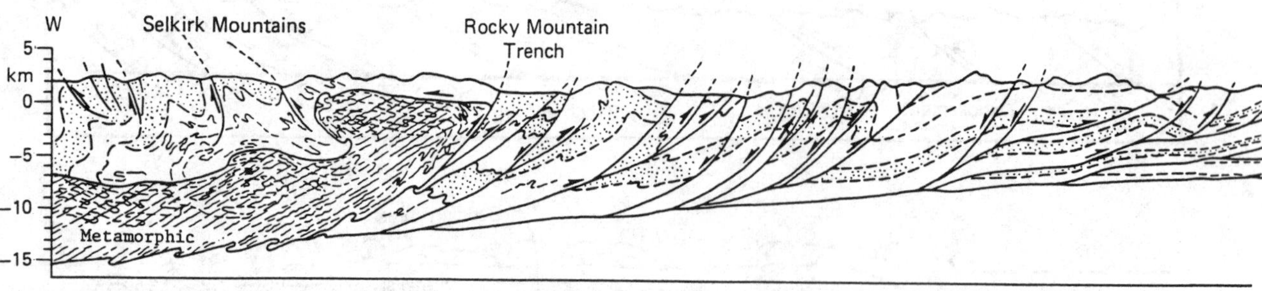

Figure 9.9 Structure section across the Canadian Rockies between the Bow and Athabasca rivers in Alberta and British Columbia. Horizontal and vertical scales are the same. (Prepared by R.A. Price from data of the Geological Survey of Canada. From Geological Association of Canada, *Special Paper*, No. 6, 1970.)

parks (Price, 1970). Here only the Cretaceous strata are involved in the thrusting, which takes the form of a large number of upwardly-concave thrust surfaces, known as *splays*. Most of these *splay faults* meet the single underlying basal fault surface, or décollement, at a strongly acute angle. We see here what is often referred to as tectonic *telescoping*—the reduction of a former sedimentary basin to a narrow orogen through the application of compression during collision. A good question to ask at this point is: In what order did these fault slices form? Would you number them in order of succession beginning at the right (first formed) and ending at the far left (last formed)? Or would it be vice versa?

9.4 Gravity Gliding and Pore-Water Pressure

Inviting speculation for almost a century has been the basic problem of great thrust sheets: How can lateral stress be transmitted through an entire rock layer that is extremely thin in comparison with its horizontal extent? Looking at a great series of nappes, whether they are viewed in nature in alpine mountains or on true-scale cross sections, it is hard to visualize an individual nappe as a strong layer capable of being pushed uphill or even horizontally by compressive stresses applied at one margin of the thrust sheet. Folding within a nappe suggests that the rock was weak and behaved as a plastic solid. We might liken a nappe to a layer of soft pastry dough rolled out on a pastry board. Even if the dough is separated from the table by a layer of flour, so that it does not stick, it may be impossible to force the entire sheet of dough to move as a unit merely by applying horizontal pressure at one edge. In this case, the dough simply does not have the internal strength to transmit the horizontal stress.

Reasoning on these lines, geologists suggested an alternative hypothesis to that of pressure applied horizontally at one source. Suppose, in the case of the sheet of dough, we tilt the pastry board. When the tilt becomes sufficiently steep, the dough begins to slide under the force of gravity. When the leading edge of the dough sheet reaches the horizontal table top it begins to buckle into folds, which pile up behind the leading edge. Our simple model illustrates the hypothesis of *gravity gliding* of overthrust sheets and nappes, proposed in 1880 by E. Reyer, a geologist familiar with the structure of the European Alps (see Holmes, 1978, p. 678-679). It postulates sufficient crustal uplift occurring along a collision zone to generate the downward gradient parallel with the base of a series of strata. Figure 9.6 shows the gravity-gliding explanation applied to décollements and nappes, since a gentle down-gradient is shown for the décollement. Reyer's theory of gravity gliding was quite widely applied in the 1940s and 1950s to the formation of tightly folded nappes in such widely separated localities as the Swiss Alps, Pyrenees, and Montana Rocky Mountains (Holmes, 1978, p. 680-683.)

The problem of sufficiently reduced friction between the gliding layer and the base on which it moves remains to be solved and can be independently approached. We might imagine that the gliding is facilitated by some natural lubricant, such as a layer of saturated plastic clay. It remained for Karl Terzaghi, a specialist in the engineering mechanics of soils, to put forward a hypothesis based on the principle that *pore-water pressure* is capable of exerting a lifting force on a mass of soil or rock and thereby counteracting, and even nullifying, the frictional effect of the weight of the overlying mass (Terzaghi, 1950, p. 92-94). The force is generated by water confined by the overlying rock layer and saturating the pore space beneath it. The mechanism is quite like that of a hydraulic jack, by means of which the power of the human arm can lift an automobile high off the ground. Although Terzaghi applied his hypothesis to the initiation of landslides on mountainsides, the principle can be applied to large overthrust sheets. This step was taken in 1959 by M. King Hubbert and William W. Rubey, who showed that in theory water trapped in interconnected pores in rock of the thrust sheet can experience a buildup of pressure to the point that the thrust sheet is actually "floated" off the thrust contact and made free to move under gravitation force.

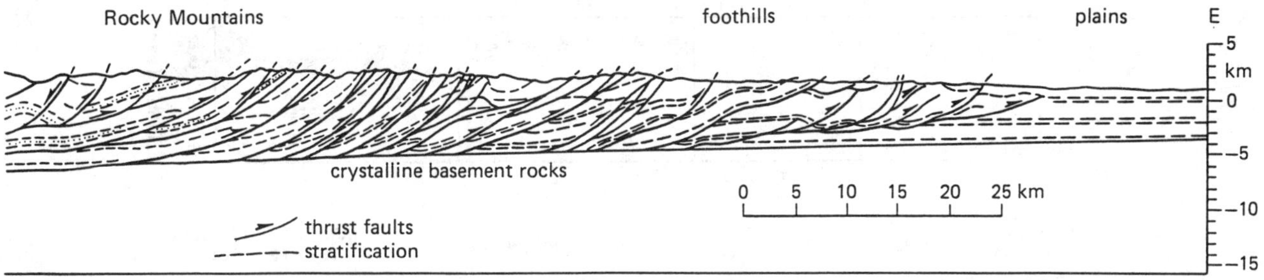

Rocky Mountains
foothills
plains
E
5 km
0
−5
−10
−15
crystalline basement rocks
0 5 10 15 20 25 km
thrust faults
stratification

The pore-water theory was challenged by three Massachusetts Institute of Technology authors: Peter L. Guth, L.V. Hodges, and J.H. Willemin (Guth et al., 1982; Willemin et al., 1980). The main thrust of their argument lies in imagining circumstances under which extremely high pore-water pressure can be held trapped in the rock of the thrust zone. These authors were addressing their criticism to papers published by two other geologists, Stephen Ayrton (1980) and P.E. Gretener (1972; 1980), who were supporting the Rubey/Hubbert hypothesis and were pressing for its application to the interpretation of gliding of nappes and thrust sheets. Ayrton suggested that as metamorphism affects sedimentary rocks deep within nappes, mineralogical changes involving dehydration (dewatering) release free water that can enter the thrust zone and replenish water lost by upward leakage. His suggestion was that periodic renewal of the pore-water supply from this source can allow movement on the thrust plane to proceed intermittently. The M.I.T. authors maintained, however, that under pressures and temperatures high enough to cause the plastic flow seen in metamorphic rocks, open and interconnected pores could not be maintained (Willemin et al., 1980, p. 405-406). They doubted that the overlying rock could maintain a sufficiently low permeability to hold in the great pore-water pressure needed for gravity gliding to occur. Furthermore, they argued, the overlying rock could not possess the tensile strength to hold in the confined water; it would break through along fractures and pressure would drop.

The debate continues among geologists, and it may well be that the arguments against pore-water pressure flotation will put that hypothesis to rest; but it is perhaps premature to anticipate that verdict just now.

As is often the case, new suggestions are put forward in an attempt to break such a deadlock. Raymond A. Price, an authority on thrust sheets of the Canadian Cordillera, pointed out in 1988 that total displacement on a large thrust sheet must be the cumulative result of many small incremental displacements, that each increment begins as a local shear failure (a seismic event), and that only a small part of the fault surface is in relative motion at any one time (Price, 1988, p. 1898). This would mean that the input of energy needed to cause fault motion is perhaps only a very small fraction of that needed to move simultaneously the entire thrust sheet. Paul A. Washington replied, finding Price's model "does not greatly change the basic mechanics necessary for thrust displacement." He also stated: "instead, the resolution of the apparent mechanical paradox can be found in the shape of the total thrust mass, which is a wedge rather than a tabular sheet as formerly assumed" (1990, p. 529-530). Price followed with his rebuttal in the same journal issue (1990, p. 531-532).

And so the discussion remains open. What we can do, however, is to go back to the crustal rock itself to see what field evidence there is that low-angle overthrust sheets actually did move long distances.

9.5 A New Look at the Deep Crust

For many years, an important geophysical tool in the search for petroleum accumulations has been the analysis of artificially generated seismic waves, sent down from the surface into the rocks beneath and picked up again after they have been reflected or refracted from various kinds of layerlike structures or abrupt rock interfaces. To apply these highly sophisticated methods to pure science, there was formed in 1973 the Consortium for Continental Reflection Profiling (COCORP). Its members have included geologists from various universities and from within the petroleum industry (Kerr, 1978). COCORP has sought to explore the continental crust to depths as great as 45 km, which is much deeper than petroleum exploration is normally carried. Equipment is mounted on a caravan of trucks that travels slowly across country. Seismic waves are generated by a hydraulically-vibrated pad. The waves travel into the crust and are reflected back to the surface, to be picked up by a long chain of geophones. The data are presented as optical images of the structures in a vertical plane of section beneath the line of geophones. The reflection method is used in conjunction with refraction studies, requiring a different kind of instrumentation. Refraction data are necessary to determine the speeds at which seismic waves travel through various rock formations, information that can be used to identify the kind of rock the waves travel through.

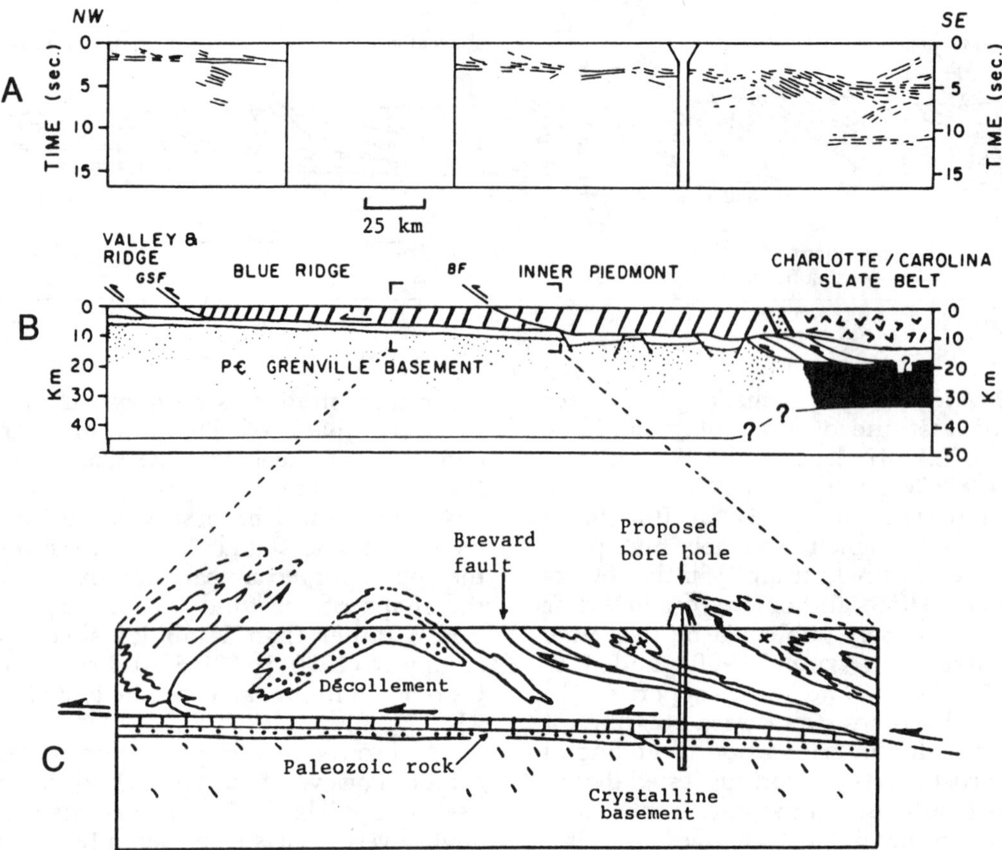

Figure 9.10 An image produced by COCORP seismic reflection sounding reveals a nearly horizontal décollement coinciding with the upper surface of a horizontal layer of Paleozoic strata. In the uppermost diagram (A) the lines are reflectors interpreted as thrust surfaces. A geological cross section (B) matches the seismic profile. Section C enlarges the Brevard fault zone and shows the location of a deep borehole that had been proposed in the early 1980s. (Section B from, F.A. Cook, *Geology*, v. 11, p. 89, Figure 4. Section C from R.D. Hatcher, Jr., in, *Geotimes*, 1984, v. 29, no. 11, p. 13. Reproduced with the permission of the publisher, the Geological Society of America, Boulder, Colorado, USA. Copyright © 1984.)

Of the COCORP crustal profiles thus far completed, an especially good example that relates to the problem of great overthrust sheets is a profile across the Southern Appalachians (Figure 9.10). This is the orogenic belt completed at the close of the Paleozoic Era by the collision of North America with Africa in Pennsylvanian time, finally eliminating the former ocean basin that lay between them. The deep profile extended across the Piedmont and Blue Ridge belts of crystalline metamorphic rock (schist, slate, and gneiss) and into the belt of foreland folds of the Newer Appalachians (Folded Appalachians), in which strata of Paleozoic age were thrown into open folds with some overturning and moved forward along a major overthrust layer as well. The crystalline metamorphic rocks of the Piedmont and Blue Ridge are comparatively ancient. They probably represent mostly early and middle Paleozoic strata metamorphosed in earlier arc-continent collisions such as one that occurred in Ordovician time (Taconian Orogeny) and another in Devonian time (Acadian Orogeny). They show complex nappe structures and some major low angle overthrust faults.

In this traverse, COCORP seismic reflection profiling revealed a startling feature. Beneath the metamorphic rocks just described, there appears to be a flat-lying rock layer, interpreted as being composed of lower Paleozoic strata (Figure 9.10). These beds were deformed by the pressures and shearing forces of overthrusting and were altered to a metamorphic rock of low grade. This relatively immobile layer rests on the Precambrian basement on which the strata were originally deposited. The crystalline thrust sheet (or sheets) above this immobile zone apparently moved forward on the nearly horizontal décollement, paralleling the underlying Precambrian surface. Overthrust sheets in this region appear to have traveled toward the continental interior over distances of several tens of kilometers along a nearly horizontal thrust fault at a depth of several kilometers. Identification of the immobile basal layer seemed reasonably certain, because the same seismic methods used have been used repeatedly in the past and have often been verified by later drilling (although at much shallower depths) in searches for petroleum accumulations. Since this pioneering seismic profile was completed, many others like it have become a fundamental source of information on the deep structure of all the continents.

9.6 Compressional Structures of Collision Tectonics

Over the past two decades or so, some new concepts and terms have come into the descriptions of compressional tectonics observed in collision orogens. Only the large-scale structures concern us here, but we should not lose sight of the importance of small-scale microstructures, such as fractures and microfolds, which are useful in interpreting large-scale features.

Different basic styles of ductile deformation can be recognized in collision orogens found in the orogenic core zones (Twiss and Moores, 1992, p. 217). One is recumbent nappe structure. A second is "thin-skinned" foreland-thrust structure. Illustrations of both of these class styles have been presented in earlier paragraphs, and they have been identified and mapped since the earliest structural studies of the European Alps.

Nappe structure of the orogenic core zones is a form of ductile deformation that goes to great depths and consequently involves metamorphism on a large scale. Figure 9.11 shows this structure in a classic region, in which we recognize some familiar names—Matterhorn, Mont Blanc, Simplon, and Saint Bernard. A feature of this structure is the enormous size of the Monte Rosa recumbent nappe, measuring some 20 km in both height and breadth. An American example of large recumbent nappes is from the Piedmont region of the Southern Appalachians, Figure 9.12.

The second major class, thin-skinned foreland thrusts, is already familiar through our examples from the North American Cordilleran frontal range (Figures 9.6, 9.7. and 9.10). These are characterized by the presence of a broad basal décollement that is nearly horizontal. Within this class, we have already recognized two quite distinct subclasses: (a) open foreland folds; (b) thrust sheets modified by secondary superimposed thrust faults. In subclass (b) we have differentiated in Figure 9.7 between a thrust sheet bearing numerous listric faults (splay faults), and one dominated by bedding thrusts.

9.7 Structures of Thin-skinned Tectonics

We concentrate next upon the structures produced in thin-skinned tectonics. The style in which numerous listric faults are generated in sequence is that of an *imbricate thrust system* (Boyer and Elliott, 1982, p. 262). It is a branching system in which two faults are joined at a very small junction angle that may be appear asymptotic, as if branching from a common stem (Figure 9.13a). Three or more such faults joined to a common stem constitute a *fan* (Figure 9.13b). This arrangement of faults can also be described as a "splaying out"; the individual branches, as "splays," or *splay faults*. The long "stem," more or less horizontal, is called the *sole thrust*. In terms of the entire system it can also be identifieid as a décollement. The splay faults are, of course, of the listric type in terms of the steepening of the dip from lower end to upper end.

The imbricate thrust system may, or may not, break through to the ground surface. If the faults terminate below the surface, they are described as *blind faults* (Figure 9.13c). Erosion that continues after faulting has ceased may later cause these blind faults to outcrop at the surface. (The specialized term *synorogenic* is applied to the land surface being produced during denudational lowering while tectonic activity is in progress.)

A single blind fault, such as one of those in diagram (c) of Figure 9.13, has its entire fault

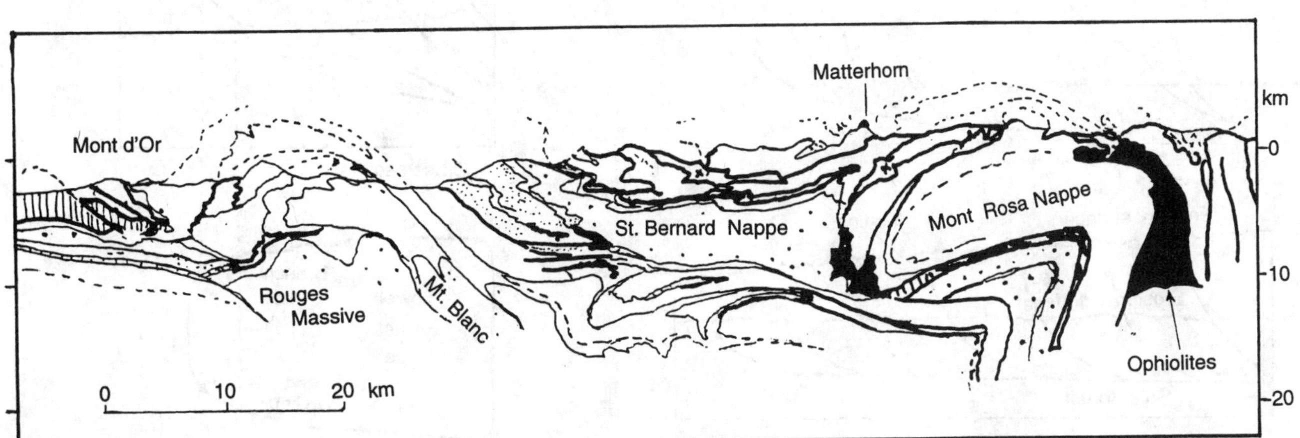

Figure 9.11 Structure section (NW-SE) through large recumbent nappes of the central region of the Western Alps of Europe. (From J. Debelmas, A. Escher, and R. Trumpy, 1983, as presented in Twiss and Moores, 1992, p. 218. Reproduced by permission.)

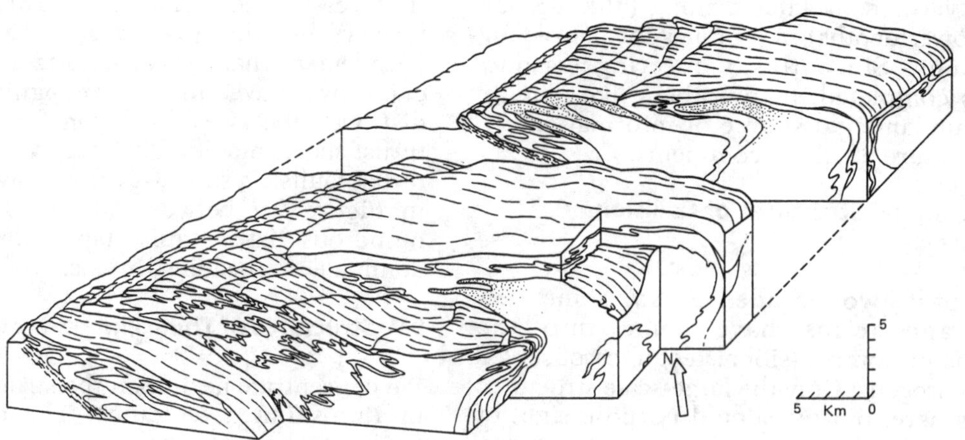

Figure 9.12 Block diagram showing reconstructed recumbent nappes of crystalline metamorphic rocks in the Piedmont region in South Carolina. (From V.S. Griffin, Jr., 1974, *Bull., Geological Society of America*, v. 85, p. 1123, Figure 13. Reproduced with the permission of the publisher, the Geological Society of America, Boulder, Colorado, USA. Copyright © 1974.)

surface intact in the form of a sheet with an irregular perimeter, called the *tip line*, as shown in Figure 9.14. A single thrust sheet in the form of a tapering wedge lies between the two thrusts.

A special composite thrust structure, of limited occurrence, is the double fan structure, illustrated in Figure 9.15. The arrangement of steep overthrusts within a basinlike structure resembles a fully open Japanese fan. The shape is described as "doubly vergent," meaning that the splay thrusts point in opposite directions—right and left—in the two halves of the fan. Two phases of tectonism were involved here. First, there was formed a foreland thrust underlain by a décollement, with eastward vergent splay faults. Second, underthrusting from the west caused regional folding into a basin-form and generated the west-verging splay faults. Thus, two orogenic events were required to produce the fan. The Selkirk Fan, shown in Figure 9.15, is an important tectonic belt some 80 km wide, lying to the west of the Southern Rocky Mountain Trench and extending north from the Canada/US border for about 500 km (Brown, Beaumont, and Willett, 1993). A mechanical model for the tectonics of doubly vergent compressional origins, such as the Selkirk fan, has been described by Sean Willett, Christopher Beaumont, and Phillipe Fullsack, of Dalhousie University in Halifax (1993). They show how the doubly vergent fan resembles mechanically a large accretionary wedge and its forearc basin.

Geophysicists have for long been faced by the long-standing problem of how a thin thrust sheet, propelled by a horizontal force acting from the rear as a ram, can be moved over a basal thrust, or décollement, as a single unit without failing. They have come up with a theory, and it has been tested

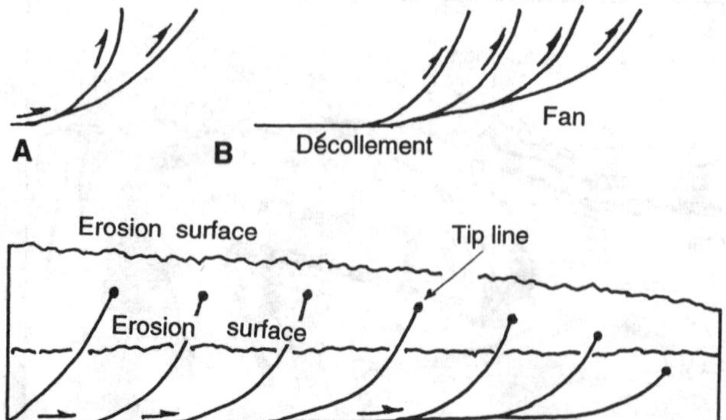

Figure 9.13 Schematic diagram of fan structure in thinskinned thrust faulting. (Copyright © by Arthur N. Strahler.)

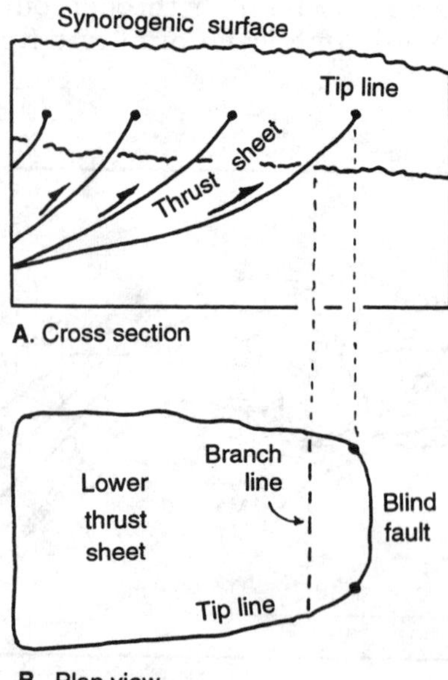

Figure 9.14 Schematic diagram of a thrust sheet in fan structure. (Copyright © by Arthur N. Strahler.)

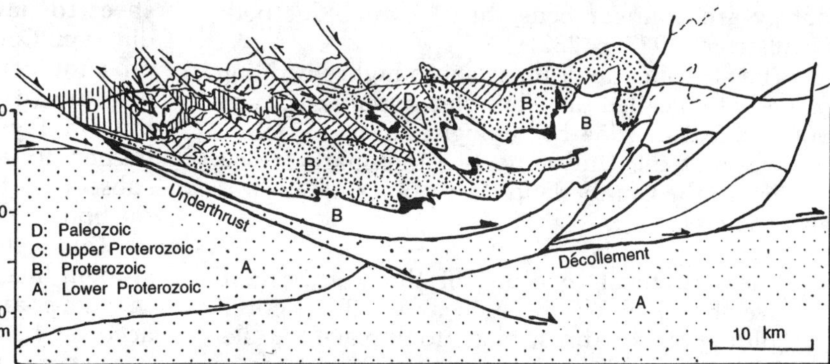

Figure 9.15 Cross section of the Selkirk Fan. (Adapted from R.L. Brown, C. Beaumont, and S.D. Willett, 1993, *Geology*, v. 21, p. 1015. Used by permission of the authors and the Geological Society of America.)

in laboratory sand-box experiments in which compression is applied and the formation of thrust faults observed. The theory they have put forward is the *critical-wedge model* (Chapple, 1978; Woodward, 1987). The thrust sheet is modeled as a uniformly tapered wedge, as shown in Diagram A of Figure 9.16. It has been established that for the wedge to move forward uniformly on the basal fault, the slope of the basal surface of the wedge must be somewhat steeper than its surface slope (topographic slope). In Diagram B, this condition is shown with those slopes having values of 10° and 6° respectively. For the sand-box experiments, the ratio of upper slope to lower slope of 6/10 (0.6) is found to be a critical value. If higher in value, the basal sliding will be continuous; if lower, it will be unstable and the structure will disrupt. Thus the wedge shown in Diagram A would be incapable of moving forward in a stable, continuous manner.

So what does this finding have to do with a foreland thrust sheet advancing during an orogeny? In reality, the thrust wedge advances by the formation of successive splay faults, the most recent of which is the leading splay fault. As this happens the wedge is both shortened and thickened (Woodward, 1987, p. 827). Thickening increases the topographic slope (but not the basal slope) and increases the slope ratio; i.e., increases the taper angle. Thus basal sliding is facilitated.

9.8 Thrusts Controlled by Bedding

We turn now to bedding thrusts that develop initially in flat-lying strata in which thin layers of weak or soft composition lie between strong, massive layers (see Figure 9.7B). Some general principles and rules need to be stated in advance of analyzing this kind of faulting (Dahlstrom, 1977, p. 232). Thrust faulting changes the shape of a rock mass but does not change the volume. In changing the shape, thickness will usually be increased, and consequently the horizontal area will be reduced. Reduction of area is accomplished by telescoping, narrowing the width of the tectonic belt. ("Width" is in the direction of compression, transverse to the strike of the folds.)

Two simple rules apply to areas where a sedimentary layers are relatively undeformed and thrust faulting is strongly influenced by the arrangement of strong and weak layers. (1) Thrusts step up into younger bedding surfaces in the direction the thrust is moving. (2) Thrusts tend to lie parallel to the incompetent layers but oblique to the bedding of competent layers. In "following" these rules, thrusting does not reverse (overturn) the age succession of the strata, except in limited zones where the fault plate is oblique to bedding. Figure 9.17 illustrates how a reversal in age sequence can occur locally by thrusting. The total thickness of the formations is increased by duplication of beds. The thrust faults do not cause beds to be omitted, nor do they thin the beds.

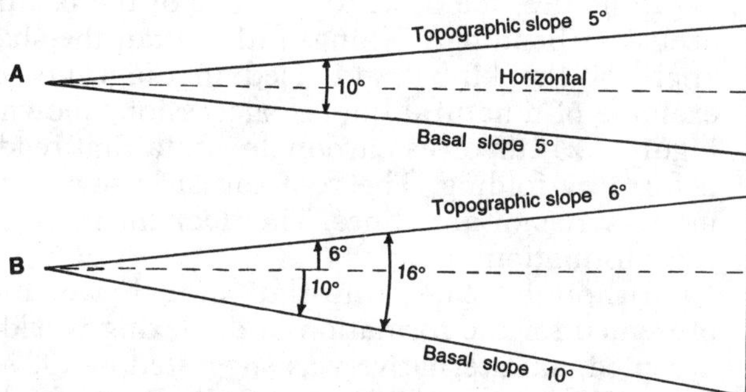

Figure 9.16 A thrust sheet modeled as a uniformly tapered wedge. The angles of topographic slope and basal slope can be varied independently. (Copyright © by Arthur N. Strahler.)

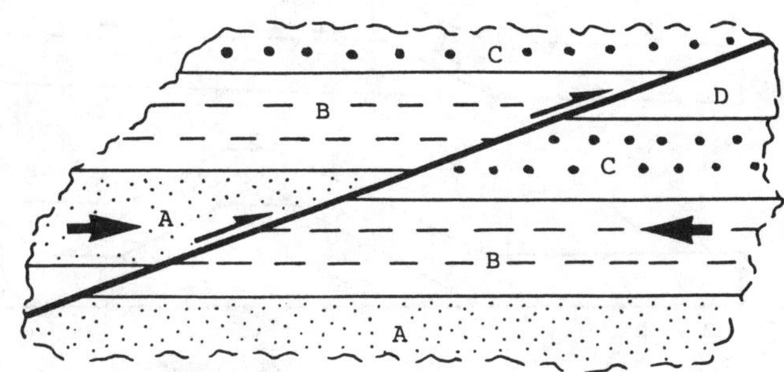

Figure 9.17 Schematic cross section of an overthrust fault, showing age relationships across the fault trace. (Copyright © by Arthur N. Strahler.)

Rarely are younger beds thrust over older beds (Dahlstrom, 1977, p. 232).

The stepping-up of thrusts into higher bedding planes, often called the "stair-step hypothesis," was put forward in 1934 by geologist John L. Rich, a professor at the University of Cincinnati. It was applied to the Cumberland thrust block of Virginia and Tennessee:

> The structural relations of the Cumberland overthrust block are such as would occur if gliding on the thrust plane took place parallel with the bedding along certain shale beds in such a way that the thrust plane followed a lower shale bed for some miles, then sheared diagonally up across the intervening beds to a higher shale, followed that for several miles, and again sheared across the bedding to the surface. (1934, p. 1584)

Figure 9.18 illustrates the stair-stepping, or "staircase," mechanism described by Rich. (a) We start with a single layer of horizontal competent beds (blank areas) lying between two relatively thin incompetent shale beds (parallel bold black lines) which contain the horizontal thrust faults. A slanting dashed line shows where a new thrust fault will form, enabling telescoping to begin. (b). The break causes the formation of a *frontal ramp*, or *riser*, lifting the bed to a new position above its former level. It then levels out, allowing it to slide horizontally over the upper surface. The wedge-shaped leading edge of the lifted bed provides a tapering down-slope. The underside of the wedge is now the hanging wall of the horizontal thrust; the top of the undisturbed bed below is the footwall. Diagram (c) shows the overlying thrust

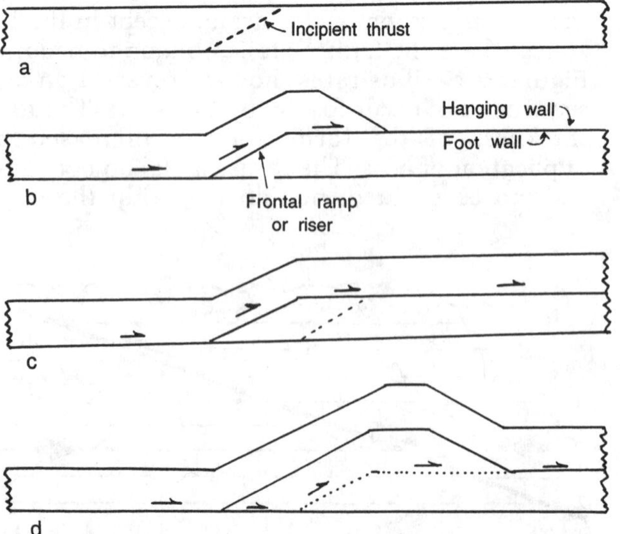

Figure 9.18 Schematic cross sections of the development of a ramp thrust repeated to produce a piggyback anticlinal structure. All lines shown here are thrust faults seen in cross section. (Copyright © by Arthur N. Strahler.)

sheet to have traveled beyond the limit of the diagram. Continuing in the same manner, we mark off another diagonal line for the next thrust. In diagram (d) the second thrust has overriden the bottom layer, lifting the first overthrust even higher to form an anticlinal structure. Thus subsequent thrust sheets are added by insertion at the bottom of the pile.

Our pictorial analysis in Figure 9.18 uses only straight lines, and these change direction abruptly in sharp angles. This stylized treatment is in accord with the principle that the original volume of rock must be retained throughout. Figure 9.19 shows what goes inside the thrust mass to maintain that constancy of volume. It is done by using abrupt changes of shape from orthogonal (right-angle) figures into parallelograms. Sharp angles are used to accomplish this transformation.

As shown in Figure 9.19A, at each sharp angle, or *kink*, an instantaneous deformation of the mass occurs. The two parallel kink lines enclose a *kink band*, and the width of the kink band remains constant (Faill, 1973, p. 1292). The thickness of beds in the kink band remains the same as in the horizontal areas on either side of it, but has been deformed by distributed shear throughout the kink prism, as shown by the parallelogram form of the kink band. Figure 9.19B is a block diagram consisting of two kink bands in geometric opposition to produce an anticlinal structure, i.e., *a conjugate fold*.

Figure 9.20 shows a somewhat different pattern of events in which a doubling of the diagonal kink band is formed and produces a *duplex* (Stage A). A duplex consists of two more-or-less parallel segments of a thrust fault, joined together by a common thrust plane, and enclosed by thrust planes on both sides. On the upper side is the *roof thrust*. On the bottom side is the *floor thrust*, which is the only active thrust plane in the duplex system. In Stage C, the duplexing operation is shown to be repeated. (You might be tempted to call the three diagonal segments a "triplex," but that term is not used.) The duplex structure we have shown here is often referred to as "piggy-backing," a noun not accepted formally as a scientific term, but nevertheless not easy to resist.

In nature, the direction change of the bedding occurs as bending (folding) rather than the sharp angle of the kink band used in diagrams. An example of a natural duplex succession, shown in Figure 9.21, involves carbonate strata that readily deform by folding. The roof thrust is segmented into a series of anticlines. The floor thrust is in a shale formation.

Although the ramp-flat model we have presented for the formation of duplexing is widely accepted, an alternative was suggested in 1987 by Gloria Eisenstadt and Declan G. De Paor of Johns Hopkins University. As shown in Figure 9.22, ramp thrusts are first formed in the competent beds, with minor offsetting. There follows a ripping through the intervening incompetent beds by

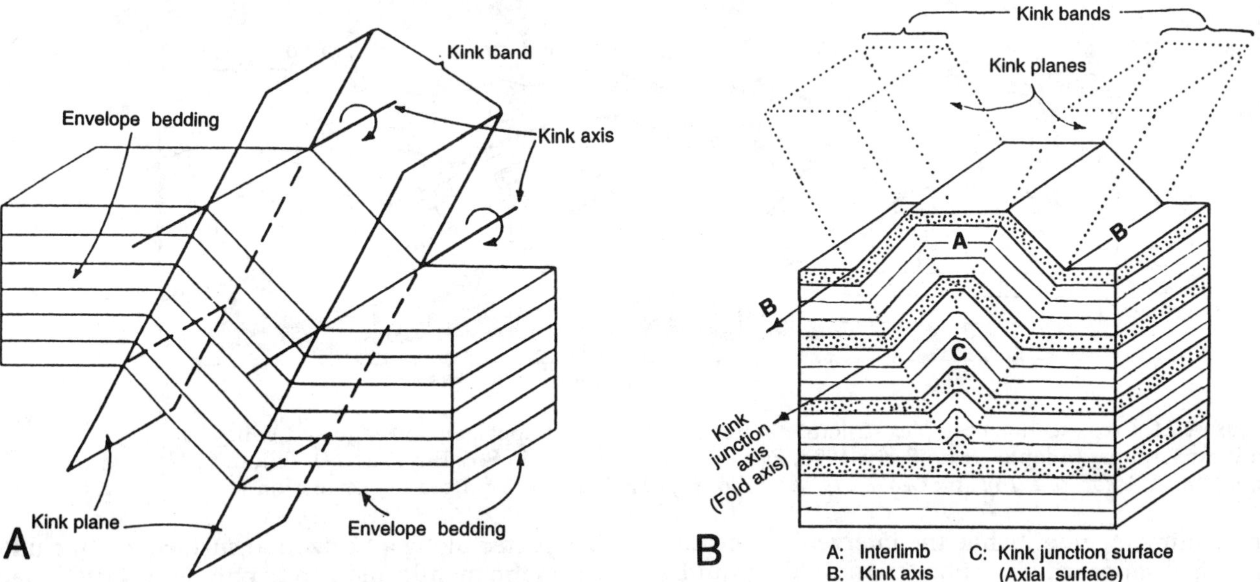

Figure 9.19 (A) A kink band between two segments of undeformed strata. (B) Idealized kink-band fold consisting of two kink bands, inclined toward each other. (From Robert T. Faill, 1973, Bulletin: Geological Society of America, v. 84, p. 1292, Figures 5 and 6. Reproduced with the permission of the publisher, the Geological Society of America, Boulder, Colorado, USA. Copyright © 1973.)

bedding faults growing away from the offsets in opposite directions and meeting in a median location. Rather than a step-by-step process in an orderly succession of growth events moving across the foreland zone in one direction, the newer model suggests a more-or-less simultaneous widespread collapse of strength throughout the entire compressional zone.

9.9 Detachment and Delamination

New ideas about the mechanics of collisions continue to appear, and with them new terms. We next take a brief look at some of the developments that were widely adopted in the 1990s. Conventional plate tectonics has assumed that during a collision of two bodies of continental lithosphere, the descending slab remains intact, eventually reaching the base of the upper mantle. Seismic reflection has, however, shown that descending slabs may experience other fates. Two events may occur: (1) a large section of the descending slab may simply separate and drop off, leaving a "stub" or "stump." This process is called *detachment*. (2) The descending slab splits laterally into two layers, the lower of which bends down to descend, while the upper layer remains horizontal and butts against the opposing plate. This process is called *delamination*.

Figure 9.23 shows how the second kind of detachment is visualized as occurring (Sacks and Secor, 1990, p. 1000). In diagram A, two continents

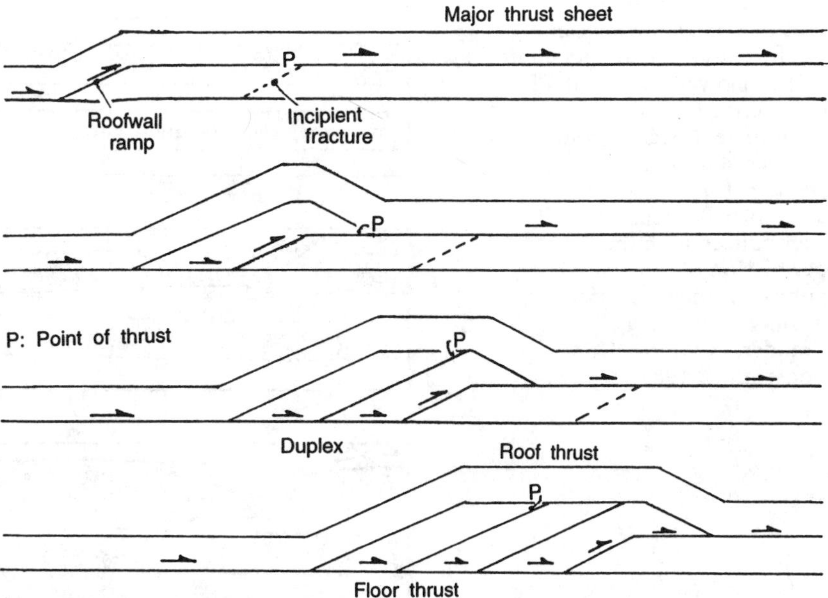

Figure 9.20 Schematic structure sections showing the development of a duplex. (Adapted from S.E. Boyer and D. Elliott, 1982, *Bull., Amer. Assoc. of Petroleum Geologists*, v. 66, no. 9, p. 1208, Figure 19. Reproduced by permission.)

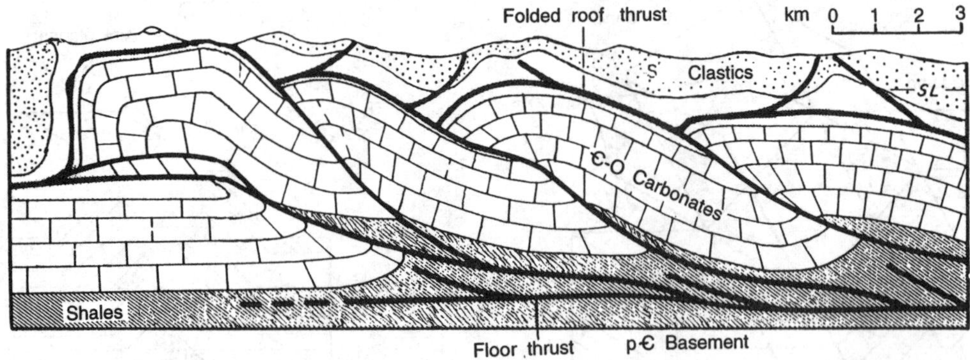

Figure 9.21 Cross section of duplex structure in folds of the central Appalachian Ridge and Valley belt in West Virginia. (Adapted from Perry, 1978, Figure 10, as presented in S.E. Boyer and D. Elliott, 1982, *Bull., Amer. Assoc. of Petroleum Geologists*, v. 66, no. 9, p. 1215, Figure 26. Used by permission.)

are coming together, while the intervening oceanic crust is disappearing by subduction. In diagram B, the continents have almost met. The basaltic oceanic crust is splitting apart from the mantle and is being obducted to lie on top of the continental crust. Below, in the mantle, a phase of stretching (ductile necking) has set in, thinning the mantle and allowing the asthenosphere to rise. In diagram C, the detached oceanic plate has moved far down into the asthenosphere and mantle thinning has continued, allowing the asthenosphere to rise even higher. So the outcome has been to produce an orogen of shallow depth, which is quite unlike the model conventionally used to show collision orogens. Because the hot asthenosphere is now at shallow depth beneath the continental crust, high-temperature metamorphism and the formation of magmas is to be expected.

Delamination, consisting of the peeling away of a layer of lithosphere from the overlying crust, is illustrated in its simplest conceptual form in Diagram B of Figure 9.24. A layer of lithosphere has parted along a horizontal surface that includes the mafic mantle and leaves only felsic crust intact (Nelson, 1992, p. 498). The layer of intact lithosphere sinks down into the asthenosphere. This generates a large vacant area on the cross section and the void is assumed to be filled continuously by rising asthenosphere. Of course, we can imagine that this downbent slab breaks off (becomes a detachment) and sinks deep into the asthenosphere. To make this concept useful it needs to be fitted into a possible collision event. In Diagram C, parting is shown to take place within the lithosphere of Plate A (right). The upper half of the plate has split away, perhaps along the Moho, and has ridden up on a thrust fault, allowing it to slide over the surface of Plate B (Rast, 1989, p. 336). This process has been called *obduction*. [The adjectival form, *obducting*, is sometimes used to refer to the stationary plate that lies over a subducting slab.] In Diagram D, a down-stepping ramp and a décollement are postulated to obtain a doubling of the crust. A similar device has been proposed in connection with the Himalayan/-Tibetan orogenic belt (see Figure 9.51).

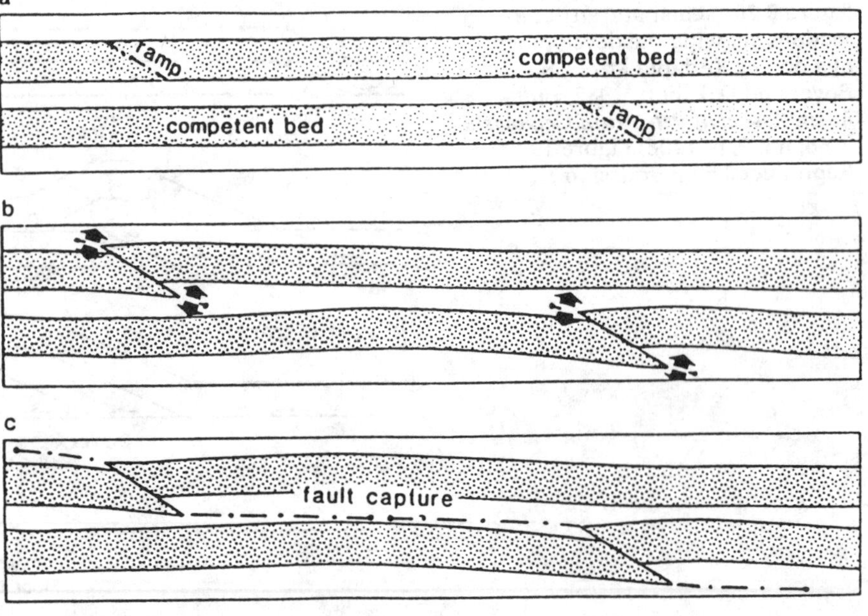

Figure 9.22 Schematic cross section showing ramp flat formation in competent beds, followed by growth of connecting thrusts in incompetent beds. (From G. Eisenstadt and D.G. DePaor, 1987, *Geology*, v. 15, p. 630, Figure 2. Reproduced with the permission of the publisher, the Geological Society of America, Boulder, Colorado, USA. Copyright © 1987.)

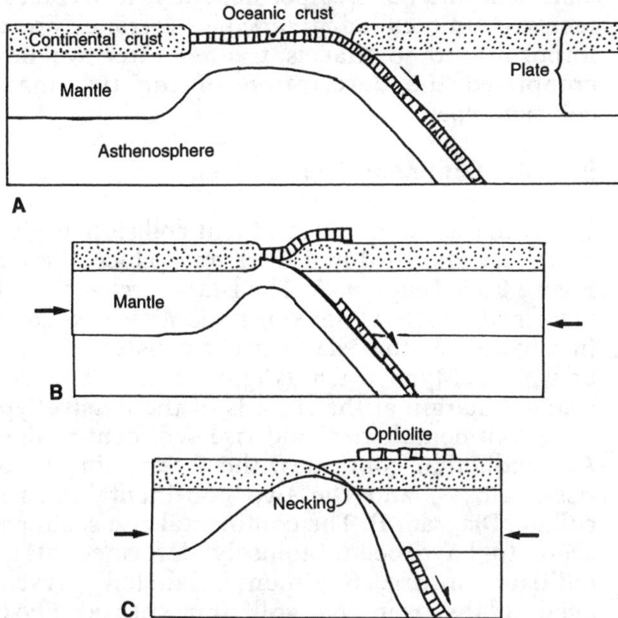

Figure 9.23 Schematic diagrams of the development of a detachment during continent-continent collision. A slab of oceanic crust has been obducted, while the mantle has been thinned by necking. Layers shown are not to scale. (Copyright © by Arthur N. Strahler.)

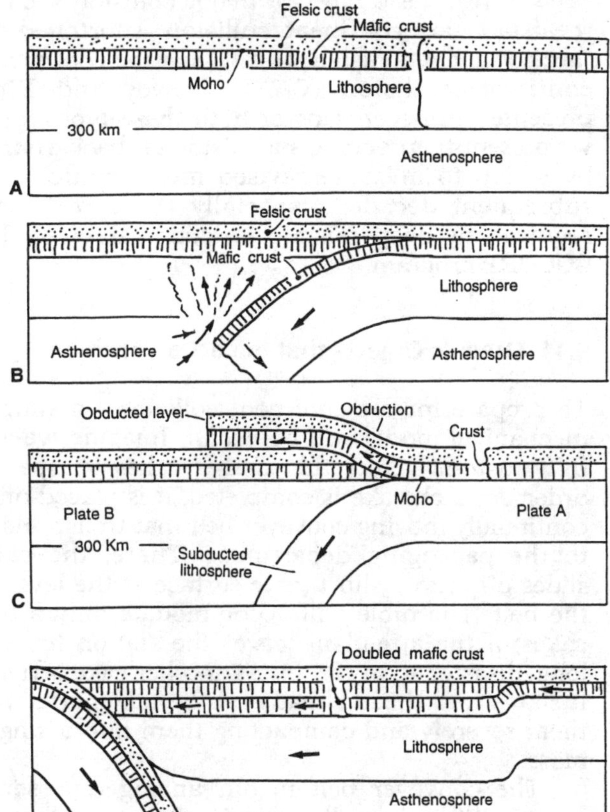

Figure 9.24 Schematic diagrams of possible forms of delamination. (Copyright © by Arthur N. Strahler.)

9.10 Basic Concepts of Collision Tectonics

With our knowledge of the tectonic structures now in place, we consider whole orogens as tectonic units, with particular emphasis on the reconstruction of stages of their development. For a historical review, we turn to a now-classic paper published in 1970, by which time the foundations of plate tectonic were firmly in place. Titled "Mountain Belts and the New Global Tectonics," the paper was authored by John F. Dewey, then of Cambridge University, England, and John M. Bird of the State University of New York at Albany. For their term "mountain belts," we substitute "orogens." This is what they wrote:

> Any attempt to explain the development of orogens must account for the following:
>
> 1. They are long linear/arcuate features.
>
> 2. They have distinctive zones of sedimentary, deformational, and thermal patterns that are, in general, parallel to the belt.
>
> 3. They have a complex internal geometry, with extensive thrusting and mass transport that juxtaposes very dissimilar rock sequences, so that original relationships have been obscured or destroyed.
>
> 4. They have extreme stratal shortening features and, often, extensive crustal shortening features.
>
> 5. They have asymmetric deformational and metamorphic patterns.
>
> 6. They are belts of marked sedimentary composition and thickness changes that are normal to the trend of the belt.
>
> 7. The bulk of the sediments involved are marine.
>
> 8. The basement beneath orogens is dominantly continental, but orogens have zones in which basic and ultrabasic (ophiolitic suite) rocks occur as basement and as upthrust slivers.
>
> 9. They have some sedimentary sequences that were deposited during very long intervals when volcanicity was completely absent in the regions of sedimentation.
>
> 10. Intense deformation and metamorphism is comparatively short-lived when compared with the time during which much of the sedimentary rock of orogens was deposited. (1970, p. 2625)

The two basic types of major collision are (1) the island arc-continent collision, shortened to "arc-continent collision" (A-CC) and the continent-continent collision (C-CC). Dewey and Bird presented full scenarios of both these types, and we present their versions as historical background by which to measure revised interpretations in subsequent decades, especially those revisions required by deep seismic reflection data of the COCORP program.

9.11 Oceanic Objects that Impact a Continent

To prepare for arc-continent collisions, a simple mechanical model will be useful. Imagine we are in a custom bakery that makes cakes on special order. As each cake is completed, it is placed on a continually moving conveyer belt that transports it to the packaging department. There, the cake slides off onto a short table surface at the level of the belt. The table will accommodate only a few cakes; if the attendant leaves the station for too long, disaster soon sets in. As another cake arrives, it slams into those already on the table, crushing them severely and compacting them into a single mass.

The conveyer belt in our analog represents oceanic lithosphere disappearing into a subduction zone. Each cake represents one of several possible crustal features that can project above the otherwise uniform abyssal surface. Small projecting objects, such as seamounts, usually cause no problem; they may be knocked off at the base by impact with the overlying plate to become incorporated into the accretionary wedge, or they may pass down unaltered beneath the accretionary wedge. We have noted earlier that the latter process is now favored. The real problem is with much larger crustal protrusions, too massive and too firmly rooted to be subducted.

What kinds of traveling crustal masses do we have in mind as capable of colliding with a large continental mass and adhering to it? One is the volcanic island arc; for example, the Kuril arc or the Marianas arc. An entirely different class of objects consists of relatively small fragments of continental crust called *microcontinents*. Some of the older island arcs with a long history of accretion qualify as microcontinents—Honshu, the Philippines, or Hispaniola, for example. In other cases a fragment of continent has been pulled away from the mainland on a widening rift that develops into a backarc basin. These islands of continental crust are thus surrounded by oceanic crust.

The objects described above can arrive at the active margin of a large body of continental lithosphere as the oceanic plate which carries them moves toward a subduction boundary. Over millions of years the impacting object can travel thousands of kilometers. As each object—a volcanic arc or a microcontinent—collides with the continent and adheres permanently, it becomes a tectonic unit called a *terrane*. Terranes are an important topic that is treated after we have completed the description of the two major collision types.

9.12 Arc-Continent Collision

The scenario of an arc-continent collision as given by Dewey and Bird in 1970 is reproduced here as Figure 9.25. Diagram A: The island arc, at the left, is formed largely of igneous rock. As we explained in Chapter 5, the island arc consists largely of continental-type crust (Figure 5.33). The continental margin at the right is of the passive type, with continental shelf and rise sediment wedges. As subduction continues, the intervening ocean basin closes, and the two continental masses collide. Diagram B: The continental rise sediments seem to have been intensely deformed at the collision suture. Sediments, labeled "flysch," accumulate over the collision suture. Flysch consists of shale and fine-grained lithic sandstone (graywacke). The shelf wedge (shown as carbonate beds) is tilted and overthrust. However, the inner shelf wedge remains intact and now serves as the foreland; it is deformed into a basin, and is accumulating sediments, labeled "molasse." The words *flysch* and *molasse* are classical European terms, applied in the early years of alpine geology, but continue to be used to refer respectively to pre-orogenic and post-orogenic sediments of terrestrial origin derived from the rising orogen. (See Chapter 11 for more details.) Diagram C: The collision orogen is complete, standing high, while molasse continues to accumulate over the foreland zone. Deep down in the suture the deformed mass has experienced blueschist metamorphism. The lower part of the arc may also have experienced deep metamorphism. Diagram D: At a later time, a new subduction boundary is formed seaward of the former volcanic arc, and we may expect a new accretionary wedge to form.

A more modern version of the arc-continental collision is shown in Figure 9.26. It is essentially a repeat of Figure 1.15, but shows only a cross section. In Diagram A, a mature passive margin is shown at the right. Subduction is occurring along the volcanic arc (at left), narrowing the expanse of oceanic lithosphere separating the two features. The accretionary wedge is growing larger as the volcanic arc increases in size and depth. In Diagram B, the intervening ocean has been completely closed. The accretionary wedge is shown as having been deformed into a doubly vergent fan, but this feature is largely conjuctural. Thrusts slice through the continental margin. As shown in Diagram C, continued compressional impact of the volcanic arc causes the overthrusting to telescope the shelf strata of the passive margin, and to extend a great thinskinned thrust slice far over the continental shield on a décollement located at the interface of the strata and the

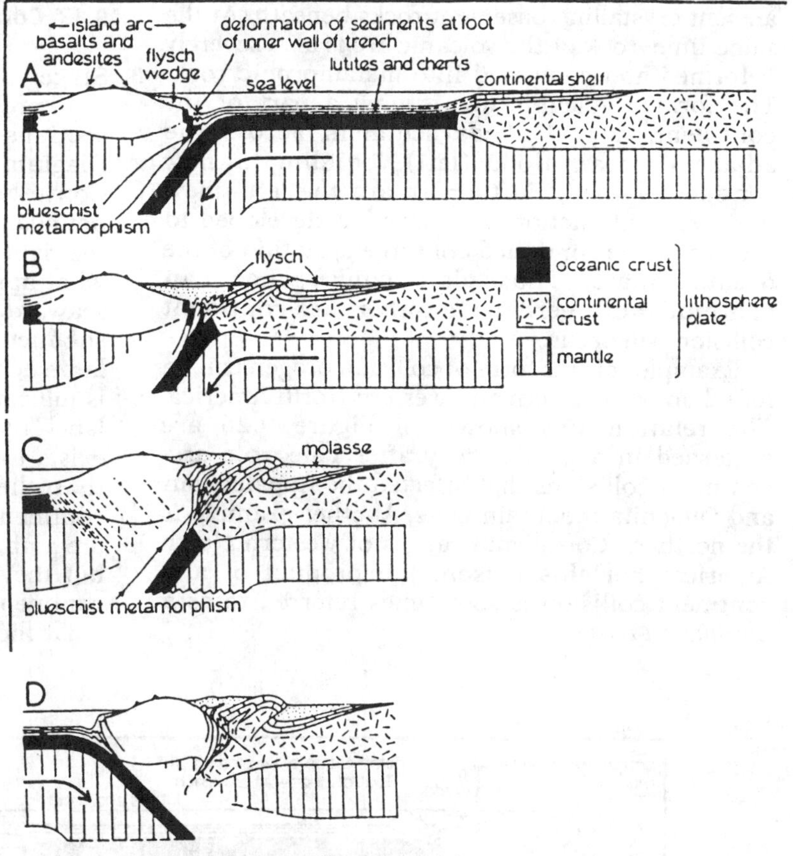

Figure 9.25 Stages in the development of an arc-continent collision. (From J.F. Dewey and J.M. Bird, 1970, p. 2561, Figure 12. Copyright © by the American Geophysical Union. Reproduced by permission.)

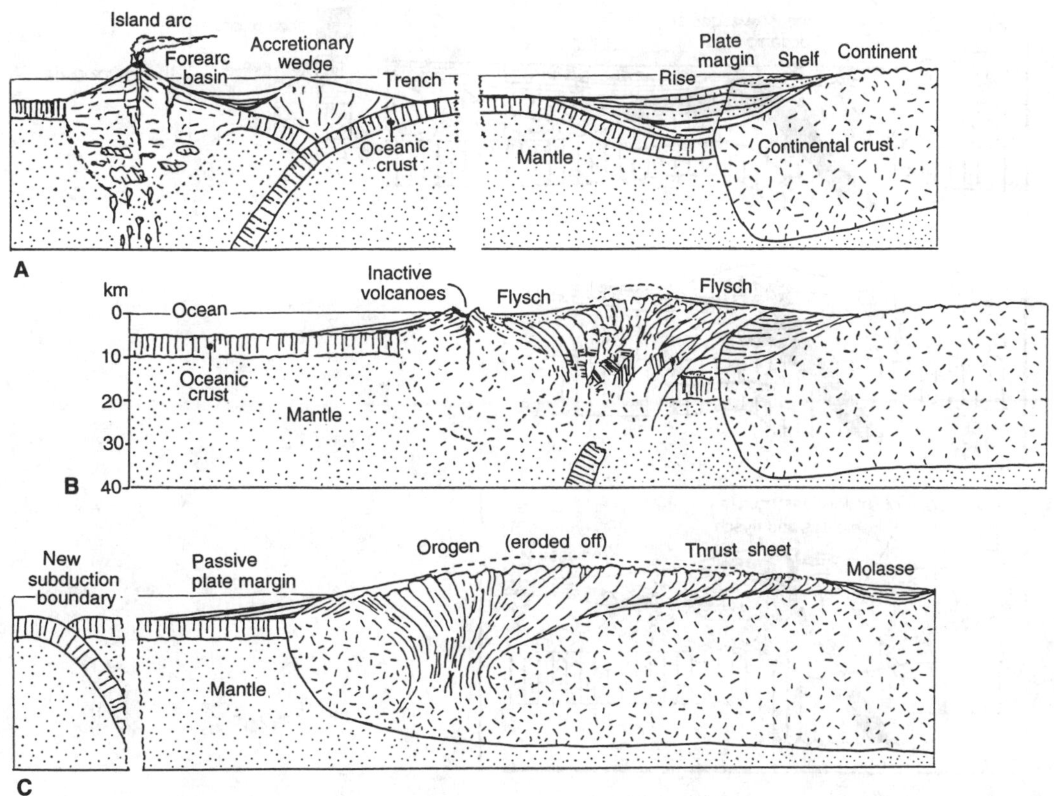

Figure 9.26 Development of an orogen during an arc-continent collision. The deep thrust structures are largely conjectural. (Copyright © by Arthur N. Strahler.)

ancient crystalline basement rocks beneath. At the same time, rock of the volcanic arc is also severely deformed and converted into metamorphic rock. The former volcanic arc is now a part of the continent, and it sheds sediment across the adjacent ocean floor (left), building a new continental shelf. Further toward the left, new midocean subduction boundary has developed to accommodate continued convergent motion of the oceanic plate. Thus plate convergence can continue and perhaps another arc-continent collision will occur.

Examples of this form of collision orogen can be found on both eastern and western North America. The relationships shown in Figure 9.26 are patterned in a general way after Paleozoic arc-continent collisions that affected the Appalachian and Ouachita mountain belts. Another example is the northern Cordilleran ranges of western North America. For this reason, the product of arc-continent collision is sometimes referred to as a *Cordilleran-type orogen*.

9.13 Continent-Continent Collision

Stages in the collision of two major continents were presented by Dewey and Bird in a set of cross sections, reproduced here as Figure 9.27. In Diagram A, final closing of an ocean is imminent. Convergence is made possible by a subduction boundary (at left). The mature passive margin at the right has a well developed continental shelf and what appears to be a continental rise continuing seaward as a thick layer of pelagic sediments. The subducting plate seems not to have developed a large accretionary wedge, but crumpled sediment is indicated beneath the bottom of the trench. The label "flysch wedge" is puzzling, as no high orogen exists to supply sediment to it. We may suppose that the sediment wedge shown is simply a continental shelf. Dewey and Bird (1970, p. 2642) are ambiguous in their description of this margin, but they note that the same setup as for an arc-continent collision can be used and, indeed, that is what they have done here (see Figure 9.25). Only

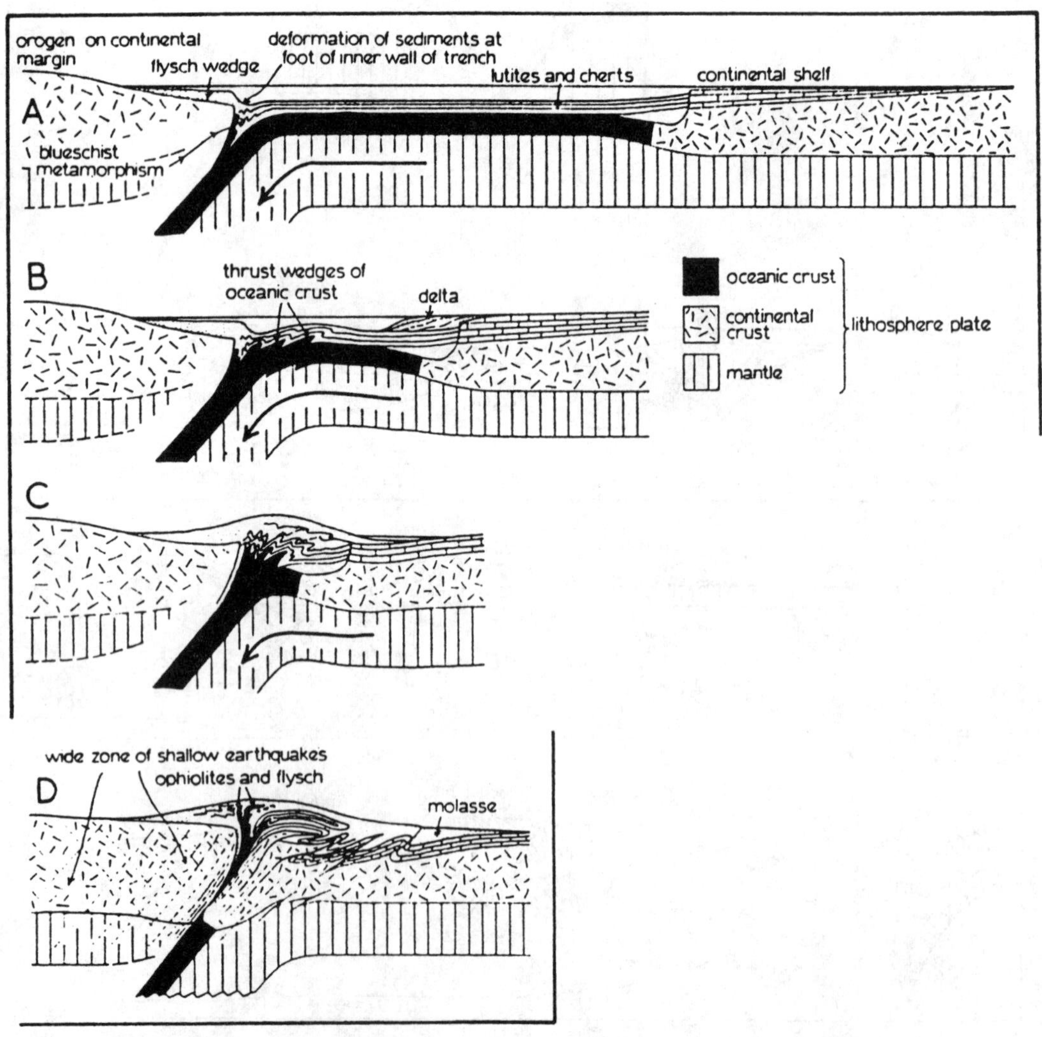

Figure 9.27 Stages in the development of a continent-continent collision. (From J.F. Dewey and J.M. Bird, 1970, p. 2642, Figure 13. Copyright © by the American Geophysical Union. Reproduced by permission.)

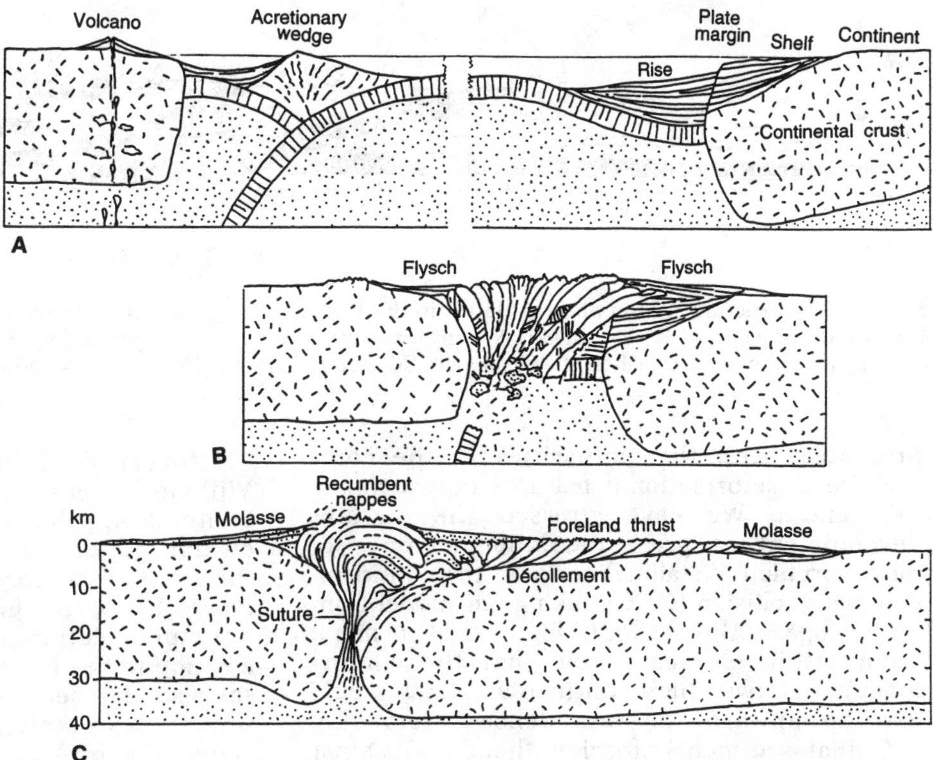

Figure 9.28 Development of an orogen during a continent-continent collision. The deep thrust structures are largely conjectural. (Copyright © by Arthur N. Strahler.)

the bodies lying left of the subduction slab are different. In Diagram B, collision has begun, with thrust wedges of oceanic crust being produced. In Diagram C, all of the intervening oceanic crust with its pelagic cover has been compressed into great pile of recumbent nappes of the type we illustrated in Figure 9.11. A wedge of flysch has been built, topping the orogen. In Diagram D, collision is complete, with continental crust from both plates in close contact and having squeezed the oceanic crust upward and outward, where it forms ophiolites within the orogen. Foreland thrusts have sliced the continental margin and its shelf strata and, finally, molasse has buried the foreland thrusts.

A somewhat different and perhaps more modern version of the continent-continent collision is shown in Figure 9.28. It takes into account more recent information on the tectonic styles found in collisions. The diagrams are similar in general form to those shown in Figure 1.16. Stage A shows two continents converging. As the ocean between the converging continents narrows, a succession of overthrust faults cuts through the oceanic crust (Stage B). The thrust slices ride up, one over the next, in an imbricate pattern, in age order from bottom to top. As the slices become more and more tightly squeezed between the converging continental plate masses, they are forced upward. The upper part of each thrust sheet, under the force of gravity, bends over to a horizontal position to form a nappe. The final nappes in the series consist in part of the slices of oceanic crust. (The structures shown here in Stage B are largely conjectural, since they are later modified into the recumbent nappes shown in Stage C.)

As you recall from Chapter 5, the oceanic crust sequence formed at a spreading plate boundary is an ophiolite suite, with rocks ranging from ultramafic peridotite at the base to mafic basalt dikes and lavas at the top. When a slice of this oceanic crust is carried up and squeezed to form a nappe, it is metamorphosed into a rock known as an *ophiolite*. It is now generally agreed that a narrow zone of outcropping ophiolites in some cases marks the line of a continental suture. Ophiolites are found at intervals along the entire collision boundary of southern Eurasia.

Continual erosion by streams and glaciers reduces the upper surfaces of the rising pile of nappes. This process is called *unroofing*. This sediment is swept to lower levels, accumulates as a flysch that may become involved in later stages of overthrusting and may be incorporated into younger nappes. As the collision reaches its final stage, a high-standing mountain mass results and the marginal ocean basin disappears. At this time, the sediment produced by land erosion becomes coarser in texture and accumulates as a thick wedge of molasse adjacent to the new mountain mass. The molasse is deposited on an exposed land surface or in very shallow coastal water as expanding deltas.

9.14 Deformational Styles of Collision Orogens

Judging from our diagrams of the two kinds of collisions, whether we are comparing those of Dewey and Bird (1970) or the newer ones

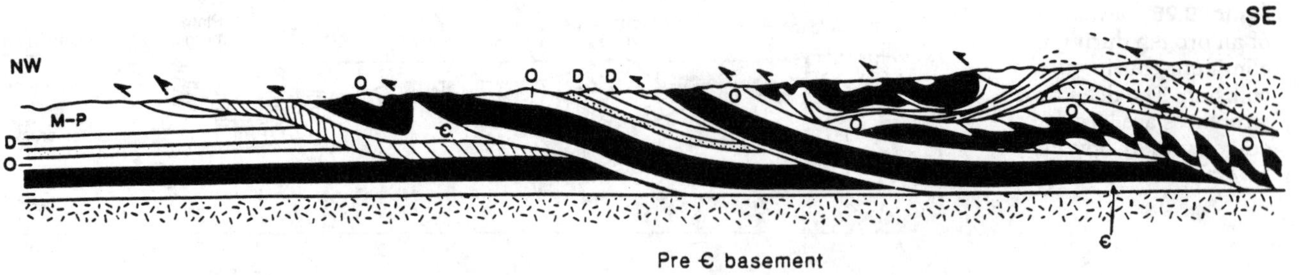

Figure 9.29 Structure section of thrust faults in the Tennessee-Virginia section of the Appalachian Valley and Ridge province. (From N.B. Woodward, 1987, *Bull., G.S.A.*, v. 99, p. 830. Reproduced with the permission of the publisher, the Geological Society of America, Boulder, Colorado, USA. Copyright © 1987.)

presented here, the similarities in the compressional deformational features outweigh the differences. We have stressed the massive development of great recumbent nappes of metamorphic (crystalline) rocks in the continent-continent collision (C-CC), taking our model from the European Alps shown in Figure 9.11. It might seem intuitively reasonable that the coming together of two thick continental plates would extrude upward the less dense intervening marginal sediments, forcing them up against gravity in a growing pile that would rise faster than it could spread out laterally. The thin foreland thrust sheets are shown as essentially alike in form in both collision types. Foreland thrusts of the Canadian Cordilleran belt, shown in Figure 9.10 resemble those of the central Appalachians, shown in Figure 9.29. Thrusts of the latter are largely the product of the Alleghanian Orogeny, a C-CC that closed the Paleozoic Era. Figure 9.30 is a schematic diagram of overthrusts of the southern Appalachians showing at the right older thrusts of the Taconian and Acadian arc-continent collisions, and at the left, those of the terminal Alleghanian orogeny. The sole thrust, or décollement, which lies deep in Precambrian crystalline rocks of the Piedmont, climbs stepwise into progressively younger stratigraphic horizons toward the west. This final telescoping also carried the Acadian and Taconian thrust sheets with it, piggyback style.

Robert B. Hatcher, Jr., and Richard T. Williams, whose extensive field work in the Southern Appalachians qualifies them as experts on this subject, have summarized differences in the styles of compressional structure in the two types of orogens. Figure 9.31 is their composite structure section drawn to show what they envision to be an "idealized orogen" (1986, p. 977; see also Hatcher, 1983, Figure 2). Not all of the several major structural elements shown (labeled across the top) are to be found in any single orogen, but some will be present in all. The model, they state, "is assumed to involve a complete Wilson cycle of opening and closing of an ocean through both transform and head-on accretion of outboard elements, then completion of the cycle through continent-continent collision." The expression "outboard element" refers to A-CCs and other collision events involving relatively small masses of continental or semicontinental lithosphere whose crust rises too high to pass beneath the subducted plate. Keep in mind that this diagram shows erosion to have already removed substantial amounts of the upper parts of the orogen. The surface profile is thus typical of high mountain belts of strong topographic relief, often deeply carved by alpine glaciers.

An important distinction is to be made between crystalline thrust sheets—made up of igneous and metamorphic rocks—and non-

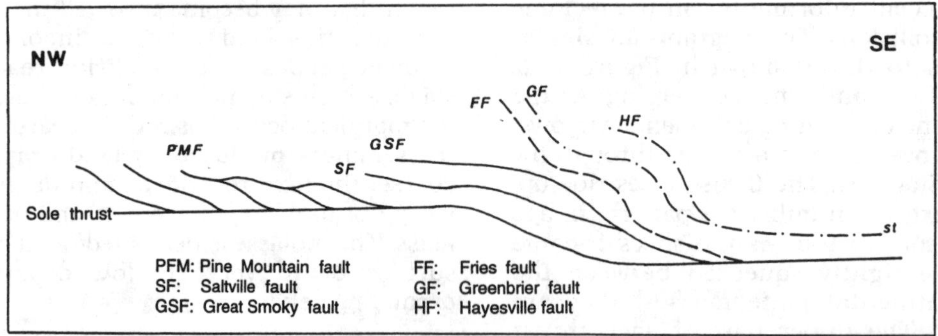

Figure 9.30 Schematic diagram of the stacking of overthrusts in the southern Appalachians. Acadian faults are in dashed lines; Taconian and Penobscottian in dot-dash. (From N. Rast, 1989, p. 339. Reproduced with the permission of the publisher, the Geological Society of America, Boulder, Colorado, USA. Copyright © 1989.)

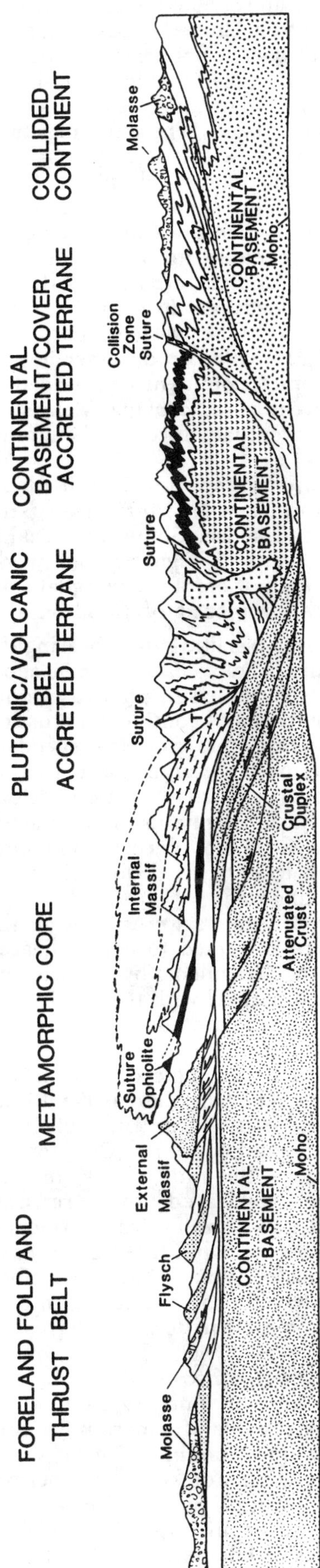

Figure 9.31 Structure section of an idealized orogen. (From R.D. Hatcher, Jr., and R.T. Williams, 1986, *Bull. GSA*, v. 97, p. 977, Figure 1. Reproduced with the permission of the publisher, the Geological Society of America, Boulder, Colorado, USA. Copyright © 1986.)

crystalline thrust sheets formed from platform sedimentary rocks. In Figure 9.31, these classes are labeled "metamorphic core" and "foreland fold and thrust belt," respectively. Ophiolites, shown in solid black, would be largely limited to C-CCs. The "plutonic/volcanic belt; accreted terrane" would apply to the A-CCs.

Perhaps the most important fundamental difference between arc-continent and continent-continent collisions lies in the outcome and future of each. In terms of the Wilson Cycle, the A-CC may be only one in a succession of such events that leave the ocean basin open, whereas for the C-CC it is the terminal event in the life of the ocean basin, locking the continents together in a strong suture that may endure for eons.

Examples of continent-continent collisions in final stages are represented by the plate boundary between Eurasia and the African, Arabian, and Indian plates. Examples of arc-continent collisions in action are not easy to find, but one good example is cited from Papaua, New Guinea, and another in the Banda arc of western New-Guinea (McCafferey and Abers, 1991, Abers and McCafferry, 1994).

9.15 Transpression on Transcurrent Faults

So far, we have assumed that the plate boundary is "straight," in the sense of being an arc of a great circle, whereas we know that subduction boundaries tend to form curved arcs. We have also presented collisions as if they involve only convergence in a direction normal to the plate boundary. Now we will look at collision boundaries in terms of their longitudinal extent and form.

Figure 9.32 is a schematic map showing that Plate B is converging with Plate A at an oblique angle. At the same time, transcurrent (strike-slip) faults are slicing diagonally across the foreland

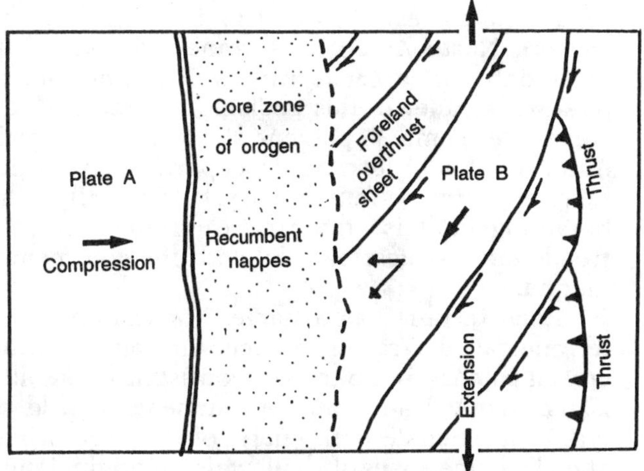

Figure 9.32 Schematic map of transpression within a foreland thrust sheet. (Copyright © by Arthur N. Strahler.)

thrust sheet. This same situation is commonly found near the ends of a curved subduction arc—for example near the western end of the Aleutian arc. The transcurrent faults affect only the thrust sheet, above the décollement. Viewed as a unit in itself, the foreland thrust sheet is undergoing longitudinal extension on an axis parallel with the orogen (Oldow et al., 1991; Oldow et al., 1993). This form of longitudinal extension combined with compression is called *transpression*. It tends to narrow the foreland thrust belt, and its effect might be sufficiently potent to offset to a large extent the forward movement and widening of the thrust sheet.

Transpression also applies to a strike-slip fault that forms a boundary between two continental plates. This feature is described in Chapter 6 as a continental transform boundary. Examples given included the San Andreas fault of California and the Alpine fault of the South Island of New Zealand. The latter fault combines the strike-slip motion with strong reverse-fault motion. The reverse-fault motion has allowed a collisional orogen to be formed; it is a young mountain range known as the Southern Alps (see Chapter 6 and Figure 6.32).

9.16 Continental Accretion of Microcontinents and Terranes

Geologists who were involved in mapping the bedrock of western North America from Mexico to Alaska came to recognize that over a zone extending inland from the Pacific coastline some 200 to 600 km it consists of a strange mosaic of crustal patches, which they called *terranes*. [Spelled "terrains" in British publications.] A particular terrane is quite distinct geologically from those that surround it, in that it has its own special rock type or suite of component rock types. If we think of this assemblage of terranes as a mosaic of tiles, we see that whereas many of the tiles are unique, others are duplicated in widely separated places. Figure 9.33 is a map of the western North American terranes, simplified to show only the larger terrane units. There are at least 50 terranes in this geologic province, which constitutes some 30 percent of continental North America. Each terrane is separated from its neighbors by a fault contact. Typically, the bounding fault is of the transcurrent type and trends more or less parallel with the continental margin.

Each terrane has a name. For example, the terrane called Wrangellia occurs in four separate crustal patches. It is a terrane consisting of basaltic island—arc volcanics and of sedimentary rocks of types that include both cherts of deep-sea origin and algal limestones of shallow-depth origin. Using paleomagnetic methods (Chapter 10), geologists sought to establish the original global location of several of the terranes. Much to their surprise, Wrangellia was calculated to have come from a location at lat. 10°S and as far distant as a spot equivalent to where New Guinea is now located—traveling since then a distance of nearly 10,000 km! It was found to have occupied that location during Triassic time, when a 3-km thickness of basaltic island-arc lavas accumulated. (These findings have since been revised.)

Obviously, a terrane can travel only by being carried along with the lithospheric plate in which it is embedded. The fragments of continental crust were embedded in oceanic lithosphere, which moved toward North America, eventually bringing each fragment to a location close to the active subduction boundary at the western margin of North America. Here a collision of lesser impact took place and the microcontinent was welded to the continent, an event called *docking*. Many such impacts took place, eventually forming the mosaic of terranes.

Each of the many terranes now identified can be regarded as a former *microcontinent*—using that term in a broad sense. Some are oceanic plateaus. Refer to Chapter 5, Figure 5.28, a world map showing the distribution of oceanic plateaus, most of which are composed of flood-basalts. Some are long, narrow basaltic ridges bearing the volcanic island chains. Figures 5.29 and 5.30 show evidence that most of the basalt plateaus would qualify as being composed of continental crust on the basis of their thickness and the speed of seismic waves that pass through them. In that sense, the term "microcontinent" is permissible. Along with more typical fragments of continental crust, they belong to a class of objects too massive and rising too high to be carried down into the mantle on a subducting slab.

Once the microcontinents were added to the continent, they were subjected to being sheared into two or more small fragments by transcurrent faults trending about parallel with the continental margin. Faults of this type are induced to form in continental crust when the subducting lithospheric plate is approaching at an angle oblique to the subduction boundary. The San Andreas Fault is an example of this type of transcurrent fault, now acting as a transform boundary (Chapter 6.) Dragged along within the fault slices, terrane fragments become separated and are now distributed up and down the entire continental marginal zone. This is what seems to have happened in the case of Wrangellia. It has since been recognized that the accretion of micro-continents to form a mosaic pattern may have also been one of the modes by which the complex Precambrian shields were constructed.

Whether the arrival and impact of a microcontinent was capable of generating a full-blown orogeny is questionable. For a small microcontinent, a few tens of kilometers across, the tectonic effect would perhaps have been localized. In the case of an impacting volcanic island arc thousands of kilometers long, a major orogeny would have ensued, strongly affecting

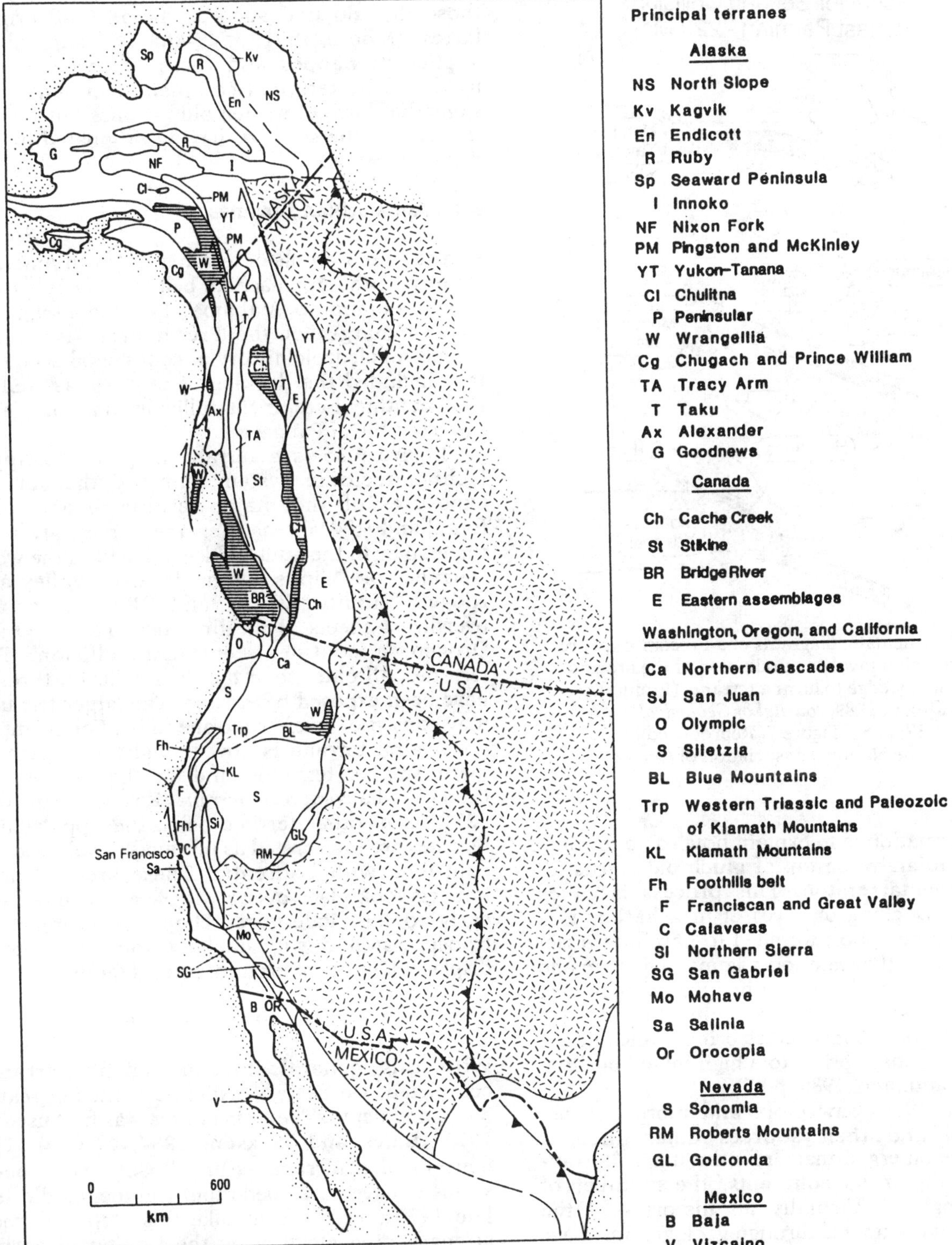

Figure 9.33 Map of terranes of western North America. Fragments of the Wrangellia and Cache Creek terranes, thought to be examples of former oceanic plateaus, are emphasized by a horizontal line pattern. (From Ben-Avraham, Nur, Jones, and Cox, 1981, *Science*, v. 213, p. 53, Figure 7. Copyright © 1981 by the American Association for the Advancement of Science. Used by permission.)

thousands of kilometers length of the continental margin. A phenomenon of this magnitude seems quite distinct from the repeated impacts of many microcontinents. However, modern practice has been to include impacting volcanic arcs as terranes, along with the lesser crustal fragments. For example, the Franciscan complex, composed of mélanges, and its adjoining Great Valley sedimentary sequence (explained in Chapter 8 and shown in Figure 8.33) are together recognized as a terrane on our map, Figure 9.33.

A real problem in our leading hypothesis of

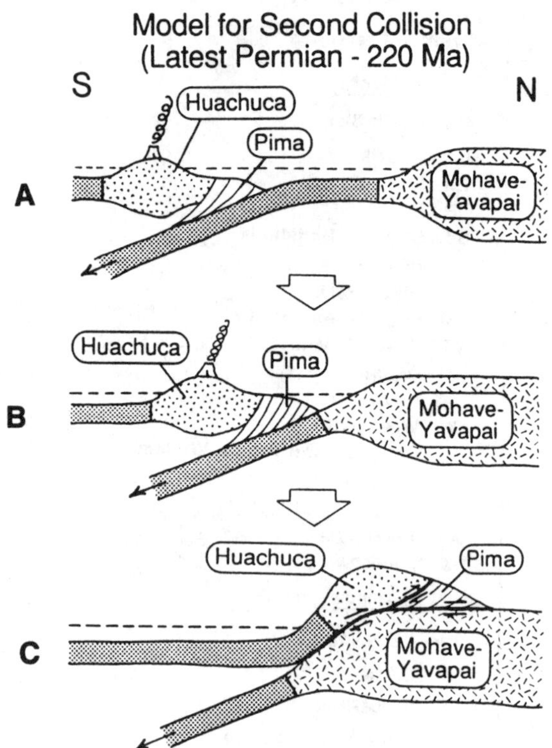

Figure 9.34 Schematic diagrams of a Precambrian arc-continent collision involving obduction of the arc and its accretionary wedge to form a terrane. (From Bykerk-Kauffman, 1989, *Journal of Geological Education*, v. 37, p. 87, Figure 7. Reproduced by permission of the National Association of Geology Teachers.)

terrane formation is to explain how some terranes managed to arrive on top of much older crust of the continental craton. This process is called *obduction*. Docking of a vessel in a harbor is a misleading metaphor; we need to have our vessel dragged out of the water on a launching ramp and pushed inland to high ground! Figure 9.34 is a schematic diagram of an arc-continent collision in which obduction is invoked to bring a volcanic arc and it accretionary prism to a high inland position (Bykerk-Kaufmann, 1989, p.87).

As the 1980s saw more and more terranes identified and their sources determined, a subscience emerged that drew the name "terranology"; and for its adherents, the moniker of "terranologists." Virtually all histories of the assembly of continents through geologic time have become exercises in terranology. (For a recent textbook of terranology, see David G. Howell, 1989.) There are, of course, some detractors who are less enthusiastic and not fully convinced that all tectonic structures are explained by terranology. Among those who advise caution in the assignment of a terrane status to every tectonostratigraphic unit in an orogen is George W. Moore of Oregon State University. He cites Celal Sengor as stressing "that a strong distinction should be made between those terranes that possess true structures along with a lithospheric basement, and those that do not, such as nappes and crustal flakes" (Moore, 1991, p. 45-46). This admonition applies to nappes and foreland thrust sheets produced by terminal continent-continent collisions that have overriden old terranes but are not terranes in the sense of having originated in far-distant locations.

9.17 Appalachian Terranes

As a second example of terranes of North America, we turn to the Appalachian belt that extends from Newfoundland to Alabama. Located along the eastern margin of the Precambrian craton, it reveals a Paleozoic history of continental accretion that included the docking of terranes as well as final continent-continent collision that completed the assembly of Pangaea.

Figure 9.35 is a terrane map of the Appalachian tectonic system showing the surface exposures of the major terranes from Newfoundland to Alabama. Terrane names, given on the map or in the attached legend, end in the word "terrane" or "klippe." Areas labeled "Valley and Ridge," "Humber Zone," and "Blue Ridge" are overthrust sheets of the final terminal Alleghany Orogen, a continent-continent collision. The terranes, all older than the final collision thrusts, have been exposed by erosion. The larger terranes may consist of smaller terrane units. For example, the Avalon terrane is now thought to consist of many smaller terranes, and for that reason has been called a *composite terrane* (Rast, 1989, p. 326-327). As in other terrane belts, the Appalachian terranes are interpreted as products of volcanic-arc collisions with Laurentia. These arc-continent impacts took place over a wide span of time from early to late Paleozoic. They were subject to transpression during docking and later lateral displacement by major transcurrent faults.

9.18 Criteria for Identifying Terranes

With this general introduction to terranes completed, we need to examine them in greater detail and depth. The term *terrane* was first used in 1972 (Bates and Jackson, 1987, p. 679). The concept of a terrane as an allochthonous body seems to have developed rapidly in the middle and late 1970s. Pressure to take this step had been strengthening steadily by the finding of earlier complex orogenic structures located landward of the great Andean-type subduction boundaries of North, Central, and South America (Kearey and Vine, 1990, p. 203). This relationship seemed puzzling because these continental subduction boundaries had been active more or less continually for many tens of millions of years, and this kind of steady subduction does not produce orogens. However, as we explained earlier, an arc-continent collision is a brief event, leaving its record in an orogen adhering to the continent, but soon followed by a return to the subduction mode.

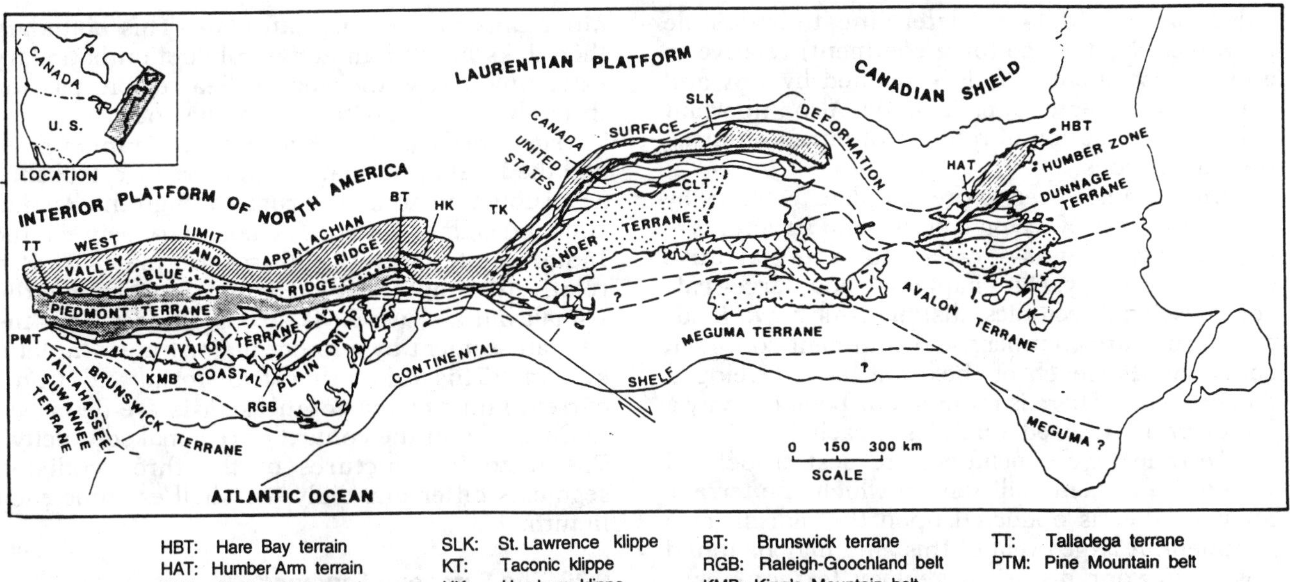

Figure 9.35 Terrane map of the Appalachian belt of eastern North America. (From N. Rast, 1989, p. 327, Figure 4. Data mainly after Williams and Hatcher, 1983. *The Geology of North America*, Chap 12. Reproduced with the permission of the publisher, the Geological Society of America, Boulder, Colorado, USA. Copyright © 1989.)

The "suspicion" that this mosaic of elongate, crustal slivers was somehow formed from allochthonous orogens plastered onto the continent led to the use of the name *suspect terranes*. The alternative terms *exotic terranes* and *displaced terranes* also came into use. The tectonic process of accumulation was referred to by such terms as *accretionary tectonics* and *mosaic tectonics*.

A formal definition of "terrane" might be given as follows: A fault-bounded, mapable crustal unit having a different geological history from those of contiguous units (Jones et al., 1983). Terranes may be bounded by transcurrent (wrench) faults, reverse faults, or normal faults, although the first of these is fundamentally the mode by which terranes are shaped and distributed. Among the lithologies commonly found in a terrane are thin ophiolites originating in oceanic crust, blueschist originating in accretionary wedges, and highly deformed flysch (Kearey and Vine, 1990, p. 203).

In actual practice, one or more of the following categories of information will often prove useful in identifying individual terranes (Shermer et al., 1984, as stated by Kearey and Vine, 1990, p. 203):

1. Stratigraphy and sedimentary history.
2. Petrogenetic affinity and magmatic history.
3. Nature, history, and style of deformation.
4. Paleontology and paleoenvironments.
5. Paleopole position and paleodeclination.

Four major types of terrane in western North America have been recognized by R.W. Simpson and A. Cox (1987). The following version of that classification is paraphrased from Kearey and Vine (1990, p. 203-204):

1. Stratigraphic terranes, characterized by the following distinct stratigraphies:

   (a) Continental fragments containing land-derived sediments, perhaps with a crystalline basement.
   (b) Oceanic fragments, containing lithologies typical of oceanic crust and sometimes overlain by sedimentary sequences that reveal travel from deep ocean to shallower continental margin environments.
   (c) Island-arc fragments containing intrusive and extrusive igneous rocks and volcanogenic sediments.

2. Disrupted terranes that contain a heterogeneous assembly of flysch, serpentinite, shallow water limestone and graywacke, with some exotic blocks of metamorphic blueschist.

3. Metamorphic terranes in which metamorphism has destroyed the original stratigraphy.

4. Composite terranes. The terrane is formed of two or more sub-terranes, amalgamated prior to accretion to the continent.

The method of using paleomagnetic poles to track the paths of lithospheric plates, now applied to terranes carried along by moving oceanic plates, was developed even prior to the arrival of modern plate tectonics. This is a subject we develop in Chapter 13, where it is applied to the history of breakup of Pangaea. The subject of use of paleomagnetic data to determine the possible positions of a terrane (or a continent) relative to another continent is fully explained by Cox and Hart (1986, Chapter 9, p. 326-331). Also important is the determination of rotation of terranes during their migrations.

Our plan has been to present plate tectonics by classes or types of tectonic events and structures— by subjects, that is— rather than as narrative historical geology. Our chapter is about large-scale compressional tectonics, distinguishing two kinds of orogens: arc-continent and continent-continent collisions. For each of these we have developed model events. There is room in our book for only a few carefully selected examples of each.

Terranes, we concluded, are best associated with arc-continent collisions in which one terrane after another is obducted upon the margin of a continent. A large event of this kind may be found posted in your historical geology textbook as a separate orogeny. Our two examples of belts of accreted terranes comprising highly complex orogen systems are the Appalachian system and the western North American (Cordilleran) system. The former is the older (Paleozoic); the latter, the younger (Mesozoic/Cenozoic). The Appalachian orogenies terminated in a final continent-continent collision, whereas the western continental margin remains active, with no termination in sight. So we must look elsewhere for examples of a great terminal collision of recent date and still tectonically active after the suturing occurred. There is only a limited choice of examples and they lie in the zone between the African, Arabian, and Indian plates as a group and the great Eurasian plate that borders them on the north.

9.19 The European/Persian/Himalayan Collision System

Continental collision has occurred in the Cenozoic Era along a great tectonic zone that marks the southern boundary of the Eurasian plate (Figure 9.36). Here we are dealing with three collision segments: European, Persian, and Himalayan. Each segment represents the collision of a different north-moving plate against the relatively immobile Eurasian plate. Depicted on small generalized world tectonic maps, such as our Figure 1.11, this entire zone is usually reduced to a single-line plate boundary between the African, Arabian, and Indian plates and the Eurasian plate. For simplicity, but giving a highly erroneous impression, the boundary between Eurasian and African plates is typically run through the Straits of Gibraltar, carried due east through the Mediterranean Sea, skirting the Italian boot and crossing the Aegean Sea to follow the southern coastline of Turkey.

On our world plate map, Figure 7.3, this boundary is depicted in more detail, but also arbitrarily in some places. A collision suture is shown across North Africa, placing the Atlas Mountains in the Eurasian plate. This boundary then links in with an active subduction boundary extending across the Aegean Sea region, passing through Crete, and following the south coast of Turkey. The boundary between the Arabian plate and the Persian subplate is quite easily established as a subuction zone that runs through the Persian Gulf and Gulf of Oman. The boundary between the Indian plate and the Eurasian plate is also relatively simply depicted on the map by the Himalayan arc, which is strongly offset from the Persian segment by another major transform fault system. (This and other transform and transcurrent faults of the southeast Asia are described in Chapter 6 in the context of regional seismicity.) The tectonic structures of the three collision segments differ markedly; we shall examine each in turn.

9.20 The European Segment

Tectonic history and structure of the European collision segment are extremely complex—so complex, in fact, that only a tectono-structural geologist specializing in this region could form a comprehensive and cohesive mental picture of what took place here through time. The tectonic history of the European collision segment goes back to the late Triassic, at which time Pangaea remained intact, but was soon to begin its breakup (see Figure 13.36-G). The Eurasian and African plates were then separated by the Tethys Sea, which is pictured as a V-shaped embayment or gulf of *Panthalassa*, that enormous ancestor of the Pacific Ocean. In earliest Jurassic time, about 205 Ma, the breakup of Pangaea had started. While the North Atlantic began to open up by continental rifting, the Tethys Sea had begun to close, a process that can be visualized as the closing of a nutcracker, the apex or pivot being about where the Strait of Gibraltar lies today. In the European segment, the closing was greatly complicated by the presence of several small lithospheric subplates, which were moved about in various ways and underwent collisions with the Eurasian plate.

Figure 9.37 is a tectonic sketch map of Europe showing the major tectonic subdivisions of what we can call the Alpine system. [Note that the map includes the ancient Caledonides and Hercynides referred to in our narrative of the closing of the Iapetus Ocean.] The dozen-or-so subdivisions of the Alpine system seem to be in disarray in terms of location, shapes, and orientations. Every one of them has its own complex tectonic history. Even the European Alps in itself is incredibly complex, differing tectonically from one section to the next. Figure 9.38 shows principal divisions of the Alps (Laubscher, 1988, p. 1314, Fig. 1). This is a single arc about 1000 km long and about 400 km wide occupying parts of France, Switzerland, Germany, Austria, and Italy. Here, we concentrate on the western Alps for the purpose of eliciting some

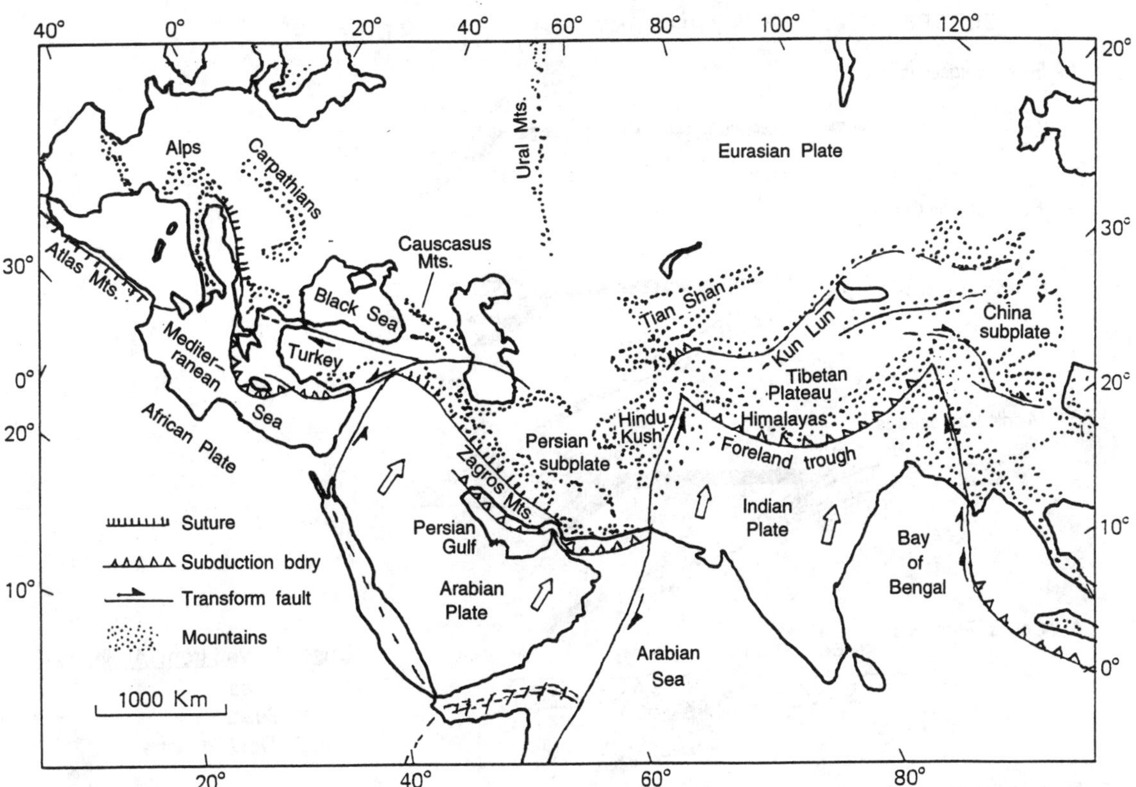

Figure 9.36 Sketch map of the three Eurasian collision segments: European, Persian, and Himalayan. (Copyright © by Arthur N. Strahler.)
p.3

Figure 9.37 Outline map of major tectonic units of Europe. (Based on data from cover of *EOS*, v. 64, no. 29, 1983, and other sources.)

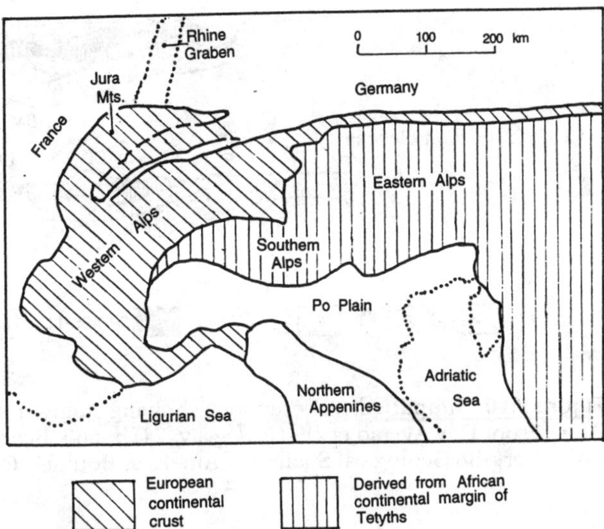

Figure 9.38 Map of principal tectonic divisions of the European Alps. (From Hans Laubscher, *Bull., Geol. Soc. Amer.*, v. 100, p. 1314, Figure 1. Reproduced with the permission of the publisher, the Geological Society of America, Boulder, Colorado, USA. Copyright © 1988.)

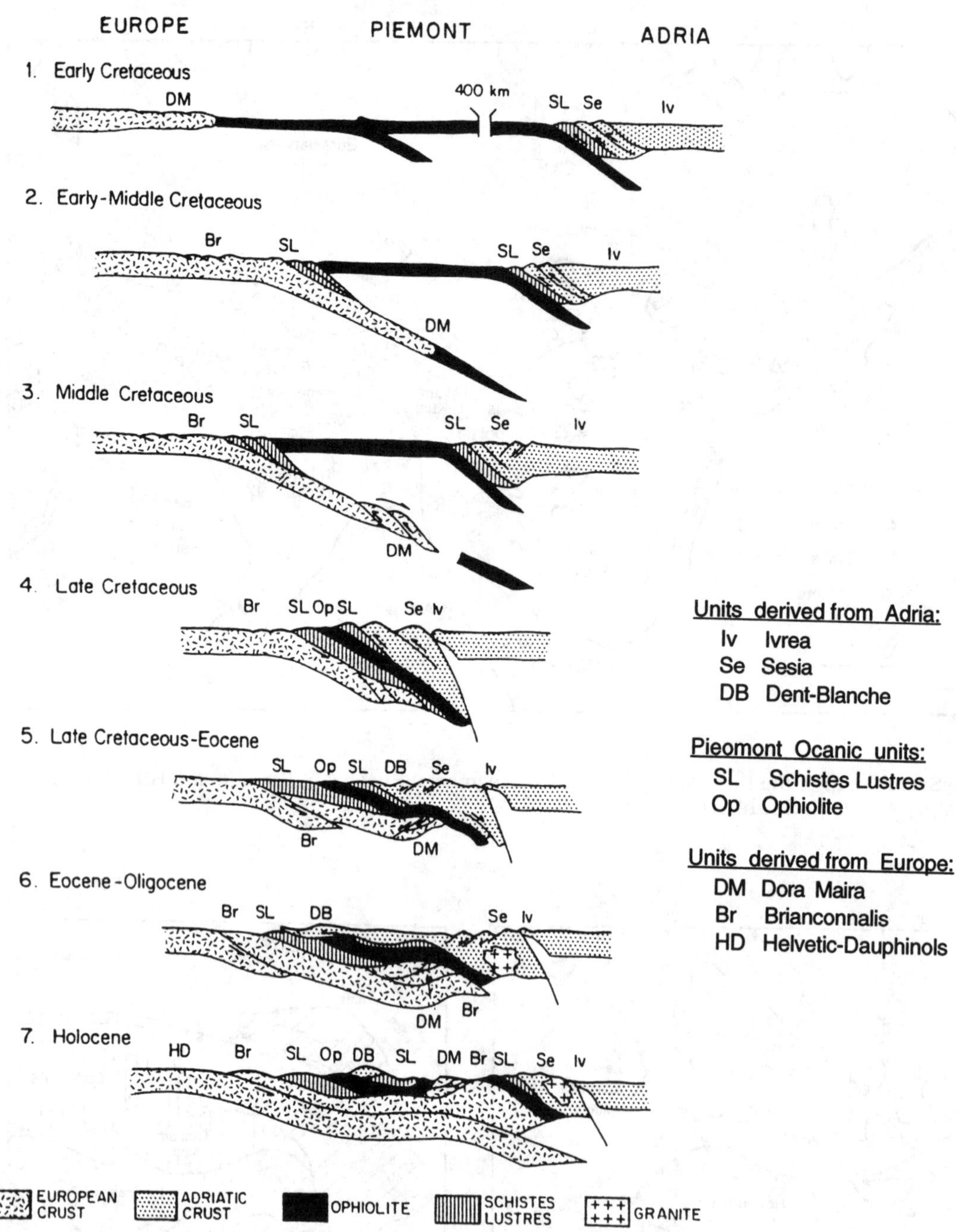

Figure 9.40 Simplified cross sections showing stages in the tectonic evolution of the Western Alps.(From Dov Avigad et al., *Geology*, v. 21, p. 660, Figure 2. Reproduced with the permission of the publisher, the Geological Society of America, Boulder, Colorado, USA. Copyright © 1983.)

generalization is not confirmed by our example. The correct version in this one example is a collision between the independent Adriatic plate which then lay to the south of Europe, separated from it by the Piemont Ocean, whereas the African plate lay much farther to the south (Belderson, 1989, p. 35). Among the many problems that need to be addressed is the history of the deep Mediterranean basins. Are they parts of the Tethys ocean floor that have not yet been closed by collision between Africa and Europe?

9.21 The Persian Segment

The Persian collision segment is dominated by two collision sutures, between which lies a zone that may be identified as the Persian subplate. These are shown on our regional map, Figure 9.41. The older of these, named the Paleo-Tethys suture, can be traced from west to east from the Black Sea, across the Caspian Sea to a common boundary with the Indian plate. It may have been formed by collision with one of the smaller continents that basic concepts or principles that may be applicable to continent-continent collisions in general. Figure 9.39 is a simplified tectonic map of the western Alps (Avigad et al., 1993, p. 659, Fig. 1). It shows a strongly curved arcuate configuration comprised of four lithologic/tectonic belts.

Figure 9.40 is a set of highly simplified cross-sectional drawings showing a recent interpretation of the tectonic history of this arc from Early Cretaceous to Holocene. The following structural features and events are worthy of noting in each section (Avigad et al., 1993, p. 660-661):

1. The two converging continents are represented by European crust (left) and Adriatic crust (right), the latter being a small continent called Adria. Between them lies the Piemont Ocean; its crust is shown in solid black and labeled "ophiolite" in the key, which it becomes in the orogen to follow. Steeply dipping thrust slices have already been produced at the subduction boundary of Adria. They are labeled in terms of the lithologic units they will later become in the ensuing orogeny: *SL* (Schiste Lustres) is a blueschist typical of high-pressure/low-temperature metamorphism. *Se* (Sesia) is sliced from Adriatic crust, coded for as *Iv*.

2. and 3. The Piemont Ocean is closing, and a second subduction boundary has formed (left). Thrust wedges of blueschist (SL) are now present on both continental margins.

4. Europe and Adria have collided, eliminating the Piemont Ocean. New thrust slices of Adria have been emplaced over the ophiolite/-blueschist slices. Underthrusting has also thickened the orogen. The actual continental suture can now be placed along the ophiolite zone. Compressional shortening has reduced to a minimum the breadth of the orogen. Because of its great thickness and height, the orogen is unstable.

5. Extensional collapse has occurred, forming normal fault slices, while at the same time continued overall compression between the two plates causes low-angle underthrusting of the European crust to continue. Denudation has exposed deeper thrusts.

6. A new thrust sheet of Adriatic crust now spreads over the earlier crust, while underthrusting at depth in the opposite direction continues. Granite intrusions have been emplaced.

7. The present structure includes a doubly thick layer of European crust extending far beneath the entire orogen.

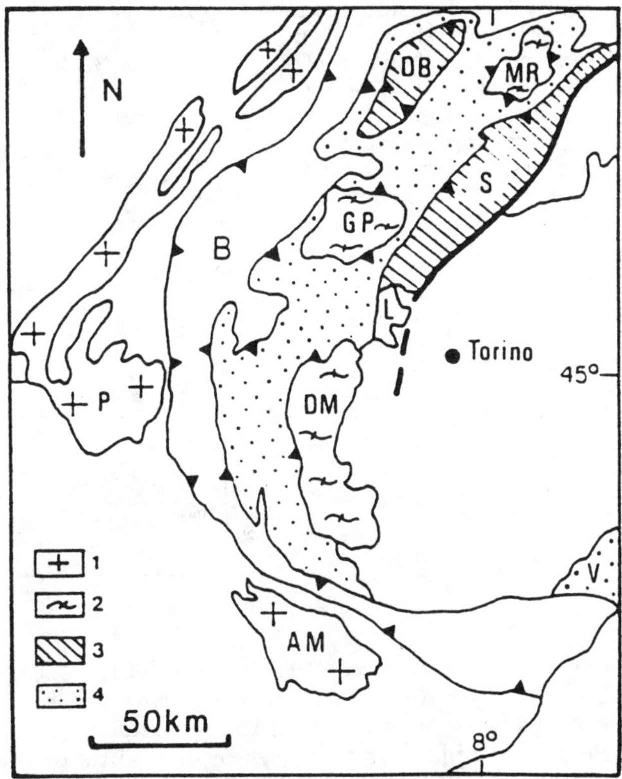

1—External crystalline massifs; 2—internal crystalline massifs; 3—Austroalpine nappe; 4—Schistes Lustres and ophiolites. AM—Argentera-Mercantour; B—Brianconnais; DB—Dent-Blanche; DM—Dora Maira; GP—Gran Paradiso; L—Lanzo; MR—Monte Rosa; P—Pelvoux; S—Sesia; V—Voltri; SA—South Alpine.

Figure 9.39 Simplified tectonic map of the Western Alps. (From Dov Avigad et al., *Geology*, v. 21, p. 659, Figure 1. Reproduced with the permission of the publisher, the Geological Society of America, Boulder, Colorado, USA. Copyright © 1993.)

The authors of the report from which our cross sections are taken show no depth scale. Deep seismic profiling across the Alps has produced images of similar thrust sheets of the lower crust extending down to depths of 15 to 20 km (Bois and Courtillot, 1988, p. 977, Figure 1).

In summary, it appears that continent-continent collision is actually a long and slow process, extending over 100 m.y. in this case. When first formed, the collision orogen may be overthickened and gravitationally unstable, after which it is thinned by lateral extension—a process of collapse. At the same time, deep underthrusting at a very low angle has doubled the thickness of the continental crust (Costa and Rey, 1995, p. 905). Isostatic compensation acts to elevate the alpine range to a great height, causing it to undergo unroofing by rapid erosion. In this stage it is deeply eroded by alpine glaciers.

So it turns out that where we have referred in earlier pages and chapters to "collision of the African Plate with the Eurasian plate," that

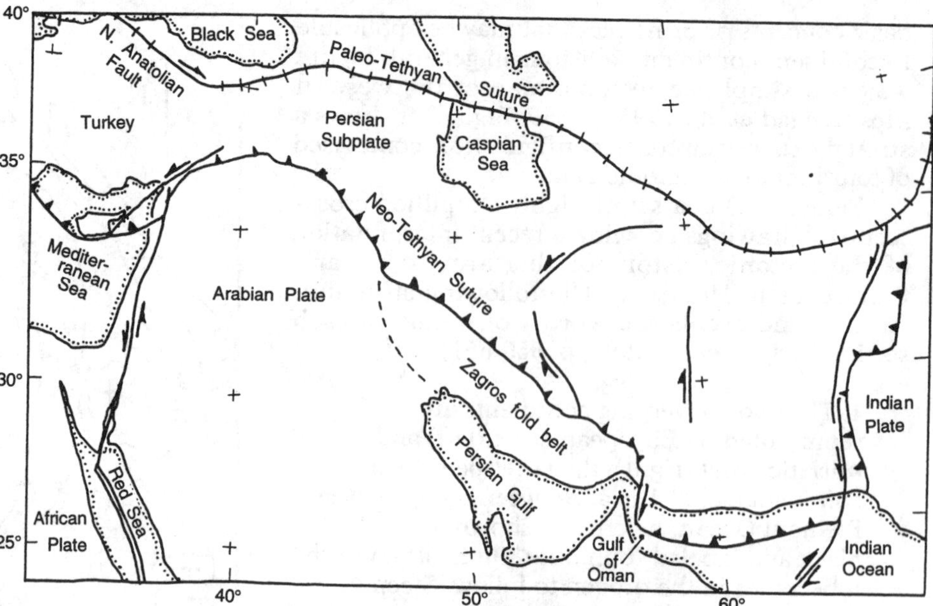

Figure 9.41 Tectonic sketch map of the Persian collision segment. (Based on data of R. Tirrul et al., *Bull., Geol. Soc. of Amer.*, v. 94, p. 135, Figure 2. Reproduced with the permission of the publisher, the Geological Society of America, Boulder, Colorado, USA. Copyright © 1983.)

earlier closed an ocean arm of the Tethys ocean. The younger Neo-Tethys suture forms the plate boundary between the Arabian plate and the Persian subplate. It also goes by the name of the Main Zagros Thrust.

South of this thrust lie the Zagros Mountains of southwestern Iran. This mountain range is remarkable in that it is a broad belt of open folds of sedimentary strata. Penetrating the Zagros fold belt in many places are great salt columns, or diapirs, called *salt domes* or *salt plugs* (see Figure 9.42). The salt originally formed as a thick bed of evaporites, largely halite, lying near the bottom of a former sedimentary basin. After folding occurred, the salt began to rise in tall stalk-like columns, forcing its way up through the overlying strata to reach the surface. The salt of a single column may form an entire hilltop or mountainside.

Geologists have reconstructed the Zagros fold belt in terms of collision of the Arabian plate with the Persian subplate in a final closing of the Neo-Tethys ocean (Figure 9.42). In Diagram A, that ocean closing was nearly complete. Thrust slices that include oceanic crust with trench deposits had already been formed as the oceanic lithosphere was subducted beneath the Persian subplate. A Cenozoic sedimentary basin on the margin of the Arabian plate was receiving sediments from the active orogen. Those sediments included carbonate strata (limestones) and red shale beds, and a thick salt formation that lay near the base of the series. In Diagram B, continuing collision has exerted

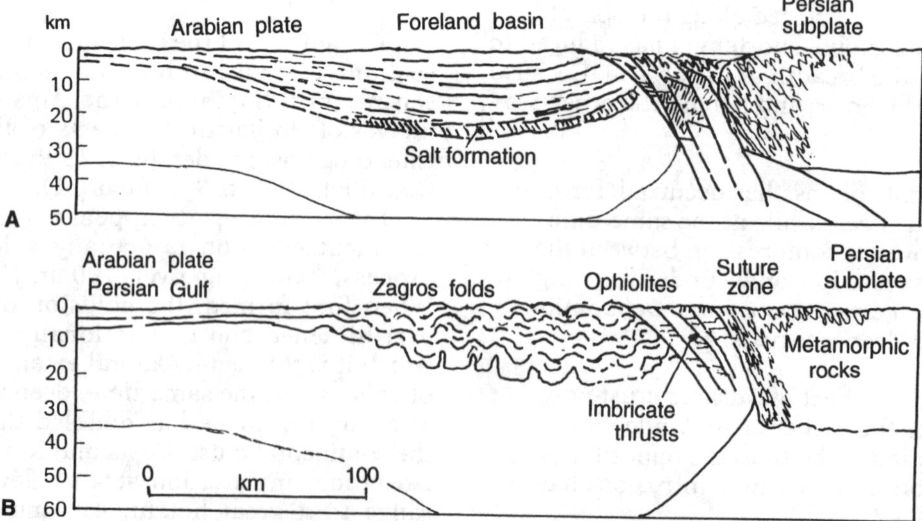

Figure 9.42 Schematic cross sections of the Zagros Mountains. (A) Final closing of Tethys Ocean is accompanied by imbricate thrust faulting of oceanic crust. (B) Structure of the Zagros today, inferred from data of exploration for petroleum accumulations. (Drawing copyright © by A.N. Strahler. Based on data of S.J. Haynes and H. McQuillan, 1974, *Bull., Geol. Soc. Amer.*, v. 85, p. 742, Figure 2, and other sources.)

compression on the basin strata, throwing them into open folds, through which salt diapirs have risen.

The Zagros Mountains are seismically active today, with numerous earthquake epicenters distributed over the entire belt. This activity suggests that the Arabian plate continues to press strongly upon the Eurasian plate and that many compressional faults are active throughout the crust beneath the Zagros folds.

9.22 The Himalayan/Tibetan Segment

The Himalayan collision segment is of particular interest to geologists because the great alpine-type Himalayan arc is bordered on the north by the Tibetan Plateau, an enormous elevated crustal mass unequaled in size anywhere on earth. Seismic activity is concentrated in the Himalayan arc and on two narrow zones nearly at right angles on either side of it—one in Pakistan, the other in Burma (Figure 9.43). A sharp tectonic change of direction is called a *syntaxis*. The seismicity shows that the boundary between the Indian plate and the Eurasian plate is tectonically active today, although the continental collision has already occurred. Lateral zones of seismic activity are located on transform faults that bound the Indian plate on the west. On the east side, major thrust faults trending north-south dominate the boundary of the Indian Plate. (Refer to Chapter 6, Seismicity of Young Continent-Continent Collisions, and Figure 6.35.)

Thick alluvial sediments fill the deep Indo-Gangetic Basin that lies adjacent to the Himalayan arc on the south. This accumulation can be regarded as a major type of sedimentary basin, namely, a foreland basin (Chapter 11). The sediment—a molasse—has been derived from the lofty Himalayan and Hindu Kush ranges by intense erosion of streams and glaciers.

Our plan of attack on the sequence of collision events is to cover the following topics:

•Precollision events, consisting of terranes accreted to southern Asia prior to the main Indian-Asian collision.

•Collision and suturing of the two plates, preceded by crumpling of the old passive margin of India.

•Formation of a great south-verging thrust fault above which sediments of the Indian plate are sliced up and deformed into nappes.

•A second major thrust fault forms farther south in the Indian plate. Above it the molasse from high mountains of the earlier underthrust is sliced up and deformed.

•Convergence continues as India pushes farther north into Asia, giving rise to great east-west strike-slip faults that accommodate much of the convergence. Rapid unroofing of the high Himalayas causes rivers to bring huge quantities of coarse molasse down to the foreland basin.

Table 9.1 charts these major activities and gives some details of the lithologic compositions and ages of the tectonic zones and the timing of the great thrusts. We start at the top, where the age is oldest, and work down. Refer to Figure 9.44, a geologic map of the Himalayan arc, and to Figure 9.45, a diagrammatic cross section of the entire orogen.

With the breakup of Gondwana, starting about in the Late Triassic (180 Ma), India had begun its northward journey. We tend to forget that the triangular piece of continental lithosphere we see on a map (such as Figure 9.47) was part of a much larger area of plate consisting of old oceanic lithosphere to the north of it, in the direction it was moving. Somewhere between India and Asia was a subduction boundary bearing an island arc, along which the Indian plate was disappearing. As an island of old continental lithosphere, India was producing a continental-shelf sediment wedge and a turbidite wedge, while at the same time pelagic sediment was accumulating on the abyssal ocean floor.

Although India was headed for a collision with Asia, at least two other microcontinents had arrived there earlier (Windley, 1985, p. 172). The first one, called "Northern Tibet," had docked about 140 Ma (Late Jurassic), the second, called "Southern Tibet," docked about 110 Ma (Middle Cretaceous). These collisions are shown schematically in Figure 9.46. In Table 9.1, the two sutures produced by these collisions are named Jinsha Suture and Bangong Suture, respectively.

The speed of northerly motion of India, read from magnetic anomalies, was exceptionally rapid in the period 65-55 Ma, the rate being 15 t0 20 cm/yr. The rate decreased rather abruptly to 5 cm/yr in the period 50 to 40 Ma (Figure 9.47). This change is interpreted as a result of the collision of the thick, strong Indian continental lithosphere with Tibet (Molnar, 1986, p. 150).

By 45 Ma, the accumulated shelf sediments of the continental margin of India began to be offscraped, forming a massive accretionary wedge. Shortly thereafter, the terminal collision occurred, closing the Tethys Sea and producing an orogen in which these sediments were overthrust into nappes, metamorphosed, and intruded by great batholiths. On our map, Figure 9.44, this orogen today appears as a zone labeled Trans-Himalayan Batholiths & Volcanoes. Immediately south of it is a line marking the suture, called Indus-Tsangpo Suture Zone (ITSZ). It is assigned an age of about 40 Ma. As shown on our general cross section, Figure 9.45, the collision piled up a great mass of Tethyan Sediments south of the suture line. Oceanic crust deformed along the suture, now

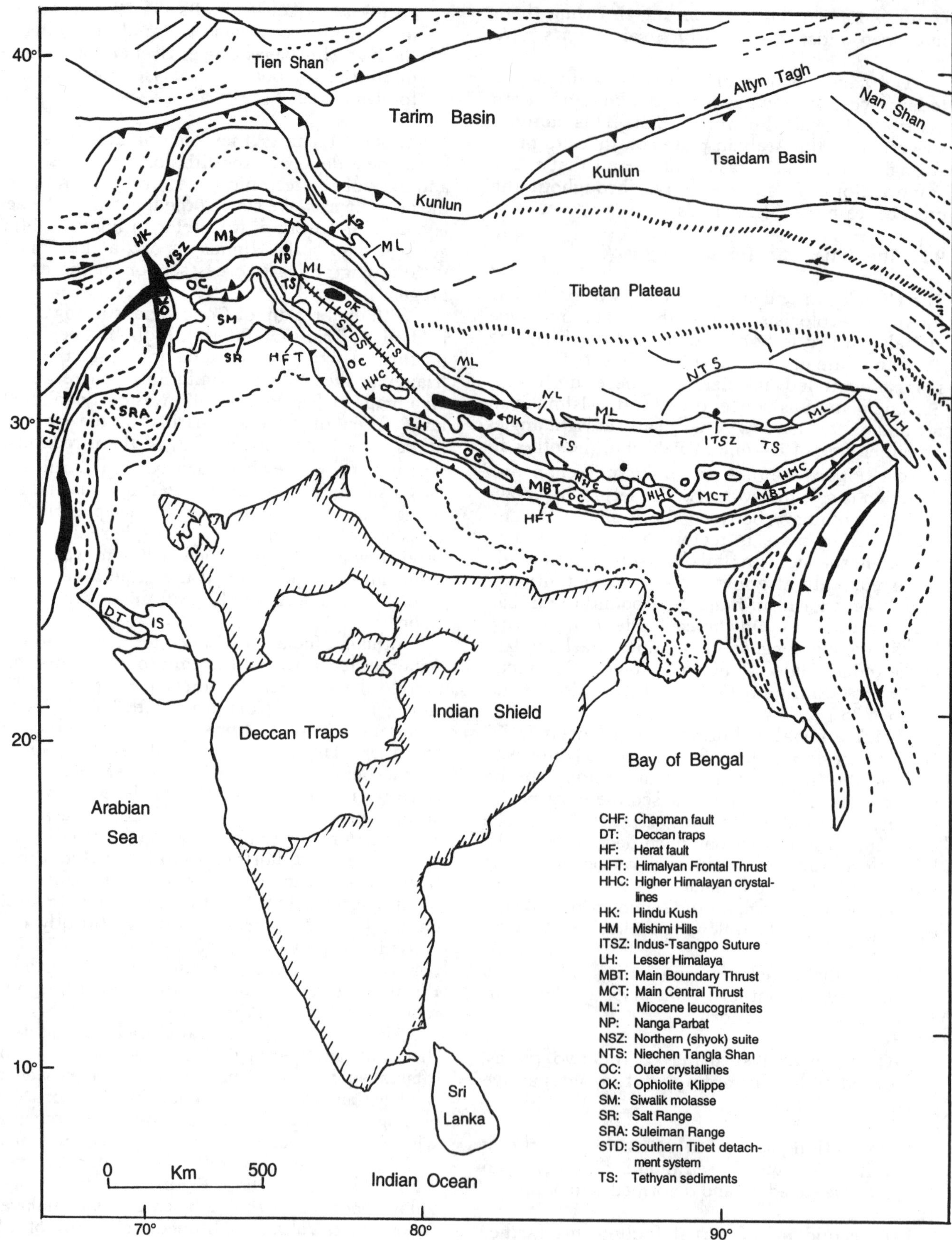

Figure 9.43 Generalized regional tectonic sketch map of the Himalayas and adjacent areas. (From R.B. Sorkhabi and E. Stamp, *GSA Today*, v. 3, no. 4, p. 88, Figure 1, and other sources. Reproduced with the permission of the publisher, the Geological Society of America, Boulder, Colorado, USA. Copyright © 1933.)

Table 9.1 Tectonic and Lithologic Zones of the Himalaya*

Morphotectonic Belts	Lithologic Composition	Thrust or Suture
Tethys (Tibetan) Himalaya		Jinsha Suture (140 Ma)
		Bangong Suture (110 Ma)
Tibetan/Indian Suture Zone	Trans-Himalayan Batholith (Gangdese belt) ITSZ Sediments	
		Indus-Tsangpo Suture Zone (ITSZ) (40 Ma)
Tethyan Himalaya	Tethys Sediments Ophiolite Klippe	
Higher Himalayan Crystallines	Higher Himalayan Crystallines Miocene Granites	
		Main Central Thrust (MCT) (20 Ma)
		[South Tibetan Detachment System]
Lesser Himalaya	Lesser Himalaya and Outer Crystallines	
		Main Boundary Thrust (MBT) (5 Ma)
Sub-Himalaya	Siwalik Molasse	
		Himalayan Frontal Thrust (HFT) (Recent)
	Indo-Gangetic Alluvial Plains	
	Indian Shield and Deccan Traps	

*Based on data of R. Sorkhabi and E. Stamp, 1994, Figure 1, B.F. Windley, 1985, Figure 1, and other sources.

designated as "Ophiolite," can also be found isolated with the sediments as the Ophiolite Klippe. Figure 9.48 gives a more detailed reconstruction of the ITSZ suture zone and its relationships with the Lhasa Block of the Asian plate and the Tibetan-Tethys Zone of the Indian Plate.

Next, as India continued to press farther into Tibet, a great new thrust surface developed within the Indian plate to the south of the suture; it is the Main Central Thrust (MCT), dated as around 20 Ma. The overriding mass was sliced by listric upthrusts and nappes, forming the Higher Himalayan Crystallines and Miocene Granites

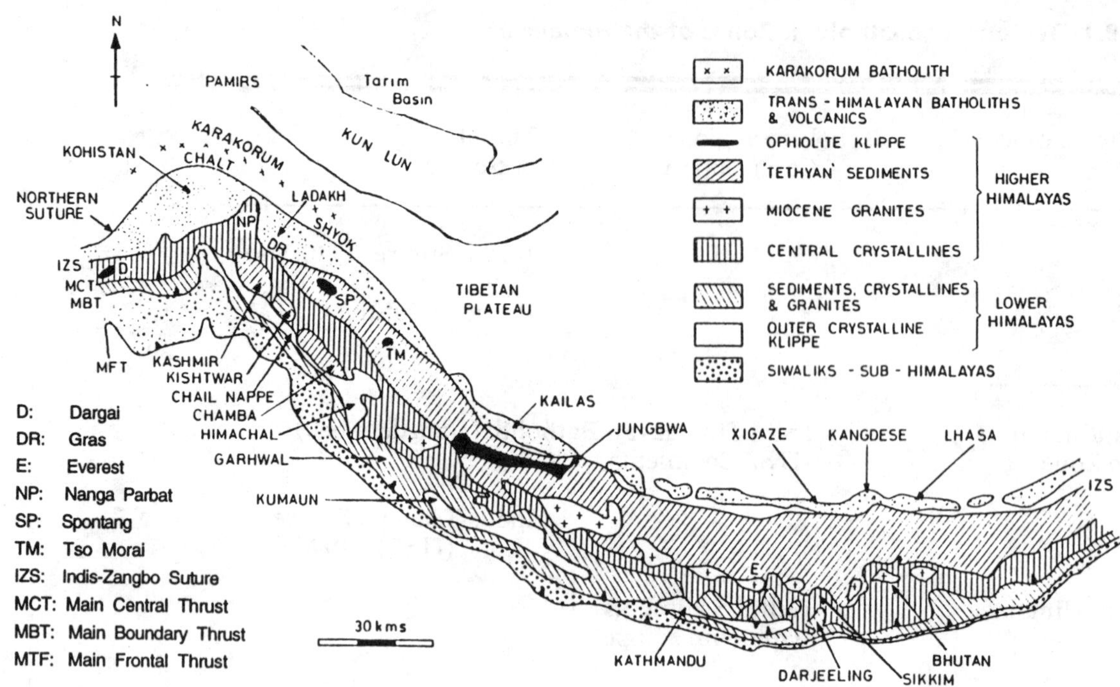

Figure 9.44 Generalized map of the main main tectonic units of the Himalayas. From Brian F. Windley, *The Evolving Continents*. 2nd. ed, p. 312 , Figure 21.2, 1984. John Wiley & Sons, Inc.)

(Figure 9.48). These now comprise a mountain belt called the Higher Himalaya. Again, a new thrust surface formed farther south on the Indian plate. Called the Main Boundary Thrust (MCT), its age is only a few million years. The thrust pushed up wedges of Tethys sediments and crystallines, and these now form the Lesser (or Lower) Himalaya.

The final event has been the accumulation of a very thick molasse at the foot of the Lesser Himalaya. Called the Siwalik Molasse, it forms the Sub-Himalaya. Thickness and width of this molasse body is greatest in the deeply indented western syntaxis, but decreases to only a very narrow zone in the eastern third of the Himalaya. Yet another thrust fault has since developed at the foot of the molasse: the Himalayan Frontal Thrust (HFT). This fault line serves to delimit the tectonically active molasse from the Indo-Gangetic Alluvial Plains.

9.23 Compression and Extension of the Himalayan Orogen

With a brief chronological description of the Himalayan continent-continent collision now completed, we turn to a closer look at important aspects of its development as a whole orogen. We tend to think of collision as dominantly a telescoping, or compressional process. The north-south extent of the main east-west arc of the entire Himalayan orogen, shown on our maps as about 500 km wide, was produced in the past 40 m.y. In

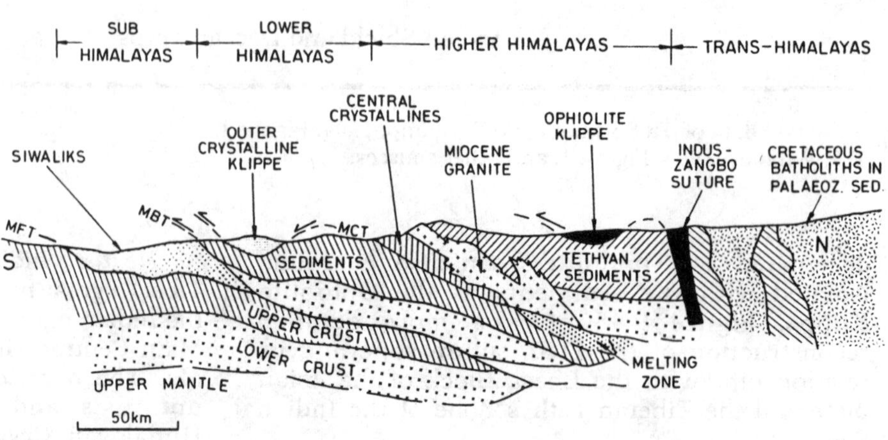

Figure 9.45 Diagrammatic cross section of the central Himalayas. (Same source as Figure 9.48, p. 313, Figure 21.3, 1984.)

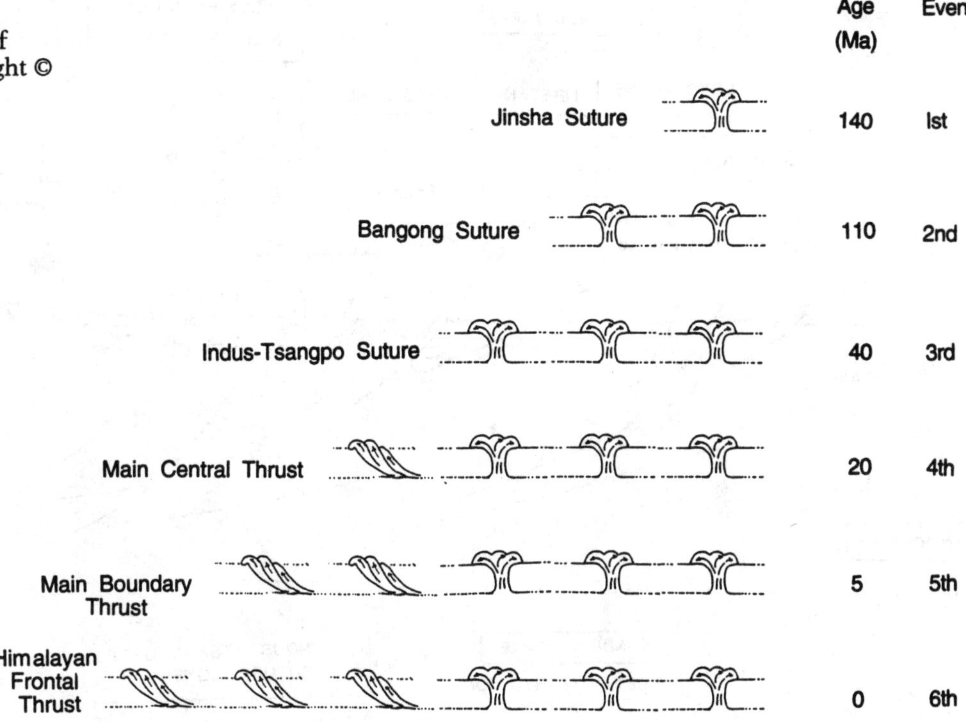

Figure 9.46 Simplified diagram of steps in the continental accretion of southern Asia. (Copyright © by Arthur N. Strahler.)

this collision and the continued orogeny, the total penetration of the Indian plate into the Asian plate has been as much as 1500 km (Molnar, 1986, p. 152). A strong, widely accepted hypothesis is that much of the total penetration has been compensated for in Tibet by lateral (west to east) crustal motion on great strike-slip faults that transect the Tibetan plateau and extend far into southeastern China. (See Chapter 6, Seismicity of Intracontinental Transcurrent Faults, and Figure 6.35.) These faults have more or less vertical planes that extend down to a ductile zone. This "pushing aside" process by lateral "extrusion" of crustal sectors between faults may account for much of the growth of Southeast Asia. It has been known since the 1970s as the "continental escape hypothesis" (Searle, 1996, p. 171).

For the Himalayan arc south of the Tibetan plateau, a quite different form of tectonic mechanism of transverse mass transfer has been proposed (Hodges et al., 1992, p. 1466-1467). Field studies in the Tibetan/Indian suture zone have revealed the presence of a persistent horizontal layering consisting of a lower layer of high-grade metamorphic rock and an upper suprastructure of weakly metamorphosed rock. Starting in Late Miocene time, the two layers became decoupled on a *detachment surface*, allowing the upper layer to deform independently of the lower layer. Figure 9.49 is our attempt to put across the detachment concept in a schematic vertical section. Thinning is going on in the upper layer while thickening is going on in the lower layer. Using the analog of an ellipse of deformation, we show that gravitational collapse in the upper layer requires simultaneous horizontal extension. In the lower layer the ellipse

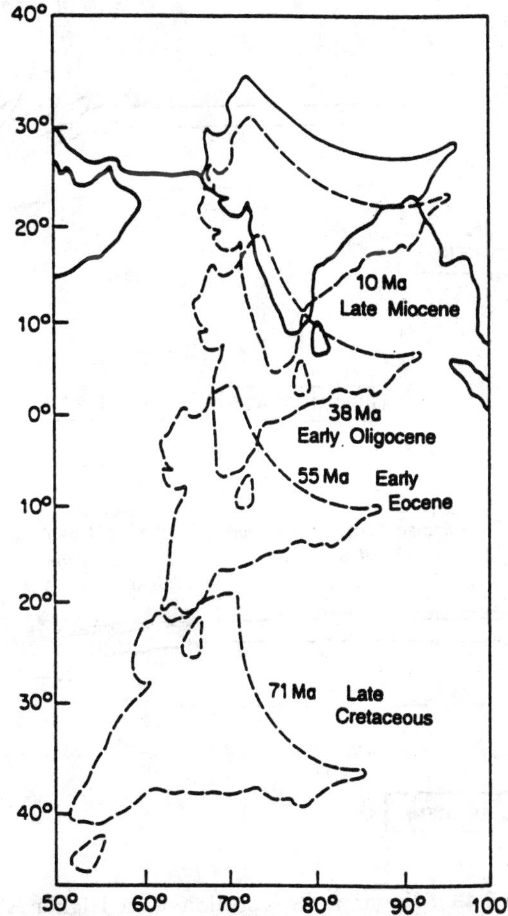

Figure 9.47 India's northward journey toward collision with southern Asia. From P.H. Molnar and P.Taponier, *Science*, 1975, v. 189, Figure 1. Copyright © by The American Association for the Advancement of Sceince. Used by permission.

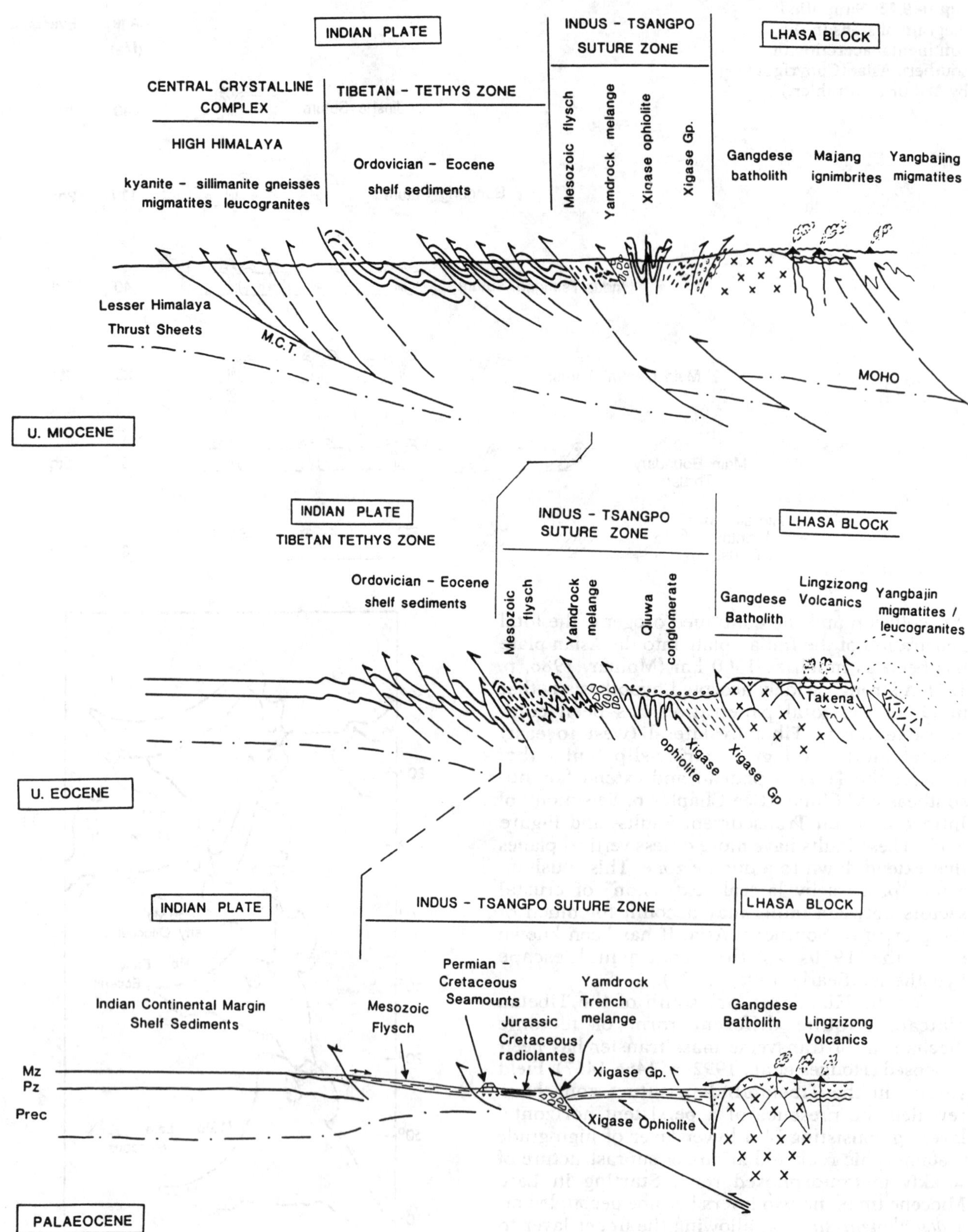

Figure 9.48 Schematic cross section of the Higher Himalaya and adjacent Tibetan plateau in Miocene time. (From M.P. Searle, et al., *Bull., Geol. Soc. Amer.*, v. 98, p. 697, Figure 12. Reproduced with the permission of the publisher, the Geological Society of America, Boulder, Colorado, USA. Copyright © 1987.)

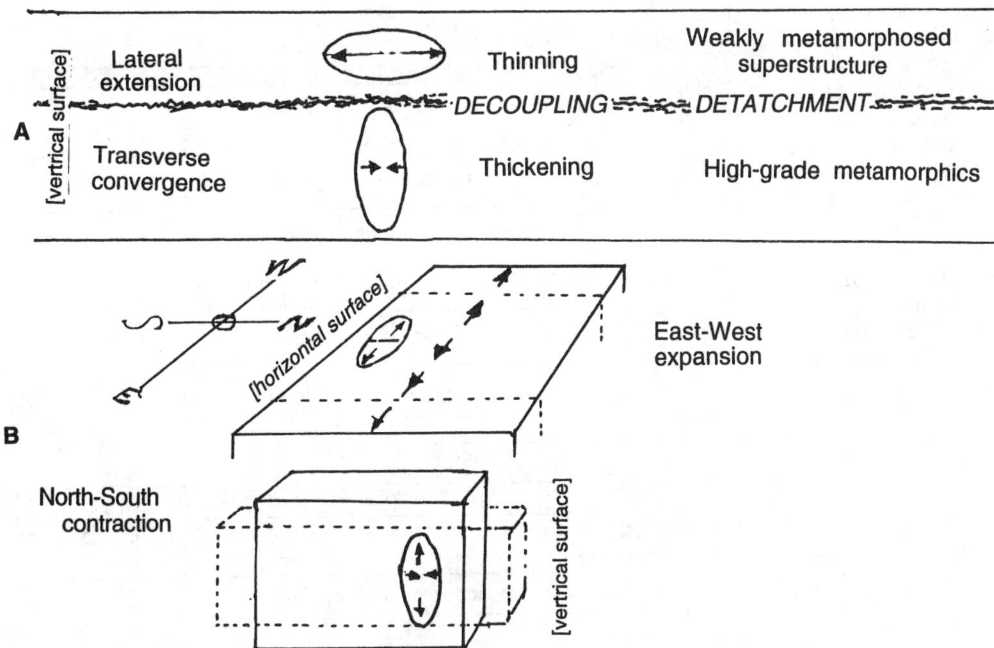

Figure 9.49 Schematic section and diagram of simultaneous lateral extension and transverse convergence. (Copyright © by Arthur N. Strahler.)

shows vertical thickening, requiring horizontal contraction. The two layers are separated by a surface of *decoupling*, also labeled as the *detachment*. To this we must add that the azimuth of relative horizontal decoupling motion of the upper layer is east-west, at right angles to that of the lower layer, which is north-south. Today, as a result of subsequent erosional denudation, the detachment is now exposed in steep mountainsides and can be mapped for a distance of over 100 km between northwest India and Bhutan. It has been named the South Tibetan Detachment System (STDS), and we have entered it on Table 9.1 as younger than the Main Central Thrust but older than the Main Boundary Thrust.

The effect of deep thickening and shallow thinning is very similar to that we described for the Western Alps (Figure 9.40. Perhaps it is a part of the normal mode of evolution of all continent-continent collisions in the later or mature phase of development. As put in K.V. Hodges et al., 1992, p. 1466: "It is commonly assumed that gravitational collapse characterizes the latest steps in the evolution of a compressional mountain belt, which correspond to a time when convergence across the orogen slows dramatically or ceases."

9.24 The Height Problem of the Tibetan Plateau

A problem that greatly interests geologists is to explain the uniformly high surface elevation of the enormous Tibetan Plateau, measuring about 3000 km latitudinally and 1300 km longitudinally in maximum extent, for a total area of nearly 2 million sq km. The surface is mostly just over 5000 m in elevation and shows remarkably low relief. Judged in terms of the total global land surface that lies higher than 4 km above sea level, the Tibetan Plateau claims 85 percent of that surface (Fielding et al., 1994, p. 163). Because the climate of the plateau is arid, surface drainage by streams and rivers stays within the plateau limits to undergo evaporation. As a result of this interior drainage, erosion is slow and detrital sediment transported by running water accumulates in topographic basins, so that over time the surface relief tends to be reduced. Normal faulting, occurring over parts of the plateau, maintains many shallow grabens, while other tectonic depressions are formed by movement on strike slip faults. These neotectonic landforms serve as sinks for drainage and sediment (Rothery and Drury, 1984).

To sustain the plateau surface at such a high level the continental crust beneath must be extremely thick and its base correspondingly deep. A thickness of continental crust of about 70 km is indicated by seismic evidence—nearly double that of typical continental crust (Molnar, 1989, p. 352). These figures bring first to mind the hypothesis that a double layer of normal crust has been formed, and scenarios for this doubling have been proposed.

Figure 9.50 uses very simple diagrams to aid us in thinking about how continental crust might be doubled during a collision, such as the penetration of the Indian plate into the Asian plate. Keep in mind that entire plates are involved in that collision and that a lithospheric plate moves as a unit over the weak asthenosphere. Our diagram (A) selects a plate thickness of 150 km, of which the crust makes up a top layer only about one-quarter

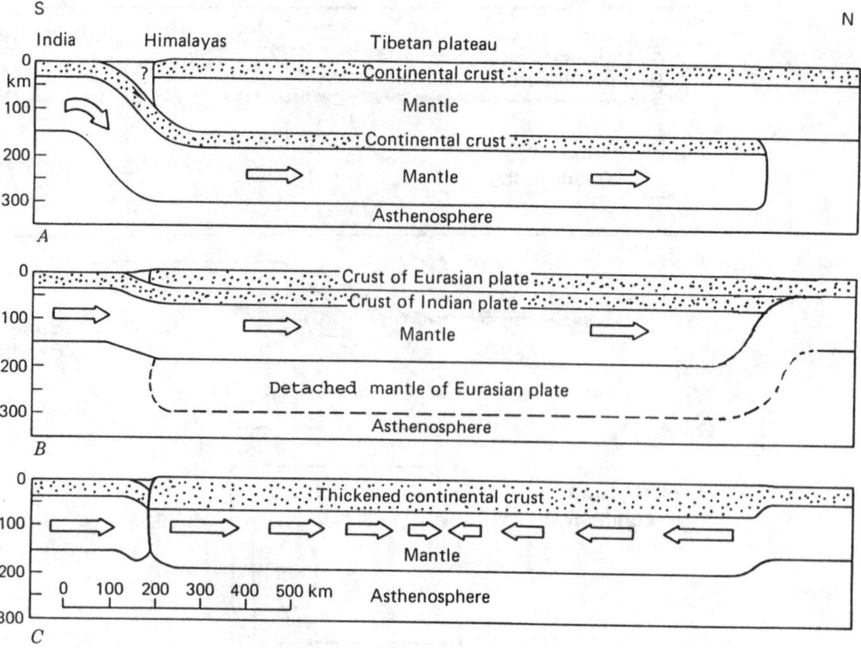

Figure 9.50 Schematic cross sections of the Tibetan Plateau showing three hypotheses of origin of a thickened crust. (A) Underthrusting of the Indian plate beneath the entire Asian plate. (B) Underthrusting with crust/mantle peeling (delamination), doubling the thickness of the crust. (C) Plate thickening under lateral compression following collision. (Drawn by A.N. Strahler. Suggested by compiled data of C.M. Powell and P.J. Conaghan, 1975, *Geology*, v. 3, p. 729, Figure 2.)

that thick. (Refer to Figure 3.15 for crust/-lithosphere data.) Most of the lithospheric plate consists of ultramafic mantle. The Indian plate has been simply subducted beneath the Asian plate. We have not doubled the crust of the Tibetan Plateau, which was our initial objective. Moreover, the sunken plate can be expected to heat up and in due time become part of the asthenosphere.

Diagram (B) inserts the Indian plate between the Tibetan crust and its mantle, achieving the crustal doubling by delamination, a process described earlier in this chapter (Figure 9.24B). Whether such a maneuver could be accomplished is highly questionable. If successful, the doubled crust would rise in isostatic compensation. Both A and B depend upon horizontal subduction on an enormous scale that calls for the subducting plate forcefully to displace the asthenosphere lying in front of it. Diagram C, shows an entirely different mechanism to achieve a doubling of the thickness of the crust: north-south lateral compression distributed through the Tibetan plate. We will return to this hypothesis in later paragraphs.

Through earlier decades of the study of plate tectonics, the subduction models were favored by many geologists. A review of these earlier models, including cross sections for comparison, is given by Powell and Conaghan (1975, p. 720, Figure 2). These date back to one produced in 1924 by the Swiss alpine geologist, E. Argand, whom we mentioned in Chapter 2. Alfred Wegener had reproduced Argand's cross section of what Argand had called the "Lemurian Compression," shown as our Figure 2.13, with the Indian continent shown to be forced under the Himalayas and the Tibetan Plateau. The cross sections given by Powell and Conaghan show only the "sialic" continental crust, and no reference is given to lithospheric plates. Other published diagrams have shown only one lithospheric plate subducting beneath another, with no attempt to delineate the crust as a separate layer.

A good example of the delamination model (B) applied to the Tibetan Plateau is presented by M. Barazangi and J. Ni in interpreting their seismological observations of the propagation of mantle shear waves (1982, p. 184). We reproduce their cross section here as Figure 9.51. Horizontal arrows suggest a great décollement separating Tibetan crust from Indian crust. Missing from the diagram is the northern termination of the Indian plate.

Deep seismic reflection profiling was carried out in the early 1990s on a traverse of the Higher Himalayan range and southern part of the Tibetan Plateau, about on the 90th meridian. Called INDEPTH, this profile has provided some firm evidence of the subduction of Indian crust beneath Tibetan crust (Zhao, Nelson & INDEPTH team, 1993, p. 557-559). A strong reflection surface sloping northward between 30 and 40 km depth is interpreted as the upper surface of the Indian crust, with its lower surface (the Moho) reflecting at a depth of about 75 km. To the limited northward extent that this profile goes, it seems to fit the delamination model, but tells us nothing about the location of the plate farther northward under the plateau.

Newer versions of the subduction model continue to be developed. Added to the possibility of the subducting plate slipping horizontally under the Tibetan crust is the possibility of abrupt downward detachment and foundering of the lower plate. This mass sinking is visualized as setting in motion an adjacent rising current of hot asthenosphere, which raises the temperature of the plateau crust and causes it to rise in elevation (Willett and Beaumont, 1994).

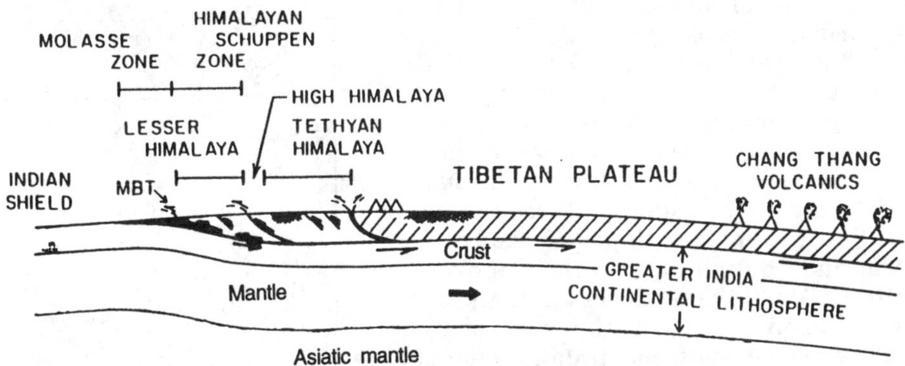

Figure 9.51 A delamination model in which crust of the Indian plate subducts horizontally beneath the Tibetan crust. (From M. Barazangi and J. Ni, 1982, *Geology*, v. 10, p. 184, Figure 7. Reproduced with the permission of the publisher, the Geological Society of America , Boulder, Colorado, USA. Copyright © 1982.)

Our third basic hypothesis (Figure 9.50-C), invokes distributed thickening of the crust beneath the Tibetan Plateau by processes that do not involve extensive plate underthrusting. This alternative fits in well with what has been stated earlier about massive north-south compression of the Tibetan plate. As the accumulating Eurasian crust underwent north-south contraction and thickening, the ductile lower part of the crust may have yielded by plastic flowage whereas the upper, more brittle part would have yielded by fracturing. The hypothesis of distributed thickening is strengthened by the presence of long transcurrent faults (mentioned above) that lie within the northern and eastern regions of the plateau. These are shown in Figure 9.43. The direction of crustal movement along these faults gives the impression that great strips of the Eurasian plate are being forced to move eastward, to "get out of the way" of (or "escape from") the telescoping Tibetan plate. If this interpretation is correct, the entire plate area that lies beneath adjacent China and Indochina is being extended southeastward as a unit, i.e., as a growing subplate. The region in which these strike-slip faults lie is remote and geologic details are not yet well known to geologists. These structures do, however, appear clearly on remote-sensing imagery that can reveal remarkably fine details of the terrain. The fault system is largely interpreted from such images.

A mechanism of plateau rise entirely different in cause from north-south compression was put forward by England and Houseman (1988) and reviewed by Peter Molnar (1989, p. 358.) If the originally cold, dense material of the mantle beneath Tibet were to be replaced by hot, less dense material, the overlying crust would be caused to rise in elevation. How could such heating be induced? Horizontal compression, as described above, would force cold mantle downward into the underlying asthenosphere, where it would be heated and would become convectively unstable, and thus be carried downward even more deeply. The sinking mantle material would be continually replaced by buoyant hot mantle, causing the crust above it to stand as much as 1000 to 2000 m higher. Crustal rise, in turn, would tend to accelerate the rate of eastward extrusion of the plateau crust, and thus maintain the plateau surface at its present high level. Should the convective activity cease to function, the plateau would subside and finally collapse to a much lower level. Molnar points out that a similar scenario of high plateau growth and subsequent collapse can be found in other parts of the world (1989, p. 358). The high Andean plateau would be placed in a stage comparable to that of the Tibetan Plateau, whereas the Basin and Range Province of the western United States would represent an advanced stage of collapse accompanied by crustal thinning. Another case of completed subsidence and thinning is the region of Greece and the adjacent Aegean Sea, beneath which relatively thin crust has been found.

9.25 Intracratonal Compressional Tectonics of Western North America

Now that we have reviewed both arc-continent collisions and continent-continent collisions, with outstanding examples of each, we turn to a rather intruiging tectonic phenomenon that also falls into the category of compressional tectonics, but is a rare end-product of foreland thrusting. First, refer back to the section early in this chapter titled The Lewis Overthrust, in which overthrust sheets of the Northern Rocky Mountains and the Canadian Cordilleran thrust belt are illustrated by cross sections in Figure 9.8 and 9.10. The orogeny in which these thrusts were formed occurred in the Late Cretaceous, when arc-continent or micro-continent collisions took place on what was then the Pacific continental margin of North America.

Traced southward in the United States, the east-directed foreland thrusts of this orogeny are found in southeastern Idaho and southwestern Wyoming and extend south into central Utah. This orogenic zone is called the Sevier thrust belt. It is labeled on our regional maps, Figures 9.52 and 9.53. This thrusting took place through the Cretaceous (DeCelles and Mitra, 1995). During that time, to the east of the Sevier thrust belt lay thick strata of an inland Cretaceous seaway. Beneath the Cretaceous strata were older and more-or-less conformable platform strata of Carboniferous, Triassic, and Jurassic age, resting on Precambrian crystallines. Starting in late Upper Cretaceous, about 75 Ma, and continuing into the Cenozoic Era to about 45 Ma (Middle Eocene), compressional stress began to affect the previously undisturbed Cretaceous platform strata in what is called the Laramide Orogeny (Dumitru et al., 1991, p. 1146). It is named for the Laramie Formation of Wyoming and Colorado. Compressional deformation seems to have progressed from west to east until the early Eocene. Some authors prefer "to rigorously separate a pre-Late Cretaceous—early Sevier orogeny from a Late Cretaceous—early Tertiary Laramide orogeny" (Oldow et al., 1989, p. 173). We will limit the term "Laramide orogeny" to the production of tectonic structures that lie east of the Sevier thrust zone.

The Laramide orogeny produced domelike structures that were pushed up locally from the underlying Precambrian craton. Strata draped over these dome or arch forms now dip outward from the summit or axis of each uplift. Intrusion of core plutons does not seem to have accompanied the forming of these *structural uplifts*, which are judged to be purely tectonic in origin. The style of crustal deformation that occurred here has been called *foreland basement deformation*.

Large structural uplifts are particularly numerous in a belt extending from Montana south through Wyoming, Colorado, and northern New Mexico. Individual uplifts in this group are from 50 to 75 km wide and 200 to 400 km long (Figure 9.52). The restored vertical dimension of the arch or dome amounts to several kilometers along the crest or summit region of the larger uplifts. Denudation has long since removed the top portions of the uplifts, exposing cores of Precambrian shield rock, but the upturned strata can be seen today along the lower flanks of the uplifts where the harder, more resistant strata form sharp-crested hogbacks (Figure 9.54).

Between the uplifts are structural basins in which the platform strata were simultaneously down-warped. Once formed, these basins received large amounts of sediment from the eroding uplifts (see Chapter 11). This accumulation of sediment continued throughout much of the Cenozoic Era. The sediments consist of coarse clastic materials deposited by streams, as well as fine textured water-laid clays, silts, and lime muds deposited in lakes that occupied the basins from time to time.

In decades prior to the coming of plate tectonics, the mechanism of formation of the structural uplifts remained an enigma. Some of the smaller uplifts, particularly those in Wyoming, showed eastward overturning of strata on their

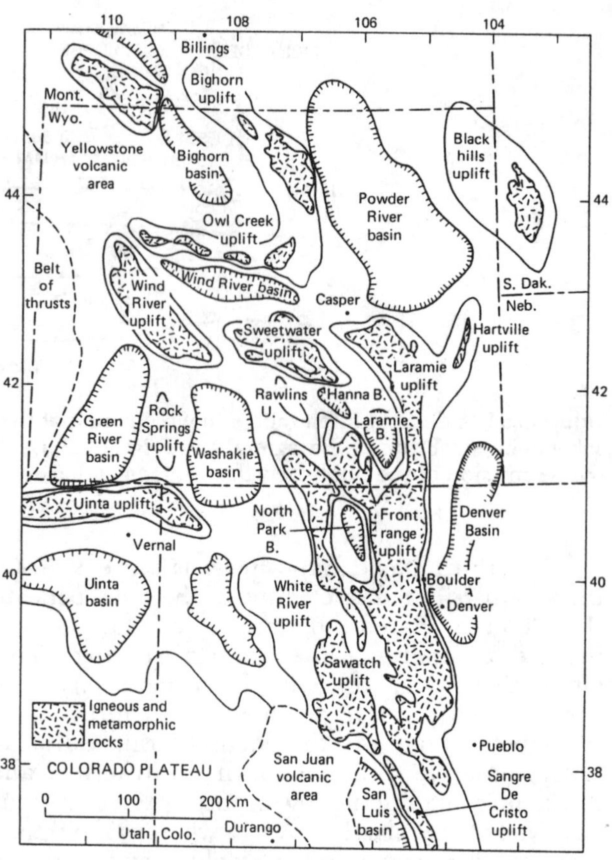

Figure 9.52 Outline map of the major structural uplifts and basins of the Middle and Southern Rocky Mountains. (Based on data of *Tectonic Map of the United States*, Amer. Assoc. of Petroleum Geologists and National Research Council, and other sources.)

flanks, and the overturned strata were seen to be cut through in places by steep thrust faults (or "reverse faults"), as shown in Diagram B of Figure 9.54. But other uplifts, such as the Black Hills dome and the Colorado Front Range, showed only moderate dips on both flanks and seemed to be lacking in thrust faults.

Soon after the theory of plate tectonics became fully stated—*ca* 1970—the role of subduction of an oceanic plate beneath a continental plate was available as a mechanism capable of producing major tectonic effects at a great distance inland. A history of the eastern Pacific basin was quickly deciphered to include the near-disappearance of a large plate (the Farallon) beneath the North American plate (Atwater, 1989, p. 46-49). Speculations soon appeared as to how the Farallon plate was situated and what its tectonic effects may have been. In 1971, three members of the U.S. Geological Survey—P.W. Lipman, H.J. Prostka, and R.L. Christiansen—published their results of a geochemical study of Cenozoic andesites exposed across the western United States. From their analyses of the ratio of K_2O to SiO_2, they could predict the depths of the points of origin of these

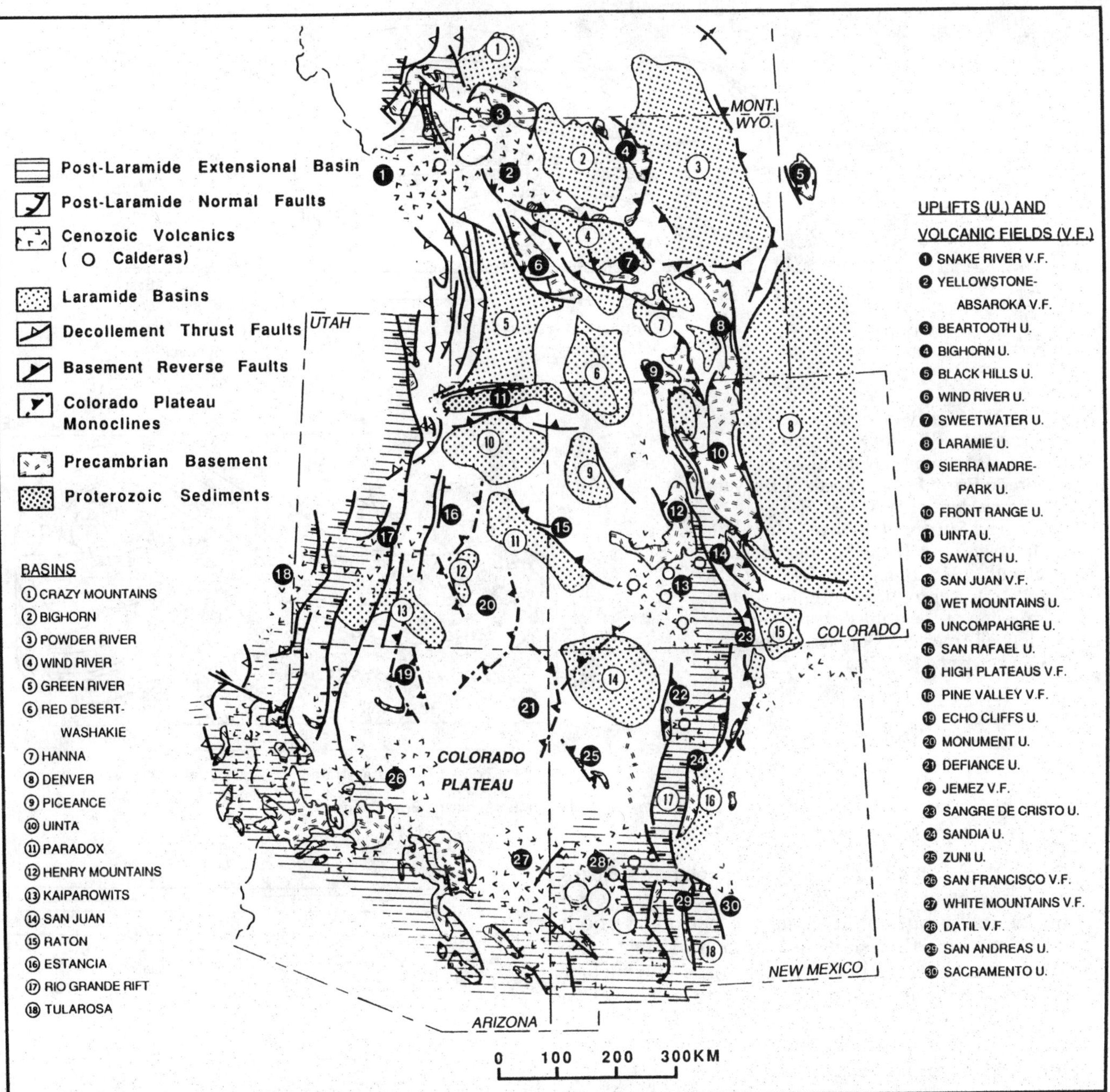

Figure 9.53 Generalized map of the central and southern Rocky Mountain region and Colorado Plateau. (From John S. Oldow, Albert W. Bally, et al., *Geology of North America*, vol. A, Chapter 8, 1989, p. 171, Figure 3. Reproduced with the permission of the publisher, the Geological Society of America, Boulder, Colorado, USA. Copyright © 1989.)

igneous bodies. The plotted points formed two northeast-sloping zones ranging in depth down to 400 km. These zones were interpreted as defining two slabs of Farallon oceanic lithosphere (1971, p. 824, Figure 3B.) Their data section, which cuts through the Utah-Colorado uplifts and basins, along with a suggested cross section of the subducted Farallon plate are reproduced here in Figure 9.55. The slab shown to lie farther east would be the older, having broken free first. This interpretation was supported by James D. Lowell in 1974, who suggested that buoyancy of the eastern slab may have exerted a lift on the overlying plate.

By the mid-1980s, most geologists had subscribed to the hypothesis that the Rocky Mountain foreland region of structural uplifts was underlain by a single horizontally subducting slab of the Farallon plate (rather than two dipping slabs) extending beneath the entire region (Dickinson and Snyder, 1978). "Geophyscists contributed to the model by showing that low-angle subduction quickly becomes horizontal due to viscous stresses even if the slab is not buoyant"

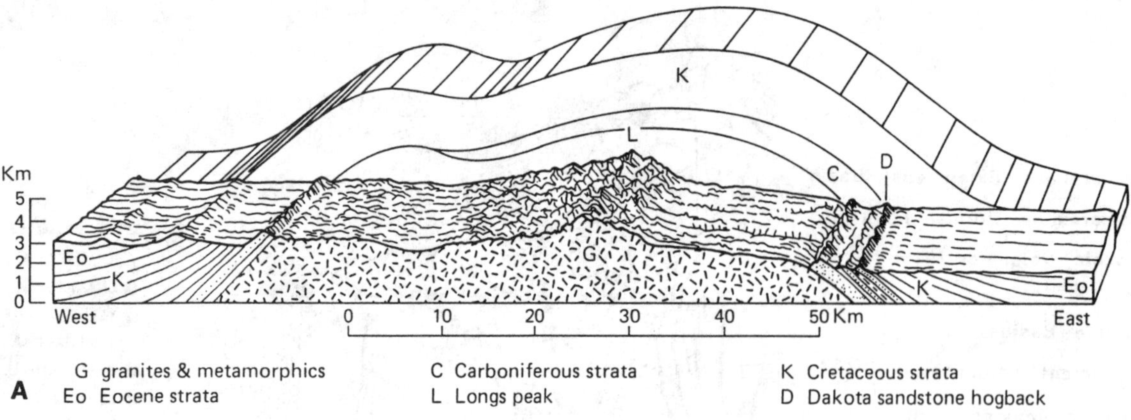

Figure 9.54 Early interpretations and restorations of Rocky Mountain structural uplifts. (Drawn by A.N. Strahler.) (A) Colorado Front Range, north of Denver (Based on data of W.T. Lee, U.S. Geological Survey.) (B) Sheep Mountain uplift, Wyoming. (Based on data of R.H. Beckwith, 1938, *Bull., Geol. Soc. Amer.*, v. 49, Plate 1. Reproduced with the permission of the publisher, the Geological Society of America , Boulder, Colorado, USA. Copyright © 1939.)

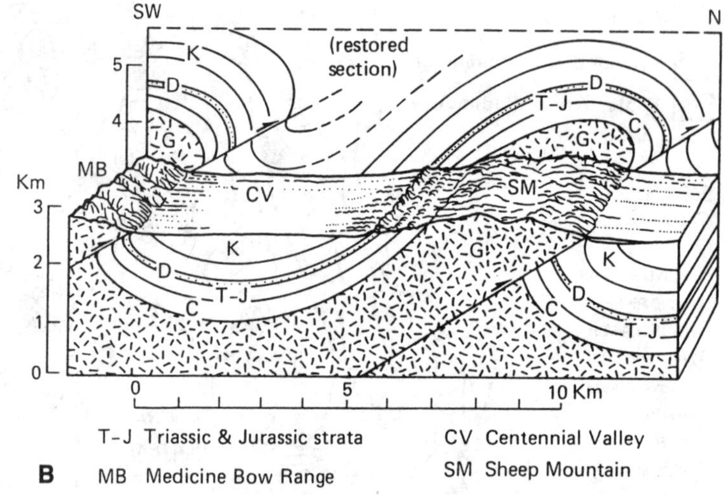

(Peter Bird, 1984,p. 742). Figure 9.56 shows Bird's schematic cross section of the completed horizontal subuction. During the period of about 70 to 40 Ma, this slab had been moving to the northeast. Whereas in Cretaceous time, the surface of this foreland region lay close to sea level in isostatic equilibrium with a crust about 33 km thick, insertion of the horizontal Farallon slab was followed by an increase in crust thickness to more than 50 km and a surface elevation of ~2 km. Crustal thickening may have been caused by shear stress (drag) exerted on the overlying North American lithosphere, which in turn transported its ductile crust northeastward to accumulate under the foreland region. This suggestion has been refuted by R.F. Livaccari and F.V. Perry (1993, p. 722). They argued instead that crustal thickening progressed eastward by horizontal end loading (horizontal pressure) originating in the subduction zone and transmitted first to the Sevier thrust belt, then finally to the region of Laramide block uplifts. They see the role of the horizontally subducted Farallon plate as serving to place a thermal barrier between the North American plate and the hot asthenosphere, and thus causing a "refigeration" of the overlying plate. Thickening of the overlying plate was thus limited to an end zone in which the Farallon plate descended at a steep

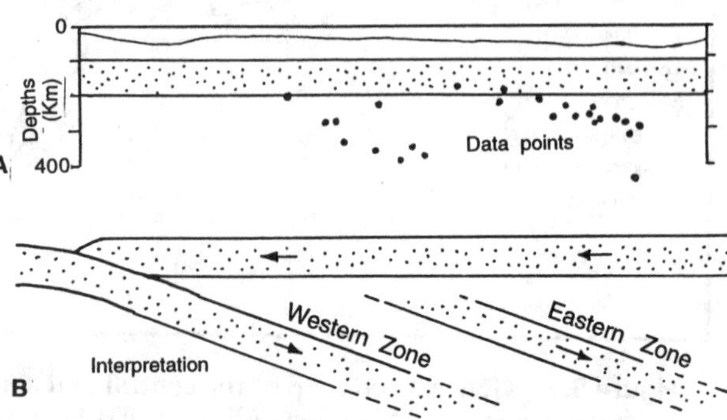

Figure 9.55 Evidence of subducted Farallon plate beneath North American plate. (A) Plotted depths of sources of andesite magmas. (B) Interpretation of data as showing two dipping subduction segments of the Farallon plate. (From P.W. Lipman, H.J. Prostka, and R.L. Christiansen, *Science*, v. 174, p. 8.24, Figure 3. Copyright © 1971 by the American Association for the Advandcement of Science. Used by permission.)0

angle. In 1995, Eugene D. Humphreys proposed that "post-Laramide removal of the subhorizontal Farallon slab occurred by buckling downward" (p. 987). His diagrams show various interesting modes of possible delamination and down-plunging (p. 988, 989).

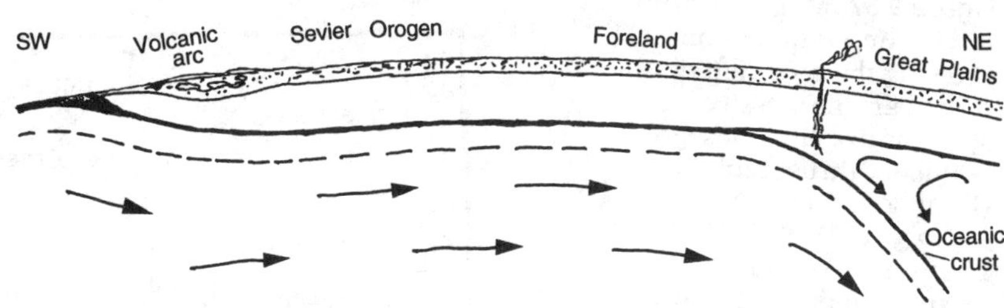

Figure 9.56 Schematic southwest-northeast cross section of western North America through the region of Rocky Mountain Laramide uplifts, showing data suggestive of horizontal subduction of the Farallon plate. (Adapted from P. Bird, 1984, *Tectonics*, v. 3, no. 7, p. 743, Figure 1. Used by permission of the author and the American Geophysical Union.)

There remained to be solved the structural mode of rise of the uplifts, which come in a wide variety of sizes and basal outlines. Two "schools" had been debating their differing tectonic modalities. One of these, called the "vertical-tectonics (or upthrust) school," drew the thrust fault planes, which are dipping moderately at the surface, as steepening to near-verticality with depth. The opposing group, called the "horizontal-tectonics (or compressional) school," drew the thrusts as listric faults, declining in dip with depth to approach horizontality (Bird, 1984, p. 741).

As in the scientific history of many major large-scale problems of geology, seismology proved to be a key to the configuration of the marginal thrust faults. Here, reflection seismology on traverse lines, both as industry exploration and by COCORP, has provided answers for some of the uplifts. A COCORP traverse of the southern end of the Wind River Range clearly showed the presence of a major thrust fault bounding the western side of the uplift (Smithson et al., 1980; Steidtmann and Middleton, 1991). The fault plane dips northeastward beneath the mountain range. The dip is on the order of 30° near the surface, and the fault surface flattens to about 15° at a depth of 40 km. Numerous minor splay faults and minor parallel faults appear to be present. COCORP tranverses of the Laramie Range revealed a boundary overthrust along the eastern base of the range. It dips westward beneath the range at a moderate angle in one traverse and at a steep angle in another, but at neither location was the fault traced to a depth of over 10 to 12 km (Brewer et al., 1982). The COCORP data lend strength to the dominant theory that crustal shortening and lateral compression are largely responsible for the Laramide uplifts.

In a comprehensive 1989 review of the Phanerozoic evolution of the North American Cordillera, John S. Oldow, Albert W. Bally, Hans G. Avé Lallemant, and William P. Leeman wrote: "In our judgement, the basement-cored uplifts of the southern Rocky Mountains are best explained within the context of intracrustal decoupling levels, including one major decoupling within the middle or lower crust. While such a basal decoupling level at this time is still inferrred, all geophysical data so far suggest that the mantle is not involved in the basement uplifts" (p. 172). More specifically, these authors postulate a regional décollement at the base of the lower crust (p. 172).

In pursuing further the hypothesis of lateral compression as the major cause of the Laramide structural uplifts, a promising source of independent evidence lies in the investigation of stress directions interpreted from small-scale tectonic structures within the bedrock of the uplifts. Recall from Chapter 6, in our section titled Stress Axes and Faulting, we explained how the compressional and tensional axes of small fracture planes can be identified in laboratory speciments or field outcrops. We also showed how these axes are related to the three basic kinds of faults. (See Figures 6.14 through 6.17.) Our next logical step is to assume that if the regional compressional axis within the crust of the Laramide uplifts is oriented horizontally in a general northeast-southwest direction, a similar geometrical relationship should be found to exist in the microstructures in the bedrock outcrops of the uplifts. If such proves to be the case, and if individual crustal units of the several uplifts have not rotated horizontally since they were uplifted, our initial hypothesis will be greatly strengthened.

Following through along these lines, geologist Robert J. Varga carried out a field program of *paleostress analysis* of these preserved stress directions (Varga, 1993). He drew his measurements from minor faults, most of which are in crystalline Archean rock, exposed near the frontal fault zones in five localities, shown in Figure 9.57. There is good independent evidence that all of the faults were formed during the Laramide orogeny. Note the wide range in orientations of the geographic long axes of the selected uplifts. The observed compass orientation of the compressional stress axis is shown by a large double arrowhead placed at each locality to summarize the field data. The most obvious visual relationship of stress axis to geology is the tendency of the axis to be orthogonal (at right angles) to the geographical long axis of the uplift and thus also to the boundary fault close to which the samples were taken. At the same time, in four out of the five locations, the stress axis has a bearing falling within the NE (or SW) compass quadrant, which shows a strong element of partial compliance with the supposed direction of movement of the

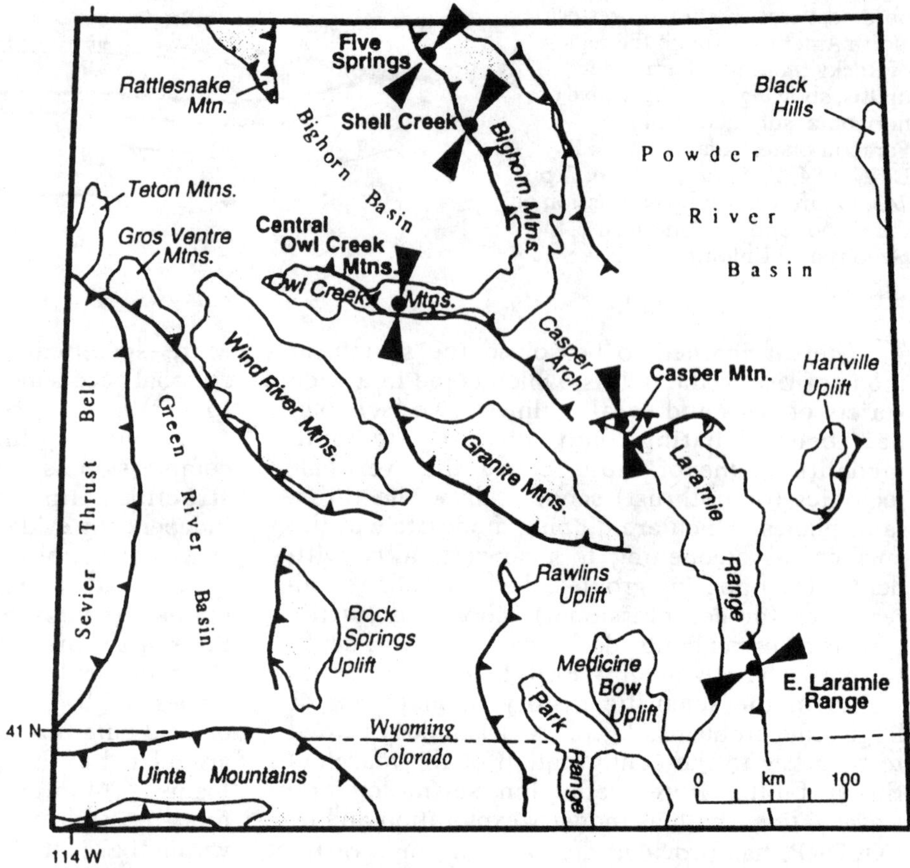

Figure 9.57 Map of central Rocky Mountain region showing the direction of principal compressive stress at five sites close to boundary thrust faults. (From R.J. Varga, 1993, *Geology*, v. 21, p. 1115, Figure 1. Reproduced by permission of the author. Reproduced with the permission of the publisher, the Geological Society of America, Boulder, Colorado, USA. Copyright © 1993.)

subducting Farallon plate.

In Chapter 6, we described three faults in the Yellowstone volcanic area: Hebgen Lake, Madison, and Centennial. Their three different orientations suggest that each individual fault block has undergone clockwise rotation. The possibility of block rotation might also be introduced into the explanation of the varied direction of the four uplifts studied by Varga. Another possibility, considered by Varga and others is that the direction of compressional stress changed as the underlying Farallon plate changed its direction of motion relative to the North American plate. A further complication is introduced by the fact that the boundary faults combine strike-slip motion in various combinations with dip slip. Varga suggests that the diverse orientations of the local stress axes "may be explained by the partitioning of strain within and near the east-trending and, to some extent, the north-trending ranges" (1993, p. 1117). This is to say that the product of two different stress vectors, each in its own uplifted range, when combined, sum to the value of the prevailing general vector. Other geologists have noted that strain partitioning commonly occurs near large strike-slip faults. This case study reveals that problems of tectonic history are seldom if ever simple. As a seemingly simple hypothesis is first investigated, it soon resolves itself into a handful of secondary hypotheses, each one difficult to resolve beause of lack of sufficient evidence.

9.26 The Colorado Plateau

Platform strata of the Colorado Plateau province were also affected by foreland basement deformation. This plateau province merges with the southern edge of the regions of Laramide structural uplifts (Figure 9.53) and is surrounded on the west, south, and east by the Basin and Range province, characteried by extensional features of a younger tectonic event. In that framework, we can think of the Colorado Plateau has having been "nibbled away" at its edges, which are steepened by tectonic and geomorphic agents. Geologically, the plateau is a sedimentary platform bearing strata of Paleozoic Mesozoic and Cenozoic ages. Between large areas of more-or-less horizontal strata are gentle anticlinal upwarps, or "swells," and sharply defined monoclines. These linear features trend mostly north-south, but may show arcuate or sinuous plan forms of varied directions. Although deeply eroded and missing large thicknesses of their original covers, exposures of the Pre-Cambrian basement are largely limited to the lower walls of deep river gorges, such as the Grand Canyon of the Colorado River.

A good example of the anticlinal uplift is the Kaibab Plateau of northern Arizona, through which the Grand Canyon has been incised. The continuation of this structure south of the Grand Canyon is the Coconino Plateau (Babenroth and

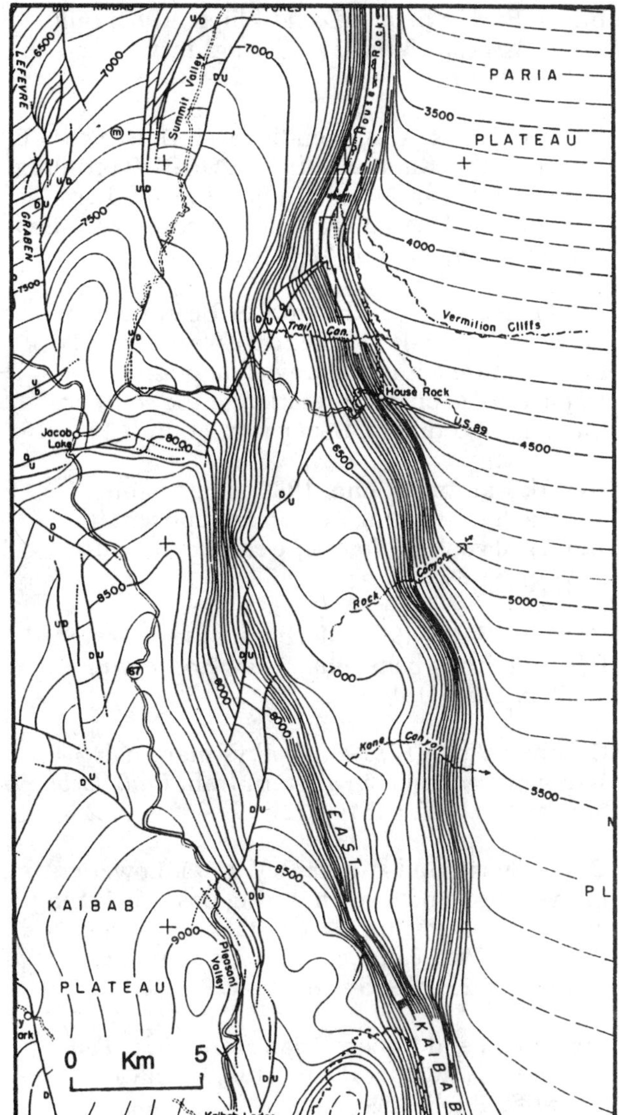

Figure 9.58 Structure contour map of a section of the East Kaibab Monocline, Arizona. (Adapted from D.L. Babenroth and A.N. Strahler, 1945, *Bull., Geol. Soc. Amer.*, v. 56, Plate 1. Reproduced with the permission of the publisher, the Geological Society of America, Boulder, Colorado, USA. Copyright © 1945.)

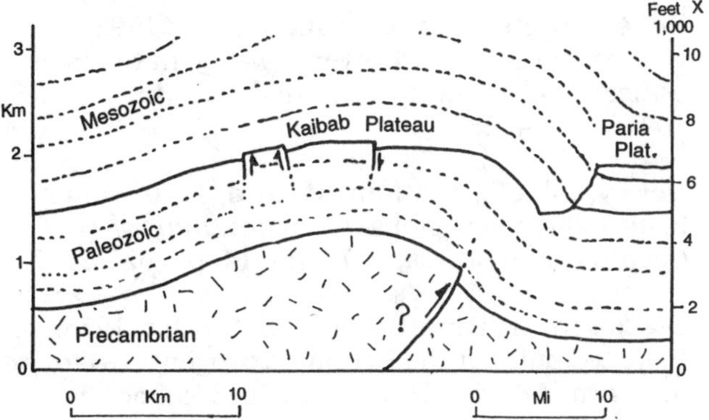

Figure 9.59 Schematic cross section of the northern part of the East Kaibab monocline. (Copyright © by Arthur N. Strahler.)

Strahler, 1945; Strahler, 1948). In combination with this broad anticline is the great East Kaibab monocline that forms its eastern flank. Figure 9.58 is a map of this structure displayed by topographic contours on a single stratigraphic horizon, which is the upper surface of the highly resistant Kaibab limestone of Carboniferous age.

Figure 9.59 is a schematic cross section through the northern part of the Kaibab Plateau and East Kaibab monocline. The dip of the strata steepens near the base of the monocline, with a maximum value of about 45°, but overturning is not observed. In this respect, the monoclines of the Colorado Plateau differ from the Laramide structural uplifts, since the latter commonly show overturning. However, both of these kinds of uplifts are thought to to be expressions of deep, steeply inclined listric upthrusts, representing crustal convergence under horizontal stress. Minor normal faults, often occuring in parallel sets as grabens, and found over the Kaibab Plateau, and these extensional features may be of younger age, brought about by the change to extensional tectonics that followed. In contrast to the Laramide uplift region, the Colorado Plateau has experienced volcanic activity in many localities. This activity, continuing into the recent epoch, includes both mafic cinder cones and silicic flows and vents. These have been dated to range in age from 5 Ma to recent (Tanaka et al., 1986).

* * * * * * * * * *

Compressional tectonics has been the main theme of this chapter. Compressional tectonics, expressed in arc-continent and continent-continent collisions, constructs and enlarges continents. Extensional tectonics, the theme of our next chapter, rifts apart continents. Logically, continent building comes first, but once that happened in the early Archean Eon, it makes little difference which modality is given priority. J. Tuzo Wilson chose continental breakup as the starting point of his plate-tectonic cycle.

References Cited

Abers, Geoffrey A., and Robert McCaffrey, 1994, Active arc-continent collision: Earthquakes,, gravity anomalies, and fault kinematics in the Huon-Finisterre collision zone, Papua New Guinea. *Tectonics*, v. 13, no. 3, p. 227-245.

Argand, E., 1924, La tectonique de l'Asie. *Comptes Rendus*, no. 5, p. 171-372, Thirteenth International Geological Congress, Brussels.

Atwater, Tanya, 1989, Plate tectonic history of the northeast Pacific and western North America. Chapter 4, p. 21-72, in *Geology of North America, Volume N*. Boulder, CO: The Geological Society of America.

Avigad, Dov, Christian Chopin, Bruno Goffé, and André Michaud, 1993, Tectonic model for the evolution of the western Alps. *Geology*, v. 21, p. 659-662.

Ayrton, Stephen, 1980a, High fluid presure, isothermal surfaces, and the initiation of nappe movement. *Geology*, v. 8, p. 172-174.

Ayrton, Stephen, 1980b, Reply to J.H. Willemin, P.L. Guth, and K.V. Hodges (1980). *Geology*, v. 8, p. 406.

Babenroth, Donald, L., and Arthur N. Strahler, 1945, Geomorphology and structure of the East Kaibab monocline, Arizona and Utah. *Bull. Geol. Soc. Amer.*, v. 56, p. 107-150.

Bally, Albert W., and Allison R. Palmer, 1989, *The Geology of North America; an Overview*. Boulder, CO: Geological Society of America.

Barazangi, Muawia, and James Ni, 1982, Velocities and propagation characteristics of Pn and Sn beneath the Himalaya arc and Tibetan Plateau. Possible evidence for underthrusting of Indian continental lithosphere beneath Tibet. *Geology*, v. 10, p. 179-185.

Bates, Robert L., and Julia A. Jackson, Eds., 1987, *Glossary of Geology*, 3rd ed. Alexandria VA: American Geological Institute.

Belderson, Martin, 1989, Third party implicated in Alpine crash. *New Scientist*, v. 121, no. 1650, p. 35.

Bird, Peter, 1984, Laramide crustal thickening event in the Rocky Mountain foreland and Great Plains. *Tectonics*, v. 3, no. 7, p. 741-758.

Bois, Christian, and Vincent Courtillot, 1988, The French ECORS program. *EOS*, v. 69, no. 43, p. 799-989.

Boyer, Steven E., and David Elliott, 1982, *Bull., Amer. Assoc. of Petroleum Geologists*, v. 66, no. 9, p. 1196-1230

Brewer, J.A., R.W. Allmendinger, L.D. Brown, J.E. Oliver, and S. Kaufman, 1982, COCORP profiling across the Rocky Mountain Front in southern Wymoming, Part I: Laramide structure. *Bull. Geol. Soc. Amer.*, v. 93, p. 1242-1252.

Brown, Richard L., Christopher Beaumont, and Sean D. Willett, 1993, Comparison of the Selkirk fan structure with mechanical models: Implications for interpretation of the southern Canadian Cordillera. *Geology*, v. 21, p. 1015-1018.

Bykerk-Kauffman, Ann, 1989, A hands-on approach to teaching the terrane concept in historical geology. *Jour. of Geologic Education*, v. 37, p. 83-89.

Chapple, W.M., 1978, Mechanics of thin-skinned fold and thrust belts. *Bull., Geol. Soc. of Amer.*, v. 89, p. 1189-1198.

Cherven, Victor B., 1986, Tethys-marginal sedimentary basins in western Iran. *Bull., Geol. Soc. Amer.*, v.97, p. 516-522.

Costa, Sylvie, and Patrice Rey, 1995, Lower crustal rejuvenation and growth during post-thickening collapse: Insights from a crustal cross section through a Variscan metamorphic complex. *Geology*, v. 23, p. 905-908.

Cox, Allan, and Robert Brian Hart, 1986, *Plate Tectonics: How it Works*. Boston: Blackwell Scientific Publications, Inc.

Dahlstrom, Clinton D.A., 1970, Structural geology in the eastern margin of the Canadian Rocky Mountains. *Bulletin of Canadian Petroleum Geology*, v. 18, no. 3, p. 332-406.

Debelmas, J., A. Escher, and R. Trumpy, 1983, *AGU-GSA Geodynamics Series*, v. 10, p. 83-97.

DeCelles, Peter G., and Gautam Mitra, 1995, History of the Sevier orogenic wedge in terms of critical taper models. *Bull., Geol. Soc. Amer.*, v. 107, p. 454-462.

Dewey, John F., and John M. Bird, 1970, Mountain belts and the new global tectonics. *Jour. of Geophysical Research*, v. 75, no. 14, p. 2625-2647.

Dickinson, William R., and W.S. Snyder, 1978, Plate tectonics of the Laramide orogeny. *Geological Society of America Memoir 151*, p. 355-366.

Dickinson, William R., Margaret A. Klute, Michael J. Hayes, Susanne U. Janecke, Erik R. Lundin, Mary A. McKittrick, and Mark D. Olivares, 1988, Paleogeographic and paleotectonic setting of Laramide sedimentary baasins in the central Rocky Mountain region. *Bull., Geol. Soc. Amer.*, v. 100, p. 1023-1039.

Dumitru, Trevor A., Phillip B. Gans, David A. Foster, and Elizabeth L. Miller, 1991, Refrigeration of the western Cordilleran lithosphere during Laramide shallow-angle subduction. *Geology*, V. 19, p. 1145-1148.

Durheim, Raymond J., and Walter D. Mooney, 1991, Archean and Proterzoic crustal evolution: Evidence from crustal seismology. *Geology*, v. 19, p. 606-609.

Eisenstadt, Gloria, and Declan G. DePaor, 1987, Alternative model of thrust-fault propagation. *Geology*, v. 15, p. 630-633.

England, P.C., and G.A. Houseman, 1988, The mechanics of the Tibetan Plateau. *Phil. Trans. Royal Soc. London*, A 326, p. 301-319.

Fielding, Eric, Bryan Isacks, Muawia Barazangi, and Christopher Duncan, 1994, How flat is Tibet? *Geology*, V. 22, p. 163-167.

Gretener, P.E., 1972, Thoughts on overthrust faulting in a layered sequence. *Bull. of Canadian Petroleum Geology*, v. 20, no. 3, p. 583-607.

Gretener, P.E., 1980, More on pore presssure and overthrusts. *Proceedings, Conference on Thrust and Nappe Tectonics*. London, Oxford: Blackwell Scientific Publishers.

Griffin, Villard S., Jr., 1974, Analysis of the Piedmont in northwest South Carolina. *Bull., Geol. Soc. of Amer.*, v. 85, 1123-1138.

Guth, Peter L., L.V. Hodges, and J.H. Willemin, 1982, Limitations of the role of pore pressure in gravity gliding. *Bull., Geol. Soc. Amer.*, v. 93, p. 611.

Harrison, T. Mark, Peter Copeland, W.S.F. Kidd, and An Yin, 1992, Raising Tibet. *Science*, v. 255, p. 1663-1670.

Hatcher, Robert D., Jr., 1983, Incorporation of new and old tectonics concepts into a modern course in tectonics. *Jour. of Geological Education*, v. 31, p. 256-265.

Hatcher, Robert D., Jr., and Richard T. Williams, 1986, mechanical model for single thrust sheet, Part I. *Bull., Geol. Soc. of Amer.*, v. 97, p. 975-985.

Heim, Albert, 1876, *Mechanismus der Gebrigsbildung.*

Heim, Albert, 1919-1922, *Der Geologic der Schweitz*, Leipzig, Tauschnitz.

Hobbs, Bruce E., Winthrop D. Means, and Paul F. Williams, 1976, *An Outline of Structural Geology*. New York, John Wiley & Sons.

Hodges, K.V., R.R. Parrish, T.B. Housh, D.R. Lux, B.C. Burchfiel, L.H. Royden, and Z. Shen, 1992, Simultaneous Miocene extension and shortening in the Himalayan orogen. *Science*, v. 258, p. 1466-1468.

Holmes, Arthur, 1978, *Holmes Principles of Physical Geology*, 3rd ed., revised by Doris L. Holmes. New York: John Wiley & Sons.

Howell, David G., 1989, *Tectonics of Suspect Terranes: Mountain Building and Continental Growth*. New York: Chapman and Hall.

Hubbert, M.K., and Rubey, W.W., 1959, Role of fluid pressure in mechanics of overthrust faulting. I. Mechanics of fluid-filled porous solids and its applications to overthrust faulting. *Bull., Geol. Soc. Amer.*, v. 70, p. 355-372.

Humphreys, Eugene D., 1995, Post-Laramide removal of the Farallon slab, western United States. *Geology*, v. 23, p. 987-990.

Jones, D.L., D.G. Howell, P.J. Coney, and J.W.H. Monger, 1983, Recognition, character and analysis of tectonostratigraphic terranes in western North America. Pages 21-35 in M. Hashimoto and S. Uyeda, Eds., 1983, *Accretion Tectonics in the Circum-Pacific Regions*. Tokyo: Terra Scientific Pub.

Kearey, Philip, and Frederick J. Vine, 1990, *Global Tectonics*, Oxford: Blackwell Scientific Publications.

Laubscher, Hans, 1988, Material balance in Alpine orogeny. *Bull., Geol. Soc., Amer.*, v. 100, p. 1313-1328.

Lipman, Peter W., Harold J. Prostka, and Robert L. Christiansen, 1971, Evolving subduction zones in the western United States, as interpreted from igneous rocks. *Science*, v. 174, p. 821-825.

Livaccari, Richard F., and Frank V. Perry, 1993, Isotopic evidence for perservation of Cordilleran lithospheric mantle during the Sevier-Laramide orogeny, western United States. *Geology*, v. 21, p. 719-722.

Lowell, James D., 1974, Plate tectonics and foreland basement deformation. *Geology*, v. 2, no. 6, pp. 275-278.

McCaffrey, Robert, and Geoffrey A. Abers, 1991, Orogeny in arc-continent collision: The Banda arc and western New Guinea. *Geology*, v. 19, p. 563-566.

Molnar, Peter, 1986, The geologic history and structure of the Himalaya. *American Scientist*, v. 74, p. 144-154.

Molnar, Peter, 1989, The geologic evolution of the Tibetan Plateau. *Amer. Scientist*, v. 77, p. 350-360.

Moore, George W., 1991, Tectonic terranes. *Geotimes*, v. 36, no. 2, p. 45-46.

Nelson, K.D., 1992, Are crustal thickness variations in old mountain belts like the Appalachians a consequence of lithospheric delamination? *Geology*, v. 20, p. 498-502.

Nevin, C.M., 1949, *Principles of Structural Geology*, 4th ed. New York: John Wiley & Sons.

Oldow, John S., Albert W. Bally, Hans G. Avé Lallemant, and William P. Leeman, 1989, Phanerozoic evolution of the North American Cordillera; Unted States and Canada. Pages 139-232 in *The Geology of North America—An Overview*, vol. A., Boulder, CO: Geological Society of America.

Oldow, John S., Albert W. Bally, and Hans G. Avé Lallemant, 1990, Transpression, orogenic float, and lithospheric balance. *Geology*, v 18, p. 991-994.

Oldow, John S., Bruno D'Argenio, Luigi Ferranti, Gerardo Pappone, Enrio Marsella, and Marco Sacchi, 1993, Large-scale longitudinal extension in the southern Appenines contractional belt, Italy. *Geology*, v. 21, p. 1123-1126.

Powell, C.McA., and P.J. Conaghan, 1975, Tectonic models of the Tibetan Plateau. *Geology*, v. 3, p. 727, 731.

Price, R.A., 1970, Geological Association of Canada, Special Paper, No. 6.

Price, Raymond A., 1988, The mechanical paradox of large overthrusts. *Bull., Geol. Soc. Amer.*, v. 100, p. 1898-1908.

Price, Raymond A., 1990, Reply to Paul A. Washington, 1990, *Bull., Geol. Soc. Amer.*, v. 102, p. 531-532.

Rast, Nicholas, 1989, The evolution of the Appalachian chain. Pages 323-348 in Bally and Palmer, 1989.

Rich, John L., 1934, Mechanics of low-angle overthrust faulting as illustrated by Cumberland thrust block, Virginia, Kentucky, and Tennessee. *Bull., Amer. Assoc. of Petroleum Geologists*, v. 18, no. 12, p. 1584-1596.

Rothery, David A., and Stephen A. Drury, 1984, The neotectonics of the Tibetan Plateau. *Tectonics*, v. 3, no. 1, p. 19-26.

Sacks, Paul E., and Donald T. Secor, Jr., 1990, Delamination in collisional orogens. *Geology*, v. 18, p. 999-1002.

Searle, M.P., 1996, Geological evidence against large-scale pre-Holocene offsets along the Karakoram Fault: Implications for the limited extrusion of the Tibetan plateau. *Tectonics*, v. 15, no. 1, p. 171-186.

Searle, M.P., B.F. Windley, M.P. Coward, D.J.W. Cooper, A.J. Rex, D. Rex, Li Tingdong, Xiao Xuchang, M.Q. Jan, V.C. Thakur, and S. Kumar, 1987, The closing of Tethys and the tectonics of the Himalaya, *Bull., Geol. Soc. Amer.*, v. 98, p. 678-701.

Shermer, E.R., D.G. Howell, and D.L. Jones, 1984, The origin of allochthonous terranes: Perspectives on the growth and shaping of continents. *Annual Review of Earth & Planetary Science*, v. 12, p. 107-131

Simpson, R.W., and A. Cox, 1977, Paleomagnetic evidence for tectonic rotation of the Oregon Coast Range. *Geology*, v. 5, p. 585-589.

Smithson, Scott B., Jon Brewer, S. Kaufman, Jack Oliver, and Charles Hurich, 1980, Nature of the Wind River thrust, Wyoming, from COCORP deep-reflecton data and from gravity data. *Geology*, v. 6 p. 648-652.

Sorkhabi, Rasoul B., and Edmund Stamp, 1993, Rise of the Himalaya: A geochemical approach. *GSA Today*, v. 3, no. 4, p. 85, 88-92.

Srimal, Neptune, 1986, India-Asia collision: Implications from the geology of the Himalaya. *Geology*, v. 14, p. 523-527.

Srivastava, Praveen, and Gautam Mitra, 1994, Thrust geometries and deep structure of the outer and lesser Himalaya, Kumaon and Garhwal (India): Implications for evolution of the Himalayan fold-and-thrust belt. *Tectonics*, v. 13, no. 1, p. 89-109.

Steidtmann, James R., and Larry T. Middleton, 1991, Fault chronology and uplift history of the Southern Wind River Range Wyoming: Implications for the Laramide and Post-Laramide deformation in the Rocky Mountain foreland. *Bull., Geol. Soc. Amer.*, v. 103, p. 472-485.

Strahler, Arthur N., 1948, Geomorphology and structure of the West Kaibab fault zone and Kaibab Plateau, Arizona. *Bull., Geol. Soc. Amer.*, v. 59, p. 513-540.

Tanaka, Kenneth L., Eugene M. Shoemaker, George C. Ulrich, and Edward W. Wolfe, 1986, Migration of volcanism in the San Francisco volcanic field, Arizona. *Bull., Geol. Soc. Amer.*, v. 97, p. 129-141.

Terzaghi, Karl, 1950, Mechanism of Landslides. *Engineering Geology (Berkey) Volume*, New York: The Geological Society of America.

Twiss, Robert J., Eldridge M. Moores, 1992, *Structural Geology*, New York: W.H. Freeman and Company.

Varga, Robert J., 1993, Rocky Mountain foreland uplifts: Products of a rotating stress field or strain partitioning? *Geology*, v. 21, p. 1115-1118.

Washington, Paul A., 1990, The mechanical paradox of large overthrusts: Alternative interpretation and reply. *Bull., Geol. Soc. Amer.*, v. 102, p. 529-530.

Willemin, J.H., P.L. Guth, and K.V. Hodges, 1980, Comment and reply on "High fluid pressure, isothermal surfaces, and the initiation of nappe movement?" *Geology*, v. 8, p. 405-406.

Willett, Sean D., and Christopher Beaumont, 1994, Subduction of Asian lithospheric mantle beneath Tibet inferred from models of continental collision. *Nature*, v. 369, p. 642-645.

Willett, Sean, Christopher Beaumont, and Phillippe Fullsack, 1993, Mechanical model for the tectonics of doubly vergent compressional orogens. *Geology*, v. 21, p. 371-374.

Williams, H., and R.D. Hatcher, Jr., 1983, Appalachian suspect terranes. Pages 33-54 in R.D. Hatcher, H. Williams, and I. Zietz, Eds., *Contributions to the Tectonics and Geophysics of Mountain Chains*. Memoir 158. New York: Geological Society of America.

Willis, Bailey, 1893, Mechanisms of Appalachian Structure, *Thirteenth Ann. Report*, Part II, Washington D.C., U.S. Geological Survey.

Willis, Bailey, 1902, Stratigraphy and structure of the Lewis and Livingstone Ranges, Montana. *Bull., Geol. Soc. Amer.*, v. 13, p. 307.

Willis, Bailey, and Robin Willis, 1934, *Geologic Structures*, 3rd. ed. New York: McGraw-Hill Book Co.

Windley, Brian F., 1977, *The Evolving Continents*, 2nd. ed. New York: John Wiley & Sons.

Windley, Brian F., 1983, Metamorphism and tectonics of the Himalaya. *Jour., Geological Soc. of London*, v. 140, part 6, p. 849-865.

Windley, Brian, F., 1985, The Himalayas, *Geology Today*, v. 1, no. 6, p. 169-173.

Woodward, Nicholas B., 1987, Geological applicability of critical wedge thrust-belt models. *Bull., Geol. Soc. of Amer.*, v. 99, p. 827-832.

Zhao, Wenjin, K.D. Nelson & Project INDEPTH Team, 1993, Deep seismic reflection evidence for continental underthrusting beneath southern Tibet. *Nature*, v. 366, p. 557-559. .

[illegible] (1938) [illegible] New York, John Wiley [illegible]

Whitney, Elmer [illegible] 198[illegible] [illegible] the origin of the Rumaila [illegible] [illegible] [illegible]

[illegible] (1934) [illegible]

[illegible] 1987 [illegible] [illegible]

[illegible] [illegible] [illegible]

[illegible] [illegible]

[illegible] (1994) [illegible] [illegible] Geological Society of America.

[illegible] Company.

[illegible] [illegible] [illegible]

[illegible]

[illegible] 1980 [illegible] [illegible] and the initiation of [illegible] movement [illegible]

[illegible] 1994 [illegible] [illegible]

[illegible]

Williams, [illegible] 1993 [illegible] [illegible] Geological Society of America.

Willis, Bailey, [illegible] Mechanisms of [illegible] [illegible] Washington D.C. [illegible]

[illegible] [illegible] and [illegible] [illegible]

Willis, Bailey and Robin Willis, 1934 [illegible] 3rd ed. New York, McGraw-Hill Book Co.

Chapter: 10 Continental Rifting and Extensional Tectonics

From compressional tectonics of collision zones, we now turn to *extensional tectonics* operating within continental lithosphere. This is a broad term we used in Chapter 9 to apply to crustal stretching that typically sets in after a compressional orogen has reached a late stage in development. We shall return to the broad-scale form of extensional tectonics later in this chapter when we examine the Basin and Range Province in western North America. A quite different category of extensional tectonics is implied by the term *continental rifting,* which involves the splitting and limited horizontal spreading of continental lithosphere to create a *rift*, or *rift valley*. This form of rifting may cease with no more than a few kilometers of spreading, or it may continue eventually to separate a continent into two subcontinents with an intervening new ocean.

On a historical note, deep continental rifting as a product of extensional stress fields received the name *taphrogeny* in the 1920s. It was coined by German geologist E. Krenkel in his treatise on African geology (Quennell, 1987, p. 673). The word is from the Greek *taphre*, meaning "trench." Krenkel thought of taphrogeny as the counterpart of orogenesis, which seems logical enough if orogenesis implies the raising up of mountains under compressional stress. The term remains current through its application to sedimentary basins of rifted continental margins (Chapter 11).

In taking up the topic of continental rifting, we are returning to Stage 1 of the Wilson cycle, and to precursory extensional activities that affect the ancient cratons before an embryonic ocean basin actually appears. At this point, it may be helpful to reread the section in Chapter 1 titled "Stages of Ocean-Basin Opening and Closing—The Wilson Cycle" and to examine the accompanying figures 1.13 and 1.14. Professor J. Tuzo Wilson, a geophysicist at the University of Toronto, had presented his cycle concept in a now-classic 1966 paper titled "Did the Atlantic close and then reopen?" (See John M. Bird, 1987, p. 836.) However, Wilson's Stage 1, rift valley as an embryonic stage (East African Rift Valley), Stage 2, narrow ocean gulf (Gulf of Aden), and Stage 3, wide ocean basin (Atlantic Basin) had been previously presented in that sequence in 1959 and 1960 by Bruce C. Heezen of the Lamont-Doherty Geological Observatory. (See our Chapter 7 and Figure 7.22.) That was perhaps the first clear and specific presentation of continental rifting leading to the forming of an ocean basin.

10.1 Continental Rifting by Mantle Plumes?

What may perhaps be described as the "mainstream" hypotheses of continental rifting have called for only internal earth agents. It also assumes the existence of a lithosphere resting on a weak asthenosphere—a structural layering that has been in place since early Archean time. Within these two constraining premises there is considerable latitude as to how rifting works.

The most common of the older working hypotheses for continental plate rifting have designated a rising mantle plume as the primary agent that heats and therefore lifts the lithosphere in a doming action. This thermal doming, or arching, of the plate in turn causes tensional stress that expresses itself in widening vertical fractures, or rifts. This theory is usually identified by the adjective "active," a word that would apply equally well to any hypothesis that involved a causative force. It would be more to the point to change the label to "uplift" to connote crustal lifting by vertical pressure from below. Lifting by a mantle plume is only one "active" option, since we might also envision lifting by a rising mantle convection current, as in the mechanism usually applied to the mid-oceanic ridge.

Geologists who proposed the plume-powered hypothesis in the mid-1970s included Kevin Burke and John F. Dewey of the State University of New York at Albany (1973, 1974). Shortly thereafter, J. Tuzo Wilson gave his endorsement to this hypothesis (Cloud, 1974. p. 879). They agreed that a domal uplift over a plume typically develops three rifts meeting at a horizontal angle of about 120° to form a "rift-rift-rift (RRR) triple junction. The three crustal wedges are capable of separating into three continental fragments (Figure 10.1). A four-branched fracture system was thought to have occurred in some instances, but the triple fracture

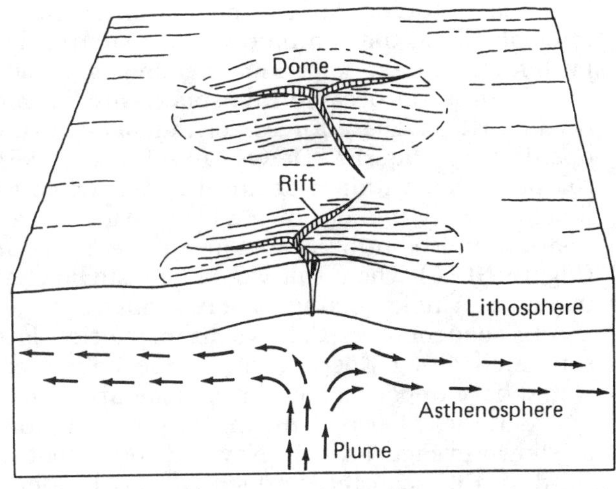

Figure 10.1 Schematic diagram of three-arm tension rifts formed by doming of the lithosphere over mantle plumes. (Copyright © by Arthur N. Strahler.)

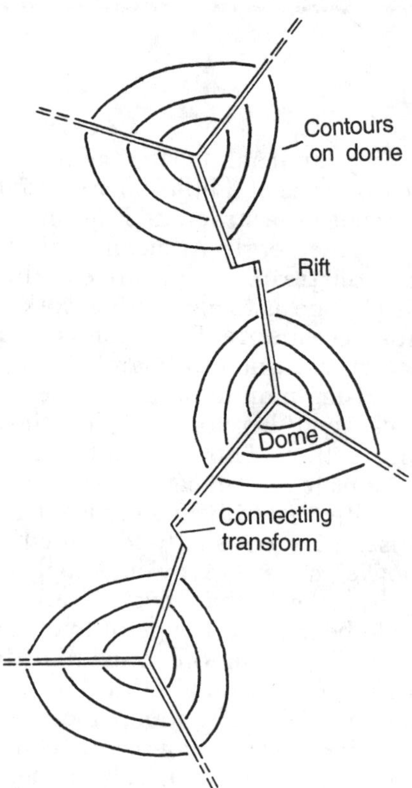

Figure 10.2 Schematic map of a chain of lithospheric domes with three-armed rifts connected in a zigzag line. (Copyright © by Arthur N. Strahler.)

was considered the most common type. A next step was to envision the simultaneous formation of an irregular line of domes (Figure 10.2). One rift extending out from a dome is approximately aligned with a rift from the next dome in the chain, so the rift domes become connected as a single continuous rift line that zigzags across the plate (Dewey and Burke, 1974, p. 58, Figure 1).

Because the facing edges of the new plates have been forced up by magma intrusion at intervals along the continuous rift system, ridge-push forces are set up in a manner analogous with those acting on oceanic lithosphere in the mid-oceanic ridge. These forces act radially outward, opening up the rift. Dewey and Burke (1974) reasoned that within a chain of linked triple rift junctions only two out of the three arms of each dome would be utilized as a new plate boundary (Figure 10.3A). The result would be a single chain made up of links joining at obtuse angles; i.e., in zigzag sequence. As the two lithospheric plates separated along this rift chain, the new ocean would have opposing coastlines made up of sharp promontories alternating with sharp indentations, as shown in Figure 10.3B. Now we notice that the third arm of each three-armed rift has become a valley extending back into the continent; it is a called a *failed arm*. In this valley, a major river flows into the new ocean and builds a large delta. Structurally, the failed arm is a fault trough, most likely an asymmetric trough with the major normal fault only on one side. This structure is known as an *aulacogen*. We will find in Chapter 11 that the sediment accumulating in the aulacogen forms a distinctive of kind of continental sedimentary basin. Notice also that thick basaltic flows ("alkaline rocks") would perhaps be found exposed in the high promontories between the aulacogens.

In early stages of rifting, parts of the rift may remain blocked off from ingress of ocean water. As plate-spreading continues, ocean water invades the widening rift from one end or both, forming a narrow ocean. Stages in widening of the new ocean basin are depicted in Figure 1.14. As the two margins of the continental plates recede from the axis of spreading, the oceanic plate is cooled and gradually sinks to a lower elevation. In Chapter 9 we explained that this slow subsidence of the plate margins allows the thickening of sediment wedges that develop on both sides of the ocean basin. (These are miogeoclinal and eugeoclinal wedges, which we will examine in Chapter 11.)

10.2 Continental Rifting by Impacting Meteorites?

A completely different hypothesis of continental rifting emerged in the 1980s and briefly caught the attention of geologists. It makes use of an external energy source. Any brittle plate that is very thin in comparison with its horizontal dimensions—a pane of glass, for example—will yield by fracturing under a sharp hammer blow. So we might envision impacts being delivered to our planet from outer space through the infall of massive solid objects—asteroids or meteorites. No doubt, as the surfaces of the Moon, Mercury, and Mars bear witness, that intense bombardment was an important early stage through which our planet also passed.

That high-energy earth-impacts by objects the size of small asteroids or asteroid fragments (meteorites) may have played an important role in plate tectonics is a hypothesis that has been seriously raised over a span of several decades. It has been suggested that a great meteorite impact might, by forming a huge crater, remove such a large piece of crust that it would set off the formation of a mantle plume. The reasoning behind this conclusion is that there would be a rapid isostatic rise of the lithosphere to compensate for the loss of crustal mass. The asthenosphere beneath would move rapidly upward as well, inducing decompression melting of the mantle, and setting off a rising magma column that would develop into a mantle plume (White, 1989, p. 1480, 1490).

Some geologists have gone even further by speculating that a number of closely grouped asteroids or large meteorites, striking the earth almost simultaneously, would have split a lithospheric plate and initiated continental rifting. The succession of mantle plumes that resulted from the impacts would have determined the

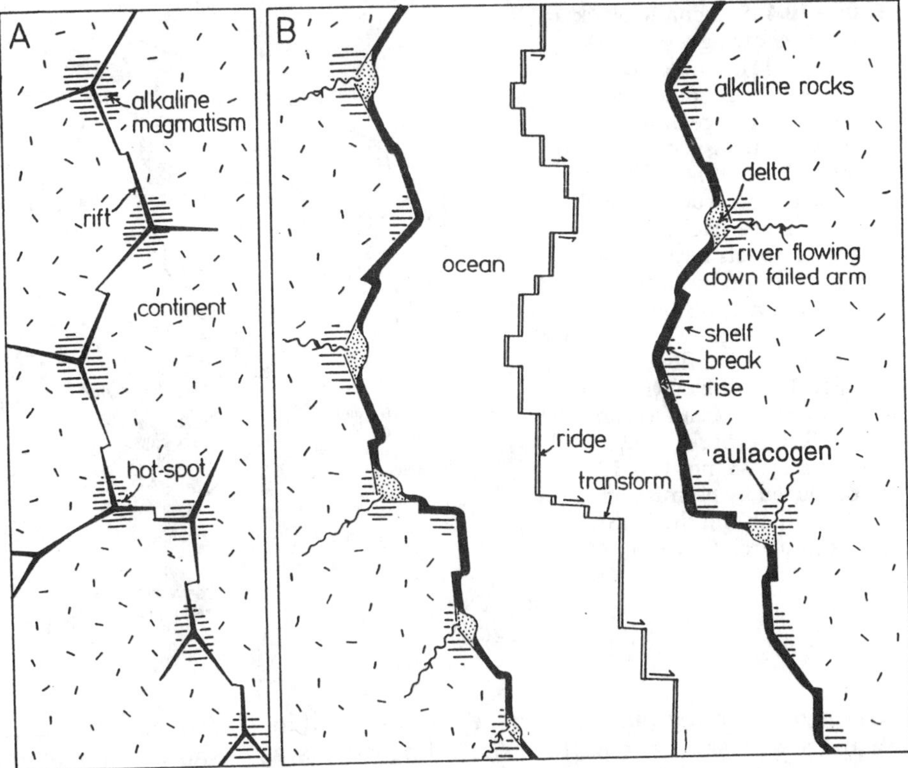

Figure 10.3 Schematic maps of early stages of the Wilson cycle. (A) Rifted domes connected into a zigzag chain. (B) New ocean formed, leaving two passive margins with failed arms in which rivers are building coastal deltas. (From J.F. Dewey and K. Burke, 1974, *Geology*, v. 2, p. 58, Figure 1. Reproduced with the permission of the publisher, the Geological Society of America, Boulder, Colorado, USA. Copyright © 1974.)

zigzag line of a new rift system. As recently as 1993, this hypothesis resurfaced to be aired in *Geotimes* by Verne R. Oberbeck of the NASA/Ames Research Center in California, whose illustration is reproduced here as Figure 10.4. You might want to respond that the supposed impact craters which started such rifting would probably have long since been obliterated by a combination of surface erosion, subsidence, and subsequent burial under the sediments of the continental margins that would have bordered the rift.

To review briefly the history of impact hypotheses of continental rifting, we can begin with a paper presented to the Annual Meeting of the Geological Society of America in 1977 by Carl K. Seyfert and John G. Murtagh of the State University of New York at Buffalo. Building on the previously proposed hypothesis that meteorite impacts could have produced mantle plumes which broke through the lithosphere (Morgan, 1972), these geologists proposed that "there appears to be an association in time of an increase in the numbers of large meteorite impacts and the times when continents begin to break apart" (Seyfert, 1987b, p. 415). They prepared a table listing epochs of impacts, including names of the impact craters (astroblemes) with their ages and diameters. The oldest epoch, in the range of 225-210 Ma, falls in late Triassic to earliest Jurassic (p. 419). One of these is the well known Manicougan Crater, 65 km in diameter, and dated as 202-210 Ma. Its outline is presently defined in the exposed shield rocks. In the youngest epoch, 2.5 Ma to present, is a possible crater in Wilkes Land, in Antarctica, with an estimated diameter of 240 km. The epoch dated as 65 Ma would include the crater or craters postulated to have been responsible for the great global Cretaceous/Tertiary biological extinction. In 1979, Seyfert elaborated upon the impact hypothesis, linking impact epochs closely with five stages in the breakup of Gondwana into subcontinents, beginning in late Triassic time and continuing through the late Tertiary, as well as to eight stages in change of direction of seafloor spreading during that same time bracket. The list of impact epochs was extended back in time to 450 Ma (Ordovician) for a total of 11 epochs (Seyfert and Sirkin, 1979, p. 383-389). Major impacts of asteroids and comets of sufficient magnitude to have set off lithospheric rifting have been postulated more recently by Andrew Y. Glickson (1995), who lists six major rifting events, ranging in age from 3.2 Ga to 0.6 Ga.

In evaluating the impact hypothesis we need to take into account factors that make difficult the assemblage of important supporting evidence. One factor is that rifting apart along a line of impact craters would separate those craters into two parts found today on opposite sides of a wide ocean. The placement of these parts in passive margins would result in their deep burial beneath younger terrestrial sediments. Another factor would be the rise of large amounts of mafic magma that could easily bury the crater and its surrounding country rock. Thus we expect a history of concealment of the necessary evidence that lies in the country rock in the form of the expected byproducts of impacting meteorites. Yet another problem arises

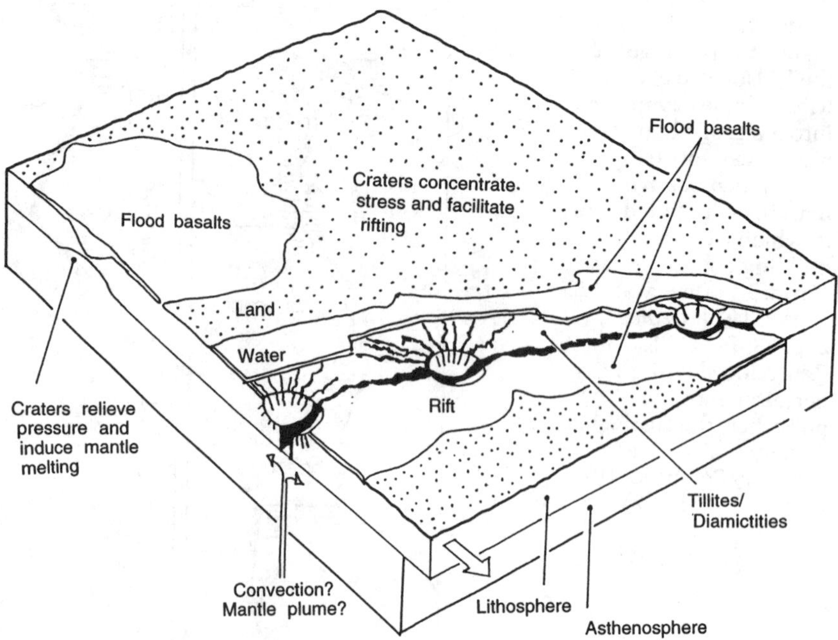

Figure 10.4 Schematic block diagram showing a continental rift energized by impacts of large meteorites. Upper left: A large crater relieves the pressure at depth, allowing rise of mafic magma to construct a basalt plateau. Lower right: Three aligned impacts have formed a rift and set in motion mantle plumes, bringing to the surface large accumulations of flood basalts. The rift has widened to form a new ocean. (From Verne R. Oberbeck, 1993, *Geotimes*, v. 38, no. 1, p. 18. Reproduced by permission of the author and the NASA-Ames Research Center.)

in the need for a group of large meteorites to fall in a more-or-less linear pattern extending across a large continental interior. The breakup of a single asteroid into two or more separated fragments by atmospheric friction or by gravitational disruption is not considered possible (Emiliani et al., 1981.) There is, however, geologic evidence from South Africa of two large impacts having occurred close together at about the same time (Vredefort Dome) and another case (Bushveld) where three overlapping ring-moats suggest three great simultaneous impacts in close proximity (Shoemaker, 1983, p. 486-487).

Looking back even further into time (*ca* 3 Ga) it seems quite likely that asteroid impacts severely affected the earth's surface when protocontinents were just beginning to be formed. What we have in mind here are impact basins on the order of 1000 km diameter that would undergo thermal and isostatic subsidence of 5 to 6 km over a period of some 10 m.y. (Grieve, 1987, p. 264). The huge craters that these impacts created may have set up major convection currents in the mantle and led to the first phases of lithospheric plate motion. Speculations of this kind are useful when based on established laws of physical behavior of the universe because they lead to the search for obscure new forms of scientific evidence we might not otherwise have investigated.

10.3 A Second Look at the Plume Hypothesis

Returning now to the mainstream hypothesis of mantle plumes, perhaps you can think of some problems arising from the Burke/Dewey scenario of rifting. You might ask: How and why does it happen repeatedly through geologic time that mantle plumes occur simultaneously in a zigzag line across an entire continent? The hotspots we attributed to mantle plumes in Chapter 5 do not show such a pattern on continents of today (Figure 5.25). Furthermore, those hotspots that have left volcanic "tracks" across the ocean floor (e.g., Walvis Ridge, Ninetyeast Ridge) trend at a large angle with the mid-oceanic ridge. There is also an even more serious problem. We surmise from the situation shown in Figure 10.3B that the plumes ceased to rise as soon as the plates began to separate, for otherwise each plume would have split in two and left its volcanic tracks from the median rift line to the continental coast. Only a few such tracks are found today in the Atlantic, Indian, Pacific, and Arctic ocean basins. Perhaps plumes were simply not involved in continental rifting. The evidences of massive magma intrusions and flows spaced along the rift are clear beyond dispute, but could they not be a result of lithospheric rifting initiated by a different and independent set of physical forces?

In a retrospective essay in *Nature* (1993, p. 393) John S. Mutter of Columbia University and the Lamont-Doherty Earth Observatory reassessed the worth of the plume hypothesis. Intensive seismic reflection imaging of rifted margins had since shown that the great igneous outpourings did not get thinner with increased distance from the rift axis. Instead, they had developed off-center to one side or the other of the axis. Mutter then added that "the effect of the inferred hotspots seemed to turn off very quickly after breakup." That is evident from the fact that oceanic crust of normal thickness now lies adjacent to the mid-oceanic ridge. Mutter continues: "Another problem was timing—why should hotspots come to life exactly at the time of rifting? These awkward features were difficult to encompass within the hotspot model, but did not prevent its widespread adoption" (p. 393).

10.4 Rifting by Penetration

An alternate hypothesis to continental rifting by rising mantle plumes switches cause and effect completely around. It envisions the rise of mafic magma under a domelike uplift of crust and mantle as the effect, rather than the cause, of splitting of a continental lithospheric plate. Careful analysis of the history of rifting of Gondwanaland suggests that wedgelike rifts appeared at the perimeter of the supercontinent. As each rift widened, it was propagated (extended) into the heart of the continent, perhaps eventually meeting another rift that had penetrated from a different marginal point.

Of course, this hypothesis requires that an extensional stress field be present over a broad expanse of the continental lithosphere and also that it be strong enough to create the rift at the edge of the continent and to sustain its propagation. The possible cause of such a stress field is a topic we treat in a later paragraph.

Under this propagation hypothesis, we can imagine that as a rift penetrates deeper into the continent it abruptly changes direction toward the right or left because of the presence of vertical zones of weakness in the lithosphere that strike at various angles to the lengthening rift. In this way, the penetrating rift might follow a zigzag path. At a point of direction change, a secondary rift might be expected, forming a triple rift. Updoming would accompany the widening of a rift, since magma would rise to fill the gap, and this rise would set off an upward movement in the asthenosphere below, perhaps through the triggering of a deep-seated phase change in the mantle rock. While this hypothesis might seem to explain the triple rifts and their domes, it leaves unexplained the basic cause and mechanism that forced the rifting to begin in the first place.

As noted above, hypotheses that invoke propagating rifts include the presupposition that the entire continental plate is being subjected to distributed extensional stress. The lower ductile region of the plate responds to this stress system by undergoing distributed thinning, while the brittle upper zone develops extensional faults (Vink, 1982; Martin, 1984). This mode of rifting is often described by the adjective "passive." In contrast to the "active theory," mentioned earlier, the "passive theory" states that the prime energizing force is a strong regional extensional stress field in the lithosphere. In other words, this stretching force pulls the lithospere apart along a line of weakness. Rise of the asthenosphere to produce domal uplifts could, of course, follow as a secondary phase, essentially as described for the "active theory".

Figure 10.5 is a schematic cross section of the upper part of a continental lithospheric plate, showing the crust, Moho, and upper mantle down to a depth of about 60 km. The uppermost 10 to 15 km is a *brittle zone* in which the rock is said to have an elastic property (Gough and Gough, 1987, p. 545). In this zone, failure occurs by faulting. Below it is a *ductile zone* in which the behavior of the rock is described as *viscoelastic*, and it deforms under stress by distributed shear, a kind of "flowage". (See Chapter 3.) This ductile property extends on down through the Moho into the mantle. To keep these zones in perspective, note that the continental lithosphere extends on down to at least 200 km in the case of the Archean cratons.

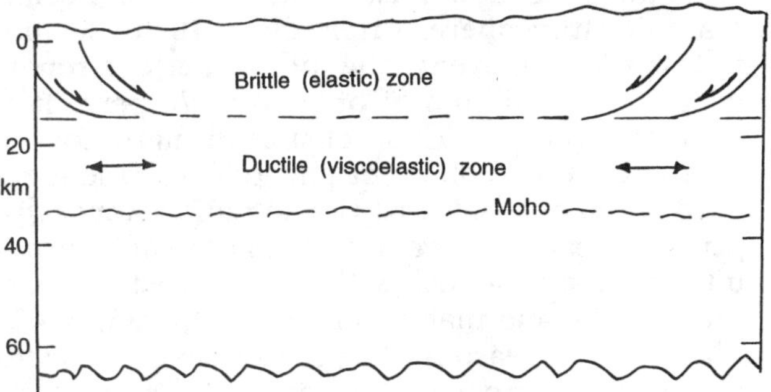

Figure 10.5 Schematic cross-section of continental crust and mantle, showing response of brittle (elastic) and ductile (viscoelastic) zones to extensional stress. (Copyright © by Arthur N. Strahler.)

Assume for the moment that a given value of horizontal extensional stress is uniformly present in the crust, tending to produce stretching outwardly left and right in the plane of the cross section. If that stress is sufficient to cause yielding, it will be manifested by brittle fracture (faulting) in the brittle (elastic) upper layer, and by continual "flowage" in the ductile (viscoelastic) zone below. Now, it is known that the stress is concentrated in the brittle (elastic) zone, and this phenomenon greatly increases the likelihood that rifting will occur (M.H.P. Bott and N.J. Kusznir, 1984; P. Kearey and F.J. Vine, 1990, p. 233). Yielding to the extensional stress is, of course, accompanied by thinning of the plate, and this allows mantle of the asthenosphere to rise, to undergo decompression, and to undergo partial melting. Thus the rise of magma may act as the effect, rather than the cause, of the rifting, but we are still in need of a hypothetical mechanism to explain the tensional stress.

The continental lithosphere is not homogeneous, however, but incorporates linear weak zones such as the deep roots of compressional orogens of largely felsic composition. It is now assumed that such linear weak zones guide the propagation process. Further analysis of the strength of continental lithosphere has been carried out by Allen F. Glazner and John M. Bartley of the University of North Carolina at Chapel Hill (1985, p. 42). Modeling has led them to the conclusion that immediately after completion of a compressional orogen the strength of the thickened lithosphere is about twice as great as normal cratonic lithosphere. After about 10 to 20 m.y. following that event, the lithospheric strength drops to a minimum of only 40 to 70 percent of normal strength. This tensile strength loss is attributed to two different phenomena. One is the deep burial of felsic crust rich in radioisotopes that generate heat. Another is the replacement of strong ultramafic mantle rock with weaker crustal rock of mixed felsic and mafic composition (1985, p. 42). These are the reasons, the authors suggest, for the common occurrence of continental rifting in old thrust belts. They note that the same observation had been made in 1966 by J.T. Wilson, and in 1984 by Vink, Morgan, and Zhao.

Figure 10.6 shows a simple map of an ideal continent subject to a uniform horizontal field of extensional stress (double-headed arrows). New rifts have begun to penetrate the continent at opposing locations, where there exist lines of structural weakness. The rifts will grow in width and depth aided by spontaneous upward forces of rising rock.

A.K. Martin of the National Research Institute for Oceanology, Stellenbosch, has modeled rift penetration using a spherical global model, as illustrated schematically in Figure 10.7. He takes into account the relative motion of the separated plates about a common Euler pole of rotation (1984, p. 612). Diagram A shows a whole continent (entire rectangle), presumably surrounded by oceanic crust (which may or may not be a part of the same plate). The vertical center band indicates a weak zone where the rift is likely to occur. We can postulate that this line lies on an old compressional orogen that has reached the stage when the lithosphere is exceptionally weak (as explained above). Diagram B shows that a widening zone of thinning crust has developed by horizontal stretching. Because of the relative rotation of the two halves of the plate with reference to the common Euler pole of rotation, the stretched zone is widest at the bottom (south) boundary and narrows toward the top (north) boundary of the plate. A critical stage is now reached at which any increase in the width (x) of the stretched zone at the bottom (south) margin will set off vertical cracking of the plate, initiated at the point entry of a rift (T). Diagram C shows a later stage in which the tip of the rift has penetrated northward, leaving in its wake a triangular wedge of ultramafic rock that has risen to fill the void, and this consists of new oceanic crust. The median line is now an active mid-oceanic ridge. Diagram D shows further penetration of the rift and in its wake a much larger and wider body of oceanic crust. Note that the area (or breadth) of continental crust has been increased by the addition of the belt of stretched lithosphere. Diagram E shows that the tip of the rift has finally reached the northern margin of the continent. From this point on in time, the ocean basin will simply widen and the distance separating the two subcontinents will increase.

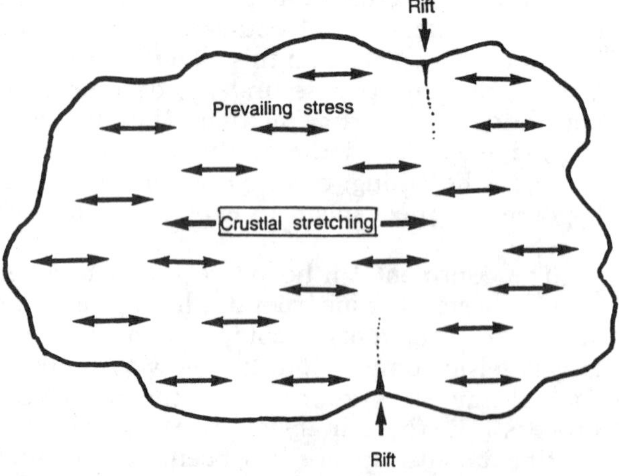

Figure 10.6 Diagram showing rifts beginning to develop at the margin of a continent subject to a uniform field of extensional stress. (Copyright © by Arthur N. Strahler.)

While the continuous through-propagation of a rift from one continental coast to the opposite side seems possible, it requires a highly uniform weak zone. More realistic may be a model in which the weak zone is interrupted by solidly locked sections where the crustal strength is high. This situation has been analyzed by Vincent Courtillot of the University of Paris (1982). Stretching in the weak sections eventually leads to fracture at a point between the locked sections, and rifts propagate rapidly away in both directions from that point toward the locked sections. Eventually, the locked sections are penetrated and full separation of the subcontinents is completed.

10.5 The Primary Cause of Intracontinental Extensional Stress?

Now we come to the final question: What primary internal agent causes a continental plate to be subjected to extensional stress sufficiently persistent and strong to cause deep rifting accompanied by the rise, emplacement, and extrusion of large quantities of mafic magmas? The most popular primary agent—a narrow mantle plume rising to form a hotspot centered in a three-armed rift—has been challenged for cogent reasons already reviewed. Does extensional tectonics within a continent—a well documented phenomenon—continue to be lacking a potent, independent causal agent?

One agent that has been favored in recent decades requires a continent bordered on opposite sides by subduction boundaries. Recall from Chapter 7, in the section "Forces Involved in Plate Motion", that geophysicists have recognized a trench-suction force that "pulls" the continental plate toward the trench. Placed in opposition, the combined pull forces of the two subduction plate

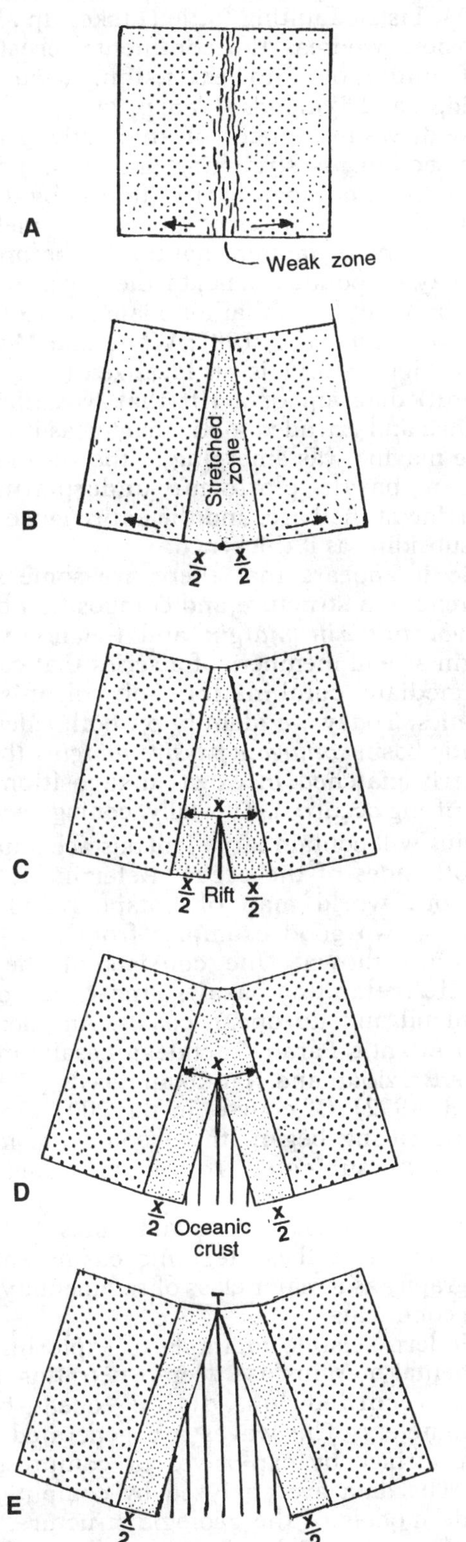

Figure 10.7 Schematic map-diagrams showing rifting of a continental plate to produce a widening stretched zone, followed by penetration of a rift and the opening up of a new ocean. (Adapted from A.K. Martin, 1984, *Tectonics*, v. 3, no. 2, p. 613, Figure 2. Used by permission of the author and the American Geophysical Union.)

boundaries would perhaps set up the necessary tensional stress system across the entire continent (Kearey and Vine, 1990, p. 234). This effect was incorporated by M.H.P. Bott in 1982 in his explanation of rift propagation. Kearey and Vine (p. 234) point out, however, that the trench-suction force cannot be applied to the East African rift system because the continent of Africa is surrounded on west, south, and east sides by divergent mid-oceanic boundaries, and that the short subduction boundaries on the north side of the African plate are incorrectly oriented relative to an east-west stress system. Nor would the explanation fit well for the Basin and Range Province, since the eastern boundary of the North American plate is a divergent mid-oceanic boundary. Stress maps show that east-west compressional stress dominates the eastern two thirds of the United States, whereas only the western one-third of the United States has extensional stress (see Figure 10.42) (Gough and Gough, 1987, p. 560, Figure 7).

A strong 'contender' for this tensional stress role has appeared through the highly successful emergence of seismic tomography of the mantle, revealing pertinent information on the thermal properties of the upper mantle down to depths of at least 400 km. (For as full discussion of this subject see Chapter 3, "Seismic Tomography of the Mantle.")

10.6 Asymmetry of Continental Rifts

Thus far our examination of continental rifting has presented the plan view of the rift as it propagates into and across a plate. We turn next to the cross-sectional view of such a rift, assuming first that it is ideally symmetrical, i.e., the right half mirrors the left half. This ideal section can be assumed first in order to show the vertical zonation with depth.

Figure 10.8 shows the brittle and ductile zones of the continental crust (A) before extension and (B) after extension. The ductile zone extends far down into the mantle, where the asthenosphere sets in. Note that the crust-mantle boundary (the Moho) lies in the ductile zone, which extends on down through the lithosphere. Extension of the continental lithosphere occurs as normal faulting in the brittle zone. These faults may be listric, lowering in dip to join tangentially a horizontal basal detachment (or décollement). The detachment surface serves to accommodate different local rates of motion between the two zones. Ductile deformation, as a form of horizontal distributed shear, may keep pace in rate of extension with the brittle faulting, and thus the entire lithospheric plate is thinned. Diagram A of Figure 10.9 is a schematic cross section showing symmetrical extension forming a symmetrical tectonic basin. In Diagram B rifting has produced a narrow ocean.

Asymmetry may be introduced into the diagram by manipulating the detachment to

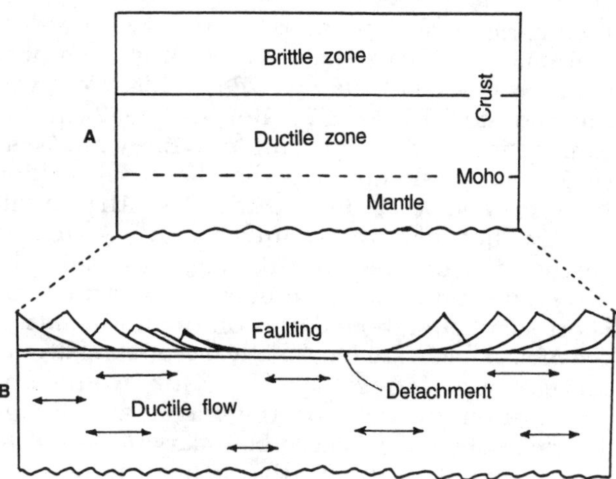

Figure 10.8 Schematic cross sections of brittle and ductile zones in extensional tectonics. (Copyright © by Arthur N. Strahler.)

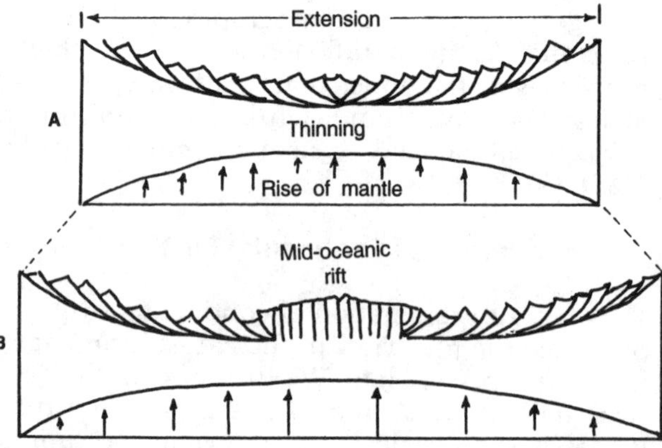

Figure 10.9 Schematic cross sections of symmetrical rifting. (Copyright © by Arthur N. Strahler.)

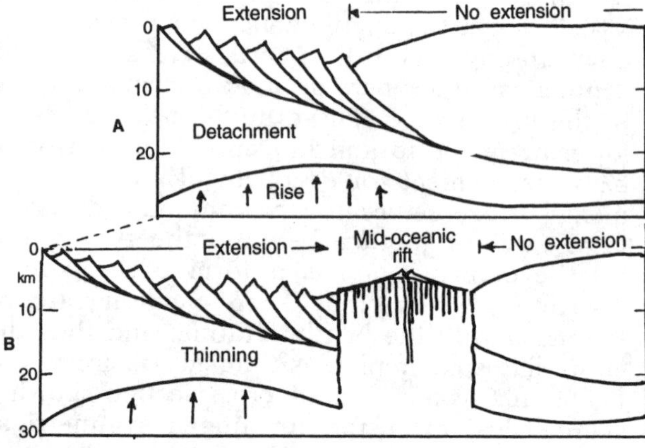

Figure 10.10 Schematic cross sections of asymmetrical rifting. (Copyright © by Arthur N. Strahler.)

become a dipping fault surface, as shown in Figure 10.10A. Listric faulting (at left) takes up all of the extension, whereas the continental crust at the right undergoes no extension. (See Lister, Ethridge, and Symonds, 1986, p. 246.)

Next, we introduce volcanic activity into the cross section. As stretching and thinning of the crust occurs, hot mantle rises to occupy the space provided. Through decompressional melting, a large volume of molten mantle can be produced, and may be ponded beneath the surface, or may erupt in basalt flows that inundate the rift (Mutter, Buck, and Zehender, 1987; White and McKenzie, 1989). Figure 10.11 is an idealized (and perhaps fanciful) diagram of a rift that was filled with intruded and extruded mafic magma as it widened. While magma was emerging at the ocean floor to form a basalt platform, underplating was occurring at the base, and the entire igneous body was subsiding as it thickened.

So it appears that there are some striking differences in structure and composition between the *volcanic rift margin* and the non-volcanic margin as end members of a series that can show intermediate combinations of volcanism and tectonics. Today we identify on both sides of the Atlantic basin *conjugate passive margins* that were formerly matched in exact juxtaposition at the time rifting occurred. Typically, conjugate volcanic margins will contain large igneous accumulations on both sides of the ocean. Referring to Figure 5.25, our world map of hotspots and basalt plateaus, two good examples from the Atlantic basin are shown. One consists of the North Atlantic/Icelandic basalts matched on the Greenland and European coasts. Another is the South Atlantic Parana/Etendeka basalts matched on the Brazilian and Namibian coasts (Harry and Sawyer, 1992). Of course, in the 200+ m.y. since Atlantic rifting began, these conjugate margins have been subjected to burial under thick accumulations of terrestrial sediments and/or constructed carbonate reefs and banks. In Chapter 11, we examine these tectonic basins and their stratigraphy as a major class of sedimentary basins of the continents.

Modern seismic methods of exploring rifted continental margins use deep-penetrating seismic waves recorded on digital ocean-bottom seismometers. The waves are generated at the ocean surface by explosives or compressed-air guns. The data are analyzed by computers that provide models of the geologic structure. Figure 10.12 shows the results of two such studies, carried out by cooperating research laboratories and universities in England and France. The data were summarized by R.S. White of the Bullard Laboratories of the University of Cambridge, England (White, 1992). Profile A is from the region near the mouth of the English Channel; it shows a typical non-volcanic margin. Profile B is from a volcanic margin near Hatton Bank, west of Great Britain. Isopleths of seismic wave velocities are

Figure 10.11 Schematic cross section of a volcanic rift margin. Not drawn to scale. (Copyright © by Arthur N. Strahler.)

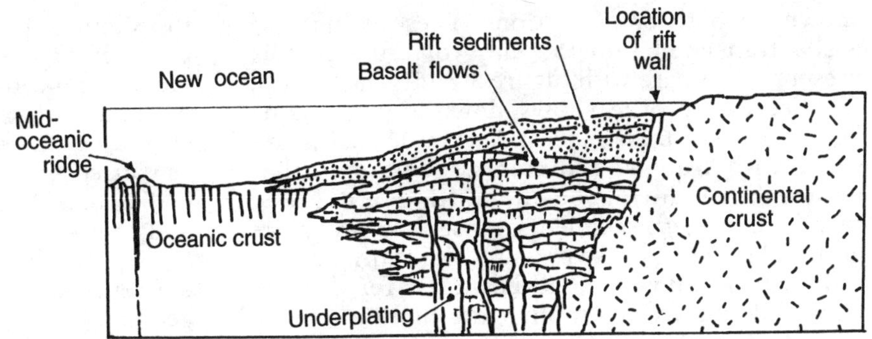

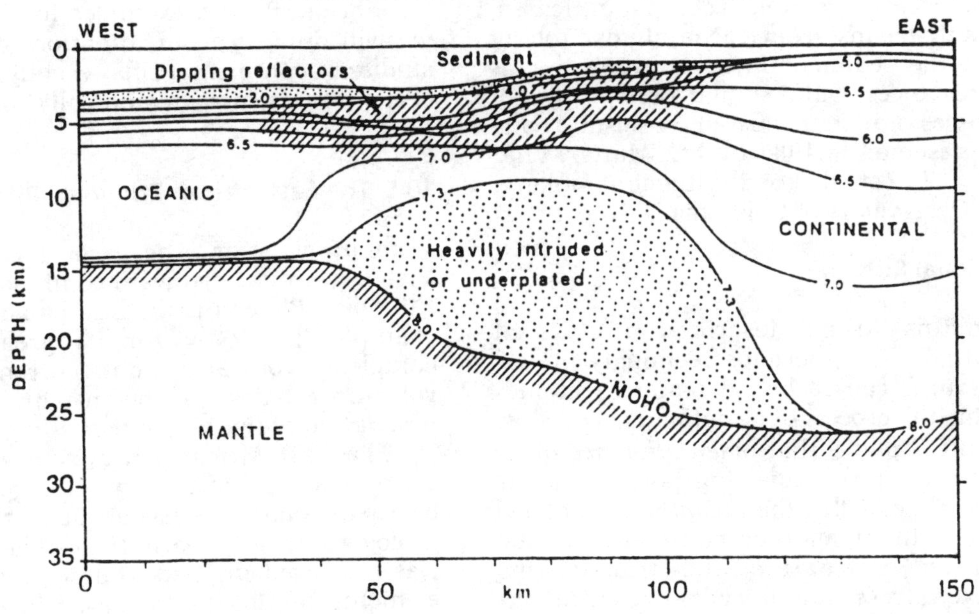

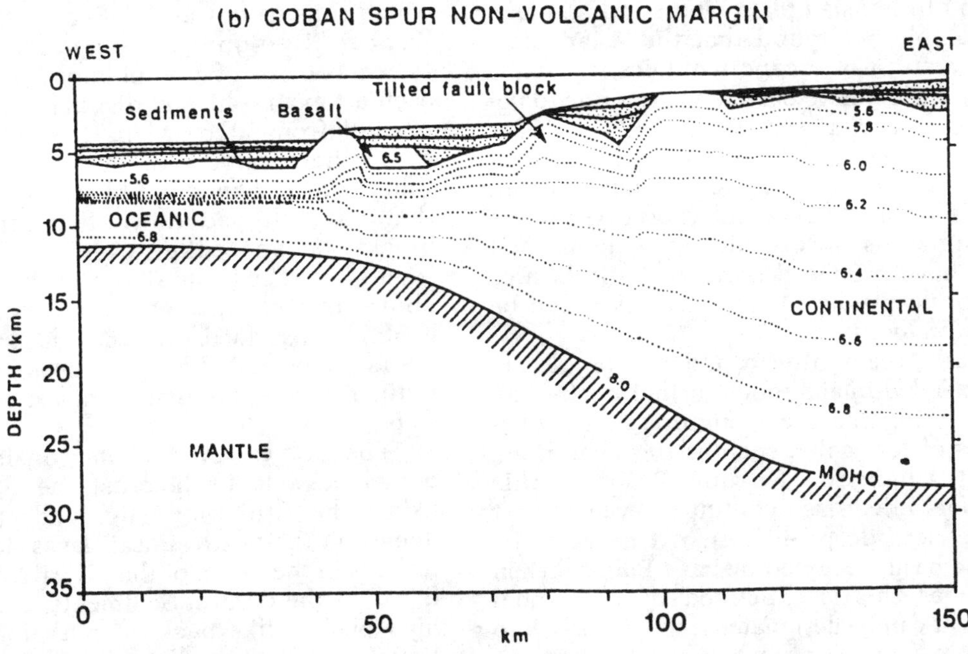

Figure 10.12 Cross sections of two kinds of rifted continental margins. (A) Non-volcanic margin with synrift sediments in fault-block basins. (B) Volcanic margin with a large mass of intruded and-or underplated igneous rock. (From R.S. White, 1992, *EOS*, v. 74, no. 5, p.58. Reproduced by permission of the author and the American Geophysical Union.)

shown on both cross sections. These values are easily translated into the class of crust that is present. (Compare with Figure 3.5.) In Diagram A, the bedrock profile shows downfaulted basins between titled fault blocks. The fault basins are filled with trapped sediments. Sediments that accumulated during basin faulting are called *synrift* (or *syn-rift*) sediments; those that have since accumulated, *postrift* sediments. The entire body of sediment in a downfaulted basin has for decades been known as a "taphrogeosyncline"; it is described in Chapter 11 as a class of sedimentary basin found in the passive continental margins. In Diagram B, a large mass of intruded and/or underplated mafic igneous rock is indicated, whereas fault basins seem to be almost totally absent and the sediment layers are continuous over long distances. Quite similar type profiles of the two classes of margins, based on seismic data, had been presented in 1987 by J.C. Mutter, W.R. Buck, and C.Z. Zehnder of the Lamont-Doherty Geological Observatory of Columbia University.

10.7 Collisional Rifts

There remains to be described a class of continental rifts that, perhaps seemingly in self-contradiction, is caused by extensional tectonics acting during the process of a continental collision. Recall from Chapter 9 that *indentation tectonics* consists of a forward projecting portion of one lithospheric plate, called the *indentor*, is rammed into the margin of another continental plate, producing an indentation and transmitting compressive stress far in advance into the receiving plate. Our example in Chapter 9 was the indentation of the Asian plate by the Indian plate. In that example, we found that the Asian plate yielded by a form of escape tectonics, in which great slices of Tibet have been (and continue to be) moved "out of the way" eastward along a series of major strike-slip faults. We also noted that over a large southeastern area of the Tibetan Plateau, eastward extension of the crust has occurred in the form of numerous north-south striking normal faults that have produced small tectonic basins. Any such basin produced by indentation can be called an *impactogen*.

Apparently, the northward indentation of Asia by India extended inland much farther north than Tibet, generating the great compressional east-west ranges of Mongolia, such as the Tien Shan, Altai, and Changain Nuruu. Perhaps this compressional effect also continued even farther north to cause a deep Siberian rift basin to be formed—the basin occupied by Lake Baikal. When a rift such as this is explained by collisional indentation, it can be designated a *collisional rift* to distinguish it from a rift produced by a rising mantle plume. The indentation scenario was proposed by P. Tapponier and P. Molnar in 1976. (See also Kearey and Vine, 1990, p. 196-198.) Whatever the merits of this hypothesis, it allows us to examine the Baikal Rift under the heading of continental rifting by indentation. On the other hand, opinions offered by Russian geologists familiar with the Baikal Rift give reasons why it should be classed with the East African rift system as caused by plate stretching independent of any collision. We postpone to a later section the pros and cons of these two interpretations.

Up to this point our chapter has covered concepts of continental rifting, including the geometry of large, deep continental rifts, and an inquiry into the possible sources of energy and the movements of matter that can initiate and/or complete the rifting. Although a few real examples have been cited as examples for our hypotheses, we will now turn our attention to regional case studies of continental rifts recently formed and, in certain cases, now tectonically and volcanically active.

10.8 The East African-Ethiopian Rift System

Without question, the great East African Rift System with its northward continuation across the Ethiopian Plateau is the best choice of a regional example, not only for its great length and complexity, but also for its current tectonic and volcanic activity. We begin with a broad-brush description of this rift system.

The East African rift system was cited by J. Tuzo Wilson as exemplary of Stage 1 of the cycle bearing his name. It has attracted the attention of geologists since the early 1900s. The term *rift valley* was first used in 1920 to describe the structural elements of this faulted area in eastern Africa (Figure 10.13). The overall length of the system, which runs from the Red Sea on the north to the Zambezi River on the south, is a full 3000 km. The system consists of a number of grabenlike troughs, each a topographically distinct rift valley ranging in width from 30 to 60 km. Geologists had noted in earlier field surveys of this system that the rift valleys are like keystone blocks of a masonry arch that have slipped down between neighboring blocks because the arch has spread apart somewhat. Thus, the floors of the rift valleys are above the elevation of most of the African continental surface, even though some of the valley floors are occupied by long, deep lakes. The sides of the rift valleys in places consist of multiple fault steps.

The rift-valley system consists of broad, domelike swells in the crust, the highest of which forms the Ethiopian Highlands (or Ethiopian dome) on the north. Basalt lavas have risen from fissures in the floors of the rift valleys and from the flanks of the domes. Sediments, derived from the high plateau-like backslopes that flank the fault troughs, have made thick fills in the floors of the valleys.

Starting at the southern end of the Ethiopian dome, the rift turns due south to become the Eastern branch, which continues through Lake

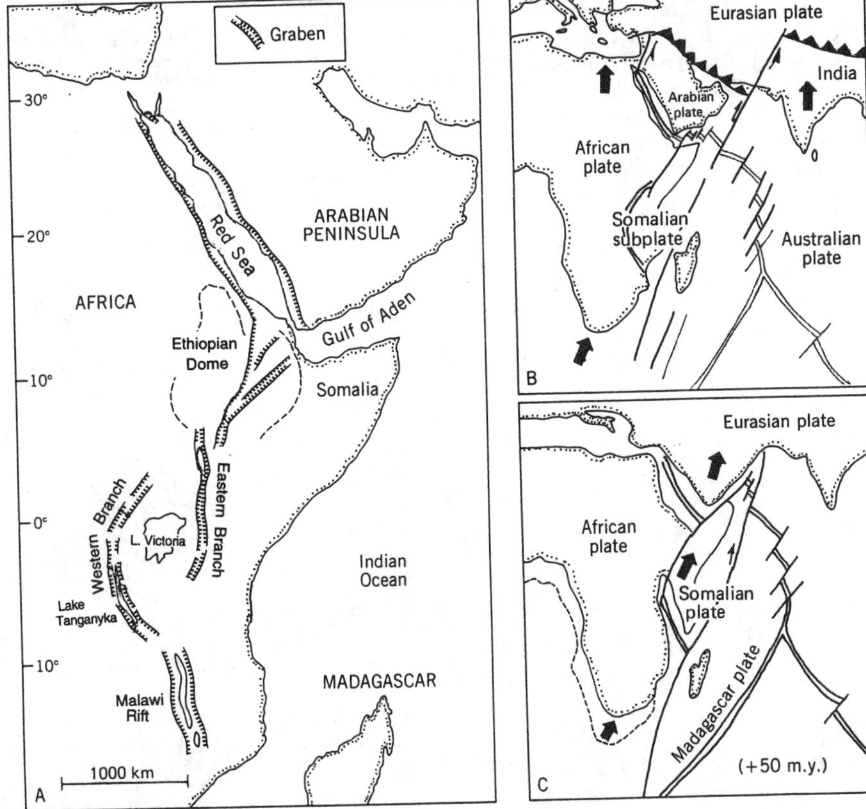

Figure 10.13 Present and possible future tectonics of eastern Africa. (A) Sketch map of the African rift-valley system and its relationship to the Red Sea and Gulf of Aden. (Copyright © by Arthur N. Strahler. (B) Delineation of a potential Somalian subplate with a new spreading boundary. (C) Prediction of a tectonic map 50 m.y. from now, during which time the new plate has moved northeast, closing the end of the Red Sea. (Panels B and C based on predictions of R.S. Dietz and J.C. Holden, 1970.)

Rudolph to become the Gregory rift (or Gregory's Rift, and also called the Kenya Rift). The Western branch, located on the opposite side of Lake Victoria, forms a great arc with Lake Tanganyika occupying its southern end. From this latitude southward, a single rift, holding Lake Malawi, forms the rift zone.

Tectonic and volcanic activity that produced the modern rift system began in this region in Eocene time and has continued sporadically ever since. The speculative suggestion was made in 1970 by R.S. Dietz and J.C. Holden that the rift system will eventually become the boundary of a detached lithospheric plate, to be called the Somalian plate. According to their interpretation of future relationships, (Figure 10.13, B, C) a spreading plate boundary will open up along the Malawi rift valley, making a new ocean basin, while a transform boundary will follow the northern part of the rift system to the Gulf of Aden. The entire plate will travel northeastward, moving past the Arabian plate.

Taking first only the rift system that lies south of the Ethiopian rift, we shift to a smaller-scale view of the tectonic features. For this information we refer to publications of Professor B.R. Rosendahl and other faculty members of Duke University, Durham, NC, who carried out Project PROBE in the 1980s. Figure 10.14 is a map outlining the major rift units, or zones. Much of the crust of this part of Africa consists of Precambrian shield rocks. Notice first that we have added rift zones to the east, west, and south of those shown in our first outline map, Figure 10.13. What has been added to the map is a much older rift system of pre-Cenozoic age, consisting of rift structures of Permo-Triassic strata of Karroo age, 230-200 Ma (Quennell, 1987, p. 678; Rosendahl, 1987, p. 446). The younger rift zones lie across these old structures in several places. The old rift structures are incomplete because of substantial erosional removal, but they are of much interest because of their possible influence on the young rift structures. A special pattern on the map (crossed diagonal lines) shows where the new structures have been superimposed on or across the old. In more than one such superimposition—the Rukwa rift zone, for example—the old structure significantly influenced the young one.

An interesting thought that comes to mind at this point is that these rifts of Permo-Triassic Karroo time did not progress into full continental breakup, as theoretically follows in the Wilson cycle. The breakup of Gondwana that began in the Late Carboniferous left this part of Africa intact. Perhaps, then we should be skeptical of predictions, such as those of Dietz and Holden, that a Somalian subplate will form and break away.

Our next map, Figure 10.15, shows the rift structures in some detail. Perhaps the feature most evident is that the border faults (main faults, with hachured lines) are relatively short segments, that many are in the form of arcs, and that these arcs are concave toward the rift axis. A chain of two or more such concave arcs comprises a "rift zone."

Figure 10.14 Major units of the East African rift valley outlined. Patterns distinguish between Cenozoic rifts and those of PermoTriassic (Karroo) age. (From B.R. Rosenthal, *Annual Reviews of Earth & Planetary Science*, v. 15, p. 447, Figure 1a. Copyright © 1987 by Annual Reviews Inc. Reproduced by permission.)

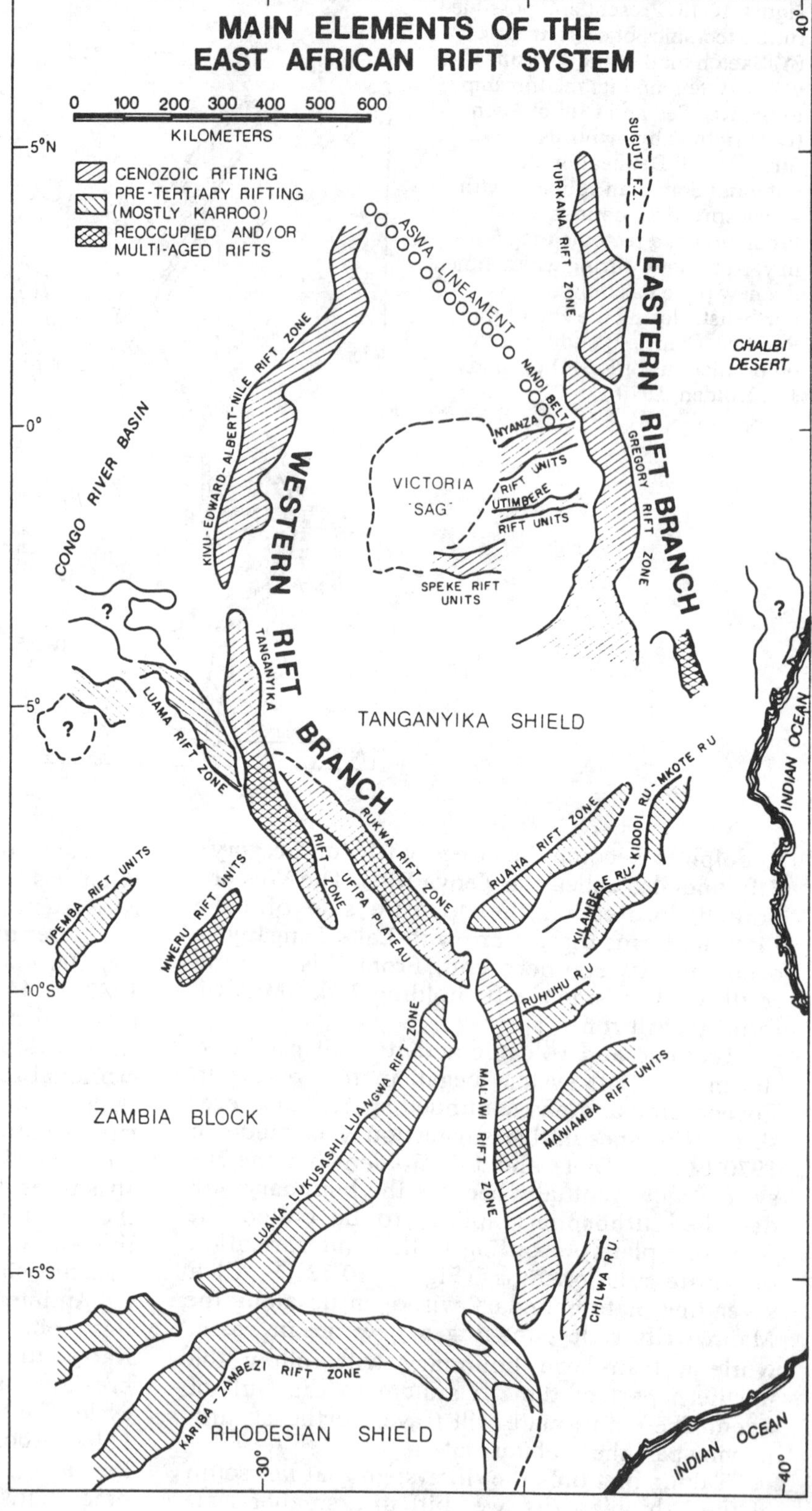

The eye also catches some long, straight fault lines. Some of these are master faults while others (lacking hachures) are labeled as "fault lineaments." Two directions dominate these linear faults: SE-NW and NE-SW. This rhomboidal pattern might suggest two sets of transcurrent (strike-slip) faults in the shield crust.

We now move in closer for a detailed study of the rift zones bordered by the inwardly-concave master fault segments, taking as an example the Gregory rift in the southwestern region of Kenya. It was named for geologist J.W. Gregory who made extensive field studies of this area, published in 1896 and 1921. Our map, Figure 10.16, shows many surface features clearly seen from the air and easily mapped from air photos and Landsat

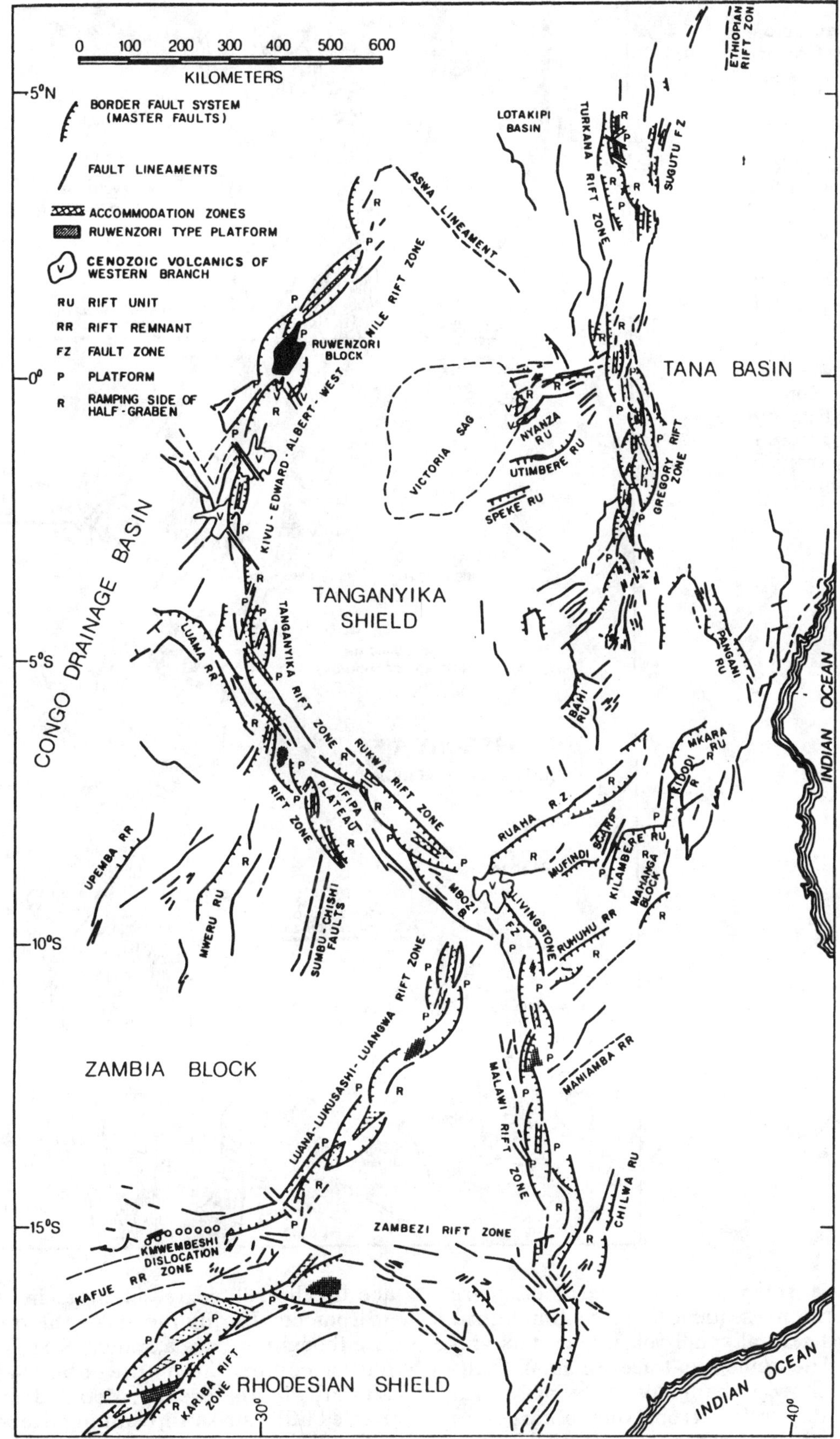

Figure 10.15 Tectonic map of the East African rift zones. (Same source as Figure 10.14, p. 449, Figure 1c. Copyright © 1987 by Annual Reviews Inc. Reproduced by permission.)

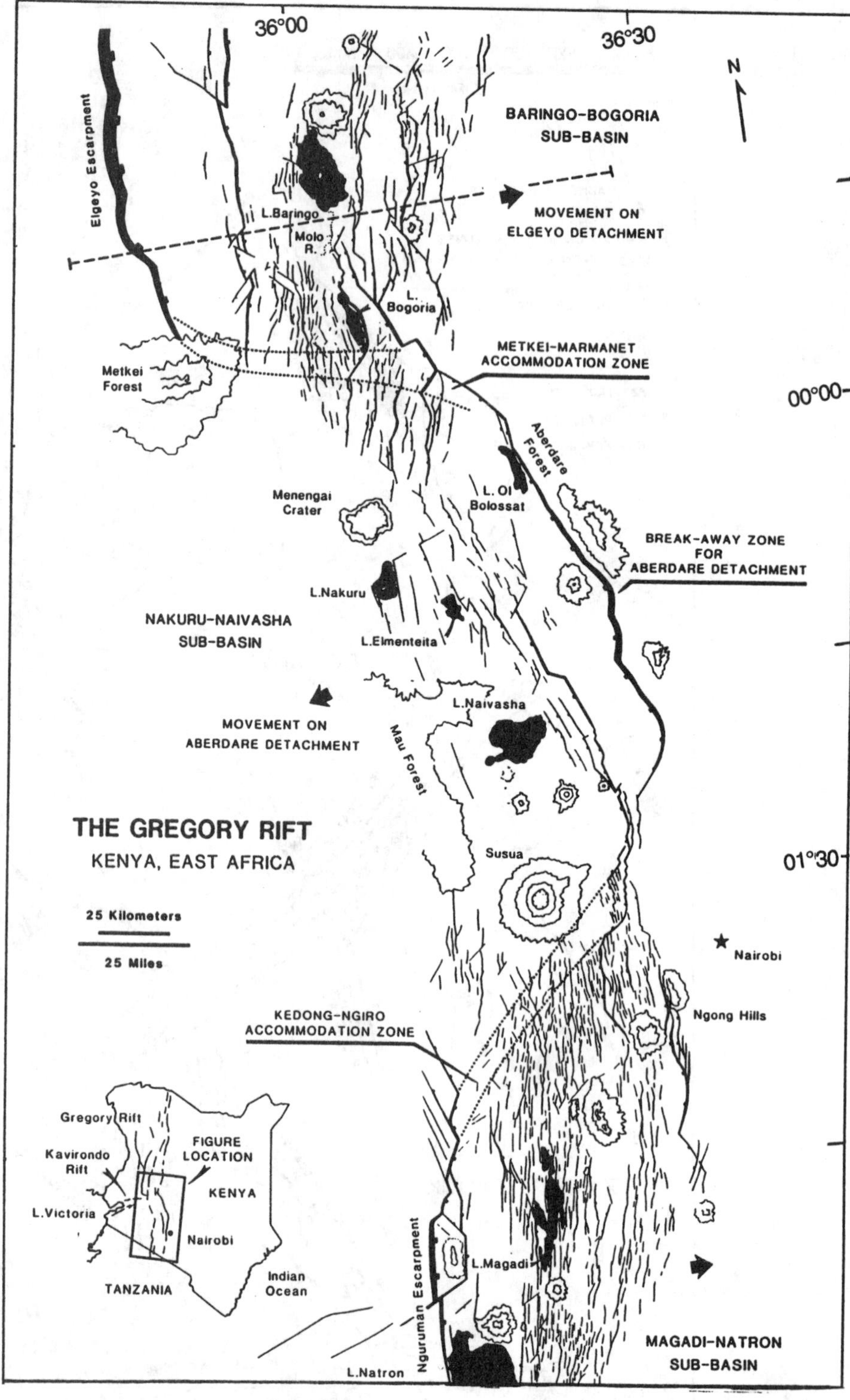

Figure 10.16 Map of tectonic and volcanic features of the Gregory rift, East Africa, using data from Landsat images, aerial photographs, and detailed topographic maps, and from surface geologic mapping. Fault traces are shown by solid lines with widths proportional the relative throw. Dashed parallel lines delineate an accommodation zone. (From W. Bosworth, J. Lambiase, and Ron Keisler, 1986, *EOS*, v. 67, no. 29, p. 577, Figure 1. Used by permission of the authors and the American Geophysical Union.)

images. Three steep arcuate escarpments are shown in alternating sequence. The continuous rift floor contains several small volcanic craters and crater lakes. The numerous traces of small faults on the floor show a change of strike of several degrees when passing from one escarpment segment to the next. Gently curved, parallel broken lines drawn diagonally cross the rift floor connect the opposing escarpments and are called *accommodation zones (AZ)* (Bosworth et al., 1986, p. 577). Within the accommodation zones are small faults known as *transfer faults*; they serve to take up the 180-degree changes in strike of the escarpments. During the 1980s the transfer zones were thought to have a system of strike-slip faults that accommodated the about-changes in azumuth. More recently, detailed mapping has revealed little strike-slip faulting (Robert J. Varga, personal communication). Instead, numerous small normal faults may supply the accommodation.

The cross section accompanying Figure 10.17 shows an interpretation of the fault structures at depth. The asymmetric structure is called a *half-*

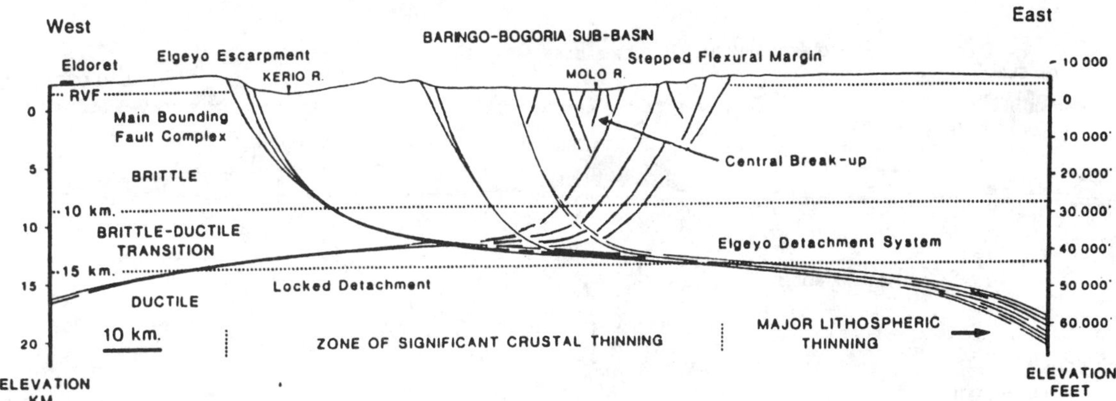

Figure 10.17 Schematic section through a sub-basin of the Gregory rift along the line indicated on the map in Figure 10.16.(Same source as Figure 10.16, p. 582, Figure 2. Used by permission of the authors and the American Geophysical Union

graben. The main bounding fault (left) descends with a steep dip, but steadily diminishes in dip as a listric fault. At about 13 km below the rift valley floor, the fault is almost horizontal and has become a *detachment zone*, which turns downward and grades into a layer of thinning in the ductile zone. (Notice how similar this cross section is compared to our Figure 10.10A.)

Viewing the same sector of the Gregory rift on a somewhat smaller scale, the same escarpments and accommodation zones are presented in Figure 10.18, showing their relationship to the great volcanoes that lie on either side: Kenya and Kilimanjaro on the east, and Elgon on the west (Bosworth, 1987, p. 398-399). Large areas of Cenozoic extrusive volcanic rocks are found on both sides of the rift axis. The lithosphere in this area is broadly domed, and often referred to as the Kenya dome.

As shown in the schematic cross section, Figure 10.19, detachment zones define planimetric zones in which the detached layers alternate in direction (Bosworth et al., 1986, p. 577). Figure 10.20 is an idealized plan view and cross section of the unit half-graben as presented by B.R. Rosendahl (1987, p. 462).

The alternating half-graben structure is considered to be a product of rift propagation in the lithosphere under uniform extensional stress. It seems that as the main normal fault is propagated, its tip is forced to turn in strike toward the rift axis. After crossing that axis, the tip is forced to reverse the curvature and again reach the center line. The three-dimensional picture that emerges for the entire under-surface of a half-graben block has been described as "spoon-shaped" (Ebinger, 1989, p. 902). To make this analogy more accurate, we might flatten the tip of the spoon into a horizontal plane and trim off the flat portion to a straight transverse edge. An alternative analogy might be an ordinary household dustpan with its flat straight edge at the front and a high upcurved rim at the rear.

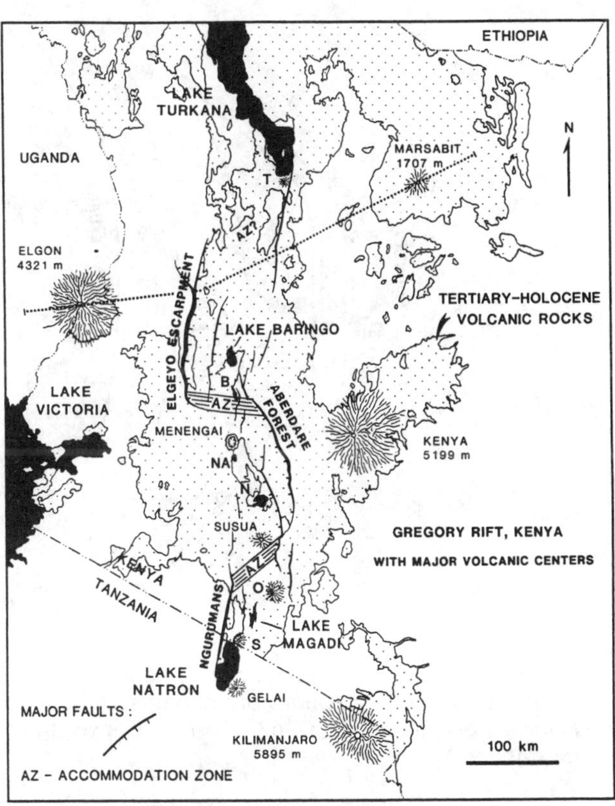

Figure 10.18. Map of the Gregory rift showing relationships between faults and volcanic features. (From W. Bosworth, 1987, *Geology*, v. 15, p. 398, Figure 1. Reproduced with the permission of the publisher, the Geological Society of America, Boulder, Colorado, USA. Copyright © 1987.)

A major explosion seismology investigation of the Gregory rift was undertaken in 1985 by an international group of seismologists. Under the name of KRISP 85 (Kenya International Seismic Programme), a team of some 70 geophysicists completed a longitudinal (N-S) traverse along the rift floor and another transverse (E-W) to it through the southernmost of the three half-

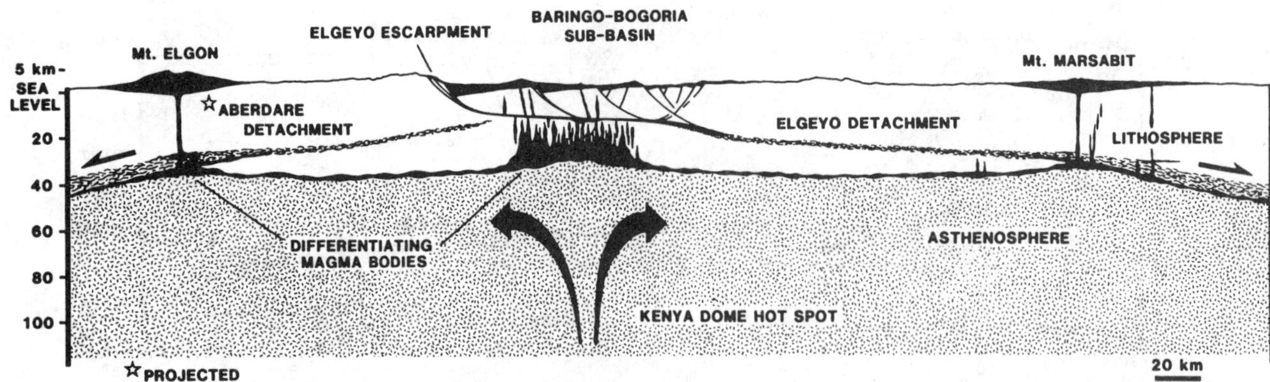

Figure 10.19 Schematic cross section along line A-B in Figure 10.18. The surface topographic profile is exaggerated x2, whereas the subsurface secton has zero exaggeration. (Same source as Figure 10.18, p. 399, Figure 3. Reproduced with the permission of the publisher, the Geological Society of America, Boulder, Colorado, USA. Copyright © 1987.)

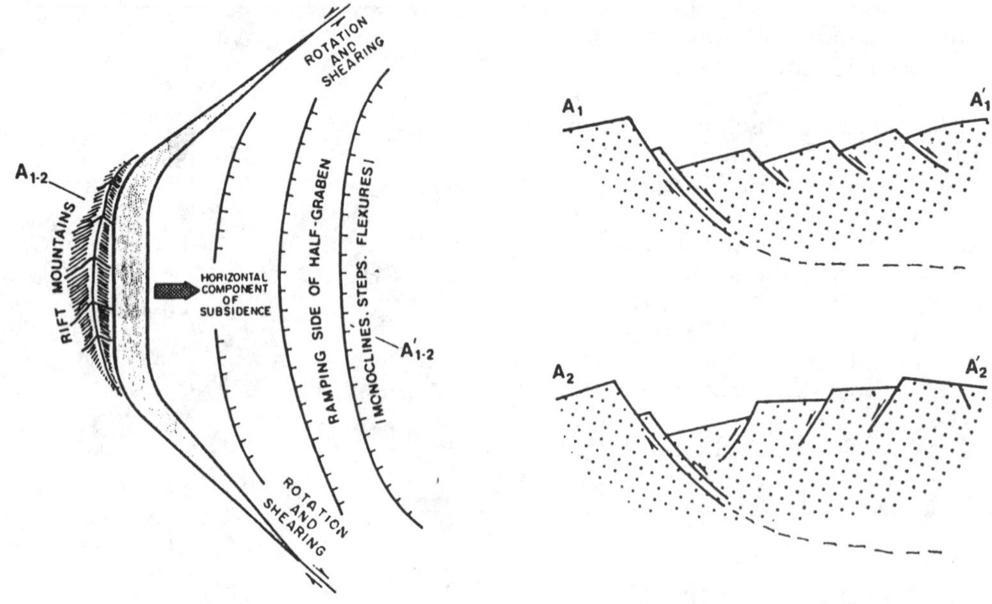

Figure 10.20 Stylized plan of an ideal half-graben, with cross sections showing two possible interpretations of the minor normal faults. (Adapted from B.R. Rosenthal, *Annual Reviews of Earth & Planetary Science*, v. 15, p. 462, Figure 3. Copyright © 1987 by Annual Reviews Inc. Reproduced by permission.)

grabens shown in Figures 10.16 and 10.18 (Khan et al., 1986). Because the KRISP 85 seismic study applied to the same rift section for which Bosworth and his colleagues had published their interpretation of these half-graben structures, it excites our curiosity as to whether that interpretation was sustained or found wanting.

Continuing immediately to the north of the Gregory rift is the Turkana rift. It, too, has been intensively studied by geologists and probed by modern explosion seismology. Our reason for examining the Turkana rift is largely because it lies in a broad lithospheric low-altitude area, called the Turkana depression. Note also that a major dome lies immediately to the north in the Ethiopian rift sector. Now, if we support the hypothesis that doming is an essential event in initiating these African rifts, how can it happen that virtually identical half-graben structures could have formed without domal uplift? This question was asked by Thomas J. Dunkelman, Jeffrey A. Karson, and Bruce R. Rosendahl of the same Duke University PROBE team that had studied the Gregory rift (Dunkleman et al., 1988). Lake Turkana occupies a long, deep basin that is almost filled with some 5 km of terrestrial sediments and volcanics ranging in age from Miocene through Holocene. The volcanics include pyroclastics and lavas ranging in composition from basalts through rhyolites. Geologic and seismic data show that the rift segment corresponding with Lake Turkana consists of a series of six half-graben units, four of which show the same curvature and alternation with connecting accommodation zones as are found in the Gregory rift (1988, p. 259). The answer to their question would seem to be that local doming is not essential to rift development.

The Western branch of the rift system also displays segmentation into inwardly concave half-graben units, but in some places two such units of opposite direction face each other directly, or with only a small offset. One explanation for this variety of relationships would be that lateral displacement has occurred along the rift axis since the graben units began to develop. This would first produce an overlap, which would continue until full opposition occurred.

Within the Western branch is what appears to be an anomalous rift. It is the Rukawa rift that lies roughly parallel with the Tanganyika rift, with which might seem to be an en echelon relationship rather than the typical end-to-end positioning. (See Figures 10.14 and 10.15.) However, the straightness of the northeastern boundary of the Rukwa rift stands out as an unusual departure from most of the other rifts, where the half-graben unit has a curved ground trace (Figure 10.21). This straight boundary is the locus of a major fault—the Lupa fault. To explain this apparent anomaly, W.H. Wheeler and J.A. Carson of Duke University postulate that the Lupa fault has followed an ancient deep-seated strike-slip fault (1994). That fault has been reactivated, but as a normal fault. Cross sections in Figure 10.21 shows the rift to be a half-graben. The older fault, which is over 1000 km long, is thought to be low in frictional strength and has been reactivated by the regional extensional crustal stress. The Rukwa rift is bounded on the southwestern side by a segmented normal fault—the Ufipa fault. Its escarpment rises to a height of 1000 m, whereas that of the Rukwa reaches only 400 m, a contrast that also seems anomalous.

Our final example is the Malawi rift, striking almost due N-S. This trend is at about a 45° to the Lupa fault of the Rukwa rift. Lake Malawi, formerly called Lake Nyasa, occupies most of the length of the rift zone. As Figure 10.15 shows, there is a connecting link provided by the Livingstone fault, similar in character to the Rukwa fault and probably also dominated by an ancient strike-slip fault in the Precambrian basement (Ring, 1994). The Malawi rift zone possesses the typical structure of the Western and Eastern branches (see Figure 10.15).

The Ethiopian rift system stands in relation to the rift systems we have described as both a close relative and a hostile predator. Look first at the big picture, shown in Figure 10.13, for the larger setting. The Ethiopian dome, also referred to as a plateau, is the largest and highest of the African uplifts, with summit elevations well over 3000 m. What strikes the eye is large V-shaped indentation squarely along the mid-axis of the dome, giving a

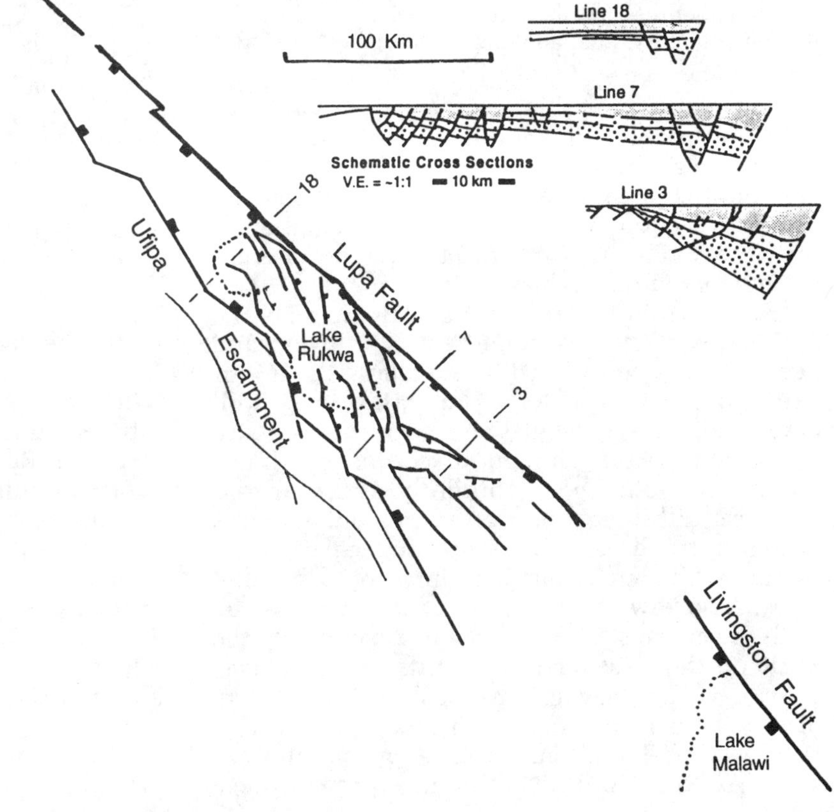

Figure 10.21 Tectonic and geologic map of the Rukwa rift and north end of the Livingstone fault. (From W.H. Wheeler and J.A. Karson, 1994, *Geology*, v. 22, p. 626, Figure 2. Reproduced with the permission of the publisher, the Geological Society of America, Boulder, Colorado, USA. Copyright © 1994.)

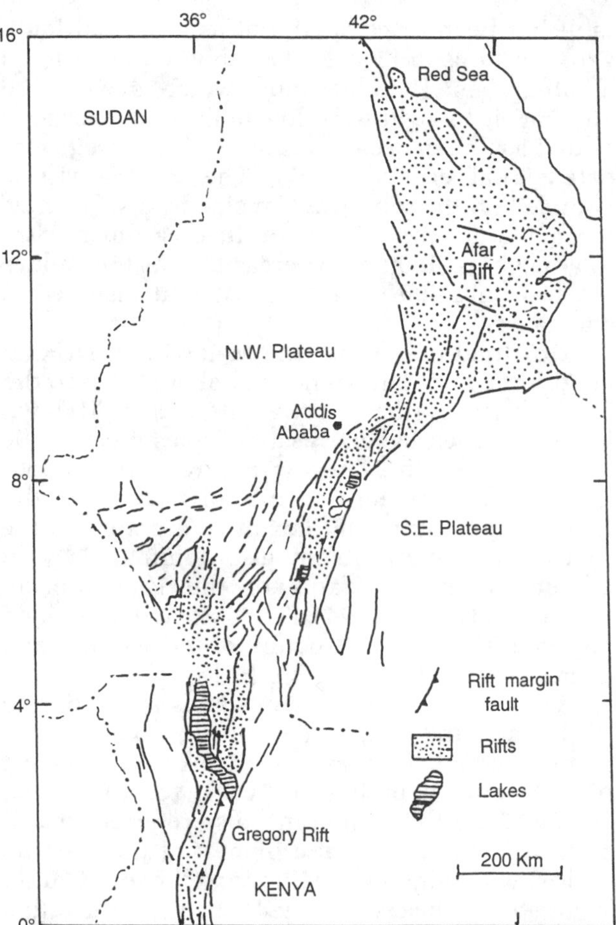

Figure 10.22 Tectonic map of the Ethiopian rift structures and their relation to the Turkana and Gregory rifts. (From G. Wolde-Gabriel and J.L. Aronson, 1978, *Geology*, v. 15, p. 430, Figure 1. Reproduced with the permission of the publisher, the Geological Society of America, Boulder, Colorado, USA. Copyright © 1978.)

tulip outline to the dome. This indentation, referred to as the Afar depression, is a lowland set off from the plateau halves by steep escarpments. In a later section, we relate the Afar indentation to the Red Sea, the Gulf of Aden, and a high promontory of the Arabian Peninsula.

As shown in Figure 10.22, a tectonic map, the Afar depression narrows to the southwest and becomes a steep-walled rift valley—the Main Ethiopian rift (MER). The MER has well developed, straight fault scarp segments on both sides, and these change direction by small increments to a more southerly strike as the southern Ethiopian border is neared. On this changing trend, the rift is not aligned with the Turkana rift, but is instead aimed on a parallel track. A northward projection of the Turkana rift leads to several short rifts on a line paralleling the MER on the west, and these rifts are no longer active. Instead, they disappear into volcanic rocks of the plateau. In a report on this region, Giday Wolde-Gabriel and James L. Aronson of Case Western Reserve University interpreted these features as failed rifts, successively abandoned as the MER, a strong propagating rift, penetrated southward (1987, p. 430, 433). Evidently, this invasive strike is tied in with the lithospheric spreading events that were forming and widening the Red Sea and Gulf of Aden.

Seismicity of the African rift system is closely related to the rift zones, with small to medium, shallow earthquake epicenters being scattered along the Cenozoic rifts. Concentration is densest along the Western branch, the Malawi rift, and the southern end of the Eastern branch. What may seem most surprising is the equally intense seismicity of certain parts the older Karroo rift zones. The northern part of the Gregory rift and the entire Turkana rift are almost free of seismic activity, as is the main Ethiopian rift. James Jackson and Tom Blenkinsop (1993) found that several earthquakes of $M_W \geq 5.5$ had occurred at depths of 25-40 km, a range "significantly greater than the 5- to 15-km range typical of most other regions of continental extension" (p. 1131). The authors associate this greater depth with an old, cold lithosphere, thicker than normal. The greater depth of occurrence is attributed to the larger-than-normal vertical and horizontal dimensions of the half-graben units (p. 1137).

To sum up, the Eastern and Western rift branches seem to be completely separate and unconnected from each other. The Eastern branch shows an offset discontinuity with the Ethiopian rift to the north. The Western rift seems to show continuity with the Malawi rift to the south. North of about the third parallel of latitude, the Eastern and Western branches and the Ethiopian rift have evolved in a Precambrian shield free of the Karroo structures that so greatly complicate the tectonic histories of the rift zones farther south. Extensional stress within the entire eastern and southern highland portions of the African continent is oriented approximately E-W (Coblentz and Sandiford, 1994, p. 833). This observation accords with our general interpretation of the stress field associated with continental regions presently undergoing lithospheric extension.

10.9 The Baikal Rift System

With information on the East African-Ethiopian rift system now presented, we can briefly compare it to the Baikal rift system in east-central Asia. Keep in mind the standing controversy as to whether the Baikal rifting was generated by the penetration of India into Asia (Tapponier and Molnar, 1979, p. 3425), or is an independent rift forced by mantle doming (Logatchev and Florensov, 1978). Figure 10.23 is a regional map showing the position of the Baikal rift between the Precambrian Siberian platform on the north and the India-Tibet collision region on the south.

The main rift of the Baikal system is a deep trough, some 600 km long and 50 km wide,

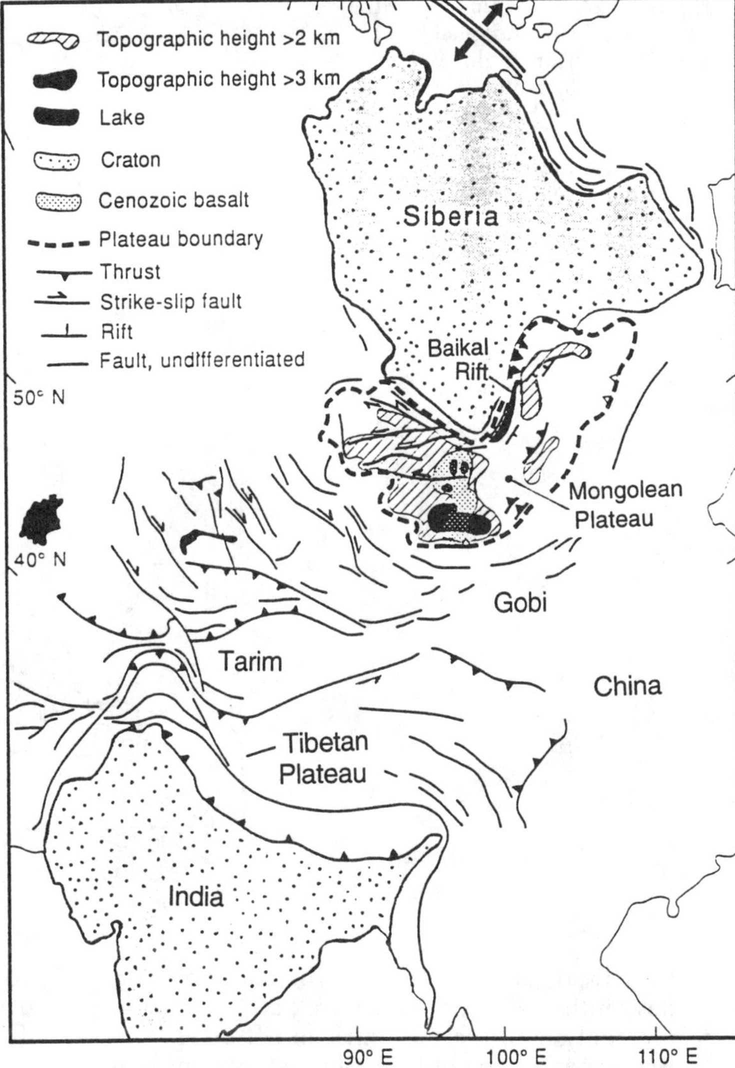

Figure 10.23 Regional map of central Asia showing the relationship of the Baikal rift to the Indian plate and the Siberian platform. (Adapted from B.F. Windley and M.B. Allen, 1993, *Geology*, v. 21, p. 296, Figure 1. Reproduced with the permission of the publisher, the Geological Society of America, Boulder, Colorado, USA. Copyright © 1993.)

occupied by Lake Baikal, which is the deepest (>1600 m) as well as the most voluminous lake on earth (Hutchinson et al., 1992, p. 589). The water surface lies at 140 m above sealevel. The age of the rift is estimated to be greater than 35 m.y. Synrift sediments have accumulated to a maximum thickness of some 10 km. Extending eastward for an additional 1500 km is a chain of isolated smaller rifts, completing the Baikal system (Seyfert, 1987, p. 681).

The Baikal trough is partitioned into four fault basins, which are half-grabens, all having the main boundary fault on the northwestern side (Figure 10.24). Because of the overall curvature of the entire rift, the boundary faults are somewhat convex toward the central axis of the lake. What is important is that there is no alternation of half-grabens facing inward to the rift axis, as is typical of the East African rifts.

Immediately to the south of the Baikal rift lies the Mongolian Plateau, a highland with surface elevations largely over 2000 m, in contrast to the low surface level of the Precambrian platform. The plateau has been described as consisting of linear crustal blocks (horsts) and intermontane basins, resembling those of the American Basin and Range province (Windley and Allen, 1993, p. 295). Some blocks exceed 3000 m in surface elevation. One of these, the Hangai uplift, lies immediately adjacent to the Lake Baikal rift basin and rises to summit levels nearing 4000 m. Geologists have long known that extensional tectonics prevailed in the Mongolian plateau in the late Mesozoic as well as during the Cenozoic, and therefore, "there is no possibility that the formation and uplift of the present-day Mongolian plateau have been the result of collision-related thickening of the crust in this region" (Windley and Allen, 1993, p. 295). On the other hand, several W-E trending strike-slip faults within the Mongolian plateau may be attributed to compression transmitted northward from the Himalayan/Tibetan indentation.

In 1989, Russian scientists carried out an extensive seismic reflection survey of the Lake Baikal sediments. A 1992 report on the results of this survey, authored jointly by Russian and American scientists, addressed the two competing hypotheses in the light of the new seismic dating (Hutchinson, et al., 1992, p. 592). Here are some of their conclusions:

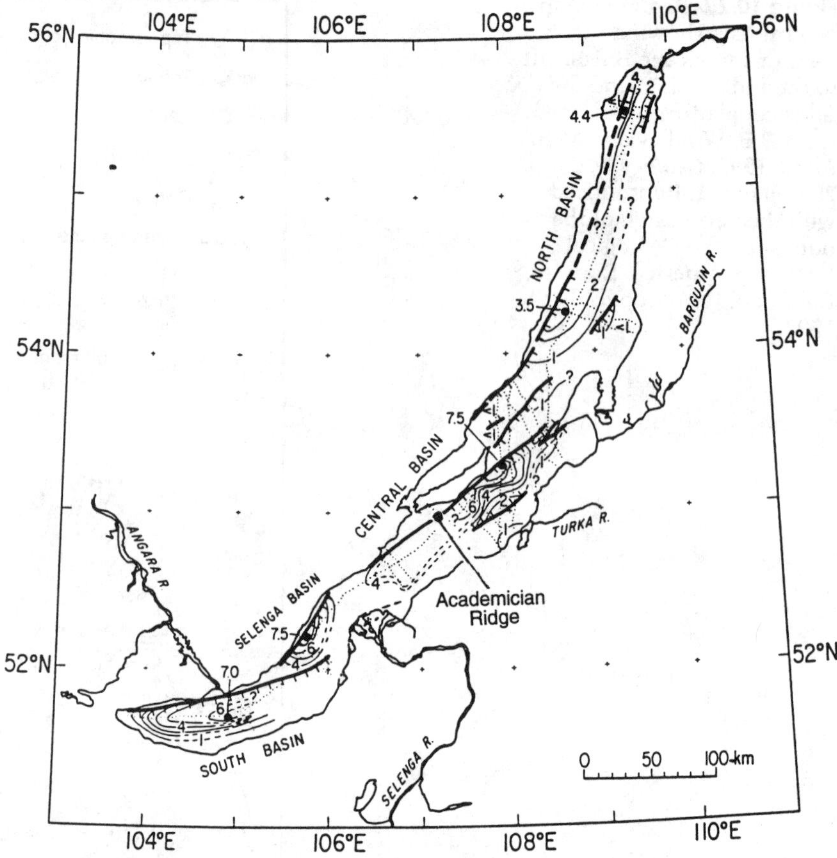

Figure 10.24 Tectonic map of the Lake Baikal rift. (Adapted from D.R. Hutchinson et al., 1992, *Geology*, v. 20, p. 591, Figure 4. Reproduced with the permission of the publisher, the Geological Society of America, Boulder, Colorado, USA. Copyright © 1992.)

Baikal does not follow the now-classic description of rift architecture developed from the analysis of the East African rift lakes. The Baikal basins do not form alternating opposing half-grabens, as do the basins in East Africa. Instead they change orientation between adjacent segments. The basins of Lake Baikal do not have curvilinear master border faults; rather, they have linear fault boundaries. The simplest explanation for these differences may lie in the fact that the East African rifts disrupt an old, stable craton, and are responding to asthenospheric stress, whereas the Baikal rifts occupy a long-lived tectonic boundary that has responded to transmitted stresses from distant plate interactions. (1992, p. 592.)

In 1992, a joint Russian-U.S. team carried out extensive multichannel seismic reflection surveys of Lake Baikal (Scholz et al., 1993, p. 465). The geophysicists concentrated on the Selenga Delta and the Academician Ridge, considered as keys to the rifting process because each is a transitional tectonic feature connecting the south and north half-grabens. The Academician Ridge cuts diagonally across the central basin, suggesting that oblique extension has been a dominant process (1993, p. 470). The evidence of oblique-slip tectonics seems consonant with the collisional mechanism in which the north-directed stress field produced by indentation generated the oblique strike-slip movement that opened and widened the rift.

10.10 The Upper Rhine Graben

Another prominent rift zone that has been attributed to collisional indentation is the Upper Rhine graben (Rhinegraben), a flat-floored valley about 40 km wide through which the Rhine River flows north-northeast, forming the boundary between France and Germany from near Basel at the Swiss border to Mannheim. There the valley turns due north to Mainz, making a total graben length of about 300 km. This structure lies within the Precambrian Rhine shield. The high "shoulders" of the graben form paired uplands—the Vosges on the west and the Black Forest (Schwartzwald) on the east.

Figure 10.25 is a tectonic map of the southernmost portion of the Upper Rhine graben showing its contact at the south end with thrusts of the Jura Mountains that border the Western Alps. (Refer to Chapter 9 and Figure 9.42.) Recall that the Jura is an arc of foreland folds that fanned out in Jurassic limestone strata, moving on a décollement. With this relationship of graben to foreland folds, the concept of indentation during the Alpine orogeny as the mechanism of graben formation looks attractive. On second thought, it

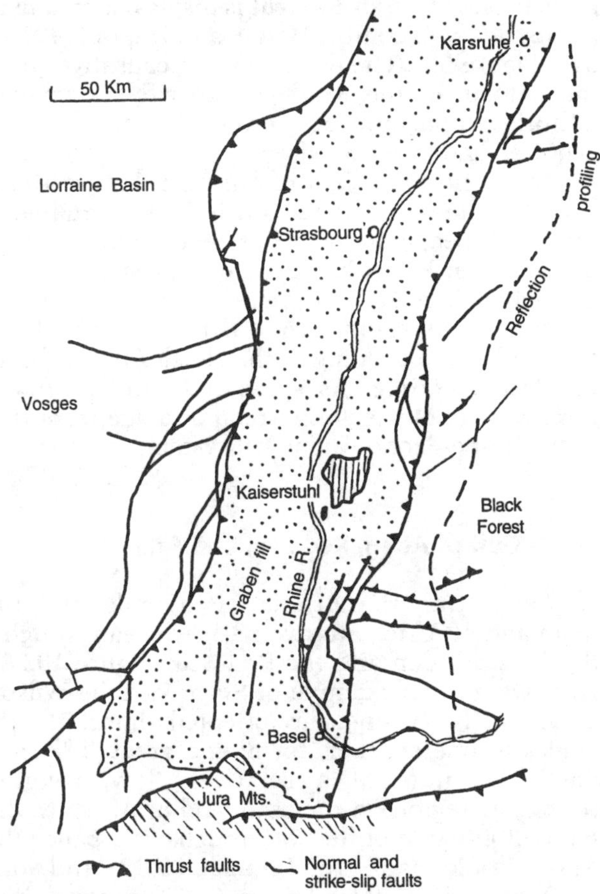

Figure 10.25 Tectonic sketch map of the southern portion of the Upper Rhine graben. (Adapted from H.P. Echtler, E. Lüschen, and G. Mayer, 1994, *Tectonics*, v. 13, no. 2, p. 344, Figure 2. Used by permission of the authors and the American Geophysical Union.)

might seem doubtful that a thin, weak thrust sheet of such foreland folds could crack the thick Precambrian crust in front of it, so perhaps we should think instead of the greatly thickened crust of the Alpine orogen as the northward-forcing indentor.

The indentation hypothesis was supported in 1976 by A.M. Celal Sengör, who put forward the following points (1976, p. 780-781): (1) The observed east-west extension is much too great to be accounted for by doming over a mantle plume. (2) The timing of the opening of the rift fits closely with the Alpine collisional orogeny. (3) The subsidence of the graben began at the south end and progressed northward, as would be expected of a rift penetrating from south to north in response to orogenic compression. (4) The uplift of the "shoulders" of the graben (i.e., an up-arching) occurred following the initial rifting.

Cross sections drawn of the Upper Rhine graben have until recently shown steeply dipping normal faults extending only to shallow depth, there having been available no evidence of what lies at greater depths. Deep reflection seismology has been able to supply that missing information. Seismic data obtained between 1984 and 1991 has been analyzed by H.P. Echtler, E. Lüschen, and G. Mayer of the Universität Karlsruhe (1994). Their interpretation of the deep structure of the Upper Rhine graben is shown in Figure 10.26. The graben is obviously asymmetric. The main normal fault flattens to become a horizontal décollement or decoupling zone within the lower part of the crust. Opposing are steep normal faults that apparently die out at shallower depth. Whereas geologic data indicates an upper crust that has undergone extension of only 10 to 15 percent, the seismic data show that the lower crust has undergone thinning of about 50 percent (Echtler et al., 1994, p. 352). The décollement has been drawn at the top of the lower crust. Notice that the Moho rises beneath the graben, indicating that substantial crustal thinning has occurred.

The Upper Rhine graben is only one element in a much longer rift zone, shown in Figure 10.27. We need to examine this full structure and its relationship to other extensional structures of northeastern Europe and the North Sea basin associated with the rifting apart of Laurentia. First, observe that aligned to the north of the Upper Rhine graben is the Hessische graben, about 160 km long and 16 km wide. If included under the indentation hypothesis, it would perhaps be the most distant of the extensional features forced by the Alpine orogeny.

Second, there lies to the southwest of the Upper Rhine graben the Saone graben, which

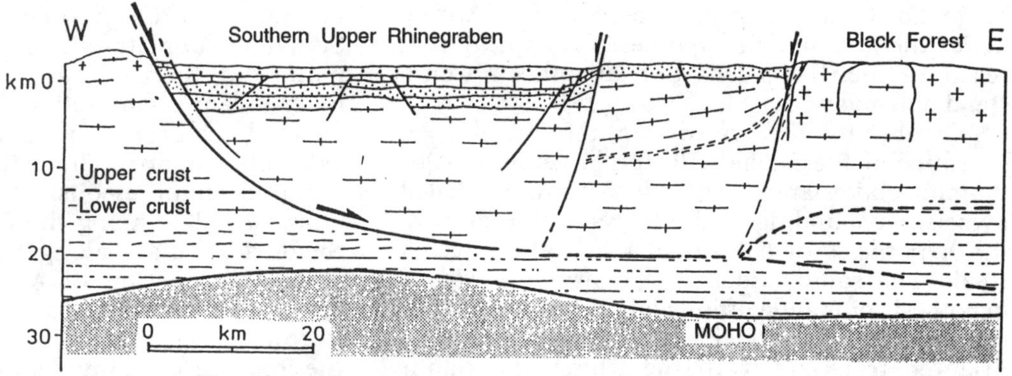

Figure 10.26 Composite cross section of the southern end of the Upper Rhine graben. (From same source as Figure 10.25, p. 352, Figure 12. Used by permission of the authors and the American Geophysical Union.)

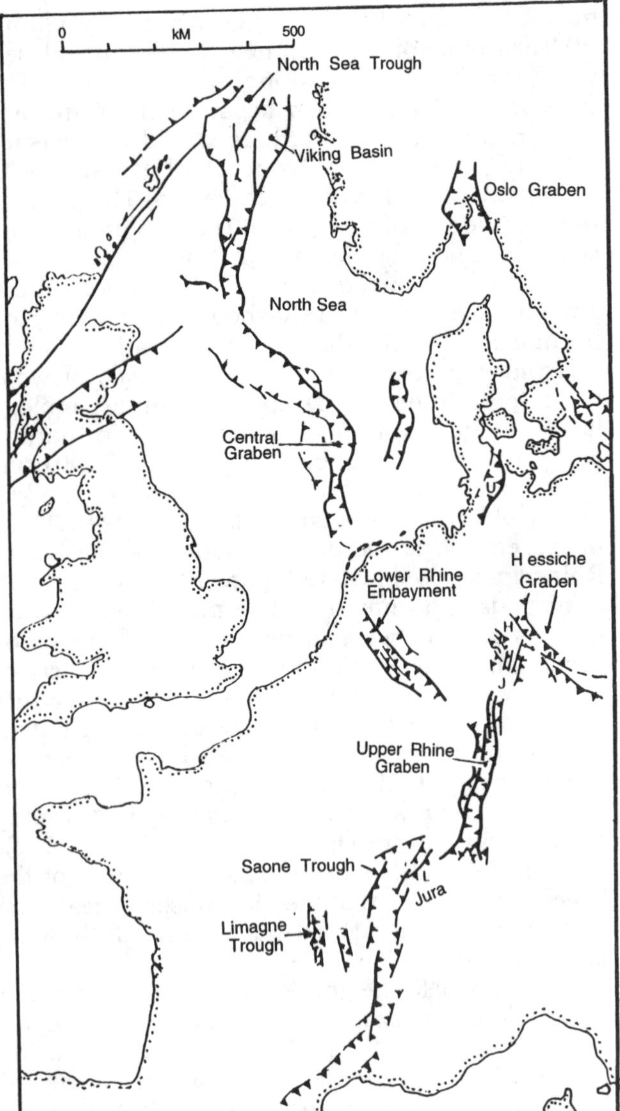

Figure 10.27 Generalized tectonic map of western Europe showing the Rhine-Saone-Rhone rift system and rifts of the North Sea Shelf. (Adapted from K. Seyfert, 1987. Page 683, Figure 6, in Seyfert, K., Ed., 1987. Used by permission of Van Nostrand Reinhold Co., New York.)

trends NE-SW. Its southern continuation is the Rhone trough, or Bresse, trending N-S and tangent to the curve of the Jura folds. That obviously tangential relationship is, of course, dead wrong under the indentation hypothesis. Accepting that reason alone, the indentation hypothesis would stand null and void.

Combining the conflicting structural relationships of the Saone with the large amount of thinning and extension of the lower crust, revealed by seismic sounding in the Upper Rhine graben, the hypothesis of collisional indentation seems weak. The same evidence is consonant with a hypothesis of mantle lifting and crustal splitting in response to a regional extensional stress field oriented transversely to the Rhine and Saone graben axes. This stress field is displayed on a map published by Lacombe, Byrne, and Dupin (1993, p. 878, Figure 5b). The debate on the causative stress mechanism of the Rhine-Saone rift system will doubtless continue as newer seismic data are acquired and interpreted.

In the northern half of our map, Figure 10.27, is a rift system positioned down the median line of the North Sea, and possibly extending into Europe as the Lower Rhine embayment. The structures lie concealed beneath sediments of the North Sea continental margin. This rift zone has been assigned to the opening of the North Atlantic basin in Mesozoic time. As such, it is an event well removed in both tectonic trend and age from that of the Rhine-Saone-Rhone rift system.

10.11 Gulf of Aden, Red Sea, and Afar

Separating the Arabian Peninsula and the mainland of Africa are two narrow ocean troughs, the Gulf of Aden and the Red Sea (Figure 10.28). Here we find an example of Stage 2 of the Wilson cycle. The two troughs are oriented almost at right angles to one another, forming a great "L". Take particular note of a relatively low, roughly triangular region on the mainland of Africa at the point of junction of the two troughs; it is called the Afar. Look back to Figure 10.22 and our description of the Afar lowland as "funneling" into the Main Ethiopian rift (MER). The Ethiopian dome might seem to be missing its northeastern quarter. Looking northeastward across to the Arabian Peninsula, you will find that "missing sector": the highlands of Yemen, a mountainous crustal mass. Thus, on the basis of topography alone, the rifting apart of a continental plate to form a new L-shaped oceanic trough is an almost irresistible conclusion, but caution is advised.

The area of our present interest involves four lithospheric plates. The Arabian, African, and Somalian plates join in a major triple junction (Figure 10.28). The Sinai Peninsula is recognized as a separate small plate and takes part in another triple junction. Boundaries of the Arabian plate, shown in full on our map, are familiar from earlier descriptions in Chapters 6 and 9. (Figure 6.28 shows details of the western transform boundary. Figure 9.45 shows the northern and western boundaries of the Arabian plate.) At present, the Somalian subplate is connected with the African plate and there is no clearly defined line of independent plate motion. This third arm, which we might call the "Afar arm," must be recognized as a potential arm. Therefore, the Arabian plate is required simultaneously to pull away from the Somalian plate along the Gulf of Suez and from the African plate along the Red Sea arm. The common direction of Arabia's relative motion along these two arms must be northeasterly (arrows in Figure 10.28). Geologic matching across the Red Sea of many distinctive rock bodies and

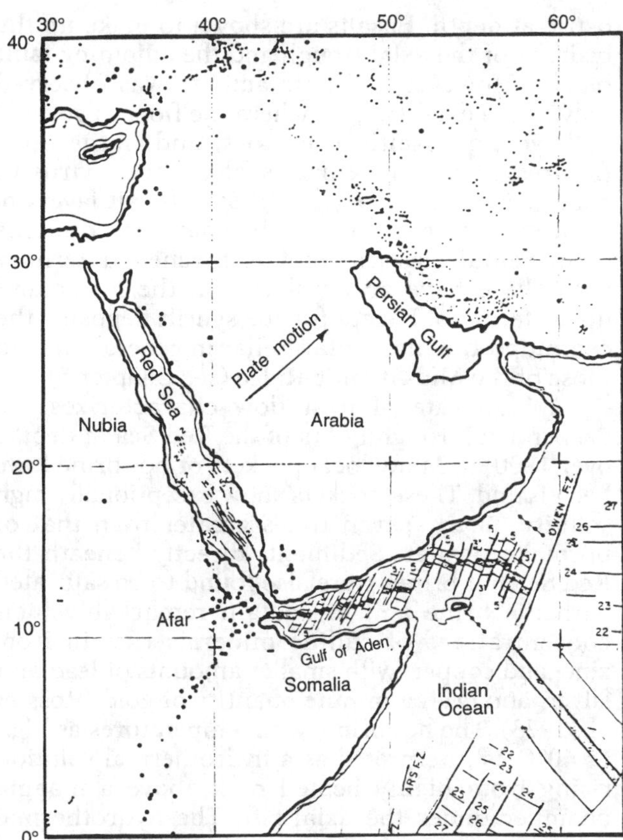

Figure 10.28 General map of the Red Sea, Gulf of Aden, and the Arabian plate. (Based in part on data of Cande et al, *Magnetic Lineations of the World's Ocean Basins*. Copyright © 1989 by the American Association of Petroleum Geologists. Used by permission.)

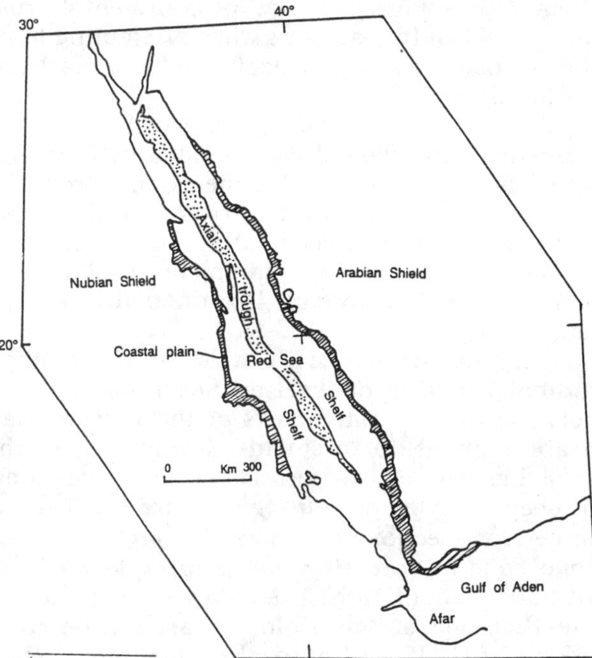

Figure 10.29 Map of the Red Sea showing the axial trough and marginal features. (Based on data of R.G. Bohannon, 1986, *Tectonics*, v, 5, p. 478, Figure 1, and other sources.)

structures within the craton confirms this direction of relative plate motion (Sultan et al., 1993).

There is abundant scientific evidence that the Gulf of Aden and the Red Sea are indeed new ocean basins. Seismic data show that the inner floors of these oceans are made up of oceanic crust. Epicenters of small earthquakes are numerous along the spreading axis of the Gulf of Aden and also along the mid-line of the southern half of the Red Sea. Both troughs exhibit a symmetrical magnetic anomaly pattern, shown in Figure 10.28. In the Gulf of Aden, the oldest recognized anomaly is number 5 (Late Miocene, 9 Ma). Numerous closely-spaced transform faults offset the spreading axis, which has all of the expected features typical of an active mid-oceanic ridge. In the Red Sea, anomaly numbers 2 an 3 are clearly recognized, but transform offsets are not shown. The anomaly zone of the Gulf of Aden tapers sharply as it nears the Afar lowland, curving southward as if to enter the Gulf of Tadjurah (see Figure 10.33). This feature brings to mind the tip of a propagating rift, and it looks as if it might now be aimed in the direction of the Main Ethiopian rift. A closer look at the Red Sea shows that it, too, narrows almost to a point as it approaches the Gulf of Aden, and also at the north end where it narrows to become the Gulf of Suez. You might jump to the conclusion that the Red Sea first rifted open in its mid-section, sending propagating tips out in opposite directions.

From these loose speculations, we turn to gather more facts, beginning with a geologic description of the Red Sea basin—a depression just over 2000 km long (Figure 10.29). Its straight, subparallel northern shorelines are about 200 km apart, but this figure widens to more than 300 km in the southern two-thirds, where the shorelines bend in and out on both sides. A narrow coastal plain borders the shoreline of the Red Sea, and from its western shore rises a prominent escarpment. This deeply eroded highland ranges in elevation to somewhat over 1000 m in the north to over 2500 m along the margin of the Ethiopian Plateau. Rising above the eastern shoreline is a comparable, but more broadly eroded escarpment that merges toward the south into the Yemen volcanic plateau, elevation over 3000 m. These opposed highland borders form the "shoulders" of the rift, in a manner similar to what we find in the East African rift system. Another feature of these opposed highlands bears noting: Volcanics lie over large areas of the eastern highlands, but are almost absent in the opposing western highlands. This contrast holds true only as far south as the Ethiopian plateau, where the Ethiopian and Yemen volcanic highlands are opposed.

Continental crust on both sides of the Red Sea extends out beneath the continental shoreline for a maximum distance of 40 to 50 km as a continental shelf. This submerged zone of continental crust must be taken into account when attempting to fit the opposing coastlines back into their original juxtaposition.

At the northern end of the Red Sea lies the triangular Sinai Peninsula, bounded by two fault trenches. The eastern fault zone extends from the Gulf of Aqaba northward through the Dead Sea depression, and has been interpreted as a transform boundary of the Arabian plate. Displacement along this transform fault is estimated to be 105 km.

Of greatest interest to us is the inner longitudinal zonation of the Red Sea floor that lies between the separated parts of the Precambrian Arabian and Nubian shields. Going first to the axial line, marked by a series of closed depressions, or deeps, lies the *axial trough*. Figure 10.30 shows three cross sections of the axial trough (or "axial zone") and its bordering *fault terraces*, located at a latitude of about 18°N. The data were obtained by the Red Sea submersible research expedition (Monin et al., 1982). The axial zone is from 2.5 to 4 km wide and lies at a depth of about 1700 m. Notice the prominent *central rise* in the axial trough. Because of the ten-fold vertical exaggeration, the normal-fault surfaces that form the terrace risers seem to be nearly vertical at the top and are drawn to suggest that the planes become listric at depth. Basalts are shown to make up the bedrock of the axial trough and the adjoining fault blocks. However, volcanic activity was observed only in the axial trough, where the floor is covered with young basaltic volcanoes, and "large open fissures appear in clusters along the extrusive zone" (Coleman, 1993, p 18). Synrift salt layers of Miocene age are covered by marine sediments (continental clastics) of Pleistocene-Quaternary age. These have accumulated on the lower and upper terraces. Except for the synrift deposits, the central profiles are quite similar in general form to those of the Mid-Atlantic Ridge (see Chapter 5).

A high rate of heat flow characterizes the deeper axial trough floors of the Red Sea at depths over 1800 m. Many local pockets of hot brine have been found. These pockets show exceptionally high salinity, nearly seven times greater than that of normal seawater. Sediments directly beneath the Red Sea hot brines were also found to be saturated with the brine and to contain remarkably high concentrations of sulfide minerals rich in iron, zinc, and copper, with smaller amounts of lead and silver, and even a minute quantity of gold (Ross et al., 1973). The hot brine, with temperatures as high as 60°C, is interpreted as a hydrothermal solution rising from highly heated rock above a magma chamber under the axial rift. The hydrothermal solution represents seawater that has penetrated

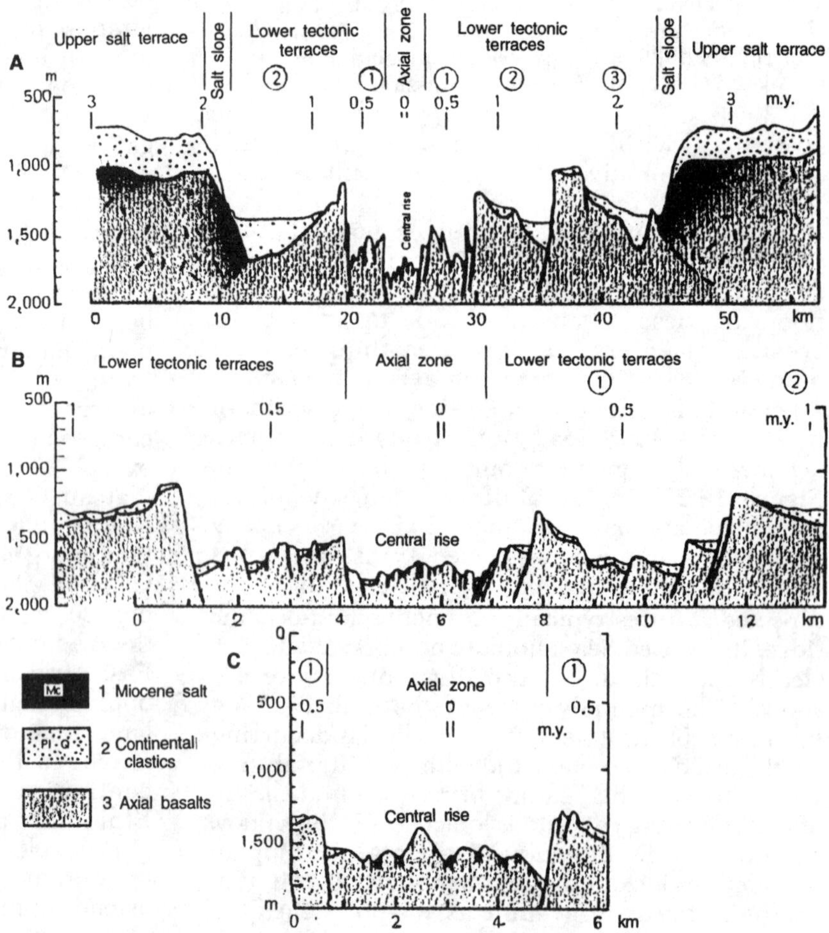

Figure 10.30 Cross sections of the axial rift zone of the Red Sea near latitude 10°N. (Data of A.S. Monin et al., 1982, *Deep Sea Research*, v. 29, p. 3671, as presented by R.G. Coleman, *Geologic Evolution of the Red Sea*, p. 91, Figure 5.4, Oxford University Press, New York. Used by permission.)

the ocean floor, moving down through permeable sediment and volcanic rock to reach the heat source. The heated water then returns to the surface charged with ions dissolved from the altered mafic igneous rock. (See Chapter 5 and Figure 5.7.)

The stratigraphic relationship between the Miocene evaporites (salts) and the Pliocene-Quaternary marine sediments is particularly important in the history of the Red Sea. Evaporite deposition was occurring as the fault terraces were being formed, and this was a time when the Red Sea was nearly isolated from the Mediterranean sea as a result of lowered sea level. However, numerous incursions of seawater furnished the Red Sea with replacements of the evaporated brine. During this period, block faulting was occurring in brittle crust that was being formed by outpourings and intrusions of basaltic magmas. At the same time, under the same extensional stress, the ductile mantle beneath was undergoing both stretching and thinning (see Figures 10.5 and 10.8). Thus most of the crust that lies between the bounding sidewalls of ancient continental crust can be labeled *transitional crust* (Bosworth, 1993). Two seismic refraction lines across the Arabian margin, Figure 10.31, support the above conclusion by showing a rapid thinning of the lower crust eastward under the coastal plain and shelf (Bohannon, 1986, p. 481, Figure 2).

The phase of extensional block faulting ended at about the same time that connection was established with a rising Mediterranean Sea, allowing a normal ocean environment to prevail. Of course, evaporite deposition ended and, instead, terrestrial sediments from the adjoining highland slopes were carried into the axial region (Coleman, 1993, p. 38, 81). At about the same time, the limit of stretching of mantle had been reached, and penetrating rift segments quickly sliced through the lithosphere to open up the initial oceanic rift along the full length of the Red Sea basin. Under this scenario, the Red Sea became a bona fide mid-oceanic plate boundary about 5 Ma, and it was largely within that time span that the "shoulders" on either side of the Red Sea rose to their present heights.

The next step we must take is to recognize that the rifting described above was not symmetrical, but at least to some degree asymmetrical, as explained in an earlier section of this chapter (see Figure 10.10). Think of the volcanic asymmetry of the northern two-thirds of the Red Sea, mentioned above, in which volcanic fields are present along the eastern highland, but absent on the western highlands. Here we may have an expression of a volcanic rift margin on the east and a non-volcanic margin on the west, although not as strongly and perfectly developed as in Figure 10.10. As suggested by geologist Robert G. Coleman of Stanford University, the first stage would have consisted of the extrusion of olivine basalts "some 150 km east of the Red Sea continental rift, forming extensive plateau basalts north from Yemen to Jordan" (1993, p. 33). During this time, crustal extension with block faulting was defining the shape of the Red Sea basin, with predominant block faulting on the western side. The main detachment surface

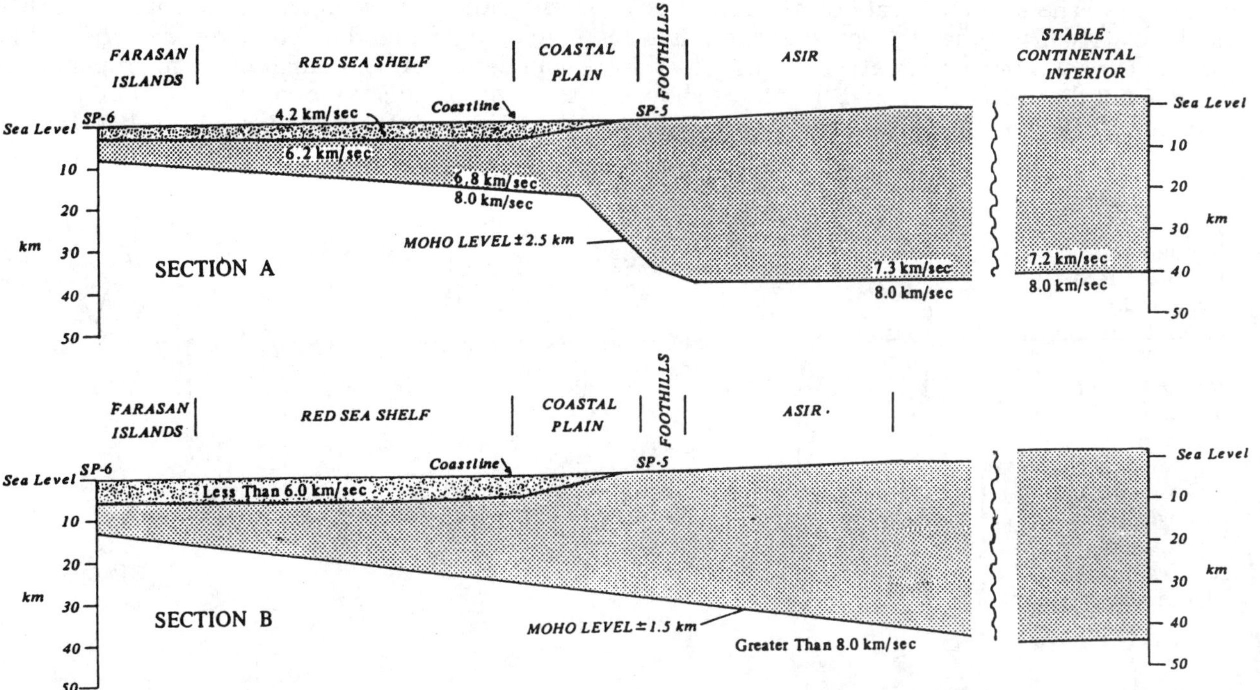

Figure 10.31 Structural interpretation of a seismic refraction profile of the Red Sea shelf and continental interior near the southern end of the Red Sea. (From R.G. Bohannon, 1986, *Tectonics*, v. 5, p. 481, Figure 2. Reproduced by permission of the author and the American Geophysical Union.)

would have originated under this block-faulted zone and dipped to the east, passing under the continental crust and down into the upper mantle. Mafic magma would have risen through dikes from above the detachment to produce the extrusive volcanic fields (Voggenreiter et al., 1988). Our cross sections of the central zone of the Red Sea rift, as presented in Figure 10.30, suggest symmetry, rather than asymmetry. On the other hand, the asymmetric location of the eastern highlands in Arabia, lying farther from the Red Sea than the corresponding western highlands, may seem to support the proposed asymmetry.

We return now to examine the magnetic anomaly data of the Red Sea axial trough, mentioned earlier. Figure 10.32 reproduces an anomaly profile at about 16°N, which is close to the southern termination of the axial trough. Two forms of anomaly profile are shown: In the center are sharply-peaked anomalies of large amplitude (up to 800 nT), whereas on either side are anomalies of broad wavelength and much smaller amplitude (300 nT). The sharply-peaked anomalies are familiar because of their resemblance to those of the mid-oceanic rift and clearly show the widening of the axial trough as a plate boundary (see Figure 7.27). The broad-wavelength low-amplitude curves are unfamiliar and require special interpretation (Coleman, 1993, p. 103-106). They span a time window between 40 and 20 Ma, and were probably produced in intruded basalt masses under thick cover of sediments. Thus they identify the early stage of block faulting while crustal thinning was in progress. In this profile we also find a strong suggestion of structural asymmetry. The spreading rate on the left (west) side is clearly faster that that on the right, as we would expect for asymmetry in which the detachment dips toward the east (right), as shown in Figure 10.10.

To complete our overview of what may be a great triple junction of three rifts we focus on the Afar, a region of bewildering tectonic complexity (Figure 10.33). Even a simplified geologic map of the Afar shows "swarms" of subparallel fault lines in various azimuthal orientations. The area that can be included under the name of "Afar" lies between the two great escarpments of the Ethiopian dome—one trending north-south and facing east, the other trending west-east and facing north. Much of the enclosed area is a low upland with summit elevations not far over 1000 m and with strong local relief. In the northern third of this area are two distinctive relief features. Bordering upon the Red sea is the Danakil horst, or Danakil Alps. With summit elevations comparable to those of the Ethiopian plateau, it has been interpreted as a continental block that separated from the Ethiopian plateau and rotated anticlockwise (Bonatti et al, 1971). This separation left an intervening depression, called the Afar depression or Danakil depression, the northern part of which lies below sealevel. It has been found that continental crust is lacking in a narrow central zone called the Afar rift (Bonnati et al., 1971, p. 468). Basaltic magmas erupted along this rift. Evaporites up to 3 km thick lie beneath the surface of the depression, and it is supposed from these deposits that periods of influx of water from the Red Sea alternated with periods of desiccation.

The name "Afar triangle" has been used to refer to a much larger region extending far to the south (see triangular broken line in Figure 10.33) (Tazieff, 1970). The Afar rift is probably not an isolated feature, and geologists have attempted to find other rift segments that connect with it in wide-angle junctions that define crustal blocks, and these can be thought of as "microplates." A rift system of this kind was presented by Franco Barberi and Jacques Varet in a 1977 article in

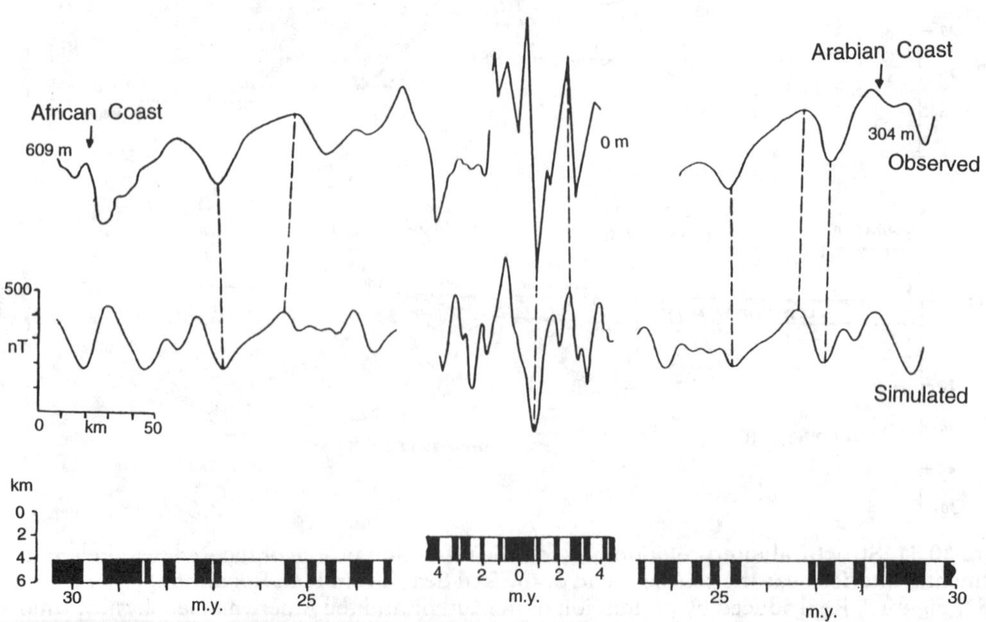

Figure 10.32 Magnetic anomaly profile across the Red Sea at latitude 16°N. (From S.A. Hall, 1989, *Jour. of Geophysical Research*, v. 94, p. 276. Also presented by R.G. Coleman, *Geologic Evolution of the Red Sea*, p. 105, Figure 6.1a.

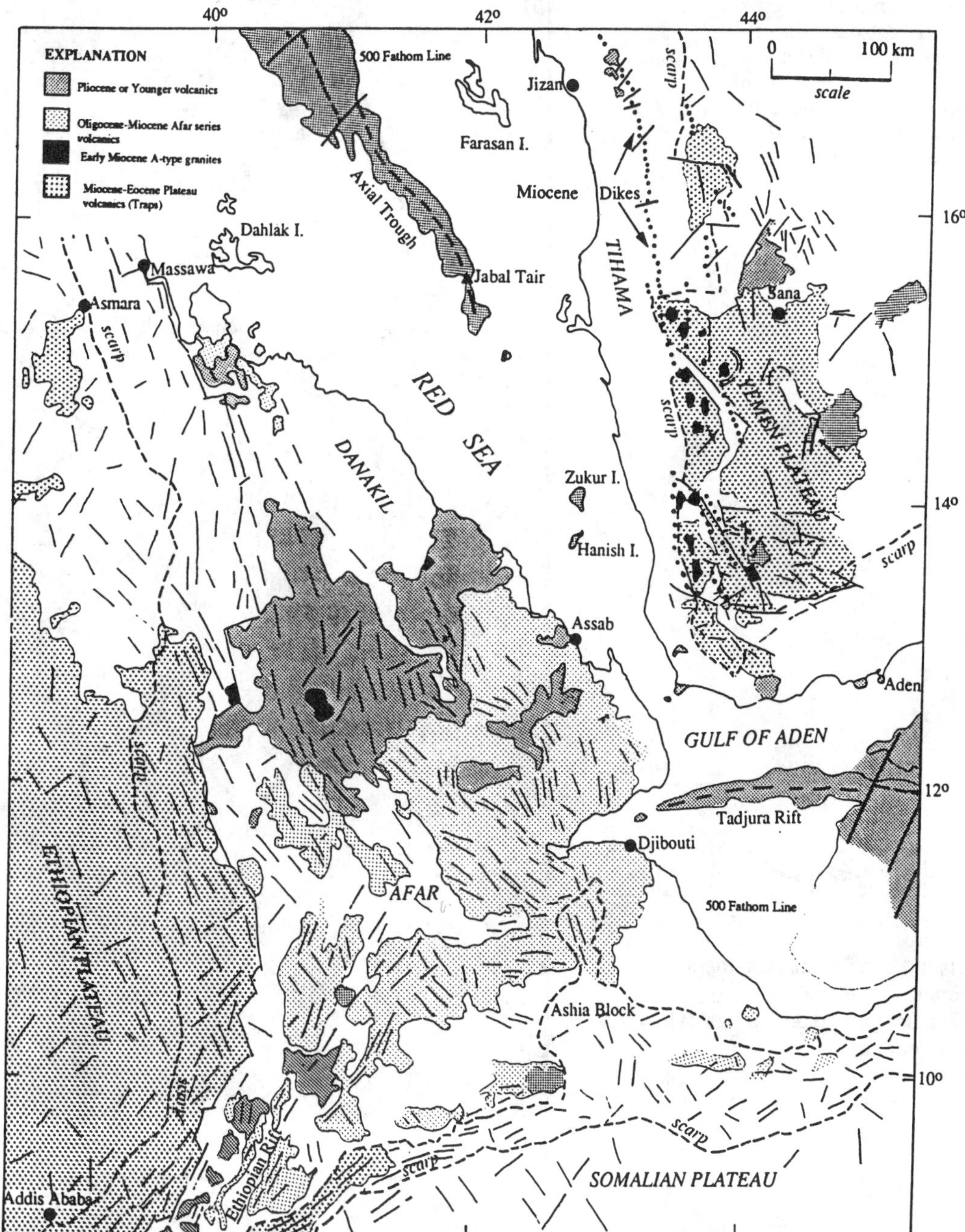

Figure 10.33 Map of the Afar-Danakil-Yemen area. (Adapted from R.G. Coleman, *Geologic Evolution of the Red Sea*, p. 91, Figure 5.4. Copyright 1993 by the Oxford University Press, New York. Used by permission of the author and publisher.)

Science. Their tectonic map is reproduced here as Figure 10.34. Although these four- and 5-sided fault-blocks, bounded by spreading rifts or strike-slip faults (transforms), are considered too small to behave as lithospheric plates, they serve collectively as a plate boundary needed to complete a triple plate junction with the Main Ethiopian rift. Notice that the Afar rift is extended northward to join with a diagonal transform connected with the Red Sea rift. The connection is now inactivated, and the of the Red Sea rift tip is shown to have a possible new transform connection into the African plate.

10.12 Basin-and-Range Extensional Tectonics

In the western United States and northern Mexico, as the long span of Mesozoic and early Cenozoic arc-continent collisions and microplate accretions drew to a close, a new mode of tectonic activity began. Over a large area, the continental crust began to break up into fault blocks bounded by normal faults. Normal faulting on a large scale produced elongate mountain ranges many kilometers wide and many tens of kilometers long, striking roughly N-S. Tectonic basins between the blocks accumulated sediment from the adjacent

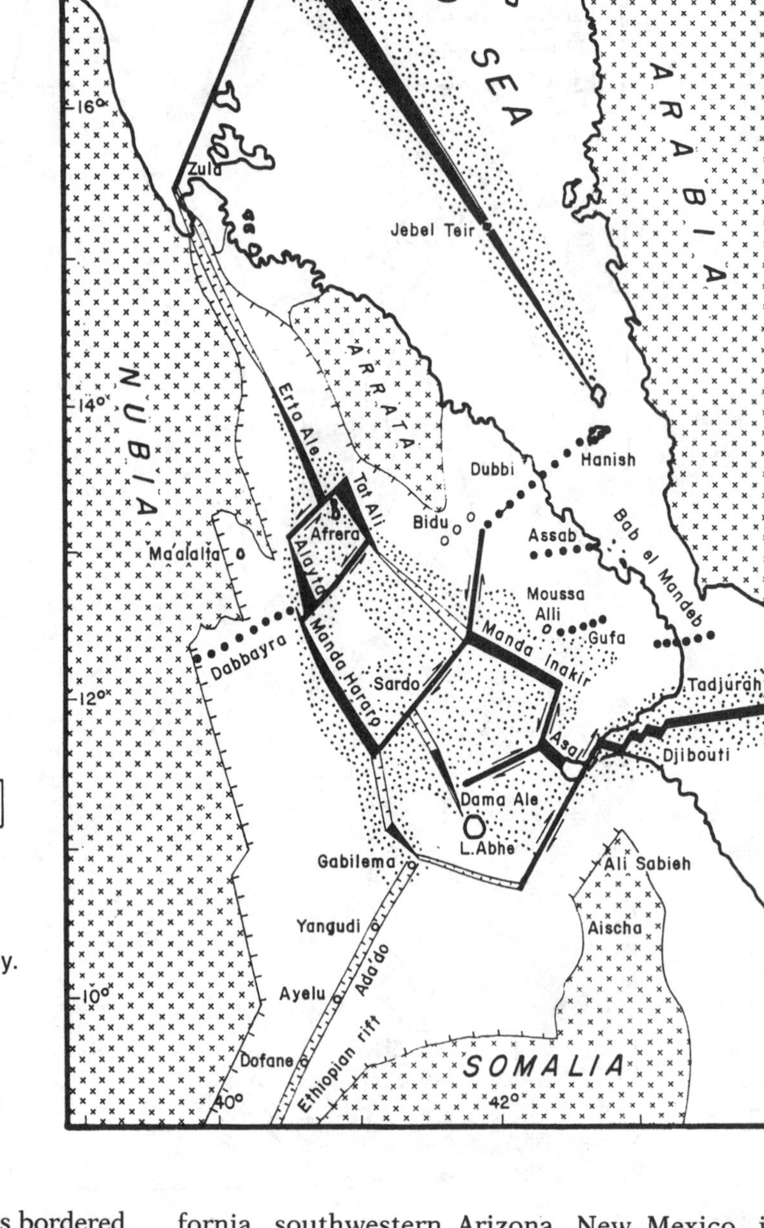

Figure 10.34 Schematic structural map of the Afar region. (Adapted from F. Barbieri and J. Varet, 1977, *Bull., Geol. Soc. Amer.*, v. 88, p. 1257, Figure 8. Reproduced by permission of the authors and the Geological Society of America.)

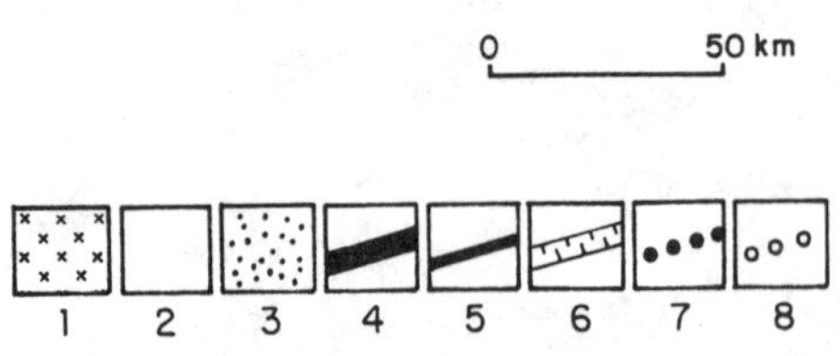

1. Outcropping continental basement
2. Continental rift material
3. Oceanic crust formed during past 3 to 4 m.y.
4. Axis of spreading
5. Relative motion along transform faults
6. Manifestation of extensional tectonics
7. Transverse volcanic structure
8. Central volcano

mountain slopes, forming alluvial valleys bordered by great alluvial fans. Thus the name *Basin and Range Province (B&R)* came to apply to the region both as a geomorphic province and as a tectonic province (Figures 10.35 and 10.36). Much of this region today lies in a desert or semidesert climate, and streams typically terminate on alluvial fan and playa surfaces within the closed basins. These hydrogeologic conditions probably prevailed over much of the Neogene and have played an important role in the tectonic evolution of the B&R. A large area in Utah, Nevada, and southern California—the Great Basin—today has interior drainage, and fluvial sediment must accumulate without reference to a sealevel base.

Block faulting began to occur in Middle Miocene time (about 15 Ma) in western Utah, Nevada, southeastern Oregon, southeastern California, southwestern Arizona, New Mexico, in parts of several neighboring states, and in northern Mexico. Extentional tectonics had, however, begun earlier (~26 Ma) in southeastern California.

Surface exposures of the principal faults of the B&R are shown in Figure 10.36. Much of this area had previously experienced overthrust faulting in the closing stages of the Cordilleran Orogeny. The docking of many terranes had added a large zone of new continental crust to the North American continental margin (see Figure 9.33). The Cenozoic normal faults cut across these older structures along new lines, providing abundant surface exposures of the older structures. These earlier events and structures were covered in Chapter 9 under the general topic of compressional tectonics.

Bordering the B&R on the east lies the Rocky Mountain region of steep overthrusts, and south of

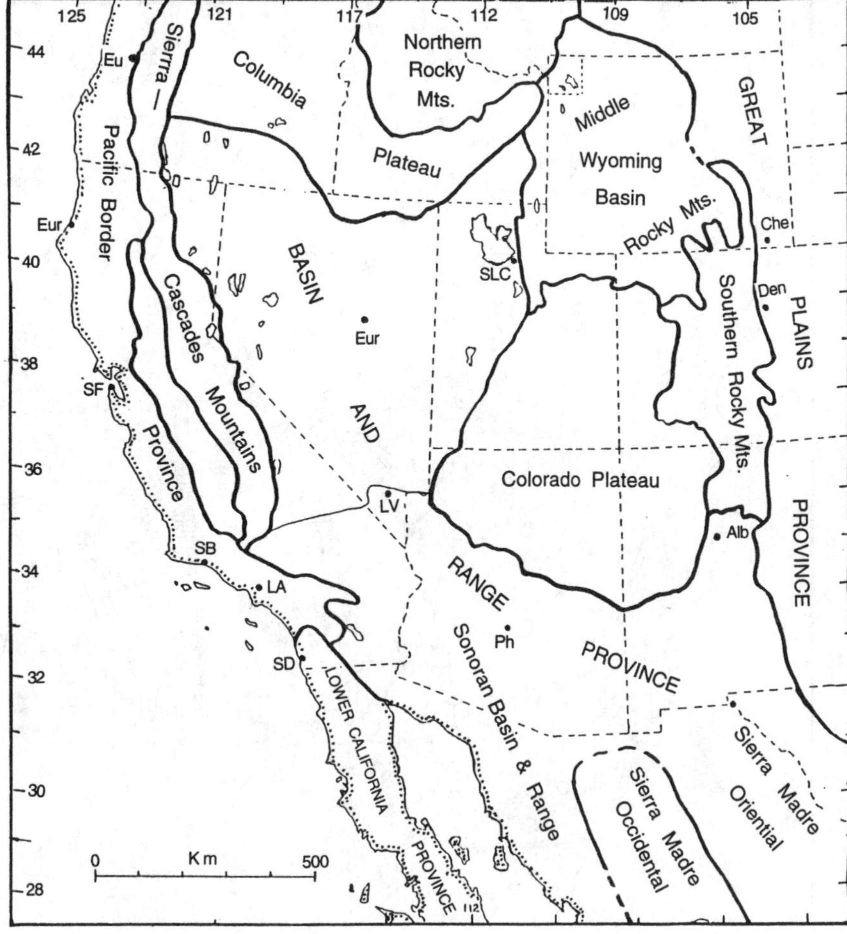

Figure 10.35 Map of geomorphic provinces of the western United States and northern Mexico as defined by Nevin M. Fenneman. (Copyright © by Arthur N. Strahler.)

that lie the weakly deformed platform strata of the Colorado Plateau (see Figure 9.57). Bordering the B&R on the west is the great Sierra Nevada uplift, often included in the B&R; and farther north, the volcanic Cascade Range. Along the northern boundary of the B&R lie the vast plateaus basalts of Oregon and Idaho, beneath which a fringe of the B&R lies concealed (see Chapter 5 and Figure 5.29). South of the Sierra Nevada the B&R projects westward in a subprovince, the Mojave Desert, that brings it adjacent to the Transverse Ranges in Los Angeles and San Bernardino counties. This region we examined in Chapter 6 in our description of the San Andreas Fault zone (see Figure 6.31). The B&R extends southeast and east across southeastern California and Arizona. It also extends far south across the border into northern Mexico in a narrow tapering zone bordering on the Gulf of California and, farther east, extends south as the Sierra Madre Occidental (Zoltan de Cserna, 1989, p. 246-248). Encircling the southern rim of the Colorado Plateau in New Mexico, the B&R forms a narrow projection aimed due north—the Rio Grande rift, penetrating the southern Rockies.

In view of the vast extent and varied crustal geology of the B&R, we will limit our description mostly to the kind of extensional deformation exhibited in the western Utah, Nevada, and southeastern California. This region offers an opportunity to follow through on a long controversy over tectonic styles, and it gives us a fine example of how science of the solid earth moves step-by-step from one hypothesis to another in the light of new geophysical findings of what lies at depth in the crust.

10.13 Crust and Mantle of the Basin and Range Province

In order to estimate the amounts of horizontal extension that have occurred in the B&R, geologists make use of a reconstruction of the upper crust at a time prior to the onset of extensional faulting (Wernicke et al., 1988. p. 1739-1741). Figure 10.37 is a map showing the former distribution of four basement-rock categories. Starting from the right is the Precambrian craton, important only in the southern region. Next is the thrust-faulted Cordilleran miogeocline, which consists of Mesozoic and older marine strata. Along the eastern border of this region is the Sevier thrust zone, with its "Sevier front." Farther west, in the more northern latitudes, are former passive-margin continental slope and rise strata, bordered on the eastern limit by the Antler thrust front. To the west of these provinces is a great north-south Mesozoic batholith belt.

Geophysical data on the crust and mantle of

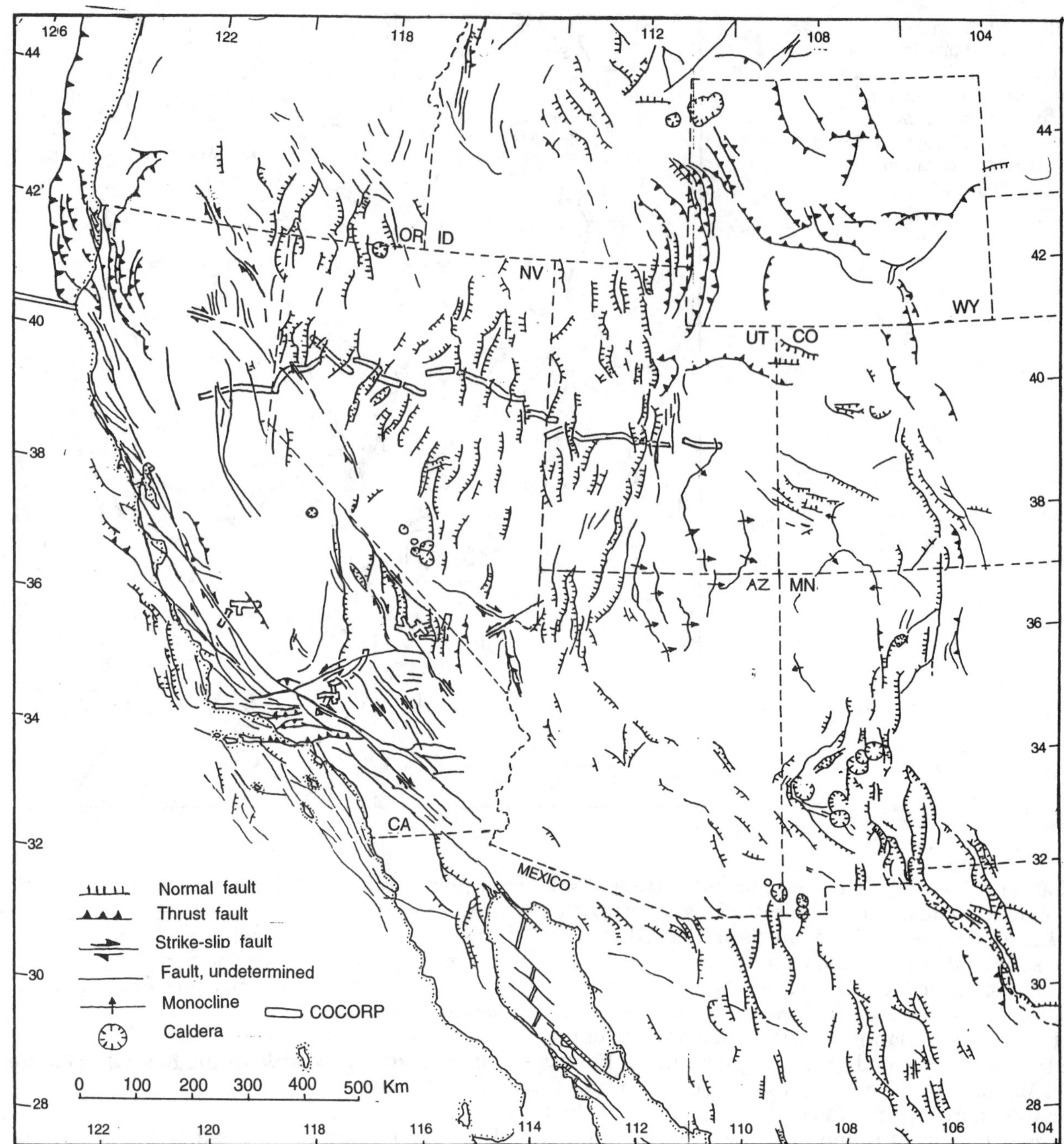

Figure 10.36 Tectonic map of the Basin and Range province and adjoining areas. (Data adapted from *Tectonic Map of North America*, compiled by W.R. Meuhlberger. Copyright © 1992 by the American Association of Petroleum Geologists. Reproduced by permission.)

the B&R were collected in the 1960s and 70s. In Chapter 3, we reproduced G.P. Woolard's 1966 gravity data along a transect of the United States (Figure 3.38). The western portion Woolard's transect is shown here as Figure 10.38. The observed Bouguer profile shows extremely large negative values beneath the B&R, as well as beneath the adjacent Sierra Nevada and Rocky Mountains, indicating that a large mass is missing at depth beneath the region. Postulating a zone of low-density mantle beneath the B&R removes most of this negative anomaly and gives profiles of small residual Bouguer and isostatic anomalies.

Furthermore, seismic refraction data indicates that the Moho beneath the B&R is shallower than beneath continental crust on both sides (Figures 10.39 and 10.40). A low velocity zone (LVZ) within the crust also showed up in the B&R seismic profile and in profiles of the Baikal rift and northern East African rift (Figure 10.41) (Kearey and Vine, 1990, p. 37-38, 111).

Observations of the thermal gradient showed

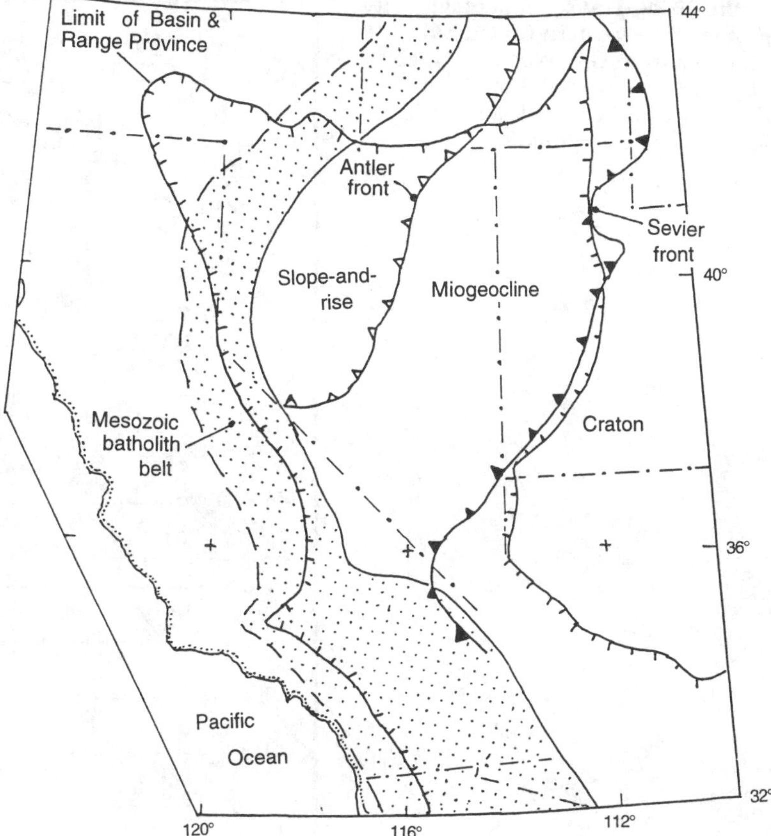

Figure 10.37 Geologic map of the Basin and Range province and adjacent areas showing pre-Miocene crustal zones. (Adapted from B. Wernicke et al., 1988, *Bull., Geol. Soc. Amer.*, v. 100 , p. 1740, Figure 2. Reproduced by permission of the authors and the Geological Society of America.)

that the rate of heat flow is high (about two heat-flow units) beneath the B&R, compared with the low rate typical of the stable continental lithosphere of the craton (about one unit). Thus the gravity, seismic refraction, and heat-flow data are commensurate with a hypothesis of large-scale horizontal extension of the lithosphere resulting in thinning of both crust and hot mantle across the entire B&R. The total extensional strain across the Great Basin that has occurred in the past 10 my has been estimated as at least 140 km, but may be substantially more (Wernicke, Axen, and Snow, 1988, p. 1739). Using as 500 km the present E-W width of this area, the percentage of extension comes to about 30 percent. However, because this recent extension is concentrated in a few zones separated by inactive zones, the ratio of extension is probably locally greater (>300%).

Crustal stress analysis gives independent evidence that extensional stress now prevails in the B&R, in contrast to the compressional stress within the North American craton to the east. Figure 10.42A shows the stress vectors on a map and in a cross section through the B&R. Note that in the central and southern Rocky Mountains, stress is also now extensional, reversing the earlier compressional stress field of Laramide thrusting (D.I. Gough and W.I. Gough, 1987, p. 560-562).

Seismicity within the B&R ranges from intense to very infrequent (Figure 10.43). A swath of intense seismic activity extends in an E-W arc from central Utah to southern Nevada, and into south-eastern California. In contrast, southern Arizona and New Mexico show quiescence, which extends far south into Mexico, and might lead us to suppose that extension in this southern belt has virtually ceased. This conclusion fits well with striking differences in topography of the two regions. Whereas terrain of the northern belt is of bold relief and relatively narrow basins, that of the southern belt shows low relief, with shrunken mountains separated by broad alluvial basins typically bordered by pediments.

What caused the long regime of Cordilleran compressional tectonics, continuing up to Miocene time, to give way to an extensional regime? As long as the Farallon plate was being subducted, compressive stresses were continuing to act across the entire North American plate [For background information, refer to Chapter 7, Evolution of the San Andreas Fault as a Boundary, and Figures 7.48 and 7.49.] In Chapter 9 under the heading of Intracratonal Compressional Tectonics of Western North America, we presented a modern version of the scenario of Farallon plate subduction. Using Peter Bird's 1984 model of a single horizontally subducting slab, shown in Figure 9.60, we may propose that soon after the San Andreas Fault had formed (ca 15 Ma) the detached Farallon plate sank deep into the mantle, perhaps breaking into two or more segments. It seems also possible that the flat slab simply heated up, softened, and disintegrated, falling away in small fragments (Severinghaus and Atwater, 1989; Atwater, 1989, p.

Figure 10.38 Transcontinental gravity profile of the western United States. (Adapted from G.P. Woollard, 1966, *Monograph 10*, p. 560. Copyright © by the American Geophysical Union. Reproduced by permission.)

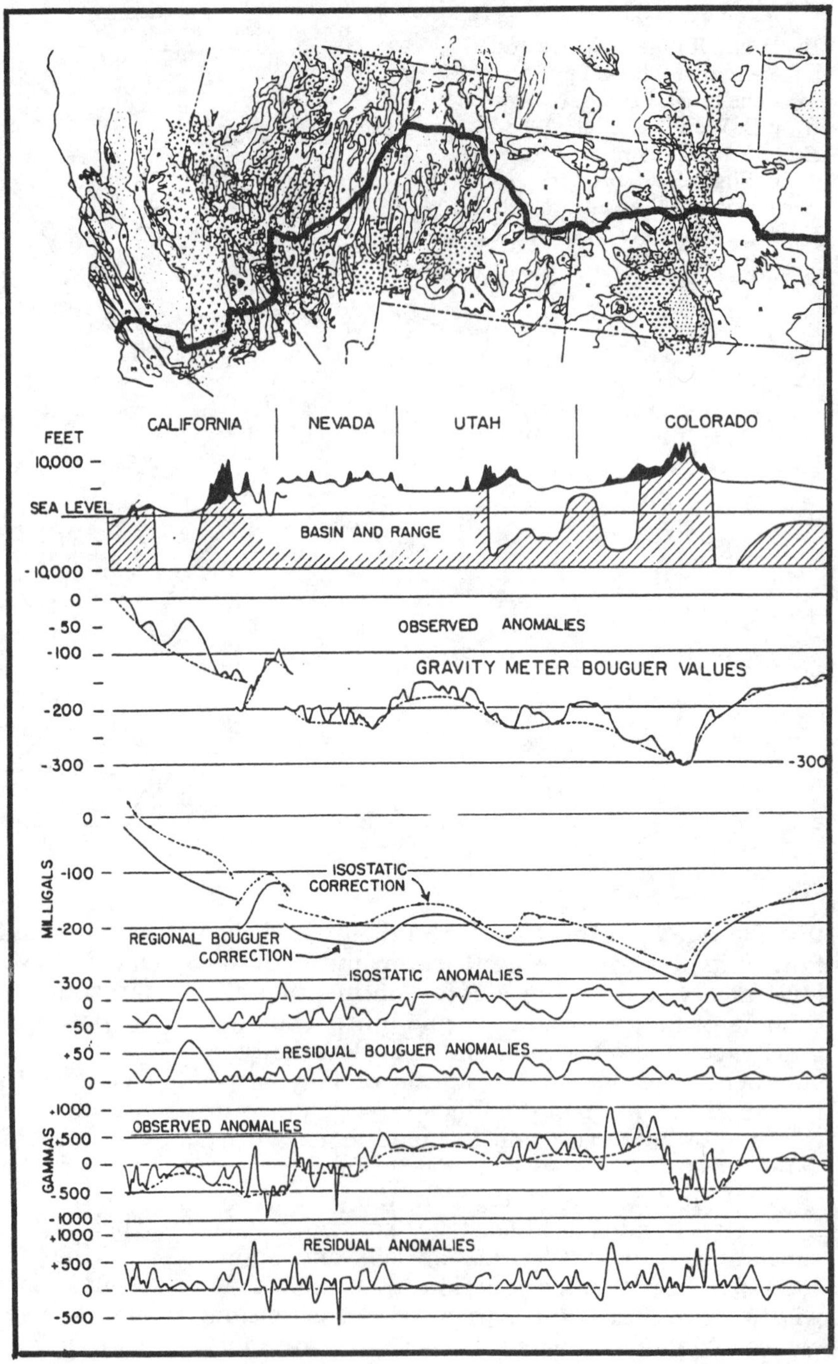

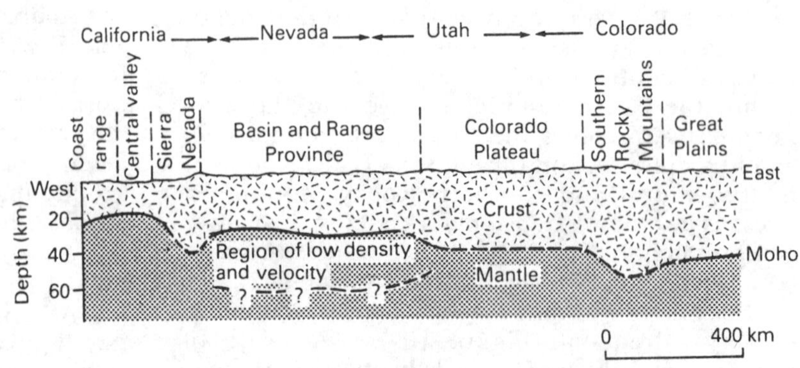

Figure 10.39 Cross section of the western United states based on seismic refraction data. (Adapted from L. Pakiser, 1963, *Jour. of Geophysical Research*, v. 68. Used by permission of the American Geophysical Union.)

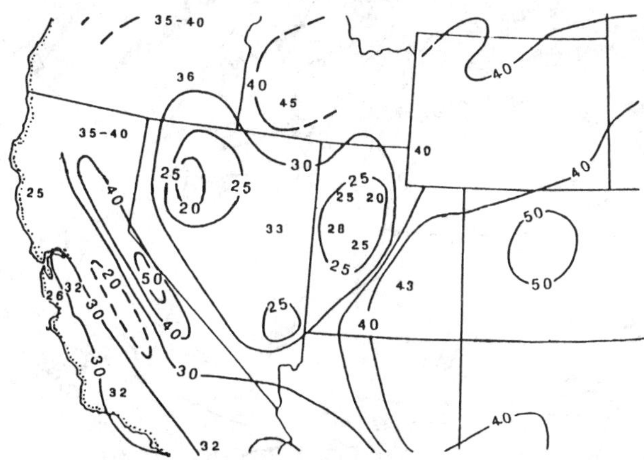

Figure 10.40 Map of crustal thickness (km) of the western United States. (Adapted from R.B. Smith, 1978, *Geol. Soc. Amer. Memoir 152*. Reproduced by permission of the author and the Geological Society of America.)

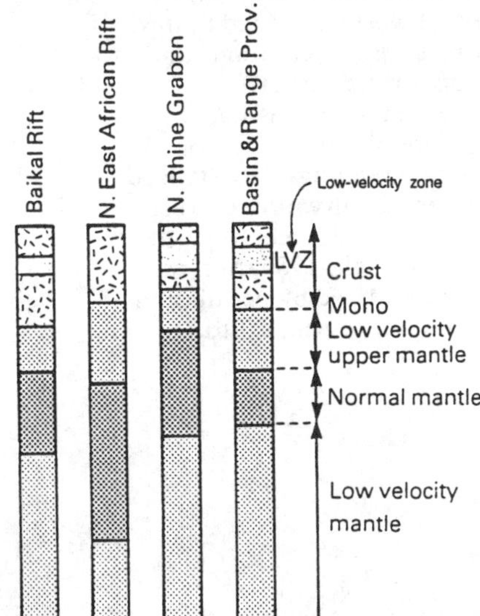

Figure 10.41 Bar graphs showing P-wave velocity zones of crust and mantle of four rift zones. (Adapted from N.N. Puzyrev et al., *Tectonophysics*, v. 45, Copyright © 1978 by Elsevier Publishers. Reproduced by permission.)

49-50). Disappearance of the slab allowed hot mantle to rise beneath what is now the B&R region. Spreading out laterally, the hot mantle exerted a horizontal drag on the overlying plate, causing extension of the crust. But since, as noted above, widespread extension began much earlier, a broader explanation seems to be called for.

Recall from Chapter 9 that in the history of the European Alps, after the strong compressional phase had ceased, there followed an extensional phase accompanied by a general collapse and broadening of the folded zone. We wrote: "When first formed, the collision orogen may be overthickened and gravitationally unstable, after which it is thinned by lateral extension—a process of collapse." This program was applied in 1996 to the B&R by C.H.Jones, J.R. Unruh, and L.J. Sonder in a paper in *Nature* titled "The role of gravitational potential energy in active deformation in the southwesterm United States." Philip England, reviewing that paper in the same issue of *Nature*, titled his piece "The Mountains Will Flow." The "flowage" involved is a viscous deformation under the principle of isostasy. High-standing crust posseses a greater gravitational potential energy and causes lateral flowage toward surrounding areas of lower potential.

With this general description of the B&R completed, we can turn to a close look at the structural modes of faulting observed in the B&R.

10.14 Fault Structures of the Basin and Range

Keeping in mind background information on extensional rift structures developed earlier in this chapter for the East African, Baikal, and Upper Rhine rifts, it will be interesting to see if similar tectonic styles can be recognized in the B&R.

Over many decades—since the pioneering studies of G.K. Gilbert, J.W. Powell, C. King, and I.C. Russell in the 1870s and then of A.C. Lawson, G.D. Louderback, W.M. Davis, and J.B. Spurr in the first decade of the 1900s—structural interpretation of the ranges was simply limited to uplifted horsts separated by down-dropped grabens, or repeated sets of tilted blocks separated by half-grabens. As late as 1980, a summary paper by John H. Stewart of the U.S. Geological Survey described three general models of B&R structure: Horst-and-graben, tilted block, and listric fault (1980, p. 461). These are illustrated in our Figure 10.44. It had also been observed that within a major tilted block there were often present smaller tilted blocks that seemed to have been formed during rotation of the large block (R.E. Anderson, 1971).

Stewart also presented a general plan for regional tilt patterns, as exhibited in Nevada and Utah (1980, p. 461-462). Stylized cross sections in Figure 10.45 show how a typical regional pattern emerges. The tilted-block mode is assumed. In Diagram A, widely separated initial graben-like tensional rifts have formed. Tilted blocks are formed in succession away from these initial rifts (Diagram B). Two chains of blocks then meet in a common horst (Diagram C). Further dislocation along the normal faults increases the regional relief (Diagram D). The initial rupture site is now referred to as an *antiformal boundary*; the central horst is referred to as a *synformal boundary*.

A similar history can be applied to the listric-fault model, which features a horizontal décollement, or detachment, shown in Figure 10.44C. Note that the motion of the blocks over the detachment is away from the antiform and toward

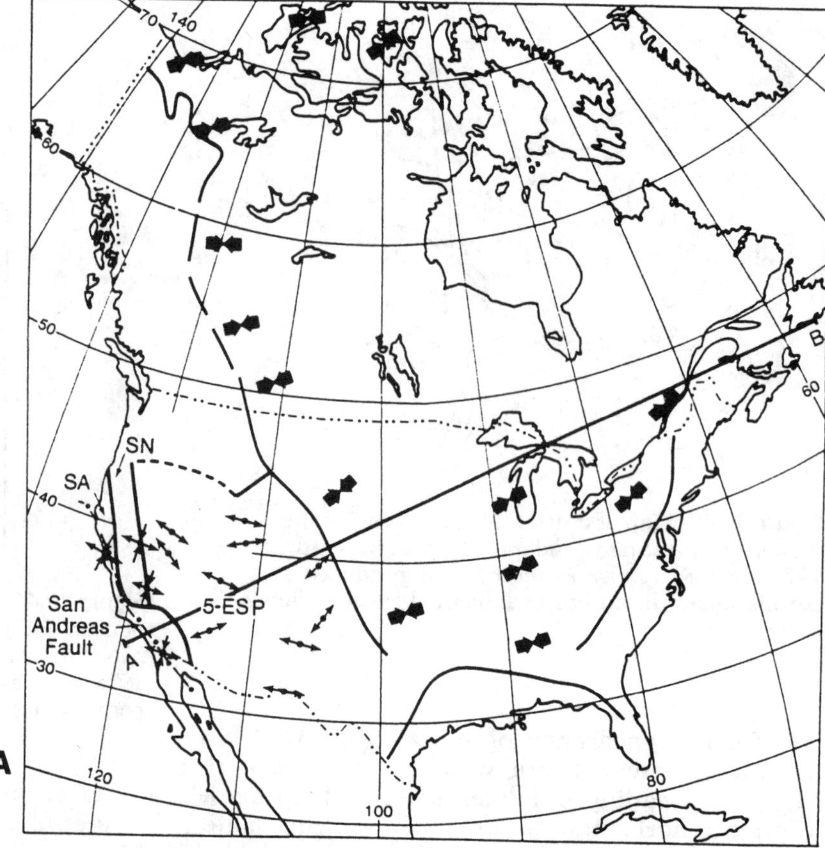

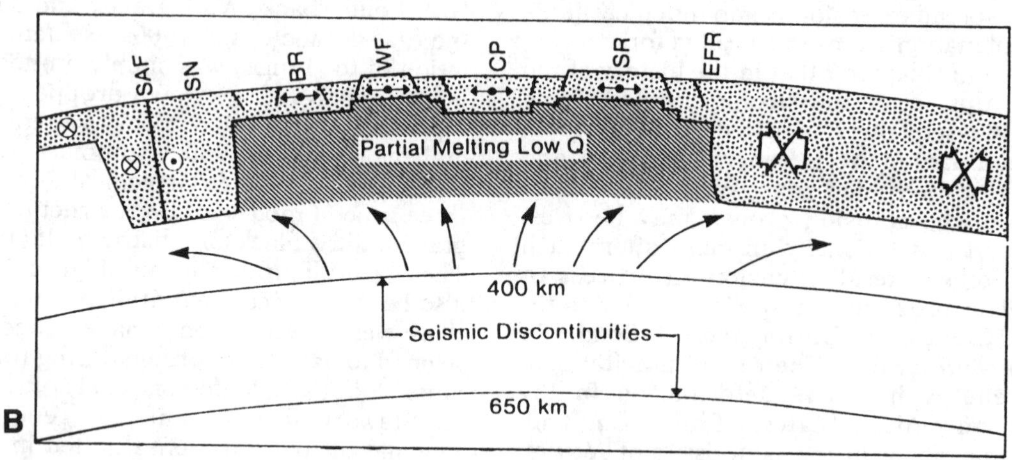

Figure 10.42 Map and cross section of western United States showing stress orientations and structure of the western Cordilleran region. (A) Each arrow symbol represents from 3 to 30 stress readings. (B) Stylized section, earth curvature correctly scaled to vertical scale. (Adapted from D.I. Gough, 1984, *Nature*, v. 311, p. 428?. Used by permission of Macmillan Journals, Ltd.)

the synform. The horizontal span across the strike of the ranges between an antiformal and a synformal boundary ranges from 50 to 250 km, while parallel to the strike the system extends over a belt 50 to 500 km wide (Stewart, 1980, p. 461).

The zone between an antiformal boundary and a synformal boundary is now called an accommodation zone (AZ), a term we have used in earlier descriptions of the African rift valleys. Note that in both regions the linked AZs alternate in direction of dip. As illustrated in Figure 10.45, the relative motion of crustal extension is from SB to AB. The distance between the two ABs has been increased. Thus the crust is undergoing thinning under the force of gravity for the same reason that a spoon of pancake batter spreads out into a thin layer over a flat griddle.

The tilted-block model of faulting, shown in Diagram B of Figure 10.44 and in Figure 10.45 is commonly called *domino-style faulting*. This term carries the obvious connotation that the blocks are rigid and undergo no internal deformation. Rigid blocks resting on a perfectly planar horizontal surface would be required to rotate on a horizontal axis. Figure 10.46 illustrates the principle. With a fault block viewed in cross-section as a rhombus, and its axis of rotation taken to lie in the lower-right corner of the rhombus, a clockwise rotation lifts the upper-left corner to a higher elevation above the basal surface. The adjacent rhombus is

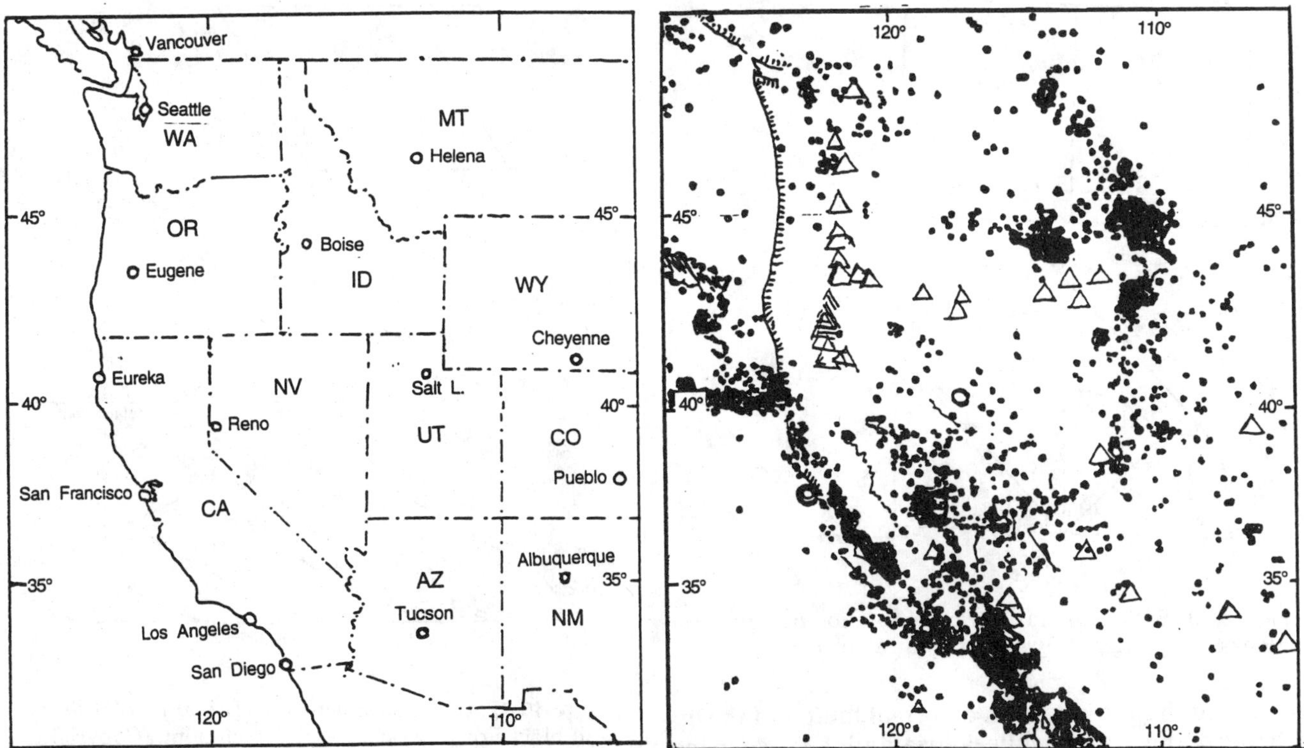

Figure 10.43 Map of seismicity of the Basin and Range province. Each small black circle marks the epicenter of a shallow-depth earthquake >M=4. Volcanoes are shown by triangles. (Adapted from *The Dynamic Planet: World Map of Volcanoes, Earthquakes, and Plate Tectonics*, 1989, compiled by Tom Simkin et al., U.S. Geological Survey and Smithsonian Institution, Washington, D.C. Reproduced by permission.)

Figure 10.44 Schematic cross sections of three models of Basin and Range structure. (From J.H. Stewart, 1980, *Bull., Geol. Soc. Amer.*, v. 91, p. 461, Figure 2. Reproduced with the permission of the publisher, the Geological Society of America, Boulder, Colorado, USA. Copyright © 1980.)

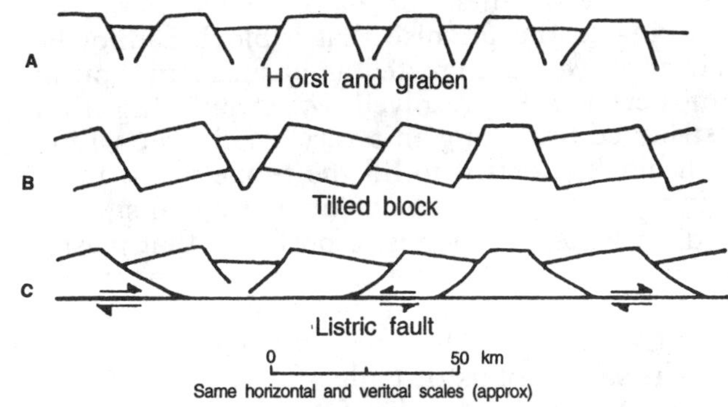

Figure 10.45 Schematic cross sections showing stages in one model of development of tilted fault blocks in the Basin and Range province. (Same source as in Figure 10.44; p. 463, Figure 5. Reproduced with the permission of the publisher, the Geological Society of America, Boulder, Colorado, USA. Copyright © 1980.)

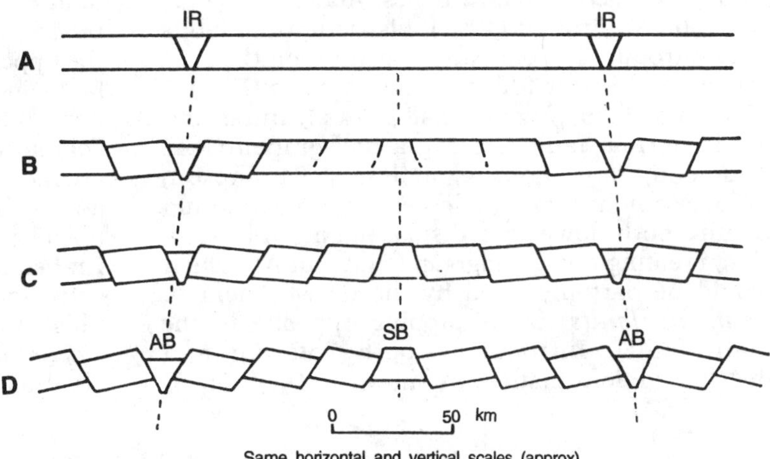

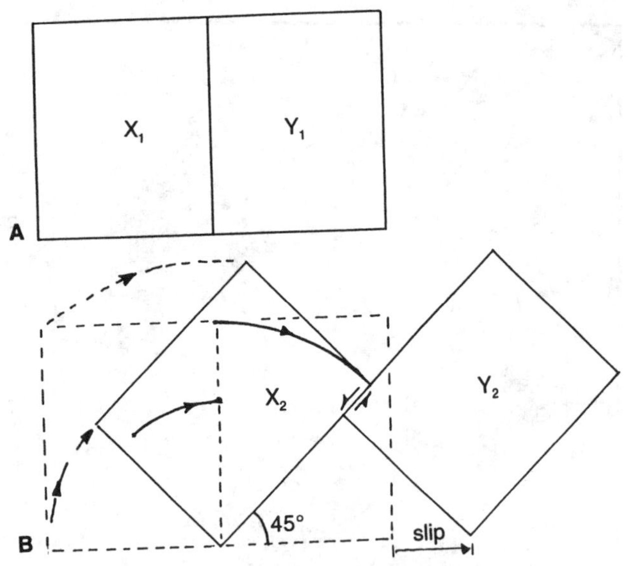

Figure 10.46 Schematic diagram of rotation of rigid blocks. (Copyright © by Arthur N. Strahler.)

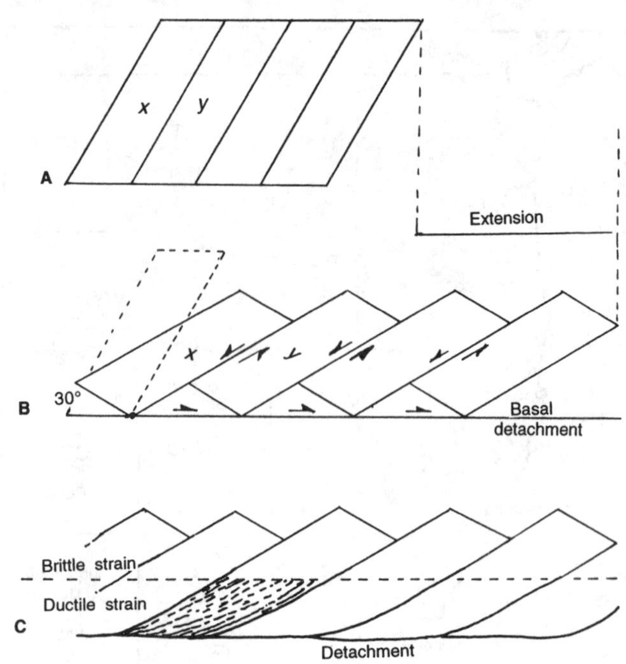

Figure 10.47 Schematic diagram of rotation of a set of fault blocks resting on a basal detachment. (Copyright © by Arthur N. Strahler.)

also required to rotate on a normal fault and to slip toward the right, while a triangular void space opens up below. Figure 10.47 shows a series of tilted blocks that have undergone extension (M.H. Anders et al., 1993, p. 1452). Diagram A shows the initial steeply dipping tensional fractures. Diagram B shows block rotation on normal faults, opening up a series of triangular voids ("tunnels" in three dimensions) above the basal surface that represents a décollement or basal detachment. By adhering to the premise that a block cannot be deformed, we have created an absurd situation. It can perhaps be resolved by stipulating that distributed fracturing on a very small scale within each block allows it to fill the tunnels, but in so doing, generates an large volume of much smaller voids. A better solution is to postulate that plastic deformation occurs in the lower region of the blocks, which lies within the ductile zone of the crust (Diagram C). This final setup can lead easily into the subject of listric faults.

Much of the credit for recognizing the importance of low-angle normal faults in the B&R goes to two geologists: R. Ernest Anderson (1977) and John M. Proffett (1997). Listric normal faults were introduced in our earlier sections on the East African and Upper Rhine graben systems (Figures 10.16 and 10.26). Figure 10.48 shows features of a listric normal fault forming a half-graben (R.E. Anderson, M.L. Zoback, and G.S. Thompson, 1983). Without rotation, descent of a block would require both downward displacement and extension, creating a widening gap (Diagram A), which would be partially filled by the development of *antithetic faults* (faults dipping opposite to the main fault). Introducing both rotation and distributed deformation, as shown in Diagram B, the stratigraphic horizons are bent down. What we need to add next is basin fill by locally derived sediments, as shown in Figure 10.49. Diagram A shows that alluvium has filled the basin, while erosional retreat of the fault scarp has left behind a pediment surface. In Diagram B, a new episode of fault movement has deepened the basin and exposed more of the footwall. In Diagram C, a second period of alluvial filling has been completed.

Figure 10.50 is an enhanced rendition of a seismic reflection profile across the Goshute Valley in Northeastern Nevada. Inferred faults are shown in solid curved lines cutting across reflecting layers in the alluvial fill. Several antithetic faults are shown but appear to have only small displacepments. Stepping next into a higher order of complexity, Figure 10.51 illustrates a two-phase fault development observed in the B&R. An older phase consists of low-dipping faults lying above the upper detachment surface, labeled *A*, and these faults in turn have been cross-cut by other, shorter normal faults. This structure is called *cross-cutting domino style* (J.C. Yarnold et al., 1993, p. 159). The second phase consists of the formation of much longer listric faults that penetrate much deeper to reach a new and lower detachment, labeled *B*. Grabens of this newer phase produced little further extension, but are now the sites of alluvial basins. This entire complex scenario goes by the name of *diachronous extensional deformation* (Anderson et al., 1983, p. 1070).

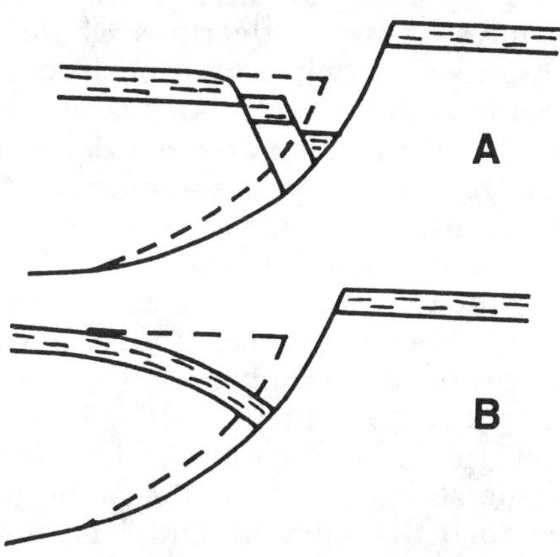

Figure 10.48 Schematic cross sections of extension by listric faulting. A. Development of antithetic faults. B. Downbending to fill potential gap. (Adapted from R.E. Anderson, M.L. Zoback, and G.S. Thompson, 1983, *Bull., Geol. Soc. Amer.*, v. 94, p. 1057, Figure 2. Reproduced with the permission of the publisher, the Geological Society of America, Boulder, Colorado, USA. Copyright © 1983.)

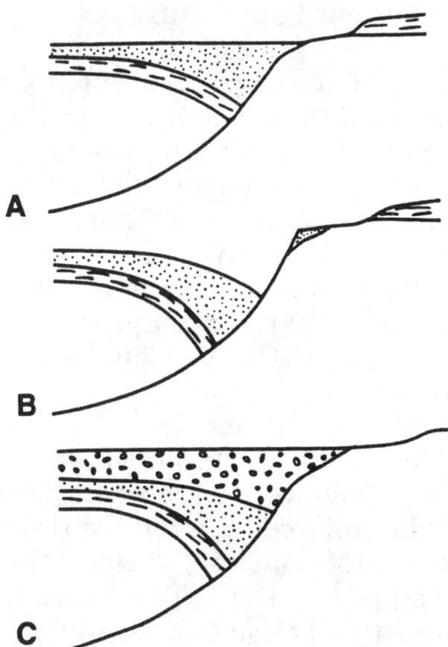

Figure 10.49 Cross sections showing two stages of basin filling and scarp erosion. (Same source as Figure 10.48; p. 1057, Figure 2. Reproduced with the permission of the publisher, the Geological Society of America, Boulder, Colorado, USA. Copyright © 1983.)

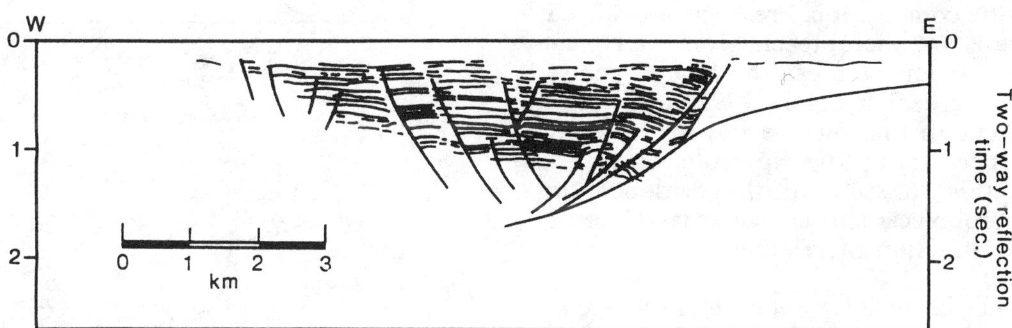

Figure 10.50 Enhanced cross section showing a seismic reflection profile across the Goshute Valley in Nevada. (Same source as Figure 10.48; p. 1063, Figure 6F. Reproduced with the permission of the publisher, the Geological Society of America, Boulder, Colorado, USA. Copyright © 1983.)

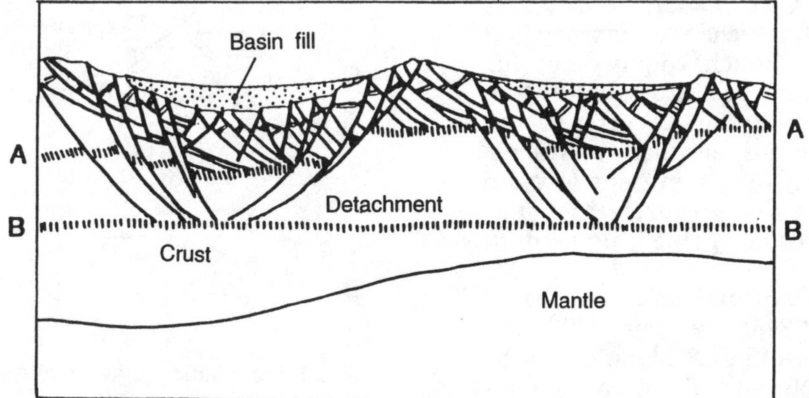

Figure 10.51 Schematic cross section showing fault pattern formed by two stages of extensional deformation. (Same source as Figure 10.48; p. 1070, Figure 10. Reproduced with the permission of the publisher, the Geological Society of America, Boulder, Colorado, USA. Copyright © 1983.

10.15 Metamorphic Core Complexes

The presence of low-dip detachments, situated deep in the brittle crust and descending farther into the ductile zone, has been presented in earlier sections as an essential part of the modern model of continental rift structure (Figures 10.16B and 10.19) as well as for broad, multi-block systems of the B&R (Figure 10.47). This is a relatively new concept, being greatly strengthened by data obtained from the COCORP and other seismic reflection traverses.

Yet, strange as it may seem, field geologists had for earlier decades been studying and mapping exposures of numerous detachments. (See Carl K. Seyfert, 1987a, for a comprehensive review of this subject.) In California alone, at least 25 exposures had been mapped in the B&R east of the Sierra Nevada and in the Mojave and Sonoran deserts (C.L. Pridmore and E.G. Frost, 1992, p. 4, Figure 1). These low-angle faults are exposed in steep erosional slopes, usually near the base of a mountain, and can often be spotted from a long distance by a sharp line of contrasting rock color or by a sharp rock ledge. In a typical case, a microbreccia ledge coincides with the fault, and below it lies a brecciated and altered mylonitic gneiss (1992, p. 3). The gneiss may, for example, be of granodioritic composition. Presence of oxidized iron in the resistant microbreccia gives it a typical reddish-brown color, whereas the altered gneiss has a distinct greenish color (1992, p. 6). The bizarre element in this picture lies in the early interpretation of these low-dip faults as thrust faults, and this in spite of the evidence on exhumed microbreccia surfaces of striae favoring the opposite direction of relative motion (1992, p. 7, Figure 4.).

Persistence of the interpretation of these low-angle faults as being overthrusts has been dubbed the "Alpine influence"—a tendency to associate any low-angle fault with alpine overthrusts such as those of the European Alps. The prevailing interpretation was that the overthrusting occurred during the earlier compressional regime of the late Mesozoic Cordilleran/Laramide orogenies. But as early as the 1950s, Peter Misch had questioned that interpretation, and in 1972 Richard Armstrong had published evidence of a much younger age for these low-dip faults (Pridmore and Frost, 1992, p. 4). In 1971, R. Ernest Anderson offered the hypothesis that normal faults, originally of steeper dips, had been rotated to their present low dip angles. The normal-fault interpretation, put forward by John M. Proffett, gained momentum through the 1970s.

A COCORP transect of the B&R was carried out in the period 1982-1984. More than 1000 km in length, it extended E-W from the Colorado Plateau to the northern Sierra Nevada, about on the 40th parallel of latitude (Allmendinger et al., 1987). Our tectonic map, Figure 10.36, shows the location of the segments of this transect and others to the south of it. These and other seismic reflection profiles have shown reflections of deep listric faults leading into what may be interpreted as detachments at great depth. An example is shown in Figure 10.51, in which an older detachment (A) has been followed by a younger and deeper detachment (B).

In the early 1980s the term *metamorphic core complex* came into use, defined as "the association of strongly metamorphosed footwall rocks and unmetamorphosed hanging wall rocks along a dome-shaped detachment fault" (Pridmore and Frost, 1992, p. 5). The first part of this definition is a petrologic statement, as is the name itself. The "dome-shaped detachment fault" is, however, a tectonic feature. What then is the nature of this doming? Figure 10.52 illustrates one scenario in which doming might occur. A shallow detachment (Diagram A) is replaced by a deep detachment (Diagram B). The inactive upper detachment becomes deformed into what is called a *roll-over fold* (Diagram C). This kind of arch is also called an *antiform*. Much later (Diagram D), a combination of uplift and erosion has led to surface exposure of the older detachment. Figure 10.53 is a diagrammatic cross section showing a deeply eroded dome

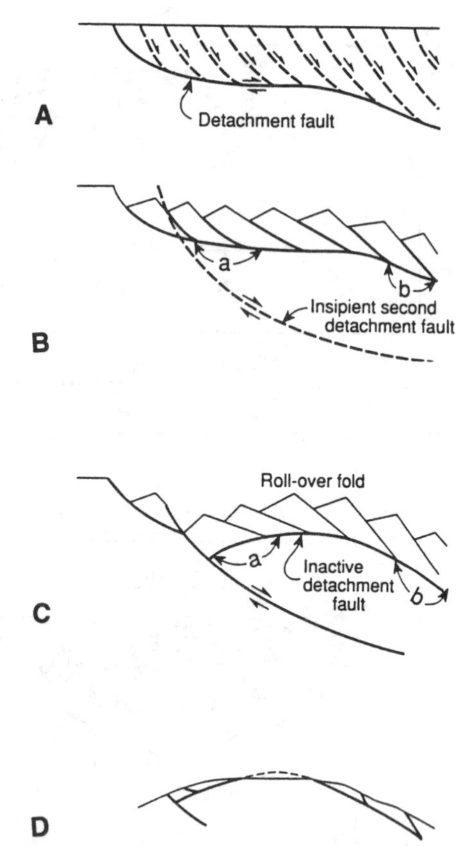

Figure 10.52 Schematic diagrams of doming of a metamorphic core complex. (From C.L. Pridmore and E.G. Frost, 1992, *California Geology*, v. 45, no. 1, p. 10, Figure 6. Used by permission of the authors and the California Division of Mines and Geology.)

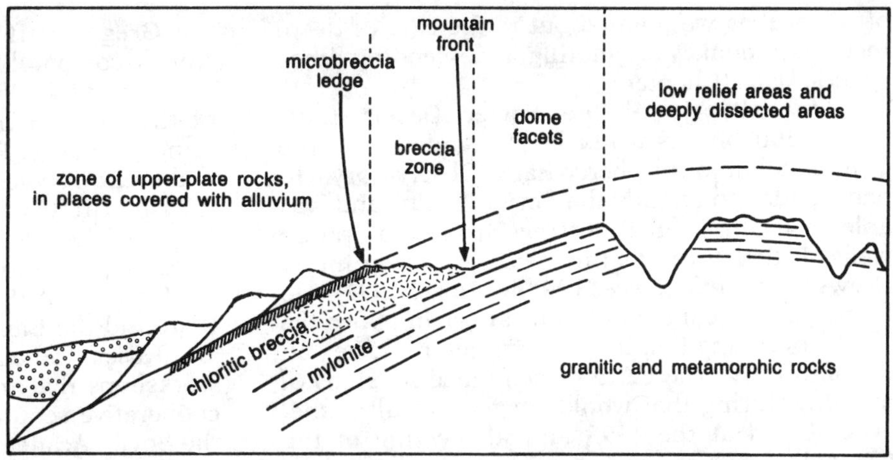

Figure 10.53 Diagrammatic cross section of landforms typical of an exposed metamorphic core complex. (From C.F. Pain, 1985, *Geology*, v. 13, p. 871, Figure 1. Reproduced with the permission of the publisher, the Geological Society of America, Boulder, Colorado, USA. Copyright © 1985.)

exposing a detachment in the zone between the main mountain front and the adjacent basin. A resistant mylonite layer with a sloping but relative smooth surface is a distinctive landform somewhat resembling a hogback flatiron of a typical sedimentary dome in the Central Rocky Mountains (C.F. Pain, 1985, p. 871).

While the existence of detachments of low dip angles seems securely backed up by their surface exposures, their recognition in deep seismic reflection imagery has been less secure and even subject to some questioning. Let us examine an actual case in which controversy developed. Beneath the Sevier Desert basin of west-central Utah, seismologists identified from the COCORP Line 1 data a detachment appearing as a gently dipping surface located in the depth range between 12 and 15 km. We reproduce here as Figure 10.54 a portion of the drawing abstracted from this seismic record (Allmendinger et al., 1983, p. 535). This remarkable reflection, which can be traced for a distance of about 70 km and to a depth of 13 to 14 km, became known as the Sevier Desert detachment. The horizontal extent of this surface was estimated to be as great as 7,000 sq km. It was also observed that reflectors of listric normal faults do not cross this detachment. The discovery was heralded in a special *Science* report by science writer Richard A. Kerr (1983). It turned out that this and other detachments had been previously observed in seismic profiles carried out by oil companies and had been made known to geologists of the U.S. Geological Survey, but those profiles could not be published (Kerr, 1983, p. 1031). The detachment hypothesis had been applied to this feature in a 1967 publication by R.E. McDonald, but seems to have attracted little notice.

Skepticism as to the physical possibility of such an enormous crustal slab sliding on a fault surface of dip on the order of 10 to 12 degrees continued to be expressed, so that the finding of what seemed to be a demonstration that such motion had occurred was disturbing to many geologists. Similar conflicts between observation and theory have frequently punctuated the history

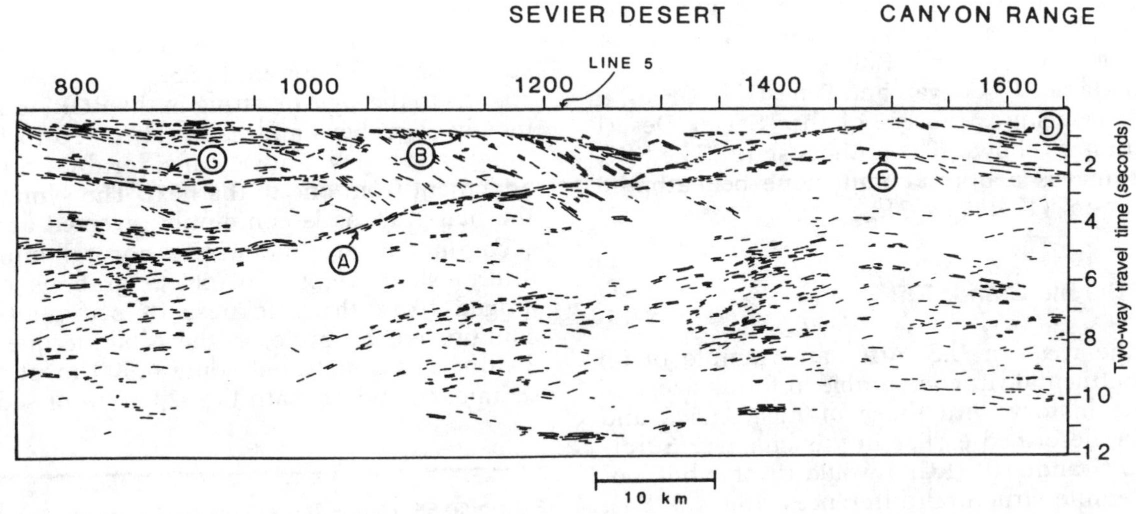

Figure 10.54 Portion of drawing abstracted from COCORP reflection seismic image of structures beneath the Sevier Desert basin of west-central Utah. (From R.W. Almendinger et al., 1983, *Geology*, v. 11, Figure 2, folded map. Reproduced with the permission of the publisher, the Geological Society of America, Boulder, Colorado, USA. Copyright © 1983.)

of science, as we pointed out in the case of deep-focus earthquakes originating in descending lithospheric slabs (Chapter 6).

One skeptic of the Sevier Desert fault interpretation was Mark H. Anders of the Columbia Lamont-Doherty Earth Observatory. He had decided to restudy the Sevier "fault," and was able to examine drill cuttings from exploration wells drilled through this seismic discontinuity (News report in *Science*, 1993, v. 262, p. 992). He found young sediment of alluvial origin above the "fault" overlying Cambrian carbonate rock, i.e., an unconformity. The cuttings contained no signs of microfracturing that would suggest a fault plane. When aired at the 1993 annual meeting of the Geological Society of America, Anders's finding was greeted with a mixed reaction, mostly skeptical in tone, since it supported none of the contending hypotheses of normal-fault evolution. About a year later, Anders and a Lamont colleague, Nicholas Christie-Blick, published in *Geology* a full account of their "no-fault" hypothesis (1994). In a balanced review of that paper, J. Wakefield (1994) included responses by leading nay-sayers in the argument: Brian Wernicke, Roger Buck, Richard Allmendinger, and Norman Sleep. To counter their negative arguments, Wakefield included the following supporting view:

> USGS geophysicist Warren Hamilton has also concluded that the fault, commonly called the Sevier Desert detachment, is a "nonexistent structure." On the basis of another set of data from industry seismic reflection profiles, Hamilton says the Sevier fault is "merely an unconformity." (Wakefield, 1994, p. 459.)

Wakefield's closing line (p. 460) quoted Cornell's Allmendinger as remarking: "This sort of debate is certainly healthy." The debate on this subject has indeed continued, with field geologists supporting low-angle extensional faults, and geophysicists rejecting that interpretation on grounds of laws of mechanics (Kerr, 1995). Published in *Geology* in 1996 by James C. Coogan and Peter G. DeCelles, a complete seismic transect of the "Sevier Desert Reflection" is shown. The authors state: "The SDR clearly marks a normal fault zone beneath the entire basin" (1996, p. 933).

10.16 The Rio Grande Rift

Does the western U.S. offer an example of an intracontinental rift comparable in form, size, and tectonic history with those of East Africa and Eurasia, described earlier in this chapter? Surely the Rio Grande rift (RGR) would fill this bill, but with definite structural differences from the East African, Baikal, and Upper Rhine rifts. An outstanding feature of the RGR is the great volume and extent of mafic extrusives that have in some places almost buried the tectonic features. Only in the Gregory rift of east Kenya is this volcanic feature comparable in extent (see Figure 10.18).

Figures 10.35 and 10.36 show the relationship of the RGR to the main area of the Basin and Range province. Figure 10.55 is a map of the RGR and areas of volcanic rock within and adjacent to it. The rift extends from Presidio on the Rio Grande River to Leadville, CO, on the north, a distance just short of 1000 km.

Because of the many similarities between the RGR and the Baikal rift, geoscientists of the U.S. and Russia joined in the summer of 1988 in field workshops that included visits to both rifts. This cooperative venture was under the sponsorship of the Soviet Academy of Sciences, the U.S. National Academy of Science, and the U.S. Geological Survey (Lipman et al., 1989).

With regard to geologic location, the RGR has developed mostly within the Proterozoic craton, and the rift truncates basement structures of the craton. The rift axis also corresponds rather closely with a compressional zone of the late Paleozoic "ancestral Rocky Mountains", and this also coincides with the region of Late-K/Early Cenozoic Laramide thrusting in Colorado. In all these respects, the RGE differs from the bedrock environment of the Great Basin region of the B&R, from which it is widely separated.

Rifting of the RGR in the north began about 27 Ma but had been active as far south as southern New Mexico as early as 32 Ma (Lipman et al., 1989, p. 578). Two active periods are recognized, with a hiatus between about 18 Ma and 10 Ma. During the earlier period, broad fault basins received sediment from relatively low bordering uplands. In the more recent period, starting about 10 Ma, normal faulting became concentrated in a narrow axial region and produced most of the tectonic features of the rift as we see it now. Great outpourings of basaltic lava, commencing about 5 Ma, inundated large areas both adjacent to the rift axis and within the rift (Baldridge and Olsen, 1989, p. 241-242). These young volcanics are shown by a special pattern in Figure 10.55.

As to the style of rifting in the RGR, it consists mostly of grabens and half-grabens 50 to 100 km long, and they show considerable offset in alignment from one to the next. The symmetry of the half-grabens is commonly reversed across an accommodation zone where normal faults are intermeshed. Depths of these grabens can be judged from the thickness of sediments they contain. For example, in the Albuquerque basin, drilling has penetrated some 4,500 m of synrift sediments, and beneath that 2,000 m of sediment

Figure 10.55 Generalized geological map of the Rio Grande rift system. (Adapted from P.W. Lipman et al., 1989, *EOS*, v. 70, no. 19, p. 579, Figure 1. Reproduced by permission of the authors and the American Geophysical Union.) →

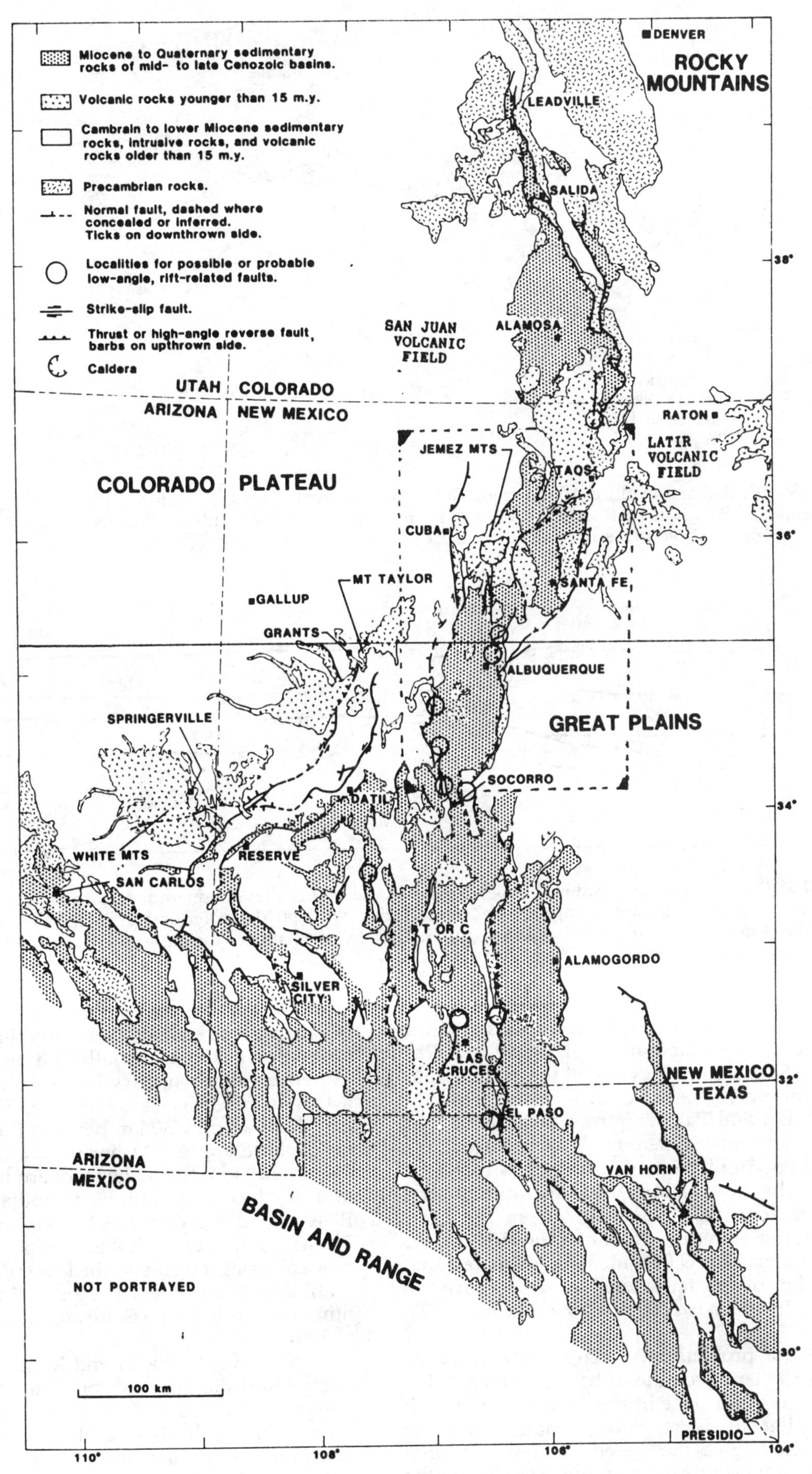

Miocene to Quaternary sedimentary rocks of mid- to late Cenozoic basins.
Volcanic rocks younger than 15 m.y.
Cambrain to lower Miocene sedimentary rocks, intrusive rocks, and volcanic rocks older than 15 m.y.
Precambrian rocks.
Normal fault, dashed where concealed or inferred. Ticks on downthrown side.
Localities for possible or probable low-angle, rift-related faults.
Strike-slip fault.
Thrust or high-angle reverse fault, barbs on upthrown side.
Caldera
DENVER
ROCKY MOUNTAINS
LEADVILLE
SALIDA
SAN JUAN VOLCANIC FIELD
ALAMOSA
UTAH
COLORADO
ARIZONA
NEW MEXICO
RATON
LATIR VOLCANIC FIELD
JEMEZ MTS
TAOS
COLORADO PLATEAU
CUBA
SANTA FE
MT TAYLOR
GALLUP
GRANTS
ALBUQUERQUE
SPRINGERVILLE
GREAT PLAINS
SOCORRO
DATIL
WHITE MTS
RESERVE
SAN CARLOS
T OR C
ALAMOGORDO
SILVER CITY
LAS CRUCES
NEW MEXICO
TEXAS
EL PASO
ARIZONA
MEXICO
VAN HORN
BASIN AND RANGE
NOT PORTRAYED
100 km
PRESIDIO
38°
36°
34°
32°
30°
110°
108°
106°
104°

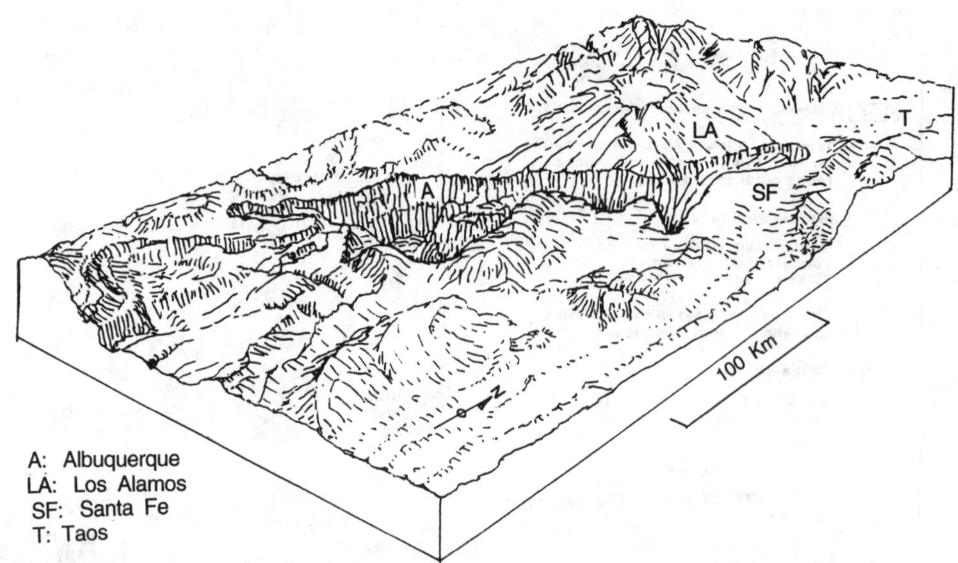

Figure 10.56 Block diagram of the Albuquerque NM region showing the configuration of the Precambrian and Paleozoic rock surface. (Adapted from a drawing by John Tubb of the Los Alamos National Laboratory. Used by permission of the artist.)

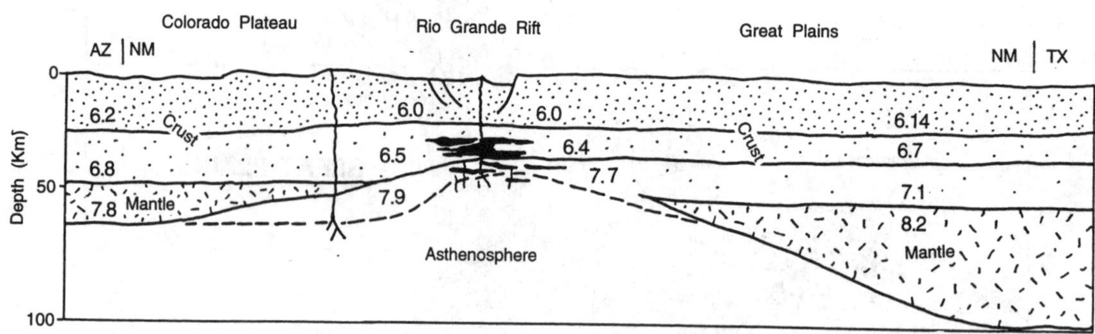

Figure 10.57 Generalized cross section through the Rio Grande rift in the Albuquerque NM area. Figures give velocities of seismic compressional waves. (From W. Scott Baldridge and Kenneth H. Olsen, 1989, *American Scientist*, v. 77, p. 246, Figure 7. Used by permision of the authors and the Society of Sigma Xi.)

brought down into an Eocene basin from Laramide uplifts (Lipman et al., 1989, p. 578). Figure 10.56 is a block diagram of the Albuquerque region depicting the configuration of the Precambrian and Paleozoic rock surface as if all younger rock and sediment could be removed from the axial region of the rift. It was drawn by John Tubb of the Los Alamos National Laboratory. Maximum total relief measured from the basin floor to the summit of the adjacent Sandia Mountains exceeds 9,000 m. It is estimated that about 8 km of crustal extension has occurred in this area in the past 25 m.y. (Woodward, 1977, p. 269).

A major problem has been to determine the origin of the large volume of basaltic magma that has reached the surface in the vicinity of the RGR and in adjacent areas. Seismic data, shown in Figure 10.57, give the speed of compressional waves as somewhat slower in the crust below the rift than to the east and west, and indicate that the lower crust is substantially thinned beneath rift. Moreover, the boundary between lithosphere and asthenosphere has risen substantially and now lies at a depth of only 30 km beneath the rift. Thus the lithosphere appears to have been greatly thinned. In comparison, the asthenosphere upper limit lies at a depth of 60 km under the adjacent Colorado Plateau and at a depth of 100 km under the Great Plains to the east. It has been suggested that molten basalt residing in the lower crust and upper mantle beneath the rift axis is in the form of numerous thin sills (Baldridge and Olsen, 1989, p. 246).

We leave the Basin and Range province with many interesting special topics unmentioned. The region continues to be intensively studied by American geologists and geophysicists and continues to yield a large number of research reports.

10.17 The Sierra Nevada Uplift

A tectonic event of major importance that took place adjacent to the Basin and Range province was the uplift of the Sierra Nevada (SN) in California and Nevada (see Figure 10.35). This lofty range is essentially an enormous westward-tilted fault block composed in large part of granite batholiths intruded from late Jurassic through the Cretaceous as typical arc magmas generated by a long-enduring subduction boundary (Atwater, 1989, p. 46). The block measures from 80 to 160 km in width and about 600 km in length. Summit elevations exceed 4,000 m in the southern part of the block. Although present as a distinctive crustal fault block of low relief throughout most of the Cenozoic, it is thought to have risen rapidly to its present high elevation during only the past 3 or 4 m.y. A system of normal faults bounds the southern SN on its precipitous eastern margin, whereas the western side remained low, now forming the border of the Great Valley of California. Figure 10.58 is a stylized block diagram of the northern section of the SN depicting in the foreground the present, heavily glaciated topopgraphy along the crest. Shown in the background is a restored surface of low relief—an uplifted peneplain—in an early phase of the rapid uplift. (For a comprehensive description of the geology and geomorphology of the SN see R.M. Norris and R.W. Webb, 1976, Chapter 2, p. 11-68.)

The principles of isostasy and isostatic crustal rise have played a major role in explaining the timing and rapid rise of the SN. In Chapter 3 (Isostasy and the Lithosphere; Figure 3.41) we explained that a high mountain mass requires a deep root of relatively low density to support it in a state of isostatic equilibrium. Andrew C. Lawson in 1936 calculated that the required crustal root for the SN extends down into the mantle to a depth of some 65 km. His estimate was substantiated in 1937 by seismologist Perry Byerly, who observed appropriate delays in travel times for waves passing under the SN (see citations in Pakiser and Brune, 1980, p. 1088). (Refer back to Figure 10.40, our contour map of crustal thickness of the western United States, on which the SN is given a thickness greater than 50 km.) Pakiser and Brune in 1980 reviewed newer seismic data and set the bottom of the root at about 55 km. That figure was endorsed by C.G. Chase and T.C. Wallace (1986, p. 730), who concurred with a conservative opinion previously stated by other authors: "About the only reasonable time for the construction of this crustal root is during the Mesozoic arc activity along the western coast of North America." The Sierra Nevada batholith was emplaced in the time frame of Late Jurassic to Late Cretaceous and it is most unlikely that a root so great could have been produced in the few episodes of minor Cenozoic igneous activity that occurred later.

So there remains the vexing question: Why, if the root was in place, did the SN block not rise until latest Miocene or in the Pliocene? Chase and Wallace suggested the possibility that, during Cenozoic erosion, isostasy was not maintained because the lithosphere had "cooled and acquired elastic strength sufficient to make the isostatic response to erosion regional rather than local" (1986, p. 731). The authors then went on to say that Basin and Range extension between 10 and 5 Ma "broke the elastic lithosphere," which freed the SN block and allowed it to rise rapidly.

An earlier hypothesis to explain the long delay in rise of the SN block in response to the presence of a thick low-density root will be familiar from reference to it in Chapter 9. As illustrated in Figure 9.60, the Farallon plate is shown as a horizontal slab in contact with the continental lithosphere and penetrating far eastward before turning

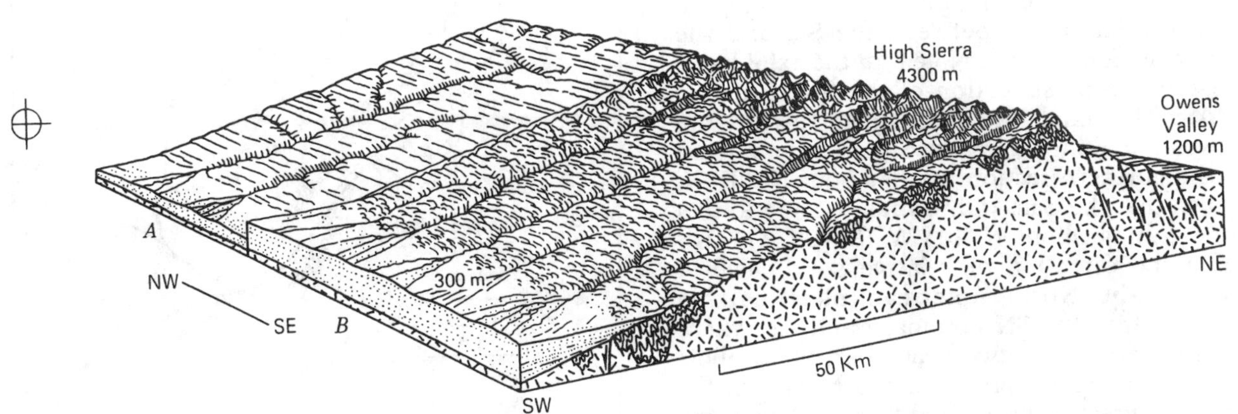

Figure 10.58 A highly stylized block diagram of the northern section of the Sierra Nevada of California. (A) The imagined sloping surface of the fault block prior to deep erosion. (B) Present mountainous landscape of the High Sierra, with deep glacial troughs and river gorges. (Suggested by drawings by Francois E. Matthes, U.S. Geological Survey. Drawn by A.N. Strahler.)

downward. This scenario, attributed to Peter Bird (1984), developed in late Cretaceous time and continued into the mid-Cenozoic. It would have followed the earlier intrusions of the Sierra batholiths. The effect of the dense lower slab would have been to "cancel out" the buoyancy of the Sierra root and prevent isostatic rise of the Sierra block. This effect terminated only when the Farallon slab was severed by initiation of the San Andreas transform boundary and sank deep into the asthenosphere where it was heated and absorbed. Edward A. Hay described this event:

> As the "slab" of the subducting lithosphere was removed, the relatively low-density root in the lower crust would no longer be "held down" by the high-density slab beneath it, thus converting a balanced situation to an imbalanced one. (1976, p. 764.)

A revised scenario for the rapid and relatively recent uplift of the Sierra block was published in 1996 in a paper in *Science* authored by Brian Wernicke and 19 coauthors. This team had collected wide-angle refraction-reflection data along profiles both transverse and parallel to the southern SN. One finding was that there is present under the high Sierra a crustal root only 3 to 5 km thick—not capable of sustaining the high block by isostasy. This thinness of crust is explained through the action of extensional tectonics known to have occurred throughout this region. This crustal layer can be responsible for only about 25% of the necessary buoyancy (Wernicke et al., 1996, p. 190). The remaining large fraction seems to consist of mantle rock, described as exhibiting an "upper mantle seismic anomaly" (p. 191). Thus there lies directly beneath the thinned crust a dense, molten mantle rock that has recently welled up to replace the normal mantle lithosphere.

Our next step is to recognize certain important relationships between the SN and its adjacent geologic provinces. These are displayed in Figure 10.59, a simplified outline map showing the geometric relationship between the SN and the San Andreas fault system. Note that the axial trend of the southernmost section of the SN is almost due N-S. The axial line then turns toward the northwest, making a broad S-curve, and from there the northern section trends about N 20° W. Note also that the San Andreas fault (SAF) in this latitude trends about N 40° W (S 40° E), also defining the direction of relative southeasterly motion of the North American plate at this latitude. Within the SN boundary and elsewhere on the map are placed two-headed arrow symbols of least horizontal compression, which is to say the direction of greatest horizontal tension. The same symbol is placed near the SAF, a right-lateral (dextral) strike-slip fault. (These symbols have been taken from Figure 10.42A.) Generally, the directions of greatest horizontal tension—i.e., of maximum extension—are roughly uniform over the entire region from Basin & Range (B&R), across the SN, and into the Coast Ranges. A bold extension symbol placed in northwestern Nevada shows the average direction of maximum extension for the Great Basin; its orientation is N 60° W (Argus and Gordon, 1991, p. 1089).

In order to understand the tectonic "role", if any, of the SN as a rigid unit during the Neogene regime of western lithospheric extension we need to tie it in with the active transform boundary that separates the Pacific plate from the North American plate. First, refer back to our section "The San Andreas Fault System" in Chapter 6, in which it is noted that the San Andreas fault (SAF) and other active adjacent dextral strike-slip faults contribute to meeting a large percent of the overall steady relative motion between the North American plate and the Pacific plate (Argus and Gordon, 1991, p. 1085). We also took note of certain faults along the eastern flank of the southern portion of the SN (Figure 6.32B). Motion on these faults combines strike-slip and dip-slip displacement. The Owens Valley fault was cited as an example. Faults such as these, along with those of the Great Basin, lying far inland from the San Andreas fault systems are called upon to supply the missing percent of relative plate motion. So we should be looking for both normal and strike-slip faulting, either in separate systems or combined in a single fault. In 1991, Richard G. Gordon of Northwestern University reviewed the advances in

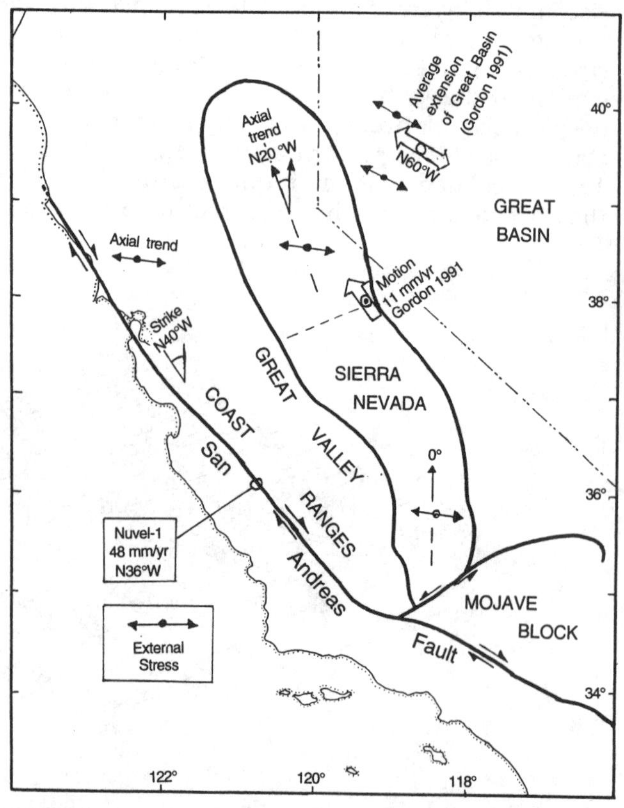

Figure 10.59 Sketch map of the Sierra Nevada in relationship to the San Andreas Fault and the Mojave Block. (Copyright © by Arthur N. Strahler.)

four preceding years of application of NUVEL-1 to plate motions. (See Chapter 7, Geodetic Measurements of Plate Motions.) The NUVEL-1 data showed that when both the San Andreas fault-system data and the extensional data of the Sierra Nevada and Basin & Range provinces are combined, they account for nearly all of the Pacific/North American interplate motion (1991, p. 573). (See also Gordon and Stein, 1992, p. 339, Figure 7.)

Lauren Wright, in 1976, published a comprehensive review of a long-lived controversy among geologists over the relative importance of normal faulting and strike-slip faulting throughout the extensional regions of the western U.S. Both groups agree that the crust of the Great Basin has been expanding westward to the accompaniment of normal faulting. Disagreement lies in the additional role of strike-slip faulting contributing to that expansion. Those giving a major role to long zones of strike-slip faults called these features *megashears*, a term used by S. Warren Carey in 1958 in promoting his expanding-earth theory. Those who placed most of the burden on normal faults called their model "simple extension." This model had been proposed by G.K. Gilbert in the early 1900s and was strongly supported in 1970 by James Gilluly. Throughout the controversy, a number of geologists and geophysicists have accepted an important role for both models: both forms of faulting serve the same extensional axis.

Figure 10.60 is a cartoon-like presentation of the two extensional systems under discussion here. The faults are to be viewed as symbols. Simple extension (Diagram A) has been covered in detail earlier in the chapter. Although the normal faults

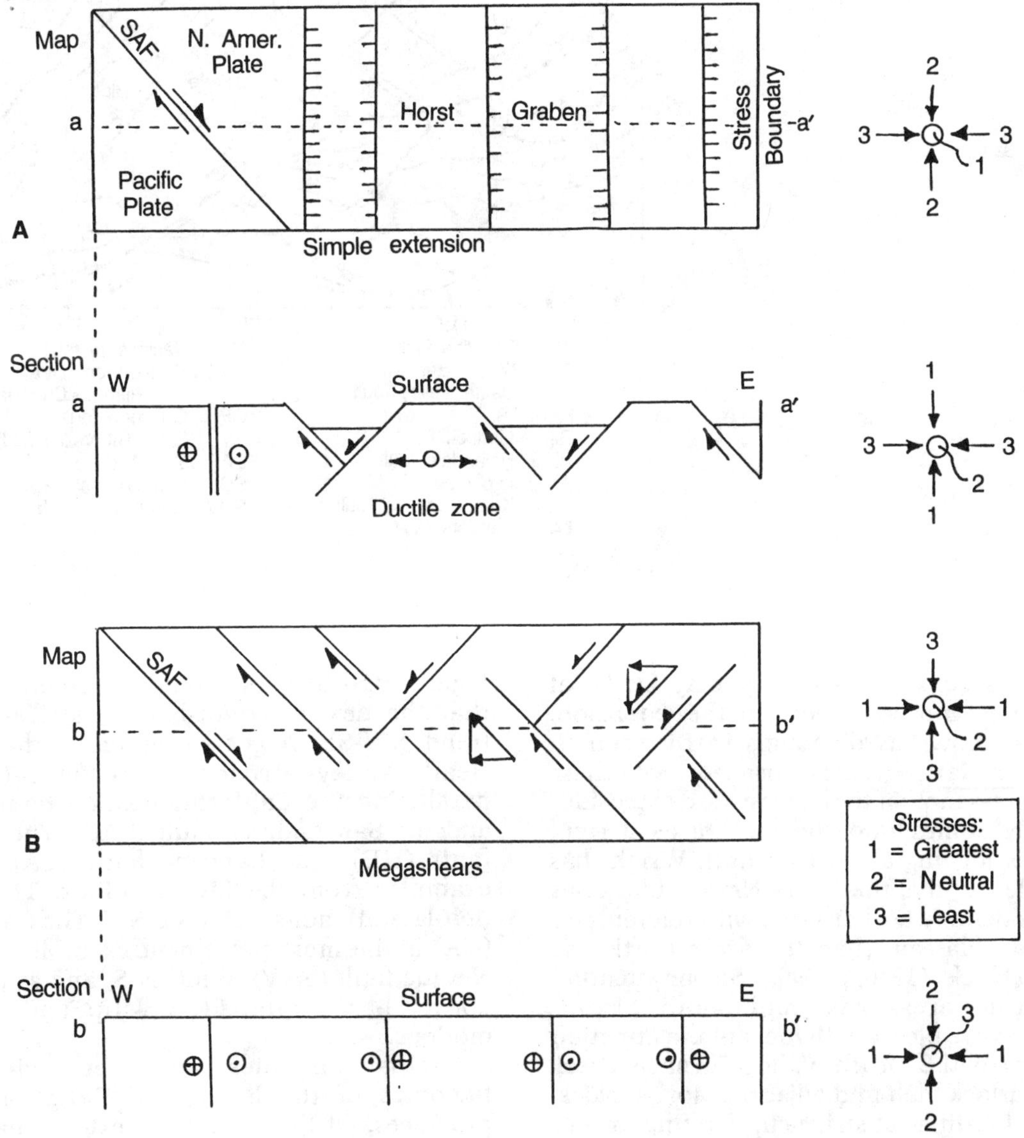

Figure 10.60 Cartoon-like presentation of two forms of extensional systems found in the Great Basin. (Copyright © by Arthur N. Strahler.)

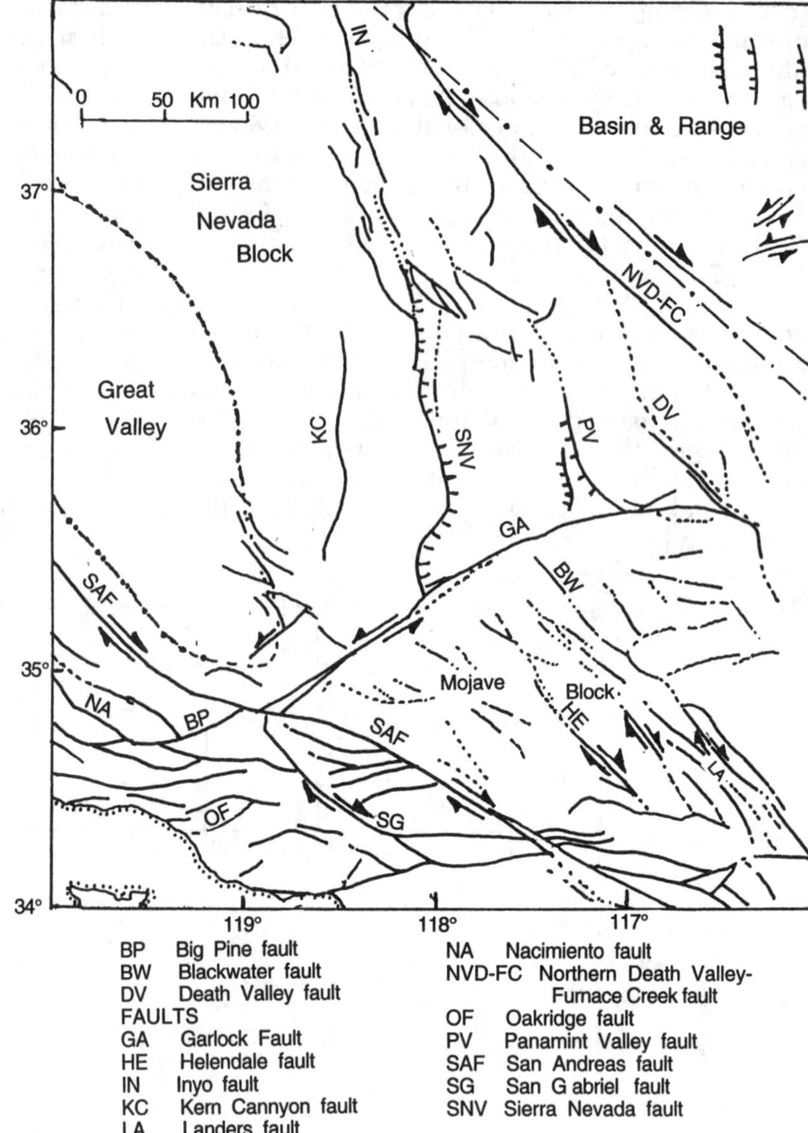

Figure 10.61 Generalized tectonic map of the region adjacent to the southern portion of the Sierra Nevada block. (Based on data from the *Geologic Map of California*, 1966, U.S. Geological Survey and California Division of Mines and Geology.)

are shown as striking N-S, they may strike at oblique angles and contribute to the extension. Megashears, shown as diagonals in Diagram B, contribute a large vector fraction of their horizontal mass motion to the westward extension.

The SN comes into the picture as a rigid crustal mass moving along as a unit. Wright has offered evidence "that the Sierra Nevada block has moved considerably farther west, with reference to the Colorado Plateau, than the areas north and south of the block" (1976, p. 490.) So our attention is directed to areas east and south of this seemingly passive block, with most of the attention being given to the Death Valley/Furnace Creek zone, the Garlock fault and adjacent Mojave block, and certain localities of strike-slip faulting farther north and east in the Great Basin.

Figure 10.36 shows this entire region, while Figure 10.61 focuses upon the southern SN. Notice that the dextral (right-lateral) strike-slip faults trend NW-SE. A good example is the Northern Death Valley-Furnace Creek fault (NDV-FC), paralleling the California/Nevada boundary line and the San Andreas fault (SAF). The Helendale fault (HE) and Landers fault (LA) are good examples from the Mojave block. The sinistral (left-lateral) faults trend NE-SW. The Garlock fault (GA) is the most prominent example. The Sierra Nevada fault (SNV) trends N-S, and as mentioned above, has combined dip-slip and strike-slip motions.

This concludes our brief review of the tectonics of the Basin and Range and Sierra provinces. Of the interesting extensional features of this part of western North America one remains to be examined.

10.18 The Gulf of California

Earlier in the chapter we examined the Red Sea and Gulf of Aden and pronounced them to be bona fide new oceans, having come into existence along lines where lithospheric rifting reached the critical point at which an oceanic plate boundary appeared and new oceanic crust began to be formed. Although the Gulf of California (GC) has resemblances to the Gulf of Aden (GA), there are significant differences in the tectonic settings of the two gulfs. The two gulfs are alike in their form, tapering to a narrow point, but whereas the GA lies between two large continental plates, the GC is much narrower and has only a thin sliver of continental lithosphere between it and the Pacific plate. Whereas the GA terminates in a triple junction where it meets point-to-point with another major rift (the Red Sea), the GC lines up nicely with the San Andreas transform plate boundary. This relationship is shown on our regional map, Figure 10.62.

There seems to be general agreement among geoscientists that the Gulf of California (GC) has had a history closely resembling that of the San Andreas transform system, which came into existence when a subduction boundary was replaced by a new transform boundary. In the GC area, prior to about 12 Ma, an active subduction boundary existed offshore of what is now the Baja Peninsula. At that time, a new plate boundary, parallel with the subduction boundary, began to

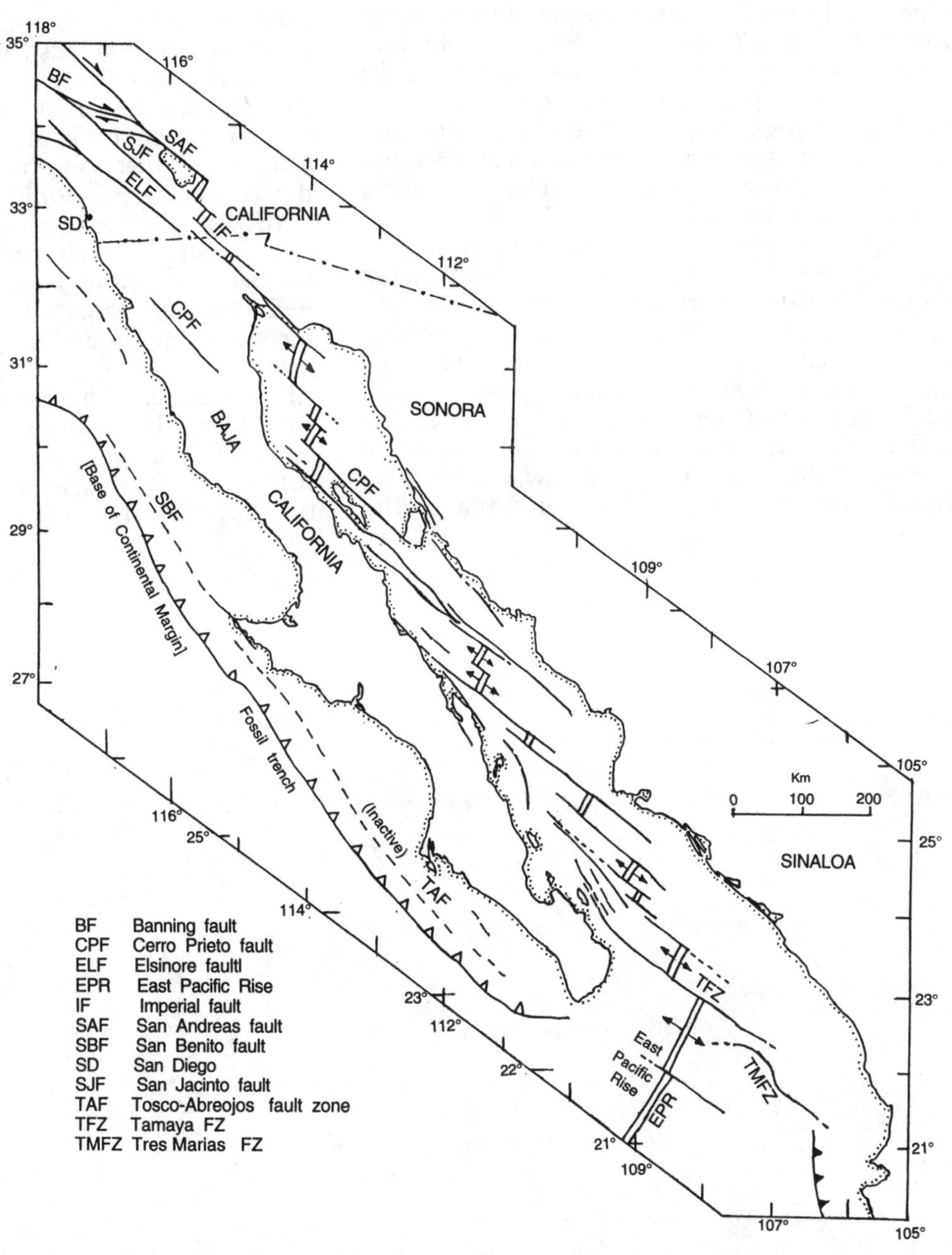

Figure 10.62 Generalized tectonic map of the Gulf of California. (Based on data of P. Lonsdale, 1989, *Geology of North America*, Volume N, p. 503. Figure 2, and other sources.)

develop along a line of strike-slip faulting located some 300 km inland (Spencer and Normark, 1989, p. 489). When the East Pacific Rise intercepted this shear zone, the plate boundary took its "jump" inland, and the strike slip zone was modified to serve the role of a plate boundary. The trace of the former subduction boundary is shown on our map with a special symbol representing a "fossil trench," and it now corresponds with the foot of the continental shelf. The East Pacific Rise (EPR) first encountered the Tamaya fault zone (TFZ) and was offset to the northwest. As the penetration of the oceanic rift continued, short segments of the EPR were formed to connect with long transform segments. The average trend of this new ocean floor is now about N 30° W.

The offsetting process has consisted of the opening up of a succession of rhomboidal pull-apart basins, and these now characterize the floor of the gulf (Lonsdale, 1989, p. 499-501). There are some 7 or 8 named basins, deepening in succession from NW to SE. Two of the basins have bottom depths exceeding 3,000 m. Tectonic features of the basins are not expressed in the present coastline of the Gulf, which has many embayments and promontories. Apparently, crustal subsidence has caused some coastal drowning that spreads over a zone of continental crust.

It seems, then, that the important tectonic role being played out in the Gulf of California is not that of rifting apart of a continent to produce an ever-widening ocean basin, but rather that of permitting continued oblique motion between the Pacific and North American plates. In other words, the GC oceanic rift serves as a southerly extension of the San Andreas fault system. Thus, a single sliver of continental lithosphere now extends from the southern tip of the Baja Peninsula to the northern terminus of the San Andreas fault at Cape Mendocino. Another such continental sliver, largely submerged, can be found along the Queen Charlotte fault on the west coast of Canada and Alaska (Chapter 6, Figure 6.34).

* * * * * * *

This chapter has completed our overview of extensional continental tectonics and the formation of continental rifts. We have covered the early stage of continental rifting to the point that oceanic lithosphere has begun to form by the rise of mafic magma in a mid-oceanic spreading rift. So this chapter could be taken as a logical prelude to Chapter 7, in which we followed the Wilson cycle through the stage of expansion of oceanic plates. Then, there would follow Chapter 8, the subduction of oceanic crust, and Chapter 9, collision tectonics and continental accretion. So the Wilson cycle stands completed.

Tectonics—the process of breaking, bending, and translocating rock—has thus far dominated our treatment of geologic processes, although igneous and metamorphic activities have not been neglected. Plate tectonics is also deeply involved with yet another major geologic process: the accumulation of sediments in large crustal basins on the interiors and margins of the continents. Sedimentary basins of several kinds have been mentioned in this and earlier chapters—e.g., flysch and molasse of orogens, shelf and slope wedges of rifted continental margins, accretionary prisms of subduction boundaries, and tectonic basins in block-faulted regions. Our next chapter treats continental basins as tectonic features serving their specialized roles in the Wilson cycle.

REFERENCES CITED

Allmendinger, R.W., J.W. Sharp, D. Von Tish, L. Serpa, L. Brown, S. Kaufman, and J. Oliver, 1983, Cenozoic and Mesozoic structure of the eastern Basin and Range province, Utah, from COCORP seismic-reflection data. *Geology*, v. 11, p. 532-536.

Allmendinger, R.W., T.A. Hauge, E.C. Potter, S.L. Klemperer, K.D. Nelson, P. Knuepfer, and J. Oliver, 1987, Overview of the COCORP 40°N Transect, western United States: The fabric of an orogenic belt. *Bull. Geol. Soc. Amer.*, v. 98, p. 308-319.

Anders, Mark H., and Nicholas Christie-Blick, 1994, Is the Sevier Desert reflection of west-central Utah a normal fault? *Geology*, v. 22, p. 771-774.

Anders, Mark H., Mark Spiegelman, David W. Rodgers, and Jonathan T. Hagstrum, 1993, The growth of fault-bounded tilt blocks. *Tectonics*, v. 12, no. 6, p. 1451-1459.

Anderson, Don L., Toshiro Tanimoto, and Yu-Shen Zhang, 1992, Plate Tectonics and Hotspots: The third dimension, *Science*, v. 256, p. 1645-1650.

Anderson, Ernest, 1972, Thin-skinned distension in Tertiary rocks of southeastern Nevada. *Bull. Geol. Soc. Amer.*, v. 82, p. 43-58.

Anderson, R. Ernest, Mary Lou Zoback, and George A. Thompson, 1983, Implications of selected subsurface data on the structural form and evolution of some basins in the northern Basin and Range province, Nevada and Utah. Bull., *Geol. Soc. Amer.*, v. 94, p. 1055-1072.

Anderson, R.E. 1971, Thin skin distension in Tertiary rocks of southeastern Nevada. *Bull., Geol. Soc. Amer.*, v. 82, p. 43-58.

Argus, Donald F., 1991, Current Sierra Nevada-North American motion from very long baseline interferometry: Implications for kinematics of the western United States. *Geology*, v. 19, p. 1085-1088.

Atwater, Tanya, 1989. Plate tectonic history of the northeast Pacific and western North America. Pages 21-72 in Winterer, Hussong, and Decker, Eds., 1989.

Baldridge, W. Scott, and Kenneth H. Olsen, 1989, The Rio Grande rift. *Amer. Scientist*, v. 77, p. 240-247.

Bally, A.W., and A.R. Palmer, Eds., 1989, *The Geology of North America*, vol. A. Boulder, CO: The Geological Society of America.

Barberi, Franco, and Jacques Varet, 1977, Volcanism of Afar: Small-scale plate tectonics implications. *Bull., Geol. Soc. Amer*, v., 88, p. 1251-1266.

Bird, John M., 1987, Wilson cycle. Pages 836-838 in Seyfert, Carl K., Ed., 1987.

Bohannon, Robert G., 1986, Tectonic configuration of the western Arabian continental margin, southern Red Sea. *Tectonics*, v. 5, no. 4, p. 477-499.

Bonatti, Enrico, Cesare Emiliani, Gote Ostlund, and Harold Rydell, 1971, Final desiccation of the Afar Rift, Ethiopia. *Science*, v. 172, p. 468-469.

Bosworth, William, 1987, Off-axis volcanism in the Gregory rift, east Africa: Implications for models of continental rifting, *Geology*, v. 15, p. 397-400.

Bosworth, William, 1993, Nature of the Red Sea crust: A controversy revisited: Comment and Reply. *Geology*, v. 21, p. 574-576.

Bosworth, William, Joseph Lambiase, and Ron Keisler, 1986, A new look at Gregory's Rift: The structural style of continental rifting, *EOS*, v. 67, no. 29, p. 557, 582-583.

Bott, M.H.P., 1982, The mechanism of continental splitting, *Tectonophysics*, v. 81, p. 301-309.

Bott, M.H.P., and N.J. Kusznir, 1984, Origins of tectonic stress in the lithosphere, *Tectonophysics*, v. 105, p. 1-13.

Braun, Jean, and Christopher Beaumont, 1989, A physical explanation of the relation between flank uplifts and the breakup conformity at rifted continental margins. *Geology*, v. 17, p. 760-764.

Burchfiel, B.C. 1980, *Continental Tectonics*. Washington DC: Nat. Academy of Sciences.

Burchfiel, B.C., 1980, Tectonics of non-collisional regimes—the modern Andes and the Mesozoic Cordilleran orogen of the Western United States. Pages 65-72 in ____(?).

Burke, Kevin, and J.F. Dewey, 1973, Plume-generated triple junctions: Key indicators in applying plate tectonics to old rocks. *Jour. of Geology*, v. 81, p. 406-433.

Chase, Clement G., and Terry C. Wallace, 1986, Uplift of the Sierra Nevada of California. *Geology*, v. 14, p. 730-733.

Cloud, Preston, 1974, Rubey Conference on crustal evolution. *Science*, v. 183, p. 878-881

Coblentz, David D., and Mike Sandiford, 1994, Tectonic stresses in the African plate: Constraints on the ambient lithospheric stress state. *Geology*, v. 22, p. 831-834.

Coleman, Robert G., 1993, *Geologic Evolution of the Red Sea*. New York: Oxford University Press.

Coogan, James C., and Peter G. DeCelles, 1996, Extensional collapse along the Sevier Desert reflection, northern Sevier Desert basin, western United States. *Geology*, v. 24, p. 933-936.

Courtillot, Vincent, 1982, Propagating rifts and continental breakup. *Tectonics*, v. 1, no. 3, p. 239-250.

de Cserna, Zoltan, 1989, An outline of the geology of Mexico. Pages 233-264 in Bally and Palmer, 1989.

Dewey, John F., and Kevin Burke, 1974, Hot spots and continental break-up: Implications for collisional orogeny. *Geology*, v. 2, no. 2, p. 57-60.

Dixon, T.H., R.J. Stern, and I.H. Hussein, 1987, Control of Red Sea Rift geometry by Precambrian structures. *Tectonics*, v. 6, p. 551-572.

Dunkelman, Thomas J., Jeffrey A. Karson, and Bruce R. Rosendahl, 1988, Structural style of the Turkana Rift, Kenya. *Geology*, v. 16, p. 258-261.

Ebinger, C.J., 1989, Tectonic development of the western branch of the East African rift system. *Bull., Geol. Soc. Amer.*, v. 101, p. 885-903.

Echtler, Helmut Peter, Ewald Lüschen, and Gunter Mayer, 1994, Lower crust thinning in the Rhinegraben: Implications for recent rifting. *Tectonics*, v. 13, no. 2, p. 342-353.

Emiliani, C., E.B. Kraus, E.M. Shoemaker, 1981. Sudden death at the end of the Mesozoic. *Earth and Planetary Sci. Letters*, v. 55, p. 317-334.

England, Philip, 1996, The mountains will flow. *Nature*, v. 381, p. 23.

Faulds, James E., and Robert J. Varga, 1997, The role of accommodation zones and transfer zones in the regional segmentation of extended terranes. *Geological Society of America, Special Paper No.*___. ___ pp.

Garson, M. S., and M. Krs, 1976, Geophysical and geological evidence of the relationships of Red Sea transverse tectonics to ancient fractures. *Bull., Geol .Soc. Amer.*, v. 87, p. 169-181.

Glazner, Allen F., and John M. Bartley, 1985, Evolution of lithospheric strength after thrusting. *Geology*, v. 13, p. 42-45.

Glikson, Andrew Y., 1995, Asteroid/comet mega-impacts may have triggered major episodes of crustal evolution. *EOS*, v. 76, no. 6, p. 49, 54-55.

Gordon, Richard G., 1991, Plate motion. *Reviews of Geophysics*, Supplement, p. 748-758. U.S. National Report to International Union of Geodesy and Geophysics 1987-1990.

Gordon, Rochard G., and Seth Stein, 1992, Global tectonics and space geodesy, *Science*, v. 256, p. 333-342.

Gough, D.I., 1984, Mantle upflow under North America and plate dynamics. *Nature*, v. 311, p. 428-432.

Gough, D.I., and W.I. Gough, 1987, Stress near the center of the earth. *Annual Review of Earth and Planetary Sciences*, v. 15, p. 545-566.

Gough, D.I., and W.I. Gough, 1987, Stress near the surface of the earth. *Annual Reviews of Earth and Planetary Sciences*, v. 15, p. 545-566.

Gregory, J.W., 1896, *The Great Rift Valley*. London: John Murray.

Gregory, J.W., 1921, *The Rift Valleys and Geology of East Africa*. London: Seeley.

Grieve, Richard A.F., 1987, Terrestrial impact structures. *Annual Review of Earth and Planetary Sci.*, v. 15, p. 245-270.

Hall, S.A., 1989, Magnetic evidence for the nature of the crust beneath the southern Red Sea. *Jour. of Geophysical Res.*, v. 94, p. 267.

Harry, Dennis L., and Dale S. Sawyer, 1992, Basaltic volcanism, mantle plumes, and the mechanics of rifting: The Parana flood basalt province of South America. *Geology*, v. 20, p. 207-210.

Hay, Edward, 1976, Cenozoic uplifting of the Sierra Nevada in isostatic response to North American and Pacific plate interactions. *Geology*, v. 4, p. 763-766.

Hutchinson, D.R., A.J. Golmshtok, L.P. Zonenshain, T.C. Moore, C.A. Scholz, and K.D. Kiltgord, 1992, Depositional and tectonic framework of the rift basins of Lake Baikal from multichannel seismic data. *Geology*, v. 20, p. 589-592.

Illies, J.H., and St. Meuller, Eds., 1981, Mechanism of graben formation. (I.U.C.G. Sci. Rept. no. 63). *Tectonophysics*, v. 73, p. 1-3.

Jackson, James, and Tom Blenkinsop, 1993, The Malawi earthquake of March 10, 1989: Deep faulting within the East African rift system. *Tectonics*, v. 12, no. 5, p. 1131-1139.

Jones, Craig H., Jeffrey R. Unruh, and Leslie J. Sonder, 1996, The role of gravitational potential energy in active deformation in the southwestern United States. *Nature*, v. 381, p. 37-41.

Kearey, Philip, and Frederick J. Vine, 1990 *Global Tectonics*. Oxford: Blackwell Scientific Publications.

Kerr, Richard A., 1983, Thin-skinned crustal extension confirmed. *Science*, v. 220, p. 1030-1031.

Kerr, Richard A., 1995, Faults stretch rocks—and theorists' imaginations. *Science*, v. 270, p. 1301.

Khan, Aftab, Peter Maguire, Bill Henry, and Martin Higham, 1986, KRISP 85-An international seismic investigation of the Kenya Rift. *Geology Today*, v. 2, no. 5, p. 139-144.

Kutina, Jan, 1987, Ore deposits of the western United States in relation to mass distribution in the crust and mantle. *Bull., Geol. Soc. Amer.*, v. 99, p. 30-41.

Lacomb, O., J. Anglier, D. Byrne, and J.M. Dupin, 1993, Eocene-Oligocene tectonics and kinematics of the Rhine-Saone continental transform zone (eastern France). *Tectonics*, v. 12, no. 4, p. 874-888

Lipman, P.W., N.A. Logatchev, Y.A. Zorin, C.E. Chapin, and V. Kovalenko, 1989, Intracontinental rift comparisons: Baikal and Rio Grande rift systems. *EOS*, v. 70, no. 19, p. 578-579, 586-588.

Lister, G.S., M.A. Ethridge, and P.A. Symonds, 1986, Detachment faulting and the evolution of passive continental margins. *Geology*, v. 14, p. 246-250.

Logatchev, N.A., and N.A. Florenzow, 1978, The Baikal system of rift valleys, *Tectonophysics*, v. 45, p. 1.

Lonsdale, Peter, 1989, Geology and tectonic history of the Gulf of California. Pages 499-521 in Winterer, Hussong, and Decker, Eds., 1989.

Martin, A.K., 1984, Propagating rifts: Crustal extension during continental rifting. *Tectonics*, v. 3, no. 6, p. 611-617.

McDonald, R.E. 1976, Tertiary tectonics and sedimentary rocks along the transition: Basin and Range province to plateau and thrust belt province, Utah. Pages 281-317 in J.G. Hill, Ed., *Symposium on Geology of the Cordilleran Hingeline*. Denver, CO: Rocky Mountain Assoc. of Geologists.

Morin, A.S., V.M. Litvin, A.M. Podreazhansky, O.G. Sorokhtin, V.I. Voitov, V.S. Yastrebov, and L.P. Zonenshain, 1982, Red Sea submersible research expedition. *Deep Sea Research*, v. 29, p. 361.

Mutter, John C., 1993, Margins declassified. *Nature*, v. 364, p. 393-394.

Mutter, John C., W. Roger Buck, and Carolyn C. Zehnder, 1987, The origin of volcanic passive margins. *Lamont-Doherty Geological Observatory Yearbook*, p. 42-43.

Newmann, E.R., and I.B. Ramberg, Eds., 1978, *Tectonics and Geophysics of Continental Rifts*. Dordrecht, Holland: D. Reidel,

Norris, Robert M., and Robert W. Webb, 1976, *Geology of California*. New York: John Wiley & Sons.

Oberbeck, V.R. et al., 19___, Impacts, tillites and breakup of Gondwanaland. *Jour. of Geology*, v. 101, p. 1-19.

Oberbeck, Verne R. 1993, Impacts and Global Change, *Geotimes*, v. 38, no. 9, p. 16-18.

Pain, C.F., 1985, Cordilleran metamorphic core complexes in Arizona: A contribution from geomorphology, *Geology*, v. 13, p. 871-874.

Pakiser, L.C., and James N. Brune, 1980, Seismic models of the root of the Sierra Nevada. *Science*, v. 210, p. 1088-1094.

Pridmore, Cynthia L., and Eric G. Frost, 1992, Detachment faults: California's extended past. *California Geology*, v. 45, no. 1, p. 3-17.

Proffett, R. Ernest, 1977, Thin skin distension in Tertiary rocks of southeastern Nevada. *Bull., Geol. Soc. Amer.*, v. 82, p. 43-58.
u
Quennell, A.M., 1987, Rift valleys. Pages 671-688 in Seyfert, Carl K., Ed., 1987.

Ring, Uwe, 1994, The influence of preexisting structure on the evolution of the Cenozoic Malawi rift (East African rift system). *Tectonics*, v. 13, no. 2, p. 313-326.

Rosendahl, B.R., 1987, Architecture of continental rifts with special reference to East Africa. *Annual Review of Earth and Planetary Science*, v. 15, p. 445-503.

Ross, David A. et al., 1973, Red Sea drillings, *Science*, v. 179, p. 377-380.

Savage, Martha Kane, 1994, Anisotropy and rift systems. *Nature*, v. 371, p. 105-106.

Scholz, Christopher A., Kim D. Kiltgord, Deborah R. Huchinson, Uri S. Ten Brink, Lev P. Zonenshain, Alexander Y. Golmshtok, and Theodore C. Moore, 1993, Results of 1992 seismic reflection experiment in Lake Baikal. *EOS*, v. 74, no. 41, p. 465, 469-470.

Sengör, A.M. Cebal, 1976, Collision of irregular continental margins: Implications for foreland deformation of Alpine-type orogens. *Geology*, v. 4, p. 779-782.

Severinghaus, J., and T. Atwater, 1987, Age of lithosphere subducted beneath western North America—Implications for the Neogene seismic history of the Cascadia slab. Abstract, *EOS*, V. 68, p. 1467.

Seyfert, C.K., and J.G. Murtaugh, 1977, Terrestrial impact epochs and their relationship to orogenies and plate movements. *Geol. Soc. of Amer., Abstracts with Programs*, v. 9, p. 1168-1196.

Seyfert, Carl K., 1987, *Encyclopedia of Structural Geology and Plate Tectonics.* New York, Van Nostrand Reinhold.

Seyfert, Carl K., 1987a, Cordilleran metamorphic core complexes. Pages 113-132 in Seyfert, Carl K., Ed., 1987.

Seyfert, Carl K., 1987b, Mantle plumes and hot spots. Pages 412-430 in Seyfert, Carl K., Ed., 1987.

Seyfert, Carl K., and Leslie A. Sirkin, 1979, *Earth History and Plate Tectonics: An Introduction to Historical Geology,* 2nd ed. New York: Harper & Row.

Shoemaker, Eugene M., 1983, Asteroid and comet bombardment of the earth. *Annual Review of Earth and Planetary Sci.*, v. 11, p. 461-494.

Spencer, Jon E., and William R. Normark, 1989, Neogene plate-tectonic evolution of the Baja California Sur continental margin and the southern Gulf of California, Mexico. Pages 489-497 in Winterer, Hussong, and Decker, Eds., 1989.

Spohn, T., and G. Schubert, 1982, Convective thinning of the lithosphere: A mechanism for the initiation of continental rifting. *Jour. of Geophysical Res*., v. 87, p. 4669-4681.

Stewart, John H., 1980, Regional tilt patterns in late Cenozoic basin-range fault blocks, western United States, *Bull., Geol. Soc. Amer.*, v. 91, p. 460-464.

Sultan, M., R. Becker, R.E. Arvidson, P. Shore, R.J. Stern, Z. El Alfy, and R.I. Attia, 1993, New constraints on Red Sea rifting from correlations of Arabian and Nubian Neoproterozoic outcrops. *Tectonics*, v. 12, no. 6, p. 1303-1319.

Tapponier, P. and P. Molnar, 1976, Slip-line field theory and large-scale continental tectonics. *Nature*, v. 264, p. 319-324.

Tapponier, P., and P. Molnar, 1979, Active faulting and Cenozoic tectonics of the Tien Shan, Mongolia, and Baykal regions. *Jour. of Geophysical Res.*, v. 84, p. 3425.

Tazieff, Haroun, 1970, The Afar Triangle. *Scientific American*, v. 222, no. 2, p. 32-40.

Vann, I.R., 1985, To stretch a continent. *Nature*, v. 316, p. 293-294.

Vink, G.E. 1982, Continental rifting and the implications for plate tectonic reconstructions. *Jour. of Geophysical Res.*, v. 87 (B13), p. 10, 677-10,688.

Vink, G.E., W.J. Morgan, and W. Zhao, 1984, Preferential rifting of continents: A source of displaced terranes. *Jour. of Geophysical Res.*, v. 89, p. _____ .

Voggenreiter, W., H. Hotzl, and J. Mechie, 1988, Low-angle detachment origin for the Red Sea Rift system? *Tectonophysics*, v. 150, p. 51.

Wakefield, J., Fault finding in Utah puts longstanding theories on the line, *EOS*, v. 75, no. 40, p. 459-460.

Wernicke, Brian, Gary G. Axen, and J. Kent Snow, 1988, Basin and Range extensional tectonics at the latitude of Las Vegas, Nevada. *Bull., Geol. Soc. of Amer.*, v. 100, p. 1738-1757.

Wernicke, Brian, R. Clayton, M. Ducea, C.H. Jones, S. Park, S. Ruppert, J. Saleeby, J.K. Snow, L. Squires, M. Fliedner, G. Jiracek, R. Keller, S. Klemperer, J. Luetgert, P. Malin, K. Miller, W. Mooney, H. Oliver, and R. Phinney, 1996, Origin of high mountains in the continents: The southern Sierra Nevada. *Science*, v. 271, p. 190-193.

Wheeler, W.H., and J.H. Karson, 1994, Extension and subsidence adjacent to a "weak" continental transform: An example from the Rukwa rift, East Africa. *Geology*, v. 22, p. 625-628.

White, Robert S., 1989, Igneous outbursts and mass extinctions. *EOS*, v. 70, no, 46, p. 1480-1490.

White, Robert S., 1992, Hot and cold rifts. *EOS*, v. 75, no. 5, p. 58.

White, Robert S., and Dan P. McKenzie, 1989, Volcanism at rifts. *Scientific American*, v. , no. p. 62-69.

White, Robert S., and Dan P. McKenzie, 1989, ____________________________. *Jour. of Geophysical Research*, v. 94, p. 7685-7729

Wilson, J.T. 1966, Did the Atlantic close and then reopen? *Nature*, v. 211. 676-681.

Windley, Brian F., and Mark B. Allen, 1993, Mongolian plateau: Evidence for a late Cenozoic mantle plume under central Asia. *Geology*, v. 21, p. 295-298.

Winterer, E.L., Donald M. Hussong, and Robert W. Decker, Eds., 1989, *The Eastern Pacific Ocean and Hawaii, The Geology of North America, Volume N*. Boulder, CO: The Geological Society of America.

Wolde-Gabriel, Giday, and James L. Aronson, 1987, Chow Bahir rift: A "failed" rift in southern Ethiopia. *Geology*, v. 15, p. 430-433.
Woodward, Lee A., 1977, Rate of crustal extension across the Rio Gande Rift near Albuguerque, New Mexico. *Geology*, v. 5, p. 269-272.

Wright, Lauren, 1976,, Late Cenozoic fault patterns and stress fields in the Great Basin and westward displacement of the Sierra Nevada Block. *Geology*, v. 4, p. 489-494.

Yarnold, John C., Roy A. Johnson, and Lowell Sorensen, 1993, Identification of multiple generations of crosscutting "domino-style" faults: Insights from seismic modeling. *Tectonics*, v. 12, no. 1, p. 159-168.

Zoback, M.L., 1992, First and second order patterns of stresses in the lithosphere: The World Stress Map Project. *Jour. of Geophysical Res.*, v. 97, p. 11,703-11,729.

Chapter: 11 Sedimentary Basins of the Continents

Perhaps the broadest definition of a *sedimentary basin* would read: "Any large accumulation of mineral and/or organic sediment held in a depression in the earth's solid surface." This would place it in the basic rock cycle familiar to students from the introductory geology course. Exposed rock and soil surfaces of the continents supply sediment that is transported by the fluid agents—running water, flowing glacial ice, turbid winds, and currents generated in bodies of standing water. The sediment is carried in suspension or dragged along in these moving agents. Over the continental surfaces sediment is most commonly moved to progressively lower elevations concentrated in narrow paths or channels. Eolian transport is a notable exception, since it includes a dispersed movement of suspended fine particles not dependent on gradient of a solid surface. Ultimately all the forms of sediment come to rest on arrival at a relatively low subaerial or submarine surface surrounded by rising surface gradients, i.e., when it arrives at the *sink* of the external flow system. Perhaps a thought that follows logically is that the ocean basins collectively comprise the "global sink," and are thus the ultimate sedimentary basin. On the continents, lesser basins can trap and hold large bodies of sediment for eons of geologic time, and these bodies may be altered by orogeny into highly deformed structures and converted into metamorphic rock.

This chapter is largely limited to sedimentary basins within the continents and in a zone immediately adjacent to the continental margins. Sediments of the abyssal ocean basins were briefly described in Chapter 4 and need not be included here.

11 .1 The Geosyncline in Classical Geology

An ancient continental sedimentary basin was recognized and studied by geologists starting more than a century ago. In the 1850s a pioneer American geologist, James Hall, State Geologist of New York, was studying the stratigraphy of the northern Appalachian Mountains. He reconstructed the total succession of strata deposited in that region in each period of the Paleozoic Era. In this way, he was able to determine at what locations the strata were thickest and how their thickness changed along a line of traverse. Because the thickest zones of these sections had been subjected to strong folding, whereas thin zones lying farther inland were only weakly folded, Hall associated the process of accumulation of thick sediment with the intense folding, i.e., "that folding was contemporaneous with downwarping" (Dickinson, 1971, p. 108).

James D. Dana, a professor of geology at Yale University, also made field studies of Appalachian structure and recognized the basin-like character of the detrital formations, using the term *geosynclinal* for the sedimentary accumulation. Dana's scenario of events was described in 1971 by Professor William R. Dickinson, then a geology professor at Stanford University, in the following paragraphs:

> Dana thus distinguished three successive phases of a geosynclinorial cycle: sedimentation, tectogenesis, and orogenesis. Metamorphism and magmatism he regarded as incidental to the scheme and dependent on local conditions during downbuckling. Familiarity led Dana to regard geosynclines as zones peripheral to continental masses. As source regions for some of the voluminous geosynclinal detritus, Dana postulated companion and parallel uplifts, or geanticlines (1971, p. 108).

Dana realized from the increasing thickness of coarse sediment in the direction away from the continent that offshore borderland mountain ranges must have existed as sources of detritus. The marine strata of the Appalachian mountain belt were deposited in each geologic period in a slowly subsiding crustal trough. While the floor of the trough was subsiding, the depth of ocean water remained shallow, because the rate of sediment deposition kept pace with the rate of crustal subsidence.

Dana's term "geosynclinal" was appropriate because, when sediment deposition has been completed, the strata are warped down into a shallow syncline. The prefix "geo" signifies that the syncline is of very large dimensions as compared with synclines produced by compressional deformation of strata. The dip of strata in a geosyncline is visualized as extremely gentle prior to the occurrence of any subsequent compressional folding.

Let us examine a particular geosyncline in order to follow the interpretive method used by a stratigrapher. Figure 11.1 is a graphic presentation of all strata of the Devonian Period in southern New York State. Diagram A shows an east-west profile of the present land surface extending from the Hudson Valley on the east to about Erie, Pennsylvania, on the west. Below the profile is a stratigraphic cross section of the rocks present today along the line of profile. The vertical scale is greatly exaggerated—about 40 times greater than the horizontal scale. This form of exaggeration is standard practice to focus attention on the details of the stratigraphy at any given point, but it greatly

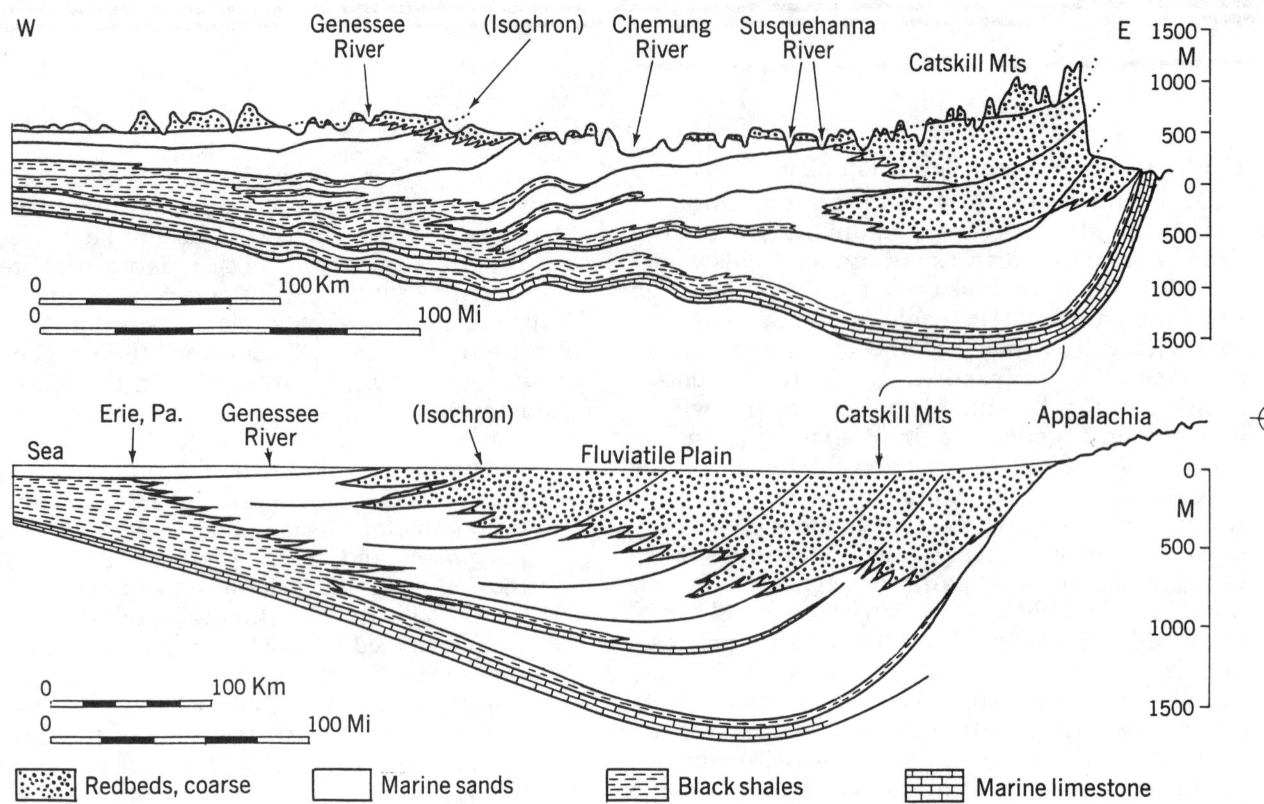

Figure 11.1 Reconstruction of a geosyncline of Devonian age in western New York State. (A) East-west surface profile and stratigraphic cross section of the Devonian strata as they are found today. (B) Restored stratigraphic section showing conditions at the close of Devonian sedimentation. (Section A after J.G. Broughton et al., 1962, New York State Museum and Science Service, Chart Series No. 5. Section B from M. Kay and E.H. Colbert, 1965, *Stratigraphy and Life History*, p. 218, Figure 11-9. Copyright © 1965 by John Wiley & Sons, Inc., New York. Reproduced by permission.)

increases the apparent dip of strata. For example, the basal limestone strata at the extreme eastern end of the section appear to have a dip of about 70°, whereas in fact the dip is somewhat less than one degree!

These strata actually show very gentle folding that occurred after they were deposited. (We now recognize that strong folding and overthrusting affected strata of the same age to the east of this locality during a post-Devonian arc-continent collision, so what we see here would now be interpreted as gentle foreland folds.) The thin strata at the base of the section are marine limestones, but all the overlying strata are clastics and range from coarse-textured red sandstones and conglomerates (red beds), through sandstone, to shales. Undulating solid lines running through the section are time lines, or *isochrones*. [Also *isochrons* or *isochronous surfaces* (Kay and Colbert, 1965, p. 111, 709.] The layer of strata between any two successive isochrones was deposited within the same time span. A stratigraphic section of this type is usually constructed from the study of rock cores obtained from boreholes, since most of the rock mass lies far beneath the present land surface.

Diagram B of Figure 11.1 is a restored stratigraphic section. It takes the information in the upper stratigraphic section and replots the vertical dimension with respect to a horizontal upper reference line. This reference line represents sea level at the end of the period of sediment deposition—in this case, the end of the Devonian Period. All undulations caused by later foldings are removed, and the isochrones become smooth curves.

Let us now interpret the restored stratigraphic section. First, we take note of the broad troughlike outline of a geosyncline. The clastic strata reach a thickness of about 1500 m in the deepest part of the trough, thinning to zero on the east and to about 250 m on the west where they are evidently typical platform strata. Evidence that a shallow sea existed here at the start of the Devonian Period lies in the nearly uniform layer of marine limestone at the base of the section. Then, for some reason that the early geologists could not explain, a trough began to form, and detrital sediment from the east was deposited in the trough. Because the sediment is coarse in texture along the eastern margin of the trough and grades into finer texture to the west, they postulated that a high mountain range, called Appalachia, had become uplifted along the eastern side of the geosyncline. It seemed reasonable that the coarse clastic sediment was part of a delta system formed by streams carrying sediment down from that mountain range. The delta surface was a low plain, only slightly above sea level. Finer sediment was spread as a sand deposit in shallow ocean water lying to the west, while clay particles were carried still farther west into the inland sea. As time passed, the coarse delta deposits spread farther toward the west. The Devonian Period, the geologists concluded, ended with a tectonic event—an orogeny—that uplifted and gently deformed the strata of the geosyncline. That conclusion represents a persistence of Hall's direct association of each geosyncline with a terminating compressional orogeny.

Actually, the Devonian strata of New York State represent only one of a succession of Paleozoic geosynclinal deposits roughly coincident with what is now the Appalachian mountain belt extending from Newfoundland on the north to Georgia and Alabama on the south. A glance through an atlas of paleographic maps from Cambrian through Silurian shows persistent marine deposition in this belt (Schuchert, 1955). A geosyncline was formed here in the Cambrian and reappeared in the Ordovician. In modern terms, these and the Cambrian strata beneath them were strongly affected by folding and thrusting in what we now recognize as successive arc-continent collisions.

After the deposition of the Devonian geosyncline we have focused upon, a Carboniferous geosyncline persisted farther south in what is now the Southern Appalachians. Figure 11.2 is a restored stratigraphic section along a line drawn across Virginia and West Virginia. This portion of the Appalachian geosyncline received a total thickness of about 8000 m of clastic sediment in the Lower Carboniferous (Mississippian) in only 20 m.y., whereas the 1500 m of Devonian strata in New York State accumulated in 50 m.y. Geologists concluded that an orogeny which closed the Devonian Period had sharply uplifted Appalachia, and this event resulted in a much faster rate of sediment deposition in the Mississippian Period than in the Devonian Period.

From the time of Hall and Dana until about the early 1940s, studies of geosynclines were based almost entirely on ancient sedimentary and metamorphic rocks seen exposed on the continents, rather than on present-day submarine troughs and shelves in which sedimentation is now taking place. Keep in mind that seismic refraction and reflection methods of subsurface exploration had not been fully developed or widely used. True, oil wells had been drilled into the geologically young strata of the Gulf Coast region, and it was understood that a great wedge of undeformed sediments, dating back to the Cretaceous Period, lay along the continental margin in that region. But that wedge of sediments did not fit the early or classical concept of a geosyncline, because there was no crustal trough bounded on the oceanic side by volcanic highlands. Instead, the sediment wedge ended in a steepened continental slope.

On the credit side of the ledger, physical oceanography had already plotted deep trenches bordering the Pacific rim, and the close parallelism of these strange features with the continental volcanic arcs was well established. The Western Pacific island arcs were also in place on the charts, with foredeeps paralleling them. But the mid-oceanic ridge remained undiscovered and, with Wegener's scenario of drifting apart of continents a forbidden dogma under the strong grip of the North American fixists, further advances in theory of geosynclines were effectively blocked. It was in this period of scientific stasis that a newcomer on the scene, Marshall Kay, attempted to organize geosynclines and other major kinds of continental sedimentary basins into a new analytical framework. Beginning this work as a geology faculty member in 1930 at Columbia University, he also influenced a substantial group of oncoming stratigraphy students over a period of 25 years. Kay became strongly interested in the writings of a German geologist, Hans Stille, published over the period 1935-1942, and the two men carried on a correspondence over the nomenclature and classification of geosynclines (see Kay, 1967). Both had independently recognized two fundamentally different kinds of geosynclines (see Dott, 1978, p. 9). One kind is almost totally lacking in volcanic rock (either as detrital particles or as dikes and flows), and was given the name *miogeosycline*. The other, called a *eugeosyncline*, "is a surface that has subsided deeply in a belt having active volcanism" (Kay, 1951, p. 4). Both of these terms were first used in Stille's publications. The distinction proved sound and was later explained fully in terms of plate tectonics. Figure 11.3 is a reproduction of Kay's restored E-W section of a miogeosyncline and a eugeosyncline in tandem across what is now the New England region between New York and Maine (Kay, 1951. Plate 9). The strata range through 130 m.y. and include the Cambrian and Middle Ordovician. Figure 11.4 is a part of a stylized paleogeographic map of the area which the cross section traverses. Kay had been strongly impressed by available knowledge of the Pacific island arcs and he made use of such an arc as located on the centerline of the eugeosyncline. Of course, the presence of a subduction zone adjacent to an island arc was unknown at that time. The presence of a "tectonic land" called "Vermontia" as a barrier between the two geosynclines (a *geanticline*) requires a tectonic uplift event near the close of the Middle Ordovician. Surely, you are curious to know how Kay's reconstruction would be reinterpreted by modern plate tectonics. An answer lies in Chapter 6, Figure 6.2, showing a "eugeosyncline" consisting of the Savu Sea and Flores Deep as basins separated by a central volcanic arc. A "miogeosyncline" is found in the China sea, which lies off to the north, but is shown on the regional map, Figure 6.1.

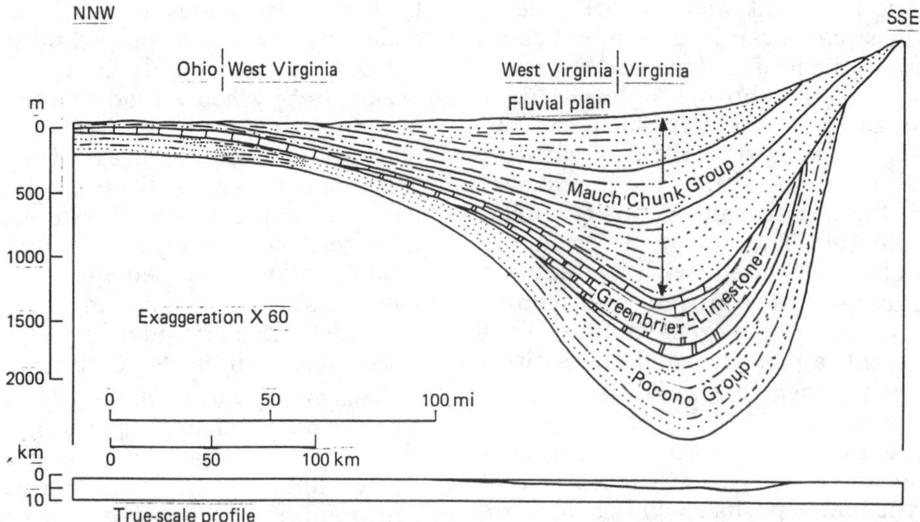

Figure 11.2 Restored stratigraphic section of a geosyncline of Lower Carboniferous age in the central Appalachians. Conditions are shown as they existed at the close of Mississippian sedimentation. (From M. Kay and E.H. Colbert, 1965, *Stratigraphy and Life History*, p. 245, Figure 12-7. Copyright © 1965 by John Wiley & Sons, Inc., New York. Reproduced by permission.)

A second example of Marshall Kay's classification system is well worth noting. He recognized coastal plains of the present continents as a distinctive type of geosyncline. His example, the "Gulf Coast geosyncline" off the northern coast of the Gulf of Mexico is restricted, of course, to what we now call the passive continental margins. He named it a *paraliageosyncline.* Today, such sedimentary bodies are known as "geoclines," explained later in this chapter and illustrated in Figure 11.19.

Altogether, Kay put forward eight types of geosynclines, each bearing a different Greek prefix. Robert H. Dott, Jr., a graduate student of Kay's, wrote later that this complicated system invoked "misunderstanding and no little verbal abuse" (1975, p. 3-4). With the arrival of plate tectonics, new explanations and names were formulated for each type, but the underlying principles and concepts of his classification remained intact. Kay himself was quick to integrate plate tectonics with the existing stratigraphic knowledge, and he had no desire to see his terminology perpetuated (Dott, 1975, p. 4).

To summarize and review, the classical geosyncline was described as consisting largely of marine sediments deposited in shallow water. Subaerial deposition of deltas or alluvial fan clastics was also a common mode of geosynclinal accumulation. It was inferred that the rate of crustal subsidence of the trough closely matched the rate of sediment accumulation (or vice versa). The geosyncline was always underlain by older basement rocks of the continents. The occurrence of thick sediment deposition on the marginal ocean floors was unrecognized. The classical geosyncline was usually pictured as having a mountain range along one side. Two geosynclinal types were envisioned. One was in a marginal location, separated from the ocean basin by a volcanic arc or a tectonic arc. Another was located well within the continent. It was bounded on one side by a mountain range, called a *geanticline,* that furnished sediment to the subsiding trough, as did a relatively low area of the craton on the opposite side. This interior variety of geosyncline was exemplified in the Cretaceous geosyncline of the Rocky Mountain region. Its adjacent geanticline was the ancestral Rockies, formed by thrust faulting in the Nevadan Orogeny that had occurred in the late Jurassic.

One of the fundamental tenets of the classical model of geosynclines was that the period of sediment deposition always ended in orogeny, destroying the geosyncline and creating from it a belt of folds and overthrust faults. This tectonic event was known as a *revolution.* A revolution terminated each geologic era. This conceptual linkage between geosynclines and orogenies was very strong—so strong, in fact, that every belt of folded strata was assumed to have originated as a geosyncline. The implication was that orogeny occurs only where geosynclinal deposition has taken place.

Acceptance of the new paradigm of plate tectonics necessitated the adoption of a new paradigm of stratigraphy. The venerable concept of the geosyncline, lying at the very foundation of continental evolution, had never proved entirely satisfactory in its century of dominance—1850-1950. The geosynclines demanded mythical borderlands—tectonic and volcanic arcs that arose where needed to supply vast quantities of sediment, then mysteriously sank into oblivion. The test of a great hypothesis is its fecundity. As it did for all the other branches of geology, plate

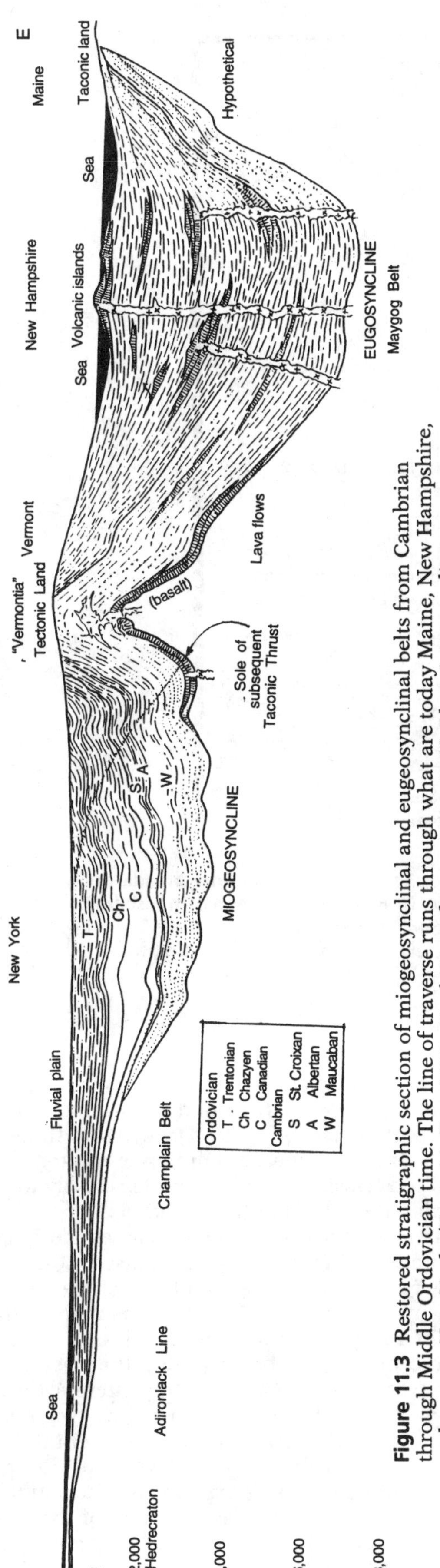

Figure 11.3 Restored stratigraphic section of miogeosynclinal and eugeosynclinal belts from Cambrian through Middle Ordovician time. The line of traverse runs through what are today Maine, New Hampshire, and eastern New York. (From M. Kay, 1951, *Geol. Soc. of Amer. Memoir 48*, Plate 9, upper diagram. Reproduced with the permission of the publisher, the Geological Society of America, Boulder, Colorado, USA. Copyright 1951.)

tectonics provided the necessary infrastructure of a New Stratigraphy.

The arrival of the great geologic revolution of the 1960s played havoc with the classical concept of the geosyncline. Some geologists tried to accommodate plate tectonics to the established varieties and forms of geosynclines. They retained the term "geosyncline" and many of the terms applied to varieties of geosynclines. Other geologists were ready to scrap the classical model entirely, even to abandoning the name "geosyncline." This entire question was discussed at a notable conference of geologists held in 1969 at Asilomar, California, under the auspices of the Geological Society of America. By this time, the fundamentals of plate tectonics had become widely accepted and much more was known about the sediment deposits of the continental margins and subduction zones.

The consensus reached by the Asilomar conference participants seems to have been that the entire subject of geosynclines needed to be heavily revised to include new knowledge of contemporary deposits of thick sediments along both active and passive continental margins. That revision has since been largely accomplished, and little remains of the original classical model. What geologists have done is to follow the principle of uniformity, which implies that "the present is the key to the past." They have looked closely at contemporary sediment deposits of the continental margins, both passive and tectonically active. Refraction and reflection profiling has allowed them to probe these and other thick sediment deposits and to discern their internal structure and the nature of the rock floors on which they rest.

We therefore say farewell to the word "geosyncline," putting in its place the term "sedimentary basin." The latter is now the accepted usage of the branch of applied geology and geophysics directed to the finding and evaluation of petroleum accumulations.

11.2 Classes of Sedimentary Basins

Refining our opening definition of a sedimentary basin and adapting it to the continental basins, it reads: A thick, rapidly accumulating body of sediment formed within a crustal downwarp or fault depression. It may appear long and narrow in plan outline, or it may be more-or-less equidimensional in outline, i.e., circular, oval, square, or rhombic in plan. A narrow, elongate sedimentary basin may accumulate in a troughlike depression with rising land slopes on both flanks, or it may accumulate on a gently descending slope (a monocline) leading down to the contact of continental lithosphere with oceanic lithosphere. Marine sediments can be deposited either in shallow water of a continental shelf or inland sea, or on the deep-ocean floor on a continental rise. Terrestrial basin sediments may accumulate in depressions called "sag basins," or in rift basins

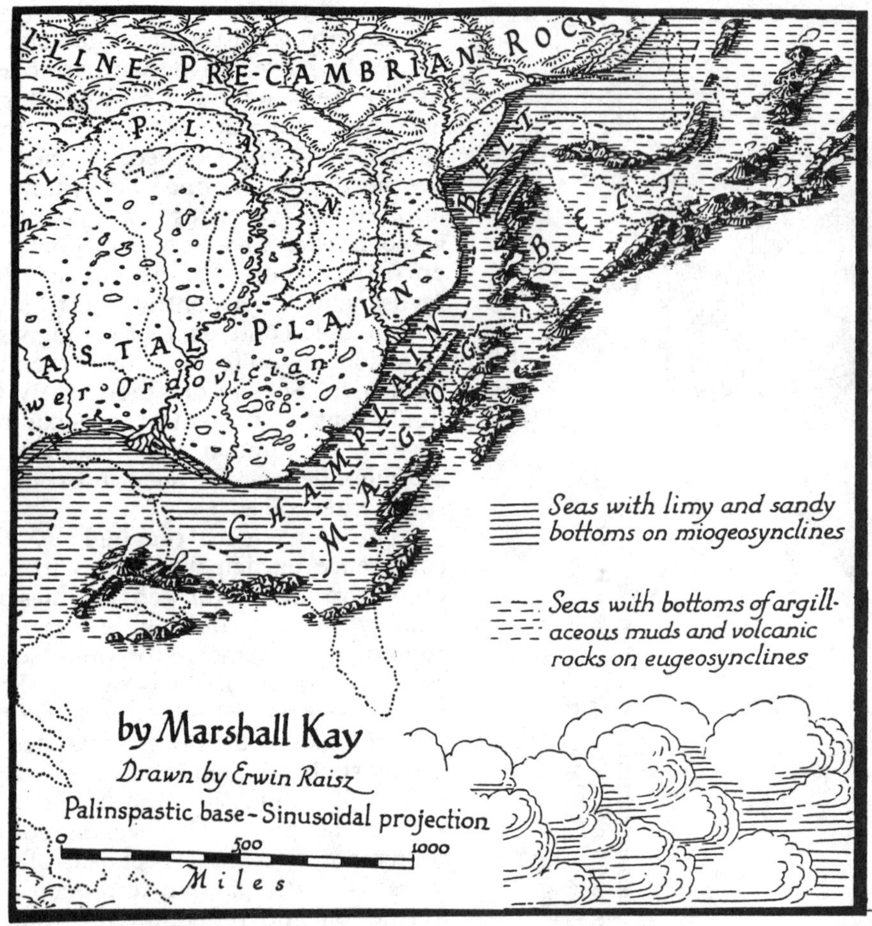

Figure 11.4 Paleogeographic map of the Appalachian region of the eastern United States and Canada showing geosynclines and highlands in Early Middle Ordovician time. (Adapted from a map composed by Marshall Kay and drawn by Erwin Raisz. From M. Kay, 1951, *Geol. Soc. of Amer. Memoir 48*, Plate 1. Reproduced with the permission of the publisher, the Geological Society of America, Boulder, Colorado, USA. Copyright 1951.)

where the land surface is well above sea level. The continental plate margin adjacent to or beneath a sedimentary basin may be either an active plate boundary, where subduction is in progress, or a passive contact between continental and oceanic lithosphere, far distant from an active plate boundary. Sedimentary basin evolution is controlled in part and to a limited degree by gravity loading or unloading, by lithospheric stretching or thickening caused by mantle flowage, and by associated mantle and crustal temperature change.

Because oceans are opening or closing more or less continually through geologic time, it is almost inevitable that a continental sedimentary basin will become caught up in an orogeny and its strata will undergo compressional deformation.

Useful basic classification systems of sedimentary basins have been presented by William R. Dickinson (1974, 1976), H.D. Klemme (1980), D.R. Kingston, C.P. Dishroon, and P.A. Williams (1983), J.A. Helwig (1985), Raymond V. Ingersoll (1988), and Albert W. Bally (1989). Drawing on these and other sources, we have attempted to put together a simplified classification that relates closely to plate tectonics at the level of this book.

First, we set up two main classes, designated by Roman numerals I and II. Class I consists of basins resting on continental lithosphere; Class II, of basins resting on oceanic lithosphere. Within each of the two classes are subclasses based on tectonic processes that produce the basins. The subclasses are designated by the letters A through E. Figure 11.5 shows schematic cross sections of examples of the five major continental basin subclasses. Table 11.1 shows the complete classification system. It expands on each subclass, giving the appropriate stage number of the Wilson cycle, the tectonic type, the basin name, and an example or two of each.

The subclasses are as follows:

Class I Continental Basins
- I-A Continental Rift Systems
- I-B Mature Passive Margins
- I-C Subduction Boundaries
- I-D Collision Boundaries
- I-E Craton Interiors

Class II Oceanic Basins
- II-A Young Oceanic Rift Systems
- II-B Mature Passive Margins
- II-C Subduction Boundaries
- (No collision subclass)
- II-E Abyssal Floors

We define below the five major subclasses of sedimentary basins (Note that these descriptions apply to both of the main classes, I and II.)

(A) Rift System Basins Crustal rifting produces tectonic sedimentary basins along new continental margins (I-A). This extensional process precedes the growth of the great sedimentary wedges along passive continental margins (as briefly described in Chapter 10) but it remains for us to study here the synrift accumulation of sediments. Also important in this subclass are basins formed in zones of interior continental rifting, such as rift valley systems of East Africa and the Basin and Range province of North America. These were covered in depth in Chapter 10. Young rift systems in oceanic crust also belong in this subclass (II-A).

(B) Mature Passive Margin Basins This subclass of sedimentary basin is found on the passive margins of the continents. In reference to surface topography, the basin underlies the continental shelf and slope (I-B, and the continental rise (II-B). These topographic features were briefly described in Chapter 4.

(C) Subduction Boundary Basins This subclass of sedimentary basins we have already covered in detail in Chapter 8, which describes subduction boundaries. It includes trench fills and the accretionary prisms that accumulate above descending slabs of oceanic crust, whether belonging to active continental margins or to island arcs (II-C). Also associated with active subduction boundaries are the forearc basin and the backarc basin, both of which are situated on continental lithosphere (I-C). These basin forms are covered in Chapter 8 and are briefly reviewed here.

(D) Collision Boundary Basins Another subclass of sedimentary basins includes those tectonically related to compressional (collisional) orogens. In Chapter 9, we described masses of accumulating sediment, known as flysch and molasse, which are pre-orogenic and post-orogenic sediments respectively, each occupying an elongate continental sedimentary basin. Here, we reexamine these deposits under the name of "foreland basin" (I-D). Note that this subclass is missing on the list of oceanic basins.

(E) Plate-Interior Basins Sedimentary basins occur within in the continental cratonic interiors, where they may seem to be unrelated to either compressional or extensional tectonics. Gravity data or seismic refraction data may indicate the presence of a deep tectonic structure, such as an ancient rift, possibly responsible for the basin subsidence. We treat these intracratonic basins in a separate category (I-E) and examine them in some detail in this chapter under the name of "sag basins.". Within the deep ocean floors and their mid-oceanic ridges are basins accumulating pelagic sediment and/or turbidity current sediments (II-E). These ocean-floor sediments were described in Chapters 4 and 8.

11.3 Mechanisms of Basin Subsidence

To introduce the principles of subsidence of a basin floor as it receives sediment from an adjacent source, we first draw upon the principle of isostasy. Fundamentals of isostasy are covered in Chapter 3 and illustrated in Figures 3.39-3.43. Familiarity with this basic information is assumed. Here, the Airy model will be used for what may be called the *gravity-loading hypothesis*, in which the force of buoyancy (Archimedes principle) is assumed to be the only actor, so that basin subsidence is not aided or otherwise affected by any other force or mechanism (Kearey and Vine, 1990, p. 242; Diecchio, 1995, p. 35).

Our model is a new or very young basin floored by a bedrock of a relatively old craton that may include platform strata, and holding at the outset very little or no sediment. The basin may be circular or trough-shaped in plan, but we will be considering only a vertical slice of unit thickness and will be dealing with only a vertical column of sediment over the deepest point of the basin. A

Table 11.1 Sedimentary Basins

Subclass and location:		Wilson stage	Tectonic type	Basin name
	CLASS I Continental Basins			
I-A	Continental rift systems	1, 2	Extensional	Rift basin (a) Marginal basin (taphrogen) (b) Aulacogen (c) Intracontinental (d) Pull-apart basin
I-B	Mature passive margins	3	Flexural geocline	Miogeocline, Delta
I-C	Subduction boundaries	4	Compressional	Backarc basin Forearc basin
I-D	Collision boundaries	5, 6	Flexural	Foreland basin
I-E	Cratonic interiors	(NA)	Thermal (?)	Sag basin
	CLASS II Oceanic Basins			
II-A	Young oceanic rift systems	1, 2	Extensional	Transitional ocean basin
II-B	Mature passive margins	3	Flexural geocline	Eugeocline
II-C	Subduction boundaries	4	Compressional	Backarc basin Forearc basin Trench fill
II-E	Abyssal floors	3		Abyssal pelagic fill Delta fan

first postulate is that the rate of deposition of sediment is uniform through time for this column.

Figure 11.6, a schematic diagram, shows the basin as a material flow system with input and output of water and sediment. Sediment retained in the basin represents system storage. The initial state (left half) shows a water body of 5 km maximum depth and no measurable sediment in place. Isostatic equilibrium prevails at this time. The question of how the initial basin came into existence is deferred for the moment. A later stage (right half) shows the completion of four time units of deposition, the oldest (earliest) being represented by the lowermost layer. The initial basin has been filled and raised to a floor level just above the former sealevel. Should the deposition continue, the sediments would be of appropriate terrestrial types. Possibly, sediment would now be transported across the basin floor and carried out of the basin over a fixed outlet.

In our model, sinking of the crust has occurred sclely in terms of isostatic response to the added load, and this is demonstrated in Figure 11.7 by vertical columns representing conditions at the end of each 10 m.y. interval. For simplicity, we have assumed that the column of sediment

CLASS I Continental Basins

	Mesozoic/Cenozoic Examples	Precambrian/Paleozoic Examples
I-A		
	Newark basin, Gulf Coast	
		Anadarko basin
	Great Basin UT-NV-CA	
	Southern California	
I-B	Atlantic passive margin Gulf of Mexico	
I-C	Indonesian subduction arc	Ordovician Appalachians
I-D	Zagreb folds; Jura folds N. Rockies foreland	Appalachian foreland
I-E		Williston basin Michigan basin
	CLASS II Oceanic Basins	
II-A	Red Sea trough	
II-B	N. Amer. Atlantic passive margin	Ordovician Appalachians
II-C	Mariana arc	
II-E	S. Atlantic passive margin; N.W. Pacific Jurassic zone	

deposited has the same height dimension as the initial water depth; i.e., 5 km. Thus, without isostatic reponse, the initial basin would have been filled to the brim in 10 m.y., replacing the water. Under the Airy model of isostatic equilibrium, the sediment load causes a subsidence according to the ratio of its bulk density to the density of the cratonic bed rock that it replaces (see Fowler, 1990, p. 378-379). In this first step we have ignored the correction for water displaced by the sediment. Density of the cratonic rock is set at 3.3 gm/cm^3, that of the sediment at 2.3 gm/cm^3. The latter figure corresponds with observed density of Gulf Coast sediments at a depth of about 5 km (Dobrin, 1960, p. 252). (We have also failed to take into consideration the effect of compaction of the water-saturated sediment under increasing load.) The ratio of the two densities, about 0.7, is used to determine the actual subsidence of the rock column, and this reduces the water depth accordingly. Continuing through a second and third calculation sees the water depth reduced to only 0.5 km, while at the end of the fourth calculation the floor of the basin is 1 km above sealevel. The rate of upbuilding of the basin floor is, for this case only, on an arithmetic-linear curve.

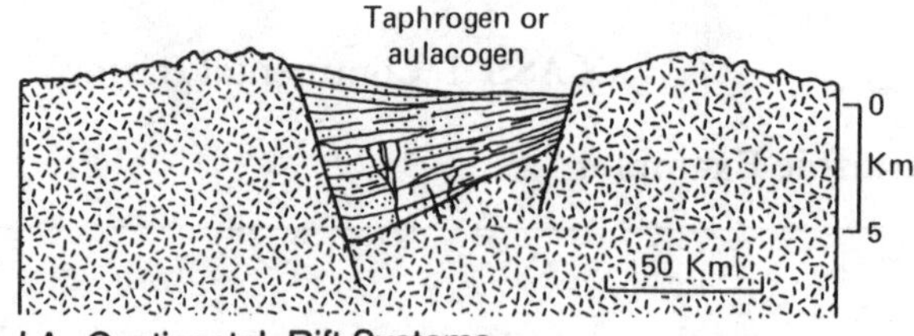

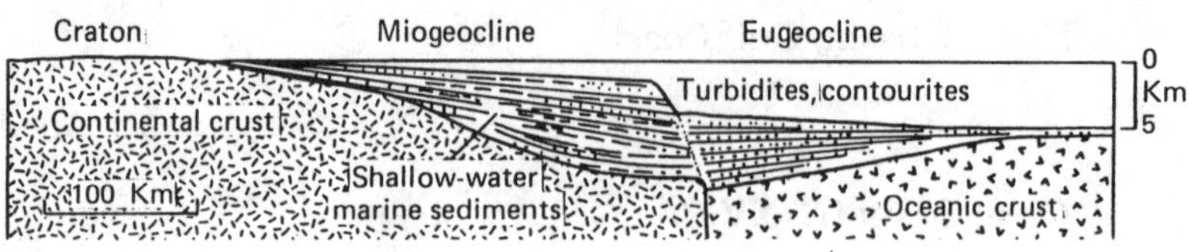

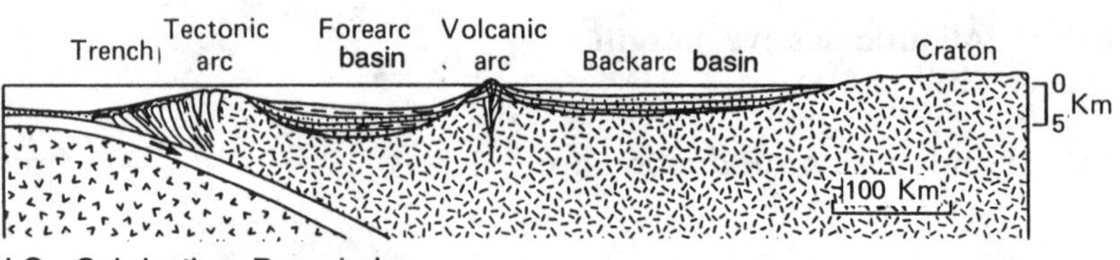

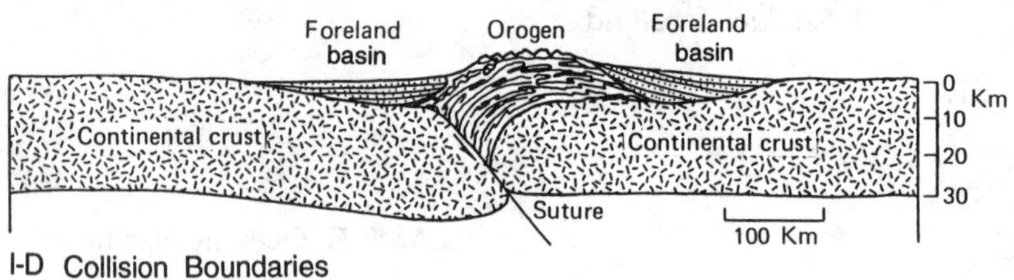

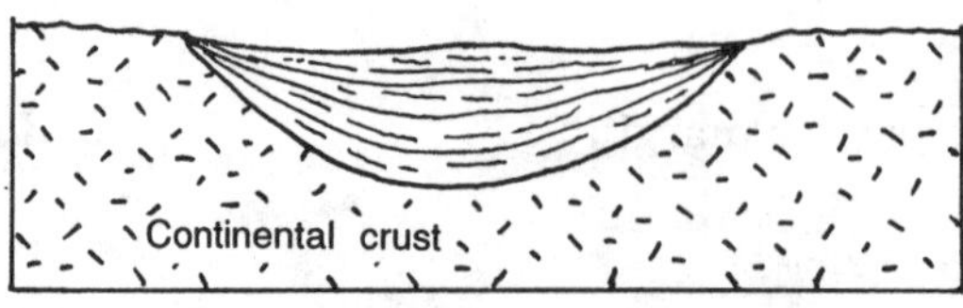

Figure 11.5 Examples of five main classes of continental sedimentary basins. See Table 11.1 for further data. (Copyright © by Arthur N. Strahler.)

Elastic deformation has occurred in the underlying lithosphere, and below this lies the depth of slow plastic flowage that merges into the soft asthenosphere. Somewhere in the asthenosphere, the depth of compensation is encountered.

Different scenarios can be calculated in the same manner. For an assumed decreasing rate of sediment deposition, the rate of rise of floor would decline exponentially without reaching the sealevel (see Diecchio, 1995, p. 39). An example is shown in Figure 11.8, in which the input of fill decreases in the same ratio as relative density of the fill, i.e., 0.70. The water depth diminishes exponentially, approaching zero. This program would fit in nicely with a situation in which an adjacent mountain range that furnishes the sediment undergoes an exponential decline in elevation (see Chapter 12). An increasing rate of sediment production, on the other hand, would hasten the filling of the basin.

It is now generally accepted that the gravity-loading hypothesis, although valid in principle and application, is not adequate to account for observed great thicknesses of basin fills (Bond and Pitman, 1982, p. 23). It has been calculated that the Airy model of isostasy "predicts a sediment fill of only about 2.4 times the initial water depth before all the available water is displaced by sediment" (Kearey and Vine, 1990, p. 242). Recall from our earlier section that the classical model of a geosyncline called for the presence of a shallow water depth at the outset of deposition and continued shallow-water deposition through to the completion of deposition. This requirement has since been verified by deep drill cores taken off the

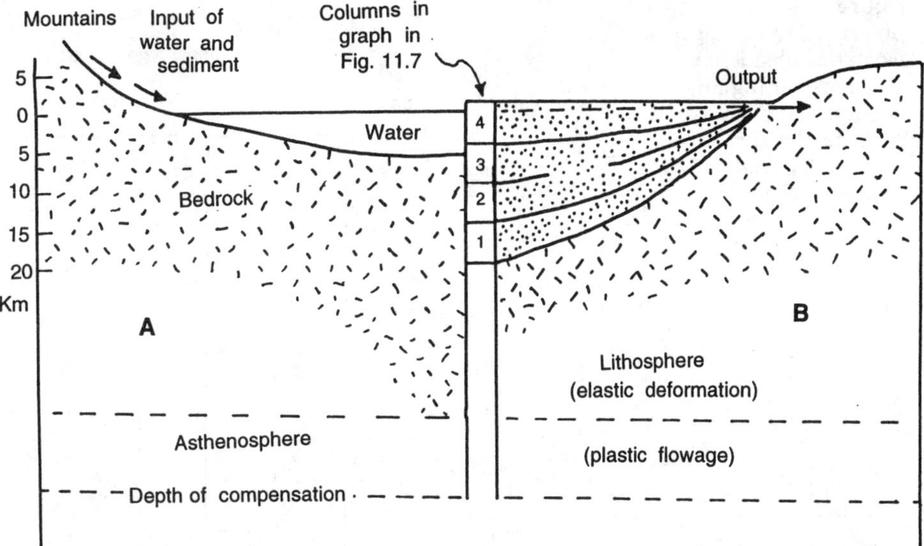

Figure 11.6 Schematic cross section of a continental sedimentary basin. (A) Initial stage with shallow water. (B) Advanced stage with thick layers of sediment. Stages of filling correspond with those shown in Figure 11.7. (Copyright © by Arthur N. Strahler.)

east coast of North America, where about 12 km of sediment has accumulated. For that thickness, an original water depth of 4 to 5 km would be required under the gravity-loading hypothesis (Bond and Pitman, 1982, p. 23). Correspondingly, if the initial depth is set at not more than 150 m, the thickness of fill is limited to about 350 m (Kearey and Vine, 1990, p. 242).

It is possible to calculate the relative magnitude of the isostatic amplification of sediment thickness in a basin by using a method called *backstripping*. The calculation tells "the depth at which the basement would have been if there had been no infilling of sediments" (Fowler, 1990, p. 379, Equations 9.2, 9.3). Bond and Pitman (1982) give the following steps in backstripping:

> (1) All sediment above a particular age horizon is removed. (2) The water depth of the upper surface of the remaining sediment is set so that the depth corresponds with that obtained from fossil evidence. (3) The remaining sediments are decompacted to give the depth to basement with a sediment load. (4) The remaining sediments are removed and the isostatic correction calculated to give the depth to basement without the sediment load. The resulting curve gives the depth to basement without a sediment load as a function of time—this is the tectonic or driving subsidence (p. 23-24).

We turn next to other geological processes that cause basin subsidence; they are large-scale tectonic or thermal processes. Fowler separates the basin-forming processes into three main classes: "(1) Those formed by thermal events, (2) those formed as the result of flexure of the lithosphere by an imposed load, and (3) those formed as the result of extension, compression or faulting of the basement" (1990, p. 380). Most of these processes

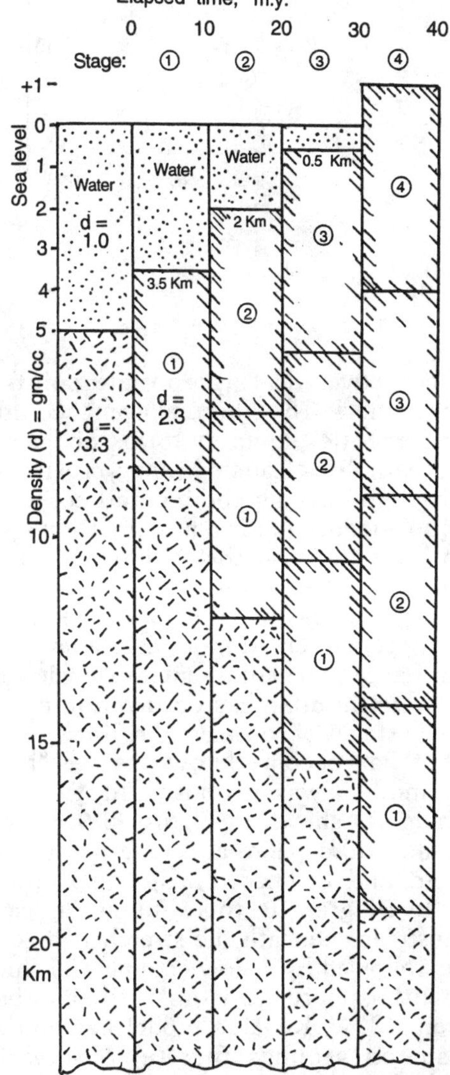

Figure 11.7 Graphic presentation of stages of isostatic subsidence in sediment filling a basin, assuming a constant rate of sediment input. (Copyright © by Arthur N. Strahler.)

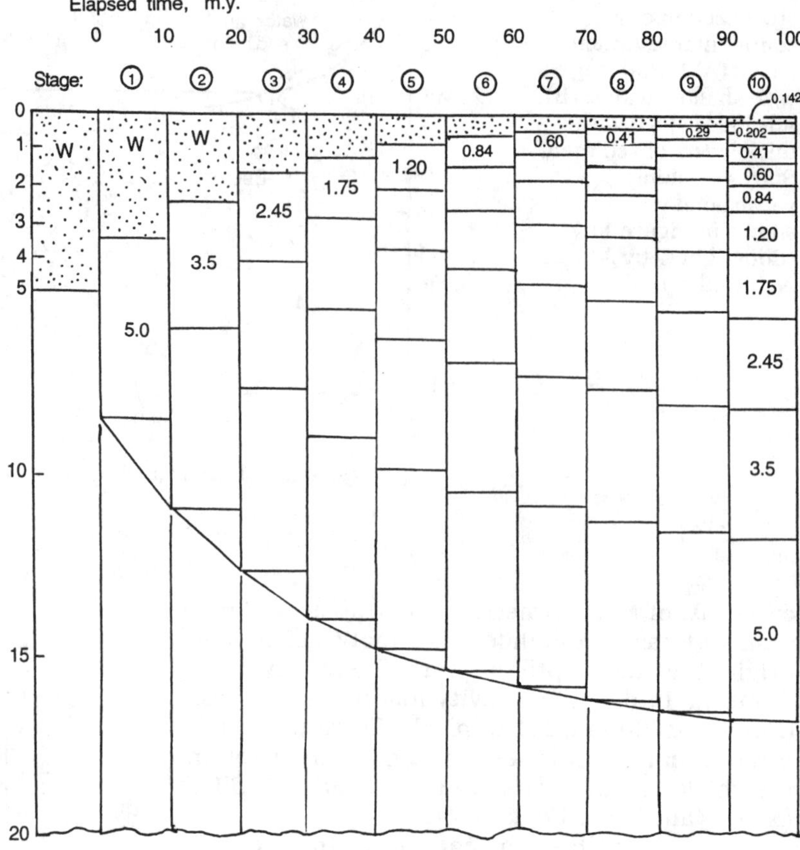

Figure 11.8 Graphic presentation of stages of isostatic subsidence of basin, assuming an exponential decrease in the rate of sediment input. (Copyright © by Arthur N. Strahler.)

have been covered at appropriate points in our earlier chapters. The "thermal event" could be the rise of a mantle plume or forms of magma rise such as batholiths, causing first a crustal doming, then through ensuing cooling and contraction, a crustal subsidence to form a basin. Circular basins within the cratons—the Michigan basin, for example—may be of this origin. Down-flexing of the lithosphere may be imposed by the growth of a collision orogen, creating a basin adjacent to the orogen. Large-scale continental extension causing lithospheric thinning has occurred in connection with early stages of continental rifting.

What has become known as the "McKenzie rifting model" was proposed in 1978 by D.P. McKenzie. As shown in Figure 11.9, Diagram A, continental lithosphere and its crust are laterally stretched and thinned, causing isostatic subsidence. In Diagram B, there follows a rise of hot asthenosphere beneath the stretched region. This stage is followed by a slow cooling and thickening of the lithosphere, causing further subsidence (Diagram C). McKenzie's model has come under criticism on grounds that (a) observations of basins have failed to reveal evidence of the large amounts of extension needed and (b) the lack of a proposed mechanism for that extension (Kearey and Vine, 1990, p. 247).

11.4 Sedimentary Basins of Newly Rifted Continental Margins

In Chapter 1, we described the opening of an ocean basin such as the Atlantic Basin, illustrated by a series of greatly simplified block diagrams (Figure 1.14). It shows first the early stage (A) in which normal faulting dominates as a tectonic process. This faulting produces tectonic basins in which terrestrial sediment accumulates. There follows a transitional stage (B) in which a new ocean basin is opening up, while the block-faulted structures of the early stage have subsided and continue to receive sediment from the adjacent continent. Stage C, much later in time, shows passive continental margins that are tectonically inactive and have great accumulations of continental-shelf, continental-slope, and continental-rise sediments.

Thus the typical history of present passive margins, formed since the breakup of Pangaea, has two stages. The first stage or phase, consists of continental rifting, often accompanied by igneous activity. Tectonics of this stage have been presented in detail in Chapter 10 in our section titled Asymmetry of Continental Rifts and illustrated in Figures 10.8 through 10.12. There is, however, a need to add here stratigraphic information with examples of the Mesozoic

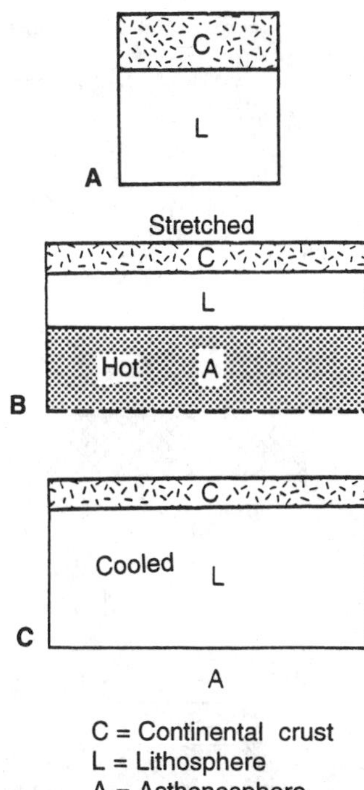

Figure 11.9 Stages in continental basin subsidence caused by lithospheric extension, followed by rise of the asthenosphere, and subsequent cooling. (Based on data of D.P. McKenzie, 1978, *Earth and Planetary Letters*, vol. 40, p. 25-32. Copyright by Elsevier Publishers. Adapted from an adapted version presented by Kearey and Vine, 1990, *Global Tectonics*, p. 246, Figure 11.16.)

tectonic basins of that phase. The second stage, occurring after the continental crust has rifted apart, is largely limited to sediment accumulation accompanied by subsidence. This stage requires further stratigraphic description, with emphasis on the evolution of the eastern North American passive margin, including the Gulf of Mexico.

The formation of rift basins in the first stage has been given the name *taphrogeny*, from the Greek *taphria* for "trench" and reading "born as a trench" (Quennell, 1987, p. 673). It was introduced in 1925, and was later used by Marshall Kay to form the name *taphrogeosyncline*, to be applied to the sedimentary fill of a rift basin. "Taphrogeny" can be considered as parallel in meaning with "orogeny." The latter produces a compressional structure that we call an "orogen." What is needed is the corresponding term *taphrogen*, to describe the extensional structure produced by taphrogeny, but that term does not seem to be recognized in the literature (see Bates and Johnson, 1987, p. 673). We have nevertheless introduced "taphrogen" in Table 11.1, where it is good company with the aulacogen.

It has become evident from studies of deep crustal structure along the Atlantic margin of North America that the continental crust was stretched and faulted just prior to the appearance of the early Atlantic Ocean basin. There were also intrusions and extrusions of magma within and upon the faulted continental crust, while synrift sediments accumulated in the fault basins. As a result, a broad zone—perhaps 100 to 150 km wide—was transformed into crust with properties intermediate between old continental crust and new oceanic crust. Perhaps the best-known modern example of the tectonic rifting stage is the Red Sea trough, described in Chapter 10 and illustrated in Figures 10.28-10.34.

Figure 11.10 covers the transition from the tectonic rifting stage (or taphrogenic stage) to the mature passive margin stage, in which sedimentation and basin deepening dominates. Diagram A shows a rifting in which symmetrical zones of stretched and faulted quasicontinental crust have been formed. Diagram B, focusing now on the left half of that symmetrical arrangement, recognizes an older graben fill of the separation phase now buried beneath basal clastics accumulated on a coastal shelf and slope. In Diagram C, which is in the mature passive stage, continental shelf sediments and continental rise turbidites form thick sedimentary wedges. Diagram D shows a special advanced stage in which continental deltaic and fan sediments have overridden the continental rise and lie directly upon oceanic crust and its pelagic cover. Sections C and D include what we have identified as geoclines (eugeocline and miogeocline), but they are not so labeled. We turn next to examples of the tectonic basin deposits of the rifting phase.

11.5 Triassic Fault Basins of the North Atlantic Margins

If our scenario of marginal stretching, faulting, and subsidence in the early stages of continental margin rifting is correct, we should find some downfaulted sedimentary basins (taphrogens) exposed today along the eastern margin of North America. Indeed, they are present and they contain rocks of Late Triassic age (225-208 Ma), which is contemporary with the early stage of opening of the North Atlantic ocean basin. Wedgelike bodies of Triassic sedimentary strata, occupying downfaulted basins, occur from the Maritime Provinces and New England to as far south as North Carolina in the Piedmont geologic province. The basins are surrounded by older gneisses and schists, which are root structures of the Caledonian and Hercynian orogens. Extensive erosion occurred during Cretaceous and Cenozoic time as the continental lithosphere underwent a series of epeirogenic uplifts, so that today all but the lower parts of the fault basins are gone.

The largest of the Triassic basins is the Newark Basin of New Jersey and eastern Pennsylvania. Figure 11.11 shows how sediments accumulated in the basin as downfaulting took place. Successive basalt flows were buried and tilted with the sediments (Sections A and B); then a massive sill of gabbro was intruded into the redbeds (Section

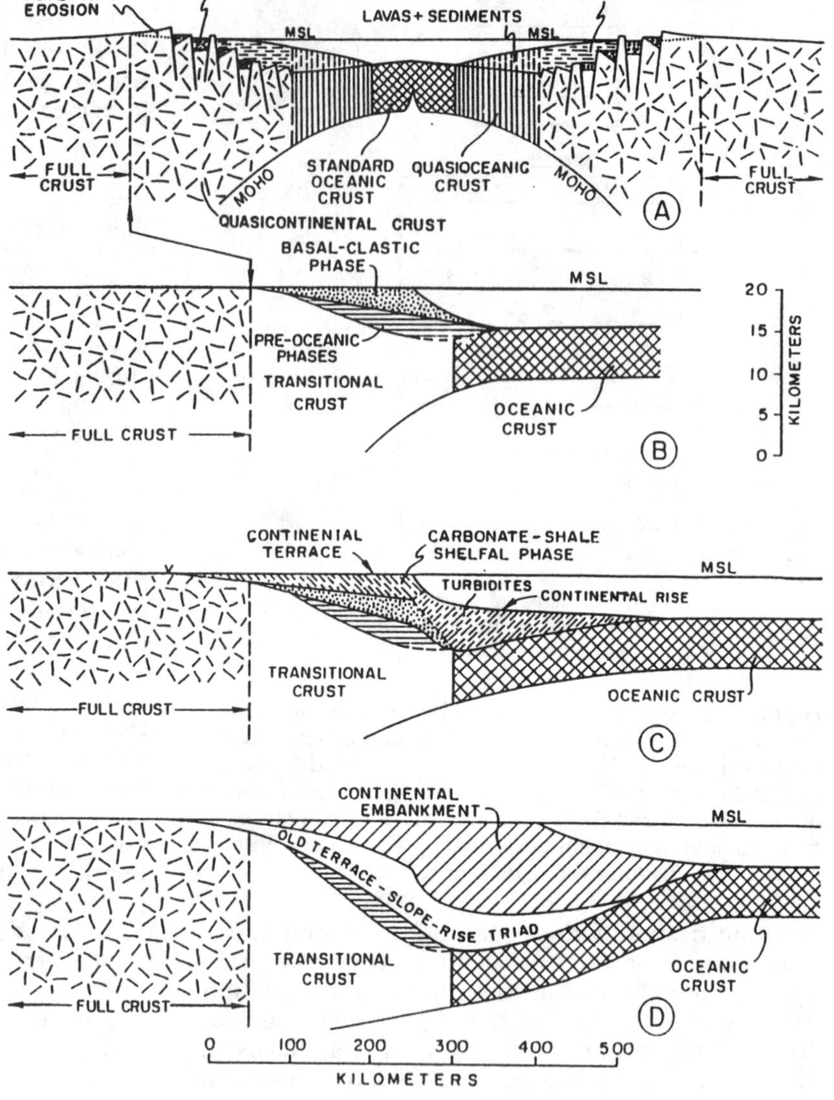

Figure 11.10 Schematic cross sections showing the typical evolution of a rifted continental margin from the tectonically active early stage to the mature passive margin stage. From R.V. Ingersoll, 1988, *Bull, Geol. Soc. Amer.*, v. 100, p. 1706, Reproduced with the permission of the publisher, the Geological Society of America, Boulder, Colorado, USA. Copyright 1988. Figure 2, as modified from W.R. Dickinson, 1976, *AAPG Continuing Education Course Notes Series 1*.

C). Today, the edge of the sill is exposed to view as the Palisades of the Hudson River (Figure 11.12), which owes its ribbed cliff form to massive columnar jointing in the gabbro.

The Triassic basins exposed along the length of the Piedmont belt represent only the westernmost of the taphrogens that formed in Late Triassic time by stretching of the heated continental crust. Other such basins lie concealed beneath Cretaceous and Cenozoic strata of the coastal plain/shelf sedimentary wedge (the modern miogeocline). They have been detected by means of detailed seismic exploration of the continental shelf. Both reflection and refraction seismology have contributed to unraveling the details of crustal structure and sedimentary deposits beneath the Cenozoic geoclines.

An excellent example of a quite different historical development of marginal rift basins can be found in northwestern Europe, in the region British Isles and Ireland, and Brittany. Opening of the Atlantic took place some 400 to 500 km to the west of the British Isles and Ireland. The continental limit lying southwest of Ireland passes around a westward-projecting continental promontory known as the Goban Spur. Figure 11.13 is a regional sketch map of the area showing the relationship of the Goban Spur to the Cornwall and Brittany peninsulas and the English Channel between them. Figure 11.14 is a composite geologic section through the succession of half-graben fault basins descending stepwise from a platform depth of -1 km to the abyssal floor below -4 km. In contrast with the opposing North American margin, thick geoclines are missing from the picture. What we are seeing is a "sediment-starved" passive continental margin (Graciansky, Poag, et al, 1985). Because of its isolated location with respect to the landmass located far to the east, synrift sediments were meager, as were the post-rift sediments. Paleogene sediments finally buried the highest horsts, while Neogene sediments were also scant and reflect the underlying structure.

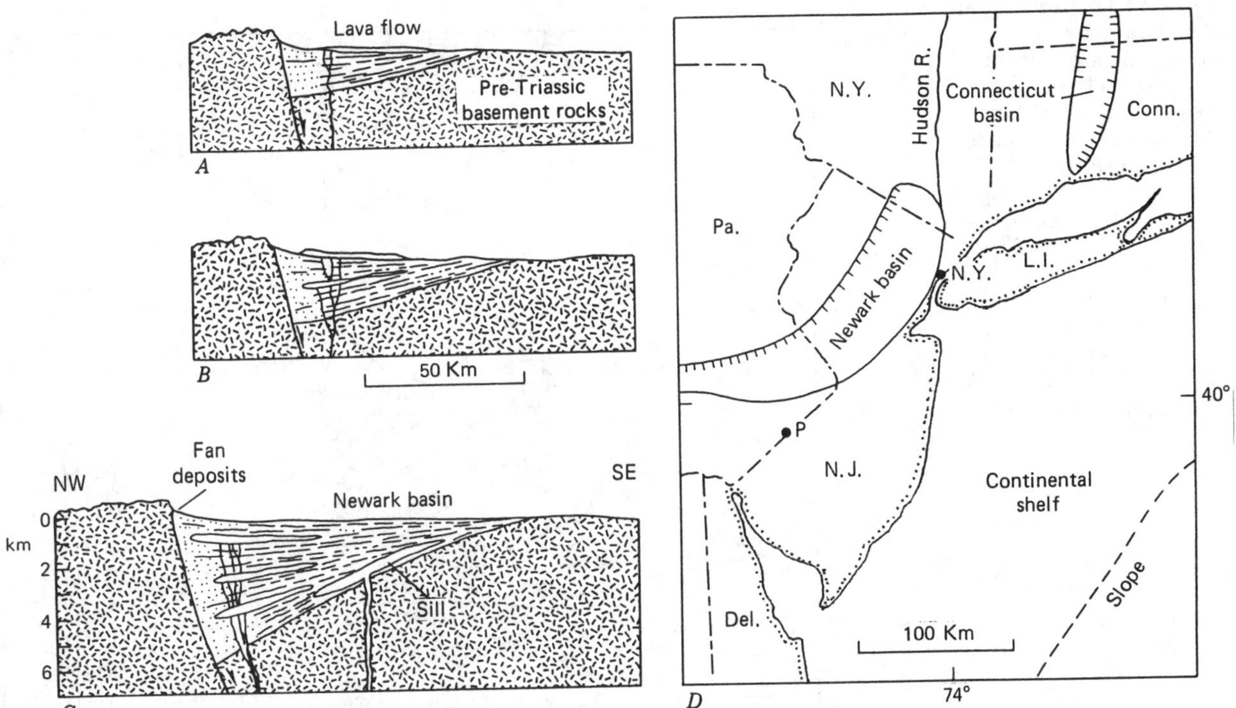

Figure 11.11 The Newark Basin formed of downfaulted Triassic sediments and interbedded lava flows. (Copyright © by Arthur N. Strahler.)

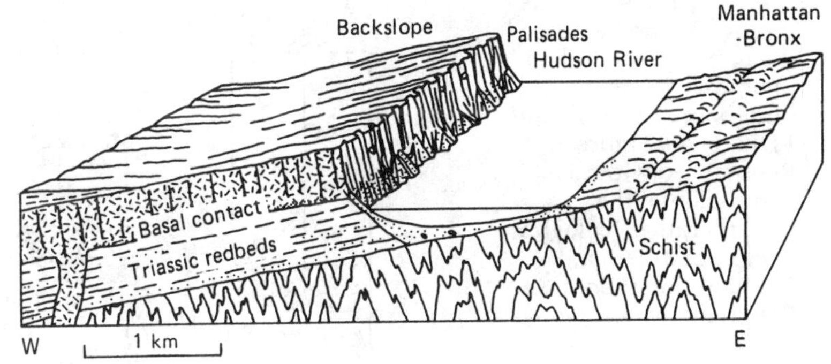

Figure 11.12 Schematic diagram of the Palisades of the Hudson River, New Jersey and New York. Relief is greatly exaggerated. (Copyright © by Arthur N. Strahler.)

11.6 The Gulf of Mexico—A Single Rift Basin?

So accustomed are we to seeing the Gulf of Mexico on maps and globes that we fail to perceive some puzzling geological relationships of the Gulf to the open North Atlantic basin. The presence of a continuous 180-degree arc of coastal plain and continental shelf extending from Florida to the Gulf of Campeche may mislead us into equating that entire arc to one continuous stretch of the Atlantic geocline.

Turning to our geologic map of the ocean floors, Figure 7.31, we find the Gulf of Mexico to be totally isolated from the unified spreading mirror-image pattern that fills the entire Atlantic basin from north to south. In the central Gulf area, known as the Sigsbee Deep, magnetic anomalies seem not to be present (Conde et al., 1989). Using this same geologic map, if we were to close completely shut the entire Atlantic ocean floor to Late Jurassic time, the Gulf of Mexico would remain isolated as a deep ocean basin floored by Late Jurassic sediments.

These general relationships are best understood by postulating that when Pangaea was in its fully compacted phase, from the late Permian (260 Ma) to perhaps as late as Middle Jurassic (180 Ma), it was South America, rather than Africa, that lay against North America along a line that today would be drawn westward from the Florida panhandle to the U.S.-Mexico line. North of this line lay the Paleozoic fold belts, the last of which were the Alleghenides of Permian time. As far back as 1970, Robert S. Dietz and John C. Holden had shown just this arrangement on their map of Pangaea at the end of the Permian (see Chapter 13 and Figure 13.34). They filled the gap that today is the Gulf of Mexico by stuffing it with the Yucatan and Honduras blocks and some other and smaller Central American blocks. In 1976, R. Van der Voo, F.J. Mauk, and R.B. French offered a new reconstruction of that part of Pangaea. By making a

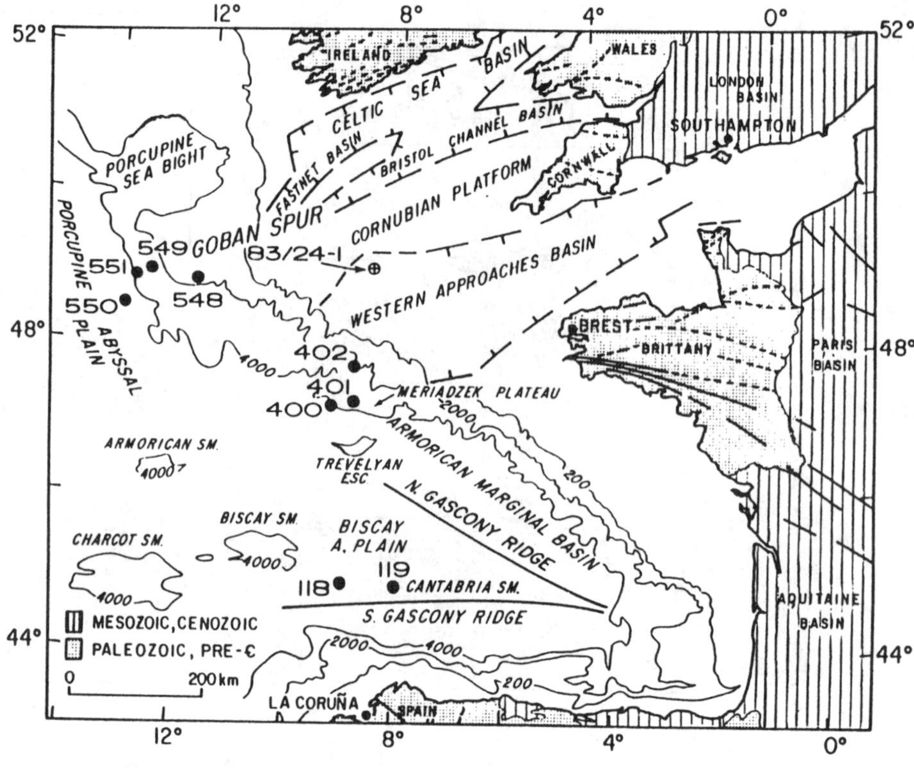

Figure 11.13 Sketch map of Goban Spur submarine area off the coasts of Ireland, Cornwall, and Brittany. Numbered dots indicate boreholes (From P.C. de Graciansky, C.W. Poag, et al., 1985, *Bull., Geol. Soc. Amer.*, v. 96, p. 59, Figure 1. Reproduced with the permission of the publisher, the Geological Society of America, Boulder, Colorado, USA. Copyright 1985.)

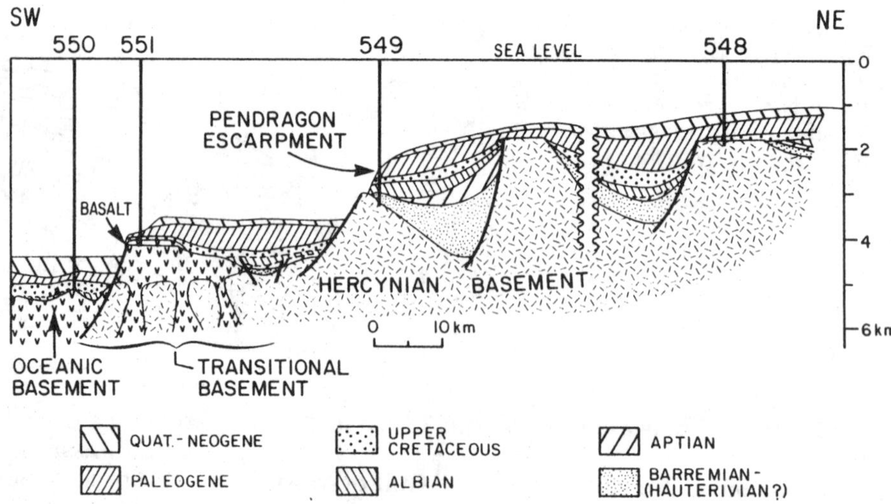

Figure 11.14 Schematic geologic section across the basins of the Goban Spur area. (From the same source as in Figure 11.13, p. 60, Figure 3. Reproduced with the permission of the publisher, the Geological Society of America, Boulder, Colorado, USA. Copyright 1985.)

clockwise rotation of S. America and Africa they brought S. America farther north and closer to N. America. In so doing, no large gulf remained in N. America. Instead, a zone of Paleozoic folds connected the two continents. In 1985, James L. Pindell presented a new paleogeographic map showing the relationship of S. America to the Alleghenides. Our Figure 11.15 is a greatly simplified version of that map.

A decade earlier, in 1974, G.W. Moore and L.D. Castillo had already drawn up a scenario that eliminated any need for a primeval oceanic gulf. Their four paleogeographic maps are reproduced here as Figure 11.16. Map A: While Africa and North America began to rift apart, S. America drew apart from N. America along a continental rift bounded by two new transform faults. Map B: By Late Jurassic, the Gulf of Mexico had fully opened, bounded on the south by the Yucatan block. Note that the main Mid-Atlantic Ridge had been extended far southward. Map C: In the Early Cretaceous a short new subduction margin arc made its way northeast between N. America and S. America. Its volcanic arc formed the ancestral Cuba-Hispaniola-Puerto Rico chain, but progressed no farther north. Map D: On this Holocene map the new Caribbean plate is shown in place. Support for this history of the Gulf of Mexico was expressed in 1994 by Hans Schouton and Kim D. Kiltgord, who proposed a revised history for the

Figure 11.15 Sketch map of a portion of Pangaea in the Late Permian showing the relationship of the Yucatan and Florida Straits blocks to North America and South America. (Simplified from J.L. Pindell, 1985, *Tectonics*, v. 4, p. 4, Figure 2. Used by permission of the American Geophysical Union.)

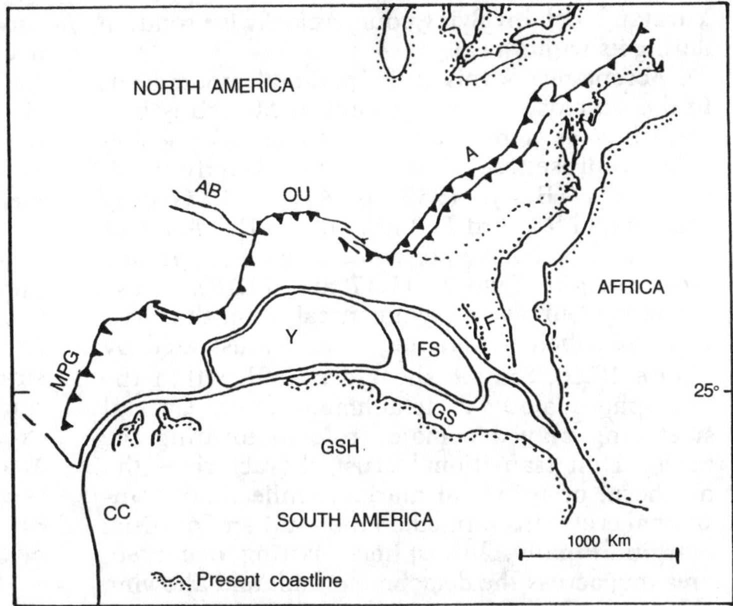

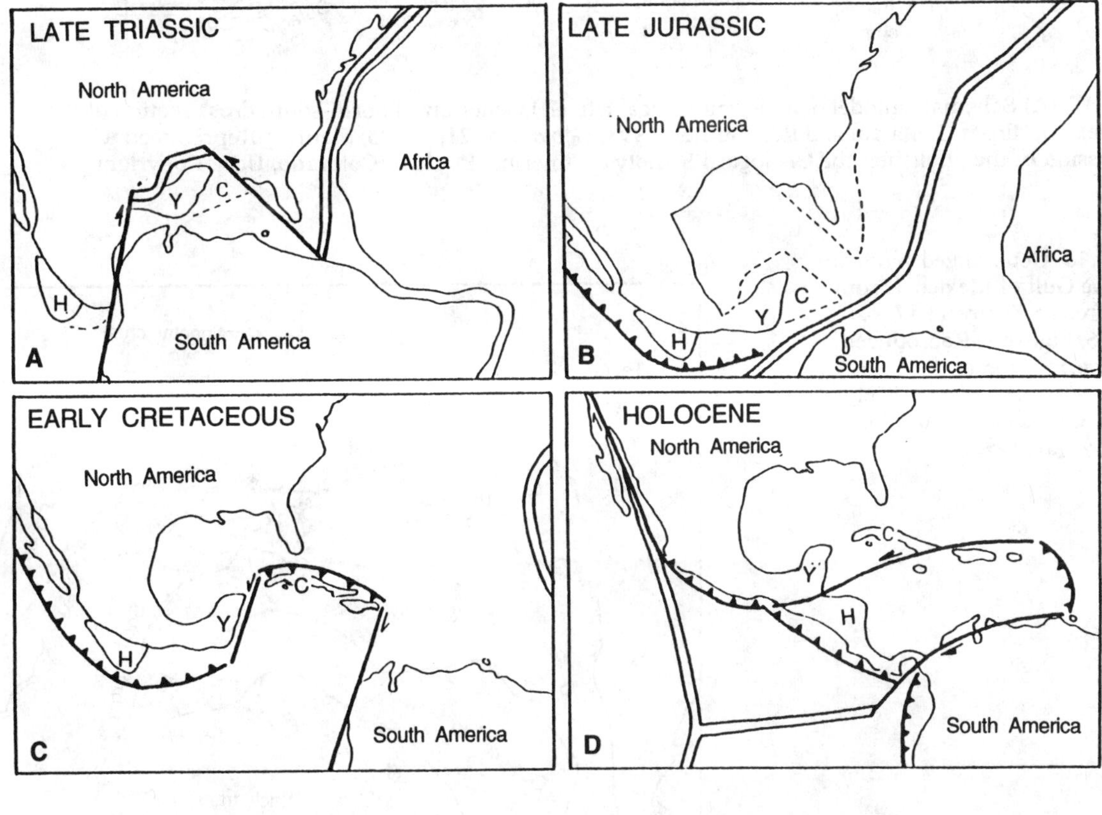

Figure 11.16 Paleogeographic sketch maps of stages in the opening of the Gulf of Mexico. (From George W. Moore and Luis Del Castillo, 1974, *Bull., Geol. Soc. Amer.*, v. 85, p. 612, Figure 9. Reproduced with the permission of the publisher, the Geological Society of America, Boulder, Colorado, USA. Copyright 1974.)

Yucatan block involving counterclockwise rotation during its withdrawal.

Acceptance of this basic "pull-out" model leads to the conclusion that the Gulf of Mexico is best identified as a mini-ocean with both opposing sides represented, but not necessarily symmetrically (Bally, 1989, p. 412-414). György Marton and Richard T. Buffler of the University of Texas at Austin have presented us with a map and cross section (Figures 11.17 and 11.18). These depict the Gulf as an asymmetrical rift of the basic type described in Chapter 10 and illustrated by Figure 10.10. Simple shear occurred within the lithosphere along a detachment fault. Crustal stretching played a major role in forming the basin. Thin transitional crust characterizes the northern, or proximal margin, while thick transitional crust was formed on the southern, or distal margin. Finally, lithospheric rifting occurred, breaking across the detachment fault and allowing production of oceanic crust. Sediments ranging in age from Upper Triassic through Cenozoic filled the northern part of the basin, with salt diapirs rising from a Jurassic salt layer. The accompanying map, Figure 11.18, shows the contrast between northern and southern halves of the basin. As expected, the belt of oceanic crust lies much closer to the southern, or distal margin than to the northern, or proximal margin. Note in the upper right corner of the map the Late Triassic basins belonging to the Atlantic rift system. The lateral margins of the Gulf are narrow and nearly straight on either side of the Sigsbee Deep. North-south striking anticlinal folds are found on the extreme western floor of the deep. The Serra Madre Oriental, shown by a west-dipping thrust, bounds the western margin of the Gulf. The eastern margin of the Gulf is bounded by the Florida Straits block.

In a later section, we review in more detail the

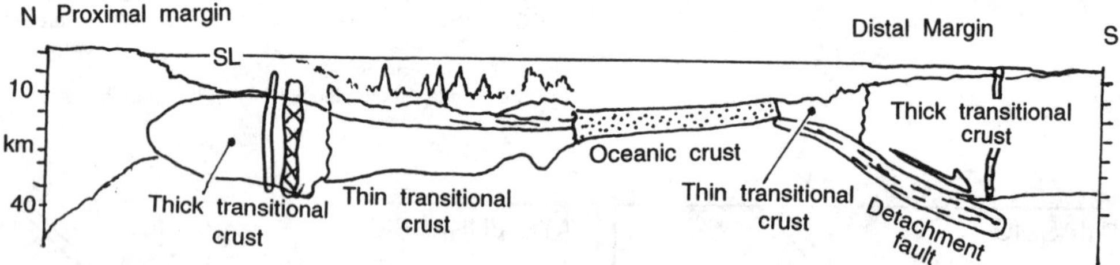

Figure 11.17 (A) Schematic model of an asymmetrical rift. (B) Generalized north-south cross section of the Gulf of Mexico. (From G. Martin and R.T. Buffler, 1993, *Geology*, v. 21, p. 495, Figure 1.Reproduced with the permission of the publisher, the Geological Society of America, Boulder, Colorado, USA. Copyright 1993.)

Figure 11.18 Generalized geologic map of the Gulf of Mexico. (From same source as Figure 11.17, p. 495,p. 476, Figure 2. Reproduced with the permission of the publisher, the Geological Society of America, Boulder, Colorado, USA. Copyright 1993.)

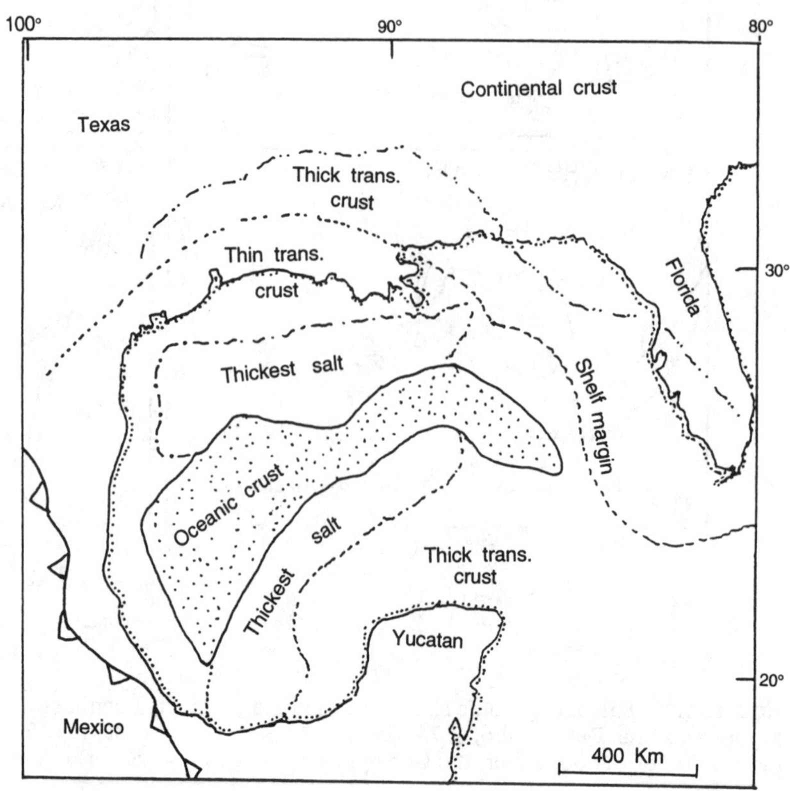

Gulf geocline of the United States. Basin deposition from Jurassic to the present comes under our Classes I-B and II-B, Mature passive margins. Salt diapirs, which are numerous around the Gulf margin, are also described in a later section.

11.7 Geoclines of the Passive Continental Margins

Thus far we have concentrated on the rifting stage of the passive continental margins. Following the rifting, continental crust separation, and block faulting there begins a prolonged period of sediment accumulation, usually lacking in large-scale faulting and volcanic activity. The body of sediment is called a *geocline*. Table 11.1, recognizes two classes of mature passive margins: Subclass I-B and Subclass II-B, both labeled as "mature passive margins, both described as "non-orogenic," and both assigned to the tectonic type *flexural geocline*. The word "flexural" refers to downflexing of the crust (and lithosphere). [This subject was presented earlier in this chapter.] Why, then, are two subclasses needed? The answer is simply that continental lithosphere underlies the first subclass, I-B, whereas oceanic lithosphere underlies the second subclass, II-B. Transitional types of lithosphere, already mentioned in this chapter, are assigned to one or the other subclass. As to basin name, Table 11.1 applies *miogeocline* to the geocline overlying continental lithosphere and *eugeocline* to that overlying oceanic lithosphere. Recall that these terms can be traced back to the 1930s, before plate tectonics was established, when Hans Stille and Marshall Kay recognized two classes of geosynclines: miogeosyncline and eugeosyncline. The use of "geocline" for passive margin basins became the term used in academic studies because these bodies of sediment are basically wedge-shaped in cross section (Dietz, 1972, p. 30; Seyfert, 1987, p. 287). This form is shown in cross-section C of Figure 11.10. In advanced stages of development, however, subsidence of the lithosphere may cause the cross section to be that of a deep, synclinally-shaped basin, as shown in cross-section D of Figure 11.10. This form is typical of large marine deltas. You should also be alert for *margin sag* as a synonym for "geocline" (Kingston, Dishroon, and Williams, 1983, p. 127). Figure 11.19 is a schematic cross section of a simple geocline with its opposing miogeoclinal and eugeoclinal wedges.

Passive margins that border the Atlantic and Indian Ocean basins epitomize the mature stage of the Wilson cycle. The rifted plate segments of Pangaea have separated by a distance of roughly 3500 to 4000 km in the 200 m.y, that have elapsed since middle Triassic time, when rifting began. These passive continental margins are, for the most part, well endowed with thick geoclines made up of strata dating back as early as late Triassic or early Jurassic time. For confirmation refer again to the geologic map of the ocean floors, Figure 7.31.

The miogeocline receives its sediments from streams that are eroding older rocks of the adjacent stable continental craton. The miogeocline also loses sediment at its outer edge, where masses slump off the edge of the continental shelf and travel as turbidity currents down the steep continental slope (see Chapter 4). The thick outer edge of a miogeocline merges into the eugeocline formed simultaneously in deep water of the continental rise. The eugeocline consists largely of turbidites with graded bedding and well-sorted sandy contourites. The eugeocline will rarely, if ever, include important quantities of volcanic materials except where a hot spot has generated an isolated volcanic seamount.

Whereas the miogeocline rests on continental crust (including intermediate stretched and faulted

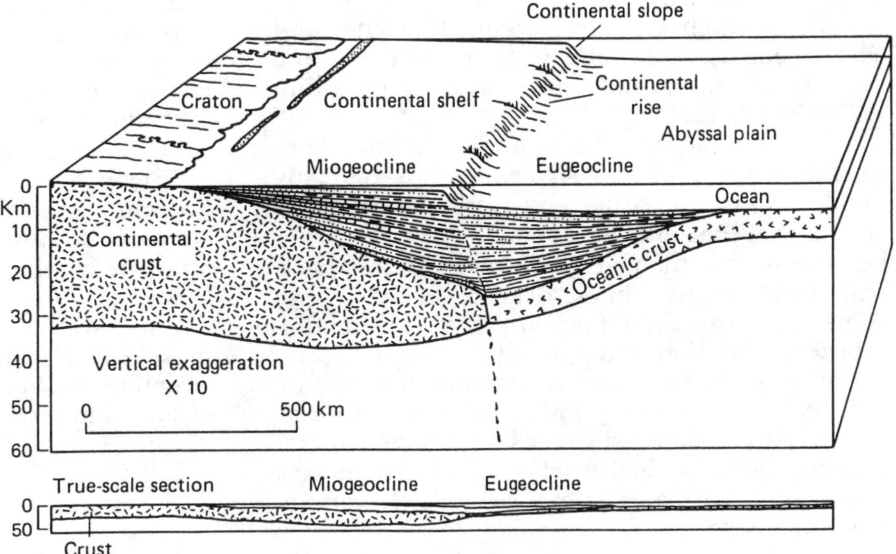

Figure 11.19 Schematic block diagram of geoclines on a passive continental margin. (Copyright © by Arthur N. Strahler.)

transitional continental crust), the eugeocline rests on oceanic crust. Thus the boundary between oceanic and continental plates is usually drawn at the base of the continental slope in cases where geophysical evidence is not available for more precise positioning.

Fortunately, there is no lack of examples of fully mature geoclines undergoing continued growth. Mature continental margins exist on both sides of the Atlantic Ocean basin, both along the American margins on the west and the western European and African margins on the east. The Atlantic Ocean basin came into existence by continental rifting that began in the late Triassic in the north, in the Jurassic in the south. Thus, continental shelf wedges and turbidite wedges have been accumulating in the North Atlantic for over 100 m.y., and it is not surprising that thick geoclines border the continental coasts for thousands of kilometers. They include no volcanic materials of importance and lack such structures as folds that might indicate significant tectonic compression. We need look no farther than the North American continent for a prime example along the East Coast Geocline.

Although we have already treated the Gulf of Mexico as a pull-apart ocean basin, its northern half is essentially a typical example of a thick miogeocline, albeit unique in possessing a large collection of salt mounds and diapirs and their related small basins. Therefore we will include the northern portion the Gulf in our further discussion of geoclines of passive margins.

Strata making up the Atlantic and Gulf Coast miogeoclines are dominantly limestones (marls), shales, and sandstones. A single formation usually shows thickening in the seaward direction, while in the landward direction it may thin to the point of disappearance. This onlap/offlap geometry is what we would expect of deposition in shallow coastal waters that receive sediment from the mouths of streams. The clastic sediment is spread seaward by currents and comes to rest in deeper water offshore. Strata in the upper part of the geocline, which are of Miocene, Pliocene, and Pleistocene ages, are mostly unconsolidated and consist of sand and mud layers, including calcareous muds.

Even the oldest strata of a miogeocline, those at the bottom of the sequence, are typically shallow-water deposits, and this may be characteristic of the entire accumulation of strata. This fact means that the marine shoreline shifted back and forth many times over a broad zone, sometimes invading far into the continental interior, and that the rate of sediment accumulation must have closely matched the rate of crustal sinking. As we pointed out earlier in this chapter, the relationship was recognized many decades ago by geologists who interpreted ancient geoclines of marine strata exposed today in various mountain belts.

11.8 Geoclines and Lithospheric Subsidence

Earlier in this chapter we briefly reviewed possible causes of basin subsidence beyond the isostatic response, which cannot alone account for sustained subsidence. Of the three main classes of geological processes named by Fowler (1990, p. 380) to account for subsidence, the class of "thermal event" includes continental rifting and the formation of passive continental margins (p. 381).

In an earlier section of this chapter we reviewed McKenzie's 1978 model of rifting, illustrated in Figure 11.9. It requires lithospheric thinning by extension prior to eventual basin subsidence. Prior thinning is essential in order that basin subsidence can later follow the rise and subsequent cooling of hot asthenosphere. McKenzie had rejected subaerial erosion in favor of the extensional thinning that occurs in the early rifting stage, prior to the final split down through the brittle lithosphere. This is a subject we have already covered in earlier paragraphs and in Chapter 10. "By the late 1970s there was general agreement that subsidence of ocean floor was controlled by cooling and thermal contraction of hot lithosphere moving away from (oceanic) ridge crests" (Bond and Kominz, 1988, p. 1924).

A basic "thermal" hypothesis of subsidence of marginal geoclines had been put forward by Norman H. Sleep in 1971. It calls upon lithospheric plate cooling accompanying the widening of the Atlantic Ocean basin. At the time of rifting, the new oceanic lithosphere would have been relatively hot because of the rise of mantle rock through the spreading rift and a general rise of hot mantle under the lithosphere. As the new continental margins separated from the spreading axis, the plate would have steadily cooled and thinned, increasing its density, and therefore slowly sinking (see Chapter 5 and Figure 5.11B). If that density increase had persisted for as long as 200 million years, its combined effect with the subsidence required by isostasy would perhaps have maintained a shallow continental shelf, and would continue to do so. However, because of the exponential decline in density, shown in Figure 5.11, the capability of the mechanism to remain active indefinitely may seem questionable.

Sleep states that during the thermal contraction of the lithosphere, thickness of sediments increases toward a final limit by an exponential function in which the decay constant is 50 m.y. (1987, p. 774). Fowler gives a simple basic mathematical model for the lithospheric subsidence (1990, p. 381). Starting with the most recently deposited bed of sediment with depth zero (d_o) at time zero (t_o), depth (d) after elapsed time (t) is given as:

$$d = d_o\,[\,e^{(t/to)} - 1\,]$$

Figure 11.20 shows a family of subsidence curves calculated by A.B. Watts (1981). For each curve, initial subsidence due to initial stretching is scaled down on the ordinate. Starting at that initial depth, the exponential curve is plotted on the abscissa through the age since rifting. Obviously, the greater the initial subsidence, the greater will be the possible thermal subsidence.

Figure 11.21 is a two-dimensional thermo-mechanical model of a passive margin constructed by M.S. Steckler in 1981. Not only does it show the accumulation of miogeoclinal and eugeoclinal strata of the continental shelf and continental rise above the synrift sediments, but also the development of an *inner flexural wedge* that accumulates on the unrifted Paleozoic hinterland as the strata onlap in progressively wider zones (Steckler and Watts, 1982). This subsidence is also caused by crustal cooling. The synrift sediment prism has rotated clockwise on a horizontal hinge axis, accommodating the accumulation of the postrift sediments. The hinge zone indicates the boundary between stretched (right) and unstretched (left) continental crust.

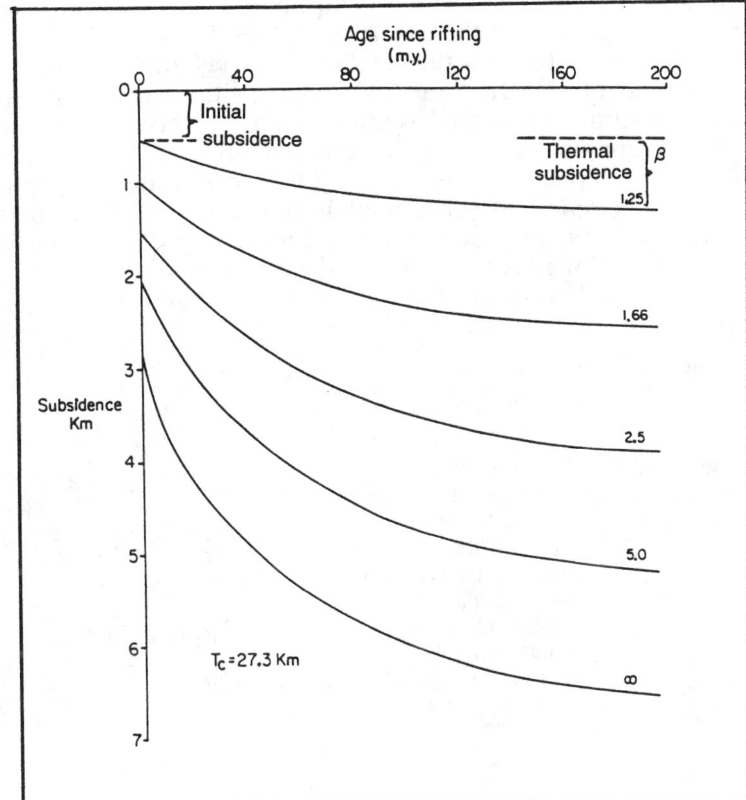

Figure 11.20 Graph of a family of thermal subsidence curves, assuming a number of values of the initial subsidence due to stretching. T_c is the initial thickness of the crust. (From G.C. Bond and M.A. Kominz, 1988, *Bull., Geol Soc. Amer.*, v. 100, p. 1928, Figure 12(b). Reproduced with the permission of the publisher, the Geological Society of America, Boulder, Colorado, USA. Copyright 1928.)

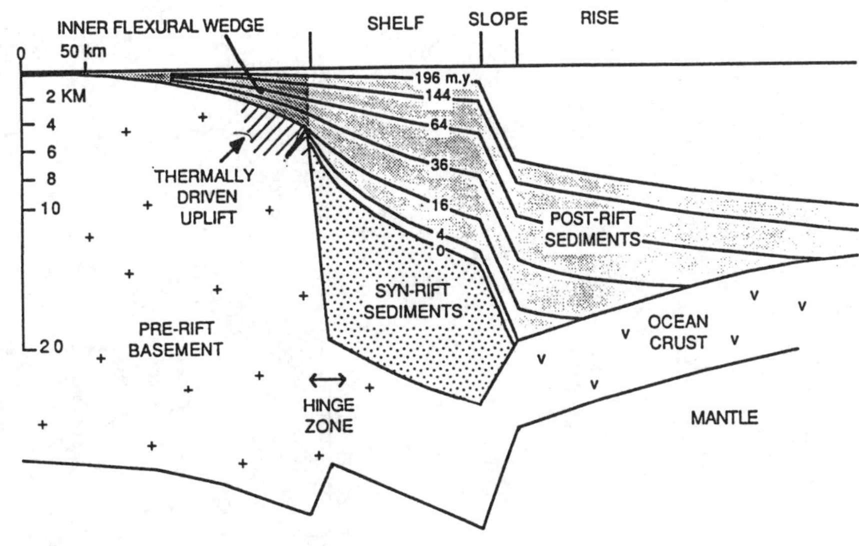

Figure 11.21 Cross section of a thermo-mechanical model of a passive continental margin, showing a schedule of subsidence of post-rift sediments and growth of a flexural wedge. (From G.C. Bond and M.A. Kominz, 1988, *Bull., Geol. Soc. Amer.*, v. 100, p. 1911, Figure 1(d).Reproduced with the permission of the publisher, the Geological Society of America, Boulder, Colorado, USA. Copyright 1911.)

11.9 Structure of the North Atlantic Continental Margin

We begin our geological description of the North Atlantic continental margin with a simplified and generalized set of block diagrams, Figure 11.22. These show steps in the formation of buried structures and sedimentary units that have been found by seismic reflection and deep drilling to underlie the Cenozoic geoclines in the Baltimore Canyon region of the Atlantic continental shelf. This is the part of the shelf lying offshore from New Jersey, Delaware, Maryland, and Virginia. Diagram A, the rift stage or "taphrogen stage," shows the geology in the late Triassic. The Triassic fault basins have been filled by red beds (Figures 11.10 and 11.11). Diagram B shows conditions in Jurassic time, when the Triassic basins had been partly removed by subaerial erosion and were being overlapped by a wedge of Jurassic marine strata. Tectonic and volcanic activity had ceased, and geoclines were beginning to form. It seems that conditions were right for the growth of a massive coral barrier reefs in a shallow water zone paralleling the coast. These reefs continued to maintain themselves as the continental margin subsided, forming a great barrier reef that separated deep ocean water on the east from a shallow marginal sea on the west. Rapid evaporation of seawater resulted in the deposition of thick salt beds landward of the reef barrier, while at the same time clastic sediment was being brought into the shallow sea from the mainland to the west. Altogether 8 to 10 km of clastic sediments and salt beds of Jurassic age accumulated in this marginal sedimentary basin. Seaward of the reef barrier and its outer slope of reef detritus, a deep-water wedge of sediments was also accumulating on the continental slope and rise.

In the Cretaceous Period, the reef barrier ceased to grow upward. North America had been migrating steadily into higher latitudes and the U.S. Atlantic passive margin now lay north of the 30th parallel. Perhaps the ocean temperature there was not high enough to allow reef corals to flourish. Or perhaps there was an increase in siliciclastic sediments, causing increased turbitity. Thus the barrier reef was buried under terrestrial Cretaceous strata. As shown in Diagram C, the Cretaceous sediments were clastics and limestones

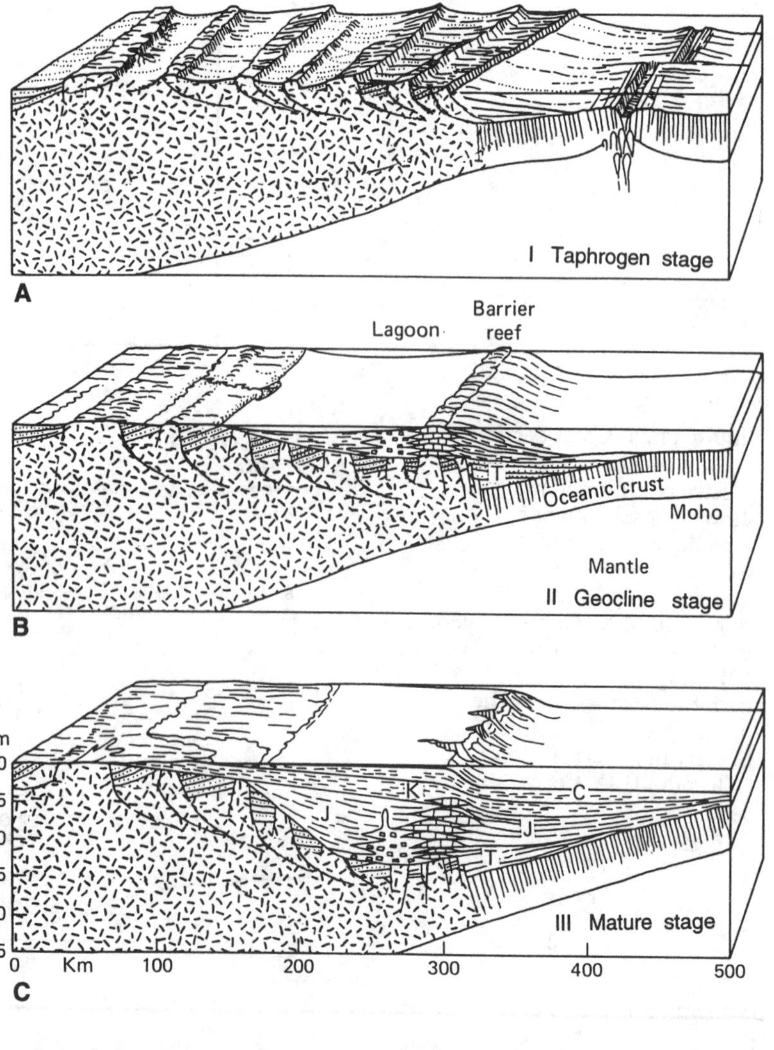

Figure 11.22 Schematic block diagrams showing stages of evolution of the North Atlantic continental margin. Vertical exaggeration about x5. (Drawn by A. N. Strahler. Based on data of J.S. Schlee et al., 1979, *Oceanus*, v. 22, no. 2, pp. 40-47; J.A. Grow et al., *Memoir 29, Amer. Assoc. Petroleum Geologists*, p. 65-83.)

on the shelf miogeocline and deep-water turbidites on the eugeocline. Deposition of flexural wedge sediments spread far inland over the early fault basins. Deposition continued through the Cenozoic Era, thickening both geoclines.

Taking a closer look at the geoclines of the North American passive margin, we focus on two representative localities. One is the Baltimore Canyon trough sector described above; the other is the Blake Plateau basin lying off the Florida coast and north of the Bahama Banks. To put these basins in tectonic perspective, Figure 11.23 is a paleogeographic map showing North America and Africa still close together about 175 Ma, in Middle Jurassic time. The tectonic rifting stage was over, and the geocline stage had begun—about as shown in Diagram B of Figure 11.22. Notice first the East Coast magnetic anomaly (ECMA) which lies on the transitional-crust/oceanic-crust boundary (Sheridan, 1989, p. 81). Farther to the east is the Blake Spur magnetic anomaly (BSMA, which has been interpreted as marking the axis of the Mid-Oceanic Ridge at the time of this map (175 Ma) (Talwani and Langseth, 1981, p. 24).

Detailed geophysical information on geoclines of the Baltimore Canyon section, off the coast of New Jersey, was obtained in the middle 1980s by the LASE Study Group. (LASE = Large Aperture Seismic Experiment.) Figure 11.24 summarizes data from both refraction seismology (code ESP) and deep commercial wells (code COST). Five classes of crustal rock are recognized. Crustal layers are marked off according to seismic velocities. The East Coast magnetic anomaly (ECMA) lies between ESP 2 and 4.

We turn next to the Blake Plateau basin, shown on a regional map, Figure 11.25. It is quite different in structure from the Baltimore Canyon basin, as is obvious from the cross section shown in Figure 11.26. Water depths over plateau range from 750 to 1000 m. A miogeocline dominates the structure, with uniform and nearly horizontal stratigraphic units extending laterally over 300 km. The Blake Escarpment, which terminates the miogeocline, is high and steep, leading down precipitously to an almost flat abyssal floor nearly 5 km deep and underlain by a relatively thin eugeocline. Near the western end of the section we

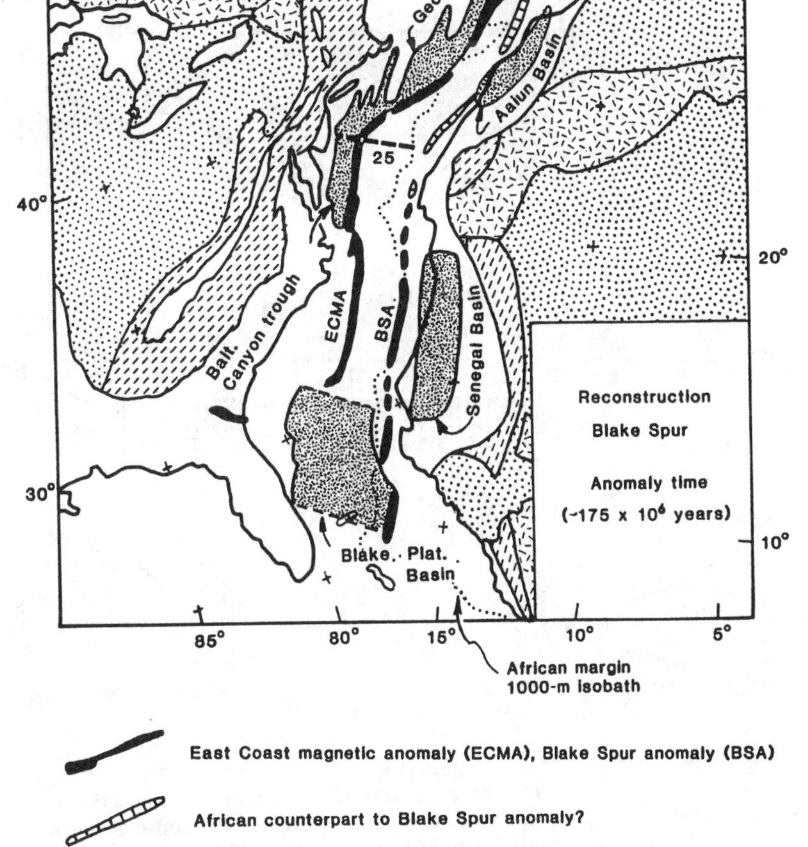

Figure 11.23 Paleogeographic sketch map of the North Atlantic about 175 Ma, showing Africa and North America beginning to separate. The Blake Spur anomaly (BSA) may represent the new mid-oceanic spreading ridge. (From Manik Talwani and Marcus Langseth, 1981, *Science*, v. 213, p. 24, Figure 2. Copyright @ 1981 by the American Association for the Advancement of Science. Used by permission.)

see the hinge zone, marking the limit of stretched crust, and to the west lie beds of the inner flexular wedge. Between this escarpment and the coastline is a zone of the continental shelf, largely isolated from the plateau by the presence of a narrow erosional trough paralleling the base of the continental slope (see Shepard, 1973, p. 215).

South of the Blake Plateau lie the Bahama Banks, which are platforms of irregularly curved outlines and have internal structures and geologic histories similar to those of the Blake Plateau. They are usually included with the latter under the title of Blake-Bahama basin. West of the Bahama Banks lies the Florida peninsula, which is also designated as a "plateau" or "platform." It is separated from the Bahama Banks by a deep trough, the Straits of Florida. We can refer to all three units jointly as the Blake-Bahamas-Florida (BBF) plateau system.

The BBF units are classed as *carbonate platforms*. Figure 11.27 is a schematic E-W cross section of the Florida and Bahamas platforms (Paull and Newmann, 1987, p. 546). The platforms have been constructed by reef building corals thriving in very shallow water depths. Constraints on modeling this process have been listed by David Bice (1988): "The platform and basin system is assumed to be isolated from any significant source of terrigenous sediment" (p. 703). The top surface of the platform is the primary source of sediment both for the plateau (miogeocline) and sediment accumulating in the adjacent abyssal floor (eugeocline). The biochemical process of production of carbonate sediment is most efficiently carried out in warm, clear marine water receiving sufficient sunlight to sustain photosynthesis. This limits significant carbonate production to a water depth between 5 and 15 m. Thus the basin surface must remain shallow while subsidence accommodates the thickening sediment accumulation. This also means that the tectonic component of the subsidence must be remarkably constant across the entire platform width. Bice uses this assumption in modeling a synthetic basin system (p. 703). Obviously we are dealing with a sedimentation system far more complex than that of a geocline nourished only by terrigenous sediments supplied from an adjacent continental surface. If sea level should rise carbonate production could be sharply reduced, or even terminated, while on the other hand a substantial drop in sea level would bring the platform surface above sea level and turn it into an eroding surface supplying terrestrial sediment to an adjacent ocean floor. (Eustatic shifts of sea level have been incorporated into the histories of the platforms, a topic treated later in this chapter.) Given these scenarios as possibilities, it seems remarkable that carbonate platforms 10 km thick were formed in the 170 m.y. between Middle Jurassic and the present.

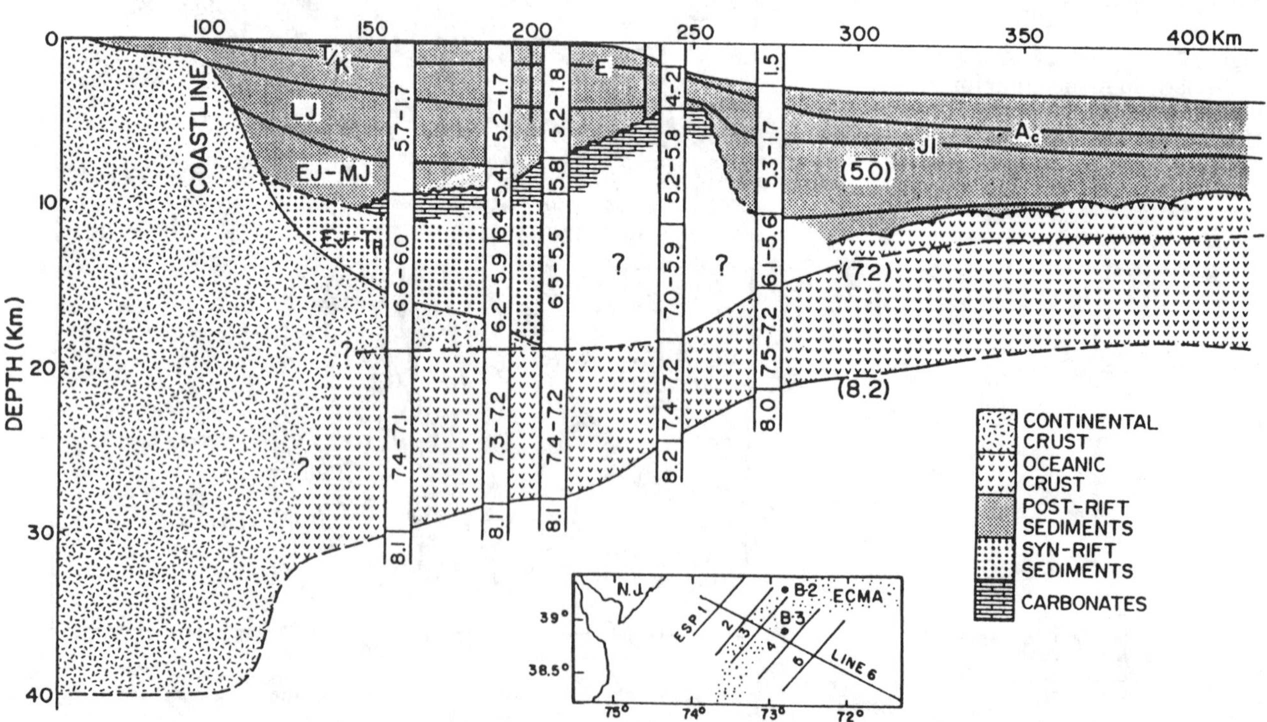

Figure 11.24 Diagrammatic cross section of the Baltimore Canyon basin of the North American passive continental margin, showing the deep seismic velocity structure. (From R.E. Sheridan, 1989, *Geology of North America*, Volume A, Chapter 6, p. 93, Figure 12. Reproduced with the permission of the publisher, the Geological Society of America, Boulder, Colorado, USA. Copyright 1989.)

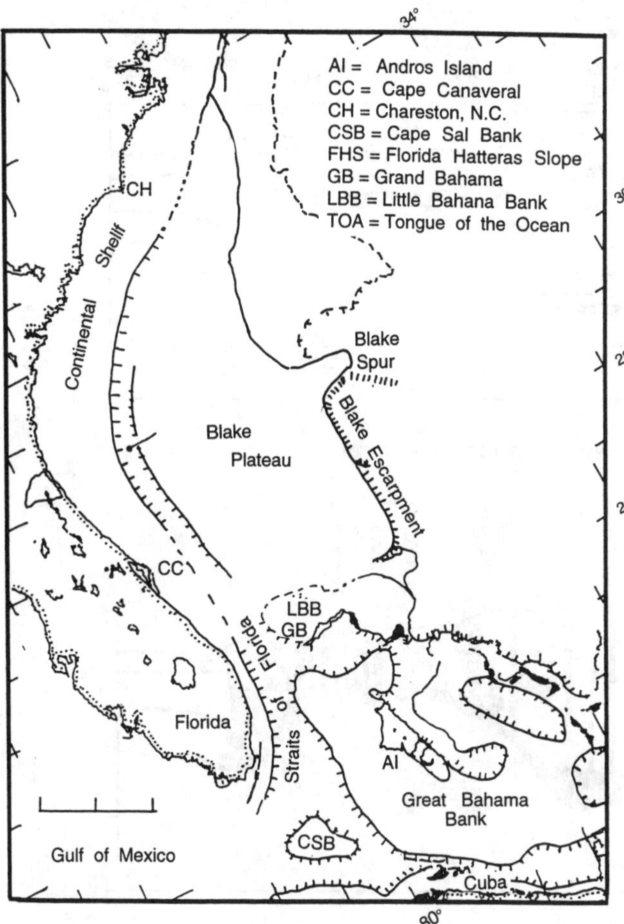

Figure 11.25 Sketch map of the Blake Plateau-Bahama Bank region of the Atlantic Ocean. (Based on data of NOAA, the AAPG, and other sources. Map copyright © by Arthur N. Strahler.)

11.10 Halotectonics of the Gulf Coast Geocline

Geoclines of passive continental margins, as depicted in Figure 11.19, show what appear to be conformable sediment layers free of any secondary structures, such as folds and faults, i.e., free of tectonic structures. We assume that thinning by gravitational compaction and water loss takes place in the geoclines, and that process is part of the normal diagenesis taking place in all sedimentary basins; it is not usually thought of as a tectonic process. However, the complete picture of a mature miogeocline will normally include both faulting and plastic deformation (folding, diapirism). Downwarping of the underlying lithosphere may trigger these processes, and for that reason a brief overview of this subject is appropriate.

Our regional subject will be the great miogeocline comprising the northern half of the Gulf of Mexico tectonic basin. (See Figures 11.17 and 11.18.) We begin with a review of the general stratigraphy of the miogeocline, using first a schematic cross section, Figure 11.28, shown devoid of secondary structures. The Gulf Coast miogeocline is thicker than the Atlantic geocline, with a maximum thickness of 15 km. Strata of Jurassic age—the Louann evaporites—form the basal member of this sediment wedge. Above are Cretaceous and Cenozoic strata. Each unit is in itself a basin-form. Each unit advances oceanward. On this framework is superimposed an entirely different system in which the basal evaporite formations demonstrate a remarkable vertical mobility. Figure 11.29, is a cross section with

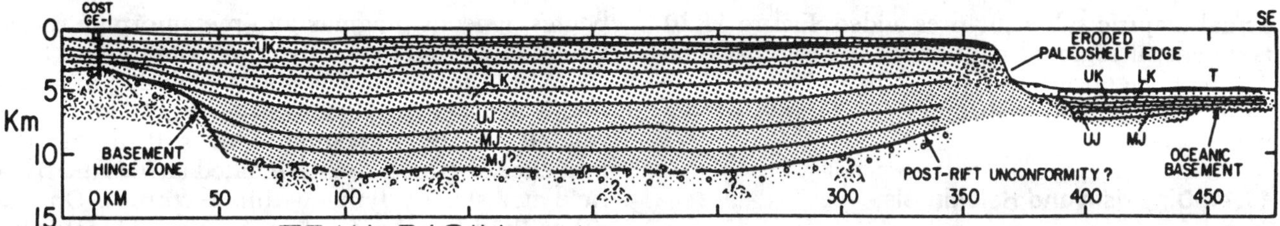

Figure 11.26 Cross section of the Blake Plateau based on deep seismic refraction profiles. (From R.E. Sheridan, 1989, *Geology of North America*, Volume A, Chapter 6, p. 84, Figure 4.Reproduced with the permission of the publisher, the Geological Society of America, Boulder, Colorado, USA. Copyright 1989.)

Figure 11.27 Schematic cross section of the Florida-Bahama carbonate platform. (From C.K. Paull and A.C. Neumann, 1987, *Geology*, v. 15, p. 564, Figure 2. Reproduced with the permission of the publisher, the Geological Society of America, Boulder, Colorado, USA. Copyright 1987.)

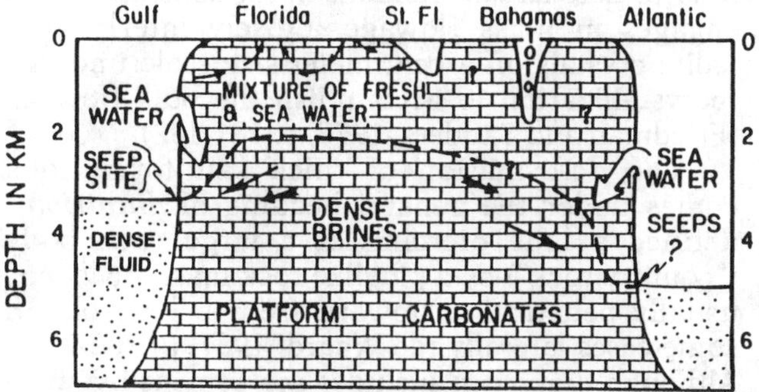

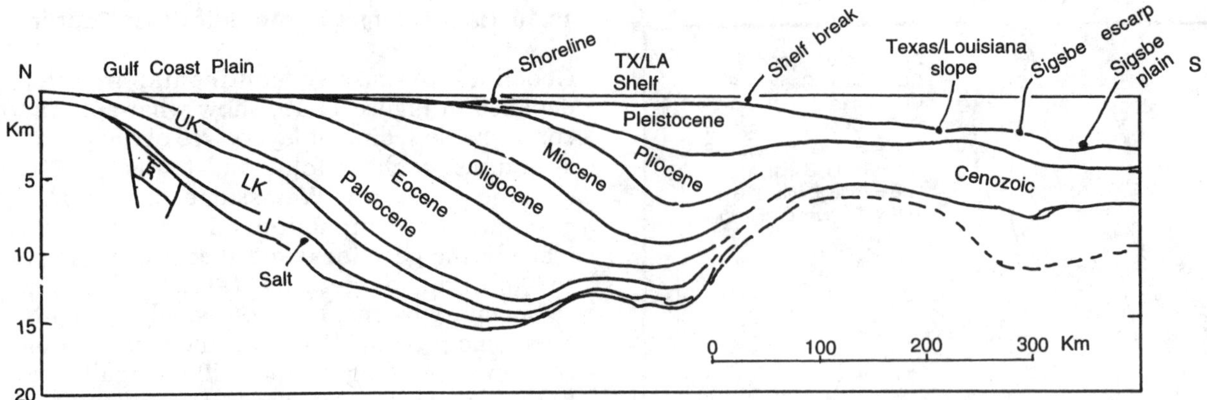

Figure 11.28 Cross section of the Gulf of Mexico geocline showing only the major stratigraphic units. (Based on data of R.G. Martin, 1978, and other sources.).

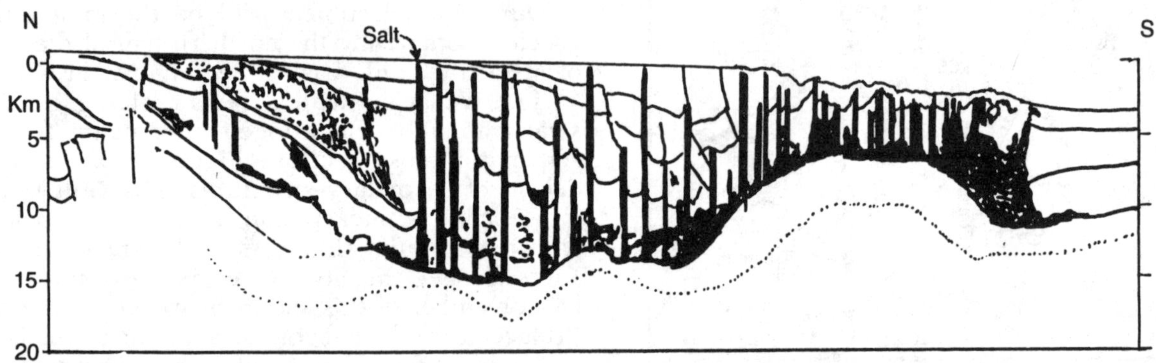

Figure 11.29 Cross section of the Gulf of Mexico geocline showing diagramatically the salt diapirs. (Based on data of R.G. Martin, 1978, as presented in D.M. Worall and S. Snelson, 1989, Chapter 7, p. 107, Figure 12, in, A.W. Bally and A.R. Palmer, 1987, *Geology of North America*, Vol. A, Reproduced with the permission of the publisher, the Geological Society of America, Boulder, Colorado, USA. Copyright 1989.)

actual diapiric salt structures added. Figure 11.30 is a general regional map of the area with which we shall be concerned. The profile in Figure 11.29 runs NW-SE, about through the middle of the map.

11.11 Diapirism and Halokinesis

The evaporites—especially *halite* (NaCl), and also gypsum ($CaSO_4{\cdot}2H_20$) and anhydrite ($CaSO_4$)—exhibit properties of bulk plastic deformation under much lower deforming stresses than most common crustal rocks. Halite rock, which we shall refer to here as *salt*, remains in the solid state as it engages in mass flowage. Closely interlocking halite crystals on a centimeter-size scale undergo recrystallization to accomplish the bulk flowage (Friedman and Sanders, 1978, p. 181-182).

The deformation of thick salt formations comes under the general heading of *diapirism*, defined as the piercing of a large rock body ("country rock") by a pluglike rock mass, or *diapir*, usually penetrating upward from below, but in some cases laterally (de Waard, 1987, p. 202-203). Although diapirism includes piercement by shale bodies, igneous magmas and metamorphic rocks, we are interested here only in *salt diapirism*.

Within the broad category of salt diapirism we find a new set of specialized terms. All processes related to the movements of salt under the influence of gravity are designated as *halokinesis*, a field not strictly lying within tectonics. On the other hand, forces of extensional tectonics (orogenic forces) may also affect the flowage of salt masses, and their activity can be distinguished as *halotectonics* (Trusheim, 1987, p. 324). Halokinesis is strictly a gravity phenomenon, based in the Archemides principle. Salt, with its low density of about 2 gm/cm^3 typically lies initially beneath sediments of greater density. Thus a supply of potential energy is present and the mass of lesser density will tend to rise to a position above all masses of higher density. Upward motion of the salt will not commence, however, unless there is sufficient load pressure to permit plastic deformation. For example, it is known that a salt layer thickness of 300 m reaches the plastic state when the overlying sedimentary cover reaches a thickness of 1,000 to 1,500 m (p. 324). Also required is a potential gradient, enabling the salt to

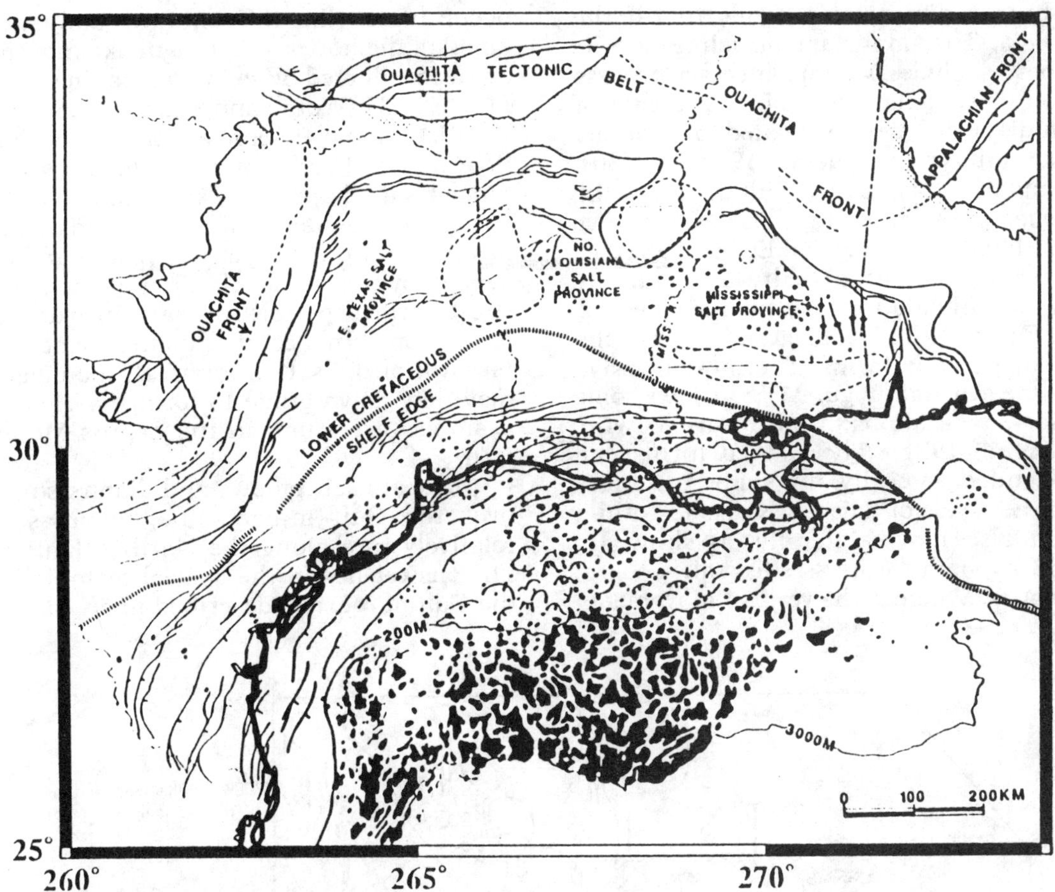

Figure 11.30 Tectonic map of the northwestern Gulf of Mexico. (Based on data of R.G. Martin, 1978, as presented in D.M. Worall and S. Snelson 1989, Chapter 7, p. 98, Figure 2, in A.W. Bally and A.R. Palmer, 1987, *Geology of North America*, Vol. A, Reproduced with the permission of the publisher, the Geological Society of America, Boulder, Colorado, USA. Copyright 1989.)

flow in the direction of least potential (p. 324). Local increase of the potential gradient can occur for a variety of reasons, including a tectonic event (e.g., slip on a fault). In gypsum, conversion to anhydrite and the accompanying volumetric reduction of 38% along with dewatering may increase the potential gradient and initiate flowage (p. 324).

Initiation of salt flow tends to be followed by a continuous and growing upward stream that is irreversible (Trusheim, p. 325). Figure 11.31 shows a set of schematic stages in upward movement of the salt. In Diagram A, a uniform salt layer is shown overlain by a shale layer and a carbonate layer. Diagram B shows a rising dome-like bulge of the salt formation, called a *salt pillow.* In Diagram C, the salt has breached the shale and carbonate layers and has begun to widen out into a "mushroom" form, which can now be identified as a diapir. Note that this upward extrusion of the salt has thinned the surrounding salt layer and required the shale and carbonate layers to subside. In this way a circular basin, called a *rim syncline*, is forming in the region surrounding the diapir. This subsidence then extends upwards to the

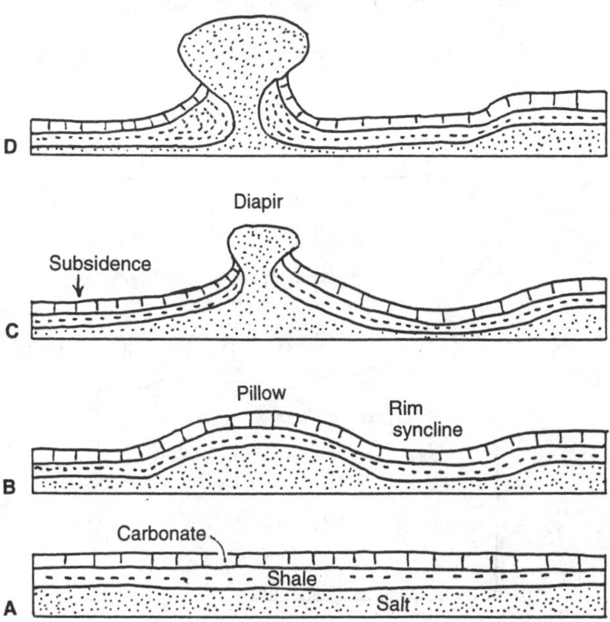

Figure 11.31 Schematic cross sections showing the rise of salt to form a pillow and a diapir. (Copyright © by Arthur N. Strahler.)

surface, where sedimentation tends to fill the depressed area. The important principle here is that halokinesis includes a complementary process of formation of sedimentary basins. The rate of rise of a salt diapir has been estimated to be on the order of 0.3 mm/yr (Trusheim, 1987, p. 330). Measurements of a sample of 20 salt domes of the Gulf of Mexico gave the average rise as 1 mm/yr over the past 11,000 y (Ewing and Ewing, 1962).

Thickness of the basal salt layer largely determines the ultimate form and massiveness of the diapirs. Figure 11.32 is a diagram showing the wide range of possible forms. The most massive structure is the salt wall. Figure 11.33 shows some further observed variations in salt forms (Lowrie, Yu, and Lerche, 1991). The stalked forms can become extended laterally, in some instances fusing with the heads of adjacent stalks to form a canopy. Salt also moves laterally, as shown in Figure 11.33 by such forms as sills, salt wedges, and salt tongues. Whereas the vertical movements occur under the influence of buoyancy (halokinetic), the horizontal, tonguelike movements are extrusions forced by sediment loading, as shown in Figure 11.34 (Worall and Snelson, 1989).

Diapirs may emerge at the land surface or sea floor. Figure 11.35 is an idealized cross section of a typical salt diapir (or "salt dome") of the Gulf coastal and deltaic plain. The rising salt column has lifted with it a layer of gypsum and anhydrite capped by limestone. Up-drag of the surrounding strata formed petroleum traps in truncated sand formations. In desert climates, where solution removal of the salt is minimal, the emerging salt may flow down grade to form *salt glaciers*. Good examples are found in the Zagros Mountains of Iran.

Why are salt pillows and diapirs so numerous over the Gulf miogeocline, whereas they are relatively rare along the North Atlantic margin? The answer lies in the special tectonic history of the Gulf of Mexico, described in an earlier section

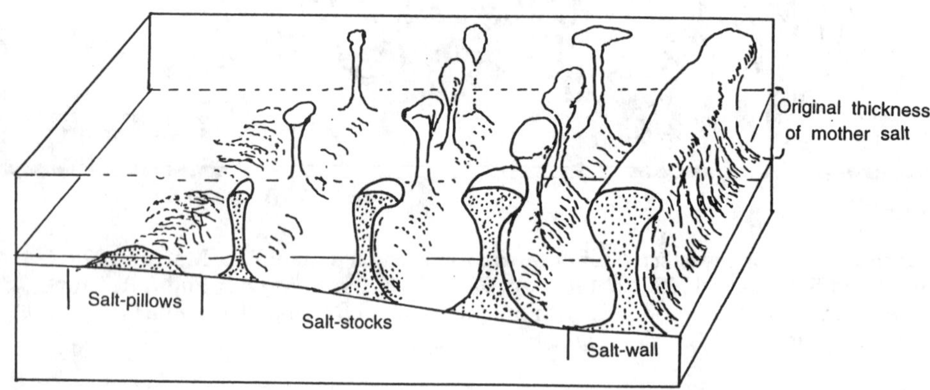

Figure 11.32 Schematic block diagram of a wide range of kinds of salt structures as related to original thickness of the salt layer. (From F. Trusheim, 1987, p. 328, Figure 4, in Seyfert, Ed., 1987, *Encyclopedia of Structural Geology and Plate Tectonics*. Copyright by Van Nostrand Reinhold Company, New York. Used by permission of the publisher.)

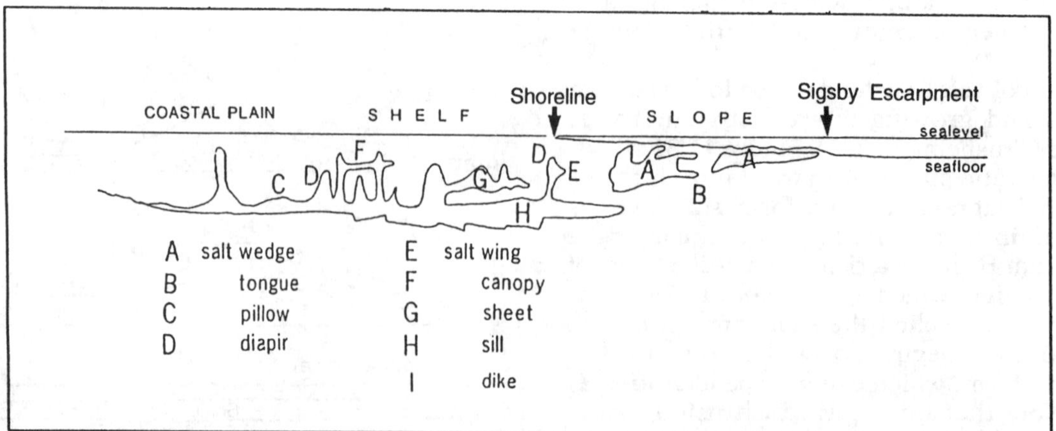

Figure 11.33 Schematic cross section showing various forms of salt structures typical of the Gulf of Mexico geocline. (From A. Lowrie, Z. Yu, and I. Lerche, 1991, *Transactions—Gulf Coast Assoc. of Geological Societies*, v. 41, p. 446, Figure 1. Used by permission the Gulf Coast Association of Geological Societies and the authors.)

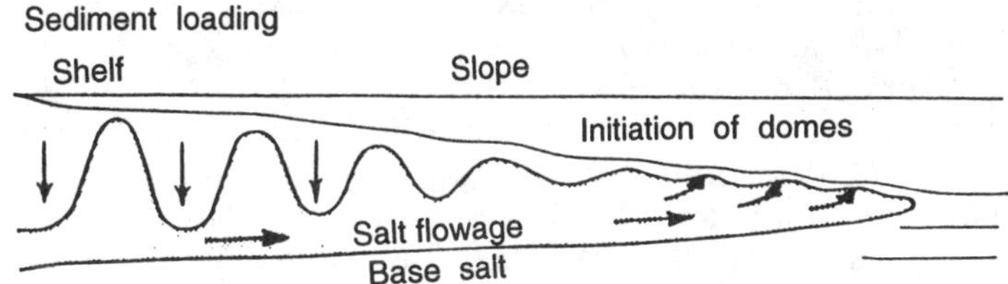

Figure 11.34 Diagrammatic cross section of the formation of salt diapirs and pillows during horizontal extrusion of salt caused by sediment loading.(From C.C. Humphris, Jr., 1979, *Bulletin of the American Association of Petroleum Geologists*, v. 63, p.782.)

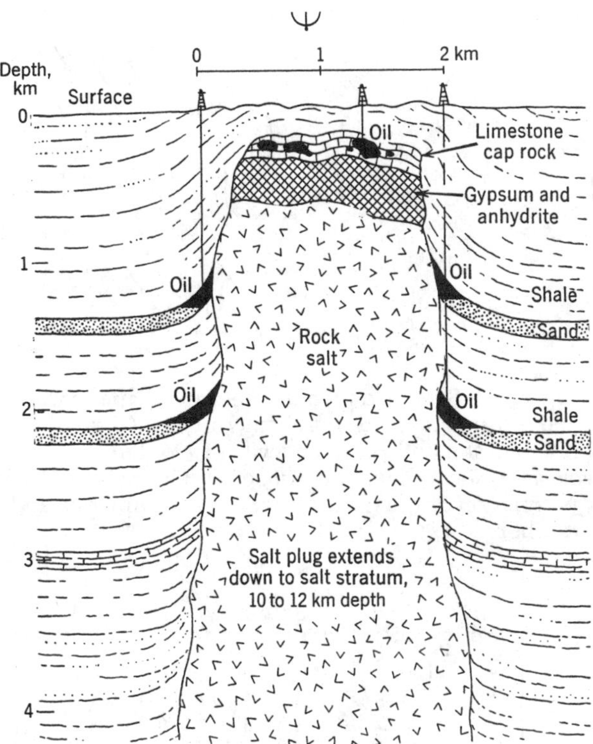

Figure 11.35 Idealized cross section of a salt dome of the Texas coastal plain. (Copyright © by Arthur N. Strahler.)

of this chapter. Coming into existence as a small new ocean basin with rather constricted oceanic passages open to the North Atlantic Ocean during Jurassic time, the Gulf served as an excellent evaporating basin.

The finding of normal faults in geoclines is a subject in tectonics deserving treatment independently of halokinetics. Large numbers of listric normal faults have been found in the Gulf miogeocline in strata ranging in ages from Cretaceous through Cenozoic. The main faults dip southward, and north-dipping antithetic faults may be present. Figure 11.36 is a schematic cross section, suggested by seismic refraction imagery, showing a normal-fault system typical of the Texas offshore zone. Over several decades, the fault systems were explained as localized gravity phenomena, quite similar to subaerial slumping that produces rotated slump blocks (Worall and Snelson, 1989, p. 106-109, 115-120). It was thought that this "slumping" could be set off by sediment loading and would continue to occur farther seaward as successively younger sediment wedges were deposited. The local-gravity hypothesis led to designation of the faulting process as *growth faulting*.

In Figure 11.36, a basal salt layer is shown to have been "flowing" down the grade of the ocean floor. This mass-flow activity has characterized the slope of the Louisiana sector of the Gulf, which receives great quantities of delta sediment. There, "regional seismic data show an enormous allochthonous mass of salt, in places as much as 8 km thick, which has been slowly but progressively overriding abyssal plain sediments since at least early Tertiary time, driven by sedimentation on the slope" (Worrall and Snelson, 1989, p. 132-133).

Careful scrutiny of accumulated seismic data has led to recent criticism of the applicability of the gravity mechanism of normal faulting. As an alternative hypothesis, salt diapirism in the Gulf is now being closely linked to regional crustal extension that has been part of the total scenario of opening of the ocean basin. Extensional tectonics has been an integral part of all openings of ocean basins, so we might expect to find a linkage between regional extension and "growth faulting" in many parts of the world ocean. M.P.A. Jackson and B.C. Vendeville of the University of Texas, Austin, surveyed 18 major salt-diapir regions and found evidence of recent thin-skinned extension in the form of numerous grabens and half grabens in the roof zones over the diapirs. "These fault structures weaken the overburden by fracturing and thinning it" (1994, p. 57). They also

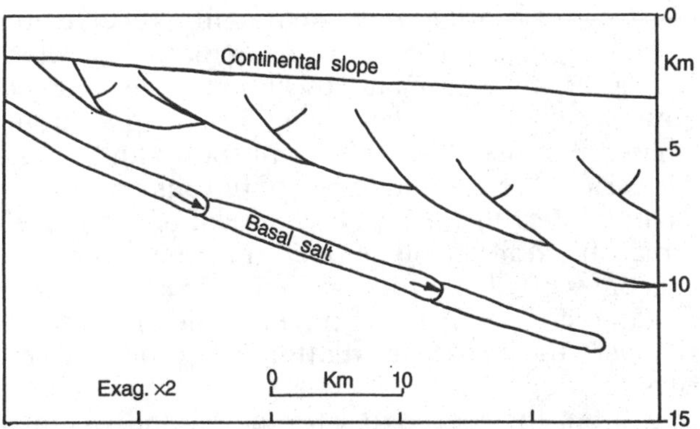

Figure 11.36 Schematic cross section of growth faults beneath the continental slope. (Copyright © by Arthur N. Strahler.)

found that where regional extension ceases, the diapirs beneath stop rising.

A specific example of the above tectonic relationship is found in the Levant Basin of the eastern Mediterranean Sea. Here normal faults have been mapped on the lower continental slope off northern Israel (Figure 11.37). Salt ridges up to 100 km in length, either exposed at the surface or buried under shallow sediment cover, show a remarkably close correlation with the normal fault traces. One might, however, raise the following question: The wide range in azimuths of the fault traces seems unlikely under uniform regional crustal extension. Instead, the faults appear to have been set in motion by growth of the diapiric walls that form over a wide range in azimuth. A second example, shown in Figure 11.38, is from the floor of the Red Sea just south of the Sinai Peninsula. Diapiric salt walls lie on or close to numerous normal faults arranged in a subparallel pattern. In this young ocean basin, extensional tectonics is strongly in control. If the observed relationship of salt tectonics to regional crustal extension proves to be a widespread phenomenon, a strong link between halokinesis and halotectonics will have been forged.

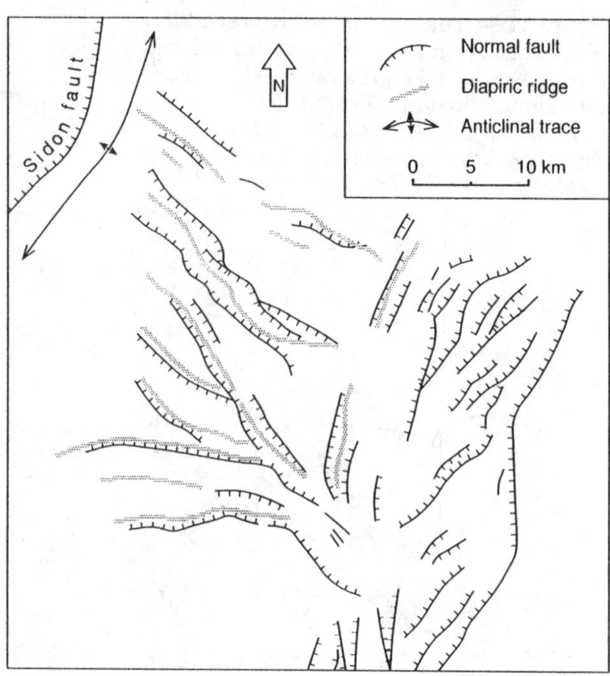

Figure 11.37 Sketched map of faults and diaperic walls on the continental slope off northern Israel.(From M.P.A. Jackson and B.C. Vendeville, 1994, *Bull., Geological Soc. of Amer.*, v. 106, p. 61, Figure 3(b). Used by permission of the Geological Society of America and the authors.)

11.12 Petroleum Accumulations in Sedimentary Basins

Plate tectonics has made a major impact upon the search for new petroleum accumulations. Today, the search extends into all of the varieties of sedimentary basins. Geologists have long been aware that the organic matter required for petroleum to be formed has accumulated in thick lacustrine and marine sediments of the continental margins. Large delta deposits of major rivers are particularly favorable for the incorporation of organic matter into the sediment. For each basin type a sediment source, whether terrestrial or marine, or both, can be identified.

A two-stage process leads to the final formation of rock reservoirs serving as petroleum accumulations of commercial value (Selley, 1985, p. 168-218; Jacobson, 1991, p. 3-5). First, petroleum *source rock* sediments receive and incorporate sedimentary organic matter, of which *kerogen* is the dominant constituent. The source of this kerogen may be algal bodies, planktonic material of marine origin, plant spores and pollen, or various fragmental forms of fibrous and woody plants (Merrill, 1992, p. *xvi*). Burial of a relatively small fraction of this organic sediment eventually becomes available for conversion into petroleum. Heat and the passage of time are then required to convert the immature matter into crude oil and gas.

From the source rock, crude oil and gas must migrate into other rocks, where they accumulate as reservoirs from which extraction is possible and profitable. Migration of oil and gas is a two-step

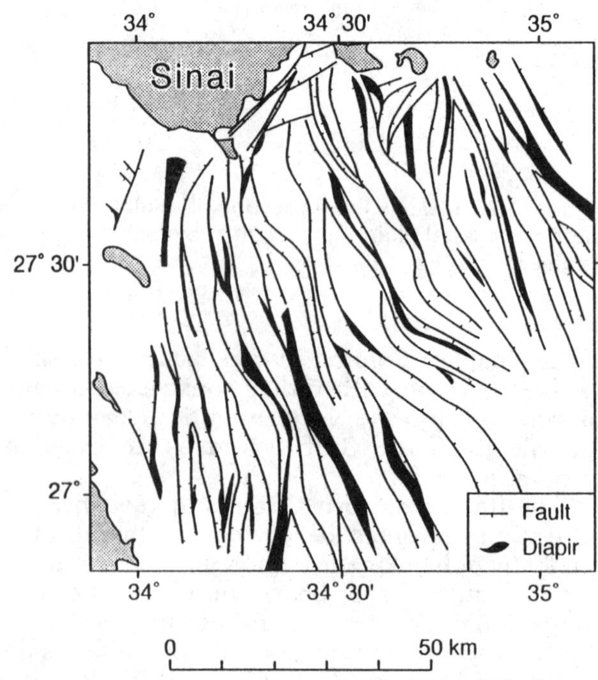

Figure 11.38 Map of a portion of the northern Red Sea showing diapiric salt walls paralleling or coinciding with normal faults of grabens and half-grabens. (From M.P.A. Jackson and B.C. Vendeville, 1994, *Bull., Geological Soc. of Amer.*, v. 106, p. 60, Figure 2. Reproduced with the permission of the publisher, the Geological Society of America, Boulder, Colorado, USA. Copyright 1994.)

process (Palciauskas, 1992, p. 13-22). Primary migration involves the expulsion of the oil and gas from low-permeability source rock so as to enter rock of relatively high permeability. This expulsion mechanism is not well understood. It has been suggested that hydrocarbon diffusion occurs through water that saturates the pore spaces, but this process is not considered adequate, since the enclosing rock is usually shale. Instead, a hypothesis of pressure-driven flow is proposed in which a certain phase of hydrocarbons moves through the shale. Another hypothesis invokes the pressure generation of a network of micro-fractures, allowing the oil and gas to move through the shale to reach permeable formations. Secondary migration through the permeable formations is an upward water-buoyant movement. The final step is the accumulation of the oil and gas in a trap where further upward movement is prevented by an impermeable barrier.

An example of how plate tectonics may facilitate the process of conversion of organic matter into petroleum can be seen in the evolution of passive continental margins. The organic matter is first accumulated in the synrift fault basins, and these are then covered by thick geoclines. Thus the accumulations of organic matter are buried to increasingly greater depths and subjected to higher temperatures, "cooking" the organic matter and converting it to petroleum. That which is buried to the greater depth becomes natural gas. A similar scenario may be applied to the other basin types.

The natural vertical motions of fluids in thick bodies of sediments and their accompanying biochemical changes, as briefly described above, are probably insignificant as agents of deformation of the crust on a scale that would be recognized as "plate tectonics."

11.13 A Paleozoic Aulacogen in North America

We turn now to another kind of basin produced by continental rifting, Subclass I-A (Table 11.1). Referring back to Chapter 10 on the subject of the initial rifting that sets off plate separation, we note that in Figures 10.2 and 10.3 the connected rift system makes use of only two of the three radial fractures formed at each dome. The third fracture is not used, but simply extends back into the continental plate for some distance. This unused fracture is called the *failed arm* of the triple rift junction. As the opposing plates recede, the failed arm becomes the site of a downdropped crustal block that may be either a graben with two boundary faults, or a downtilted fault block with a major normal fault on only one side (i.e., a half-graben). In either case, it forms a trenchlike feature that leads from the new coastline of the continent into the continental interior, thus making the failed arm a natural site for a major river, as shown in Figure 10.3B.

The river mouth occupies a V-shaped indentation in the plan of the coastline where the sediment carried by the river accumulates in a delta. Sediment also accumulates in the floor of the failed arm, and continued downsinking of the floor of the failed arm allows more and more sediments to accumulate until they may reach a total thickness of several kilometers. This deposit has been given the name *aulacogen*; it was recognized as a special form of sedimentary basin of the continental crust as early as the early 1940s. The name had been coined from Greek words that mean "born of furrows," but the origin of the "furrow," or trough, was not understood at that time in the framework of plate tectonics. Instead, the rift was considered to form at right angles to a geosyncline that lay along a continental margin, or to an orogen that had been formed from such a geosyncline (Segnör, 1987, p. 18).

A good example of an aulacogen of Paleozoic age that conforms to the above model—projecting from a Paleozoic fold belt into the adjacent craton—had been identified long before plate tectonics came on the scene. It lies in western Oklahoma, almost due west of Oklahoma City and directly beneath the city of Sayre. Geologists call this aulacogen the Anadarko basin. There is almost nothing to show for it in the landscape, but wells drilled here prove the presence of Paleozoic sediments nearly 10 km thick in a narrow, one-sided fault basin, or half-graben. A map and cross section of the Anadarko basin are shown in Figure 11.39. The sedimentary basin is bounded on the southwest side by an ancient fault cutting the Precambrian shield rocks, which appear at the surface to the southwest in the Wichita Mountains. The fault basin seems to orginate about at the inner limit of the Ouachita Mountains, which are part of the Appalachian fold system, completed in the final Paleozoic orogeny in Permian time. But while this relationship satisfied the older concept of an aulacogen, much of the deposition of the Anadarko basin sediments had already occurred long before the Ouachita folds were produced. We must go back into late Precambrian time, when the continental rifting apart of ancestral North America took place to form the Iapetus Ocean and the Appalachian-Hercynian ocean. It was then that rifting produced the failed arm in which Paleozoic sediments of this aulacogen began to accumulate.

The above scenario is illustrated schematically in Figure 11.40. Following the formation of a triple rift over a possible mantle plume and hot spot in late Precambrian time (Diagram A), the Appalachian-Hercynian ocean opened fully. (See Chapter 13.) In early Paleozoic time (Diagram B), marine strata of Cambrian, Ordovician and Silurian ages were deposited in the Anadarko basin, which was then an arm of the ocean. In Carboniferous (early Pennsylvanian) time (330 Ma), as the ocean basin was closing, a massive tectonic uplift—a compressional orogen—formed across the mouth of the aulacogen. Streams eroding the uplift brought great quantities of coarse clastic sediment (molasse) into the

Figure 11.39 Map and cross section of the Anadarko basin. (A) Map contours show depth to the Precambrian basement. (B) Vertical exaggeration is about ×10. (Based on data of P.B. King and others, *Tectonic Map of the United States*, Amer. Assoc. of Petroleum Geologists. Used by permission.)

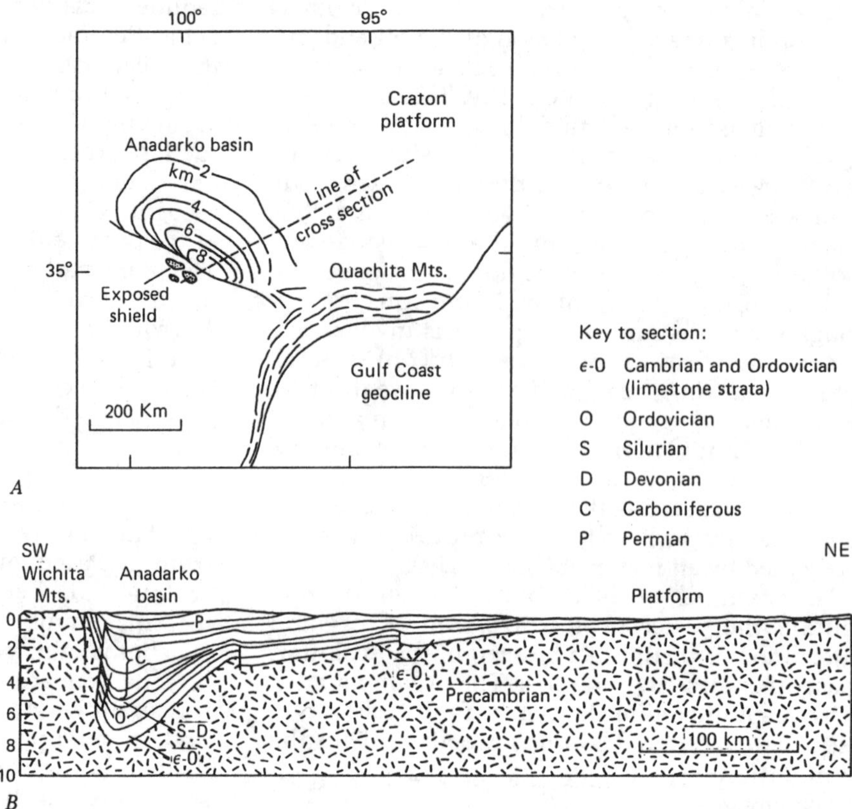

Figure 11.40 Hypothetical stages in the evolution of the Anadarko basin as an aulacogen. (Copyright © by Arthur N. Strahler.)

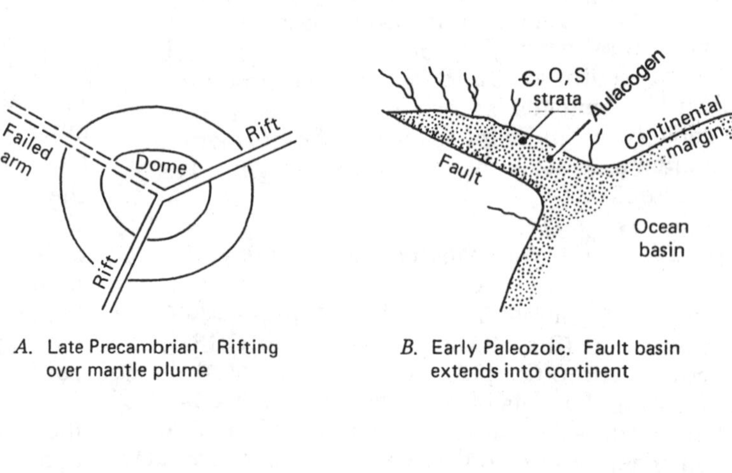

A. Late Precambrian. Rifting over mantle plume

B. Early Paleozoic. Fault basin extends into continent

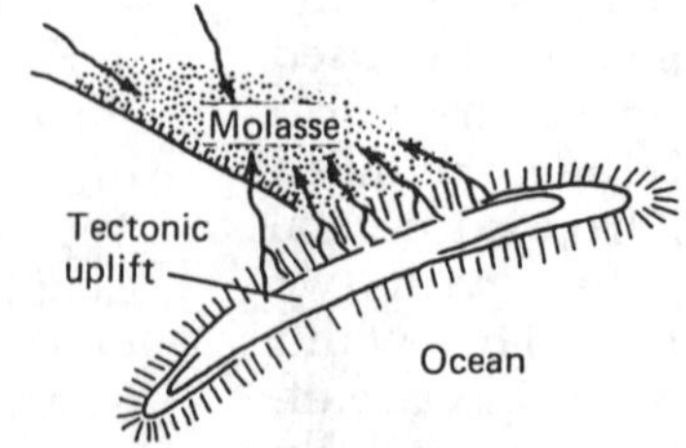

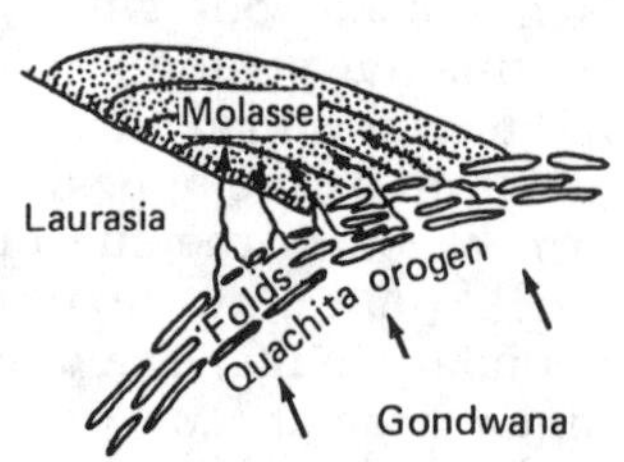

C. Early Pennsylvanian. Tectonic uplift of continental margin

D. Late Pennsylvanian. Continental collision forms Quachita orogen

Anadarko basin. About 7 km of conglomeratic strata accumulated during this period, (Diagram C). Then, in late Pennsylvanian time, the final continent-continent collision occurred, forming a belt of Appalachian-type foreland folds that are today the Ouachita Mountains (Diagram D). Molasse from this orogen poured into the aulacogen, and as it accumulated, the floor of the aulacogen subsided.

Figure 11.41 shows five model stages in the evolution of an aulacogen (Ingersoll, 1989, p. 1708-1709). It makes use of a symmetrical basin (Hoffman, Dewey, and Burke, 1974). Stage A: One of three rift arms that are equally developed by mantle upwelling is a failed rift. Stage B: Grabens of the failed arm fill with alluvium. Stage C: Downwarping stage in which mantle cooling causes subsidence, inunduating the grabens and initiating marine deposition. Stage D: Marine strata fill the subsiding basin. Stage E: As a compressional orogen impinges on the continental margin, a medial fault block drops down into the mantle. Evidently, the mechanisms acting here are of two kinds, one following the other. In stages A through C, thermal expansion of the mantle is followed by thermal contraction. In stages D and E, loading caused by the advancing orogen down-flexes the lithosphere and at the same time the indenting continental mass applies longitudinal compression along the axis of the aulacogen. In some ways, this final stage resembles that of the Lower Rhine Graben, described in Chapter 10 (see Figure 10.27.) There, the arcuate Jura foreland fold pushed northward and exerted compression upon the European Hercynide crustal block (see Figures 9.41 and 9.42). Perhaps what we are seeing there and in the Anadarko basin is the final stage in the formation of an impactogen! (Segnör, 1987, p. 24).

Hypotheses of initiation of aulacogens rest heavily on the more basic scenarios of triple junction formation during continental rifting that leads directly to the widening of a new ocean basin. This subject was covered in Chapter 10, where the aulacogen was introduced briefly. There, we reviewed two independent hypotheses of initiation of such rifting: (1) rise of mantle plumes and (2) bolide (asteroid) impacts. Development of the mantle-plume hypothesis in the 1970s is credited in large part to Kevin Burke and John F. Dewey, who recognized the need for a failed arm that develops into an aulacogen (Burke and Dewey, 1973; Dewey and Burke, 1974). The impact hypothesis was strongly supported by geologists Carl K. Seyfert of the State University of Buffalo and Leslie A. Sirkin of Adelphi University (Seyfert and Sirkin, 1979, p. 96-97, 383-389; Seyfert, 1987b, p. 415-420). Whatever may be the merits and deficits of the two hypotheses, their importance is to some extent muted, because a bolide impact is postulated to have initiated a plume-like rise of hot mantle.

What is more relevant here is to note the general agreement that chains of triple junctions

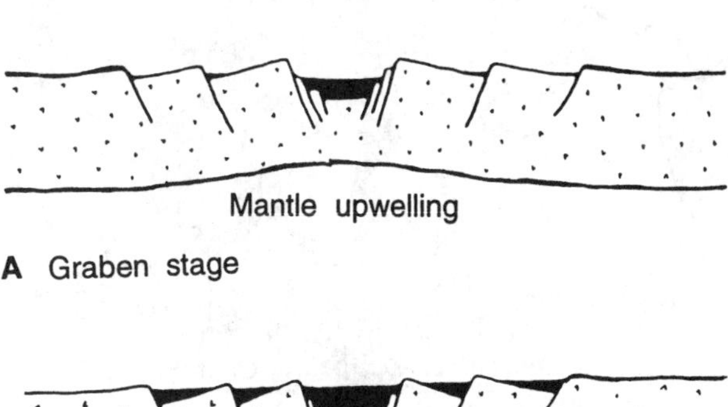

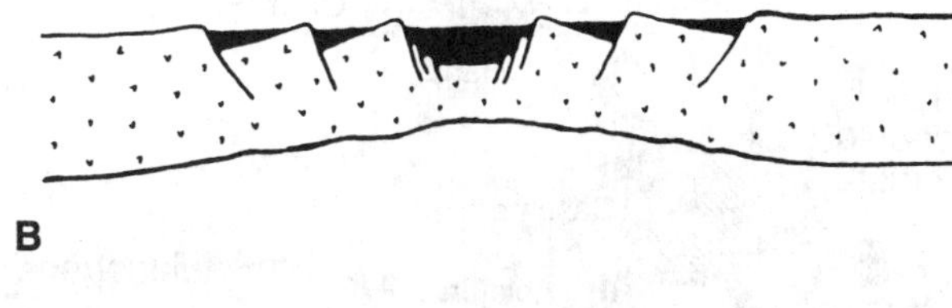

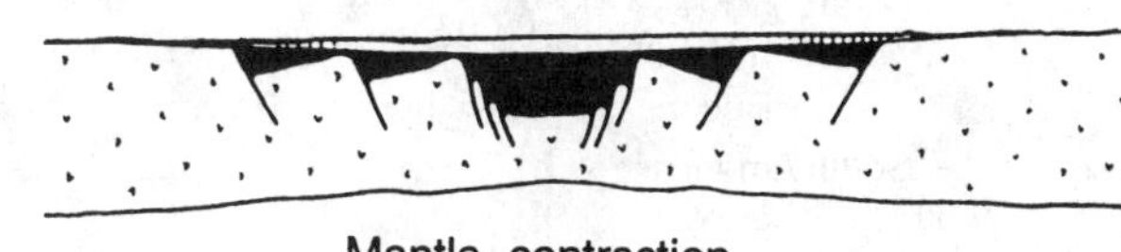

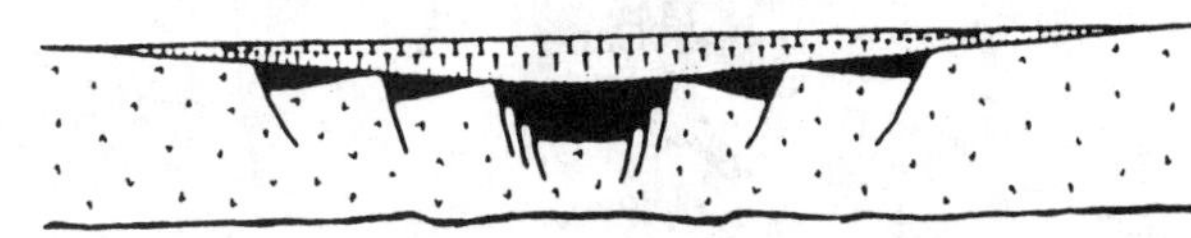

Medial block founders

E Compressional stage

Figure 11.41 Five model stages in the evolution of an aulacogen. (From P. Hoffman, J.F. Dewey, and K. Burke, 1974, *Soc. of Economic Paleontologists and Mineralogists*, Special Publication 19. Reproduced by permission.)

appeared on a global scale during at least two major episodes of continental breakup. One was the late Proterozoic rifting, mentioned above and exemplified in the Anadarko basin; the other was the breakup of Pangaea that began in the Late Triassic. These events are summarized in Chapter 13. Figure 11.42 shows the locations of a number of aulacogens thought to have developed during the Late Triassic opening of the South and North Atlantic oceans.

In summarizing his 1987 article on aulacogens, A.M. Celal Segnör pointed out that their reactivation over long spans of time is typical and "may be ascribed to the observation [made by J.

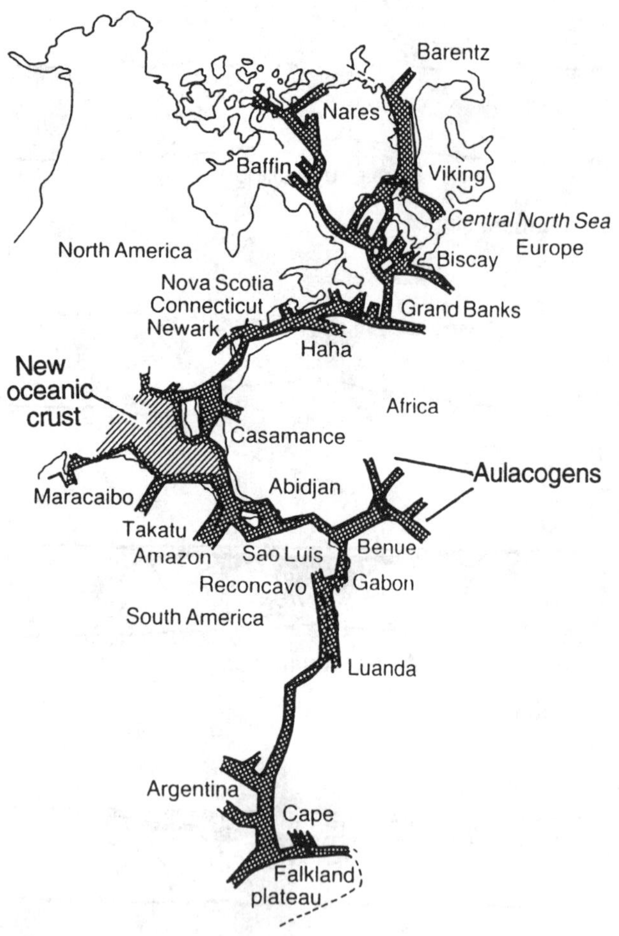

Figure 11.42 Generalized map of an early breakup stage of Pangaea showing aulacogens and other new rift basins. (From Kevin Burke, 1977, *Tectonophysics*, v. 36, as adapted by P. Kearey and F.J. Vine, 1990, in *Global Tectonics*, p. 140, Figure 7.30, Blackwell Scientific Publications, Oxford, UK. Used by permission of the publishers.)

Tuzo Wilson in 1966] that oceans tend to open and close roughly along the same places and that the marginal structures such as aulacogens may serve to nucleate new ones as well" (p. 24).

11.14 Wrench Faults and Pull-Apart Basins

Our fourth and last rift-basin type under the subclass I-A, Continental rift systems, is the pull-apart basin, formed by certain patterns of deep crustal displacement along strike-slip (transcurrent) faults. In the section heading above, we substituted *wrench fault* for "strike-slip fault." There is a special motive in our selection of the term, explained by geologist Arthur G. Sylvester of the University of California, Santa Barbara:

> "Wrench fault" pervades the literature of petroleum geology, perhaps because of the prominence gained from the 1953 paper by J.D. Moody and M.J. Hill entitled "Wrench Fault Tectonics," as well as its usage in a subsequent series of important papers in the American Association of Petroleum Geologists *Bulletin* by T.P. Harding and his associates in the 1970s. (Sylvester, 1984, p. v.)

Keeping this choice of usage in mind, we return to the use of "strike-slip fault," used in other chapters of this book.

The recognition of major strike-slip faults came about comparatively recently. Since the dawn of tectonic geology in the late 1800s, emphasis had been on compressional tectonics involving overturned folds and overthrust faults in typical alpine structure (see Chapters 2 and 9). The concept of normal faults being involved in the formation of grabens and horsts was also established at an early date. It was not until the 1940s and 50s, however, that great strike-slip faults were identified in Scotland (Great Glen fault), California (San Andreas fault), New Zealand (Alpine fault), and the Near East (Dead Sea fault). The idea that horizontal offsets of the magnitude of hundreds of kilometers had occurred along these faults was not easily swallowed, but it was thoroughly demonstrated in 1953 for the California region by two American geologists—Mason Hill and Thomas Dibblee—and backed up in 1962 by John Crowell (Sylvester, 1984, p. v).

In presenting these great strike-slip faults as interplate transforms (Chapter 7) we made no mention of the possibility that strike-slip faults could also produce alternating uplifts (horsts) and basins (grabens). Since the time of the early geological surveys of the arid western United States, block mountains and their adjacent sedimentary basins were simply interpreted as products of normal faulting. We may have promoted this concept in Chapter 10 in presenting the modern interpretation of the Basin and Range province as simple extensional phenomena and by mentioning oblique strike-slip faults as contributing to that extension.

What seems to have long eluded geologists was the idea that a single isolated block mountain (a "horst") in proximity to a single isolated sedimentary basin (a "graben") might be the products of vertical components of earth motion on closely adjacent segments of strike-slip faults. Just how these "up" and "down" motions are generated will be explained as we describe a series of relationships in which two strike-slip fault segments are found in a "side-by-side" geometrical relationship.

Figure 11.43 shows three relationships between crustal blocks separated by a single, continuous strike slip fault (Crowell, 1974, p. 198). Diagram A is the typical illustration of a perfectly straight right-slip (dextral) strike-slip fault crossing a land surface that is a perfect horizontal plane (see Chapter 6 and Figure 6.15). Under these circumstances, slip motion produces no vertical deformation hence no lift or sinking of the land

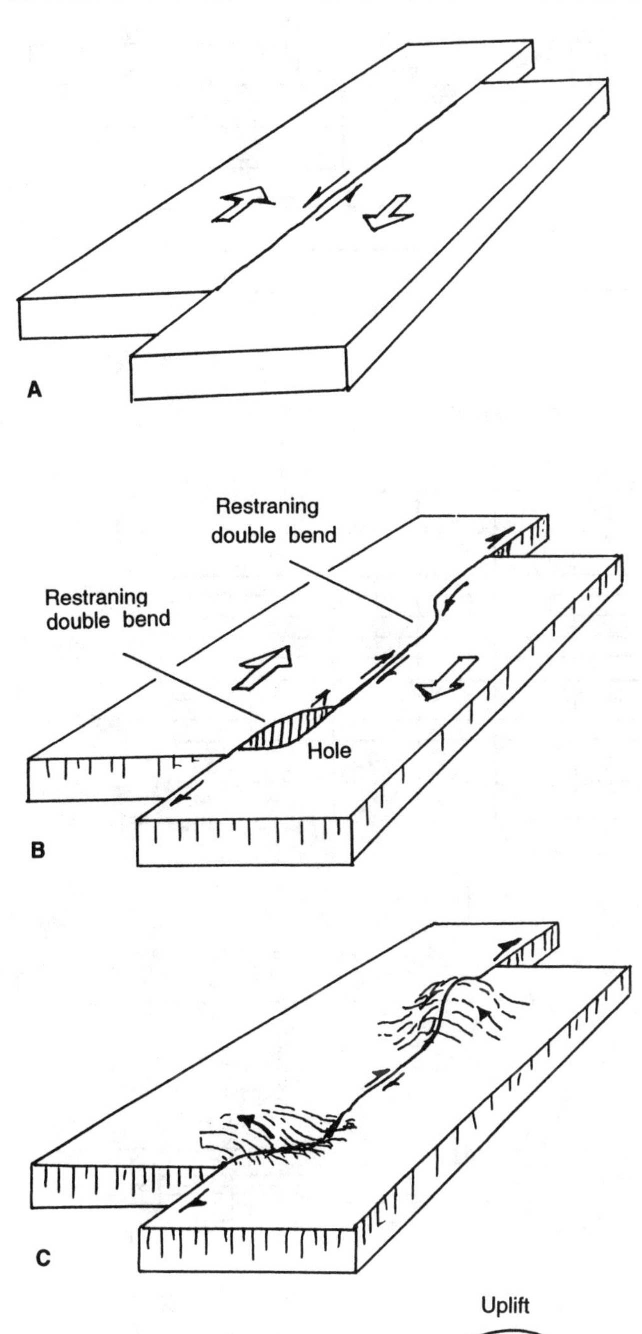

Figure 11.43 Stylized block diagrams showing the relationship of basins and uplifts to bends in a single strike-slip fault. (Copyright © by Arthur N. Strahler. Based in part on similar diagrams by John C. Crowell, 1974, Figures 2, 3, and 4, in W.R. Dickinson, Ed., *Soc. of Economic Paleontologists and Mineralogists*, Special Paper 22.)

surface. (Existing topographic features, when offset by the fault, do produce minor closed depressions and isolated hills, but these are not taken into account here.)

Diagram B shows a strike-slip fault in which the strike undergoes a gentle "double bend," veering first to the right, then to the left. (The block is assumed to be rigid in its behavior under stress, and not capable of distributed plastic flowage. Instead, it may rupture by discrete fractures.) In the bend closest to the front of the block, a tensional fracture can readily occur and the two surfaces of the fault will undergo separation, leaving a curious "cavity" with sheer walls. Accordingly, this class of double bend is called a *releasing double bend*. In the distant double bend (turning first to the left, then to the right) the original straight alignment of the fault is resumed. Obviously, horizontal forward motion is solidly blocked, and if motion is to occur the crust must yield by brittle deformation, breaking into angular blocks that are forced upward and outward, and perhaps creating a sort of "pile" or hill over the fault trace. Something must be wrong with our model and it needs correction.

Diagram C of Figure 11.43 introduces a new factor into the tectonic response. The crust is now assumed to be readily deformable and capable of being stretched or thickened in a manner depending on how the stresses are applied. This behavior can be stated in more formal terms of structural geology. Instead of applying the deformational mode of *simple shear* (as in a deck of cards) used in Diagram B, we have now substituted *pure shear*, in which distributed shortening on one axis is accompanied by elongation on the other.

Figure 11.44 compares simple shear and pure shear. In both modes, volume is held constant, so in these two-dimensional diagrams, area of cross section area is held constant. Pure shear is also known as *homogeneous flattening*. For example, you take a sphere of modeling clay and compress it between two parallel boards, converting it into a pancake form. Figure 11.45 shows how the homogeneous flattening diagram can be superimposed on a plan view of the double bend to achieve the correct results.

Returning to Figure 11.43, Diagram C, shows the tectonic effect of applying the pure shear model. At the releasing double bend the crust is stretched transversely over the fault zone and must subside to form a depression. Thus we have a tectonic basin with little or no formation of a gaping cavity or open pit. At the restraining bend, lateral compression causes the excess crust to be expelled upward and the land surface to be elevated. When this two-fold deformation program is continued over a long period of time, a deep sediment-filled basin develops, while in the region of elevation, uplift may be countered by fluvial erosion and only low a group of low hills appears. Sediment thus released may be fed into the basin. If, however, the uplifted bedrock mass is highly resistant to fluvial erosion, a mountain of substantial proportions can be sustained.

Continuing the description of various forms of basins related to strike-slip faults, we consider the case where the main fault appears as if completely

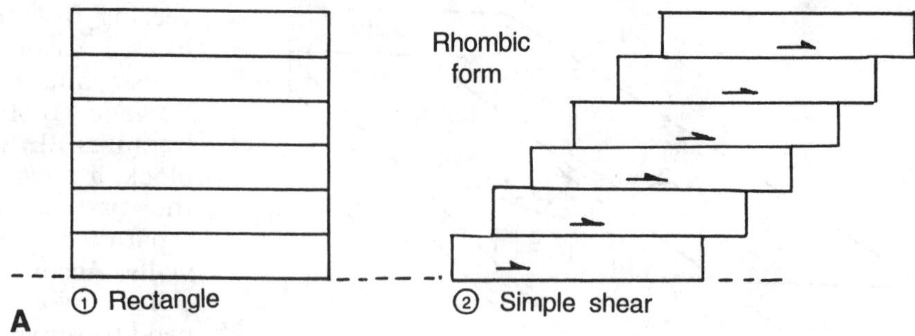

Figure 11.44 Schematic diagrams of the principles of simple shear and pure shear. (Copyright © by Arthur N. Strahler.)

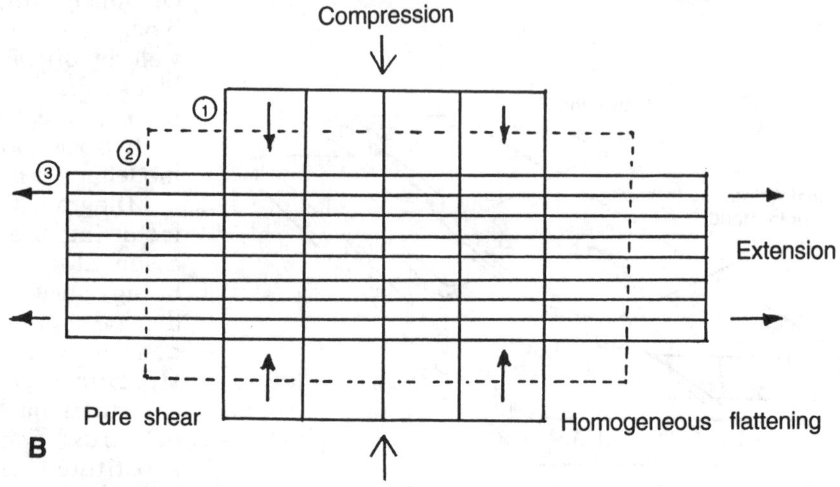

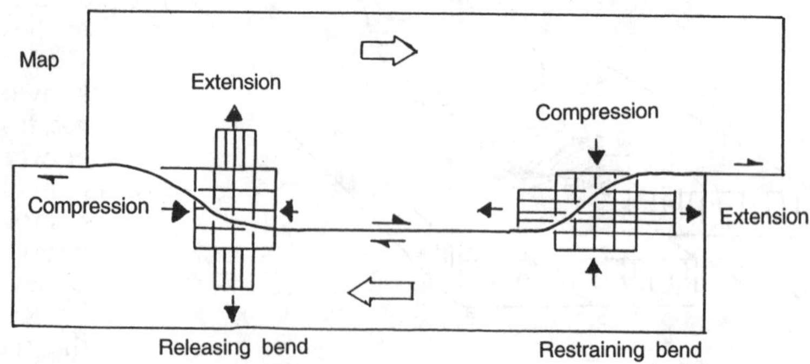

Figure 11.45 Schematic plan of pure shear superimposed on bends in a strike-slip fault. (Copyright © by Arthur N. Strahler.)

severed and the two free ends are substantially offset, as shown in Figure 11.46. The adjective *en echelon* is used to describe offsetting and overlapping of the two fault segments. This configuration is also called a *stepover*. Two modes of stepover are possible for an offset right-lateral (dextral) strike-slip fault: The *left-stepping* mode is shown in Map A; the *right-stepping* mode, in Map B (Rodgers, 1980, p. 346).

The offset may be imagined to have occurred rather suddenly as a jump, leaving the abandoned section of fault inoperative. Relative motion between the two continental plates must nevertheless continue, so a tensional stress would immediately be exerted in the intervening zone between the two ends, and this would need to be relieved by crustal deformation. Uncoupling of the crust from the mantle would probably take place at a depth of about 20 km.

Figure 11.47, Map A, shows the initiation of a tensional rift between the offset ends of the fault. Map B shows a full-fledged right-stepping *pull-apart basin*. As seen in the cross section in Figure 11.47, sediment from surrounding highland surfaces would have kept the basin filled as it lengthened. Mafic magma would perhaps have emerged through the basin floor, solidifying as sills and dikes. Figure 11.48 is an idealized block diagram of the pull-apart basin.

Note that our description of a pull-apart basin closely resembles that of the basins on the floor of the Gulf of California, described in Chapter 10 and shown in Figure 10.62. The Gulf basins are floored in large part by new oceanic crust. Intermediate in

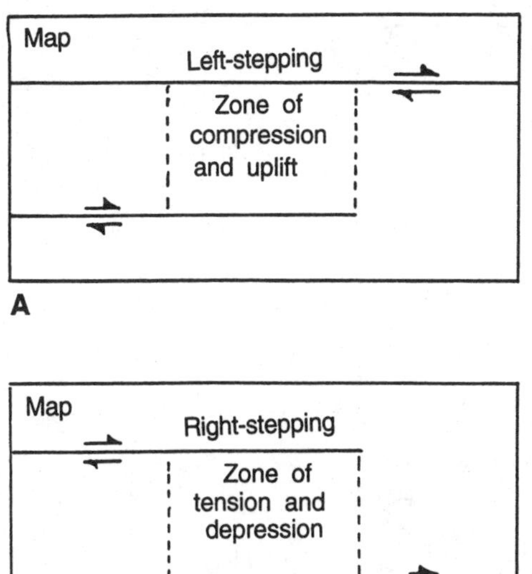

Figure 11.46 Schematic plan of *en echelon* left-stepping and right-stepping strike-slip faults. (Adapted from Donald A. Rodgers, 1980; page 346 in Sylvester, Ed., 1984.Copyright © by

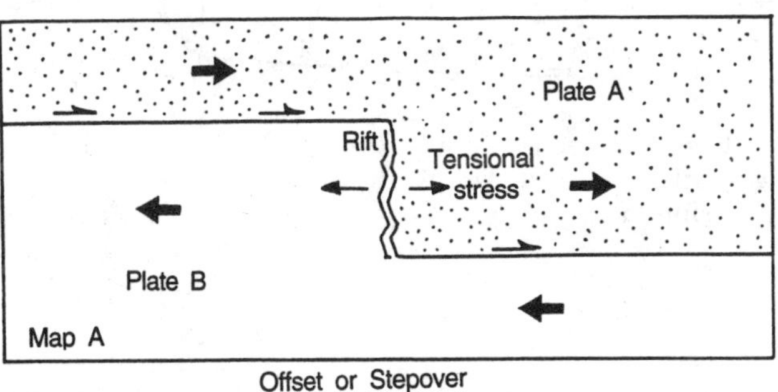

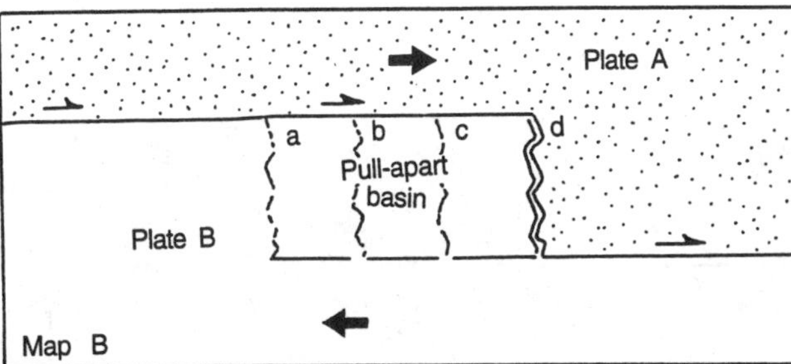

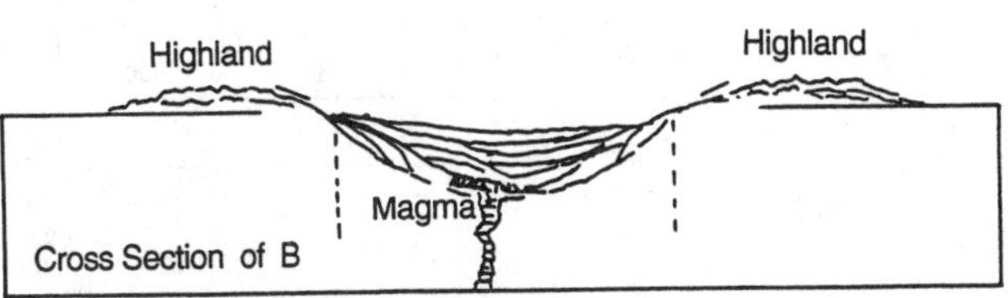

Figure 11.47 Schematic map and cross section of formation of a pull-apart basin. (Adapted from John C. Crowell, 1974, Figure 8, in W.R. Dickinson, Ed., *Soc. of Economic Paleontologists and Mineralogists*, Special Paper 22.)

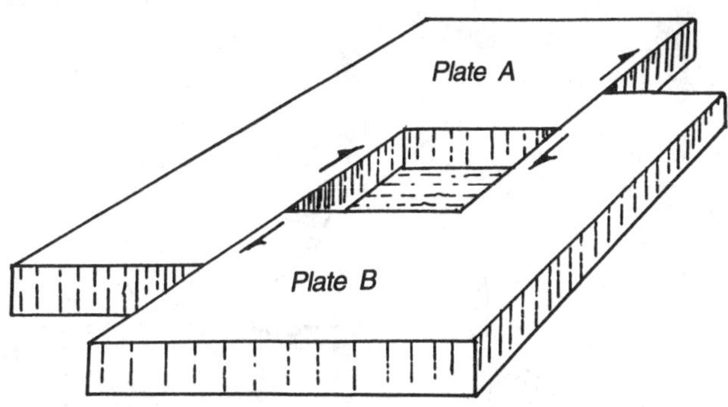

Figure 14.48 Schematic block diagram of a simple pull-apart basin. (Copyright © by Arthur N. Strahler.)

position as a link between the Gulf of California and the San Andreas fault is the Salton basin (see Chapter 6 and Figures 6.35, 6.36). Figure 11.49 is a sketch map showing the position of the Salton basin in relation to the major strike-slip faults and to the Gulf basins. It may be interpreted as a large and complex pull-apart basin (Crowell, 1974, p. 200). Our map suggests a rhombic area that can be interpreted as deeply buried oceanic floor. Two short segments of spreading oceanic plate boundary are shown to be present in the basin floor (Muehlberger, 1992). That recent and ongoing volcanic activity occurs in this geothermal area is substantiated by high heat-flow rates and the large volumes of hot water brought to the surface from deep wells. While the northeastern margin of the basin is quite clearly defined by the San Andreas fault and its continuation in the Sand Hills fault, the southwestern margin is not easily defined. If the parallel San Jacinto and Imperial faults are selected, the separating distance is about 40 km. Several lesser strike-slip faults lie within this zone and may serve to divide it longitudinally into two or more parallel pull-apart sub-basins.

For another example of the pull-apart basin, we turn to a locality presented in Chapter 6 as an example of seismicity along major strike-slip plate boundaries: the northern boundary of the Caribbean plate that crosses Central America through Guatamala (Figures 6.32 and 6.33). The area of special interest is shown here on a larger scale in Figure 11.50. The two great left-lateral (sinistral) boundary strike-slip faults are the Motagua fault and the San Agustin fault. Between these two faults lies the Motauga Valley. Some 55 km north of the Motauga Valley lies the Polochic fault, also a left-lateral strike-slip, that passes along the north shoreline of Lago de Izabal. Along the south shore of the lake lies a parallel branch fault, thus defining the Lago de Izabal tectonic basin. The Polochoc fault may serve to absorb a substantial percentage of the total necessary plate boundary displacement. Both of these valleys are amenable to interpretation as pull-apart basins (Aydin and Nur, 1982, p. 95-96). If that hypothesis

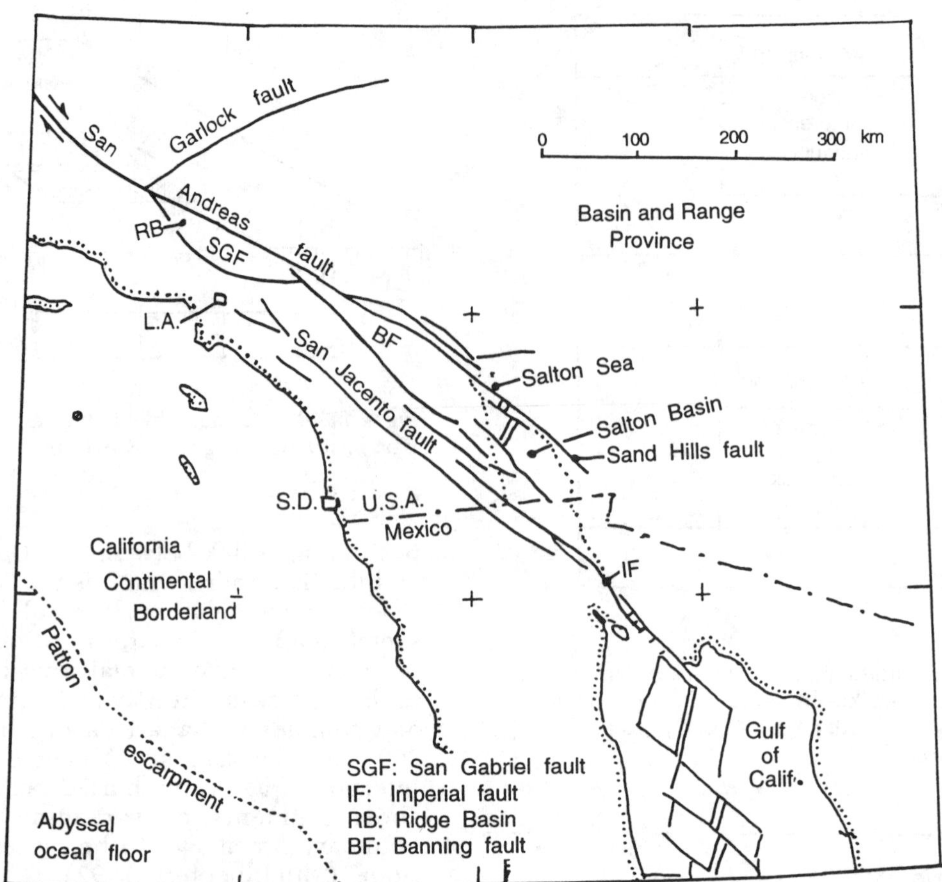

Figure 14.49 Sketch map of the region surrounding the Salton basin. (Based on data of William R. Muehlberger, Compiler, 1992, *Tectonic Map of North America*, Southwest Sheet. Tulsa, OK, Amer. Assoc. of Petroleum Geologists. Copyright @ 1992. Reproduced by permission.)

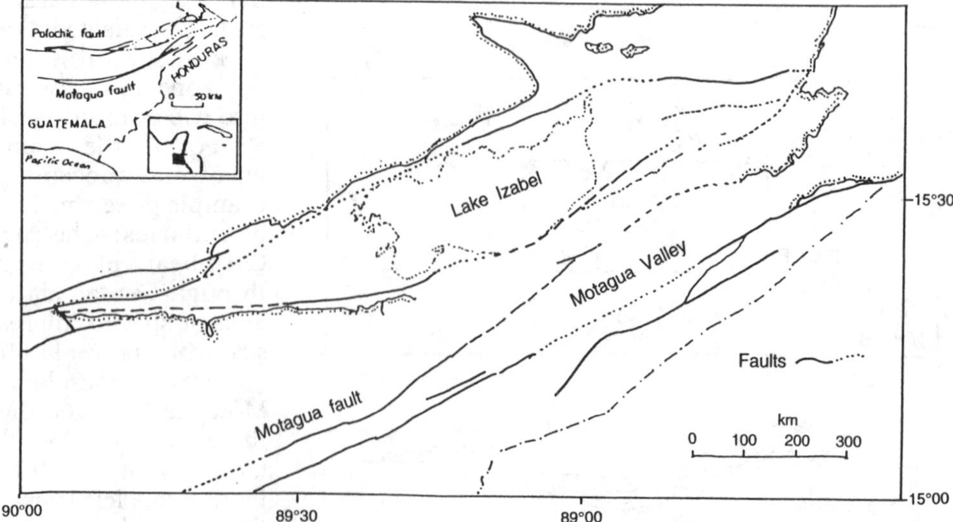

Figure 14.50 Fault map of the Montagua Valley/Lake Izabal region of Guatemala and Honduras. (Adapted from A. Aydin and A. Nur, 1982, *Tectonics*, v. 1, no. 2, p. 95, Figure 2e. Used by permission of the American Geophysical Union.)

is correct, they would rank in areal extent near the top of a worldwide list: Motauga basin, length ~50 km, width ~20 km; Izabal basin, length ~50 km, width ~25 km. The Salton basin would perhaps outrank them, however, with a maximum length of ~150 km and width of ~80 km.

We turn next to other configurations of strike-slip faults important in basin formation. One is the branching off of a major strike-slip fault to become a *splay*. Typically, a splay follows a major fault for some distance, then rejoins it to mark off a rhomboidal section of crust, as shown in Figure

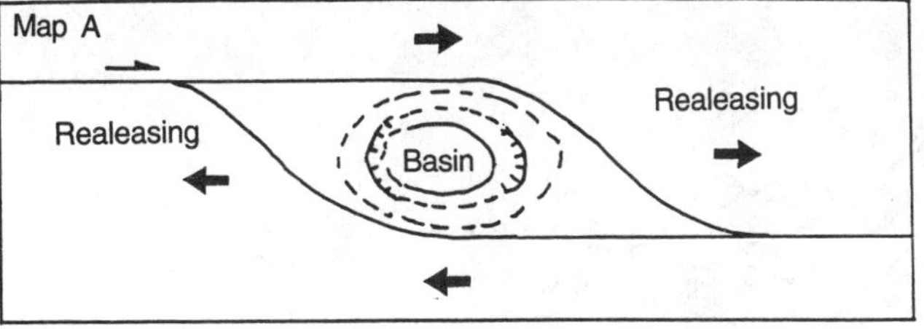

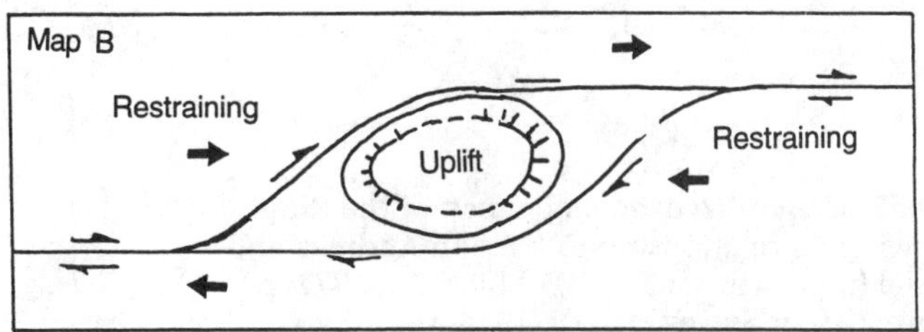

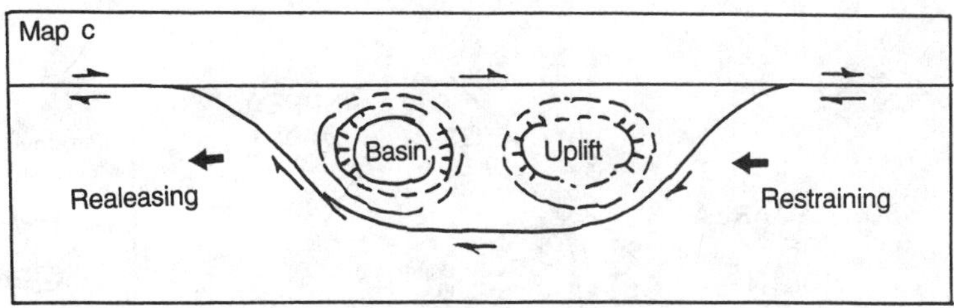

Figure 14.51 Schematic maps showing the relationship of curving plate boundary faults to basins and uplifts. (Copyright © by Arthur N. Strahler. Based on data of T.J. Dibblee, Jr., 1977; page 169 in Sylvester, Ed., 1984.)

11.51, Map A (Dibblee, 1977, p. 169, Figure 2.11). The relative opposite motion of the two plates is unimpeded, while the enclosed rhomb is relatively motionless. However, we have two releasing bends face-to-face, so that the rhomboid is free to lengthen. Extension acts on the rhomboid, bringing about subsidence, and a sedimentary basin (graben) is formed. In Map B, the curvatures are to the left, producing two restraining bends. Here, lateral compression acts to form an uplift, or horst. In Map C, maps A and B have been combined to produce a hybrid section of crust bearing both a basin and an uplift. One might predict that as time passes the basin will migrate to the left, lengthening the basin.

Figure 11.52 is an example of a hybrid basin containing both basin and uplift. Known as the Ridge basin, it lies between the main San Andreas strand and the San Gabriel fault. It is located in the northwest corner of Los Angeles County, due north of the Malibu coast. Angelenos will recognize the locality as near the site of "The Grapevine," a notorious grade on Interstate 5. On the geologic map, the location is easily spotted by the junction of the Garlock fault with the San Andreas fault at Gorman. Ridge Basin is mapped as an area of Pliocene/Pleistocene sediments, mostly unconsolidated. Some 12 km thickness of both marine and non marine sediments accumulated within a narrow basin. A gradual lateral shift in the depositional site allowed this great thickness of sediment to accumulate (Crowell, 1974, p. 198). Figure 11.53 is a schematic block diagram of the Ridge basin. North is toward the right. The bulk of the sediment came from the highlands to the north. Subsidence of wedgelike sections on the north side of the San Gabriel fault left a sheer S-shaped basin wall. Eventually, the main plate boundary shifted from the San Gabriel fault to its modern position farther north, and the basin became inactivated (Ingersoll, 1988, p. 1716-1717).

A review of the California sedimentary basins would not be complete without mention of basins of the California Continental Borderland, a submerged region of continental crust some 200 to 300 km in width (see Figure 11.49). On the landward side of the Borderland is a narrow continental shelf. Figure 11.54 shows the locations and outlines of the major basins. For the most part they are elongated on axes trending NW-SE, and they seem to fall into rough rows paralleling the mainland coast. Figure 11.55, a structural map of the northern half of Figure 11.54, emphasizes this linearity by anticline symbols showing axes or crests of the linear highs and by syncline symbols along the axes of the basins. If strike-slip symbols should be introduced, they would probably show a network of right-lateral faults converging and diverging to enclose rhomboidal areas. Thus the Borderland as a zone participates in the tectonics of the total San Andreas system. In marked

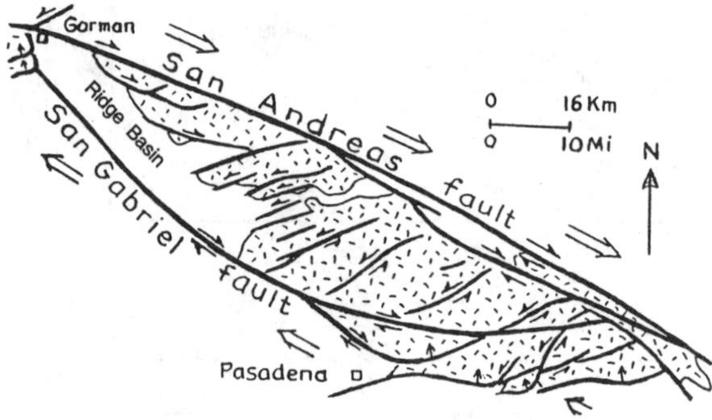

Figure 14.52 Generalized geologic map of the Ridge basin showing its relationship to the San Andreas and San Gabriel faults. (From T. W. Dibblee, Jr., 1977; p. 168, Figure 2.10 in Sylvester, Ed., 1984. Used by permission of the San Joaquin Geological Society and the author.)

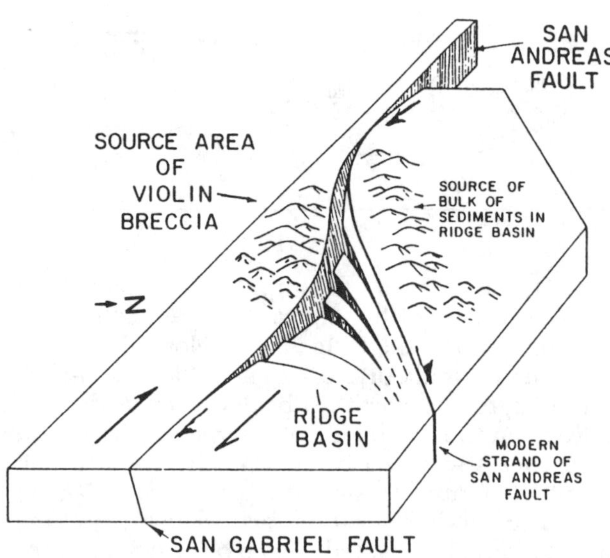

Figure 11.53 Schematic block diagram of Ridge basin. (From John C. Crowell, 1982, Publication 22 of *the Society of Economomic Paleontologists and Mineralogists*. Reproduced by permission of the author.)

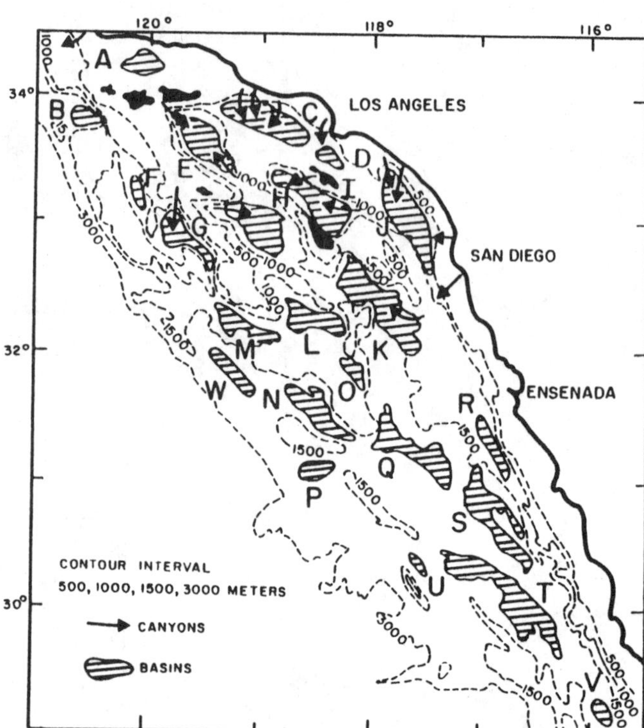

Figure 11.54 Map of the California Continental Borderland showing basins and topographic highs. (From D.S. Gorsline and L.S.-Y. Teng, 1989; Chapter 10, p. 472, Figure 1, in *Geology of North America*, Vol. N., Boulder, CO, The Geological Society of America. Reproduced with the permission of the publisher, the Geological Society of America, Boulder, Colorado, USA. Copyright 1989.)

exception to this general structural plan is the Santa Barbara basin and its bordering chain of Channel Islands. Here the high and low axes trend E-W and are obviously within the system of western Transverse Ranges. Basins close to the mainland coast receive large quantities of terrestrial sediments, brought into the basin deeps in submarine canyons. Thus the Santa Barbara, Santa Monica, and San Pedro basins have high rates of fill of hemipelagic sediment. Basins farther seaward receive some terrestrial sediment by overflow of the inner basins over sills, while basins farthest out receive mostly pelagic sediment. Farther north off the mainland coast lies a narrow borderland zone that continues to the termination of the San Andreas system at Cape Mendocino. Three elongate pull-apart basins occupy much of this foreland: Offshore Santa Maria, Bodega, and Point Arena (Atwater, 1989, p. 64-65).

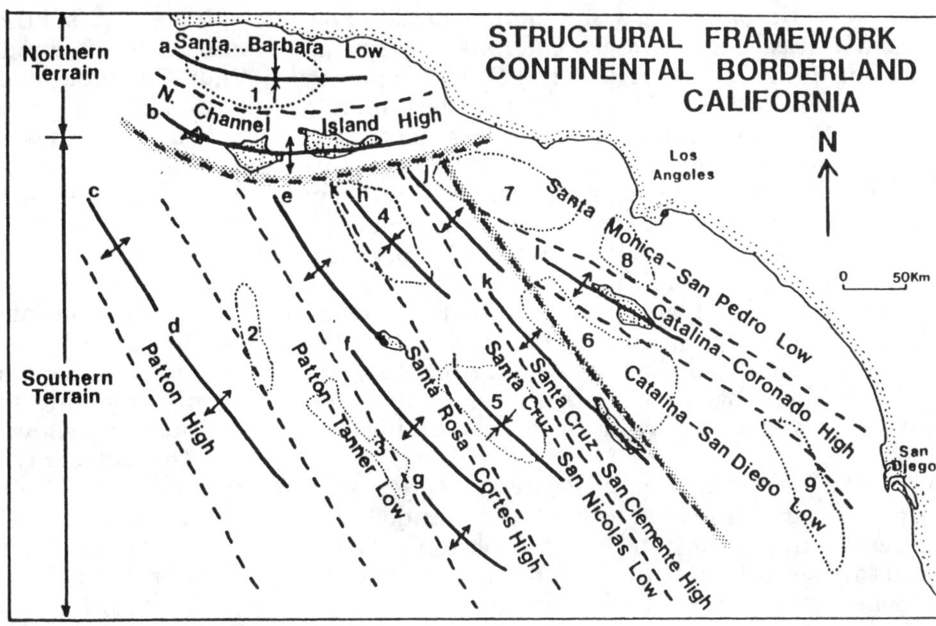

Figure 11.55 Map of major structural elements of the northern zone of the California Continental Borderland. (Same source as Figure 11.54, p. 474, Figure 2. Reproduced with the permission of the publisher, the Geological Society of America, Boulder, Colorado, USA. Copyright 1989.)

11.15 Backarc Basins and Forearc Basins

Under the heading of Subduction boundaries, Subclasses I-C and II-c, two kinds of basins of the compressional tectonic type are listed: backarc basin and forearc basin. Both of these types have been fully treated in Chapter 8 under the subject of subduction tectonics. Seismicity related to these basin types was covered in Chapter 6. A familiarity with Chapters 6 and 8 is assumed.

Because of the great extent of active subduction plate boundaries, there is no lack of active backarc and forearc basins to examine. These are mostly located around the circum-Pacific "Ring of Fire," but are also well developed in other locations: Sumatra-Java arc in Indonesia, Lesser Antilles volcanic arc of the Caribbean Sea, Scotia arc of the South Atlantic, and Aegean Sea arc of the Mediterranean basin.

This chapter has been limited largely to sedimentary basins resting on continental crust and lithosphere, so much of the subject matter of oceanic backarc basins covered in Chapters 6 and 8 is not relevant. We defined two basic kinds of subduction boundaries: Class A (Chilean type) is subduction of an oceanic plate beneath the margin of a continental plate, producing volcanic continental mountain arcs. This class appears in Table 11.1 as subclass I-C. Class B (Mariana type) is subduction of one oceanic plate beneath another oceanic plate. This class is shown as subclass II-C. Basins of this subclass are floored by oceanic crust at abyssal depths and accumulate a layer of pelagic sediment. Delta fan sediments are also found spreading far out over the abyssal floors.

Subduction boundaries of the Class A (Chilean type) hold the continental basins of interest in this chapter. Figures 8.1 and 8.2 give a good overview of the positioning of both forearc and backarc basins in relation to the volcanic arc that separates them, but at the same time furnishes a large supply of sediment to both. The forearc basin owes its existence to the continual growth of the accretionary prism, which rises to form a ridge-like tectonic arc. Where the tectonic arc rises above sea level as a chain of islands it can also shed sediment into the forearc basin. In this example, the backarc basin may be completely above sea level as a terrestrial basin (Cross sections A and B), or it can be a seaway accumulating terrigenous sediment (Cross sections C and D). The abyssal depth of these troughs in the vicinity of the Flores Deep and Banda Sea is of special interest, because it suggests stretching and thinning of the deep crust and upper mantle, causing subsidence. This eastern section of deep submergence is also of great interest because of the possibility that it is floored in part by continental crust. Warren Hamilton (1988, p. 1511, Figure 2) shows on his tectonic map several "continental fragments" within the Banda Sea.

The Class A subduction boundary is illustrated in some detail in Figure 8.19. The forearc basin is shown as resting partly on continental crust and partly on the accretionary wedge. Figure 8.22 shows stages in the growth of the accretionary wedge and with it a growing forearc basin. Variations in the form of the forearc basin have been presented by W.R. Dickinson and D.R. Seely (1979, p. 5-7, 25-26).

We turn next to further discussion of the Class A backarc basins, using as the example the central Andes of South America. Keep in mind that the western margins of the North and South American plates were probably active subduction margins long before the breakup of Pangaea that opened up the Atlantic basin. This subduction mode dates from at least the Early Carboniferous (Seyfert and Sirkin, 1979, p. 324, Figure 11.12). In Chapter 9, we described the accretion of the western margin of the North American plate by a long succession of docking terranes, consisting of microcontinents of various kinds and places of origin. Arc-continent collisions also occurred and produced orogens. It is reasonable to assume that a similar history must have prevailed along the western margin of the South American plate. In long periods of steady subduction between such collisional events, the central Andes would have produced a set of forearc and backarc basins on either side of the high volcanic arc, as is now the case in the Sumatra-Java arc.

The volcanic arc of Peruvian Andes is a massive structure of andesitic lavas intruded by a great number of interlocking plutons. Great quantities of detritus from this arc were transported eastward to accumulate as a sub-Andean zone of continental sediments, resting on the Brazilian shield. This deposit constituted the initial backarc basin, formed in a regime of crustal extension during the early Cretaceous. By middle Cretaceous, the regime had changed to a compressional regime of more rapid subduction. This change led to overthrust deformation of the backarc basin, making an orogen called the Andean Cordillera (Ramos, 1989, p. 449).

11.16 Foreland Basins of Compressional Origin

Plate collisions, both continent-continent and arc-continent varieties, generate a variety of sedimentary basin known as the *foreland basin* (Table 11.1) That name was applied in 1973 by R.A. Price, an authority on the overthrust structures of the Canadian Rockies (see Chapter 9). He explained the basin as a lithospheric flexure in response to loading by the overthrust sheets. An alternate name, *foredeep*, has been used by A.W. Bally (1989, p. 402), but is avoided here because of possible confusion with the deep oceanic trench of an active subduction boundary (i.e., a trench fill). Actually, an early deep-water phase, characterized by deposition of turbidites, can be recognized in some cases (Bally, 1989, p. 406-407).

Figure 11.5(I-D) uses as a model of the foreland basin a continent-collision in which two foreland basins are formed. They are opposed in direction, and each lies on continental lithosphere. Refer back to Chapter 9 and Figure 9.28, showing the foreland thrust and a foreland molasse accumulating beyond it. At the same time another molasse is accumulating on the opposing plate from sediment derived from the recumbent nappes. Two examples of the continental-continental collision are also shown in Chapter 9. Figure 9.42 shows a foreland basin lying on the Arabian plate. A second example is from the India-Asia collision. Figure 9.45 shows a belt of molasse skirting the southern margin of the Himalayan ranges and its modern extension south across the Indo-Gangetic lowland. Here is a great foreland basin in the process of being loaded. Several foreland basins were also formed on the northern side of the Himalayas in earlier stages that included arc-continent collisions. These basins were then involved in younger northward-thrust slices. The recent rise of the great Tibetan plateau prevents the development of a foreland basin. As for an arc-continent collision, a single foreland basin is generated. Figure 9.26 shows the deposit of molasse beyond the thrust sheet which is furnishing the sediment. An early stage of subsidence is shown.

The tectonic type of the foreland basin is given in Table 11.1, Subclass I-D, as a flexural basin. Much thought has been given to the development of models of flexural basin development. First, however, we need to examine an actual example of such a basin. It is the Western Canada foredeep. This foreland basin and others in North America are shown on our map, Figure 11.56. The cross section of the Western Canada foredeep is shown in Figure 11.57. The great vertical exaggeration of ×20 gives the cross section a strange look but it will be familiar from Chapter 9 and Figure 9.9, showing the complex thrust planes in western Canada moved forward on a décollement and overriding undisturbed strata of the adjacent plains region. The thrusts are in Cretaceous strata, and the thrusting occurred in the Laramide orogeny of Late Cretaceous and Paleocene time. The same strata that are strongly telescoped at the left correspond with undeformed platform strata that make up the floor of the Western Canada basin. The basin strata are sandstones, subdivided into early and late groups. The thrust region has been deeply eroded and a substantial part of the original basin sequence has also been removed by erosion. Notice how (a) the basin sequence merges gradually into the platform sequence farther east and (b) that the platform strata and Precambrian basement plunge sharply down beneath the fold belt. This "plunge" has been referred to as form of "subduction," but this usage does not imply that a new plate boundary is being created. Obviously, the extending fold belt has consumed much of the older western portion of the basin strata, during which time the locus of continuing basin sedimentation has been shifted eastward.

Telescoping thickens the crust under the fold belt, increasing the load upon the lithosphere, which in turn responds by yielding, and as it sinks draws down a large region of lithosphere below the limit of the folds. The principle is the same as that of the subsidence of the crust under the increased load of an ice sheet, as explained in Chapter 3 and illustrated in Figure 3.45.

Geologists and geophysicists who have been modeling foreland basin evolution have been divided on an important premise of physics. A.W. Bally has explained this division as follows:

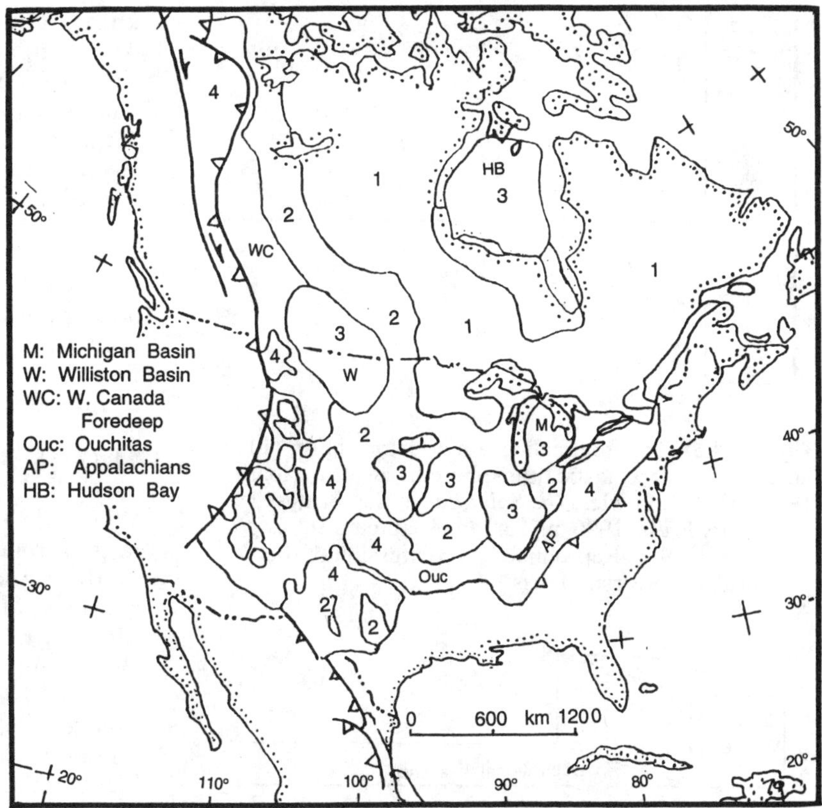

Figure 11.56 Simplified map of sedimentary basins of the North American craton. (Adapted from A.W. Bally, 1989, Chapter 15, p. 398, Figure 1 in *The Geology of North America*, Volume A. Reproduced by permission of The Geological Society of America and the author.)

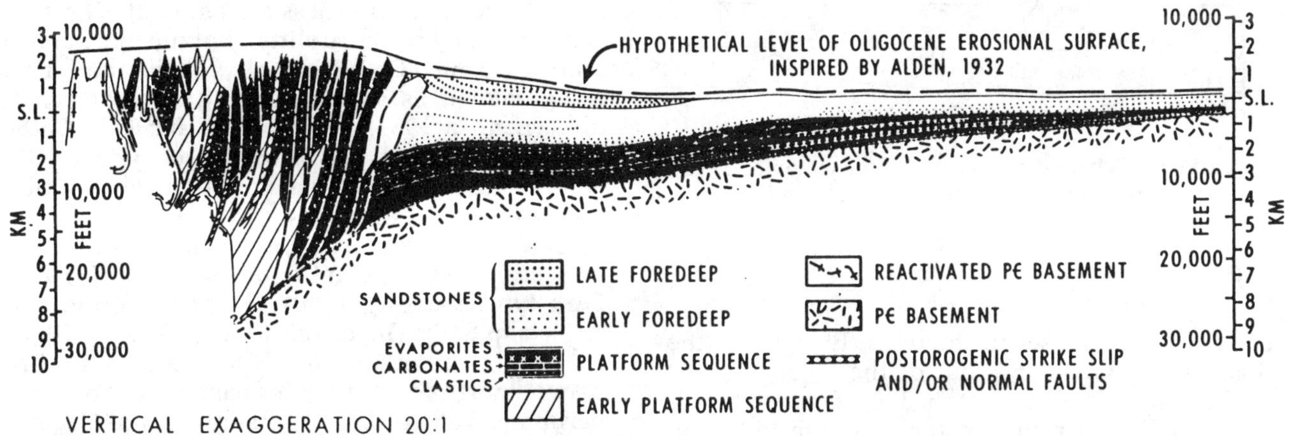

Figure 11.57 Structure section of the Western Canada Foredeep, a sedimentary basin. (From Bally and Snelson, 1980, as presented in A.W. Balley, 1989, Chapter 15, p. 407. Figure 5, in *The Geology of North America*, Volume A. Reproduced with the permission of the publisher, the Geological Society of America, Boulder, Colorado, USA. Copyright 1998.)

Some authors visualize an elastic lithosphere, while others assume a viscoelastic lithosphere. Both assumptions lead to acceptable models for foreland subsidence... Elastic models permit rapid relaxation of the lithosphere. On the other hand, viscoelastic models provide for slower relaxation (1989, p. 402).

Figure 11.58 is a schematic diagram of the response of a viscoelastic lithosphere to emplacement of a single load, represented by the block above the horizontal line indicating the initial horizontal ground surface. Equal units of elapsed time (1, 2, 3) are marked off. In the first period the strain is equal to that of an elastic lithosphere, then becomes reduced in the second

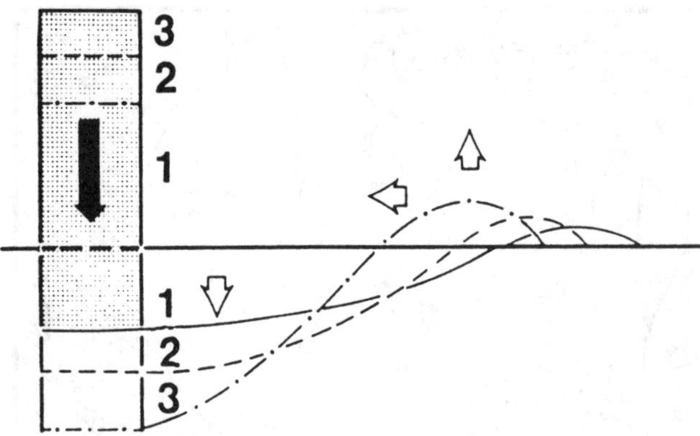

Figure 11.58 Schematic diagram of deformation of the surface of a viscoelastic lithosphere by a surface load. (From C.M.R. Fowler, *The Solid Earth*, Cambridge University Press, 1990, p.383-384. Adapted from C. Beaumont, 1981. Reproduced by permission of the Cambridge University Press.)

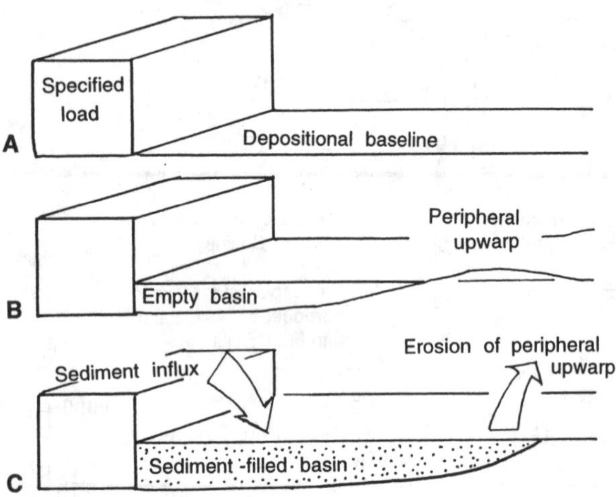

Figure 11.59 Schematic diagrams of the tectonic loading of a foreland basin.(Same source as in Figure 11.58.)

period, and increases in the third. Eventually, the final profile would be that of the local isostatic equilibrium (Fowler, 1990, p. 383). Figure 11.59 is a cartoon-like drawing of the response to a load emplaced on a flat surface (Diagram A). Sinking of the load produces an empty basin with a peripheral upwarp (Diagram B). With further subsidence the basin is filled with sediment and the upwarped peripheral zone has been eroded away (Diagram C). Figure 11.60 is a model of the Alberta foreland basin showing the loads as vertical columns and the corresponding sediment wedges (Beaumont, 1981). Erosional truncation has been great over the thrust pile and has also affected the basin sediments, largely removing the peripheral bulge.

Another important belt of foreland basins borders the Appalachian chain (Figure 11.56). We know it by the provincial name of the Folded Appalachians, or Valley-and-Ridge province (see Figure 9.34). The basin zone is continued westward into the E-W trending Ouachita Mountains, where the Arkansas sedimentary basin is situated. The Appalachian foreland basin contains a sequence of strata (mostly clastics) ranging in age from Cambrian through Pennsylvanian with a total maximum thickness of over 8 km (Bally, 1989, 407-408). Loading occurred over a long period of time that included two continent-continent collisions: Caledonian and Alleghany. Permian folding of the basin strata followed, terminating the life of the basin.

11.17 The Rocky Mountain Basins

When we trace southward the Canadian belt of large foreland basins, it seems to terminate about at the Canada-U.S. boundary Figure (11.56). In southern Montana, there begins the zone of Rocky Mountain uplifts, extending southward through Wyoming and Colorado. These uplifts were described in Chapter 9 with accompanying maps, Figures 9.52 and 9.53, showing the basins that lie among the uplifts. Figure 11.61 is the same map as 9.2, which shows, showing both basins and uplifts. Recall that the uplifts were formed during Paleocene and Eocene time, and the deformation was superimposed on an older foreland basin of Cretaceous age. Notice the positioning of the frontal flank overthrust belt lying to the west of the Rocky Mountain uplift/basin region.

The basins vary greatly in outline form, dimensions, and thickness of sediment. The same can be said for the uplifts that lie between or among them. Consequently, there has been disagreement as to a basic pattern that can be discerned. In 1981, S.M. Chapin and C.E. Cather recognized three types of basins: (1) Green River type: large, equidimensional or elliptical in outline, and bounded on three or more sides by uplifts. (2) Denver type: elongate basins, asymmetric synclinal in section, with an uplift on one side. (3) Echo Park type: narrow, highly elongate, bounded by strike-slip faults (Ingersoll, 1988, p. 1715). William R. Dickinson et al. in 1988 recognized three parallel north-south zones of basins: (1) An eastern perimeter zone of broad, shallow basins draining out to the east. (2) An axial central zone of mostly small basins. (3) An inner (western) zone of ponded basins lying close to the boundary overthrust belt.

Our interest here is not so much in the sedimentology and stratigraphy of the basins, but rather their tectonic origin. Are they causally related to the basement uplifts, described in Chapter 9? Refer back to Figure 9.53, a map showing both basins and uplifts. Notice the widespread occurrences of basement reverse faults along the boundaries between uplifts and adjacent basins. Compressional tectonics is now the favored interpretation of this faulting, and this regional

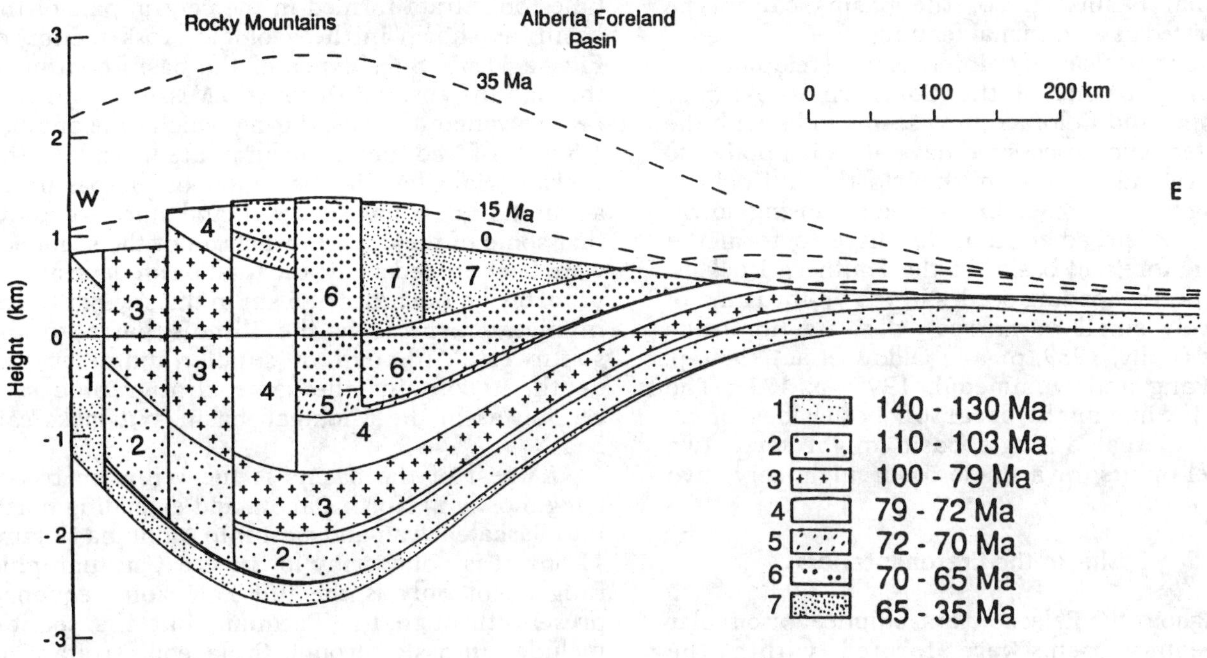

Figure 11.60 Schematic cross section of a model loading of the Alberta Foreland Basin. A vertical loading column is shown for each wedge of basin sediment accumulation. (Same source as in Figure 11.58.)

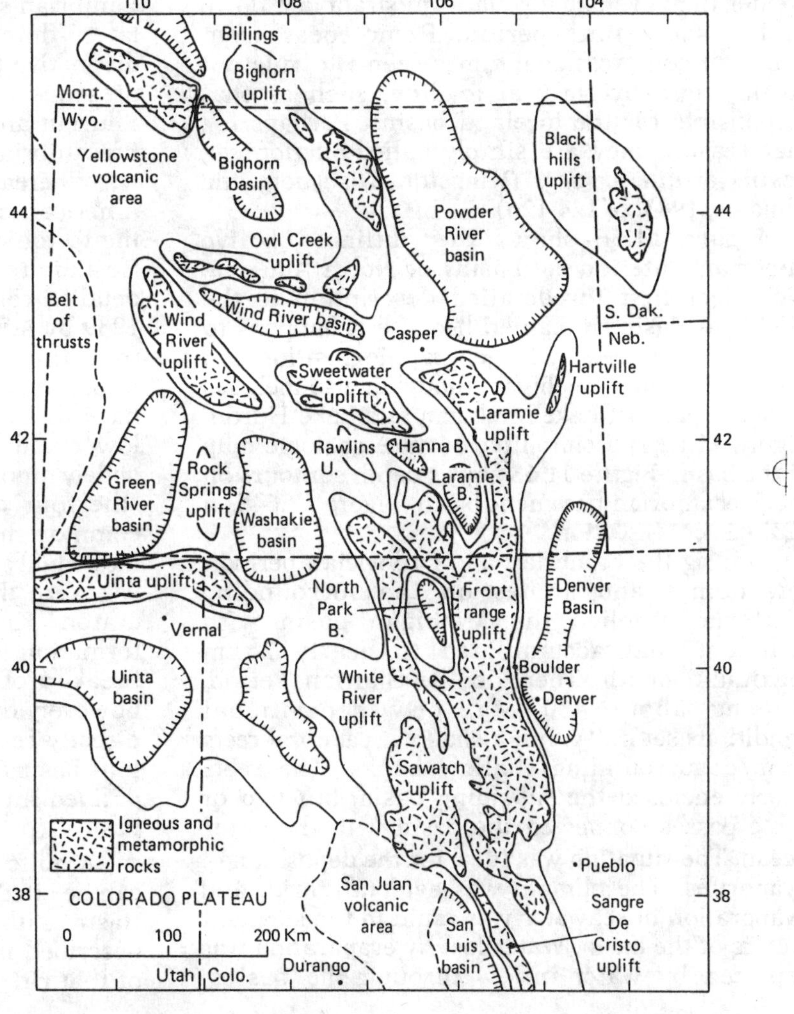

Figure 11.61 A simplified map of uplifts and sedimentary basins of the Southern Rockies. (Based on data from the Tectonic Map of the United States, National Research Council, and other sources. Map copyright © by Arthur N. Strahler.)

compression must have also applied to the synclinal basins. If so, the basins cannot be interpreted as extensional features.

The consensus of opinion as to development of the many basins of the Southern Rockies in Wyoming and Colorado now seems to lie with the same tectonic process we have already applied to the foreland basins in the Northern Rockies: loading by telescoped thrust sheets, causing down-flexing of the adjacent lithosphere to form the tectonic foreland basin. In the Southern Rockies, however, the loading occurs in the up-thrusting of relatively small or narrow, discrete horst-like blocks (Bally, 1989, p. 403; Oldow et al., 1989, p. 173; Pang and Nummedal, 1995, p. 173). The down-flexing might occur on both sides of an uplift, so that a single basin might serve two parallel uplifts (or a single basin might serve two uplifts).

11.18 Sag Basins of the Craton Interiors

Throughout the Paleozoic era, elliptical or circular sedimentary basins were formed within the interior regions of the continental cratons. Marine sediments deposited in shallow water in these subsiding basins reached thicknesses on the order of 1 km during a single geologic period lasting 30 to 50 m.y. This thickness is some four to five times greater than average for platform strata laid down in the same time period. Remoteness from marginal compressional zones seems to rule out basin origin by flexural loading, such as that responsible for the foreland basins. Perhaps for that reason, they are simply called *interior sag basins* or *interior sags* (Kingston, Dishroon, and Wiliams, 1983, p. 124-126).

Figure 11.56 shows the outlines of five important interior sag basins of North America. We select first for detailed description is the Michigan Basin, so named because it happens to coincide quite closely in geographic position and extent with lower Michigan, though it also includes adjacent parts of Lake Michigan and Lake Huron. Figure 11.62 is a simplified surface geologic map of the basin; Figure 11.63 shows depth contours on the Precambrian basement basin; Figure 11.64 is a geologic cross section.

During the Cambrian and Ordovician periods, low domes and arches on the surrounding platform supplied the Michigan basin with sediment that accumulated to nearly 2 km maximum depth. Then, in the Silurian Period, starting about 430 Ma, new depositional conditions set in. Within a shallow sea, coral reefs formed surrounding shallow banks. The reefs nearly enclosed the subsiding basin, but two or three passes connected the basin with the outer ocean. The situation was ideal for the deposition of evaporites. The climate was evidently arid, and evaporation of seawater was rapid in the stagnant waters of the basin. Water lost by evaporation was replaced by water inflow through the passes. Nearly 1 km of salt beds and interbedded limestone strata formed in the central part of the basin, as shown in the geologic cross section of Figure 11.65. Subsidence of the basin continued through the ensuing Devonian, Mississippian, and Pennsylvanian periods, during which time another 1.5 km of sediments accumulated. Today, the Precambrian floor in the center of the basin lies about 4.5 km below sea level, and since we know that some of the uppermost strata of the sequence were later eroded away, the total basin deposit was probably on the order of 5 km in thickness. Similar in many respects is the Illinois basin to the southwest. Although of smaller diameter and depth, it contains the same stratigraphic succession as in the Michigan basin, but lacks salt beds.

Largest of the basins is the Williston basin, lying mostly in North Dakota and extending north into Saskatchewan and west into Montana (Figure 11.66). It is noteworthy for its great stratigraphic range. Not only is the full Paleozoic sequence present through the Permian, but the section includes Jurassic through Cretaceous strata. The Cretaceous strata alone make up a full one-third of the total basin thickness.

A fourth example is the Hudson Bay basin, shown in Figure 11.56. It contains Ordovician, Silurian, and Devonian strata. The absence of Cambrian strata shows that the basin began to fill later than the other three basins. Another distinctive feature of the Hudson Bay basin is the presence of normal faults that cut through the Silurian and Ordovician strata and penetrate the Precambrian basement (Bally, 1989, p. 404).

Whereas the depositional histories of the North American cratonic sag basins seem clear enough, the tectonics of subsidence—over and beyond the isostatic response to loading—remains obscure. A detailed review of this problem was presented in 1989 by A.W. Bally. Here, we paraphrase or quote from that review. Bally points out that there are important dissimilarities among the four basins we have described. We have already noted that the lower and upper stratigraphic limits differ quite widely among them. Moreover, Bally observes that "the four cratonic basins did not subside to a common rhythm; instead they developed their own individual subsidence rates and history" (p. 405).

Were these basins initiated by rifting of the craton? Klein and Hsui (1987) linked the basin formation to extensional rifting accompanying the breakup of the Proterozic supercontinent. Bally, however, finds that "no extensional event can be directly related to the subsidence patterns of the four basins" (p. 405). "Thus, the search for a well-defined initial rifting event is elusive for all four basins" (p. 403).

A quite different relationship of basins to rifts can be cited in a possible connection of the Illinois Basin with the Reelfoot rift system, which we described in Chapter 6. Figure 6.64 shows details of that rift. Bally notes that "the southern Illinois

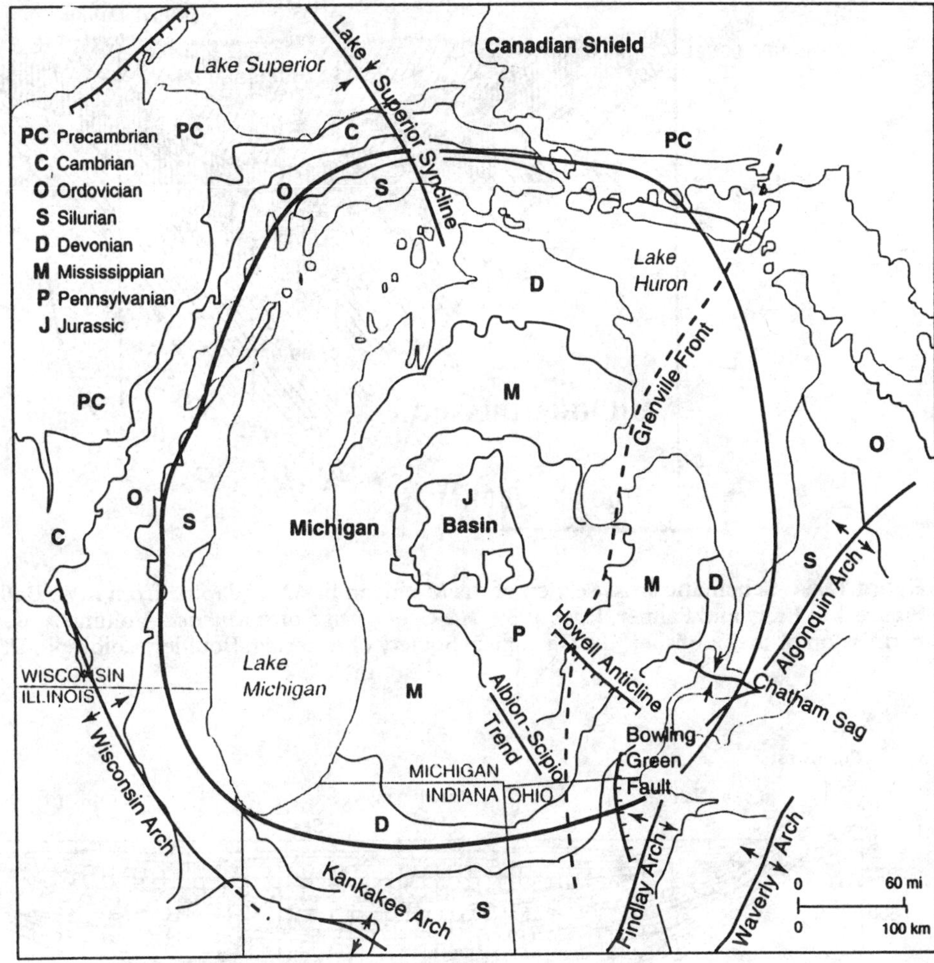

Figure 11.62 Geologic map of the Michigan basin. (From P.A. Catacosinos et al.,1990, *Structure of the Michigan Basin*, in M.W. Leighton et al, Eds.,Interior Crationic Basins: Am. Assoc. Petroleum Memoir 51, Fig. 30.1, p. 652. Reproduced by the AAPG, Tulsa, OK.)

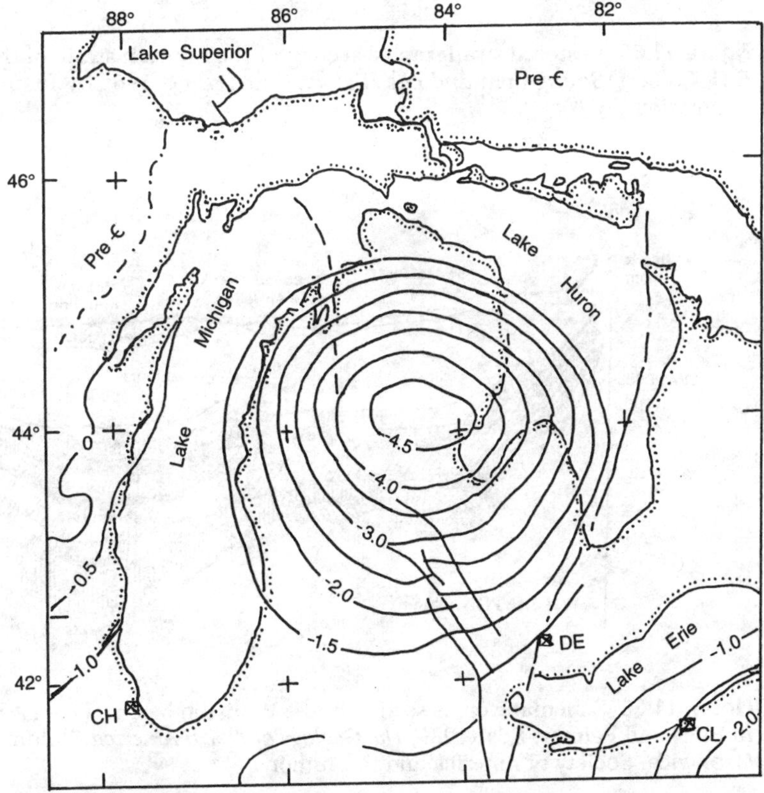

Figure 11.63 Contour map of the Precambrian basement of the Michigan basin. Countours in kilometers.(Data from *Tectonic Map of North America*, Copyright © 1992 by the American Association of Petroleum Geologists. William R. Muehlperger, Compiler. Used by permission.)

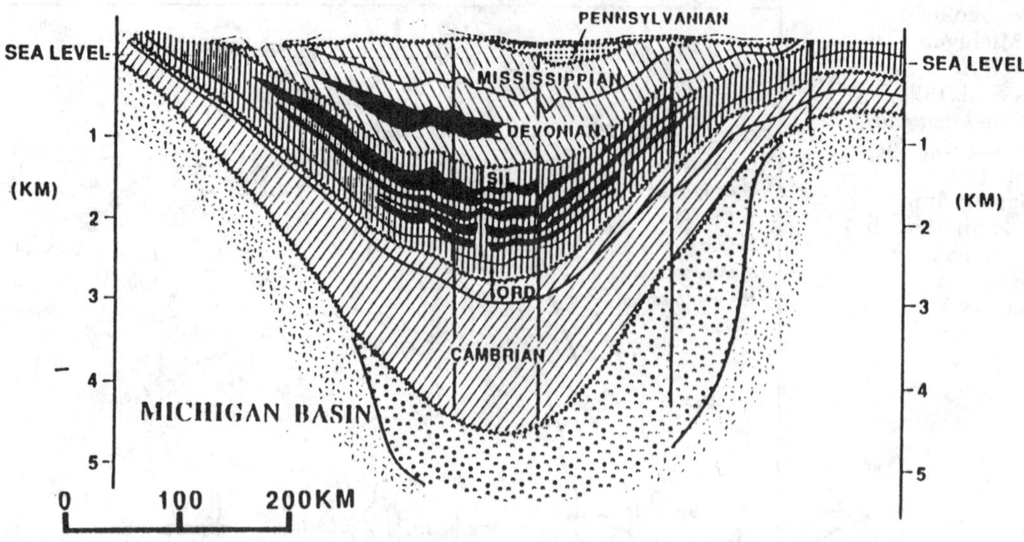

Figure 11.64 Schematic cross section of the Michigan basin. (Adapted from A.W. Bally, Chapter 15, p. 404, Figure 3 in Bally and Palmer, Eds., 1989, *The Geology of North America*, Volume A. Reproduced with the permission of the publisher, the Geological Society of America, Boulder, Colorado, USA. Copyright 1989.)

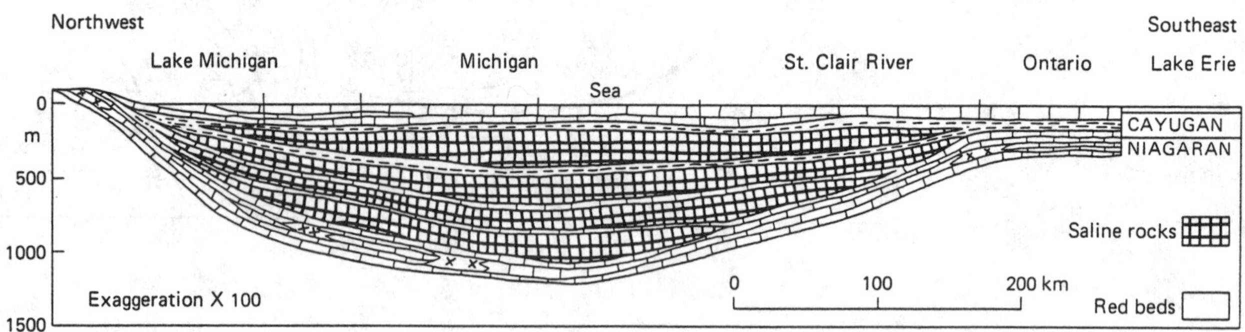

Figure 11.65 Restored stratigraphic section of the Silurian strata of the Michigan basin. (From M. Kay and E.H. Colbert, *Stratigraphy and Life History*. Copyright © 1965 by John Wiley & Sons, Inc., Reproduced by permission.)

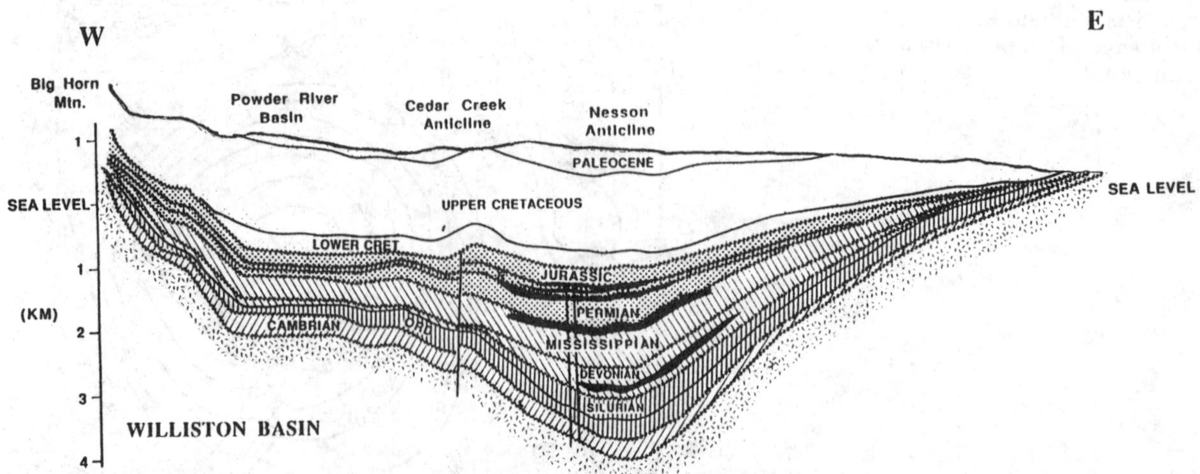

Figure 11.66 Schematic cross section of the Williston basin. (From A.W. Bally, Chapter 15, p. 404, Figure 3 in Bally and Palmer, Eds., 1989, *The Geology of North America*, Volume A. Used by permission of the Geological Society of America and the author.)

basin perhaps represents the extension of the Reelfoot graben system" (p. 403). However, the alignment of rift with basin is rather poor. A possible connection of the Michigan basin with a Keewenawan rift system extending from the Lake Superior region to the southeast has been pointed to by other authors, but that rift system "is at least 550 m.y. older than the overlying Cambrian sediments" (Bally, 1989, p. 403).

What remains is the general thermal hypothesis of basin origin presented earlier in this chapter under the name of "McKenzie rifting model" (see Figure 11.9). A "thermal event" is required to initiate the process, and is followed by cooling and subsidence. This hypothesis can be modeled to suit the stratigraphy of a given cratonic basin, "but again the physical evidence for any thermal event such as rifting is lacking" (Bally, p. 405). Models of thermal contraction have been fitted by Sleep et al. (1980) to both the Illinois and Michigan basins, but the data suggest that two thermal events may have occurred (see Fowler, 1990, p. 380, 382). Subsidence can also be attributed to a gabbro-eclogite phase transition, but that hypothesis is no more than "an ad hoc mode when all other explanations fail!" (Bally, 1989, p. 405)

A serious problem with application of the general thermal model is that the cratonal basins are essentially circular and have a radial symmetry in their stratigraphic properties. Lithospheric extension, on the other hand, fits linear, troughlike structures, but not the circular form. Instead, we may substitute a mantle plume of narrow stalklike form, i.e., a hotspot. Circular doming would occur first, followed by erosion, and finally by collapse to form the basin. A one-time occurrence of the hotspot, perhaps followed by secondary recurrence, might suffice. The hotspot hypothesis would not seem to apply to low, anticlinal uplifts, known as *intracratonal arches*, that are found on the continental sedimentary platforms. We refer to these in a following section.

Bally offers a good closing statement for this section: "And so, the deceptively simple cratonic saucers of our continent remain unexplained. In addition, the origin of many of the apparently equally simple intracratonic arches is even more obscure. Obviously we need more information, including more and better geophysical data concerning both the lower crust and the mantle underlying the cratonic basins and arches" (1989, p. 405).

11.19 Sedimentary Platforms of the Cratons

Over large areas of the continental cratons, a layer of flat-lying or gently tilted sedimentary rocks now covers the ancient shield rock (Figure 11.67). This sedimentary cover of Paleozoic and younger strata constitutes a *continental platform* (Bates and Jackson, 1987, p. 510). Platform areas of North America are shown in Figure 11.56. Figure 11.68 is a world map of platforms showing their relationship to Precambrian shields. These are Phanerozoic platforms resting on an erosion surface of low relief (a peneplane) which cuts across all older rocks, i.e., rests on a great nonconformity. Typically, the platform strata are of marine origin, deposited in shallow water, and consist of limestones, shales, well-sorted quartz sandstones, and conglomerates. The maximum total thickness of platform strata at any one place averages some 1 to 2 km, because the rate of platform sediment deposition has been comparatively slow, and because many periods of exposure to erosional removal have intervened.

Rising and sinking motions of the continental lithosphere over large areas, without appreciable deformation of the surface rocks, are called *epeirogenic movements*. The process is referred to as *epeirogeny* to distinguish it from orogeny that results in compressional or extensional deformation of strata. Epeirogeny is one of the various forms of tectonics. It can be thought of as a flexing

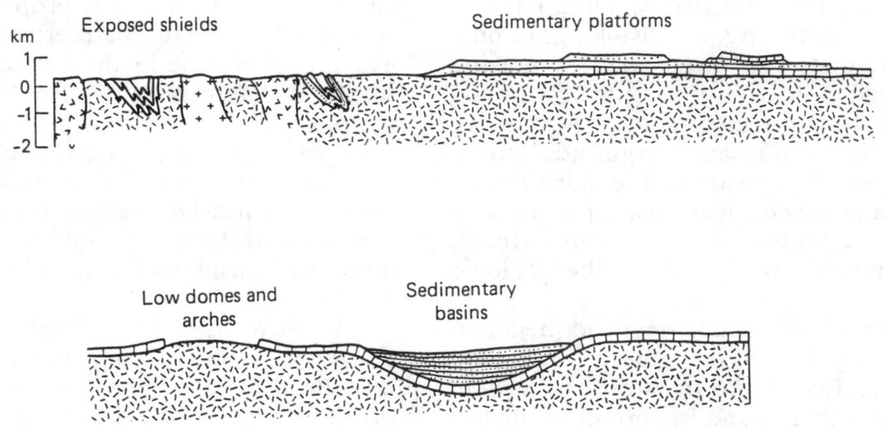

Figure 11.67 Schematic cross section of sedimentary platforms and sag basins. (Copyright © by Arthur N. Strahler.)

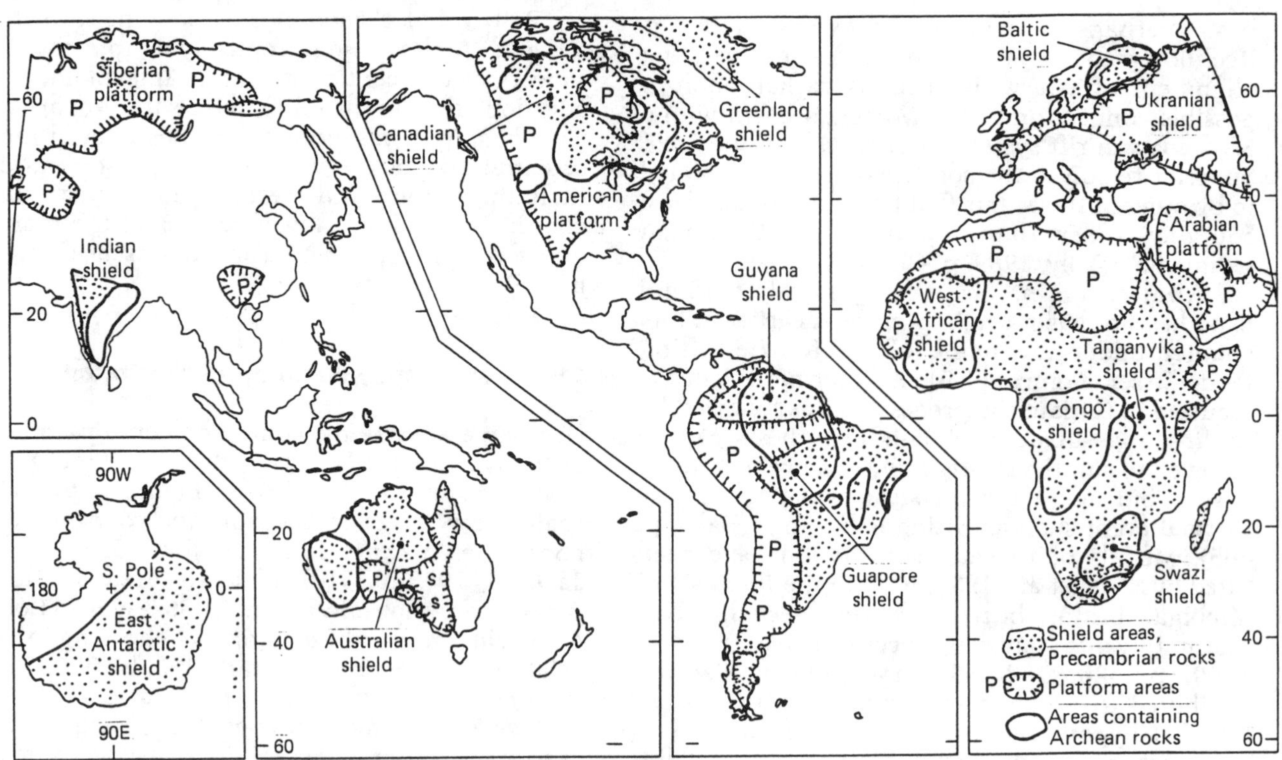

Figure 11.68 Generalized world map of continental shields and platforms. The continental nuclei lie within the areas encircled by a bold line. (Based in part on data of R.F. Murphy, P.M. Hurley, and J.R. Rand, and other sources. Goode Base Map.)

of the lithosphere—up or down—that warps the crust into low domes or basins, and into low arches or troughs. Thus epeirogeny grades into orogeny. Of course, crustal flexing (if done without stretching) must be accompanied by some degree of crustal shortening. To illustrate, a sheet of paper lying flat on a desktop, cannot be arched up without shortening the distance between opposite edges.

Epeirogenic movements have been of great importance in the history of the stable interior cratons of the continental lithosphere. Here, a negative epeirogenic flexing (downsinking) of only a few hundred meters allowed shallow marine waters to spread over a large proportion of the continent, creating an *epeiric sea*. A positive epeirogenic flexing of the same magnitude caused the shallow sea to retreat to the continental margins, exposing previously deposited strata. This process was repeated innumerable times, producing many disconformities in the geologic record.

Many alternations of positive and negative epeirogenic flexing affected the cratons throughout the Phanerozoic Eon. Platform strata of a wide range of ages are thus found in correct sequence, but the sequence found in one region will be uniquely different from sequences found in other regions. During periods of time when the platform surface stood above sea level, strata deposited in earlier periods were subject to erosion by running water. During these long episodes of denudation, part or all of the older platform sequence was removed. The detrital sediment was transported by streams to the ocean shoreline, from which it was swept by currents into an adjacent oceanic trench or across a continental shelf. An advance of the marine shoreline over the craton is called *transgression*; shoreline retreat is called *regression*.

Epeirogenic movements of the stable cratons are difficult to explain, but working hypotheses can be advanced. We may propose that epeirogeny is a distant and weaker effect of orogeny. For example, the same loading effect that generates a foreland basin might also produce a broad updoming on the craton beyond the basin. This peripheral "rim" effect was mentioned in an earlier section of this chapter. Recall also that in late stages of a passive margin, sediment loading has flexed down the continental margin, allowing the ocean to transgress far inland (Figures 11.21 and 11.22).

A quite different hypothesis is free of dependence on orogeny. Recall from Chapter 3 that the Moho has been interpreted as marking the phase transition from gabbro to eclogite which occurs at a particular combination of pressure and temperature. Suppose, now, that the temperature just above the Moho should be increased above the critical phase-transition point. A layer of gabbro at the base of the crust would be transformed into eclogite, which is denser than the gabbro. The result would be a sinking of the lithosphere to a lower level in order to reach isostatic equilibrium. The opposite change, from eclogite to gabbro, would result in the rising of the lithosphere to a new level of equilibrium. Temperature changes that would cause such epeirogenic movements of the crust could result from changes in the rate of heat flow upward through the mantle, and these in turn could be related to mantle convection systems.

11.20 Eustasy and Plate Tectonics

Another possibility to consider in explaining the stratigraphy of continental platforms is that marine inundation of a low, plainlike craton surface (a peneplane) might occur because of a global rise of sea level rather than a negative epeirogenic crustal movement. Changes in the position of the marine shoreline caused by rise or fall of the ocean level are known as *eustatic changes*. The process is called *eustasy*. Eustasy is paired with epeirogeny as alternate systems in explaining the ups and downs of sea level with respect to the continents. An essential difference between the two is that whereas epeirogeny is confined locally to a given section of a continental craton, eustasy always acts globally in both time and direction (up or down). Epeirogeny refers to the solid rock surface of the earth, whether it be the surface of the continent exposed to the atmosphere, or to the solid rock surface covered by standing water. Eustacy refers only to the free water surface of the world ocean.

A simple lab model for eustacy would be a water tank with vertical sides and a flat square bottom, as shown in Figure 11.69. First we build up for a "continent" on the tank floor a pile of six cement slabs, each one of base area half that of the tank. Water for an "ocean" is then added to reach the level of the contact of slabs 3 and 4, which amounts to half the volume of the slab pile. Next, the topmost slab is removed and placed on the adjacent tank floor. The water level now rises to the level of the base of slab 2. Our interest is in the change in the "freeboard," which is the vertical distance between the water level and the flat "deck" of the slab pile. (These nautical expressions come from John W. Rodgers, 1993, p. 35). Transfer of one more slab would see the entire continent covered by water.

In nature, mass transfer of rock from continent to ocean floor results in eustatic sea-level rise. This transfer occurs as sediment is eroded from the continental surface and deposited on the ocean floor, and thus forces a global rise in sea level. Isostatic compensation would take place accordingly, so the net difference in freeboard would be less than the tank diagram shows. The system of production of sediment and its transport to the ocean basin for deposition is a geomorphic system,

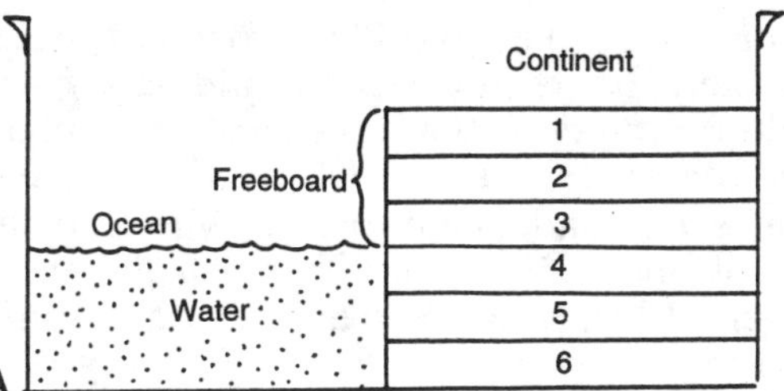

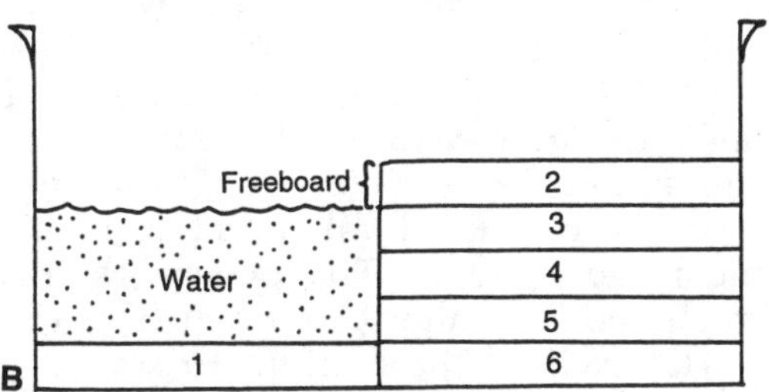

Figure 11.69 A simple water tank model to illustrate eustasy by mass transfer. (Copyright © by Arthur N. Strahler.)

powered by solar energy. We might call this system "geomorphic eustasy," but that term is not now in use.

A second possible mechanism causing rise and fall of sea level would be a simple increase or decrease in the total volume of water in the world ocean. In our water tank model this mechanism simply requires that new water be poured into the tank, or that some water be withdrawn. In nature, the new water is *juvenile water*. It could come from the upper mantle, released from magma rising at the mid-oceanic spreading boundaries (Pitman, 1978, p. 1389). Volume increase from this source has probably been very slow, and perhaps insignificant from Archean time to the present (Rodgers, 1993, p. 35). A possible natural mechanism of removal of water from the world ocean would be the hydrolysis of the mafic minerals in oceanic crust and their subsequent permanent transfer to continental crust at subduction margins.

As an example of mass water transfers between continent and oceans, consider a popular prediction featured in the news media. As a consequence of global warming, there arises the unpleasant prospect that the great ice sheet on Antarctica may rapidly melt, causing sea level to rise and drown many of the great coastal cities of the world. Unquestionably, the alternate growth and melting of great Pleistocene ice sheets caused substantial eustatic changes of sea level. This mechanism is called *glacio-eustasy*. Rhodes W. Fairbridge, who made intensive studies of Pleistocene sea-level oscillations, shows the vertical range between glacial minimum levels and interglacial maximum levels to have spanned from 75 to 100 m (1966, p. 480). Because ice ages were episodic throughout the Phanerozoic, it does not seem likely that their eustasy would have governed the alternate deposition and erosion of platform strata. Moreover, the vertical range estimate given above seems inadequate to cope with a measured range of about 500 m in Phanerozoic sea levels (Rodgers, 1993, p. 36). The discrepancy—some 400 to 425 m—would need to be made up by tectonic causes, to which we turn next.

Eustasy controlled by tectonic processes is *tectono-eustasy*, a term introduced by Rhodes W. Fairbridge in 1961. Several mechanisms linked to plate tectonics have been proposed as effective in causing important eustatic changes in sea level through Phanerozoic time. One mechanism is based on the estimated volume changes of mid-oceanic ridge systems. The principles involved were reviewed by Walter C. Pitman II in 1978 (p. 1391). He credited the concept to several other authors, including Menard (1969), Hallam (1963), Russell (1968), Valentine and Moores (1972), and Hays and Pitman (1973). [See Pitman, 1987, for references cited.]

As we explained in Chapter 5, oceanic lithosphere recently formed along a spreading axis stands high in elevation. As the lithosphere moves away from the spreading plate boundary, the plate becomes cooler and denser, subsiding gradually to a lower level (see Figure 5.9). Suppose that the rate of spreading is greatly increased—say, from 2 cm/yr to 10 cm/yr. In that case, the width of the two belts of higher-standing lithosphere adjacent to the axis will be increased, displacing a certain volume of water from the ocean basin. As shown in Figure 11.70, world sea level will be raised, and this positive eustatic change will cause a transgression of the ocean over the low cratons. When the spreading rate then slows, the former profile will be resumed, and a greater volume of water can again be accommodated in the ocean basin. A negative eustatic change will occur and the cratons will experience a regression.

Past spreading rates can be estimated from the widths of magnetic anomaly belts. In the case of the Cretaceous Period, a transgression that is known to have occurred between 110 Ma and 85 Ma is matched by an episode of exceptionally rapid seafloor spreading, followed by a return to a lower rate. Plate tectonics thus offers a potent hypothesis to explain transgressions and regressions.

A second hypothesis based on plate tectonics uses the possibility that a spreading plate boundary can drift toward a subduction boundary and that eventually the entire mid-oceanic ridge is consumed by subduction (Pitman, 1978, p. 1392). During this process, the oceanic lithosphere that is being consumed is progressively younger and more high-standing, which means that the average age of the entire unsubducted oceanic lithosphere must increase, and so must the average depth of the ocean basins. The result will be eustatic lowering of sea level and regression. Later, as new spreading boundaries appear and an increased amount of new oceanic lithosphere is generated, average depth of the ocean basins will again decrease and a positive eustatic movement will bring on transgression.

Carrying this last speculation a bit further, consider the effect of the opening up of a new backarc basin by extension, following the model explained in Chapter 8 (see Figure 8.4). During this process, new hot lithospere within the backarc basin replaces in areal extent the old, cold lithosphere lost by subduction in the trench on the outward side of the laterally moving island arc. The substitution of new lithosphere for old would decrease the average depth of the ocean basins, as required for transgression.

Yet another tectono-eustatic process that has been brought forward is the rise of mantle plumes within oceanic lithosphere (Hallam, 1992 p, 206). Presumably, these plumes are not implicated in mid-oceanic ridge volcanism, but rise in areas far from plate boundaries. The plumes would raise domes on the abyssal sea floor and thus force sea-level rise. Modeling of this process suggests that it would have a negligible effect on sea level (Huffman, Fahlquist, and McCartney, 1990).

Largest in terms of scale of magnitude is a totally global tectonic mechanism that has been called upon to explain eustatic rise and fall of sea level; it is the breakup of a supercontinent (Hallam, 1992, p. 206-207). The breakup of Pangea, starting in Triassic time, is well documented. (See Figures 1.17 and 13.36.) Seafloor magnetic anomalies have been mapped over much of the world ocean floor. Prior to the breakup, a single great ocean, *Panthalassa*, surrounded Pangea. Much of the crust of that ocean was relatively cold. Supercontinents are thought to be short-lived because the huge dimensions of the single plate allow heat to build up rapidly in the mantle and cause mantle doming leading to continental rifting (Chapter 10). This

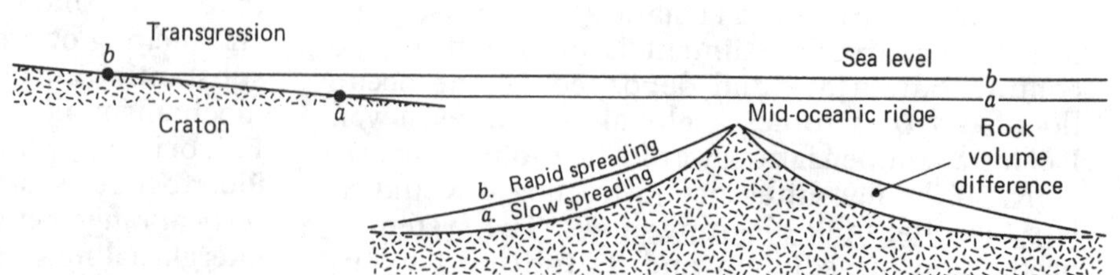

Figure 11.70 Schematic cross sections showing sea-level rise caused by an increase in spreading rate. (Copyright © by Arthur N. Strahler.)

hypothesis was put forward by seismologist Don L. Anderson in 1982. During fragmentation and separation of the parts, new hot oceanic crust will be formed in large quantities. At the same time, the old, cold oceanic crust is being consumed at subduction margins along the advancing margins of the dispersing fragments. The dispersing continents finally reach a zone of mantle downsinking where the continents also subside, and this brings on a substantial eustatic rise in sea level (Worsley, Nance, and Moody, 1984).

11.21 Eustasy and the Geoid

So far, we have not taken in to account that the earth is not a perfect sphere. Even the ellipsoid form of the earth, produced by its rotation, is not an adequate representation of the configuration of global sea level. Refer back to Chapter 3 and reread the section titled The Geoid and Global Geoidal Maps. As Figure 3.40 shows, the surface of the geoid lies below the ideal ellipsoid of reference and coincides with the undisturbed sea surface over the ocean basins. The geoid passes beneath the continental surface in a location above the ellipsoid. If one imagines a tunnel to be excavated at the level of the geoid from coast to coast, the water surface would be found in that tunnel. However, this simple a relationship could only happen for a solid earth of perfect internal homogeneity. In reality, inhomogeneities in the crust and mantle are large and actually govern the height of the geoid. When you look closely at a modern world map of the geoid, Figures 3.42 and 3.43, the geoidal surface seems scarcely to relate to the configuration of continents and oceans. The southern tip of the Indian craton lies in one narrow sector of a nearly circular negative geoidal depression, or "hole" occupied mostly by oceanic crust. "A ship sailing across that hole would drop by almost 100 m and then rise again by the same amount, all without doing work against gravity!" (C.M.R. Fowler, 1990, p. 165) Over Australia, a cratonic block, a geoidal gradient from negative to positive over a large range of values covers the block from southwest to northeast. The large negative depression centered on Hudson Bay clearly agrees with the glacio-eustatic model, as expected. Over the central Andes of South America we find a conspicuous high flanked with large expanses of low values over the Pacific ocean on the west and the great craton to the east. The Andean high makes sense because of its excess mass, but why are the adjacent ocean floor and craton so similar in geoidal height? What we are probably seeing is a large-scale geoidal control operating deep in the mantle.

You may also be puzzled by the lack of correspondence of the continental coastlines with the zero value of geoidal height. Take for example the west coast of South America. Near the southern tip of the continent, at the shoreline the geoid reads +6 m. Should you travel northward off the shoreline by boat, that figure would rise to higher values, reaching a maximum of over 40 m in northern Chile where the great Altiplano mountain mass lies inland. You have actually moved farther from the center of the earth by the difference in geoidal height, but here again, "all without doing any work against gravity."

Is it possible that changes in the form of the geoid, acting as an independent factor, cause transgressions and regressions? If so, would these be global eustatic changes comparable to those caused by changes in volume of the world ocean? The concept of such "geoidal eustasy" was first introduced by Rhodes W. Fairbridge in 1961 and was developed further in 1976 by Nils-Axel Mörner of Stockholm University. The hypothesis requires that the geoidal surface is undergoing constant change in its form by simple warping in response to local changes in mantle density from place to place. At any given locality, upwarping of the geoid would cause transgression, while downwarping would cause regression. However, true global eustatic change such as results from changes in volume of the world ocean are not provided for.

Figure 11.71 is a schematic drawing showing how mantle convection currents might produce corresponding variations in height of the geoidal surface. It is based on results of modeling carried out by Michael Gurnis of the University of Michigan (1990, 1992, 1993). Diagram A shows the mantle layer with its imagined convection system. Heating from below powers a rising current that spreads out laterally and feeds into a descending current in a region of cooling from above. The system is driven by density differences in the mantle. As shown in Diagram B, these differences cause the geoidal surface (sea surface) to be high over the hotter mantle and low over the cooler mantle. (Do not be misled by enormous differences in the vertical scales of the two diagrams!)

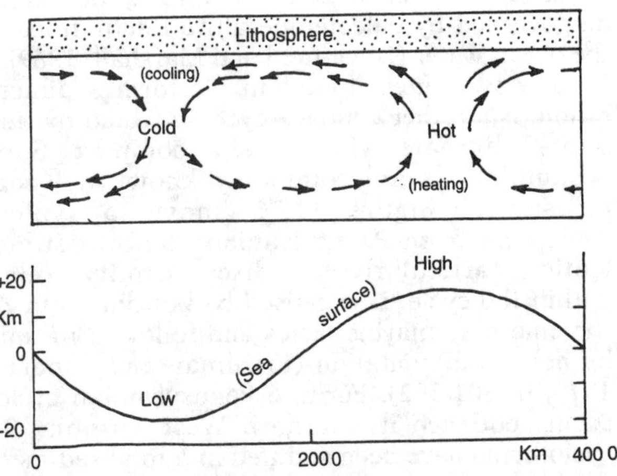

Figure 11.71 Schematic diagrams of the possible effect of mantle convection currents on the geoidal surface profile. (Copyright © by Arthur N. Strahler.)

11.22 Sequence Stratigraphy and the Vail Curve

We have now reviewed two processes of great importance in the field of stratigraphy: epeirogeny and eustasy. Whereas epeirogeny is clearly a tectonic process involving flexing of lithospheric plates, eustasy is restricted to global sea-level change. As we have shown, eustasy can come about through the action of plate tectonics, but eustasy can also be attributed to non-tectonic processes that involve only the global water balance. (The water balance is a flow system of water in any of its three states through the atmosphere and hydrosphere.) Stratigraphy is a major geoscience discipline with which we assume our readers are familiar, while the water balance is a topic within the geophysical branch of hydrogeology (or geohydrology). In this, our final chapter section, we describe briefly one part of the subject of modern *sequence stratigraphy*.

Heavily involved in sequence stratigraphy is a general field known as *cyclic stratigraphy*. A brief background statement about cyclic stratigraphy may be helpful. "Cycle" refers to a specific succession of upward changes in lithology or texture, repeated many times over with very little variation, other than thickness. Strata showing such successions are often called *rhythmites*. Examples familiar to most geology students are varved clays in terrestrial glacial deposits and turbidites of the abyssal sea floors. Both of these are formed by fluctuations in subaqueous sedimentation. Varves are not linked to tectonism, but turbidity currents are known to be triggered by earthquakes. Other rhythmites are linked in to the earth's tidal cycle, which has changed gradually through time. Regional earthquakes, a tectonic mechanism, have been called upon to explain sedimentary cycles within a cratonal basin. Appropriately, these rhythmites have been called *seismites* (Pratt, 1994, p. 1091). Interbedded chalks and marls of the Upper Cretaceous "White Cliffs of Dover" on the Kent coast of southeast England are an example of rhythmites thought to be governed by paleotemperature fluctuations of the ocean water (Ditch-field and Marshall, 1989).

The *cyclothem*, found in platform sedimentation, is a rather complex cycle in which marine strata alternate with a delta complex. Such accumulations are commonly known as "coal measures." Figure 11.72 shows a typical cyclothem from Pennsylvanian platform strata. Notice particularly the disconformity found within the cycle. It is caused by bottom scour of the emerging marine facies and followed in time by delta sedimentation (Friedman and Sanders, 1978, p. 301-302). For one Pennsylvanian cyclothem sequence in southern West Virginia, 90 cyclothems have been counted in a total sediment thickness of about 1500 m. The average thickness of a cyclothem is thus about 17 m and perhaps required about 400,000 years to complete. Eustasy is an obvious mechanism for cyclothems. Perhaps the mechanism is glacio-eustacy, in which case we have a further choice of the several possible causes of glaciations and interglaciations.

Turning now to sequence stratigraphy, we concentrate on one aspect only, that of Phanerozoic transgressions and regressions that occurred on the passive margins of the continents. Stratigrapher H.E. Wheeler is recognized as a pioneer in sequence stratigraphy (1958). The tectonic aspects of this process have already been explained in earlier parts of this chapter. Recall that in mature stage of the passive margin the geocline thickens and advances over the continental crust (Figures 11.10C and 11.21). The shelf sediments and their landward extension as an inner flexural wedge are the subject of our attention. Following the breakup of Pangea this sediment body began to form at the close of the synrift stage, so the miogeoclinal strata would date from about the Early Jurassic, ~200 Ma. Sequence stratigraphy can also be carried back through the entire Phanerozoic eon by study of ancient passive margins deformed by orogenies of the Paleozoic Era, such as those of the Appalachians.

Studies of the miogeocline on both sides of the Atlantic began many decades before plate tectonics appeared, and the stratigraphic sequence was well established on the Cretaceous and younger coastal plains. Through core drilling, information was extended some distance seaward over the shallow continental shelf. Then seismic reflection came into wide use, enabling the established disconformities to be identified directly from the reflection images. Figure 11.73 is an example of the appearance of typical reflection imagery and its interpretation in terms of stratigraphic units. Identification and correlation of passive margin strata became known as *seismic stratigraphy*. It was developed intensively during the 1970s for use in petroleum exploration. A set of principles and a style of graphic presentation for applying this form of stratigraphy were put forward in 1977 by a team of Exxon geologists and geophysicists led by Peter R. Vail (Vail, Mitchum, Todd, Widmer, Thompson, Songree, Bubb, and Hatlelid, 1977). Vail had been a graduate student of stratigrapher Laurence L. Sloss of Northwestern University, who had developed basic concepts of sequence stratigraphy as applied to cratonic interiors (1963). [See Anthony Hallam, *Phanerozoic Sea-Level Changes*, 1992, for a historical review of the development of sequence stratigraphy and seismic stratigraphy.]

Because our book is about plate tectonics, the following review of the Vail system and its graphic expression in the "Vail curve" is brief and incomplete, giving only what is essential to make intelligible an assessment of the role, if any, that plate tectonics plays in shaping the Vail curve. Three figures will be helpful in serving this purpose. Figure 11.74 leads from the conventional

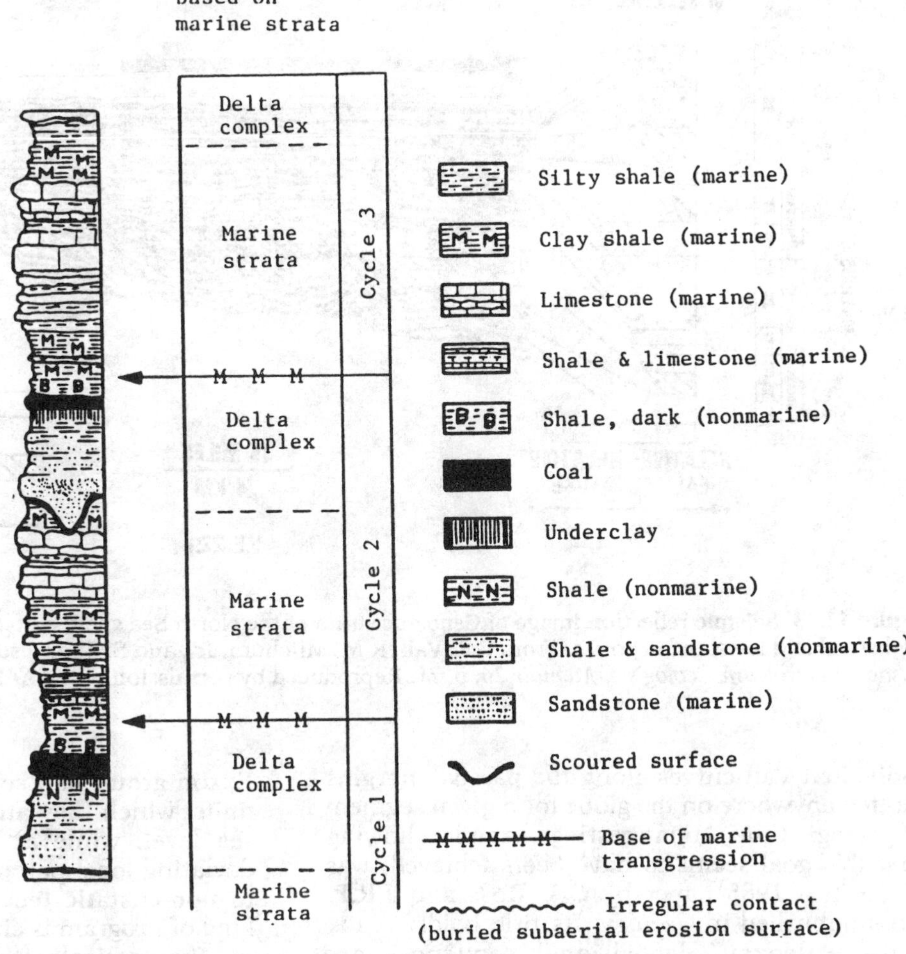

Figure 11.72 A modern interpretation of a typical Pennsylvanian cyclothem. (From G. Friedman and J.E. Sanders, *Principles of Sedimentology*, p. 302-303, Figure 10.28. Copyright © 1978 by John Wiley & Sons, Inc. Reprinted by permission of the publisher.)

presentation of stratigraphy into the Exxon/Vail presentation. Diagram A is a stratigraphic cross section depicting the sedimentary geology of a typical miogeocline. It shows bedding surfaces and disconformities. Two kinds of facies are shown: marine and coastal. The sequence is divided up into an age succession of *cycles*, labeled *A*, *B*, *C*, *D*, and *E*. Bold vertical arrows indicate coastal aggradation. Diagram B is a chronostratigraphic chart, on which age in m.y. is scaled on the ordinate. Horizontal distance is scaled on the abscissa, as in Diagram A. Key points on the discontinuities are marked with dots, which are connected, leaving a large unoccupied area, labeled "hiatus." Diagram C shows the data of Diagram B converted into the format known as the *Vail curve*. Horizontal distance has as its zero point the initial shelf edge of cycle *A*. Increments of coastal aggradation are plotted as steps rising up to the left to reach a "highstand." For a "stillstand," a vertical line is entered. Fall from a highstand is indicated as a horizontal line pointed to the right. A fall that extends to the right beyond the zero point measures a "lowstand." The time units labeled A through E now become designated as *cycles*. All changes of level are taken to be relative. Figure 11.73 includes an example of the Vail curve derived from a real reflection seismic image. It shows the full Cenozoic record of a locality on the continental shelf of the North Sea. We see here only the equivalent of diagrams A and C of Figure 11.74, omitting diagram B.

Notice next that Diagram C of Figure 11.74 recognizes a division of the cycles into two *supercycles*. Cycles *B*, *C*, and *D* are grouped into one *supercycle*, but cycles *A* and *E* are incomplete (truncated) as shown here. A hierarchical system of cycles prevails and has four levels, called *orders*. Figure 11.75 (right) shows cycles of the second order; they are supercycles of the entire Phanerozoic. At the left, first-order cycles have been fitted as an envelope over the second-order cycles (supercycles). Well known to stratigraphers for many decades is the great rise in sea level throughout the Cambrian, a near-constancy of sea level through the Permian, Triassic, and Jurassic periods, and the great inundation of Cretaceous time followed by a great withdrawal through the Cenozoic. (We show no examples of third- and fourth-order cycles.)

The final goal of seismic stratigraphy as developed by the Exxon/Vail group was to demonstrate the synchroneity of profile of

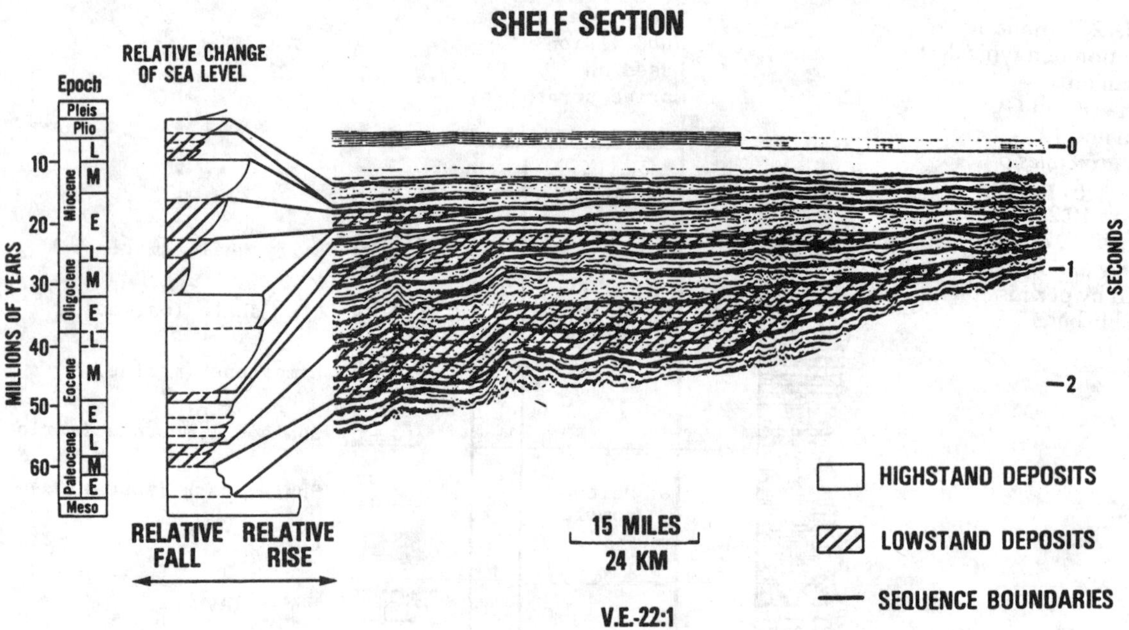

Figure 11.73 Seismic reflection image of Cenozoic strata of the North Sea shelf, edited to define layers of highstand and lowstand deposits.(From P.R. Vail, R.M. Mitchum, Jr., and S. Thompson, III, 1977, *Amer. Assoc. of Petroleum Geologists, Memoir 26*, p. 71. Reproduced by permission of the AAPG.)

individual Vail curves along the passive margins plotted anywhere on the globe for a given segment of geologic time. An interesting example, showing that this goal seems to have been achieved, was given in a 1985 paper by C.A. Ross and J.R.P. Ross published in *Geology*. Its title boldly reads "Late Paleozoic depositional sequences are synchronous and worldwide." The authors assembled more than 50 transgressive/regressive depositional sequences from Carboniferous through Lower Permian time on stable cratonic shelves. Vail-like curves for northwestern Europe, the Russian Platform, and the Mississippi valley, compared side by side, appear remarkably similar in form and timing throughout 30 oscillations (1985, Figures 1-3). This time span is, of course, coincident with an intact Pangea prior to the start of its rifting apart, and is within a span of geologic time having very small sea level fluctuations.

Immediately following its publication in the early 1970s, the Exxon/Vail program experienced strong but mixed reactions that began to appear in print from members of the academic and government geoscience community. Science writer Richard Kerr summarized these reactions in a 1980 article in *Science*. Obviously, the Vail curve (VC) was based on an enormous quantity of data, but most of it was denied access to those outside the petroleum industry. Thus the supporting evidence was hidden from view and could not be used by the "outsiders" (OUTs) to test the product. Nevertheless, upon applying the VC, the OUTs were finding that it was generally accurate in timing. In preparing the VC, the Exxon group had selected only the synchronous units, which they attributed to global changes of sea level, while at the same time leaving out deviating local patterns that had to be attributed to non-eustatic tectonic causes. Of course, this kind of program is circular in its logic.

Pragmatically, the VC was hailed by some as great success, for it resulted in some major discoveries of petroleum accumulations. One specific point on which the OUTs could make a clear objection was the manner in which the VC shows a precipitous decline of sea level at the end of each period of sea level rise (Kerr, 1980, p. 485). (This feature is shown in Figure 11.74, Diagram C, where a "fall" is shown as a horizontal line.) To the contrary, evidence of a retreat (regression) on a time schedule matching that of the advance (transgression) had been obtained by Earle Kauffman of the Smithsonian's National Museum (Kerr, p. 485). Although the Vail group had held that glacio-eustasy was the mechanism for their cycles, we should treat it as a secondary hypothesis independent of the empirical data of the VC itself.

A major event in the enduring saga of the VC was the 1987 publication in *Science* of a revised version of the curve (Haq, Hardenbol, and Vail, 1987). It was reviewed in the same issue by science writer Richard A. Kerr (1987). Because of the great increase in both data and curve detail, it was seen by the VC team as a "new generation curve." To rectify their reliance on sequestered oil company data, the VC team tied in the revised curve to data of some 40 accessible rock outcrops that serve as type sections. Another novel feature

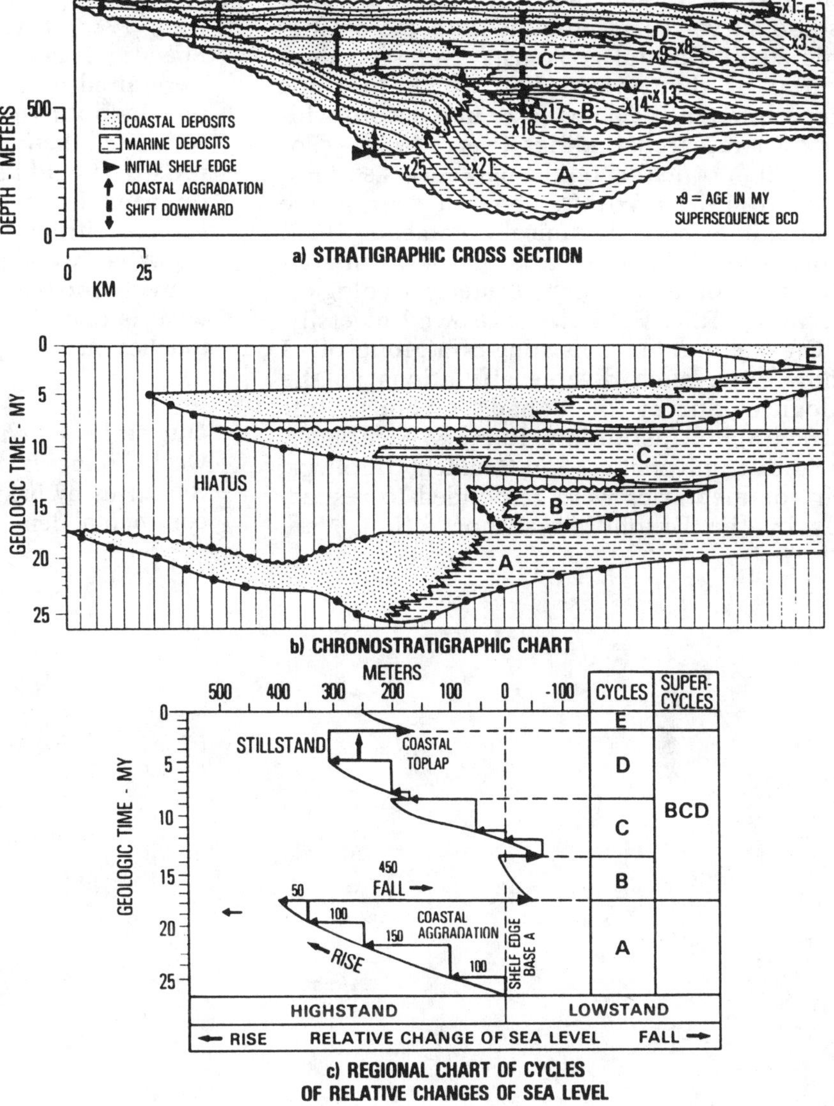

Figure 11.74 Cross-sectional diagrams showing three steps in producing the Vail curve from seismic reflection data. (From P.R. Vail, R.M. Mitchum, Jr., and S. Thompson, III, 1977, *Amer. Assoc. of Petroleum Geologists, Memoir 26*, p. 74. Reproduced by permission of the AAPG.)

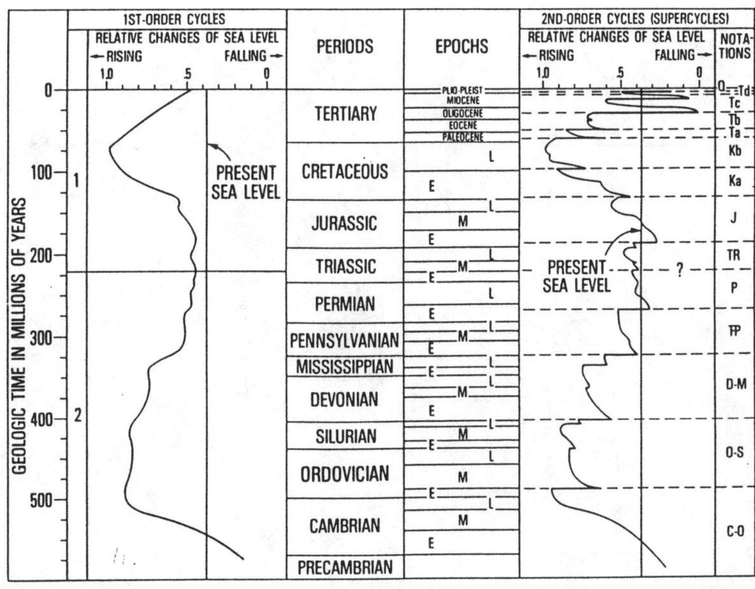

Figure 11.75 The Vail curve of the Phanerozoic Eon as presented in 1977. (From P.R. Vail, R.M. Mitchum, Jr., and S. Thompson, III, 1977, *Amer. Assoc. of Petroleum Geologists, Memoir 26*, p. 84. Reproduced by permission of the AAPG.)

of their revised table was the inclusion of a "eustatic curve" corresponding with the stratigraphic curve. Several geologists expressed their approval of the revised VC, which in some respects brought the data closer into accord with their own research findings (Kerr, 1987). (For additional information on the new curves see also Weisburd, 1987.) Within about a year, there appeared in *Science* (Technical Comments, 1988) responses by three adversarial parties: Christie-Blick et al. of the Lamont-Doherty Geological Observatory; R.K. Matthews of Brown University; and Gradstein et al., consisting of a group of 13 authors from such diverse affiliations as the Geological Survey of Canada, Woods Hole Oceanographic Institution, Rutgers, McMaster, and Purdue universities, and Occidental College. Their commentaries were responded to respectively by the Exxon/Vail authors (Haq, Vail, Hardenbol, and Van Wagoner, 1988; Vail and Haq, 1988; Haq, Hardenbol, and Vail, 1988). Specific areas of agreement and disagreement were aired by the groups on both sides. Staff of the Lamont-Doherty Geological Observatory continued their adversarial investigations into the revised VC and its implications. Their results were reported in several issues of their periodical, *Lamont*, through 1988, 1989, and 1990.

What we have been able to offer here is scarcely more than the briefest of overviews of what is one of the great geoscience debates that touches on concepts of plate tectonics.

* * * * * * *

Our series of chapters on "how plate tectonics works" remains incomplete. Chapter 12 completes the series by briefly examining the interaction of continental denudation with plate tectonics.

References Cited

Amer. Assoc. of Petroleum Geologists Education Course Note Series, No. 19, Chapter 2.

Anderson, Don L., 1982, Hot spots, polar wander, Mesozoic convection, and the geoid. *Nature*, v. 297, p. 391-393.

Atwater, Tanya, 1989, Plate tectonic history of the northeast Pacific and western North America. Chapter 4, p. 21-72 in *Geology of North America*, Vol. N, Boulder, CO: The Geological Society of America.

Aydin, Atilla, and Amos Nur, 1982, Evolution of pull-apart basins and their scale independence. *Tectonics*, v. 1, no. 1, p. 91-105.

Bally, Albert W., 1989, Phanerozoic basins of North America. Chapter 15, pages 397-446 in Bally and Palmer, Eds., 1989.

Bally, Albert W., and Allison R. Palmer, Eds., 1989, Vol. A of *The Geology of North America: An Overview*. Boulder, CO: The Geological Society of America.

Bates, Robert L. and Julia A. Jackson, Eds., 1987, *Glossary of Geology*, 3rd ed., Alexandria: American Geological Institute.

Beaumont, C., 1978, The evolution of sedimentary basins on a visco-elastic lithosphere: Theory and examples. *Geophys. J. R. Astronomical Soc.*, v. 55, p. 471-497.

Beaumont, C., 1981, Foreland basins. *Geophys.J. R. Astronomical Soc*., v. 65, p.291-329.

Bice, David, 1988, Synthetic stratigraphy of carbonate platform and basin systems. *Geology*, v. 16, p. 703-707.

Bond, Gerard C., and Michelle H. Kominz, 1988, Evolution of thought on passive continental margins from the origin of geosynclinal theory (~1890) to the present. *Bull., Geol. Soc. Amer.*, v. 100, p. 1909-1933.

Bond, Gerard, and Walter C. Pitman III, 1982. The evolution of sedimentary basins. *Lamont-Doherty Yearbook*, v. 8, p. 23-27.

Burke, Kevin, 1977, Development of graben associated with the initial ruptures of the Atlantic Ocean. *Tectonophysics*, v. 36, p. 93-112.

Burke, Kevin, and John F. Dewey, 1973, Plume-generated triple junctions: Key indicators in applying plate tectonics to old rocks. *Jour. of Geology*, v. 81, p. 406-433.

Chapin, C.E., and S.M. Cather, 1981, Eocene tectonics and sedimentation in the Colorado Plateau-Rocky Mountain area. *Arizona Ceological Society Digest*, v. 14, p. 173-198.

Christie-Blick, Nicholas, Gregory S. Mountain, and Kenneth G. Miller, 1988, Sea level history. *Science*, V. 241, p. 596.

Conde, S.C., J.L. LaBrecque, R.L. Larson, W.C. Pitman III, et al., 1989, *Magnetic Lineations of the World's Ocean Basins* (Map). Tulsa OK: Amer. Assoc. of Petroleum Geologists.

Crowell, John C., 1974, Origin of late Cenozoic basins in southern California. Pages 190-204 in W.R. Dickinson, Ed., 1974, *Tectonics and Sedimentation*. Society of Economic Paleontologists and Mineralogists Special Paper 22. Also, pages 195-208 in Sylvester, Ed., 1984.

Crowell, John C., 1982, The tectonics of Ridge Basin, southern California. Pages 25-41 in Crowell, J.C., and Link, H.M., Eds., Soc. of Economic Paleontologists and Mineralogists, Publication 22.

deWard, D., 1987, Diapirism. Pages 202-203 in Seyfert, Ed., 1987.

Dewey, John F., and Kevin Burke, 1974, Hot spots and continental break-up: Implications for collisional orogeny. *Geology*, v. 2, no. 2, p. 57-60.

Dibblee, Thomas J., Jr., 1977, Strike-slip tectonics of the San Andreas Fault and its role in Cenozoic basin evolvement. Pages 26-38 in T.H. Nilsen, Ed., 1977, *Late Mesozoic and Cenozoic Sedimentation in California*. Bakersfield, CA, San Joaquin Geological Society. Also, pages 159-171 in Sylvester, Ed., 1984.

Dickinson, William R., 1971, Plate tectonics in geologic history. *Science*, v. 174, p. 107-113.

Dickinson, William R., 1974, Plate tectonics and sedimentation. *Society of Economic Paleontologists and Mineralogists Special Publication 22*, p. 1-27.

Dickinson, William R., 1976, Plate tectonic evolution of sedimentary basins. *Amer. Assoc. of Petroleum Geologists Continuing Education Course Notes Series 1*, p. 1-62.

Dickinson, William R., and D.R. Seely, 1979, Structure and stratigraphy of forearc regions. *Bull., Amer. Assoc. Petroleum Geologists*, v. 63, no. 1, p. 1-30.

Dickinson, William R., Margaret A. Klute, Michael J. Hayes, Susanne U. Janecke, Erick R. Lundin, Mary A. McKittrick, and Mark D. Olivares, 1988, Paleogeographic and paleotectonic setting of Laramide sedimentary basins in the central Rocky Mountain region. *Bull., Geol. Soc. Amer.*, v. 100, p. 102-1039.

Diecchio, Richard Joseph, 1995, Isostasy for geoscience labs. *Jour. of Geological Education*, v. 43, p. 35-42.

Dietz, Robert S., 1972, Geosynclines, mountains, and continent-building. *Scientific American*, v. 226, no. 3, p. 30-38.

Dietz, Robert S., and John C. Holden, 1970, Reconstruction of Pangaea: Breakup and dispersion of continents, Permian to present. *Jour. Geophysical Res.*, v. 75, p. 4939-4956.

Ditchfield, P., and J.D. Marshall, 1989, Isotopic variation in rhythmically bedded chalks: Paleotemperature variation in the Upper Cretaceous. *Geology*, v. 17, p. 842-845.

Dobrin, Milton B., 1960, *Introduction to Geophysical Prospecting*. New York: McGraw-Hill Book Co.

Dott, Robert H., Jr., 1974, The geosynclinal concept. Pages 1-12 in *Modern and Ancient Geosynclinal Sedimentation*, R.H. Dott, Jr., and Robert H. Shaver, Eds., Soc. of Economic Paleogeologists and Mineralogists, Special Publ. No. 19.

Dott, Robert H., Jr., 1975, Memorial to Marshall Kay 1904-1975. Boulder, CO: The Geol. Soc. of Amer.

Dott, Robert H., Jr., 1978, Tectonics and sedimentation a century later, *Earth Science Reviews*, v. 14, p. 1-34.

Ewing, M., and J. Ewing, 1962, Rate of salt dome growth. *Amer. Assoc. Petroleum Geologists, Bull.*, v. 46, p. 708-709.

Fairbridge, Rhodes W., 1961, Eustatic changes in sea level. Pages 99-185 in L.H. Ahrens et al., Eds. *Physics and Chemistry of the Earth*, v. 4. New York: Pergamon Press.

Fairbridge, Rhodes W., 1966, Mean sea level changes, long-term—eustatic and other. Pages 479-485 in Fairbridge, Ed., 1966.

Fairbridge, Rhodes W., Ed., 1966, *Encyclopedia of Oceanography*, New York: Reinhold Publishing Corp.

Fowler, C.M.R., 1990. The Solid Earth*: An Introduction to Gelobal Geophysics*. Cambridge, UK: Cambridge Unversity press.

Friedman, Gerald M., and John E. Sanders, 1978, *Principles of Sedimentology*. New York: John Wiley & Sons.

Gorsline, D.S., and L.S.Y. Teng, 1989, The California continental borderland. Chapter 24, p. 471-487 in *Geology of North America*, Vol. N, Boulder, CO: The Geological Society of America.

Graciansky, P.C. de, C.W. Poag, et al., 1985. The Goban Spur transect: Geological evolution of a sediment-starved passive continental margin. *Bull., Geol. Soc. Amer.*, v. 96, p. 58-76.

Gradstein, F.M., et al., 1988, Sea level history. *Science*, v. 241, p. 599-601.

Graham, Stephan Alan, 1983, Evolving concepts and teaching approaches in tectonics and sedimentation. *Jour. of Geologic Education*, v. 31, p. 266-276.

Gurnis, Michael, 1990, Ridge spreading subduction and sea level fluctuations. *Science*, v. 250, p. 970-972.

Gurnis, Michael, 1992, Long-term controls on eustatic and epeirogenic motions by mantle convection. *GSA Today*. v. 2, no. 7, p. 141-157.

Gurnis, Michael, 1993, Depressed continental hypsometry behind oceanic trenches: A clue to subduction controls on sea-level change. *Geology*, v. 21, p. 29-32.

Hallam, Amthony, 1992, *Phanerozoic Sea-Level Changes*, New York: Columbia University Press.

Hamilton, Warren B., 1988, Plate tectonics and island arcs. *Bull., Geol. Soc. Amer.*, v. 100, p. 1505-1527.

Haq, B.U., Hardenbol, and P.R. Vail, 1988, Sea level history, *Science*, v. 241, p. 601-602

Haq, B.U., P.R. Vail, J. Hardenbol, and J.C. Van Wagoner, 1987, Sea level history, *Science*, v. 241, p. 596-597.

Haq, Bilal U., Jan Hardenbol, and Peter R. Vail, 1987, Chronology of fluctuating sea levels since the Triassic. *Science*, v. 235, p. 1156-1167.

Helwig, J.A., 1985, Origin and classification of sedimentary basins. *1985 Proc. of the Seventeenth Annual Offshore Technology Conference*, v. 1, p. 21-32.

Hoffman, P., J.F. Dewey, and K. Burke, 1974, Aulacogens and their genetic relation to geosynclines with a Proterozoic example from Great Slave Lake, Canada. In R.H. Dott, Jr., and R.H. Shaver, Eds., *Modern and Ancient Geosyncline Sedimentation*. Society of Economic Paleontologists and Mineralogists, Special Publication 19, p. 38-55.

Huffman, A.R., D.A. Fahlquist, and K. McCartney, 1990, Gravity effects of large mantle plumes and the correlation between hot spot initiation, mass extinctions, and sea level change. *Geol. Soc. Amer. Abstracts* 280.

Ingersoll, Raymond, V., 1988, Tectonics of sedimentary basins. *Bull., Geol. Soc. Amer.*, v. 100, p. 1704-1719.

Jackson, M.P.A., and B.C. Vendeville, 1994, Regional extension as a geologic trigger for diapirism. *Bull., Geol. Soc. Amer.*, v. 106, p. 57-73.

Jacobson, S.R., 1991, Petroleum source rocks and organic facies. Pages 3-11 in Merrill, Ed., 1991.

Karner, Garry D., and James L. Pindell, 1992, The role of late-stage sedimentation in the generation of gas, Gulf of Mexico. *Lamont-Doherty Geological Observatory, 1990-91 Report*.

Kay, Marshall, 1951, *North American Geosynclines*. Memoir 48, Geol. Soc. of Amer.

Kay, Marshall, 1967, On geosynclinal nomenclature. *Geological Magazine*, v. 104, no. 4, p. 311-316.

Kay, Marshall, and Edwin H. Colbert, 1965, *Stratigraphy and Life History*, New York: John Wiley & Sons.

Kearey, Philip, and Frederick J. Vine, 1990, *Global Tectonics*. Oxford: Blackwell Scientific Publications.

Kerr, Richard A., 1980, Changing global sea levels as a geologic index. *Science*, v. 209, p. 483-486.

Kerr, Richard A., 1987, Refining and defending the Vail sea level curve. *Science*, v. 235, p. 1141-1142.

Kingston, D.R., C.P. Dishroon, and P.A. Williams, 1983, Global basin classification system. *Amer. Assoc. of Petroleum Geologists*, v. 67, no. 12, p. 2175-2193.

Klein, G. de V., and A.T. Hsui, 1987, Origin of cratonic basins. *Geology*, v. 15, p. 1094-1098.

Klemme, H.D., 1980, Petroleum basins—classification and characteristics. *Jour. of Petroleum Geology*, v. 3, no. 2, p. 187-207.

Lowrie, Allen, Zhihuai Yu, and Ian Lerche, 1991, Hydrocarbon trap types and deformation styles modeled using quantified rates of salt movement, Louisiana margin. *Trans-Gulf Coast Assoc. of Geological Societies*, v. 41, p. 445-459.

Martin, R.G. Jr., 1978, Northern and eastern Gulf of Mexico continental margin: Stratigraphic and structural framework, Pages 21-42 in A.H. Bouma, G.T. Moore, and J.M. Coleman, Eds., *Amer. Assoc of Petroleum Geologists Studies in Geology, No.* 7.

Matthews, R.K., 1988, Sea level history, *Science*, v. 241, p. 597-598.

McKenzie, D.P., 1978, Some remarks on the development of sedimentary basins. *Earth and Planetary Science Letters*, v. 40, p. 25-32.

Merrill, Robert K., Ed., 1991, *Source and Migration Processes and Evaluation Techniques: Treatise of Petroleum Geology*. Tulsa, OK: Amer. Assoc. of Petroleum Geologists.

Moore, George W. and Luis Del Castillo, 1974, Tectonic evolution of the Southern Gulf of Mexico. *Bull, Geol. Soc. of Amer.*, v. 85, p. 607-618.

Morgan, W.J., 1968, Pliocene reconstruction of the Juan de Fuca ridge (Abstract). *Trans., Amer. Geophys. Union*, v. 49, p. 327.

Mörner, Nils-Axel, 1981, Revolution in Cretaceous sea-level analysis. *Geology*, v. 9, p. 344-346.

Muehlberger, William R., 1992, *Tectonic Map of North America*. Tulsa, OK: Amer. Assoc. of Petroleum Geologists.

McKenzie, D.P., A.B. Watts, B. Parsons, and M. Roufosse, 1980, Planform of mantle convection beneath the Pacific Ocean. *Nature*, v. 288, p. 442-446.

Oldow, John S., Albert W. Bally, Hans G. Ave Lallemant, and William P. Leeman, 1989, Phanerozoic evolution of the North American Cordillera; United States and Canada. Chapter 8, Pages 139-232, in Bally and Palmer, Eds., 1989.

Palciauskas, V.V., 1991, Primary migration of petroleum. Pages 13-22 in Merrill, Ed., 1991.

Pang, Ming, and Dag Nummedal, 1995, Flexural subsidence and basement tectonics of the Cretaceous Western Interior basin, United States. *Geology*, v. 23, p. 173-176.

Paull, Charles K., and A. Conrad Newmann, 1987, Continental margin brine seeps: Their geological consequences. *Geology*, v. 15, p. 545-548.

Paull, Charles, K., and William P. Dillon, 1980, Erosional origin of the Blake Escarpment: An alternative hypothesis. *Geology*, v. 8, p. 538-542.

Pindell, James L., 1985, Alleghenian reconstruction and subsequent evolution of the Gulf of Mexico, Bahamas and proto-Caribbean. *Tectonics*, v. 4, no. 1, p. 1-39.

Pitman III, Walter C., 1978, Relationship between eustasy and stratigraphic sequences of passive margins. *Bull., Geol. Soc. Amer.*, v. 89, p. 1389-1403.

Pratt, Brian R., 1994, Seismites in the Mesoproterozoic Altyn Formation (Belt Supergroup), Montana: A test for tectonic control of peritidal carbonate cyclicity. *Geology*, v. 22, p. 1091-1094.

Price, R.A., 1973, Large-scale gravitational flow of supracrustal rocks, southern Canadian Rockies. Pages 491-502 in de Jong and Schotten, Eds., *Gravity and Tectonics*, New York: John Wiley & Sons.

Quennell, A.M., 1987, Rift valleys. Pages 671-688 in Seyfert, Ed., 1987.

Ramos, Victor A., 1988, The tectonics of the Central Andes: 30° to 33° latitude. *Geol. Soc. Amer. Special Paper 218*, p. 31-54.

Ramos, Victor A., 1989, The birth of South America. *Amer. Scientist*, v. 77, p. 444-450.

Rodgers, Donald A., 1980, Analysis of pull-apart basin development produced by *en echelon* strike-slip faults. Pages 27-41 in P.F. Ballance and H.G. Reading, Eds., Oxford, England, International Association of Sedimentologists; also pages 345-359 in Sylvester, Ed, 1984.

Rodgers, John W., 1993, *A History of the Earth*. New York: Cambridge University Press.

Ross, Charles A., and June R.P. Ross, 1985, Late Paleozoic depositional sequences are synchronous and worldwide. *Geology*, v. 13, p. 194-197.

Schouten, Hans, and Kim D. Kiltgord, 1994, Mechanistic solutions to the opening of the Gulf of Mexico. *Geology*, v. 22, p. 507-510.

Schuchert, Charles, 1955, *Atlas of Paleogeographic Maps of North America*. New York: John Wiley & Sons.

Segnör, A.M. Celal, 1987, Aulacogen. Pages 18-25 in Seyfert, 1987.

Selley, Richard C., 1985, *Elements of Petroleum Geology*. New York, W.H. Freeman & Co.

Seyfert, Carl K., 1987a, Cratonic basins, domes, and arches. Pages 141-158 in Seyfert, Ed., 1987.

Seyfert, Carl K., 1987b, Geosynclines and geoclines, Pages 287-309 in Seyfert, Ed., 1987.

Seyfert, Carl K., 1987c, Mantle plumes and hot spots. Pages 412-430 in Seyfert, Ed., 1987.

Seyfert, Carl K., and Leslie A. Sirkin, 1979, *Earth History and Plate Tectonics*, 2nd ed., New York: Harper & Row.

Seyfert, Carl K., Ed., 1987, *Encyclopedia of Structural Geology and Plate Tectonics*, New York, Van Nostrand Reinhold Co.

Shepard, Francis P., 1973, *Submarine Geology*, 3rd Ed., New York: Harper & Row, Publishers.

Sheridan, Robert E., 1989, The Atlantic passive margin.

Sleep, N.H., J.A. Nunn, and L. Chou, 1980, Platform basins. *Annual Reviews of Earth and Planetary Science*, v. 8, p. 17-34.

Sleep, Norman H., 1971, Thermal effects of the formation of Atlantic continental margins by continental breakup. *Royal Astron. Soc. Geophys. Jour.*, v. 24, p. 325-350.

Sleep, Norman H., 1987, Subsidence of Atlantic continental margins. Pages 773-775 in Seyfert, Ed., 1987.

Sloss, L.L., 1963, Sequences in the cratonic interior of North America. *Bull., Geol. Soc. Amer.*, v. 74, p. 93-114.

Steckler, M.S., 1981, The thermal and mechanical evolution of Atlantic-type continental margins. Ph.D. thesis, Columbia University (Lamont-Doherty Geological Observatory), New York.

Steckler, M.S., and A.B. Watts, 1978, Subsidence of the Atlantic-type continental margins. Pages 184-196 in Scrutton, R.A., Ed., 1982, *Dynamics of passive margins*. Amer. Geophysical Union Geodynamics Series, v. 6.

Sylvester, Arthur G., 1984, Wrench fault tectonics—Introduction. Pages v-ix in Sylvester, Ed., 1984.

Sylvester, Arthur G., Ed., 1984, *Wrench Fault Tectonics. AAPG Reprint Series No. 28*. Tulsa, OK: American Association of Petroleum Geologists.

Talwani, Manik, and Marcus Langseth, 1981. Ocean crustal dynamics. *Science*, v. 213, p. 22-30.

Trusheim, F., 1987, Halokinesis. Pages 324-332 in Seyfert, Ed, 1987.

Vail, P.R., R.M. Mitchum, Jr., R.G. Todd, J.M. Widmer, S. Thompson III, J.B. Songree, J.N. Bubb, and W.G. Hatlelid, 1977, Seismic stratigraphy and global changes of sea level. *Amer. Assoc. of Petroleum Geologists Memoir 26*, p. 49-212.

Vail, Peter R., and Bilal U. Haq, 1988, Sea level history, *Science*, v. 241, p. 599.

Van der Voo, R., F.J. Mauk, and R.B. French, 1976, Permian-Triassic continental configurations and the origin of the Gulf of Mexico. *Geology*, v. 4, p. 177-180.

Vine, F.J., and Hess, H.H., 1970, Sea floor spreading. Pages 587-622 in A.E. Maxwell, Ed., *The Sea*, v. 4, part 2. New York: Wiley Interscience.

Watts, A.B., 1981, The U.S. Atlantic continental margin: Subsidence history, crustal structure and thermal evolution.

Weisburd, Stefi, 1987, Sea cycle clock. *Science News*, v. 131, p. 154-155.

Wheeler, H.E., 1958, Time stratigraphy. *Bull., Amer. Assoc. of Petroleum Geologists*, v. 42, p. 1047-1063.

Wilson, J. Tuzo, 1966, Did the Atlantic close and then reopen? *Nature*, v. 211, p. 676-681.

Worrall, D.M., and S. Snelson, 1989, Evolution of the northern Gulf of Mexico, with emphasis on Cenozoic growth faulting and the role of salt. Chapter 7, pages 97-138 in Bally and Palmer, Eds., 1989.

Chapter: 12 Geomorphology and Plate Tectonics

Geomorphology, the branch of geology concerned with the evolution of landforms—those of both the continental and ocean-basin surfaces—is linked with plate tectonics in two quite different ways. First, geomorphic processes can influence the rates and amounts of tectonic uplift and subsidence. In this relationship, geomorphic process acts as a causative or regulatory agent. Second, erosional landforms, such as marine terraces, can allow rates and amounts of tectonic uplift to be measured. In this second role, geomorphology provides useful information on tectonic processes. In this chapter, we explore both of these roles under the title of *tectonic geomorphology*.

To develop the role of tectonic geomorphology, we need to analyze the two disciplines—plate tectonics and geomorphology—in terms of systems of energy and matter. The geomorphic system carries out the role of *denudation*, consisting of weathering, erosion, transportation, and deposition of crustal rock. In this process, solar energy powers the system through the pathways of the hydrologic cycle, including processes of condensation, precipitation, runoff, and evaporation. The tectonic system, in contrast, is a material system within the solid earth, powered by internal heat energy resources, including residual heat and radiogenic heat. These two systems have been given the names of *exogene system* and *endogene system*, respectively. Atmosphere, hydrosphere, and biosphere comprise the exogene system; minerals comprise the endogene system. The two systems are not by any means completely self-contained within the medium associated with each: For example, water moves within and between both systems in its three states. Nature abhors the categories that humans strive to perfect, and frustrates us with complex cases of interconnections and feedbacks.

If we are so naive as to pronounce that "geomorphology is the study of landforms," some contradictions immediately arise in application. *Landforms* are varied configurations of the interface between the solid earth and its overlying cover of air or water. Now, some of those landforms turn out to be products of the endogene system. A freshly congealed lava flow would be a good example; so would a freshly broken fault scarp. To accommodate all varieties of landforms, two classes of landforms are generally recognized: Class I. Volcanic and tectonic landforms; Class II. Denudational landforms. The volcanic and tectonic landforms are dominated by the endogene processes. The denudational landforms are dominated by the exogene processes.

The exogene processes lower the land surface by agents of erosion (fluvial, eolian, glacial) coupled with rock decomposition and disintegration (weathering) and mass wasting (gravity movements). The total process of reduction or down-wasting of the continental surfaces is covered in the term denudation. Dominating this total process are the fluvial agents, which include the action of water of precipitation flowing over the land surface as runoff in overland flow and stream flow (channel flow). Hence we are dealing here largely with *fluvial denudation* when analyzing the reduction of most continental surfaces lying above sea level. Denudation consists of a sequence of erosion, transportation, and deposition in one more-or-less continuous operation. Deposition accounts for the great sedimentary basins we have examined in Chapter 11. Nevertheless, denudational processes and landforms are not *per se* subjects of this book, and we assume that the reader has a knowledge of general geomorphology, along with other basic geologic topics, such as mineralogy, petrology, sedimentology, stratigraphy, and structural geology.

Tectonic geomorphology probably began to be perceived as a subdiscipline in the mid-1980s, when it was the subject of the 1983 Penrose Conference convened by the Geological Society of America. The 1985 report of this conference introduced tectonic geomorphology as "a rapidly evolving discipline that examines the interaction of vertical and horizontal deformation with erosional and depositional processes" (Bull and Wallace, 1985, p. 216). (The term *morphotectonics* was also used in this context.) The scope of tectonic geomorphology was described and illustrated by William B. Bull of the University of Arizona in 1984. Further publicity was given to the subject by the 15th Annual Geomorphology Symposium held in 1984 at SUNY Binghamton (Graf, 1985). In retrospect, these early descriptions of a "tectonic geomorphology" revealed some confusion with the concept of relative recency of the landforms produced by tectonic events *vis-à-vis* the concept of a causal relationship between geomorphic processes and crustal tectonics that has operated throughout deep geologic time. To clarify this seeming uncertainty of goal, we need to digress in order to compare tectonic geomorphology with a related subject topic named "neotectonics."

12.1 Neotectonics

What is "neotectonics"? This term is frequently seen in the titles of geological journal articles and even of entire books. "Neo," a form of the prefix *ne*, is from the Latin *neos*, meaning "new." We can safely translate "neotectonics" to mean "tectonics of recent time." Is neotectonics a part of tectonic geomophology, or is tectonic geomorphology a part of neotectonics? The standard glossary definition of neotectonics reads: "The study of the post-Miocene structures and structural history of the Earth's crust" (Bates and Jackson, 1987, p. 445). This is a time-bracketed definition combined with a subject definition. Its time-frame starts with the Pliocene, ~5 Ma, and continues through the Pleistocene and Holocene to the present. Our glossary definition seems to agree closely with the title of C. Vita-Finzi's 1986 book: *Recent Earth Movements: An Introduction to Neotectonics*. To check this meaning against that of the Geological Society of America, we can turn to a 1991 volume of the Decade of North American Geology series, titled *Neotectonics of North America.* Most of its chapters and "Neotectonic Maps" describe and document seismicity of North America, while several chapters are given to tectonic stress and heat flow in the North American crust. A single chapter covers the Late Quaternary glacial isostatic recovery of North America, Greenland, and Iceland, which is a topic we cover later in this chapter. Thus all the neotectonics topics covered in the GSA volume are under the aegis of geophysics. Seismicity is the main theme of our Chapter 6, and since all instrumental records of earthquakes are of very recent age, it perhaps qualifies as a bona fide chapter on neotectonics. In their 1996 textbook, *Active Tectonics*: *Earthquakes, Uplift, and Landscape*, Edward A. Keller and Nicholas Pinter of the University of California, Santa Barbara, cover a wide range of neotectonic subjects as well as those we cover here as tectonic geomorphology.

Over many decades, structures of seismic origin—faults and fault systems—were studied within structural geology. Impetus for renewed and intensified research in the field of seismicity under the title of neotectonics has come from the search for evidence of the Neogene history of past earthquakes along established major fault lines. The San Andreas transform system offers one important example. Neotectonics focuses on unraveling the history of a given sequence of tectonic events along the fault zone. Each significant fault displacement triggers an erosional/depositional response preserved in a stratigraphic sequence. Through application of dating methods, a chronology of fault displacements can be established and perhaps provide a basis for earthquake prediction.

Neotectonics *per se* is not covered in our chapter.

12.2 Tectonic Geomorphology

Edward A. Keller describes the present state of the term "tectonic geomorphology" as follows: "Tectonic geomorphology is being defined today in several ways. The first is that tectonic geomorphology is the study of landforms and processes produced by tectonic processes. A more utilitarian definition is that tectonic geomorphology is the application of geomorphic principles to examine and solve tectonic problems. Considering the latter definition, then the term 'neotectonics' is the broader field of study and tectonic geomorphology is a part of it" (Personal communication, 1996).

Our first major topic in tectonic geomorphology relates to fluvial denudation in general, as a system linked with plate tectonics through the effects of thickening of continental crust and lithosphere during orogeny. There rises to high elevation a great crustal mass (a *landmass*) that is destined to be carved up and destroyed by the denudational processes. We shall focus on the schedule of tectonic uplift, which may be related either to epeirogeny or orogeny (or a combination or both). In line with the first role of tectonic geomorphology, we look for the ways in which the removal (unroofing) of an orogen influences the further development of the active orogenic structures.

We then examine the change in rate of denudation that starts with the tectonic uplift and normally continues long after the orogen is completed. An isostatic response to lithospheric unloading comes into play here: this epeirogenic response is a flexing of the lithosphere. We are interested in the gross form and dimensions of the lowering land surface viewed as an envelope, rather than in the individual landforms of smaller dimension, such as valleys, ridges, and stream networks.

Processes of marine erosion and planation, always active along the exposed coasts of continents and islands, are related to plate tectonics in terms of epeirogenic and orogenic crustal movements. Much of what needs to be said about this activity in the framework of plate tectonics can be combined with the broader problems of marine transgression. One specific phase of coastal geomorphology—that of cutting and episodic uplift (or depression) of marine terraces—can be singled out as a research subject of tectonic geomorphology. One phenomenon for study is the spasmodic crustal rise and tilting accompanying underthrust faulting along an active subduction boundary. Another might be the spasmodic epeirogenic uplift of the coast of a passive continental margin to produce a succession of elevated marine terraces. Mantle doming provides yet another independent cause of formation of stepped marine terraces.

Streams draining the flanks of active or recently completed orogens normally develop entrenched alluvial channels in their lower reaches across alluvial fans and aprons. Normal and reverse faulting transverse to the stream channels upsets the grade of the channel, causing aggradation or degradation of channel segments. Here, tectonics is dictating morphological changes, and in so doing is leaving a landform record useful in establishing the tectonic history.

Where ice-sheet loading of the crust has produced a localized crustal basin by isostatic response, the removal of the ice sheet is followed by crustal rise, typically documented by a succession of uplifted marine shorelines marked by beach ridges and other features.

Note that in the above examples, tectonic geomorphology is used as a source of information about the tectonic events that took place. This informational function is the second role of tectonic geomorphology we treat throughout this chapter.

12.3 The Concept of a Denudation System

Processes of fluvial denudation can, of course, be studied effectively without reference to plate tectonics, but when we look to a larger dimension of denudation in terms of its initiation by crustal uplifts, plate tectonics plays a dominant role. Denudation is initiated and strongly intensified by the rise of volcanic arcs and orogens. We need to think in terms of rates of crustal uplift. Perhaps for a collision orogen the uplift of a mountain range occurs relatively swiftly and ends abruptly, whereas for a tectonic forearc rising above an accretionary prism, uplift may be continuous over a period of tens of millions of years. The former is the case of a two-stage sequence in which a brief initial event of compressional tectonics is followed by a long-lasting period of denudation. The latter is a continuum of combined isostatic tectonics and denudation over a vast period of time.

Denudation deals with that portion of the continental crust that lies above baselevel. As we define it here, *baselevel* is an imaginary surface of zero elevation (sea level) extended beneath the land surface. The layer of rock lying above the baselevel surface is the *available landmass*; it is the crustal mass available for removal by denudation. This might seem simple enough and perhaps too obvious to need discussion, until we consider the principle of isostasy, namely, that removal of rock by denudation is compensated for by an upward isostatic movement, whereas the deposition of sediment in another place is accompanied by downward isostatic movement under the added load (see Chapter 3 and Figure 3.43).

To the available landmass as it exists at any one moment must be added the crustal mass that will rise under isostasy to replace part of the rock mass removed in the denudation process. Estimates vary as to what factor to allow for isostatic replacement, but ratios on the order of 4/3 or 5/4 are considered realistic. Arthur Holmes in 1945 had estimated the ratio to be 4/3, based on the replacement inflow of mantle (1978, p. 372-373). James Gilluly in 1955 had used the ratio 5/4. Stanley A. Schumm reviewed these and other estimates, selecting for Gilluly's figure (1963, p. 9). Thus, the removal of 5000 m of rock would be accompanied by uplift of 4000 m and would result in a net lowering of the land surface of only 1000 m.

The available landmass provides potential energy for a denudation system activated by the external agents powered by solar energy. Geomorphic work has been quantitatively analyzed by Nel Caine (1976, p. 137-139). Two forms of work must be done within this system. First, energy must be expended to reduce the strong, dense bedrock to a clastic state or weaken it greatly so that it can be moved to lower levels by mass wasting or by processes of overland flow. Weathering performs the preliminary physical and chemical changes essential to denudation. Energy for weathering processes comes from external sources—from atmospheric heat and heat stored in water in its liquid and vapor states, and to some degree directly from solar radiation. Chemical energy is also released through mineral hydrolysis.

The second form of work is that of abrasion and transportation by overland flow and channel flow. This fluid flow is a system of mass transport and energy transformation powered by gravity. Potential energy that water and rock particles possess because of their elevated position is transformed into kinetic energy of flow, which is ultimately dissipated as heat through frictional resistance to flow. Water is brought to high elevations on land by atmospheric processes, which are powered by solar energy. Rock is caused to rise to high elevations by tectonic forces, powered by the same sources of energy that cause lithospheric plates to move.

12.4 Rates of Orogenic Uplift

Let us take up now the case of an active orogenic belt. Disregarding the horizontal movements involved in folding and overthrust faulting (telescoping), consider for the moment only the vertical component of lift of the crustal mass. In a compressional tectonic event, such as a continent-continent collision, a given prism of crust can be visualized as being narrowed in breadth and at the same time increased in height, as shown in Figure 12.1. Not shown in this figure is the isostatic response, which is a sinking of the prism. The isostatic response partially offsets the rate of vertical rise of the prism, as explained in an earlier paragraph. Using the same ratio of 5/4, for every 5000 m of increase in vertical dimension of the prism, the net increase in vertical rise would be only 1000 m. Uplift rates discussed below are the net values.

Rates of net uplift during orogeny can be roughly estimated from the ages of late Cenozoic strata found today at high positions in the mountain zone. Of course, these estimates deal with long time spans within which uplift rates were certainly unevenly distributed. The long-term averages thus obtained are likely to be much lower

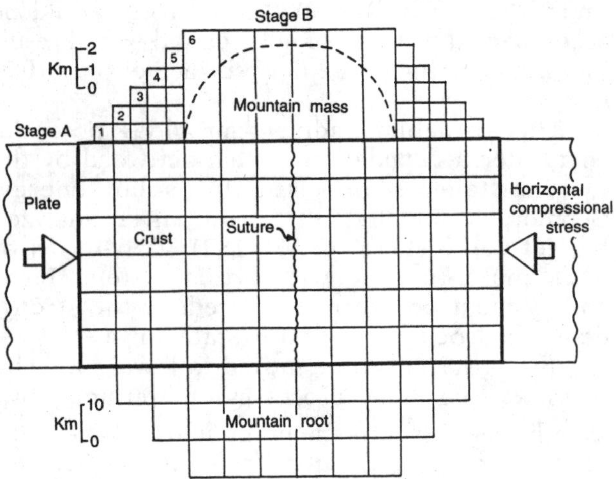

Figure 12.1 Schematic cross-sectional diagram of continental crust in which two plates have been joined by collision. Continued compressional deformation by pure shear raises a mountain mass while also producing a mountain root. (Copyright © by Arthur N. Strahler.)

than what actually occurred during a single orogenic event.

A more realistic estimate of maximum rates of uplift by active orogenic processes can perhaps be obtained from the data of geodetic surveys. Precise determination of ground elevations above sea level has been repeated in a number of instances along survey traverse lines crossing active mountain blocks. Units of millimeters per year (mm/yr) are used for such short periods of observation. A number of such measurements in California listed by Gilluly (1949), as collated by Schumm (1963, p. 7), showed rates of uplift ranging from 5 to 13 mm/yr, with an average of about 8 mm/yr. Comparable rates have been measured in orogenic belts in such widely separated places as in the Persian Gulf area and in Japan. Schumm (1963, p. 7) notes that precise leveling in the Los Angeles area revealed uplift at a rate of 4 mm/yr in the Santa Monica Mountains and 6 mm/yr in the San Gabriel Mountains (Stone, 1961). In contrast, epeirogenic uplift of certain parts of the stable continental cratons is estimated to be very much less—on the order of 1 mm/yr.

A caveat that must be observed in interpreting such geodetic data is not to accept the elevation of a bench mark on a summit as providing a true measurement of crustal rise over that region. As we explain in a later section, deepening of the valleys may cause the summits to rise, whereas the mean elevation of the surrounding region is actually falling. (See Figure 12.10.)

A second caveat that must be applied to the use of geodetic data of uplift is that isostatic compensation is thought to occur episodically (a subject explained later in this section). We do not know where our present century lies temporally in such an episodic sequence.

Using what may be a very high net rate of uplift of 5 mm/yr, and disregarding the removal of mass by denudation, a mountain summit might rise from sea level to an elevation of 5 km in about 1 m.y. This calculation suggests that a full-sized mountain range might be created in a time span less than the duration of the Pleistocene Epoch, taken as 1.6 m.y. Considering the much longer durations of the individual epochs of the Cenozoic Era, orogenic uplift during a continent-continent collision appears to be an extremely rapid process in comparison with the long, uninterrupted spans of time in which denudation operates. Schumm stressed this "marked imbalance between the rates of orogeny and denudation" (1963, p. 7).

Data summarized above were obtained prior to about 1960, through a period predating the arrival of modern plate tectonics in the late 1960s. Schumm and others were making the general assumption that orogenies are relatively brief events, and this holds firm for collisional events, whether arc-continent or continent-continent collisions. On the other hand, plate tectonics includes plate subduction that tends to be prolonged over spans of several or many tens of millions of years. In the subduction regime, continuous, steady growth of an accretionary prism would be expected, and thus continuously lift the tectonic arc above it. At the same time, underplating and rise of magma beneath the continental plate would cause continuous uplift of the volcanic arc. Thus, we have to deal with two scenarios of tectonic uplift, one brief and intense, the other prolonged and with small fluctuations of intensity. These two scenarios are recognized in sections to follow.

12.5 Observed Denudation Rates

Geologists and hydrologists have made a number of attempts to estimate the rates of continental denudation by using long-term measurements of suspended and dissolved solids in major streams. For example, Sheldon Judson of Princeton University published the following estimates of denudation rates in three large continental areas

(1968, p. 367, Table 2):

	mm/yr
Amazon River basin	0.047
Congo River basin	0.020
United States	0.030
Weighted mean	0.036

An unknown factor in such calculations is the effect of humanactivity in increasing the rates of soil erosion through deforestation and agriculture. Judson made a generous allowance for this factor. A large part of all three regions consists of a low-lying, stable craton, and the rates are extremely small in comparison with our estimate of rapid tectonic uplift.

Keep in mind that rate of denudation describes the rate at which mass is removed from a land surface, expressed as volume per unit time or as mass per unit of area per unit of time. To compare rates as intensities on a uniform basis, irrespective of areal extent, we state only the average depth (thickness) of the layer removed per unit of time. Isostatic compensation is not included in this definition, but must be included when the rate of lowering of the land surface elevation above sea level is described.

Denudation rates are strongly influenced by elevation of the surface of a landmass above baselevel. Given a crustal block of fixed basal width, the higher it rises, the steeper will be the slopes of the eroding land surfaces as will be the gradients of stream channels carving into that mass. Figure 12.2 shows this geometric relationship, but in reverse, since it illustrates the down-wearing of a mountain block previously raised to full height. We must also take into account the increased rate of rock breakup with increasing altitude because of intensified frost action.

Both stream abrasion and transportation ability (in terms of either capacity or competence) increase strongly as gradients become steeper. For this reason the rate of surface denudation will generally be most intense for the most highly elevated crustal masses and will diminish with time as elevations become lower.

Based upon measured volumes of sediment brought by streams from small watersheds in mountainous areas, denudation rates of 1 to 1.5 mm/yr are about the maximum that can be expected as average values for high mountain masses. These rates are very much greater than Judson's figures for large continental areas of moderate to low elevation. For example, Schumm reviewed the data of Khosla (1953, p. 111) on the sediment yield from the Kosi River basin that drains 60,000 sq km, including the highest mountain peaks in the world. The average denudation rate of that basin was calculated as 1 mm/yr. Schumm concluded: "A denudation rate of 1 m per 1000 years [1 mm/yr] may not be excessive during the early stages of the erosion cycle when relief is high" (1963, p. 4). This conclusion, based on measured rates of today's mountain watersheds, left open the possibility that actual denudation rates in young collision orogens may have been higher in relatively brief periods of the past.

Rates of denudation of an orogen can also be estimated from the rates of sediment accumulation in a foreland basin. In the case of a continent-continent collision, such as the Himalayan front range, the record lies in the sediments of the Indo-Gangetic foreland and the Bengal fan. The results of an analysis of these sediments has been reported in detail by D. W. Burbank, L.A. Derry, and C.

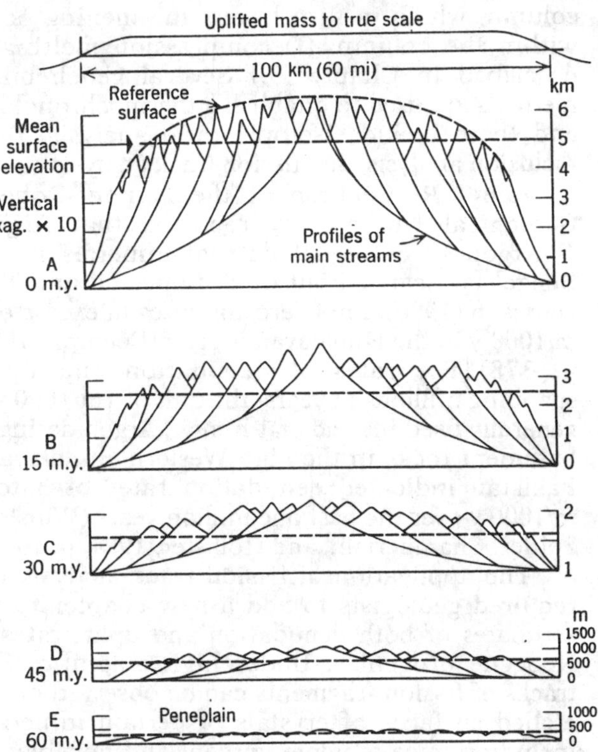

Figure 12.2 Schematic diagrams of landmass denudation. In this model, the mean surface elevation is reduced by one-half every 15 m.y. (Copyright © by Arthur N. Strahler.)

France-Lanord (1993). Changes in accumulation rates are observed to have occurred, one being a sharp decline that occurred about 8 Ma. This decline in rate may have resulted from "reduced intensity of tectonic activity, decreased intensity of Himalayan glaciation, or slope stabilization from dense plant cover" (p. 48).

12.6 Establishing Denudational Chronologies

Establishing firm chronologies and estimates of rates of uplift and denudation of orogens in the Neogene requires that new investigative methods be applied to the orogen itself, as well as to detrital sediments lying outside the boundaries of the orogen. The effects of both tectonic uplift and denudation need to be combined so as to yield the net rate of denudation.

A modern approach, using geochemistry and geophysics, concerns itself not only with changing elevation during orogeny, but also the consequences of that simultaneous uplift and denudation on the petrology of the rock types comprising the orogen. Thermochronology traces the temperature changes within the orogen. Changes in temperature result in petrologic change. When rock heating occurs during unroofing, deep-seated rock will undergo melting or metamorphism. This happens because unroofing causes decompression within the rock column, which in turn lowers the melting point within the column. (Decompression melting is described in Chapter 5.) Several geochemical methods are used to establish a thermochronology, and these include isotopic ratio analysis, fluid inclusion analysis, and fission track analysis.

James R. Cochran of the Lamont-Doherty Geological Observatory reported that Argon-40/Argon-39 dating of detrital minerals in the Bengal fan, carried out by P. Copeland and T.M. Harrison (1990), imply erosion rates in excess of 5 m/1000 y in the Himalayan orogen (Cochran, 1993, p. 378).[For rates of denudation and uplift spanning millions of years, the unit of 1m/1000 y is generally used instead of 1 mm/y.] Argon dating of basement rocks in the high Western Himalaya of Pakistan indicated denudation rates of 3 to 6 m/1000 y over the past one million years (Winslow, Zeitler, Chamberlain, and Hollister, 1994, p. 1075).

The application of fission track analysis has required geologists to add a new chapter to the estimates of both denudation and uplift rates in Neogene orogenies. Under high magnification, tracks of fission fragments can be observed on the etched surfaces of crystals of certain minerals, including mica, epidote, zircon, and hornblende. Spontaneous fission decay particles of U-238, for example, produce these fission tracks, which increase in density with time. However, because the tracks are obliterated by heating, they can also record decompressional heating events (Fleischer, Price, and Walker, 1965, 1972). Fission track dating was successfully applied in combination with K-Ar dating to chronologies of mid-oceanic spreading boundaries and magnetic anomalies, and in another example, to confirming the K-Ar age of Bed I in the Olduvai Gorge (1972, p. 367).

In the early 1990s, fission track dating was applied to rates of uplift and denudation in the Himalayan region. David A. Foster, Andrew J.W. Gleadow, and Greg Mortimer applied the method to the Karakoram Range in Pakistan (1994). Analysis of apatite crystals taken from rock between 5 and 8 km elevation on Mt. Godwin Austen (K2) yielded ages in the range of 2 to 4 Ma. This and other fission track dating led to the estimate of an initial denudation rate of 1.2 m/1000 y, commencing after 5 Ma, and a total amount of denudation (mass removal) of ~6000 m (1994, p. 21, Figure 4).

Another thermochronological study of denudation rates, published in 1993 by N.O. Arnaud, M. Brunel, J.M. Cantagrel, and P. Tapponnier, was made of the Kongur Chan mountains of the Pamir range north of the Tibetan Plateau. It was estimated that surface uplift at the rate of 3 to 5 m/1000 y has been going on over the past 2 m.y. (1994, p. 1345).

12.7 Exhumed Landscapes

Geologists and geochemists who have been pioneering in the new kinds of research we have just described above have come to use the terms "erosional unloading" and "exhumation" for the mass removal process to which we have applied the term "denudation." A brief comparison of terms may be helpful. For example, Paul F. Hoffman and John P. Grotzinger state: "High rates of uplift could have been balanced by erosional unloading" (1993, p. 195). This reference is to Precambrian orogens of North America and their denudation by orographic precipitation during tectonic uplift. The usage seems acceptable and the word "unloading" is appropriate. Philip England and Peter Molnar (1990) use "exhumation" in the same sense as we have used "denudation." For example, they say: "The rate of exhumation is simply the rate of erosion" (p. 1173).

In geomorphology, the term *exhumed landscape* has been in use for many decades to apply to ancient relief features, such as monadnocks, that were buried under younger sediments and much later uncovered by regional denudation. Our glossary definition of "exhumation" reads: "The uncovering or exposure by erosion of a pre-existing surface, landscape, or feature that had been buried," while "exhumed" means "resurrected" (Bates and Jackson, 1987, p. 227). Rhodes W. Fairbridge has reviewed the literature of these usages (1968, p. 339-342). He mentions that the term *resurrected relief* has also been used. Exhumed Precambrian monadnocks are good examples, one being the Baraboo Range in Wisconsin, a truncated syncline of Precambrian quartzite, now partially uncovered from Paleozoic strata that had formerly buried it.

Pinter and Keller (1991, p. 1053), in their comment on England and Molnar's paper (cited above), use "denudation and "denudation rate," but also describe "exhumation of antecedent high-standing topography," for which they give as an example the exhumed mountain ranges of the Ridge-and-Valley Appalachians. This is a correct usage under the hypothesis that Paleozoic strata, folded in the Late Permian orogeny, were buried under Cretaceous marine strata and finally exhumed during the Cenozoic.

Unroofing is another term introduced in recent publications with much the same meaning as erosional unloading. The word has long been in use in petrology to refer to the erosional exposure of a batholith, which is of course younger than the country rock. Used in a different context, an "unroofed anticline" means an anticline from which one or more resistant formations have been removed by denudation, creating a longitudinal valley flanked by homoclinal ridges.

12.8 A Model Denudation System

Using certain reasonable assumptions, we can devise a model of the denudation process and from it perhaps obtain some idea of the order of magnitude of time spans involved in reduction of a mountain mass to a low, undulating plain called a "peneplane."

First, we need to model the process of relatively rapid uplift of a high mountain mass, ending quite abruptly. The model should be simple in concept and based on a sound principle. We select from among several varieties of continent-continent collisions, all of which can produce a high mountain range and a deep mountain root. (See Moores and Twiss, 1995, p. 234-237.) In Figure 12.1 we offered a schematic diagram of a continental suture joining two continental plates. Stage A shows an elongate section of sutured crust lying below the surface. As horizontal compressive stress continues to act on the rectangular crustal prism, deformation by simple shear increases the vertical dimension while shortening in horizontal dimension. Stage B is the terminal stage in which the mountain mass is completed along with a newly formed mountain root. Because we are using pure shear, the cross sectional area of the prism has remained constant. The growing mountain must be sustained by the mass of the lengthening root. Notice also that the mountain range is being narrowed in width as it grows, suggesting the likelihood of severe internal compressional deformation of the mountain mass.

Figure 12.2 shows cross sections of the idealized mountain mass in several stages of erosional reduction. Arbitrarily, we have assigned a width of 100 km to the uplifted mass, for this is about the order of magnitude of width of a number of long but narrow ranges, including the western European Alps, the Carpathians, the Pyrenees, the Caucasus, the Alaska Range, the Sierra Nevada, and the Rocky Mountain Front Range. Length of the uplift mass is not important in this analysis—a segment some tens of kilometers long will do.

The uplifted mass is bordered by low areas, at or below sea level, which can serve as receptors of detritus. An initial surface of reference at sea level has been raised to a summit elevation of 6 km. In Figure 12.2, a dashed line shows a reference surface (restored surface) at the close of the orogenic uplift. Figure 12.3 is a graph on which elevation is plotted against time. The surface rise during orogeny is shown by the steeply rising line. The tectonic uplift is given a span of 5 m.y, and uplift ceases at zero reference time.

Denudation has been in progress during the uplift, increasing in intensity as elevation increases. The elevated mass has been carved into a maze of steep-walled gorges organized into a fluvial system of steep-gradient streams. The profile of the rugged mountain mass and the main stream system are suggested in greatly exaggerated scale in Stage A of Figure 12.2. Let us assume that at time zero the mean (average) elevation of the eroded surface lies at 5 km. Thus, a rock layer averaging 1 km in thickness has already been removed during tectonic uplift.

Starting at time zero, an average denudation rate of 1 m/1000 y is assumed for the entire

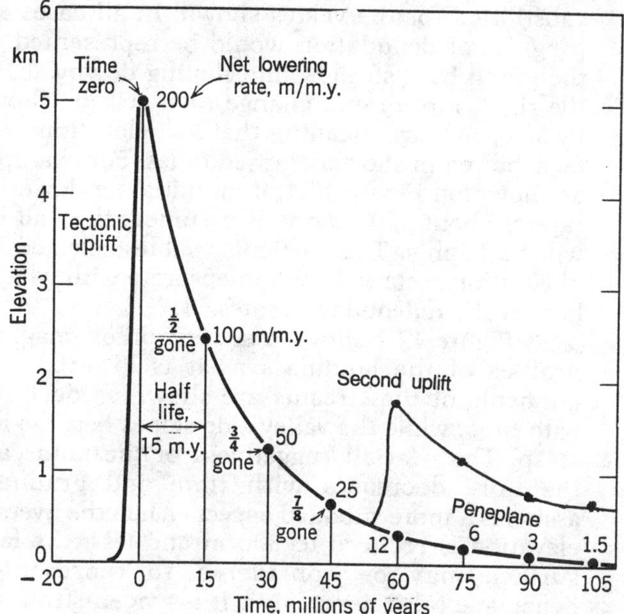

Figure 12.3 Arithmetically scaled graph of elevation change with time during landmass denudation, assuming a half-life of 15 m.y. and an initial net lowering rate of 200 m/m.y. (Copyright © by Arthur N. Strahler.)

surface. However, as average elevation declines, the rate of denudation itself diminishes in such a constant ratio that one-half of the available landmass is removed in each 15 m.y. period. We call this time unit the half-life of the available mass. We make an additional assumption that isostatic restoration occurs constantly in the ratio of 4/5. The initial rate of net lowering of the surface will be only one-fifth of the denudation rate, or 0.2 m/1000 y. In million-year units, used on the graph, this net lowering rate is 200 m/m.y. at time zero. As shown by labels on the descending curve of the graph, when the elevation is reduced to 2.5 km at the end of 15 m.y., the net rate of lowering will have fallen to 100 m/m.y. At the end of 30 m.y. (two half-lives), average elevation and denudation rate are again reduced by one-half, to one-quarter of the initial values. Now three-quarters of the mass is gone and the average altitude is down to 1.25 km.

What we are describing here is a negative-exponential decay process not unlike the mass rate of decay of radioactive isotopes. The curve of elevation flattens with the passage of time. Rates of denudation comparable to those observed today in the central and eastern United States are attained when the average elevation is about 0.3 km (300 m), after a lapse of some 45 m.y. Thereafter, further decline in elevation is extremely gradual.

Figure 12.4 shows the exponential decay of elevation with time on a semi-logarithmic graph. Here the curve of Figure 12.3 appears as a straight line. Any one of a large number of arbitrary initial values of elevation and net lowering rates might be substituted for the values shown. In all cases the progress of denudation would be represented on the graph by a straight line sloping downward to the right. More rapid change rates will be shown by steeper lines, meaning that low elevations will be achieved in shorter elapsed times. For example, as shown on Figure 12.4, if an initial net lowering rate of about 320 m/m.y. is assumed, the half-life will be 10 m.y. The particular values selected for illustration seem to be commensurate with what is known about denudation rates.

Figure 12.2 shows a succession of imagined profiles of the landmass as it is lowered. The gradients of the streams are shown as declining with time, while the valley-side slopes become less steep. The over-all ruggedness of the landscape therefore decreases with time and gradually assumes a more subdued aspect. When the average elevation is reduced to 300 m and less, the land surface may be considered to represent a peneplane (also peneplain). It is evident from the nature of the exponential-decay curve that zero elevation can never be reached. Instead, elevation approaches zero as time approaches infinity. Thus our model of denudation has no ultimate stage.

The word "peneplain" was coined by prominent Harvard geomorphologist William Morris Davis (Davis, 1889; 1909, p. 350-351). The term was derived from two words: the Greek pene ("almost") and "plain;" hence an "almost-plain." Use of the word "plain" was unfortunate, because that word is descriptive of a land surface of low, undulating relief. We need to substitute "plane" to signify the ultimate surface as a geometrical sealevel plane in the established geodetic sense of a geoidal surface. An attempt to substitute the scientifically correct term peneplane was made by geomorphologist Douglas W. Johnson of Columbia University (Johnson, 1916, p. 443-445). Through ensusing decades, "plain" won acceptance over "plane." Our Glossary of Geology (Jackson and Bates, 3rd. ed., 1987) lists both forms but gives preference to "peneplain." Inadvertently, however, the Glossary selects for "plane" in its definition of the process of peneplanation. Encouraged by this rational support, we shall use "peneplane" throughout this chapter.

Attainment of a peneplane in an uninterrupted denudation span of 40 to 70 m.y. is not an unreasonable guess. Most of the Phanerozoic geologic periods are about of that order of duration. Continuous sedimentation throughout a single geologic period might thus be roughly equated to the contemporaneous denudation of a mountain mass produced by orogeny at the start of the period (or at the end of the previous period).

The denudation process can be interrupted at any point by renewal of orogenic uplift. A new

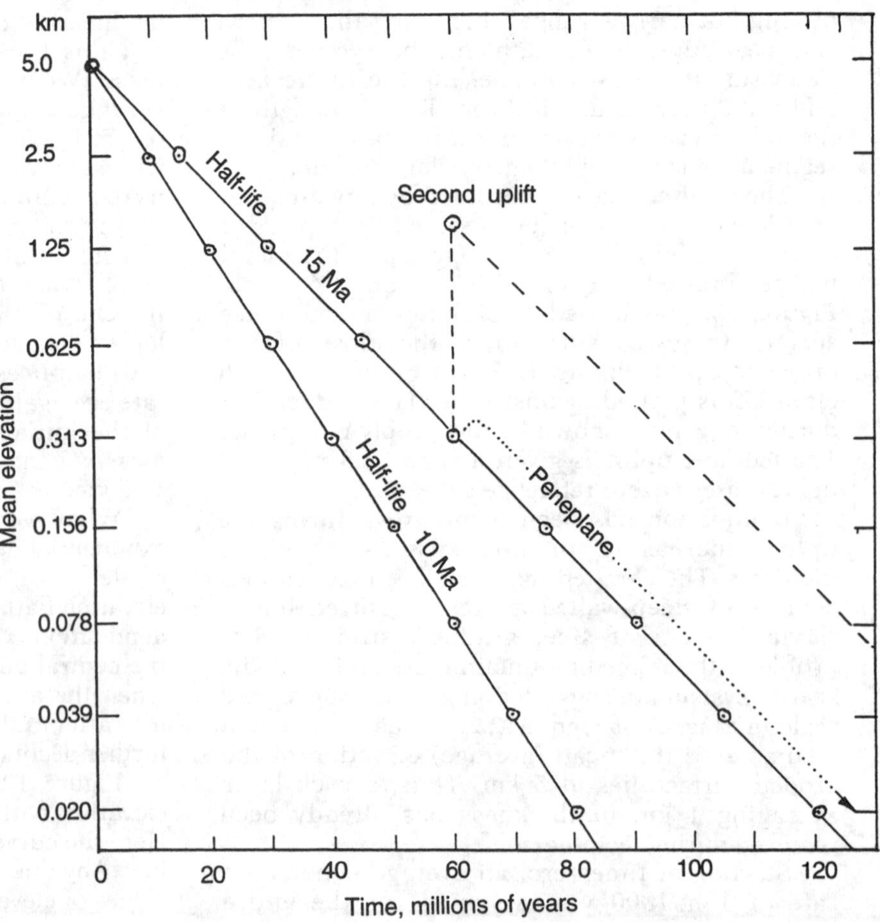

Figure 12.4
Semilogarithmic plot of the same denudation data as in Figure 12.3. (Copyright © by Arthur N. Strahler.)

curve of denudation then follows the cessation of uplift (Figures 12.3 and 12.4). Interruption can occur early in the denudation process, when elevations are high and relief is strong, or it may occur in the peneplane stage, when relief is low and even a minor crustal uplift can have radical effects.

12.9 Landmass Rejuvenation

Peneplanes that have been uplifted several hundred meters above present baselevel are easily identified as upland surfaces of low relief. Following epeirogenic uplift, the streams that flow across a peneplane quickly begin to degrade their channels and develop deep, steep-walled rock gorges. The process of uplift of a peneplane followed by trenching of the major streams is called rejuvenation.

Figure 12.5 is a series of block diagrams that illustrate rejuvenation of a peneplane formed on an exposed shield area of a craton not far inland from a continental margin. Block A shows the peneplane immediately after an uplift of several hundred meters. In Block B, major streams have deeply trenched the peneplane, which is now seen as an upland surface between steep-walled stream valleys or gorges. As the stream valleys are deepened and widened, the remaining peneplane surface is reduced in area and is finally totally destroyed. Block C shows the region in a rugged condition with steep slopes and narrow divides. From this point on, relief declines and slopes become more gentle (Block D). The major streams have become graded with respect in the new baselevel. Block E shows that a second peneplane has been formed. Now, if epeirogenic uplift again occurs, the region will revert to the conditions shown in Block A, and the denudation cycle will be repeated. The question now arises: What mechanism of plate tectonics can explain repeated epeirogenic uplifts of a stable craton?

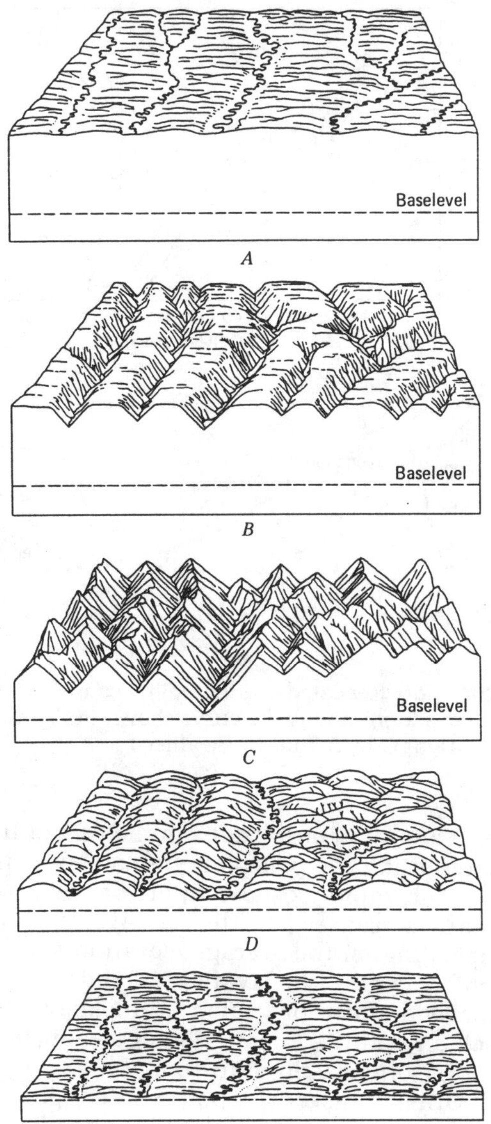

Figure 12.5 A denudation cycle caused by uplift of a peneplane. followed by a rejuvenation of the stream system. An uplift of the peneplain shown in Block E will bring a return to conditions shown in Block A and the cycle will be repeated. (Copyright © by Arthur N. Strahler.)

To explain repeated rejuvenations in the advanced stage of fluvial denudation, our simple model of denudation, shown in Figures 12.2 and 12.3, needs an important modification. We have assumed that isostatic compensation occurs uniformly and constantly as denudation proceeds, but this is probably not the case. It is more reasonable to suppose that isostatic compensation occurs spasmodically. Because the lithosphere is a massive, strong layer, it resists being lifted until a certain minimum thickness of rock has been removed. Then, beyond the critical point of strength, any further removal triggers a rapid uplift, restoring the equilibrium. This scenario of events was presented in detailed by Schumm (1963, p. 9-12), who outlined a program of spasmodic isostatic compen-sation that can be superimposed on our denudation model. As each critical thickness of mass is removed, an isostatic uplift occurs. Figure 12.6 shows this program, using a vertical line for the instantaneous uplift, followed by denudation on the exponential decay schedule. The result is a sawtooth curve, plotted on the assumption that full isostatic compensation occurs abruptly after 300 m of rock has been removed. The uplift, however, amounts to only 80% of the amount removed, or 240 m.

Our revised model shows that isostatic uplifts are triggered at short intervals during the early stages of denudation, when gradients are steep and relief is great. Because the abrupt changes in elevation are only a small relative fraction of the total elevation, there may be no easily observable changes in the profiles of the slopes and stream channels. In contrast, the effects of spasmodic

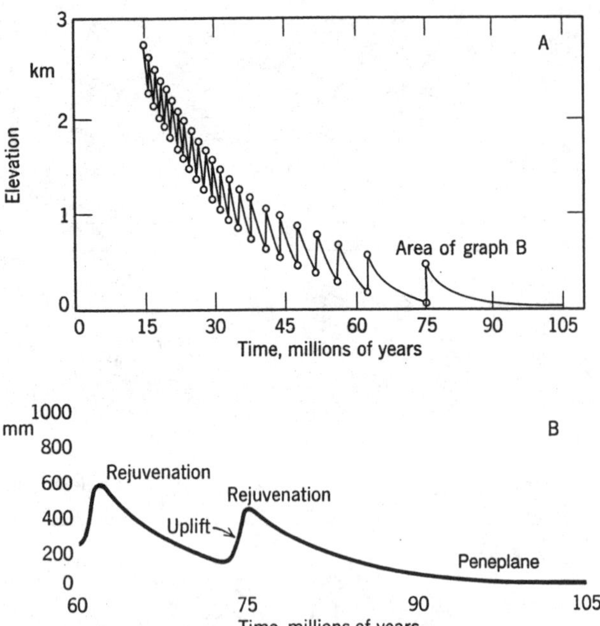

Figure 12.6 Repeated sudden uplifts caused by isostatic compensation modify the curve shown in Figure 12.3. (Copyright © by Arthur N. Strahler.)

uplift are very conspicuous in the part of the graph representing the peneplane (area shown in Graph B). Each rapid isostatic uplift brings a relatively great increase in the available landmass. Depending on the average elevation at which this uplift occurs, the available landmass may be quickly doubled or tripled in thickness. Following such an uplift, a long period of steady denudation follows, often lasting 5 to 10 m.y.

Other causes of epeirogenic uplift are not excluded by our model of spasmodic isostatic uplift. For reasons that are obscure, epeirogenic movements, both up and down, can be expected as a result of large-scale motions of a continental lithospheric plate. We may postulate that the underlying asthenosphere has a somewhat undulating upper surface, so that when a plate is moving over the crest of a "bump" on the asthenosphere, it undergoes epeirogenic upwarping. Irregularities in the upper surface of the asthenosphere might result from differences in rock temperature and density from place to place in the upper mantle. The presence of a large mantle plume or an upward moving convection current might be responsible for an upward bulge in the asthenosphere.

A negative isostatic anomaly can be interpreted as meaning that the lithosphere is being forcibly held down against a tendency to rise. Now, we find that negative isostatic anomalies on the order of 20 to 40 milligals exist over wide areas of the stable continental lithosphere of central and eastern North America (see Figure 3.38). There are also many small areas of positive anomalies in these regions, but the tendency toward negative values is quite marked.

George P. Woollard, an authority on gravity measurements and their interpretation, stated in 1966 that "changes in crustal thickness due to surface erosion (are) going on at a faster rate than can be compensated through crustal buoyancy" (1966, p. 548). He went on to state that all mountain ranges show a history of reduction to a peneplane followed by epeirogenic uplift. In old mountain ranges, such as the Appalachians, this sequence has been repeated several times. In the Rockies, uplift has occurred at least once since the range was reduced to low relief following its rise during the Cordilleran Orogeny of Cretaceous time. Woollard predicted that the isostatic anomalies will be about zero when a mountain range is originally formed, but that negative anomalies will develop after reduction to a low surface of erosion. Positive anomalies might be expected following isostatic uplift if the momentum of crustal uplift carried the base of the crust to a level above that required for perfect equilibrium.

12.10 Comparing the Models of Davis and Penck

Before attempting to construct a model for the compressional orogens, another historical note is in order. Our model denudation system shown in Figures 12.2 and 12.3, featuring a rapid and brief tectonic uplift followed by a very long denudation period, has been associated with W.M. Davis, mentioned earlier as author of the term "peneplane." Davis had produced a schematic diagram quite similar to ours (1909, p. 255) under the name of "the geographical cycle." It reflected the views of his English and American predecessors and was generally adopted by many geomorphologists who followed him.

At about the same time the German geophysicist Alfred Wegener was presenting his highly controversial version of continental drift, another German geoscientist, Walther Penck, published a theory of landform evolution that differed in several ways from that of Davis and his supporters. Penck had developed models that required long-enduring periods of both crustal uplift and denudation. Just as in the great debate between supporters of continental drift and those English and American supporters of "fixism" or "vertical tectonics" (covered in our Chapter 2), a heated controversy followed the posthumous publication in 1924 of Penck's volume *Die Morphogologische Analyse.* An English translation, titled *Morphological Analysis of Landforms*, appeared in 1953. In both these controversies, Wegener and Penck were strongly supported by several prominent southern-hemisphere geologists. Penck also gained a few adherents among American geologists (see O.D. Von Engeln, 1940). However, the theories of the two German authors were about entirely different and completely unrelated subjects: Wegener's was about great sialic plates in motion;

Penck's, about the configurations of landforms.

Following now the "Davis/Penck" controversy in the pre-plate tectonics period, it is essential to make a clear distinction between the contexts and goals underlying the two landform evolution models. Davis interpreted denudational landforms as products of a three-fold control system (a) the exogene processes acting on the rock surface (formative agents), (b) rock structure and composition (resistance to the agents), and (c) the stage of development reached in a cycle of denudation. Endogene processes, although responsible for the formation of an entire class of "initial" landforms (the volcanic and fault forms) were simply assumed to be inactive during the program Davis had set up for analytical consideration.

The following lines paraphrase or quote from Chapter 1 of Penck's 1924 work: Penck held that landforms are functions not only of erosion process and geologic structure, but also of crustal activity. We can observe and evaluate exogene forces at work, hence we can solve for the unknown, which is endogene force in the form of crustal movement. Landform serves as an indicator of crustal movements. The ultimate objective is the determination of crustal movement, and this objective can be attained because various rates and amounts of deformation produce distinctive landforms. Morphological analysis can provide altogether different knowledge than that which can be had from tectonic research based on structural evidence. The factor which governs the shapes of the earth's landforms is the intensity ratio between endogene and exogene translocations of matter. Penck evaluated Davis's "geographical cycle," noting that it is valid, as is the deductive method of obtaining it, but it is only one special case—that of one rapid uplift completed before significant erosion was accomplished. Davis's program of lowering of surface gradients with time was appropriate, and the peneplane concept was also valid. Penck noted that Davis himself had recognized the imposed conditions to be special cases.

Of course, neither Penck nor Davis knew of the basic plate boundary processes of plate tectonics. They did know of the telescoping structural forms (alpine structure) obviously produced by compressional deformation, and they knew that continental rifting is an expression of crustal extension.

An example to illustrate the basic difference in the two approaches can be taken from Penck's analysis of slope profiles. A *slope profile* is a line extending from a point on a drainage divide downward to the nearest stream channel, and following a path orthogonal to the topographic contours. Several forms of slope profiles are common: upwardly concave, upwardly convex, sigmoidal, straight, segmented. Usually the upper part of the profile lies on a rock surface undergoing erosion, while a lower part may lie on a surface of deposition, such as on talus or a fan. Now, the Davisian interpretation would explain the profile form simply in terms of equilibrium with the exogene forces, including weathering, mass wasting, and overland flow of runoff.

The Penckian interpretation would explain the slope profile form in terms of time rate of change of tectonic uplift in one of three uplift velocity modes. Figure 12.7 illustrates these modes. Categories of uplift rate are arranged for display in sequence from left to right. Starting at the left with a low, flat plain, a mode of increasing relief is followed; it is represented by an upwardly concave line indicating that both velocity and acceleration are positive. For this mode, slopes follow a *waxing development* (*Aufsteigende Eentwicklung*) in which divides are broadly rounded and all slopes are upwardly convex. Next, the uplift rate continues positive but without acceleration, and relief remains constant.

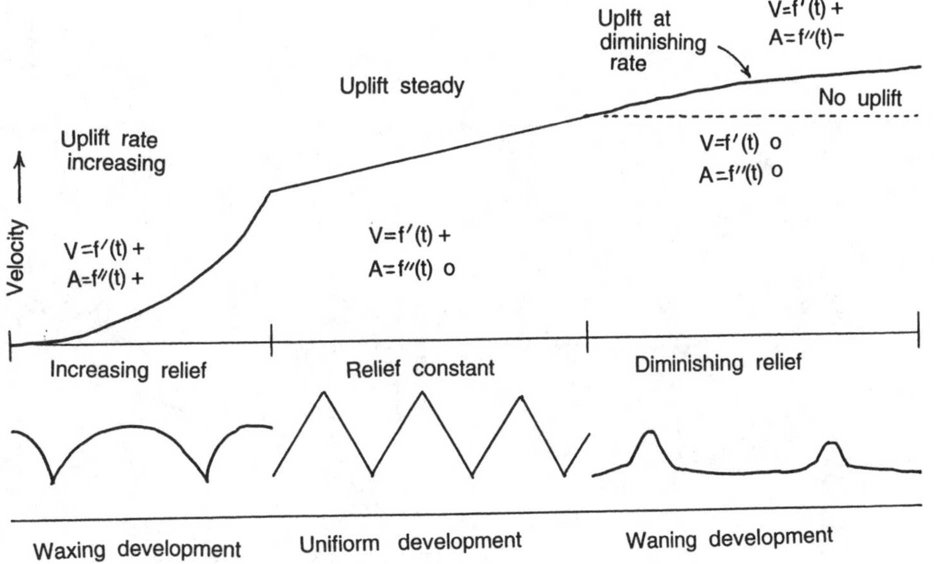

Figure 12.7 Three forms of slope profile development envisioned by Walther Penck as developing under different combinations of velocity and acceleration of uplift. (Copyright © by Arthur N. Strahler.)

This is called *uniform development* (*Gleichförmige Eentwicklung*). The slope profiles are straight from bottom to top. Next comes uplift at a diminishing rate, with velocity positive and acceleration negative. This mode is *waning development* (*Absteigende Eentwicklung*) and produces a profile formed of the steep-sided isolated erosional remnants (inselbergs) separated by pediment surfaces of gentle up-concavity. (Also shown is a fourth mode, that of no uplift.) We make no attempt here to pass judgment on Penck's decisions as to the appropriate slope form for each uplift mode. The Davisian explanation for each of these profile types would consist of a different set of causative factors, none of which calls upon rate of tectonic uplift.

12.11 Subduction and Steady State Denudation

Along active subduction boundaries, which can persist for long periods of time, the relationship between uplift and denudation is quite different from that of the collision-caused orogens, although both cases are in the broader category of compressional tectonics. Referring back to Chapter 8 and Figure 8.2, focus on two kinds of mountain arcs: (1) an outer tectonic arc and (2) a volcanic arc. Where these arcs rise above sea level, they are landmasses undergoing uplift that may continue as long as plate subduction continues. As soon as an arc landmass of this kind rises above sea level, it is subject to denudation. Recall also that in Chapter 8 we described the origin of a volcanic island arc constructed on oceanic lithosphere (Figures 8.4B, 8.5, and 8.6). In the course of time, this oceanic arc thickens by accretion of rising magma and develops a core of continental crust. In this same case, growth of an accretionary wedge may cause the emergence of a tectonic arc.

In the case of the mountain arc described above, we are dealing with crustal rise that is an isostatic response. As horizontal compression of two plates occurs, diminishing the horizontal dimension of a crustal block, there occurs a lengthening of the vertical dimension of the block as a column. Because subduction is continuous, although with possible fluctuations in the convergence rate, a suitable denudation model for the outer tectonic arc will feature a more-or-less steady rate of isostatic uplift. The same may perhaps be predicted for the inner volcanic arc.

We now attempt to formulate a model using uplift rate and denudation rate as the two variables, as given in Figures 12.3 and 12.4. Figure 12.8 shows that at time-zero, the summit of an outer arc, which is an accretionary prism, has reached the ocean surface, after being built up from the abyssal ocean floor. Marine erosion will, of course, be active and may be sufficiently effective to keep the arc summit planed off to wave base for a significant span of time. We will, however, overlook this complication, and show denudation as starting from a zero rate and increasing exponentially with elevation. The uplift rate is assumed to be constant, shown as a straight line. While in a transient state, denudation thus lags behind but eventually intersects the uplift rate, and the two rates are then equal. Thereafter, the mean elevation of the land surface remains constant, as shown in the upper diagram. This is the steady-state phase, and it may continue indefinitely. Relief and slope would also hold constant with time.

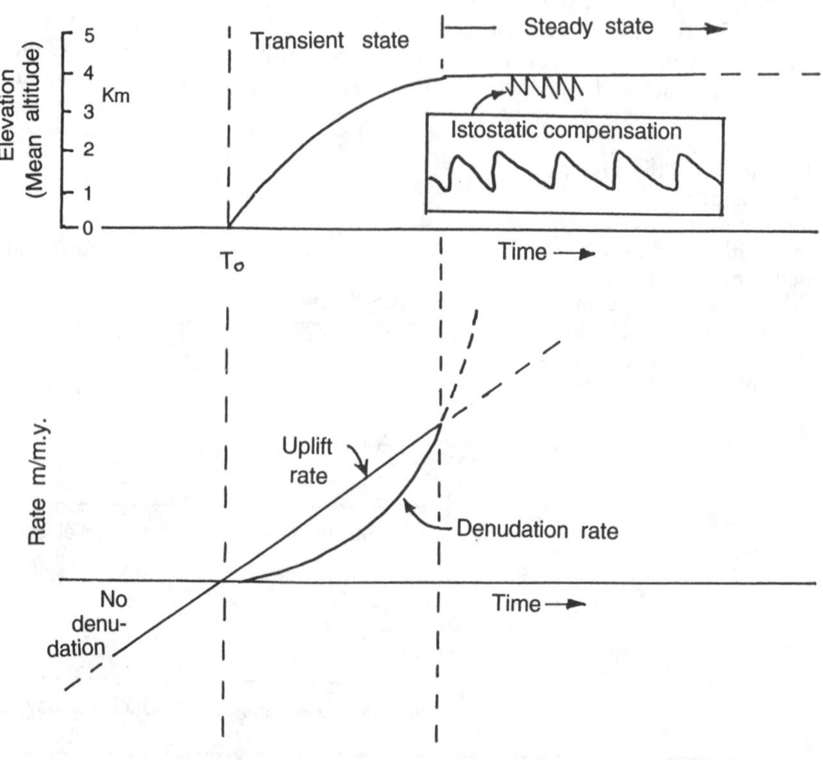

Figure 12.8 Steady-state model in which net uplift rate and net denudation become equal, so that elevation holds constant. (Copyright © by Arthur N. Strahler.)

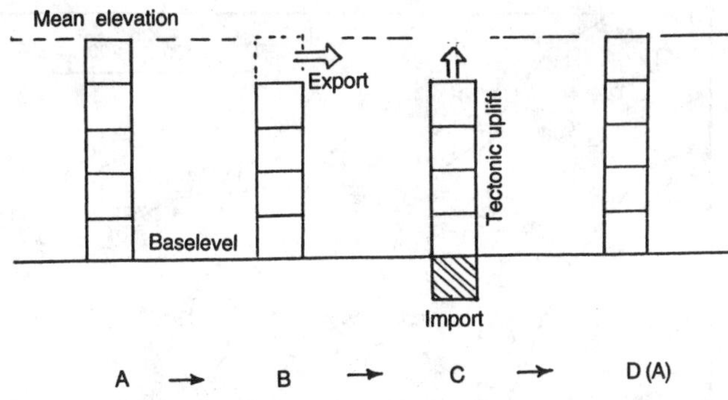

Figure 12.9 System analysis of the steady-state model of an orogen. (Copyright © by Arthur N. Strahler.)

Ultimately, the system is disrupted by another tectonic event, such as an arc-continent collision.

It can be anticipated that the accretionary prism will experience lateral (horizontal) growth as well as upward growth. Lateral growth accompanies (or causes) a migration of the descending plate away from the opposing plate (Summerfield, 1991b, p. 195-196). To the extent that horizontal growth occurs, it will detract from the vertical growth, assuming that volume production of the wedge holds constant. We can predict the possibility of a steady state in which the prism summit remains below sea level. A similar program might apply to the continental volcanic arc, which could also widen, with a steady lateral shift of the line of active volcanoes, matching the rate of migration of the subducting plate away from the continent.

As before, a refinement of this model would be the inclusion of episodic isostatic compensation, in this case a drop of the landmass elevation. This program, shown in Figure 12.6B, is the opposite of the isostatic uplift program in the exponential decay model.

Continuing with the subject of system analysis of the steady-state regime, we now look at the orogen as an open material system of input and output of matter. Figure 12.9 uses a tall prism to stand for that part of an orogen which rises above sea level and constitutes the mass available for reduction and ultimate removal. In (A), the prism is marked off into volume units of rock mass. The

line. While in a transient state, denudation thus lags behind but eventually intersects the uplift rate, and the two rates are then equal. Thereafter, the mean elevation of the land surface remains constant, as shown in the upper diagram. This is the steady-state phase, and it may continue indefinitely. Relief and slope would also hold constant with time. Ultimately, the system is disrupted by another tectonic event, such as an arc-continent collision.

It can be anticipated that the accretionary prism will experience lateral (horizontal) growth as well as upward growth. Lateral growth accompanies (or causes) a migration of the descending plate away from the opposing plate (Summerfield, 1991b, p. 195-196). To the extent that horizontal growth occurs, it will detract from the vertical growth, assuming that volume production of the wedge holds constant. We can predict the possibility of a steady state in which the prism summit remains below sea level. A similar program might apply to the continental volcanic arc, which could also widen, with a steady lateral shift of the line of active volcanoes, matching the rate of migration of the subducting plate away from the continent.

As before, a refinement of this model would be the inclusion of episodic isostatic compensation, in this case a drop of the landmass elevation. This program, shown in Figure 12.6B, is the opposite of the isostatic uplift program in the exponential decay model.

Continuing with the subject of system analysis of the steady-state regime, we now look at the orogen as an open material system of input and output of matter. Figure 12.9 uses a tall prism to stand for that part of an orogen which rises above sea level and constitutes the mass available for reduction and ultimate removal. In (A), the prism is marked off into volume units of rock mass. The horizontal line across the top of the diagram represents mean surface elevation, which remains constant. In (B), a unit of mass is removed (exported) from the prism by denudation (exogene process). This is the total amount of removal, corrected for isostatic response. Denudation is the mass export channel of the system. In (C), a unit of rock mass is imported from below by tectonic

Figure 12.10 Schematic diagram showing how mean elevation can remain constant as local relief increases, giving the effect that the divides and summits are rising in elevation. (Copyright © by Arthur N. Strahler.)

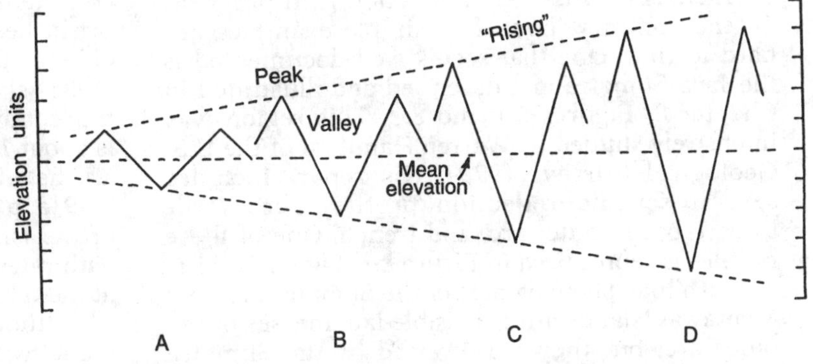

activity (endogene process). This rate is also appropriately compensated for by isostatic sinking. Both export and import are going on simultaneously, and in steady state are exactly balanced over a long period of time. Thus, in (D) the prism remains unchanged in elevation (assuming prism density is unchanged.)

A further refinement in the steady-state model takes into account landform development on a smaller morphological scale. Looking back at Figure 12.2, note that a fluvial denudation system is forming on the uplifted crustal mass. It consists of water-carved valleys with steep side slopes and narrow drainage divides. As time passes, mean surface elevation declines, accompanied by a decline in slope and channel gradients. Here, we are interested in an earlier steady-state stage shown in Figure 12.8. Figure 12.10 is a schematic diagram focusing on the development of valleys and their divides. Stage A shows a valley and its two confining divides. Through stages B, C, and D, the depth of incision is increased by equal vertical units, leaving the horizontal dimension constant. This treatment allows us to show that the valley side slopes steepen, and presumably the stream channels also steepen in gradient, so that intensity of erosion is increased. But denudation rate is assumed to be compensated for by isostatic and tectonic uplift, so the mean elevation remains flat. What emerges is the strange illusion that the divides (and with them the mountain summits) are actually rising in elevation. This is not illusion, but a reality forced on us by the stated terms and parameters. The distinguished English geologist Arthur Holmes, called attention to this phenomenon in his popular textbook (1978). Considering it a "normal accompaniment of a cycle of erosion," he stated that "it involves the curious effect that during late youth and early maturity the summits of peaks and divides become elevated above the initial surface." He also refers to "the bearing of this remarkable result on the high altitudes of the Himalayan peaks" (p. 372-373, 388). More recently, this mechanism has been reexamined, quantified, and applied to the European Alps by A.R. Gilchrist, M.A. Summerfield, and H.A.P. Cockburn (1994. p. 963-966).

One might suppose that examples of the steady-state model are abundant throughout the island and continental-margin arcs that ring the Pacific basin, wherever subduction is in progress. To the contrary, bona fide simple examples are hard to find. One that seems well documented is the Java-Sumatra arc, described and illustrated in Chapter 8, Figures 8.1 and 8.2. This region was intensively studied by Warren Hamilton of the U.S. Geological Survey (1979). His report includes several seismic reflection profiles across the forearc basin, outer arc, and trench. One of these profiles is reproduced in Figure 8.3. Figure 12.11 is a sketch map showing part of the Sumatra arc. The Mentawai Islands are the visible landmasses of the outer arc, but they are dwarfed by the Sumatra

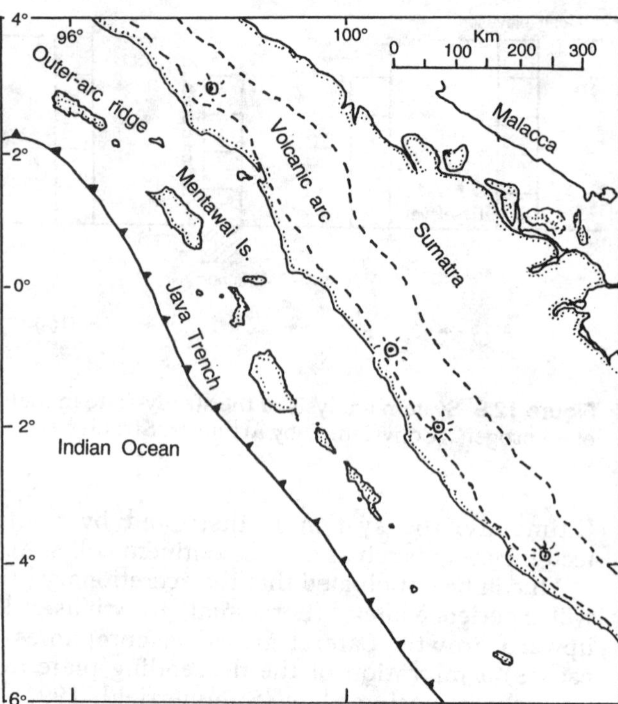

Figure 12.11 Sketch map of a part of the Sumatra arc, showing the Mentawai Islands of the outer arc. (From Warren Hamilton, 1979, *U.S. Geological Survey Professional Paper 1087*, p. 34, Figure 12.)

volcanic arc. Peak elevations of the Mentawai islands, composed mostly of melanges, range between 0.2 and 0.9 km in elevation, whereas the volcanic peaks have summits at 2 to 3 km. Why is this discrepancy in height and volume so great? It would seem obvious that melting of the downgoing slab provides a very much greater volume of rock to the volcanic arc above it than does the transfer by offscraping and underplating from the upper surface of the slab to the base of the accretionary prism. Whether this entire system is now in steady state is not known. Possibly, the volcanic arc has been accumulating for a much longer time than the outer arc and contains the remains of several arc-continent collisions.

Another case of possible steady state is the Island of Honshu in central Japan, referred to in Chapter 8 and illustrated in Figures 8.9 and 8.10. Here the modern volcanic arc rises from a wide zone of complex crust produced by earlier arc-continent collisions. The modern accretionary prism lies offshore below sea level. Summerfield (1991a, p. 398-399) cites data of T. Yoshikawa (1985) showing that the Quaternary uplift rate in this central zone of the volcanic/metamorphic arc is about 1 m/1000 y, which is about the same value as the observed denudation rate. Summerfield (1991a, p. 467-468) also cites the high central range of the island of Taiwan as being in steady state, with rates of uplift and denudation being matched at the very high rate of 5 m/1000 y.

Although we have associated the steady-state model with the process of subduction, it may also

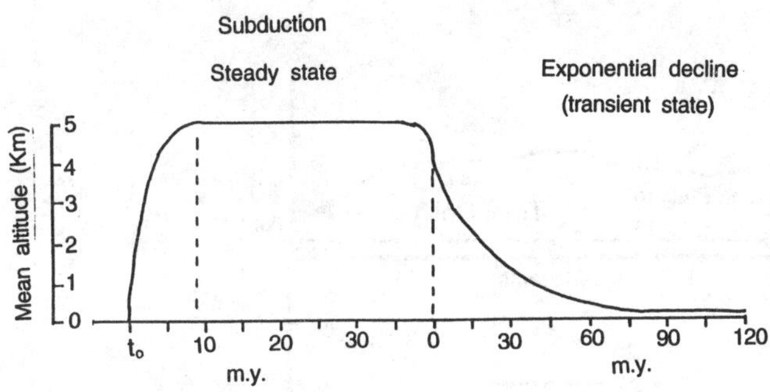

Figure 12.12 Model of steady-state denudation being followed by a transient state of exponential decay. (Copyright © by Arthur N. Strahler.)

be applied to continental collision, in which a rapidly rising orogen reaches a point of balance with increasing denudation rate. A period of steady state could follow, but full closure of the two plates would perhaps abruptly terminate the compressional phase and its steady state, initiating an exponential decline. Thus, our two basic models of denudation can be related sequentially in time at a given location. Figure 12.12 illustrates this suggested sequence. On the assumption that the steady-state period is typically much briefer in duration than the exponential decline, we have applied a different time scale to the two modes.

12.12 Unroofing and Tectonic Asymmetry

Referring back to our section on exhumation chronologies, we apply the rapid rates of denudation found in the Himalayan collision orogen to a special case of the steady-state model, using the term *unroofing* in place of "exhumation," commonly used in modern journal articles. Whereas "exhumation" emphasizes the petrological aspect of the rock formations exposed; "unroofing" fits better into the problem of rate of denudation versus rate of uplift. Whereas the orogen has been first visualized as symmetrical in cross section, as drawn in Figure 12.2, we now postulate that because of the orographic effect of prevailing seasonal winds on the distribution of precipitation, denudation rate will be much more rapid on the windward side of the main drainage divide than on the lee side. Thus, the transverse profile of the mountain range would need to be redrawn to accommodate the orographic phenomenon.

Figure 12.13 is a N-S topographic profile across the Himalayan range and the Tibet plateau. It was compiled from digitized elevation data (D.W. Burbank, 1992, p. 483). Besides a profile of mean elevation, it shows profiles of maximum and minimum elevation, so that the variation in local relief is displayed.

Geologist Peter O. Koons of the University of Otago, New Zealand, investigated the phenomenon of tectonic and geomorphic asymmetry of collisional orogens (1987; 1989; 1990). In our Figure 12.14 he has presented the essential data of two good examples of asymmetry of orogens: (A) The Himalayan range and Tibetan plateau; (B) The Southern Alps of the South Island of New Zealand. We have described both of these ranges in earlier chapters. [Southern Alps: Chapter 6, Seismicity of Continental Transform Plate Boundaries and Figure 6.32. Himalayas and Tibet: Chapter 9, Himalayan Collision Segment, Table 9.1, and Figures 9.43-9.48.] The Himalayan cross section (A) shows the steep southern descent from the Higher Himalaya to the Indo-Gangetic plain. Extremely heavy precipitation falls on this slope during the southwest monsoon season. A broken line indicates the total surface uplift. Greater precipitation causes more rapid denudation, causing more rapid isostatic crustal rise. The total

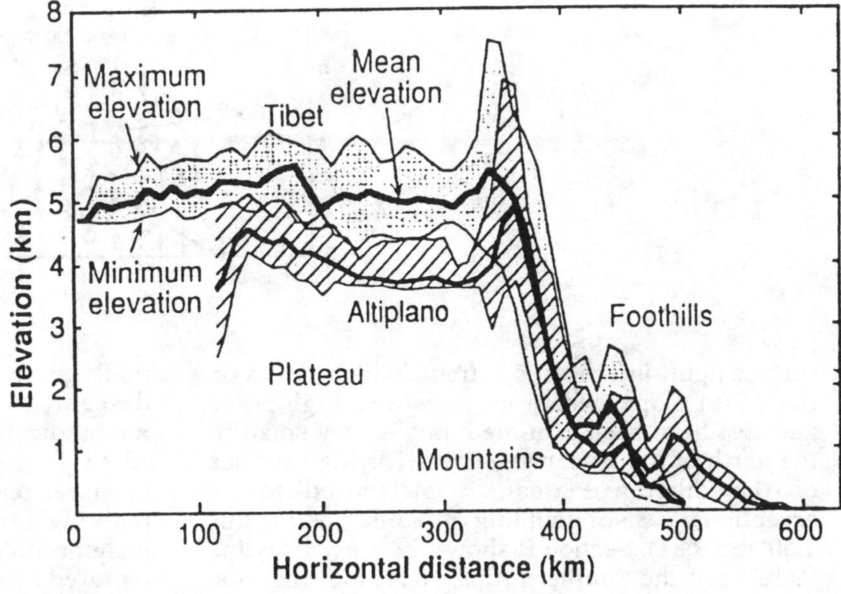

Figure 12.13 Transverse profiles of the Himalayan ranges and the Tibet Plateau. Mean, maximum, and minimum profiles compiled from digitized altitude data. From D.W. Burbank, *Nature*, v. 359, p. 483. Copyright © 1992 by Macmillan Magazines Ltd. Used by permission of the author and publisher.

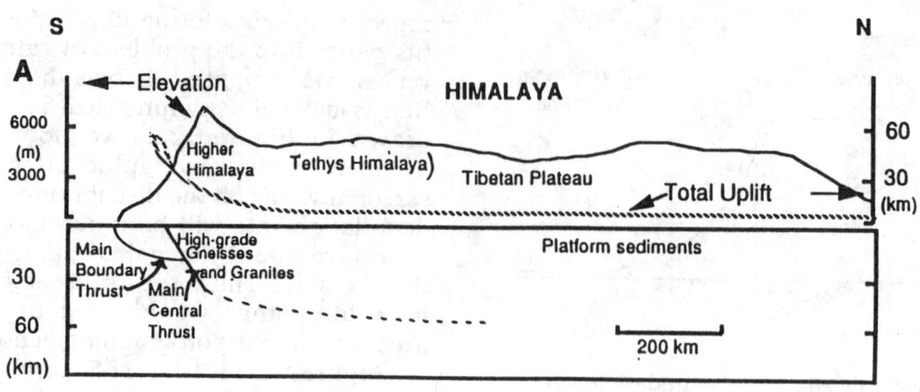

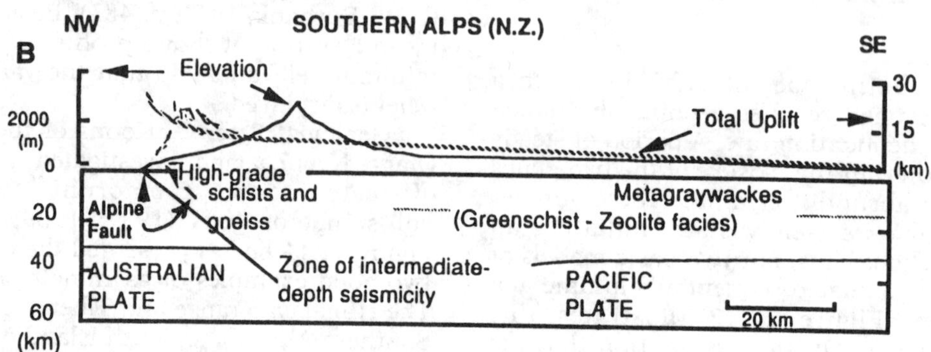

Figure 12.14 Schematic transverse profiles and sections of (A) the Himalaya and (B) the Southern Alps, showing the large range in total uplift. (Adapted from Peter O. Koons, 1990, *Geology*, v. 18, p. 681, Figure 2. Reproduced with the permission of the Publisher, the Geological Society of America, Boulder, Colorado, USA. Copyright 1990.)

Figure 12.15 Schematic diagram of (A) precipitation profile and (B) the relation between total mass uplift and steady-state surface elevation. (Copyright © by Arthur N. Strahler.)

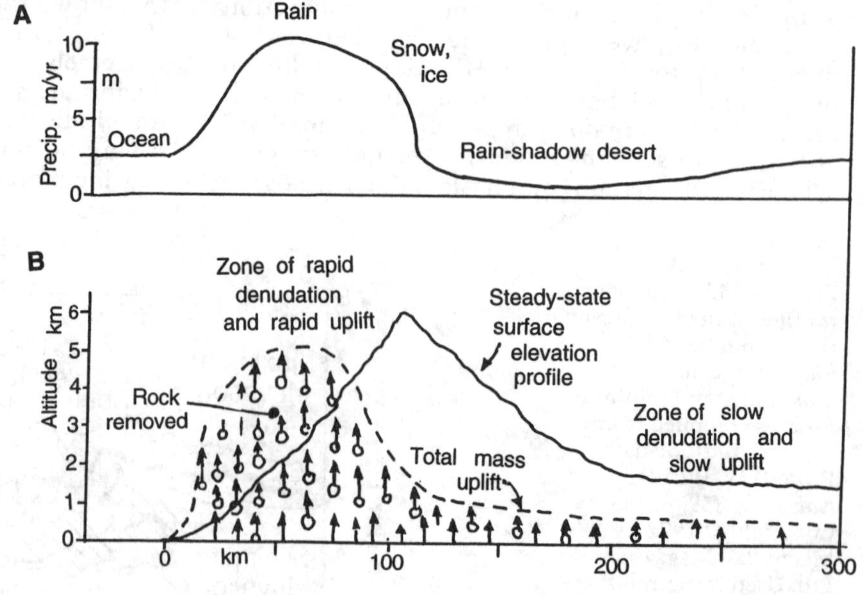

surface uplift increases to extremely high values on the south slope, where granites and high-grade gneisses have been exhumed, but is very small to the north of the Himalayan crest. The high surface of the Tibetan Plateau is attributed to an exceptional case of doubling of plates (see Figures 9.50 and 9.51). Section B shows the corresponding features of the Southern Alps, Here, too, the total uplift curve turns sharply upward across the steep descent to the wet windward coast, where metamorphic rocks have been exhumed. Figure 12.15 is a cartoon diagram sum-marizing the essential features of the two examples. The up-pointing arrows express the rise of deep-seated metamorphic rock, a large mass of which has been removed by denudation.

12.13 Antecedent Streams and Orogens

One theme of this chapter has been to show ways in which evolving landforms can provide independent evidence of rates and dates of tectonic activity. A good example is the relationship between streams and actively growing tectonic structures, such as folds and fault blocks. Diagram A of Figure 12.16 shows a thrust fault, or thrust ramp, steepening upward and having slowly raised an anticline across the path of a major stream. Channel degradation has kept pace with the uplift. This *antecedent stream* has carved a *watergap* for itself. Diagram B shows a similar development in which a major stream has maintained its course across a rising fault block. Note that in both examples small streams have carved steep ravines on the rising tectonic slopes and have built alluvial fans at the foot of the mountain. Petrologic studies of the fan gravels will show a reversed age sequence to that of the source area strata (P.G. DeCelles, 1988).

Foreland folds of late Neogene age can perhaps provide the best type examples of antecedent streams and their watergaps traversing rising anticlines. Favorable regions would be the Jura Mountains of Europe, the Zagros Mountains of Iran, and the Siwalik Range of Pakistan. Figure 12.17 attempts to reconstruct the early phase of growth of open folds in strata of varied lithologies, ranging from pebbles and sand through clays of recent deposition. Block A shows parallel anticlines undergoing erosion as they are forming. Sediment removed from the anticlines is accumulating in the synclines. The stream pattern is of the trellis type with a dominant set of streams parallel with the fold axes. Transverse antecedent elements provide regional drainage across the folds, leading away from the core of the orogen and toward a marginal seaway. As time passes, the strata at depth have undergone diagenesis that includes cementation of the sands into hard quartzitic sandstones and conglomerates. Block B shows the exhumation of a highly resistant quartzite formation that forms bold anticlinal mountains. The antecedent streams have been able to maintain their locations and have cut deep windgaps. Figure 12.18 is a carefully drawn block diagram of a portion of the Jura Mountains on the northern fringe of the eastern European Alps. The river gorge contains an antecedent stream that has carved a succession of watergaps. The anticlines are mostly of the plunging type. Tear faults, produced during the compressional orogeny have offset the Jura ridges in several places and may have in part controlled the transverse drainage.

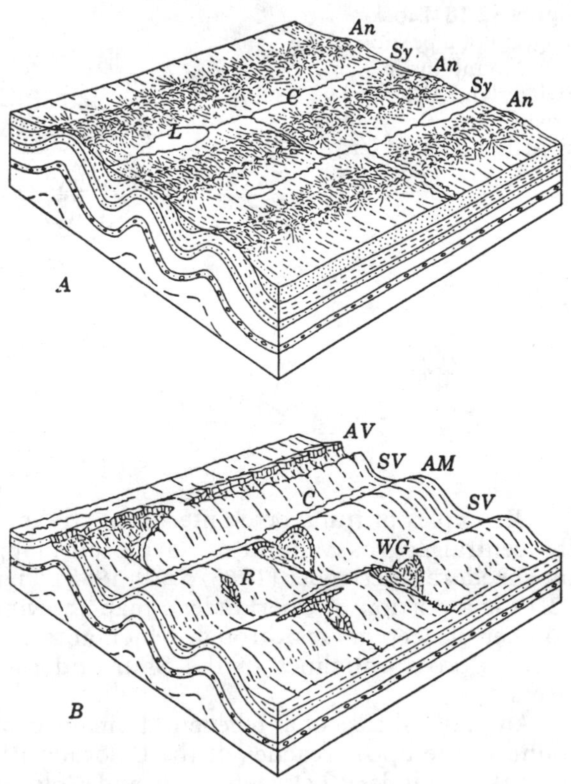

Figure 12.17 Block diagrams of erosional development of open folds. (A) Early stage with transverse antecedent streams. (B) Later stage of fold denudation and carving of deep watergaps. (Copyright © by Arthur N. Strahler.)

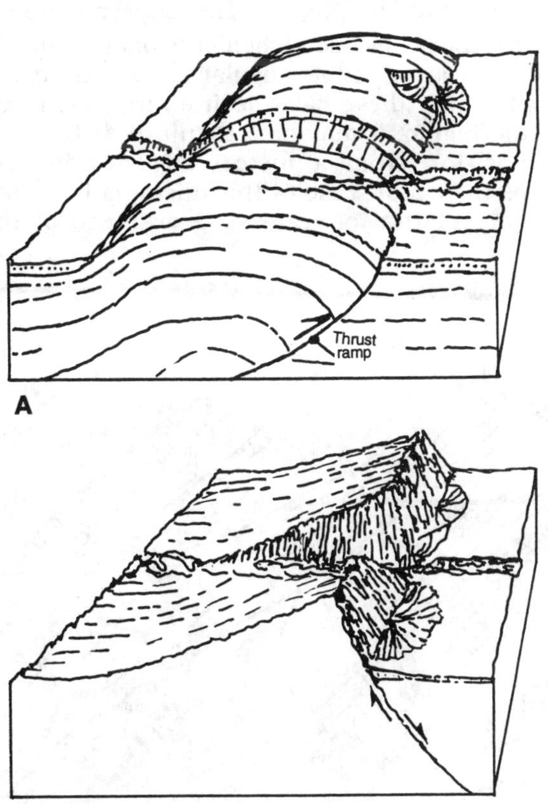

Figure 12.16 Block diagrams of gorges of antecedent rivers across (A) a rising anticline and (B) a rising fault block. (Copyright © by Arthur N. Strahler.)

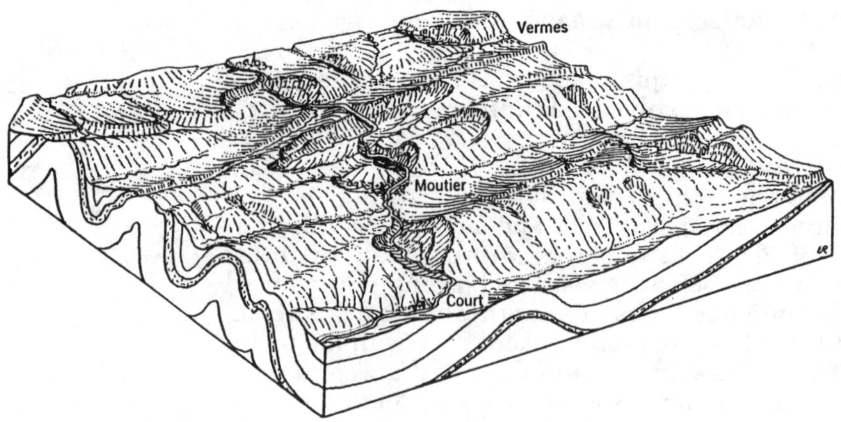

Figure 12.18 Block diagram of a portion of the Jura Mountains in Switzerland. (Drawn by Erwin Raisz. Copyright © by Arthur N. Strahler.)

Examples of transverse antecedent streams in the central Zagros Mountains have been mapped by Theodore Oberlander (1965, p. 79; 1985). Figure 12.19 is a portion of Oberlander's map showing a number of deep gorges through which antecedent streams cross anticlines of the Shur and Karun rivers.

An unusual case of antecedent drainage can be found in the upper reaches of the Colorado River near the boundary between Utah and Colorado. Here the Colorado and its tributary, the Dolores River, cross several anticlines at about right angles. These structures are called "salt anticlines" because they were pushed up by elongate salt diapirs. Subsequent solution removal of salt and gypsum caused collapse of the anticlinal crests, so that each structure holds an narrow elliptical strike valley (Eardley, 1962).

Antecedent streams that run transverse to fold and fault structures need to be clearly distinguished from superposed streams of non-tectonic origin. *Superposition* of a drainage system occurs where a relatively young layer of horizontal or gently-dipping platform strata overlies much older tectonic structures that had been previously reduced to an erosional surface of low relief (a peneplane), and perhaps bearing low monadnocks. This stratigraphic relationship is classed as an angular unconformity (Strahler, 1981, p. 130-132). Epeirogenic uplift allows the drainage system on the peneplane to initiate a vigorous new cycle of erosion, as shown in Figures 12.3 and 12.5. The trunk streams have the erosional capability of cutting through the underlying anticlines or fault blocks that may be present. This superposition is easily diagnosed as such when erosional remnants of the cover layer and its angular unconformity are present, but if these have been entirely removed from the region, it may be difficult to distinguish superposition from a history of antecedence. Perhaps the classic case of this dilemma has been the interpretation of transverse drainage of the

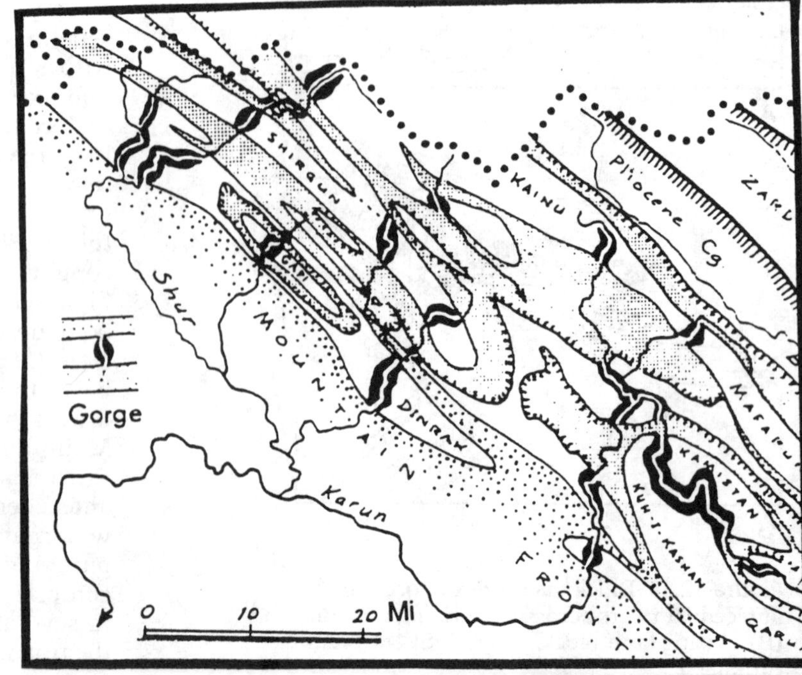

Figure 12.19 Sketch map of a portion of the Zagros Mountains showing transverse gorges classified as antecedent in origin. (From Theodore Oberlander, 1965, *The Zagros Streams*, Syracuse Geog. Series, No. 1, p. 79, Syracuse University Press. Used by permission of the author and publisher.)

central Appalachians, in which chains of great watergaps are conspicuous. (See Douglas Johnson, 1931, and A.N. Strahler, 1945, for comprehensive reviews.)

Another well known case study is about several deep gorges that cut through the Rocky Mountain uplifts of Wyoming, Montana, Utah, and Colorado. Tectonic histories of these uplifts and the basins that lie between them were presented in earlier chapters. [Chapter 9: Intracratonal Compressional Tectonics of Western North America; Figures 52-54. Chapter 11: The Rocky Mountain Basins; Figure 11.61.] Figure 12.20 shows nine such canyons occupied by major streams of the area. Perhaps the most spectacular is the Ladore Canyon cut into the eastern end of the Uinta range. John Wesley Powell, whose party ran its rapids in June 1871 on his great canyon voyage, used the Green River as an example of an antecedent stream. This explanation was accepted for many decades. As the geologic history of the region was unfolded, the alternative of superposition gained acceptance. W.W. Atwood, Sr., and W.W. Atwood, Jr. (1938) argued that deep partial burial of the uplifts in debris shed from the mountain slopes raised the level of the surface drainage to the point that stream channels shifted their courses to positions over buried uplifts, or were diverted by stream piracy through cols or passes. In the denudation phase that followed, the new paths were carved to their present depths in Precambrian rock.

Finally, we turn to the great Himalayan range for possible examples of antecedent river gorges. In an earlier section of this chapter we investigated the rapid exhumation of the windward slopes of the Higher Himalayas and the establishment of a comparatively recent date of rapid rise of the chain of high peaks. Figure 12.21 is a drainage map of the Himalayan-Tibetan region with locations of the chains of highest peaks and other information about the tectonic zones we described in Chapter 9 (see Figures 9.43, 9,44, 9.45). Arthur Holmes gave special attention in his textbook to the origin of the Himalayan rivers (1978, p. 386-389). He pointed out that the mere downcutting of stream channels as the entire crust rises is not what is meant by

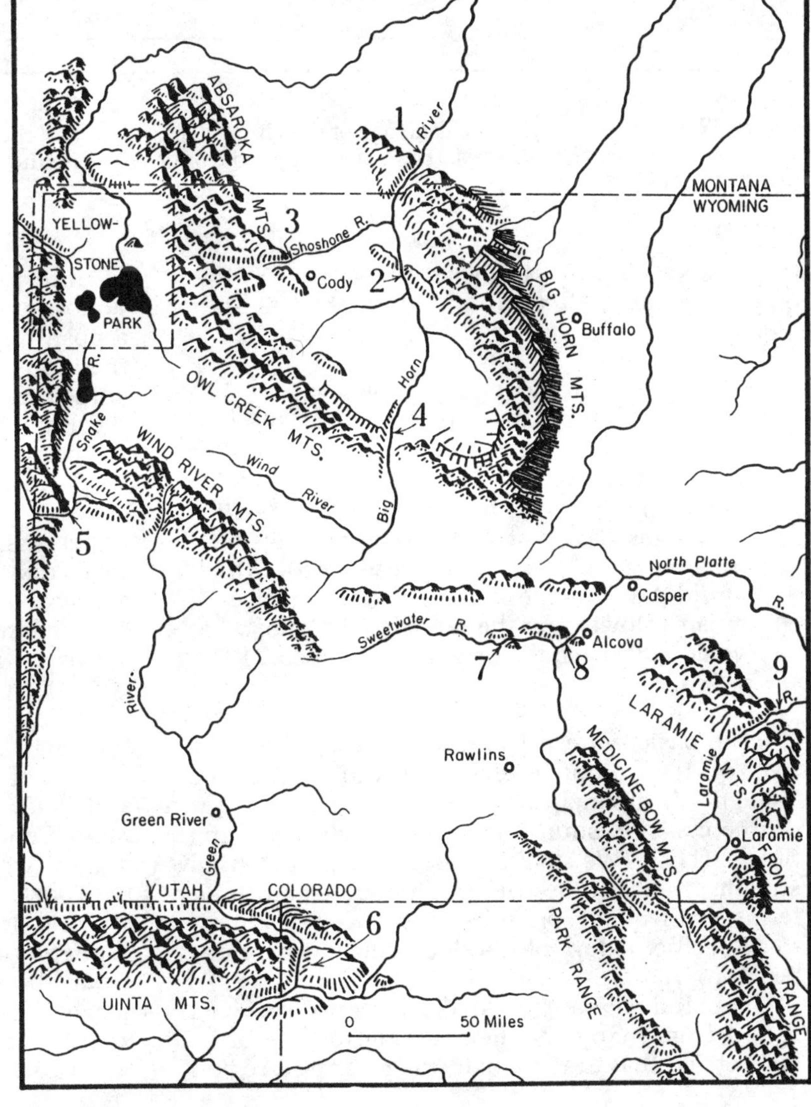

Figure 12.20 Sketch map of a part of the central Rocky Mountain uplifts, showing gorges of superposed streams. 1. Bighorn Canyon through Bighorn Mountains. 2. Bighorn River near Greybull. 3. Shoshone Canyon. 4. Wind River Canyon. 5. Snake River Canyon. 6. Lodore Canyon of the Green River. 7. Devil's Gate of Sweetwater River. 8. North Platte River near Alcova. 9. Laramie River. From W.W. Atwood, Sr., and W.W. Atwood, Jr., 1938, Bull., *Geol. Soc. of Amer.*, v. 49. Reproduced with the permission of the Publisher, the Geological Society of America, Boulder, Colorado, USA. Copyright 1938.)

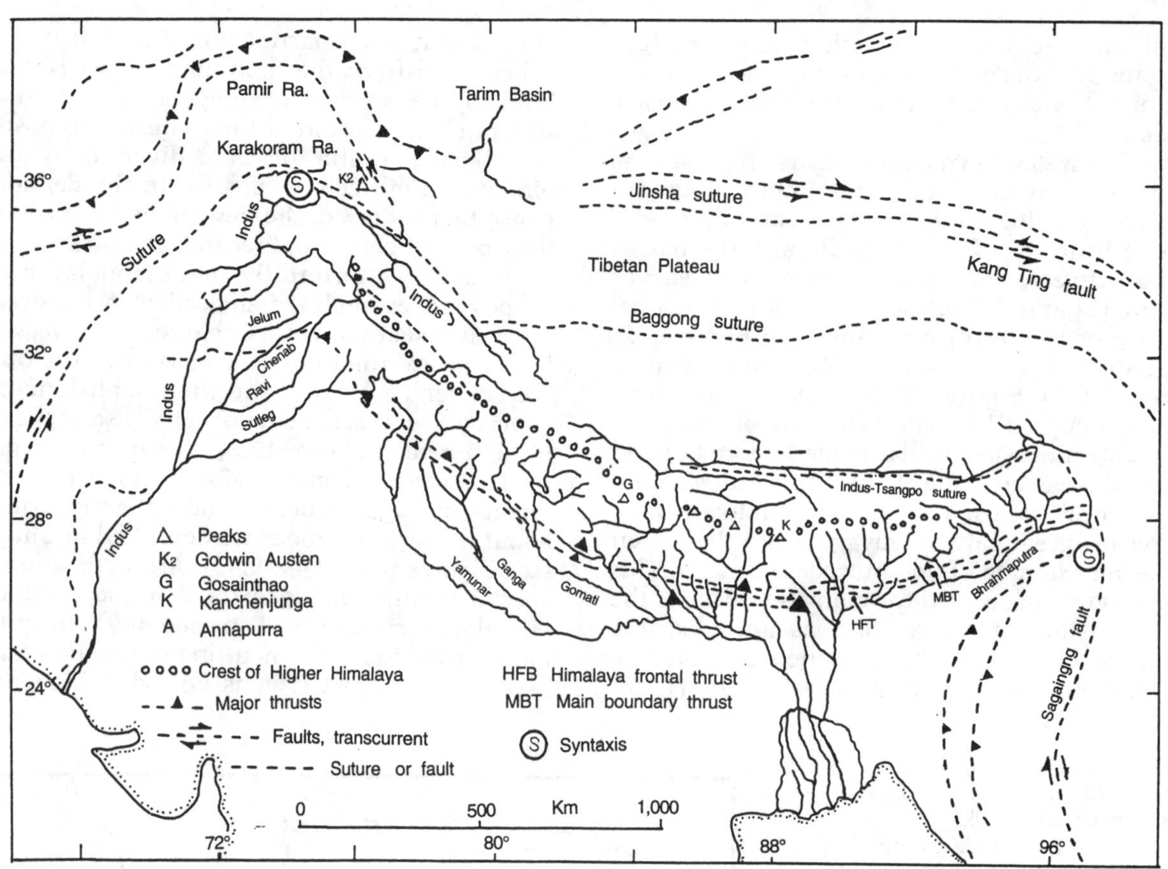

Figure 12.21 Sketch map of the drainage of the Himalayan ranges and the Tibetan Plateau in relation to the major thrusts and sutures. (Drainage complied from NASA satellite imagery. Map copyright © by Arthur N. Strahler.)

antecedence, since if that were the case, it would apply to nearly all drainage systems. He then added:

> The significant criteria in the case of the Himalayan rivers are (a) that the river has sawn its way through ranges with peaks that now rise high above the level of the source; and (b) that the deep valleys and gorges traversing the ranges have not resulted from headward erosion (e.g. by waterfall recession), which would have made possible the capture of streams flowing on the far side (Tibet) of what would have been the original watershed. (1978, p. 386)

The basic pattern Holmes saw was, first, that two of the major rivers—the Indus and the Tsangpo (Brahmaputra)—taken together lie about on the collision suture named the Indus-Tsangpo Suture (ITZ). (We shall categorize them as "strike streams," since to use the traditional geomorphic terms "consequent" or "subsequent" would commit to a specific history of development that may not be appropriate.)

The Indus-Tsangpo strike streams received runoff from many channels arising to the north, but beyond that to the north was perhaps a region of interior drainage, as we find there today. Following on the map the Indus River northwest to a position south of the Karakoram Range, we see the Indus turn sharply left, passing through a great gorge across the high crest and continuing down to the Punjab lowland. This bend is in the western structural syntax of the Himalayan arc. Following the Tsangpo eastward, it makes a sharp right turn, crossing the high crest and flowing south into the upper Assam lowland. This abrupt change is the eastern syntax connecting to the southern Asiatic arc system. Both exit courses can be classified as antecedent streams, since they cross ranges younger than the ITZ suture (Summerfield, 1991, p. 423).

We now direct attention to the up-thrusts forming the line of the highest peaks, which are formed of Miocene leucogranites (see Figure 9.44 and 9.45). This high crest was raised along the Main Central Thrust (MCT) and, as it rose ever higher, would have acted to cut off streams that previously flowed south to the Ganga-Brahmaputra lowland, forcing the drainage to overflow into the Tsangpo or Indus systems. Only those streams of great abrasional power would have been able to survive as antecedent streams. According to Table 9.1, the MCT was active about 20 Ma, which was some 20 m.y. after the suturing of India with Tibet.

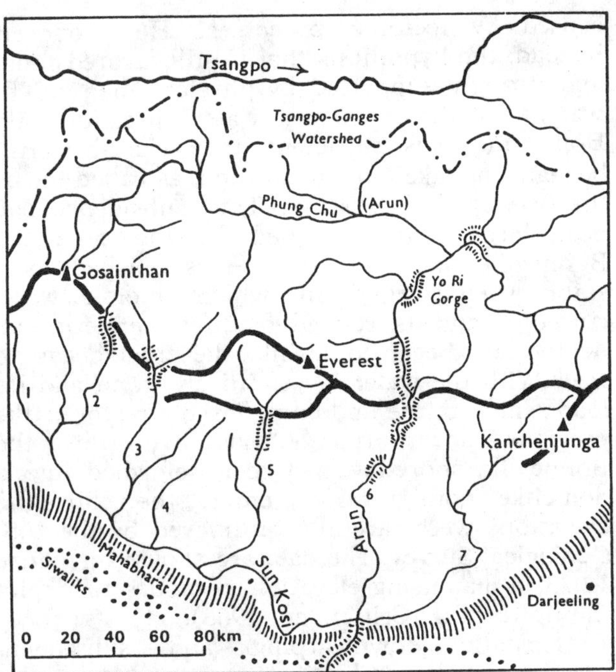

(1) Indrawati. (2) Sun Kosi (3) Bhote Kossi (4) Tamba Kosi
(5) Dubh Kosi (6) Arun (7) Tamur

Figure 12.22 Sketch map of a portion of the Himalayas surrounding Mount Everest. (From Arthur Holmes, 1978, *Holmes Principles of Geology*, 3rd Ed., revised by Doris L. Holmes, p, 387, Figure 19.36. Copyright © 1936. Reprinted by permission of Thomas Nelson & Sons, Ltd.

Holmes focused attention on a group of south-flowing streams in the vicinity of Mount Everest that converge to form the Kosi River on the IndoGangetic lowland. This area is shown in Figure 12.22. Attention focuses on the Arun River, which flows from north to south on a course passing some 40 km east of Everest. North of the crestline of the great peaks the Arun drains a large area that is bounded on the north by the watershed of the Tsangpo-Brahmaputra system. At an elevation of about 4000 m, the Arun turns south and passes through the Yo Ri gorge. Some 20 km farther downstream, it enters a deep gorge some 50 km long through the high mountain chain. The steep descent of the channel brings it down to about 1200 m. Two other tributaries of the Kosi also pass southward through the main mountain crestline in deep gorges: Sun Kosi and Bhote Kosi.

Although the case for an antecedent origin of this great gorge sequence seemed strong, Indian geologists had argued for an alternative development: headward erosion and capture of the drainage north of the mountain crestline (Holmes, 1978, p. 386-387). In defense of the antecedent theory, it was argued by L.R. Wager (1937) that because the gorge has been carved in highly resistant gneiss, rather than in a nearby zone of relatively weak schist, stream piracy is unlikely.

Perhaps it has come to your mind that the rapid rise of the great barrier chain would have also formed a trap for atmospheric moisture (Figure 12.15). This orographic effect is one that we have relied on in the earlier section to produce a rainshadow desert (as it does today). A satisfactory response might be that snowmelt forming on the north facing slopes of the watershed would provide the stream discharge needed to sustain the erosion of the south-flowing antecedent streams. Holmes tells us that there have indeed been brief periods when the Arun lacked the erosive power necessary to keep its flow going as tectonic uplift tended to back it up. Remnants of lake sediments laid down during periods of ponding can be found today along the walls of the antecedent gorge (1978, p. 388).

In bringing this section to a close we note that antecedent streams, such as those of the Himalayas, leave clinging to the walls of their gorges alluvial deposits that may be subjected to age dating and thus reveal rates of tectonic uplift and isostatic response (Burbank et al., 1996). A similar information link between geomorphic process and tectonics can be found in uplifted marine terraces and coral reefs, a subject we turn to next.

12.14 Isostatic Crustal Rebound

Loading of the crust, requiring isostatic compensation by crustal sinking to a new equilibrium level, occurs not only when sediment from an adjacent region is deposited, but also when an overlying layer of ocean water, lake water, or ice is added or thickened. When that water layer is thinned or removed, crustal rise occurs. Here, we illustrate with examples of (a) increase in depth and extent of a Pleistocene inland lake and (b) growth and disappearance of Pleistocene ice sheets.

Rise and fall of water levels in some inland lakes of arid and semiarid regions during the Pleistocene Epoch have been correlated with glacial and interglacial stages. Such lakes occupied intermontane basins of the western United States, and most had no outlet to the sea. They are called *pluvial lakes*, suggesting the increase in depth and extent of the lakes as a result of a combination of reduced evaporation and the increased precipitation over nearby mountains. Largest of the western pluvial lakes was Lake Bonneville, of which the shrunken remnant is now Great Salt Lake (Figure 12.23). At its maximum extent Lake Bonneville was almost as large in area (52,000 sq km) as present Lake Michigan and attained a maximum depth of about 330 m. At the maximum level of its cycles of waxing and waning, Lake Bonneville overflowed into a tributary of the Snake River. At that time the highest of the shorelines was carved into mountainsides by wave action and is now found at an elevation of about 1615 m (Figure 12.23).

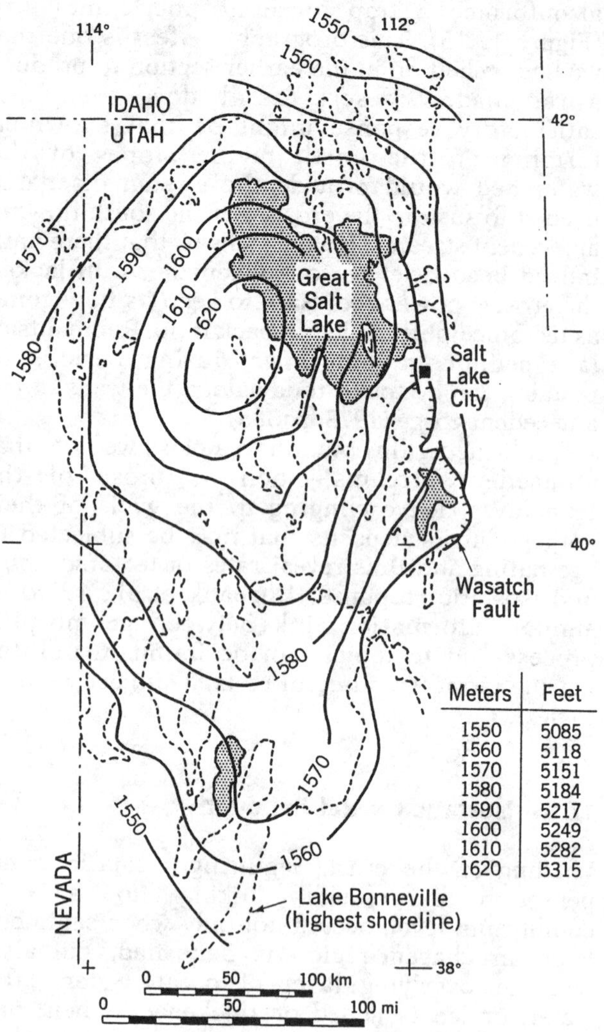

Meters	Feet
1550	5085
1560	5118
1570	5151
1580	5184
1590	5217
1600	5249
1610	5282
1620	5315

Figure 12.23 Deformation of the highest shoreline (dashed line) of Lake Bonneville, Utah, shown by elevation contours in meters. (After M.D. Crittenden, Jr., 1963, *U.S. Geological Survey, Professional Paper 454-E.*)

American geologist Grove Karl Gilbert made the first major field survey of the relict features of Lake Bonneville; the results were published in 1890 in a monograph of the U.S. Geological Survey. Gilbert's survey party determined the elevation of two of the high shorelines. It might be expected that the height of each shoreline above the present lake surface elevation would be the same at all points throughout the area; but this proved not to be the case. The highest shoreline—called the Bonneville shoreline—is higher in elevation near the former center of the ancient lake than in the peripheral zone, the difference being on the order of 60 m. (The shoreline can be found carved into islands that occupied the central part of the lake in its highest stages.) Clearly, the former high geoidal water surface has been warped upward into a domelike surface. Gilbert ruled out the possibility that the up-doming could have been caused by tectonic processes. He proposed, instead, the hypothesis that is still favored today and strongly supported by physical theory. The weight of the maximum water mass of Lake Bonneville was sufficient to cause the crust beneath the lake floor to subside, as called for by the principle of isostasy. This subsidence had been largely accomplished by the time the Bonneville shoreline became established as a stable water level, during which time the wave-cut notch and its related features were formed. As the lake began to shrink, the crust began to rise. With the water layer entirely gone and its load removed, the updoming largely restored the previous downwarp, but as a result, the Bonneville shoreline had been deformed into a domelike configuration. Later, the shoreline elevations were carefully resurveyed by the U.S. Geological Survey. The data are shown in Figure 12.23, a map using elevation contours to depict the upwarping (Crittenden, 1963).

Isostatic downwarping and subsequent recovery has been identified on a much grander scale in two major centers of ice sheet accumulation. One of these is the former site of the Laurentide Ice Sheet, centered about on what is now Hudson Bay and the Laurentian Highland immediately to the east. The other is the former site of the Scandinavian Ice Sheet, centered on what is now the Gulf of Bothnia. In both cases the ice load depressed the crust into saucerlike basins that became flooded by the ocean as sea level rose. Along the shores of these epicontinental seas, wave action marked the new shoreline with a wavecut notch or a ridge of cobblestones (a beach ridge). Crustal rebound set in immediately following the rapid thinning and final disappearance of the ice, so that each shoreline marker was lifted above the limits of wave action, becoming an elevated *strandline*. Large numbers of strandlines lie abandoned in the coastal belt of Hudson Bay, and elevated strandlines can also be identified in the lands surrounding the Gulf of Bothnia.

Postglacial uplift of the Baltic region had been recognized in the mid-1700s, but until the glacial theory was proposed in the mid-1800s no suitable explanation was forthcoming. By 1860 a Scottish geologist, T.F. Jamieson, had identified upraised shorelines in his country and applied the principle of isostasy (first proposed in 1855) to the problem. He suggested that the crust is weak and flexible, allowing it to subside under the ice load, and to rise again after the ice had disappeared. The explanation became universally adopted and, as we have seen, was tested by Gilbert in the analogous case of Lake Bonneville.

Geophysicists came forward with evidence substantiating the hypothesis. One of these was the seismologist Beno Gutenberg, who in 1941 offered the following lines of support, as restated by R.F. Flint (1971, p. 343):

1. In both Fennoscandia and North America the outer limits of the upwarped region parallels the limit of the latest glaciation. 2. In both regions the isolines (lines connecting points on any strandline that have been equally uplifted) are concentric to the area in which, according to independent evidence, the former ice was thickest late in the process of deglaciation. 3. In both regions antecedent downwarping is suggested by the presence of marine deposits now bent up above sealevel, and in turn overlying subaerial deposits. 4. In both regions rate of uplift is of the same order of magnitude. During the last few thousand years the rate of uplift of Fennoscandia has slowed down from an earlier, much greater rate. 5. In both regions even the incomplete data obtained thus far show that the gravity anomalies are negative, and that they increase toward the central parts of the glaciated areas, indicating that crustal equilibrium in these regions has not yet been reached. 6. In other regions of former glaciation or former greater glaciation, such as Britain, Greenland, Svalbard, Novaya Zemlya, Siberia, Patagonia, and Antarctica, where postglacial upwarping is expectable, evidence of it has been observed.

Point 5 needs special explanation. Although the crustal downwarping is elastic in nature, like the flexing of a steel spring, the mass displacement below the crust is accomplished by plastic flowage in the soft asthenosphere. This flowage is directed radially outward from the area of loading into the unloaded peripheral zone, where the crust is actually forced to rise very slightly, as shown in the deformation curve in Figure 12.24. An example of lithospheric subsidence under load is seen in the Hawaiian Islands, where the loading and downflexing of the crust by volcano building has caused a bathymetric moat to form (McNutt, 1987, p. 356). On the bathymetric map this moat is identifiable on both sides of the island chain.

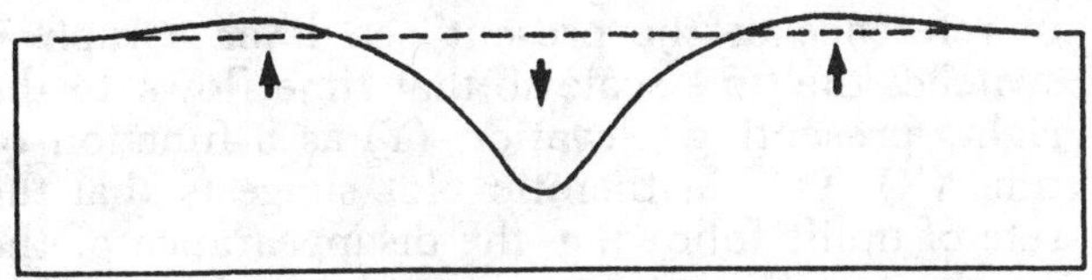

Figure 12.24 Idealized diagram of deformation of the earth's crust under a concentrated vertical load. The vertical scale is greatly exaggerated. (After W.A. Heiskanen and R.A. Vening Meinesz, 1958, *The Earth and Its Gravity Field*, p. 322, Figure 10A-3, The McGraw•Hill Book Companies, New York. Used by permission.

The Maui and Hawaii deeps on the north sides of their respective islands are closed depressions more than 5.5 km below sea level; the deep axis clearly curves around the southeastern side of Hawaii. To the northeast beyond the deep moat is a bathymetric arch with its crest about 1 km above the general level of the Pacific seafloor (Macdonald and Abbott, 1970, p. 279-280).

What has happened since the ice sheets rapidly disappeared is described by geophysicists W.A. Heiskanen and F.A. Vening Meinesz:

> At the present time the flow of the subcrustal material should be directed toward the center. Since all of the mass that flowed outward during the glacial period has not had time to move back, there is too little mass under the uplift, and the gravity anomalies are therefore negative, being as high as -50 milligals in the center of the area. The existence of negative anomalies in the uplift area is of great significance. If the subcrustal masses had moved only vertically downward during the glacial period and upward later on, the mass under the glacial areas would not have changed, so that there would be no reason for the systematically negative gravity anomalies. The existence of the negative gravity field in this area is evidence of the horizontal movement of the subcrustal masses. (1958, p. 212-213)

Geoid contours for the two ice sheet centers referred to—Laurentide and Scandinavian ice sheets—are shown in Figure 12.25). Centered over Hudson Bay is a deep closed depression of the geoid, going down to negative elevations of more than -48 m. Centered about over Finland is a deep trough, opening out to the northeast, in which the geoid surface plunges deeply. Although not a closed depression, it is nevertheless a true depression, shaped like a hand-scoop used to dispense nuts or candies.

Heiskanen and Vening Meinesz cite the opinion of another geophysicist, E. Niskanen, that in the Baltic region the land has yet to rise about 200 m before complete isostatic equilibrium prevails (Niskanen, 1939). It is not expected that the entire amount of recovery will be achieved, but recovery will continue perhaps as long as 15,000 years (Flint, 1971, p. 349). Modern rates of uplift have been obtained by two programs of precision geodetic leveling in Finland, separated by a period of 40 to 50 years. (Heiskanen and Vening Meinesz, 1958, p. 212). They show a maximum rate of 0.9 m/100 y. On the Swedish side, the rate may be as high as 1.0 m/100 y (Figure 12.26).

By the mid 1980s, postglacial isostatic rebound was actually observed by the geodetic satellite *Lageos* (Rubincam, 1984, p. 1077, 1085). Observations over a 5-year period had

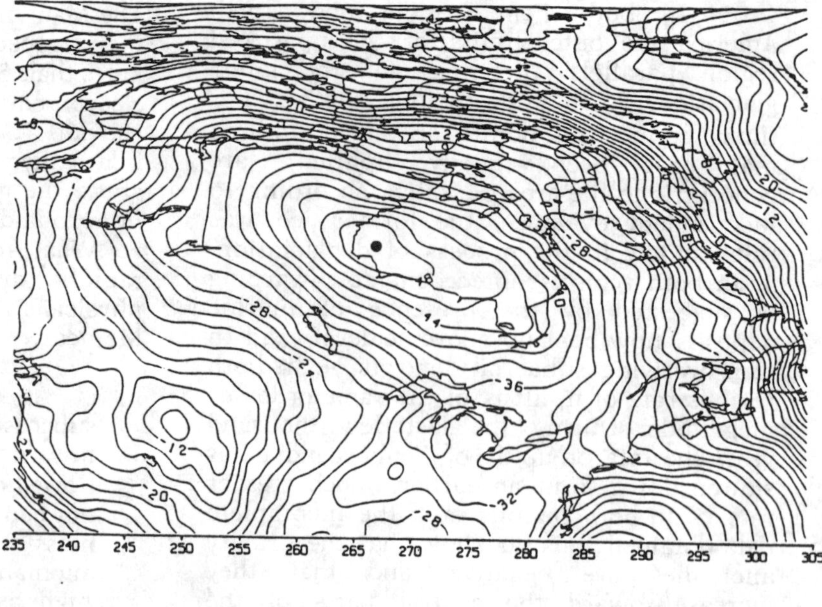

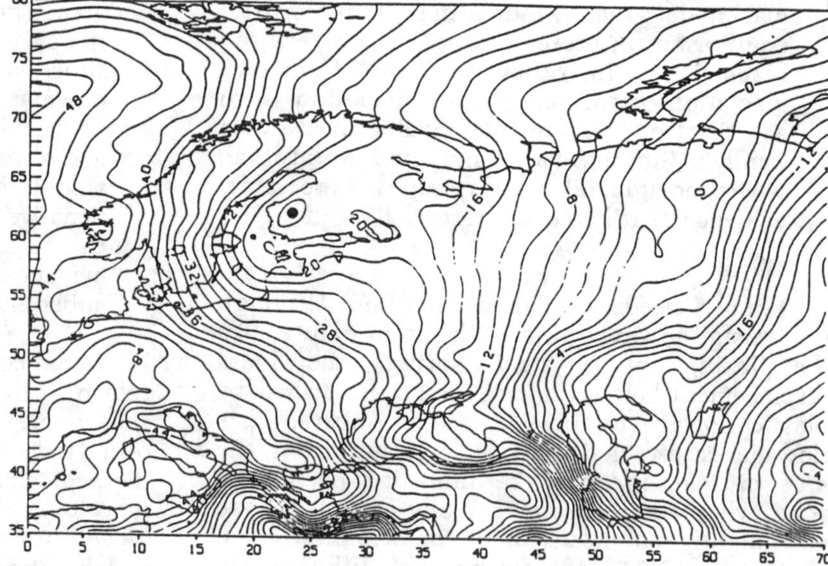

Figure 12.25 Portions of a world map of the global gravity geoid, based on satellite data, and showing depressions centered over the former sites (above) the Laurentide Ice Sheet and (below) the Scandinavian Ice Sheet. (NASA Goddard Space Flight Center.)

revealed the fact that the node of Lageos's orbit was undergoing a small acceleration, and this was attributed to a combination of postglacial rebound and the ocean tide. When the effect of the tide was removed, the residual acceleration due to rebound was computed. These data have also made possible the confirmation of previously calculated values of the effective viscosity of the earth's mantle (Chapter 3).

Isostatic rebound of areas formerly depressed by the Laurentide Ice Sheet has been documented and dated by surveys of a great succession of strandlines, marked by beach ridges. Figure 12.27 is a map of *isobases* (contours of former sea levels) of the Hudson Bay region, covering the last 6000 years (Andrews, 1970; 1991, p. 481). The crust has risen over 100 m in that period.

Geologists and geophysicists have presented an arithmetic graph showing the observed relationship between altitude of isobase as a function of time (Farrand, 1962; Flint, 1971, p. 345; Walcott, 1972). Figure 12.28 is an example, showing data from Scandinavia and North America. Graph A is the conventional presentation showing the uplift of strand lines in reference to the present sea level. Graph B switches the time scale so that time flows to the right, presenting elevation (Y) as a function of time (X). This arithemtic plot suggests that the rate of uplift following the disappearance of the ice sheet is a negative exponential function. This would agree with theory, since the pressure differential of the sinking crust would be decreasing with reduction in altitude. This type of curve is indicated by the field evidence consisting of elevation measurements of strandlines and carbon-14 age fixes (Farrand, 1962; Flint, 1971, p. 345, Figure 13-1). Graph C shows the three curves plotted on semi-

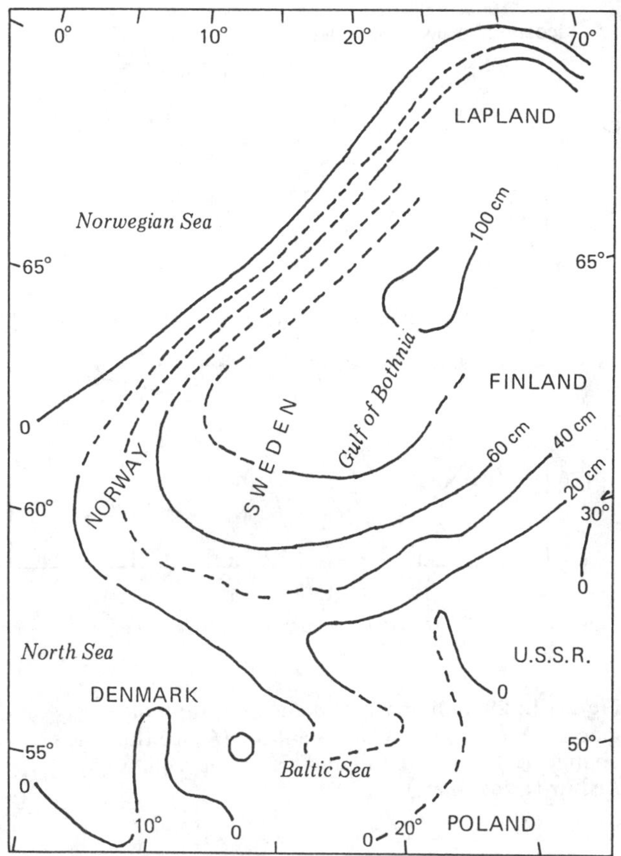

Figure 12.26 Map of present rate of uplift of the Baltic region, showing contours of equal uplift in centimeters per century. (Adapted from data in J.A. Jacobs, R.D. Russell, and J.T. Wilson, 1959, *Physics and Geology*, p. 98, Figure 4-5. The McGraw•Hill Book Companies. Used by permission.)

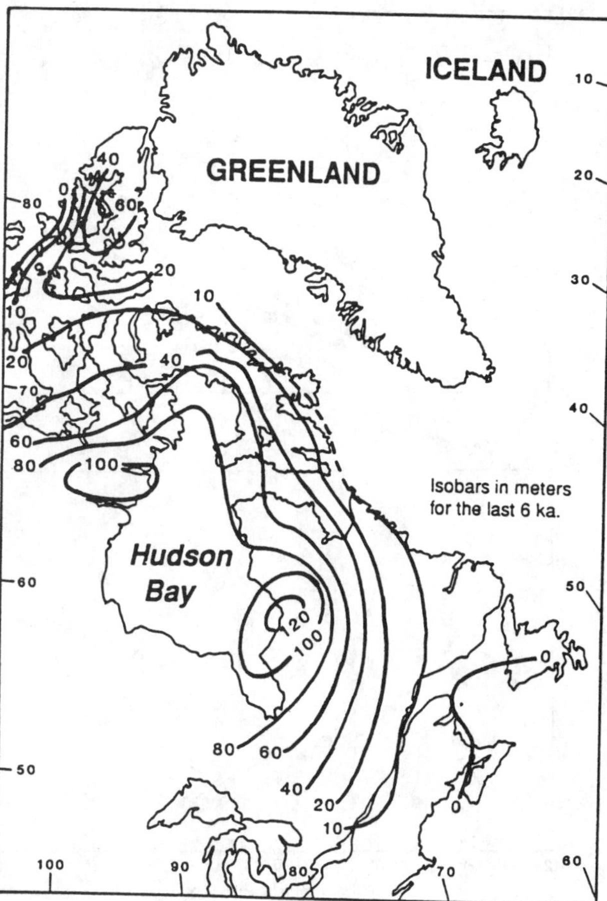

Figure 12.27 Map of isobases of sea level change over the past 6,000 years in the central region of the Laurentide Ice Sheet. (From John T. Andrews, 1991, p. 481, Figure 10, in *Neotectonics of North America, Decade Map Volume*. Copyright © by the Geological Society of America. Reproduced with the permission of the Publisher, the Geological Society of America, Boulder, Colorado, USA. Copyright 1991.)

logarithmic graph paper, and the result is a fairly close fit of the plotted points to straight lines.

Figure 12.29 is an attempt to diagram the program of glacio-isostatic crustal movement during a cycle of glaciation followed by a rapid deglaciation. (Purely elastic deformation is not shown). Both downwarping and upwarping are taken to be represented by exponential or logarithmic curves: rapid change at first, then slowing contin-uously to a much lower rate.

A region of strandlines stretches from Lake Superior to Newfoundland. These are shown on a regional map, Figure 12.30. The strandlines came into existence during recessional substages of the Wisconsinan Stage as ice evacuated topographic basins that formed temporarily between the ice front and higher ground elevations to the south. Our map includes strandlines that are either marine shorelines or lake shorelines. A dashed line shows the southern limit of warping, or *hinge line*, which is approximately equivalent to the limit of Wisconsinan ice advance in the New England region. Several other hinge-lines are shown farther north over the Great Lakes area. These refer to sets of lake levels in the order of younger age from south to north.

Figure 12.31 is a schematic diagram to illustrate the principle of isostatic upwarping as it applies to the Great Lakes region. In Phase 1, the crust is shown to be warped down beneath the ice sheet while a proglacial lake lies to the south of the ice front. Wave action in this lake will produce a horizontal strandline. In Phase 2, the ice front has receded some distance and the crust has risen, warping the first strandline so that it increases in elevation toward the north. In this phase a new horizontal strandline is formed at lake level. In Phase 3, further ice recession has permitted additional crustal rise, upwarping the strandlines of both the first and second phases.

That updoming continues today in this region is established by tide-gage records. Figure 12.32 shows contours of equal rate of uplift as presented by Gutenberg (1941). The zero contour is the present hinge line for this deformation. These rates are comparable with

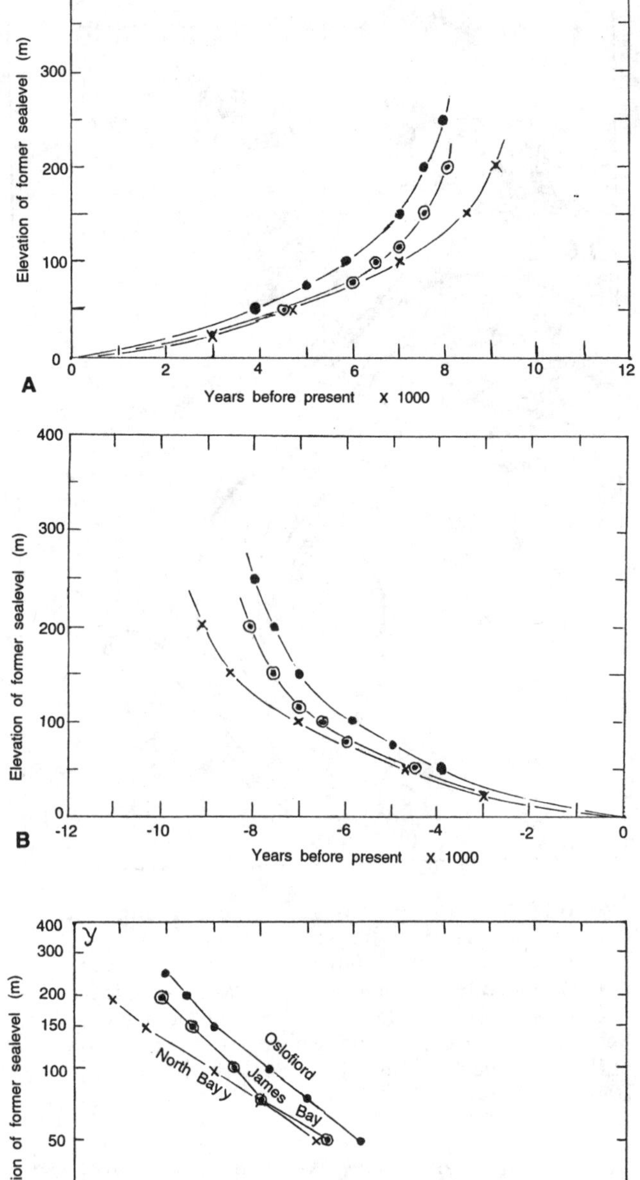

Figure 12.28 Graphs of the Holocene crustal uplift in Oslofjord, James Bay, and North Bay. (A) Conventional presentation. (B) Reversed time scale. (C) Semilogarithmic plot. (Copyright © by Arthur N. Strahler.)

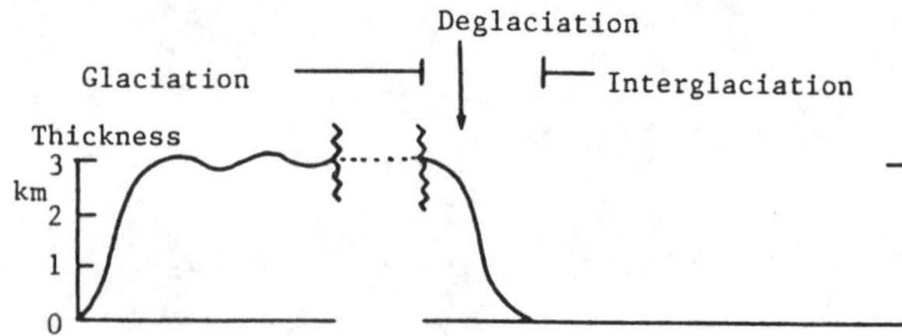

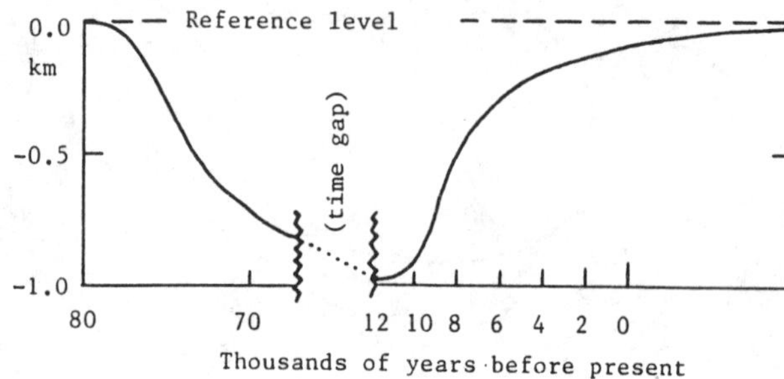

Figure 12.29 Schematic time/height graph of glaciation followed by deglaciation. (A) Ice thickness change. (B) Sea level fall and rise. (Copyright © by Arthur N. Strahler.)

those of the Baltic region, Figure 12.26, for the southerly marginal zone of the respective ice dome.

J.T. Andrews has called attention to the phenomenon of episodic uplift that we introduced earlier in this chapter (1991, p. 482-483). Whereas we have assumed that postglacial uplift occurs at a steady pace, although slowing gradually with time, a punctuated response may have been the prevailing mode. In this connection, consider the phenomenon of seismicity as a manifestation of episodic uplift. In Chapter 6, a brief account is given of scattered earthquakes or earthquake groups in New England, the Adirondacks, the St. Lawrence estuary in Quebec, and the Ungava Peninsula (see Figure 6.43). Andrews states that "there appears to be a growing consensus that glacial isostatic unloading has reactivated tectonic structures" (1991, p. 483).

Although much of the data we have cited in this section dates back into the 1940s and 1950s—long before modern plate tectonics came on the scene—they continue to be held generally valid and useful. Principles of isostasy had been put in place by Airy and Pratt in the 1850s, and the concept of a viscous (plastic) earth interior beneath a rigid crust had been firmly established by G.K. Gilbert (1877. p. 97) as a working hypothesis. Perhaps the reason that such a successful geophysical program has endured lies in the fact that the explanation for isostatic warping requires no reference to lithospheric plates and their motions.

A recapitulation of the long history of the isostatic deformation of the Great Lakes region was summarized in 1994 by James A Clark, Mark Hendriks, Thomas J. Timbermans, Calvin Struck, and Kenneth J. Hilverda (p. 19-20). Newer data and modeling have brought some

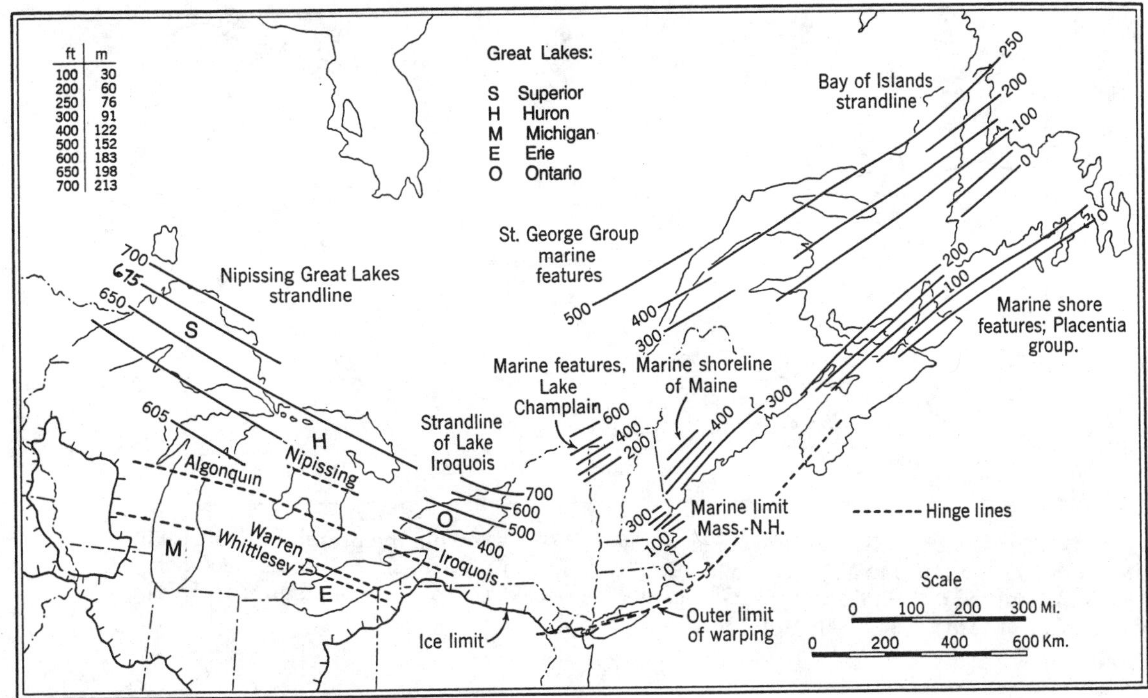

Figure 12.30 Map of strandlines and hinge lines of eastern North America, extending from the Great Lakes across New England and the Maritime Provinces. (Strandlines are modified and simplified from a map by R.F. Flint, 1975, *Glacial and Pleistocene Geology*, p. 251, Figure 14.6, Copyright by John Wiley & Sons, New York. Used by permission.)

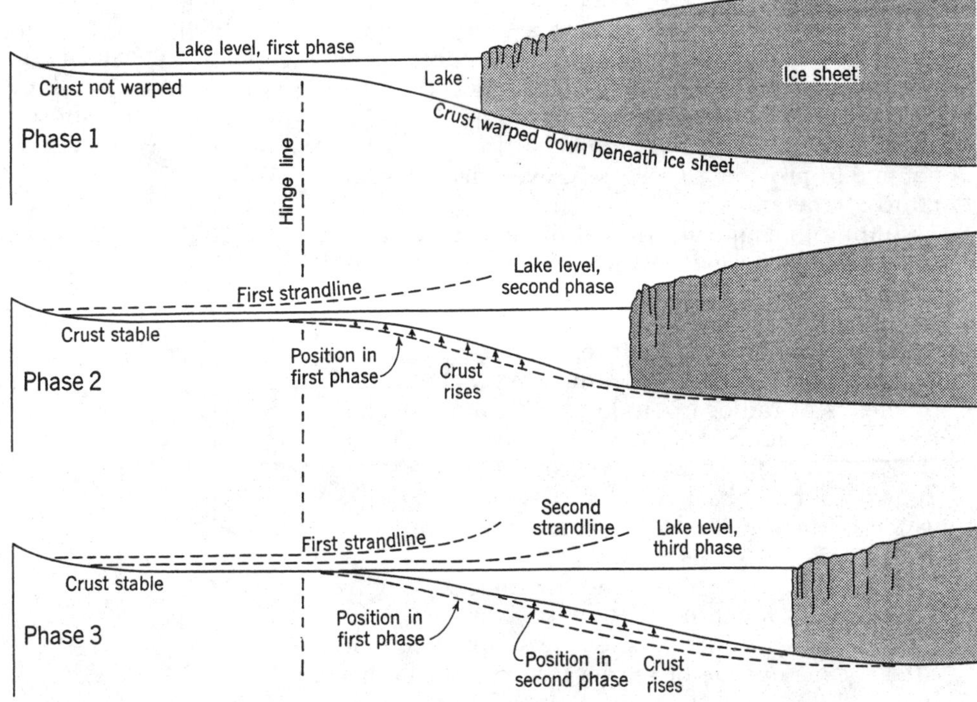

Figure 12.31 Schematic cross sections showing crustal warping and strandline deformation accompanying ice retreat. (Adapted from R.F. Flint, 1957, *Glacial and Pleistocene Geology*, p. 252, Figure 14.7. Copyright © by John Wiley & Sons, New York. Used by permission.)

revisions in the chronologies of the advances and retreats of the ice margin and have suggested alternatives to the hinge-line concept. A high-viscosity asthenosphere is ruled out, but on the other hand, one of low viscosity is not likely. Estimates of the full thickness of the ice sheet continue to be uncertain, but the possibility of a thickness as low as 700 m in this marginal region has been proposed (1994, p. 22).

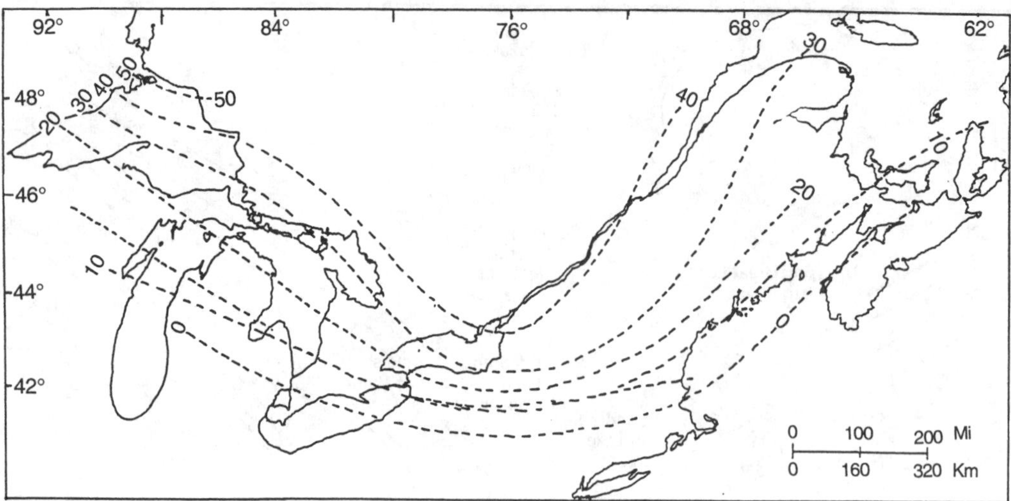

Figure 12.32 Sketch map of the same region as in Figure 12.30, showing the present rate of rise in elevation (cm/100 y) relative to a theoretical datum. (Data from Gutenberg, 1941, *Bull., Geol. Soc. Amer.*, p. 743, adapted by R.F. Flint, 1957, *Glacial and Pleistocene Geology*, p. 250, Figure 14.5, John Wiley & Sons, New York. Used by permission of the publisher.)

12.15 Glacial Lowering of Sea Level

Simultaneous with the growth of ice sheets during the Pleistocene was a global eustatic reduction of sea level. During a deglaciation, a rise of sea level would correspondingly have occurred. At the present time (the Holocene Epoch), although the great ice sheets have disappeared from North America and Eurasia, a huge amount of ice remains in the Antarctic and Greenland ice sheets along with reduced alpine glaciers of high mountain ranges. The Antarctic Ice Sheet alone now holds sufficient water volume to provide a gross sea level rise of some 60 to 90 meters, should all of that ice be melted. Assuming that the added load of this water upon the oceanic crust would cause a eustatic downwarping of 20 m, the net sea level rise would still over 40 m.

The record of sea level lowering in the Wisconsin Stage is now quite well documented by means of radiocarbon dating of samples taken from the floors of the passive continental shelves. Certain types of bottom materials are known to have been produced in very shallow water or at sea level. Examples are salt-marsh peat, oyster shells, oolites, corals, algae associated with corals, and beachrock. Figure 12.33 shows a depth-time curve of sea level for the Atlantic continental shelf. Assuming that the order of magnitude of sea level lowering the last major glacial advance is at least 100 m, the Atlantic continental shelf would have been exposed out to a distance of 100 to 200 km beyond the present shoreline off the northeastern United States. To this figure we may add an additional 30 m of emergence due to isostatic rise in response to load removal. Thus the shoreline may have reached a point close to the shelf break. In making the above statements, we are assuming that no other force was acting to cause a relative change in sea level. In particular, it is assumed that no epeirogenic or other tectonic rising or lowering of the crust was occurring independently. Blake W. Blackwelder (1981, p. 439) states that for the stretch of coast from New Jersey to Florida "similar elevation of similar-age samples shows that the coastal region has been relatively stable for the past 12,000 yr," and that "these largely undeformed shorelines show the tectonic stability of this region." (See also Blackwelder, 1980.)

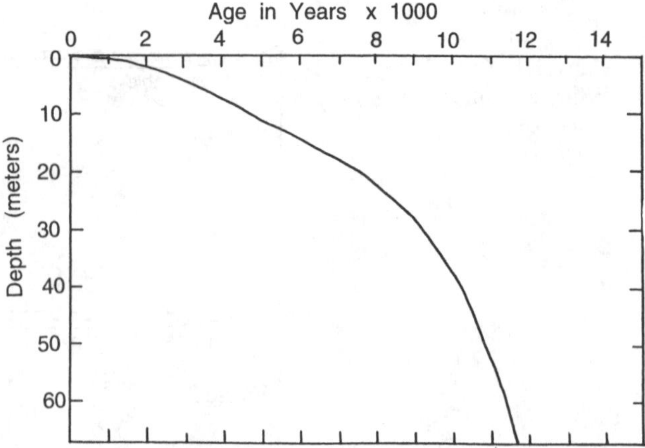

Figure 12.33 Age-depth graph of sea level rise over the inner continental shelf off Massachusetts during Holocene time. (From R.N. Oldale and C.J. O'Hara, 1980, *Geology*, v. 8, p. 104, Figure 2. Reproduced with the permission of the Publisher, the Geological Society of America, Boulder, Colorado, USA. Copyright 1980.)

12.16 Epeirogeny and Marine Terraces

We next consider tectonic activity as a possible second "player" or agent in explaining elevated strandlines of Pleistocene and Holocene time, and particularly those strandlines not directly connected with areas formerly lying beneath ice sheets. For this category of strandlines, we need to go to global locations well removed from glaciations. The raised features under discussion include the following: (A) Raised marine beaches, called simply *beach ridges*. The beach ridge may have been a barrier island with a lagoon behind it, such as we find today along the Texas coast. (B) *Marine terraces*, carved into older bedrock and typically bearing beach sediments. (C) Elevated *coral reefs*.

Now that our time window has been expanded to include the entire Pleistocene, lasting over a period of at least 1.6 m.y, we take note of a series of beach ridges and/or marine terraces that can be identified along the Atlantic coastal plain of the eastern U.S. and the Gulf of Mexico. More than a half-century ago, an assemblage of some eight marine terraces had been identified on the Atlantic coastal plain of New Jersey, Maryland, and Virginia. A concise description of these "classic" terraces was given by Nevin M. Fenneman in 1938 (p. 25-55). C. Wythe Cooke, one of the outstanding investigators of these terraces, had set up an idealized arrangement and classification of the terraces (1931). Given in descending order (oldest to youngest) they are as follows: Brandywine (82 m), Coharie (66 m), Sunderland (52 m), Wicomico (30), Penholoway (21), Talbot (13 m), Pamlico (8 m), Princess Anne (4 m). Each marine terrace can be traced into the valleys of major transverse streams as a stream terrace. Cooke assumed absolute stability of the coastal plain throughout the Pleistocene, meaning that no epeirogenic activity occurred. He extended his correlation of terraces by the simple criterion of elevation so as to include terraces of the Carolinas, Georgia, and Florida. Keep in mind that in those days radiometric ages could not be determined.

Charles D. Winker and James D. Howard have updated the history of investigation of the Atlantic coastal plain terraces (1977, p. 123). Correlation by elevation continued to be used into the 1970s by some researchers, but another group "introduced new terms for geomorphic features and stratigraphic units." "New paleogeographic reconstruct-ions were necessary, and these turned out to contradict much of the previous work and to suggest that the coastal plain was, in fact, warped during Pleistocene time" (p. 123). Winker and Howard showed that a warping of the innermost elevated shoreline—a low sand ridge known as Trail Ridge—has clearly occurred, since its elevation drops from 100 m to about 30 m as it is traced from South

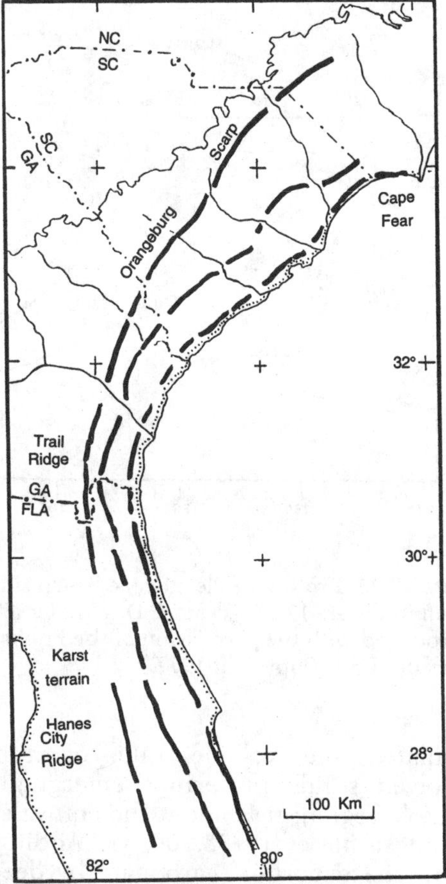

Figure 12.34 Sketch map of Pleistocene beach ridges of the Atlantic coastal plain south of Cape Fear. (From C.D. Winkler and J.D. Howard, 1977, *Geology*, v. 5, p. 124, Figure 1. Reproduced with the permission of the Publisher, the Geological Society of America, Boulder, Colorado, USA. Copyright 1977.)

Carolina into Georgia (Figures 12.34 and 12.35). A similar but lesser warping shows in the next lower shoreline. For both these ridges, the age seems to remain constant along the length of the ridge (p. 123-124). So, it would seem that an epeirogenic crustal sinking took place during the same period of time that these shore levels were being established.

In 1984, N.D. Opdyke, D.P. Spangler, D.L. Smith, D.S. Jones, and R.C. Lundquist of the University of Florida added a new chapter to the evolution of the southeastern coastal plain and its elevated shorelines. Notice on our profile diagram (Figure 12.35), a ridge gap between the 28th and 29th parallels, and the label "karst terrain" inserted in the gap. Both Trail Ridge and Haines City Ridge rise rather sharply in elevation toward this gap. This upturn in elevation requires that epeirogenic movement was locally upward, in contrast to the downsinking that occurred farther north. Could the rapid solution removal of limestone beneath this gap account for the local uplift? The U. Florida team made use of this mechanism. They

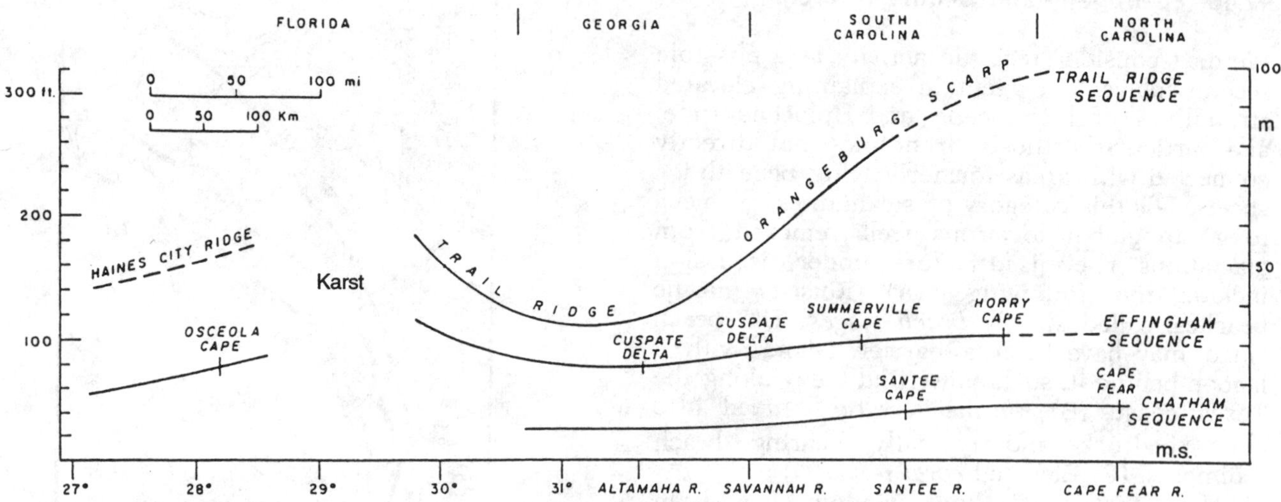

Figure 12.35 Profiles of Pleistocene beach ridges of the Atlantic coastal plain south of Cape Fear, shown in Figure 12.34. (From C.D. Winkler and J.D. Howard, 1977, *Geology*, v. 5, p. 126, Figure 3. Reproduced with the permission of the Publisher, the Geological Society of America, Boulder, Colorado, USA. Copyright 1977.)

calculated the volume rate of removal of dissolved solids in springs emerging from the sinkhole region; it is about the equivalent of 1 m of limestone every 38,000 yr. Adding to that figure the export of carbonate by deep seepage directly into the ocean, the total export could be as rapid as 1 m per 12,500 yr. The growth of cavities in the limestone would reduce the average density of the rock. Isostatic uplift in response to this density reduction was calculated and found to match closely the observed elevation excess of 42-49 m (1984, p. 228). The absence of shoreline ridges over the karst region is, of course, attributed to solution removal.

Turning next to the northeast Gulf Coast of western Florida and its extent into Mississippi, we find two low but clearly defined escarpments that parallel the Gulf shoreline. These are the Citronelle scarp (CS) and the Big Ridge scarp (BRS), shown on our sketch map, Figure 12.36. Notice that the CS consists of segments, and that these are not aligned, but instead change abruptly in strike. The BRS is relatively short, but forms a simple arc parallel with the coastline lineaments. Ervin G. Otvos (1981) noted the strange trend of the major streams, which are parallel and strike obliquely to the CS. This configuration suggests the possibility that the CS segments are scarps of normal faults that dip toward the Gulf. Although not sharply defined now, their heights are from 9 to 16 m. Figure 12.37 is a schematic cross section showing the scarps as possible faults and the stratigraphic succession associated with them (Etvos, 1981, p. 402). To develop this hypothesis of normal faulting, we need to look back into Chapter 10 to the text section on the Gulf of Mexico and Figures 11.15 through 11.18. Recall that the Gulf is postulated to have formed as a pull-apart basin with transforms as lateral boundaries. One of these transforms is shown to lie parallel with what is now the northeast Gulf Coast. If that historical interpretation is valid, reactivation of this ancient fault zone may explain the tectonic lineaments.

In this selective study of geomorphic features of the Atlantic coastal plain, we have held to one purpose of this chapter: to show that geomorphology can provide quantitative information on the age of flexing of the crust and lithosphere and of possible crustal faulting as well.

12.17 Marine Terraces of Subduction Margins

Subduction boundaries (convergent boundaries), where oceanic lithosphere is plunging beneath continental lithosphere surround the Pacific Ocean basin. Along the eastern margins of the Pacific basin, subduction carries the oceanic lithosphere beneath the massive American continents. Along the northern and western Pacific rim, narrow island arcs are typical, and we should include the Sumatra-Java arc in the list.

A striking geomorphic feature found on many exposed coasts of the Pacific Basin is a stair-like succession of marine terraces, typically arranged in age sequence from youngest at the bottom to oldest at the top. Two classes of such terraces can be recognized. One class is the *wave-cut terrace*, excavated by breaking waves and surf and having a marine cliff with an abrasion platform at its base (Figure 12.38A). It is largely an erosional landform. The second class of marine terrace, found in tropical waters, is the elevated coral reef (or *coral terrace*) attached to bedrock (Figure 12.38B). It

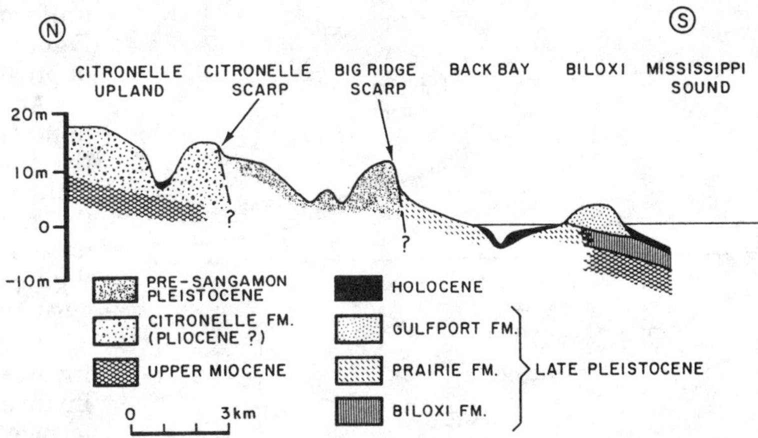

Figure 12.36 Sketch map of the northeast Gulf Coast showing escarpments in relation to drainage patterns. Circlred "X" indicates location of abrupt stream-course.(From E.G. Etvos, 1981, *Geology*, v. 9, p. 399, Figure 1. Reproduced with the permission of the Publisher, the Geological Society of America, Boulder, Colorado, USA. Copyright 1981.)

may lack an abrasional cliff, and may instead be built of a horizontal or gently sloping layer of coral conglomerate overlying layers of framework reef (Chappell and Veeh, 1978, Figure 4).

As an example of a great succession of coral terraces, we might select those on the Huon Peninsula on the north coast of Papua New Guinea, shown in a sketch map in Figure 12.39. The highest terraces rise to an elevation of over 600 m and can be traced nearly 900 km along the coast (Chappell, 1974), p. 553). The age of each of 10 levels of terraces has been determined to range from 30,000 y to 220,000 y.

It has been conventional practice to interpret each terrace as formed at the full height of a single glacio-eustatic cycle of sea level rise and fall. When standing by itself, this scenario requires that each successive cycle diminish in amplitude, as shown in Figure 12.40A. This program is not shown in paleo-temperature curves based on oxygen-isotope

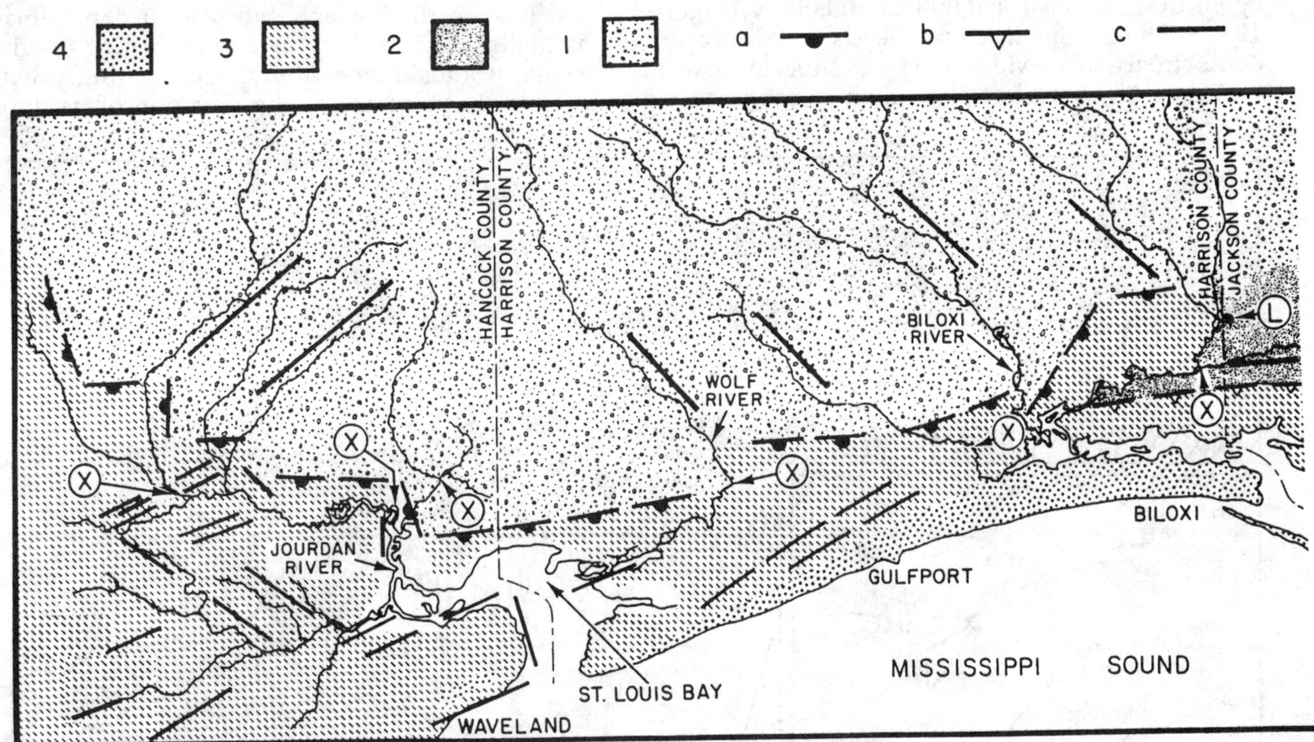

1: Citronelle Formation **2**: Pre-Sangamon Pleistocene **3**: Prairie Formation
4: Gulfport Formation **a**: Citronelle scarps **b**: Big Ridge scarps
c: Drainage and shoreline lineament

Figure 12.37 Schematic N-S cross section through formations and escarpments of the northeast Gulf Coast, approximately along the Harrison-Jackson County line. (From E.G. Etvos, 1981, *Geology*, v. 9, p. 402, Figure 5. Reproduced with the permission of the Publisher, the Geological Society of America, Boulder, Colorado, USA. Copyright 1981.)

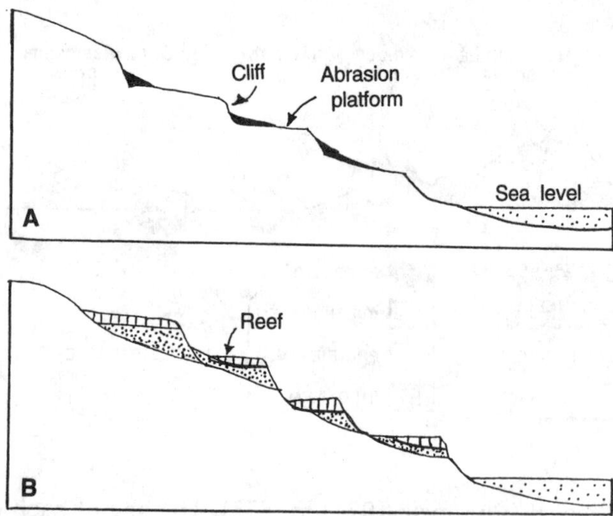

Figure 12.38 (A) Wavecut terraces. (B) Reef terraces. (Copyright © by Arthur N. Strahler.)

ratios, in sea-surface temperature curves, or in curves of incoming solar radiation. These data show instead no significant long-term trend up or down over the past 400,000 to 500,000 y (Figure 12.41). The decline in terrace levels can, however, conform to this evidence if we superimpose a program of tectonic uplift upon a program of uniform rise and fall of sea level, as shown in Figure 12.40B. The net change is a set of terraces of progressive lower elevation, as in Figure 12.40C.

An applied example of this program of tectonic uplift is shown in Figure 12.42, in which the lower five Huon reef terraces are shown in cross section along with the inferred positions of the shoreline (Veeh and Chappell, 1970). An interpretation of the data in terms of crustal rise is shown in Graph A of Figure 12.43. Graph B shows the corresponding curve of glacio-eustatic sea-level change.

What can be said of the tectonic processes involved in the crustal rise we interpret as involved in the formation of elevated marine terraces? We need to consider the two major kinds of plate boundaries rimming the Pacific Basin: subduction boundaries and continental transform boundaries. How does subduction generate crustal rise? Refer to Chapter 8 and Figures 8.19 through 8.22, showing the growth of the accretionary prism and the rise of the structural high, or outer arc. Where this outer arc rises above sea level, it forms islands capable of carrying marine terraces. An example might be the Mentawai Islands of the Sumatra-Java Arc (Figure 12.11). Farther to the east, where this outer arc is submerged, the Java coastline lies against the volcanic arc, where marine terraces would be expected (Figures 8.1 and 8.2). Here, not only does the rising of magma add load to the surface, but also at depth forms batholiths that thicken the crust. Loading requires isostatic subsidence of the lengthening crustal column, but also raises the elevation of its upper

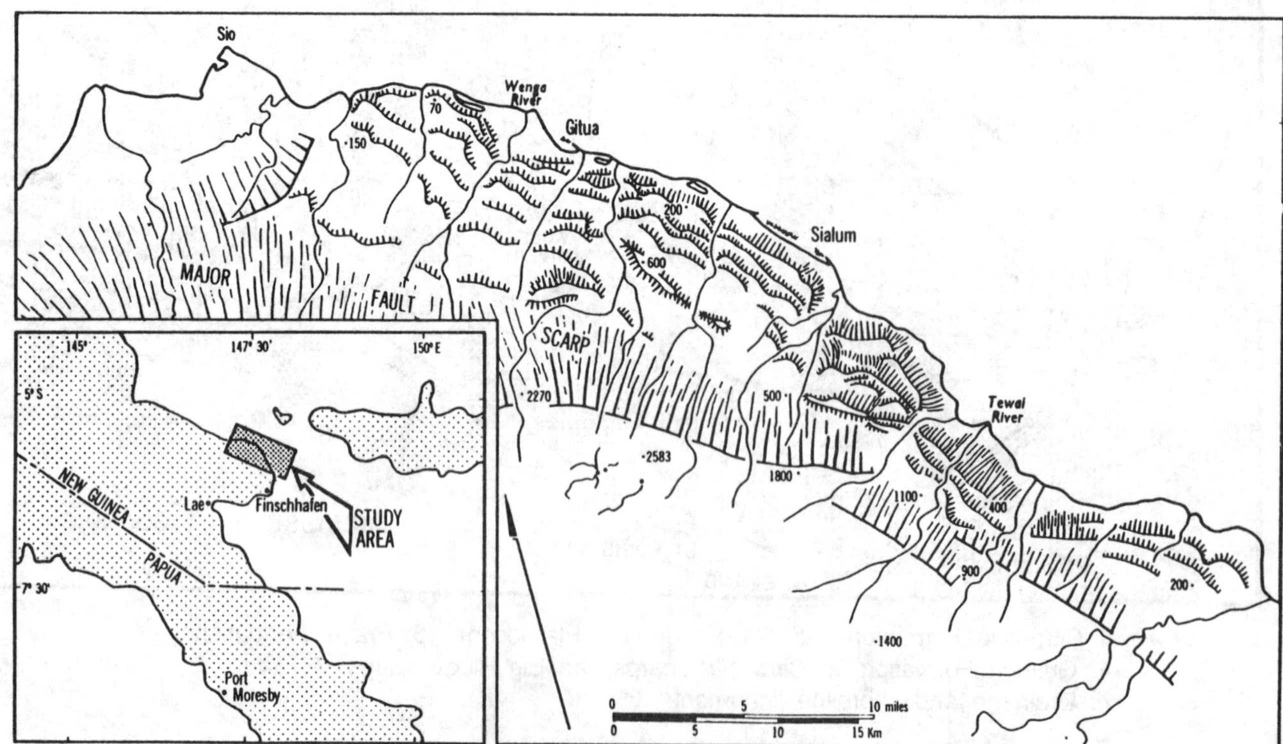

Figure 12.39 Sketch map of reef terraces on the Huon Peninsula, Papua New Guinea. (From J. Chappell, 1974, *Bull., Geol. Soc. Amer.*, v. 85, p. 553, Figure 1B. Reproduced with the permission of the Publisher, the Geological Society of America, Boulder, Colorado, USA. Copyright 1974.)

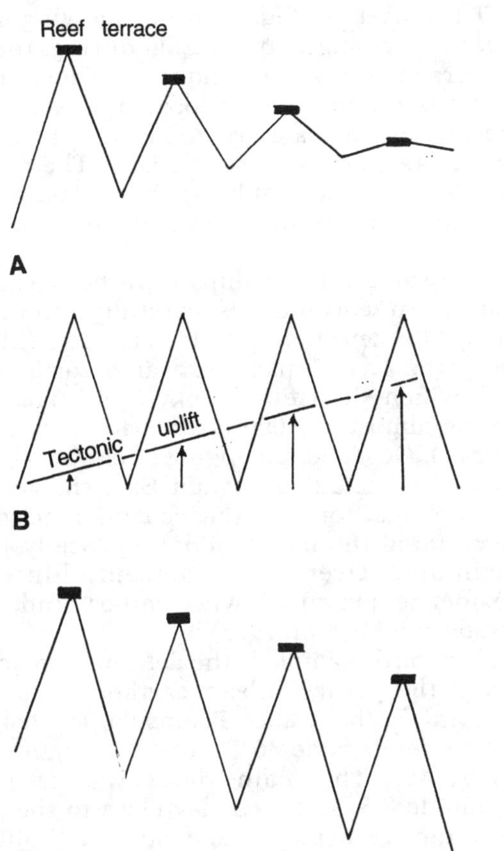

Figure 12.40 Schematic diagrams showing two possible glacio-eustatic sequences: (A) without tectonic uplift; (B) combined with tectonic uplift. (Copyright © by Arthur N. Strahler.)

surface.

But what about those stretches of the Pacific plate boundary where a continental transform is present, replacing the subduction boundary? Examples are the San Andreas fault of California and the Queen Charlotte fault of British Columbia (Chapter 6). A pure strike-slip fault boundary would not seem to qualify as a mechanism of uplift, but in these two examples there is present a strong compressional force vector. In the case of the continental sliver located on the western side of the San Andreas fault, regional compression has caused the uplift of crustal blocks that make up the Coastal Ranges and several offshore islands, known as the Channel Islands, that lie in the California Continental Borderland (Figures 6.35 and 6.40). One of these, San Clemente Island, has 20 terraces. Another, San Nicolas Island, has 14 terraces. Their ages have been dated from solitary corals on several of the islands. The long-term rate of uplift of San Clemente Island has been estimated at 0.2 to 0.3 mm/y (Muhs, 1985, p. 58). So here we have observed how coastal geomorphology can contribute to the calculation of rate of crustal uplift.

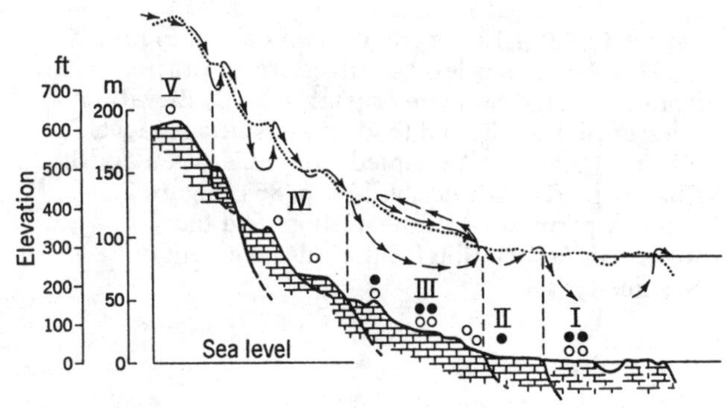

Figure 12.42 Cross section of the lower five reef terraces of the Huon Peninsula shown in Figure 12.39. Arrows on the upper profile show inferred positions of shoreline during falling and rising of sea level. Solid circles indicate carbon-14 dates; open circles, thorium-230 dates. Compare with Figure 12.43. (From H.H. Veeh and J. Chappell, 1970, *Science*, v. 167, p. 863, Figure 1. Used by permission of the authors and the American Association for the Advancement of Science.)

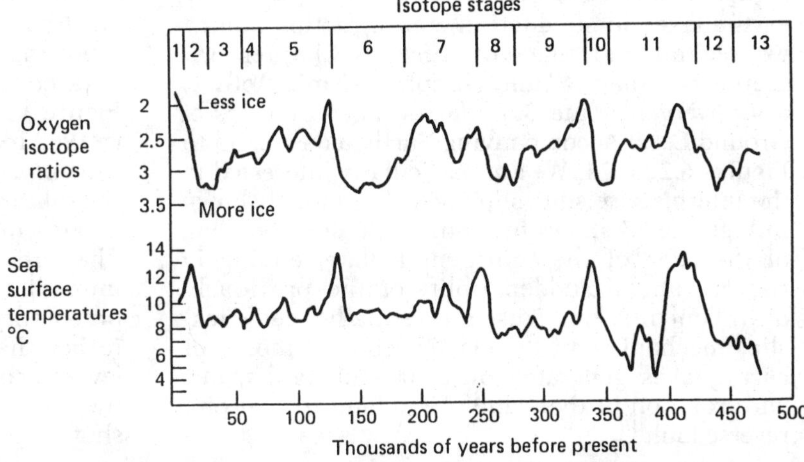

Figure 12.41 Curves of oxygen-isotope ratios (above) and inferred summer sea-surface temperatures (below) from two deep-sea cores in the subarctic ocean. (From J.D. Hays, J. Imbrie, and N.J. Shackelton, 1976, *Science*, v. 194, p. 1130, Figure 9. Copyright © 1976 by the American Association for the Advancement of Science. Used by permission.)

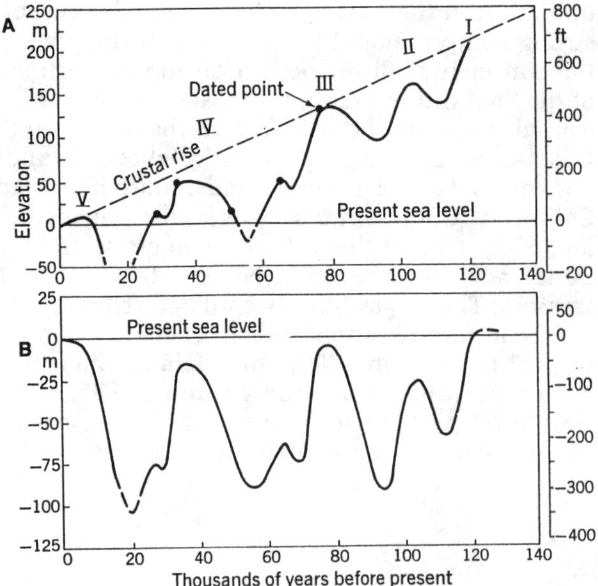

Figure 12.43 (A) Interpretation of data of Figure 12.42. Inferred sea level changes are subtracted from estimated uniform crustal rise. (B) Elevation difference is attributed to glacio-eustatic sea level change. (Diagram A adapted from H.H. Veeh and J. Chappell 1970, *Science*, v. 167, p. 864, Figure 2. Used by permission of the authors and the American Association for the Advancement of Science.)

12.18 Earthquakes and Land Elevation Changes

Another question for study is the tempo of tectonic uplift. Is it continuous and uniform in rate, or is it spasmodic? Earlier in this chapter we introduced spasmodic epeirogenic uplift as a mode to be expected during landmass denudation. Isostatic rise seems to occur spasmodically, with the onset of rise being delayed until a certain threshold value of stress is reached. But does a similar mechanism apply for uplift of strandlines, which are closely linked to the tectonic activity of a subduction boundary?

The answer may lie in the examination of abrupt land elevation changes accompanying large earthquakes in subduction zones. At this point we recommend that you turn to Chapter 6, sections headed "Shallow-Depth Seismic Activity at Convergent Plate Boundaries" and "Changes of Ground Level Accompanying Earthquakes," and to Figures 6.22-6.24. We are particularly interested in the interplate seismic slip zone. The model shown in Figure 6.23 shows first an elastic downbending of the edge of the continental plate, ending in rupture and a sudden uplift of the previously downbent margin. This is essentially the "stick-slip" mechanism of the elastic-rebound theory of earthquakes generated on strike-slip faults, but with rotation in the plane of the fault to that of a reverse fault.

Turn next to Figure 6.24, showing ground eleva-tion changes occurring during the 1964 Anchorage, Alaska, earthquake. The dominant feature is the uplift zone located seaward of the epicenter and focus. Here uplift was 1 to 2 m over a large area, and 4 to 8 m locally. The region of subsidence on the landward side is noteworthy, but is not provided for in the ideal model of Figure 6.23.

The same relationships have been shown in other great earthquakes carefully studied and mapped for detection of sudden elevation changes. One is the great Japanese Kwanto earthquake of 1923 which devastated Tokyo and Yokohama, causing almost 100,000 deaths (Richter, 1958, p. 567-571). Geodetic remapping of elevations over a large area, including Sagami Bay, showed uplift over a large zone of the coastal land margin surrounding the bay, amounting locally to 2 m maximum. Over the adjacent hinterland, subsidence prevailed with values under 1 m (Terada and Miyami, 1928).

Our third example is the deformation accompanying the great Chilean earthquake of 1960, occurring in the Arauco Peninsula, located about in the latitude zone 36°S. to 39°S. (Figures 12.44 and 12.45). The main shock was of Richter magnitude 8.5. The focus lay close to the axis of the Chile Trench. Ground surface uplift was measured in a range of coastal mountains between the Chile Trench and the Central Valley that lies at the western foot of the Andes volcanic range. Uplift was mostly from 1 to 2 m, with some small areas up to 3 m (Kaizuka, Matsuda, Nogami, and Yonekura, 1973, Figure 14, p. 29). This location seems to lie along the crest of an outer arc formed along an accretionary prism. It is of historical interest that a major earthquake had occurred in 1835 along this coast at about lat. 37°N., and that Charles Darwin, during the 1830s voyage of the *Beagle*, had studied the evidence of land uplift in this area. That uplift seems to have been on the order of 2 to 3 m in the vicinity of the epicenter, located not far southwest of Conception (see Lomnitz, 1970).

The event of sudden uplift (or subsidence) of the land surface accompanying a major earthquake can also be viewed in an observational time frame starting several years before the event and following it up with continued observations. The data consist of a set of geodetic measurements. Figure 12.46 graphs a data set ranging from 1890 to 1960 for a great earthquake that occurred on the Japanese island of Shikoku in 1946 (Yoshikawa, Kaizuka, and Ota, 1964). After a steady sinking of about 1 m in 35 years, the rate began to accelerate. The sudden jump of about 5 m was followed immediately by subsidence. In other cases, the precursory gradual change has been one of rise, rather than sinking, followed by abrupt drop in level accompanying the earthquake. Records for the 1964 Nigata, Japan, earthquake, M = 7.5, showed precursory slow change over 60 years as a

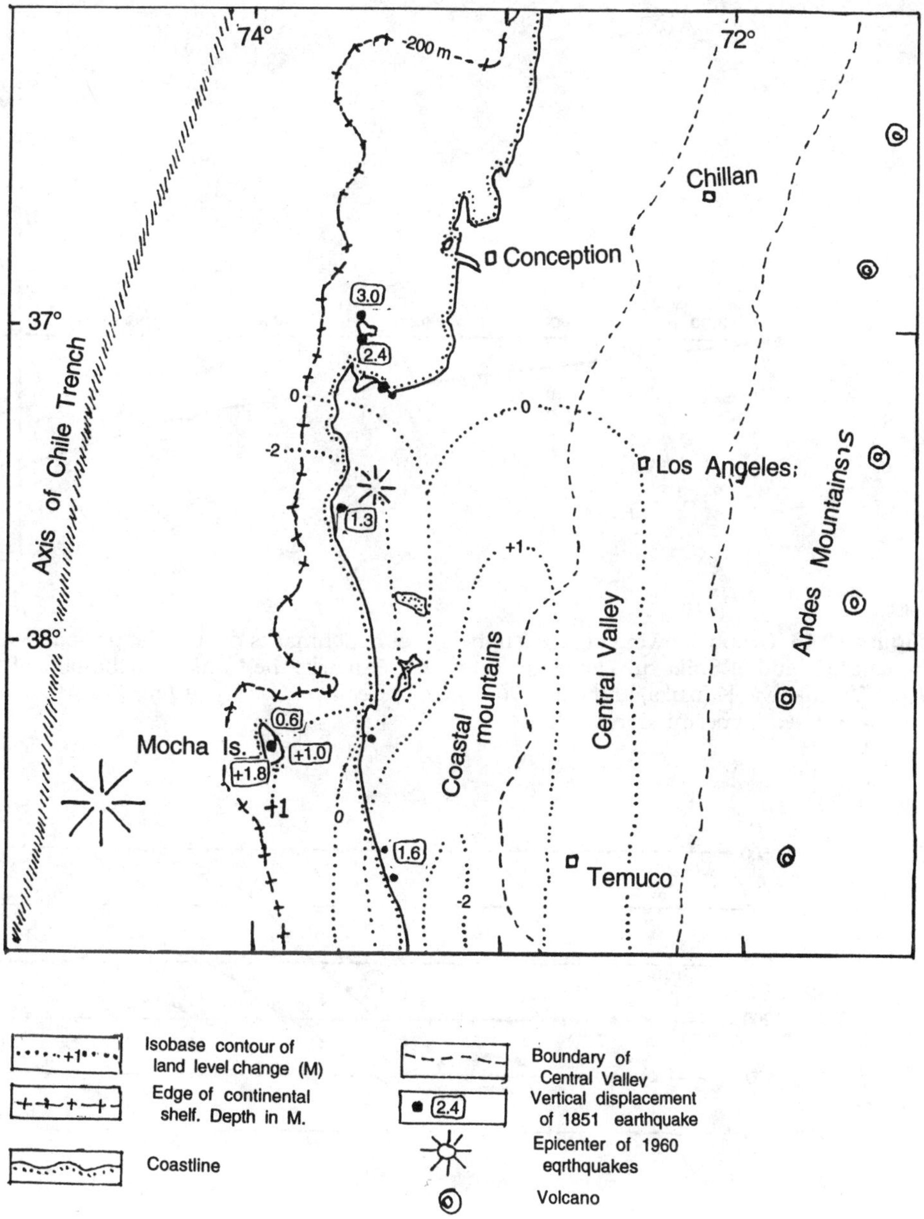

Figure 12.44 Generalized map of the Arauco Peninsula, Chile, showing land surface elevation changes accompanying the great earthquake of 1960. (Adapted from Kaizuka, Matsuda, Nogami, and Yonekura, 1973, *Geographical Reports of Tokyo Metropolitan University*, no. 8, p. 29, Figure 14, and including data of Plafker and Savage, 1970, *Bull., Geol. Soc. Amer.*, v. 8, p. 1001-1031. Reproduced with the permission of the Publisher, the Geological Society of America, Boulder, Colorado, USA. Copyright 1970.)

Isobase contour of land level change (M)
Edge of continental shelf. Depth in M.
Coastline
Boundary of Central Valley
Vertical displacement of 1851 earthquake
Epicenter of 1960 eqrthquakes
Volcano

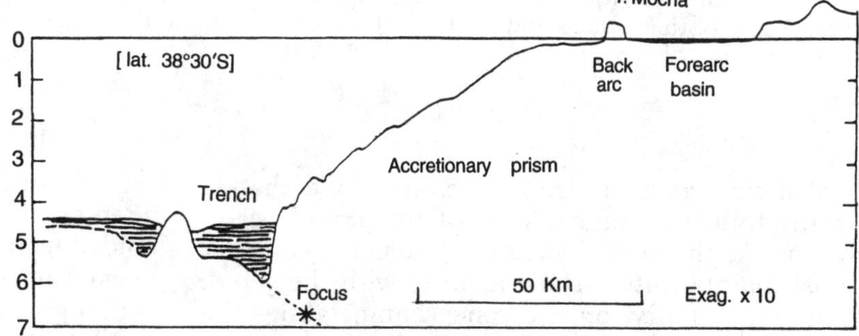

Figure 12.45 Generalized cross section through the Island of Mocha and adjacent trench. (Adapted from the same source as Figure 12.44. Data attributed to Sholl et al., 1968, 1970, and to Chart No. 3075 of the Hydrographer of the Navy, U.K.)

rise in elevation in one area and a decline in another area (Bolt, 1978, p. 138, Figure 2).

In these examples, tectonic movement is obviously in progress near active plate boundaries, and when extrapolated far back in time would (with cyclic eustasy) readily account for stepped multiple coastal terraces. There still remains the question of how to establish direct evidence that such terraces are genuinely tectonic features rather than terraces formed during the cycle peaks of a diminishing succession of glacio-eustatic sea level changes. Pure eustasy is, by definition, a process of

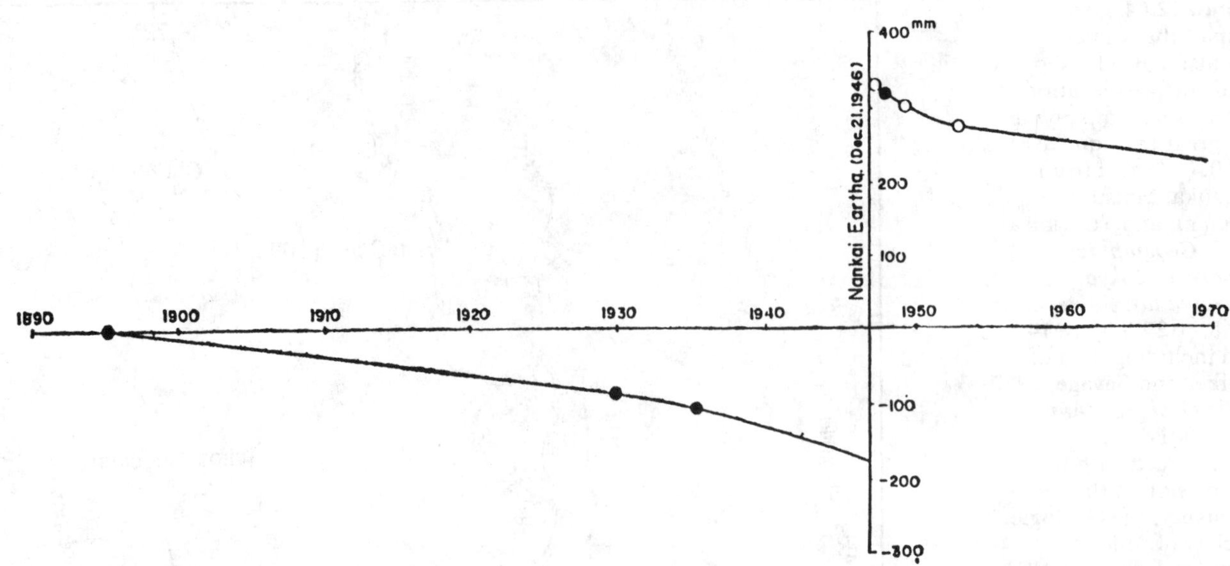

Figure 12.46 Graph showing changes in height of benchmarks during the period 1890 to 1970 on the Japanese island of Shikoku. The large vertical offset marks the Nankai earthquake of 1946. (Adapted from Yoshikawa, Kaizuka, and Ota, 1964, *Jour. of Geodetic Society of Japan*, v. 10, nos. 3-4, p. 120, Figure 3. Used by permission.)

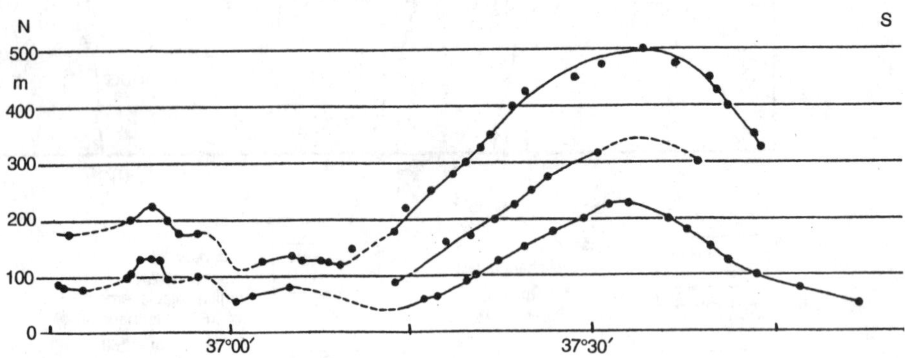

Figure 12.47 Longitudinal profiles of three elevated marine terraces on the Chilean coast south of Conception. See Figure 12.44 for location. (Adapted from Kaizuka, Matsuda, Nogami, and Yonekura, 1973; *Geographical Reports of Tokyo Metropolitan University*, no. 8, p. 29, Figure 12, p. 26. Used by permission of the authors and publisher.)

global change of the sea level caused by a change in the total volume capacity of the global ocean basins. As the eustatic sea level change occurs, it must maintain its surface identity with the geoid. Tectonic activity, on the other hand, taking the form of successions of fault displacements, will warp previous strand lines that may have conformed with the geoid. Each fault displacement diminishes and dies out in both directions away from the epicenter and is thus deformed into a dome-like surface. Such an increment of up-arching of the crust also deforms all of the previous terrace levels above it. Geodetic surveys reveal these upwarpings.

For an example, we return to the Auraco Peninsula of central Chile to examine profiles of older terraces drawn on a north-south line from near Conception on the north (lat. 35°45′ S.) and ending about at lat. 38°00′S., a distance of about 140 km. Figure 12.47 shows the longitudinal profiles of the three principal marine terraces. (See map, Figure 12.44 for location.) The highest terrace crests at about 500 m, which is about 400 meters higher than its lowest points to the north and south. Clearly, tectonic uplift has been concentrated in the vicinity of the known major earthquakes in this stretch of the Chilean coast.

* * * * * *

In this chapter we have given examples of how the geomorphic processes of denudation can influence the rates and amounts of tectonic uplift and subsidence. We have also shown how the study of certain erosional landforms can help us to determine the rates and amounts of tectonic uplift.

Many other examples of how erosional and depositional landforms can provide information on rates of tectonic activity can be found in the field of fluvial landforms, e.g, in stream channel profiles and gradients, in rock terraces and alluvial terraces, and in drainage patterns. Many of these topics have been presented in depth by Edward A. Keller and Nicholas Pinter in their 1996 textbook *Active Tectonics* (see Chapters 4 and 5).

References Cited

Andrews, John T., 1970, A geomorphological study of post-glacial uplift with particular reference to Arctic Canada. *Institute of British Geographers*, Special Publication 2.

Andrews, John T., 1991, Late Quaternary glacial isostatic recovery of North America, Greenland, and Iceland; A neotectonics perspective. Pages 473-486 in *Neotectonics of North America*, Decade Map Volume, Decade of North American Geology. Boulder, CO: Geological Society of America.

Arnaud, N.O., M. Brunel, J.M. Cantagrel, and P. Tapponier, 1993, High cooling and denudation rates at Kongur Shan, Eastern Pamir (Xinjiang, China) revealed by 40-Ar/39-Ar alkali feldspar thermochronology. *Tectonics*, v. 12, no. 6, p. 1335-1346.

Atwood, W.W., Sr., and W.W. Atwood, Jr., 1938, *Bull, Geol. Soc. of Amer.*, v. 49.

Bates, Robert L., and Julia A. Jackson, Eds. *Glossary of Geology*. Alexandria VA: American Geological Institute.

Blackwelder, Blake W. 1980, Late Wisconsin and Holocene tectonic stability of the United States mid-Atlantic coastal region. *Geology*, v. 8, p. 534-537.

Blackwelder, Blake W., 1981, Comment and reply on 'Late Wisconsin and Holocene tectonic stability of the United States mid-Atlantic coastal region. *Geology*, v. 9, p. 439.

Bolt, Bruce A., 1978, *Earthquakes: A Primer*. San Francisco: W.H. Freeman & Co.

Bull, William B., 1984, Tectonic geomorphology. *Jour. of Geologic Education*, v. 32, p. 310-324.

Bull, William B., and Robert E. Wallace, 1985, Tectonic geomorphology, *Geology*, v. 97, p. 216-217.

Burbank, Douglas W., 1992, Characteristic size of relief. *Nature*, v. 359, p. 483-484.

Burbank, Douglas W., Louis A. Derry, and Christian France-Lanord, 1993, Reduced Himalayan sediment production 8 Myr ago despite an intensified monsoon. *Nature*, v. 364, p. 48-54.

Burbank, Douglas W., John Leland, Eric Fielding, Robert S. Anderson, Nicholas Brozovic, Mary R. Reid, and Christopher Duncan, 1996, Bedrock incision, rock uplift and threshold hillslopes in the northwestern Himalayas. *Nature*, v. 379, p. 505-510.

Caine, Nel, 1976, A uniform measure of subaerial erosion. *Bull., Geol. Soc. Amer.*, v. 87, p. 137-140.

Chappell, John and H.H. Veeh, 1978, Late Quaternary tectonic movements and sea-level changes at Timor and Atauro Island, *Bull., Geol. Soc. Amer.*, v. 89, p. 356-368.

Chappell, John, 1974, Geology of coral terraces, Huon Peninsula, New Guinea; A study of Quaternary tectonic movements and sea-level changes. *Bull., Geol. Soc. Amer.*, v. 85, p. 553-570.

Clark, James A., Mark Hendriks, Thomas J. Timmermans, Calvin Struck, and Kenneth J. Hilverda, 1994, Glacial isostatic deformation of the Great Lakes region. *Bull, Geol. Soc, Amer.*, v. 106, p. 19-31.

Cochran, James R., 1993, Two-phase uplift of Higher Himalayas since 17 Ma: Comment and Reply. *Geology*, v. 21, p. 378-379.

Cooke, C. W., 1931, Seven coastal terraces in the southern states, *Jour., Washington Acad. Sci.*, v. 21, p. 503-513.

Copeland, P., and T.M. Harrison, 1990, Episodic rapid uplift in the Himalaya revealed by $^{40}Ar/^{39}Ar$ analysis of detrital K-feldspar and muscovite, Bengal fan. *Geology*, v. 18, p. 354-357.

Crittenden, Max D., 1963, Effective viscosity of the earth derived from isostatic loading of Pleistocene Lake Bonneville. *Jour. of Geophysical Research*, v. 68, p. 5517-5530.

Dahlen, F.A., and J. Suppe, 1988 Mechanics, growth, and erosion of mountain belts. Pages 161-178 in *Processes in Continental Lithospheric Deformation*, S.P. Clark, Jr., and J. Suppe, Eds., Geological Society of America Special Paper 218.

Davis, William Morris, 1889, Topographic development of the Triassic Formation of the Connectiucut Valley. *Amer. Jour. Science*, 3rd. Ser., v. 37, p. 430.

Davis, William Morris, 1909, *Geographical Essays*. Boston: Ginn and Company. (See also reprint of 1954. New York: Dover Publications.)

De Celles, Peter G., 1988, Lithologic provenance modeling applied to the Late Cretaceous synorogenic Echo Canyon Conglomerate, Utah: A case of multiple source areas. *Geology*, v. 16, p. 1039-1043.

England, Philip, and Peter Molnar, 1990, Surface uplift, uplift of rocks, and exumation. *Geology*, v. 18, p. 1173-1177.

Fairbridge, Rhodes W., 1968, Exhumed landscape. Pages 339-342 in Fairbridge, Ed., 1968.

Fairbridge, Rhodes W., Ed., 1968, *Encyclopedia of Geomorphology*. New York: Reinhold Book Corp.

Farrand, William R., 1962, Postglacial rebound in North America. *Amer. Jour, of Science*, v. 260, p. 181-198

Fenneman, Nevin M., 1938, *Physiography of the Eastern United States*. New York, McGraw-Hill Book Co.

Fleischer, Robert L., P. Buford Price, and Robert M. Walker, 1965, Fission track dating of Bed I, Oldwai Gorge. *Science*, v. 148, p. 72.

Fleischer, Robert L., P. Buford Price, and Robert M. Walker, 1972, Fission track dating. Pages 366-367 in R.W. Fairbridge, Ed., *Encyclopedia of Geochemistry and Environmental Sciences*. New York: Van Nostrand Reinhold Co.

Flint, Richard F., 1957, *Glacial and Pleistocene Geology*. New York: John Wiley & Sons.

Flint, Richard F., 1971, *Glacial and Quaternary Geology*. New York: John Wiley & Sons.

Foster, David A., Andrew J.W. Gleadow, and Greg Mortimer, 1994, Rapid Pliocene exumation in the Karakoram (Pakistan) revealed by fission-track thermochronology of the K2 gneiss. *Geology*, v. 22, p. 19-22.

Gilbert, Grove Karl, 1890, *Lake Bonneville*, U.S. Geological Survey, Monograph 1. Washington, D.C.: Government Printing Office.

Gilbert,Grove Karl, 1877, *Report on the Geology of the Henry Mountains*. Washington, D.C.: U.S. Government Printing Office.

Gilchrist, A.R., M.A. Summerfield, and H.A.P. Cockburn, 1994, Landscape dissection, isostatic uplift, and the morphologic development of orogens. *Geology*, v. 22, p. 963-966.

Gilluly, James, 1955, Geologic contrasts between continents and ocean basins. *Geol. Soc. Amer. Special Paper 62*.

Graf, William L., 1985, Morphotectonics topic of 15th annual meet. *Geotimes*, v. 30, no. 3, p. 10-11.

Gutenberg, Beno, 1941, Changes in sea level, post-glacial uplift, and mobility of the earth's interior. *Bull., Geol. Soc. Amer.* v. 52, p. 721-772.

Hamilton, Warren, 1979, *Tectonics of the Indonesian Region*. Geological Survey Professional Paper 1087. Washington, D.C.: U.S. Government Printing Office.

Heiskanen, W.A., and F.A. Vening Meinesz, 1958, *The Earth and Its Gravity Field*. New York: McGraw-Hill Book Co.

Holmes, Arthur, 1978, *Holmes Principles of Physical Geology*, 3rd ed., revised by Doris L. Holmes. New York: John Wiley & Sons.

Johnson, Douglas W., 1916, Plains, planes, and peneplanes. *The Geographical Review*, v. 1, (June), p. 443-447.

Johnson, Douglas, 1931, *Stream Sculpture on the Atlantic Slope*. New York: Columbia University Press.

Judson, Sheldon, 1967, Erosion of our lands, or "What's happening to our continents?" *American Scientist*, v. 56, no. 4, p. 356-374.

Kaizuka, S., T. Matsuda, M. Nogami, and N. Yonekura, 1973, Quaternary tectonic and recent seismic crustal movements in the Arauco Peninsula and its environs, central Chile. *Geographical Reports of Tokyo Metropolitan University*, No. 8, p. 1-38.

Keller, Edward A.,and Nicholas Pinter, 1996, *Active Tectonics: Earthquakes, Uplift, aned Landscape*. Upper Saddle River, NJ: Prentice Hall.

Koons, Peter O., 1987, Thermal and mechanical consequences of rapid uplift in continental collision; an example from the Southern Alps. *Earth and Planetary Science Letters*. v. 86, P. 307-319.

Koons, Peter O., 1989, The topographic evolution of collisional mountain belts: A numerical look at the Southern Alps, New Zealand. *Amer. Jour. of Science*, v. 289, p. 1041-1069.

Koons, Peter O., 1990, Two-sided orogen: Collision and erosion from the sandbox to the Southern Alps, New Zealand, *Geology*, v. 18, p. 679-682.

Lomnitz, C., 1970, Major earthquakes and tsunamis in Chile during the period 1553-1955. *Geol. Rundschau*, v. 59, p. 938-960.

Macdonald, Gordon A., and Agatin T. Abbott, 1970. *Volcanoes in tbe Sea: The Geology of Hawaii*. Honolulu: University of Hawaii Press.

McNutt, Marcia K., 1987, Isostasy. Pages 354-358 in Sirkin, 1987.

Moores, Eldridge M., and Robert J. Twiss, 1995, *Tectonics*. New York: W.H. Freeman and Co.

Muhs, Daniel R., 1985, Amino acid age estimates terraces and sea levels on San Nicolas Island, California, *Geology*, v. 13, p. 58-61.

Niskanen, 1939, On the upheaval of land in Fennoscandia. *Publ. Isos. Institute IAG* (Helsinki), no. 6.

Oberland, Theodore, 1965, *The Zagros Streams.* Syracuse Geographical Series, No. 1, Syracuse, N.Y.: Syracuse Univ. Press.

Oberlander, Theodore, 1985, Origin of drainage of transverse to structures in orogens. Pages 155-182 in M. Morisawa and J.T. Hack, Eds., *Tectonic Geomorphology*. Boston and London: Allen and Unwin.

Oldale, Robert N., and Charles J. O'Hara, New radiocarbon dates from inner continental shelf of southeastern Massachussetts and a local sea-level-rise curve for the past 12,000 yr. *Geology*, v. 8, p. 102-106.

Opdyke, N.D., D.P. Spangler, D.L. Smith, D.S. Jones, and R.C. Lindquist, 1984, Origin of the epeirogenic uplift of the Pliocene-Pleistocene beach ridges in Florida and development of the Florida karst. *Geology*, v. 12, p. 226-228.

Otvos, Ervin G., 1981, Tectonic lineaments of Pliocene and Quaternary shorelines, northeast Gulf Coast. *Geology*, v. 9, p. 398-404.

Penck, Walther, 1924, *Die Morphologische Analyse.* Stuttgart: Verlag Von J. Engelhorns Nochf.

Penck,Walther, 1953, *Morphological Analysis of Landforms*. Trans. by Hella Czech and Katherine C., Boswell, London, Macmillan and Co.

Pinter, N., and E.A. Keller, Comment on England and Molnar in *Geology*, v.18, p. 1173, p. 1173-1177. *Geology*, v. 19, p. 1053.

Plafker, G., and J.C. Savage, 1970, Mechanism of the Chilean earthquakes of May 21 and 22, 1960. *Bull., Geol. Soc. Amer.*, v. 81, 1001-1031.

Plafker, George, 1965, Tectonic deformation associated with the 1964 Alaska Earthquake. *Science*, v. 148, p. 1675-1687.

Richter, Charles F., 1958, *Elementary Seismology*, San Francisco: W.H. Freeman and Co.

Rubincan, David Parry, 1984, Postglacial rebound observed by Lageos and the effective viscosity of the lower mantle. *Jour. of Geophysical Res.*, v. 89, no. B.2, p. 1077-1087.

Scholl, D.W., R. von Huene, and J.B. Ridlow, 1968, Spreading of the ocean floor; undeformed sediments in the Peru-Chile trench. *Science*, v. 169, p. 869-871.

Schumm, Stanley A., 1963, The disparity between present rates of denudation and orogeny. U.S. Geological Survey, Professional Paper 454-H.

Slemmons, D.B., et al., Eds., 1991, *Neotectonics of North America*. Decade Map Volume. Boulder Co: Geological Society of America.

Stone, Robert, 1961, Geologic and engineering significance of changes in elevation revealed by precise leveling, Los Angeles area, California (abstract). *Geol. Soc, Amer., Special Paper 68*. p. 57-58.

Strahler, Arthur N., 1945, Hypotheses of stream development in the Folded Appalachians of Pennsylvania. *Bull., Geol. Soc. Amer.*, v. 56, p. 45-88.

Strahler, Arthur N., 1981, *Physical Geology*. New York: Harper & Row.

Summerfield, M.A., 1991a, *Global Geomorphology.* New York: John Wiley & Sons.

Summerfield, M.A., 1991b, Tectonic geomorphology, *Progress in in Physical Geography*, v. 15, no. 2, p. 193-205.

Terada, T., and N. Miyabe, 1928, Displacements of the Sagami Bay area after the great Kwanto earthquake of 1923. *Proceedings of the Imperial Academy* (Japan), v. IV, No. 2, p. 45-55.

Thornbury, William D., 1965, *Regional Geomorphology of the United States*. New York: John Wiley & Sons.

Veeh, H. Herbert, and John Chappell, 1970, Astronomical theory of climatic change: Support from New Guinea. *Science*, v. 167, p. 862-865.

Vita-Finzi, C., 1986, *Recent Earth Movements: An Introduction to Neotectonics*. London, Academic Press: Harcourt Brace Jovanovich, Publishers.

Von Engeln, Oscar D., 1940, Symposium: Walther Penck's contribution to geomorphology. *Annals, Association of Amer. Geographers*, v. 30, no. 4, p. 219-284.

Wager, L.R., 1937, The Arun River drainage pattern and the rise of the Himalaya. *Geographical Journal*, v. 89, p. 239-250.

Walcott, R.I., 1972, Late Quaternary vertical movements in eastern North America: Quantitative evidence of glacio-isostatic rebound. *Reviews of Geophysics and Space Physics*, v. 10, no. 4, p. 849-884.

Winker, Charles D., and James D. Howard, 1977, Correlation of tectonically deformed shorelines on the southern Atlantic coastal plain. *Geology*, v. 5, p. 123-127.

Winslow, David M., Peter K. Zeitler, C. Page Chamberlain, and Lincoln S. Hollister, 1994, Direct evidence for a steep geotherm under conditions of rapid denudation, Western Himalaya, Pakistan. *Geology*, v. 22, p. 1075-1078.

Woollard, George P., 1966, Regional isostatic relations in the United States. Pages 557-594 in *The Earth Beneath the Continents*, Geophysical Monograph 10, Washington, D.C.: The Amercan Geophysical Union.

Yoshikawa, T., 1985, Landform development by tectonics and denudation. Pages 194-210 in A. Pitty, Ed., *Themes in Geomorphology*, London: Croom Helm.

Yoshikawa, T., S. Kaizuka, and Yoko Ota, 1964, Crustal movement in the Late Quaternary revealed with coastal terraces on southeast coast of Shikoku, southwestern Japan. *Jour. of Geodetic Soc. of Japan*, v. 10, nos. 3-4, p. 116-122.

Chapter: 13 The Accretion and Breakup of Continents

In contrast to most of the previous chapters of this book, our theme here is largely focused on the history of our planet through geologic time. Of course, many historical events have been previously cited as examples of tectonic processes. For example, continent-continent collision was illustrated by the India/Asia collision. An unique succession of tectonic events—suturing and thrusting—was recognized and dated. That particular narrative consists of time-bound knowledge, and it is only one of several such examples from which we tried to uncover the essential elements of a general dynamic model applicable to most continent-continent collisions contained within the geologic record.

13.1 Precambrian Cratonization and Continental Growth

Looking back into the Proterozoic Era, we will find only the roots of orogens, and in the Archean Era only patches of crust that have been strongly metamorphosed. In contrast, the oldest oceanic crust found intact on the ocean floor is of Jurassic age. What this means is that our description of how plate tectonics works is "guaranteed" (so to speak) for only about one-sixth of geologic time. How far back into the Proterozoic and Archean eons can we with assurance apply what we have learned about plate tectonics? This is a question that has worried geologists for as long as plate tectonics has been in place, and we must address it here, too.

To prepare for a long look back into deep time requires a brief description of the most ancient sections of continental crust. In terms of areal extent, most of the continental crust is composed of rocks of Precambrian age, ranging from close to 4 Ga to somewhat less than 0.6 Ga.

Continental crust that is now tectonically stable—meaning that it is largely unaffected by present or recent plate-boundary activity—bears the name of *craton*. (The term *hedreocraton* has also been used.) Although substantial areas of continental crust bearing orogens of early Phanerozoic fold belts (such as the Appalachians and Caledonides) qualify as craton under this definition, most global geologic maps will restrict "craton" to Precambrian crust. In terms of the type of rock exposed at the surface, a craton appears to consist of one of two kinds: shields and platforms. A *shield* is an area of craton over which ancient (Precambrian) igneous and metamorphic rocks are exposed. A *platform* is a part of a craton covered by flat-lying or gently dipping sedimentary rocks, which are usually strata younger than Precambrian. In other words, a platform is a *covered shield*. In most cases, the strata rest unconformably on an erosion surface (an ancient peneplane). Compared with the total thickness of the continental crust, the sedimentary cover represents a very thin skin, but it is effective in obscuring the shield rocks beneath from direct geological observation.

Figure 13.1 is a world map showing the present extent of five age categories of continental crust, along with adjacent belts of early Phanerozoic orogens. The categories are (1) exposed Archean shields, (2) exposed Proterozoic shields, (3) covered Archean and Proterozoic shields (i.e.,sedimentary platforms), (4) Paleozoic orogenic belts, and (5) Mesozoic and Cenozoic orogenic belts (Durrheim and Mooney, 1991, p. 606).

The process of craton growth may be referred to as *cratonization*. On the reasonable assumption that the continental crust has grown in area throughout geologic time by accretion from collision impacts of oceanic volcanic arcs, we should look at the distribution patterns of rock ages within cratons. Perhaps they will reveal a growth pattern of diminishing age from a central zone to an outer zone. The oldest rocks of the cratons (older than about 2.5 Ga) are of the Archean Eon. On our map they are found in relatively small shield patches that have been called *continental nuclei* (Figure 13.1). These continental nuclei are surrounded by or are contiguous with larger areas of shield rock with maximum ages falling in Early and Middle Proterozoic time. On our map, these areas are the Proterozoic shields and the Proterozoic platforms. We should not expect to see a good concentric zoning of age belts because continents that were once joined have since separated or broken apart and were also moved far apart. This breaking up and rejoining, accompanied by rotations of the traveling continents, may have occurred more than once since Archean time.

Figure 13.2 shows the Precambrian shield rocks of North America zoned into crustal provinces according to ages of the oldest intrusives (Condie, 1989, 1993; Hoffman, 1988). Covered shield areas are not shown on this map, but the full extent of the underlying craton has been inferred from rock cores of holes drilled through the sedimentary covers and from magnetic and gravity surveys. Seven major Archean provinces, older than 2.5 Ga, are labeled: Slave, Rae, Hearne, Wyoming, Superior, Torngat, and North Atlantic (Table 13.1). As an example of the lithologic makeup of one of these cratonic units, the

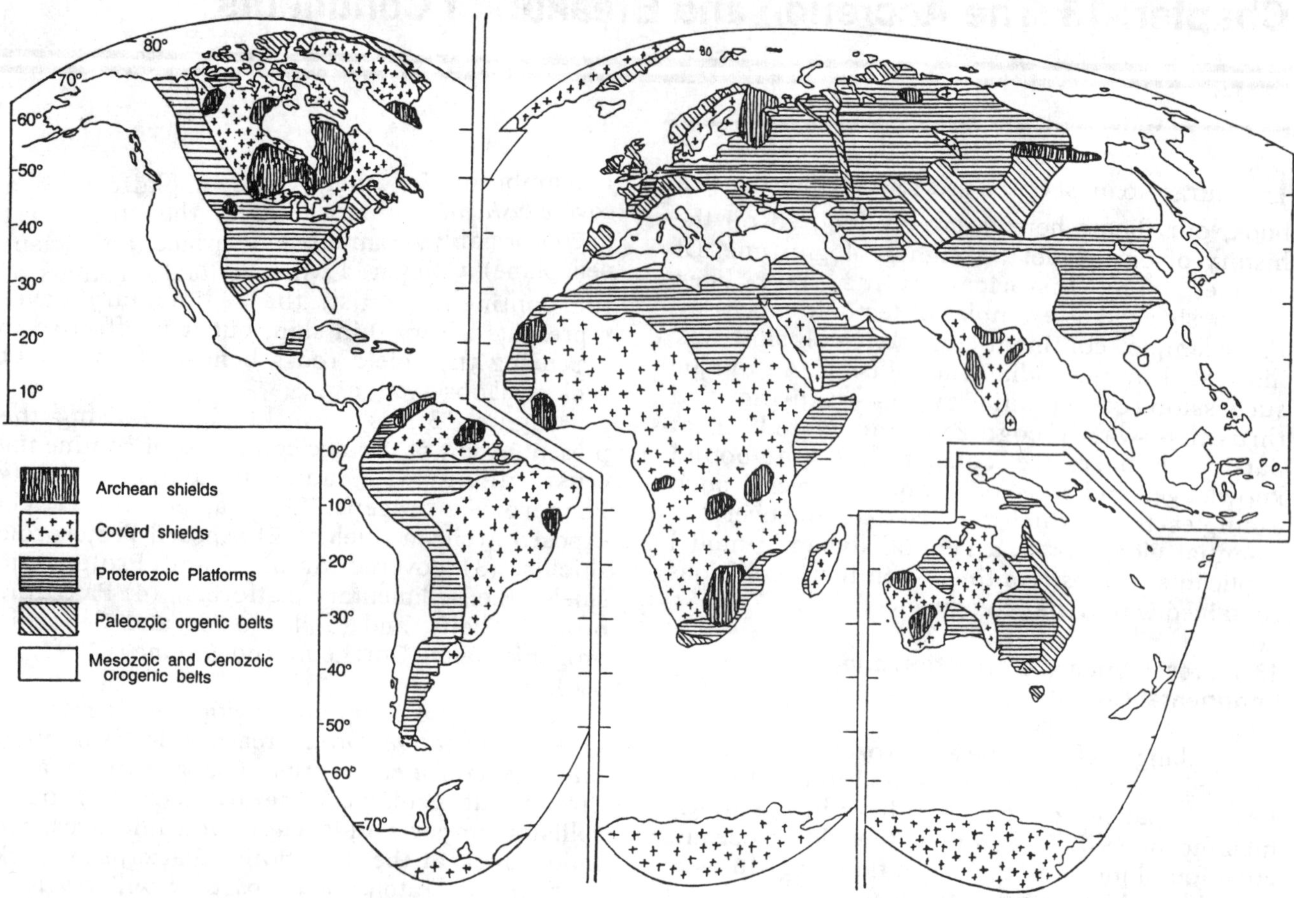

Figure 13.1 Generalized global map of age-provinces of continental crust. (Based on Goode's map. Data adapted from Richard E. Murphy. Copyright © by Arthur N. Strahler.)

Superior Province is shown to be a mosaic of four mapped types: plutonic, volcanic-plutonic, metasedimentary, and high-grade gneiss (Card and Ciesielski, 1986). Figure 13.2 also shows by special line treatment two kinds of sutures between adjacent provinces. A toothed line shows a collision suture, while the symbol of a strike-slip fault astride a narrow black line indicates a former continental transform boundary.

A comparatively new practice is the designation of certain of the provinces as "orogens." These are typically long, narrow zones for which the crust is interpreted as having been emplaced by arc-continent collisions that added new crust to an existing continent (Kerr, 1985, p. 230). Suppose that two cratons, separated by an ocean, are slowly approaching one another, and that new crust is accumulating along the margin of either craton, or on the margins of both. This phase of growth was followed by a continent-continent collision, closing that ocean. In this way a new compressional orogen has come to lie between two cratons of the same age, and the orogen is, of course, younger than both of them. An orogen of this kind has been classed as an *interior orogen* by J. Brendan Murphy and R. Damian Nance (1991, p. 469). It is placed in contrast to the *peripheral orogen*, which forms on the outer margins of a large continent by repeated arc-continent collisions. These two basic classes of orogen differ markedly in their structure and igneous petrology, as described in the final section of this chapter (Hoffman, 1989). An example of an interior orogen is the Trans-Hudson province, a product of compressional orogenies; it now lies between the Superior province and the Wyoming and Hearn provinces. An example of the peripheral orogen would be the Penokean province of Proterozoic age that lies to the southeast of the Superior province and north of the Yavapai province; it consists of arc-continent collisional crust accreted to the Superior province at about the same time as the Trans-Hudson province. Both of these orogens are of the age bracket 2.0-1.8 Ga.

Also shown on the map in south-central United States and northern Mexico are two provinces, the Yavapai and Mazatzal-Pecos. The first is in the age range 1.8 to 1.75 Ga (Early Proterozoic); the second, 1.75 to 1.6 Ga (Middle Proterozoic). South and east of these orogens lies the Grenville Province, a separate province of age 1.2 to 1.0 Ga (Middle Proterozoic). It represents the most recent of the Precambrian additions to the North American shield.

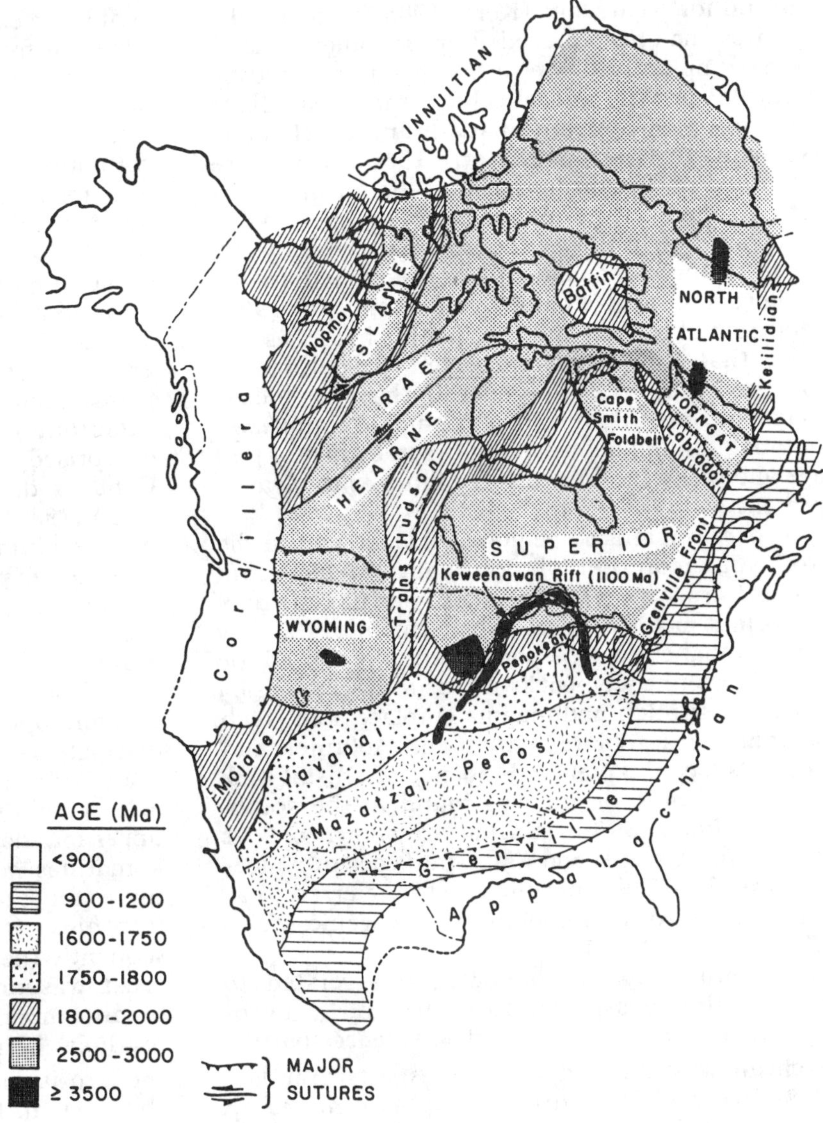

Figure 13.2 Generalized map of North American crustal provinces and sutures between provinces. (From Kent C. Condie, 1989, *Plate Tectonics & Crustal Evolution*, 3rd. Ed., p. 355, Figure 10.12, Oxford, England, Pergamon Press Ltd. Modified after P.F. Hoffman, 1988, *Annual Reviews of Earth and Planetary Science*, v. 16. Reproduced by permission of the publishers.)

13.1 Archean Tectonics

We turn now to the question: In what ways, if any, did the plate tectonics of the two Precambrian eons differ substantially from each other and from the plate tectonics of the Phanerozoic Eon? Possible points of difference that have been discussed are included the following categories: (1) Process of generating of new oceanic and continental crust. (2) Rate of production of continental crust. (3) Average thickness of continental crust. (4) Petrologic composition of continental crust and its seismic properties. These categories are interrelated and impossiblle to isolate completely.

Addressing the first category, during the first two decades of plate tectonics (ca 1960-1980) it was claimed by some geologists that the Precambrian crust does not contain ophiolites, and that their absence casts doubt on the formation of new mafic oceanic crust in mid-oceanic spreading plate boundaries comparable to those of the Proterozoic. In the mid-1980s the oldest known ophiolite suite, found in Morocco, was dated as having been formed about 800 Ma (Late Proterozoic). E.M. Moores of the University of California at Davis had accepted the absence of ophiolites in rocks older than about 1 Ga, and he offered a hypothesis to explain that absence, while allowing for continental collision and continental rifting (Moores, 1986). He proposed that ethroughout all of Precambrian time oceanic crust was much thicker than in the Phanerozoic and that at the same time ocean basins were much shallower. He reasoned that under these conditions ophiolites would not have formed during arc-continent collisions. However, such drastic differences of crust formation did not need to be introduced after it became evident that ophiolites actually are present within Precambrian orogens. These crustal remains differ from standard ophiolites in the absence of ultramafic crust that normally lies beneath the mafic crust in an ophiolitic suite. The need for a special explanation was finally nullified when in 1985 geologist Gregory Harper discovered in Wyoming a bona fide ophiolite in late Archean rock dated as at least

2.65 billion years old (Kerr, 1986, p, 670). His discovery had been preceded by two other finds of Archean ophiolites; one in South Africa found by Maarten de Wit, and another near Great Slave Lake in north-central Canada found by Herwart Helmstaedt (Kerr, 1985, p. 1365). So there remained no reason to question the formation in late Archean time of oceanic crust and its incorporation into new continental crust by the same tectonic mechanism as functioned in the Proterozoic and Phanerozoic eons. In 1993, Moores had revised and restated his hypothesis to read that ophiolites emplaced in collisional orogens prior to 1 Ga generally have a thicker magmatic crust than younger ophiolite complexes, but maintaining his view that oceanic crust of that age and older was two or three times as thick as at present.

There remains some good evidence that in the Archean, accretion of continental crust from oceanic crust by plate collisions was not the only important mechanism of enhancement of the very old cratonal crust. The phenomenon proposed for this other enhancement is a crustal thickening by volcanic eruption and magma emplacement, such as that we associate with mantle plumes and hotspots (see Chapter 5). Evidence of crustal rock of this volcanic origin was found in the south-central United States in what are shown on our map as the Yavapai and Mazatzal-Pecos provinces (Figure 13.2). This volcanic crust is referred to as "anorogenic rock" (implying "not-orogenic rock") (Kerr, 1985, p. 1366).

Turning now to the categories related to crustal thickness, composition, and rate of production, there is substantial evidence that the Archean crust differed in these respects from late Proterozic and Phanerozoic crust. As summed up by H. Martin of the Université de Rennes, in Archean time, although the general scheme of plate-tectonic processes "appears to be the same as now, several details were different, as indicated by the nature and relative proportions of rocks emplaced during the Archean" (Martin, 1986, p. 753).

That high values of global heat production existed in Archean time is strongly indicated by the emplacement of *komatiites*. These are from low-viscosity mafic lavas having an exceptionally high content of magnesium (Renner, 1993, p. 23). Their presence in Archean rock was first discovered in 1969 in the Barberton Mountains of South Africa, near the Komati River. Exposures were soon thereafter found in Archean greenstone belts in Canada, Australia, and Finland.

Another important feature of the Archean rocks is the abundance of *granitoids* (grantitic rocks) of a distinctive suite designated as TTG, an acronym for "tonalite-trondhjemite-granodiorite." Granitoid abundance, taken in combination with the presence of komatiites, has suggested to some geologists that the production of continental crust during the Archean had some unique features, and that the scenario we need to construct will be quite different from the arc-continent collision scenario that prevails through ensuing eons. The revised scenario must accommodate voluminous mafic and ultramafic lava emissions as well as the formation and rise of felsic plutons to achieve the end result of a thick crust made up largely of greenstones (the metamorphic product of mafic lavas) and granitoid bodies.

Two quite different versions of early Archean evolution of continental crust were proposed in the 1980s. Kent C. Condie in 1980 visualized the existence of midoceanic spreading rifts offset by transforms, parallel with a system of "sinks" functioning as subduction boundaries. These comprised the equivalent of a lithospheric plate. Condie's diagram is reproduced here as Figure 13.3A (1989, p. 353). The komatiite magma rose in mantle plumes at intervals along the spreading rifts. Other plumes appeared as isolated volcanic islands, resembling those we are familiar with in the Pacific ocean of today. Notice the large impact crater, a carryover phenomenon from an earlier period of heavy impaction. This primitive "plate" system, operating about 4.0 Ga, was able to dissipate heat some four to six times more rapidly than is needed today. "Komatiite crust (density 3.2) is slightly more dense than a partially molten upper mantle (density 3.1) and should sink. Hence komatiites may have provided the major driving force for the onset of the Earth's first plate tectonics" (Condie, 1989, 1993, p. 342). Subsequently (perhaps by about 4.2 Ga), the sinking crust was only partially melted and produced tonalite magmas. These rose to the surface to produce "tonalite arcs," the equivalent of the modern island arcs (p. 355). Figure 13.3B shows this system. For the first time, continental crust would have been produced above a subduction zone.

A very different model for the growth of the earliest continental crust had also been recognized by Condie (1980). As it is described by Alfred Kröner in 1985 (p. 55-56, Figure 3), the model calls for the growth of large volcanic edifices fed from sources in a partly melted mantle (Figure 13.4). Diapiric granitoid magmas, segregated near the base of the crust rose through the volcanic layers, solidifying as granitoid batholiths.

A newer model of the Archean crust was offered in 1991 by R.P. Rapp of Princeton University, who drew upon data from his laboratory experiments of rock melting under high pressures (1991, p. 221, 229). Figure 13.5 shows a hybrid model combining his input with that of earlier models by Kröner (1985) and M.E. Wilks (1988). The dominant feature shown is a mantle plume providing rising magma that builds a volcanic edifice to which a keel is added by underplating. Komatiite lavas would be present here. Obviously, a previously formed "crust" is assumed, so we need to suggest that this volcanic structure is built into a primeval mafic or

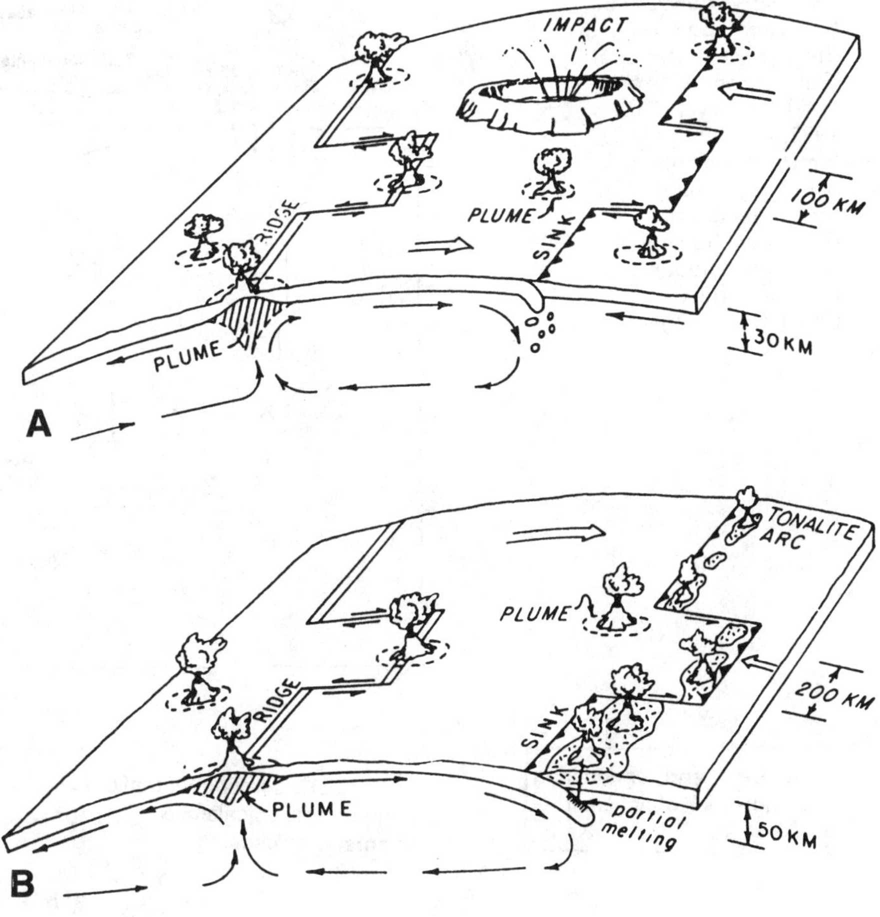

Figure 13.3 Schematic diagrams showing development of the early Archean crust. (A) Primitive komatiitic crust. (B) Early continental tonalite crust. (From Kent C. Condie, 1989, *Plate Tectonics & Crustal Evolution*, 3rd. Ed., p. 353, 354, Figures 10.10, 10.11, Oxford, England, Pergamon Press Ltd. Reproduced by permission of the author and the publisher.)

ultramafic oceanic crust, solidified at an earlier time from a layer of molten mafic magma. Also shown in the volcanic edifice are plutons of TTG that have formed by partial melting of amphibolite and eclogite. Plume structures of this kind may have been numerous and closely spaced in a polygonal arrangement, comprising a system dubbed (perhaps facetiously) "polygonal tectonics." An added tectonic feature of this model, shown to lie to either side of the plume, is a subduction phenomenon, analogous to the formation of a new subduction boundary in oceanic crust. Within the subducting crustal slab is shown the formation of TTG plutons that are rising to invade the crust. The dense eclogite residue is shown to be detaching from the crust and sinking into the mantle below. A second version of the above model was presented by Kröner and P.W. Layer (1991); it also makes use of mantle plumes and volcanic edifices in which plutons of granitoid magma are generated. Speculation on the nature of the Archean crust will doubtless continue unabated for many years to come.

Continuing now on the subject of rate of production of continental crust, it seems rational that the rate of growth of continents would be closely tied in with the rate of total activity of the entire plate-tectonic system, which in turn would be proportionate to the global production of radiogenic heat and the required rate of dissipation of that heat. The latter subject was introduced early in Chapter 5, where we showed that the total heat production has fallen exponentially with time (Figure 5.4). At the same time, the important radioisotopes were undergoing concentration in the felsic upper part of the continental crust, and this may have tended to facilitate the global dissipation of the radiogenic heat. Over the total span of geologic time for which the plate-tectonic mechanism was in operation, dissipation of mantle heat was carried out by insertion of magma into the spreading plate boundaries and the rise of magmas above subducting lithospheric plates. Thus it might seem reasonable to propose that the rate of formation of new crust, both oceanic and continental, would have been increasingly faster, going back into geologic time.

R.B. Hargraves of Princeton University has reviewed the subject of heat dissipation and plate-tectonic activity (1986). To start this analysis, he postulated that "dissipation of more heat from a hotter early Earth by the plate-tectonics

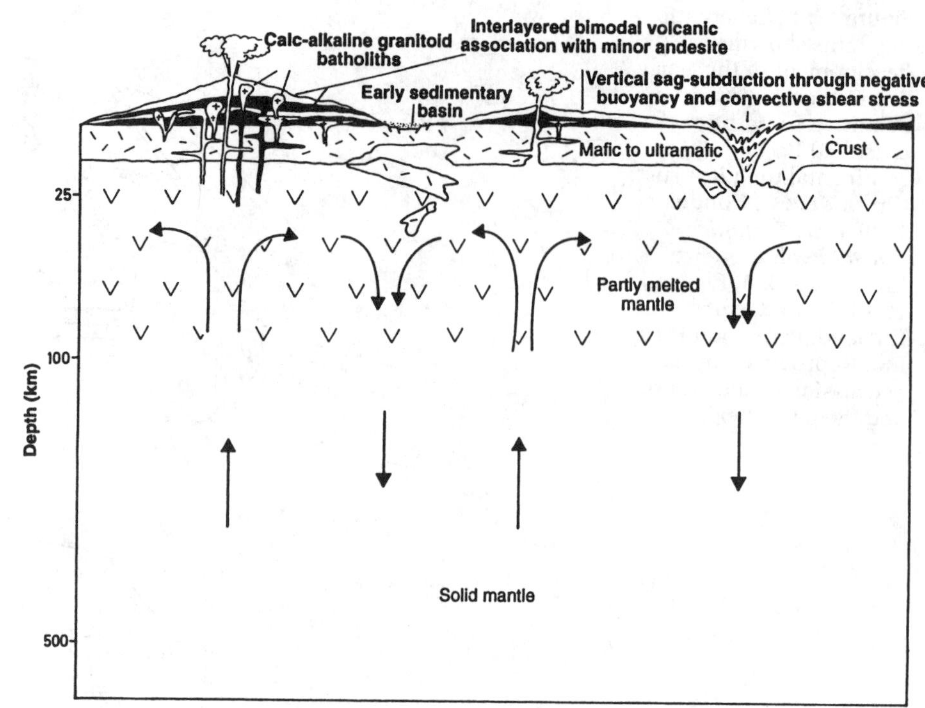

Figure 13.4 Schematic, speculative diagram of the origin and growth of the earliest continental crust. (From A. Kröner and P.W. Layer. *Science*, 1992, vol. 256, p. 1407, Figure 3. Reproduced with the permission of the publisher, the Geological Society of America, Boulder, Colorado, USA. Copyright 1992.)

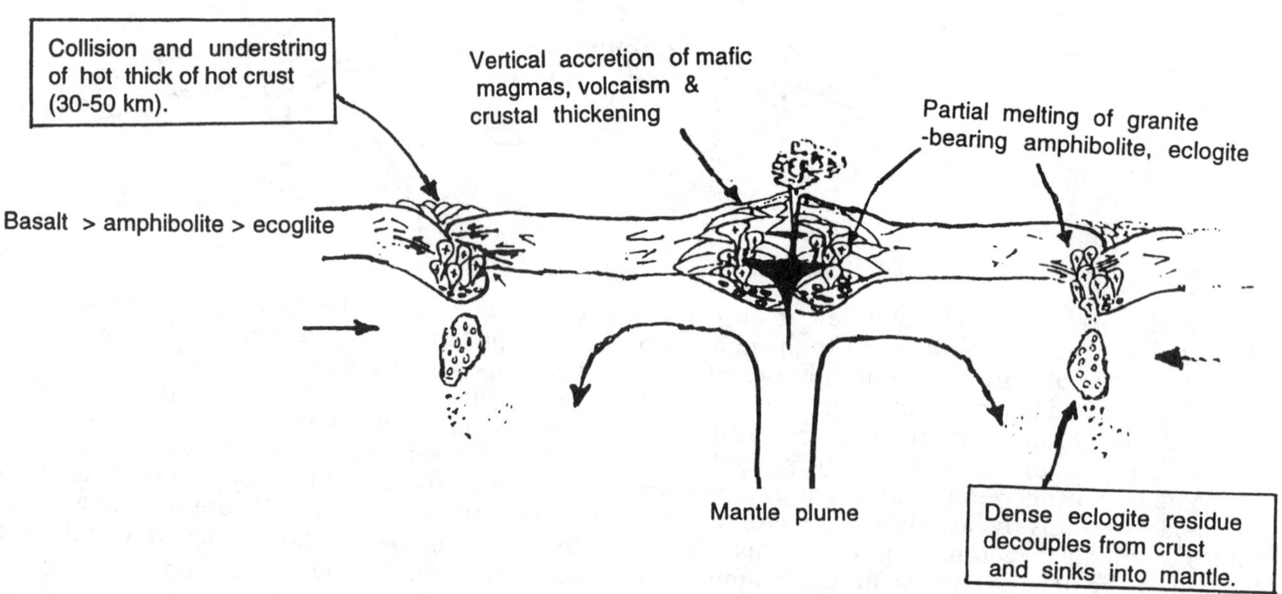

Figure 13.5 Cartoonlike depiction of a model for Archean crustal thickening by mafic volcanic magmas and the intrusion of TTG felsic Magmas. (Adapted from R.P. Rapp, 1991, *EOS*, v. 72, no. 20, p. 229. Used by permission of the author and the American Geophysical Union.)

mechanism would require subduction of, on average, younger lithosphere" (p. 750). Younger lithosphere is, of course, hotter than old lithosphere (See Chapter 5, Heat Flow and Spreading Plates, and Figure 5.11.) If you were in control of the global tectonic system, you could increase the rate of global heat dissipation in one of two ways. First, the average spreading rate could be increased, keeping all other factors unchanged. This alternative would, however, run into a snag because younger oceanic lithosphere, being less dense, subducts more slowly than old lithosphere, and in consequence, the system steady state could not be sustained. Second, the total global length of spreading boundary could be increased, keeping the spreading rate constant. This change, too, would increase the global heat output. Now, since the globe is assumed to hold to a constant radius and surface area, ridge length increase would most likely require an increase in number of plates, and those plates would need be smaller in area. Thus Hargarves has been led to suggest "that the Archean Earth was covered by many small plates moving slowly." Using an equation in which oceanic heat loss varies as the cube root of ridge length, he estimates that "if Archean heat flow was 3 times that of the present, 27 times as much ridge [length] would have been required" (p. 750). Similar arguments favoring greater ridge length had been offered by other authors (see Abbott and Hoffman, 1984, p. 438). Accepting the need for greater ridge length requires rejection of the commonly proposed hypothesis that Archean crustal spreading rates were much faster than today. Carrying this conclusion forward into the future, we might visualize that the numbers of continents will have become fewer and the average areal extent of each will have become greater.

Calculations and estimates of the rates of addition to the continental crust have been carried out since plate tectonics first emerged as a successful paradigm. In a paper published in *Tectonics* in 1984, Arthur Reymer and Gerald Schubert reviewed these estimates and also made their own computation of rates of crustal growth. Their equation for the growth of the continents as a function of decline in terrestrial heat flow yields an approximately constant rate since Archean time (1984, p. 63). That rate is approximately one cubic kilometer per year (1 km^3/yr). For the Archean Eon, they estimated a rate between 3 and 4 times greater. Most of the earlier models presented for comparison show a substantially faster rate for the Archean than for post-Archean time. In the model we presented in earlier paragraphs for Archean continental crust development, an explanation for the faster rate of crust accumulation may lie in the mechanism of mantle plumes ("polygonal tectonics") that may have contributed large volumes of magma, serving to thicken a preexisting primordial crust.

The above analysis of rates of production of continental crust seems to include the assumption that little or none of that crust was also undergoing destruction by melting and reabsorption into the mantle. Samuel A. Bowring and Todd Housch, in a paper on the earth's early evolution wrote: "A major outstanding question in the Earth sciences is whether the volume of continental crust today represents nearly all that formed over the Earth's history or whether the rates of creation and destruction have been approximately balanced since the Archean" (1995, p. 1535). Based on their analysis of neodymium isotopic data, they concluded that crustal recycling had been important during the formation of the oldest Archean crust. The authors suggest that the surviving crustal fragments are those that had developed thick lithospheric roots, and that the conditions for such thickening were unusual p. 1539).

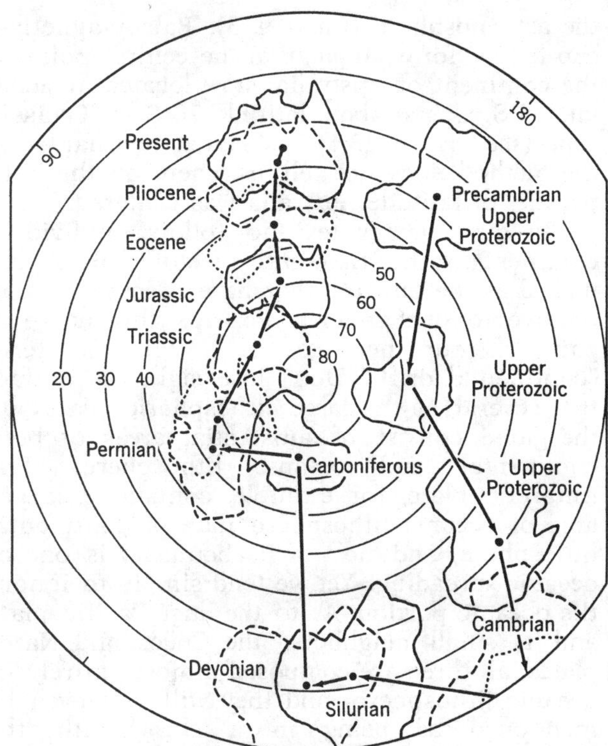

Figure 13.6 Positions of Australia relative to the present South Pole from the Upper Protozoic to the present. Straight-line segments connect the maps to emphasize the path of polar wander. (The dots are not paleopoles.) Conformal polar stereographic projection. (From a map by S.K. Runcorn, 1959, *Science*, v. 129, p. 1007, Figure 6. Used by permission of the American Association for the Advancement of Science.)

13.3 Paleomagnetism, Paleopoles, and Polar Wandering

Before undertaking an historical account of plate accretions, breakups, and collisions through geologic time, it is necessary to understand the geophysical method by which paleomagnetism can reveal the past locations and motions of a single lithospheric plate. Be sure that you are familiar with the introductory information in Chapter 7 under the headings of Geomagnetism and Paleomagnetism. Especially important is the method of obtaining and analyzing rock core samples. Also important is Figure 7.16, showing an ancient magnetic pole—a *paleopole*—and its relationship to a former magnetic latitude. Review also in Chapter 7 sections titled Relative Plate Motions and Plate Motions relative to Hot Spots.

Polar wandering, the plate motion we describe here, is motion of a lithospheric plate relative to the underlying mantle and core, which together are assumed to be fixed with respect to the earth's magnetic axis. The horizontal shear that allows plate motion is distributed within the asthenosphere (Chapter 3). Paleomagnetism can tell us, for example, that the central point of the continent of Australia, now located at about lat. 25°S, was at about latitude 70°S in Triassic time (see Figure 13.6). As stated in Chapter 7, the method does not tell us where on the 70th parallel of latitude Australia was centered.

In our chapter text to follow, individual continents, rather than entire tectonic plates, are named as the entities that have been in motion relative to one another. Perhaps this usage is part of our heritage of Wegener's term "continental drift." Don't lose sight of the fact that several of the large lithospheric plates on the globe consist of substantial areas of both continental and oceanic lithosphere. The Antarctic plate, for example, contains a larger area of oceanic lithosphere than of continental lithosphere, and most of its boundary is one of oceanic spreading. Yet we tend simply to ignore the oceanic portion. As to the huge Pacific plate and its small neighbors, the Cocos and Nazca plates, all three are composed almost entirely of oceanic lithosphere, and they will not even be mentioned as being in a class with the "continents" that are in motion over the asthenosphere. We must also keep in mind that one continent can move relative to other continents only when boundary processes of subduction, spreading, or strike-slip faulting are in action. When two widely separated continents seem to be approaching each other—like two ships on the ocean—the intervening oceanic lithosphere must be undergoing a process of disposal by subduction beneath one or the other of the two plates.

Paleomagnetic evidence that continents had moved large distances relative to one another preceded by more than a decade the arrival of plate tectonics as a full-blown theory. In Chapter 7, we set the arrival year of plate tectonics with the publication of Robert S. Dietz's June 1971 paper in *Nature*. Continental separation along a mid-oceanic spreading boundary had been previously nailed down by Bruce C. Heezen in 1960, but his text lacked the essential concept of plate disposal by subduction that Dietz added. A dozen years earlier, S.K. Runcorn had published in *Science* his seminal article titled Rock Magnetism (1959). Runcorn, a geophysicist, was then Director of the Department of Physics of King's College, University of Durham, England. Rock magnetization data had been accumulated during several years prior to this time. Reversals of polarity had been observed and their significance was understood. In collaboration with N.D. Opdyke and others, Runcorn had recorded the phenomenon of polar wandering and had plotted paleopoles for Great Britain, North America, and Australia Figure 13.6 is a copy of Runcorn's 1950 map of the successive positions of Australia from the Upper Proterozoic to the present. For a detailed historical review of this early discovery period of paleomagnetism and continental drift, see E. Irving, 1988. As a geophysicist working under Runcorn's direction at Cambridge, Irving in the early 1950s contributed key evidence from the Deccan traps showing "that India once could have been in the southern hemisphere" (1954). A highly significant factor in the success of the work of Runcorn and his group of students was the adoption of statistical probability methods established by Sir Ronald Fisher, professor of genetics at Cambridge. Fisher's tests of significance of sample data proved essential to the handling of the raw field observations (Irving, 1988, p. 99).

Runcorn had also interpreted the paleomagnetic data as consistent with a separational movement between North America and Europe (1956, p. 1006, Figure 5). His map of polar wandering is reproduced here as Figure 13.7. [Explanation of the paths follows in later paragraphs.] It is clear from the approximate parallelism of the European and North American paths that these two great landmasses were joined together from as early as the Cambrian to as late as the Triassic. Other investigators had documented considerable amounts of what they called "continental drift" among the southern hemisphere continents in Mesozoic time (Runcorn, 1959, p. 1008). It goes without saying that many geologists in Europe and in the southern hemisphere were enthusiastic over such independent evidence of "continental drift" much as Alfred Wegener had envisioned it (See Chapter 2).

In 1960, an important international symposium was held in Atlantic City, NJ, to discuss the impact of the new paleomagnetic discoveries on the Wegener concept of continental drift (Munyan, Ed., 1963). At that time, seismic evidence from deep-focus earthquakes had not yet been interpreted as convincing evidence of deep underthrusting at the active Pacific continental margins. (See Chapter 5 and Oliver and Isacks, 1967.) On the other hand, seafloor spreading was becoming an inescapable interpretation based on the configuration and seismic activity of the mid-oceanic ridge (see Chapter 7 and Heezen, 1959). Of particular historical interest is the symposium paper by geologist Warren Hamilton of the U.S. Geological Survey summarizing the geological evidence for the grouping of Antarctica, Australia, and Africa into a Paleozoic supercontinent (1963). He reproduced Du Toit's map of the reconstructed continents (p. 91) and ventured the following cautious statement: "Drift is not required by the new interpretation, but it certainly provides new coincidental relationships which are much more easily explained with drift than without" (1963, p. 90).

A high point of the 1960 symposium was the imposing display of polar wandering paths,

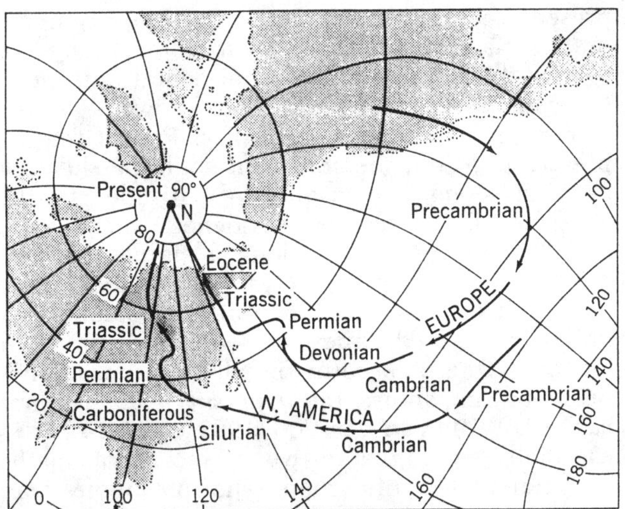

Figure 13.7 Generalized polar wandering paths of North America and Europe, plotted on the oblique Mercator projection. (Simplified from a map by S.K. Runcorn, 1963, in *Polar Wandering and Continental Drift*, A.C. Munyan, Ed., Tulsa, OK, Soc. of Econ. Paleon. & Mineral., p. 51, Figure 2. Used by permission.)

Figure 13.8 Polar wandering paths for Eurasia and North America. (From C.K. Seyfert and L.A. Sirkin, 1979, *Earth History and Plate Tectonics*, 2nd. Ed.,Harper & Row, p. 123, Figure 7.12.)

which left little doubt in the minds of many that the continents had indeed been united in Pangea and that they had later separated (Runcorn, 1963; Deutsch, 1963). Although paleomagnetism had finally won a victory for Alfred Wegener, many geologists still did not see it that way. The nonbelievers were not going to give their approval until an acceptable geophysical model could be produced to explain how continents could drift apart. Several years were to elapse before plate tectonics provided that physical model. An interesting parallel study in this early period was the paleomagnetic investigation of ancient wind directions, called "paleowind directions." Opdyke and Runcorn made a field study of cross laminations of desert dunes of the Coconino Sandstone of Arizona and the New Red Sandstone of Great Britain in an attempt to determine whether the prevailing winds they indicated were consistent with their paleolatitudes (1960).

13.4 Polar Wandering Paths

As explained in Chapter 7, determination of the approximate geographic location of the north magnetic pole at a given time in the geologic past—a *paleopole*—can be made by measurements of the ancient residual magnetism in a rock specimen dating from the time the rock was formed. When a series of such determinations is made for rocks of successively younger ages within the single continent that behaved as part of a single intact plate, the data can be plotted to reveal a *polar wandering path*. An early example of such a plot is shown in Figure 13.7.

Before going into more technical details of polar wandering paths, we offer two simple examples of how they can be interpreted. Figure 13.8 shows a relatively recent version of the polar wandering paths for North America and Europe for the past 400 m.y. Both paths terminate at the present location of the magnetic north pole, but going back into time, the two paths separate, with the distance of separation increasing rapidly to about 100 Ma. Here the two paths cross, and then continue to separate as far as the paths are shown, ending at about 400 Ma.

At this point, you can try an experiment. Using a small piece of tracing paper, trace the North American curve. Poke the point of a pin through the pole point on the tracing paper and also into the page at the pole position. Now rotate the tracing paper slowly counterclockwise until the two curves coincide. Coincidence is almost perfect between 200 and 400 Ma, but now the curve portions between 0 and 100 m.y. become widely separated.

When we began to rotate the tracing paper, we also moved North America and Greenland closer to Europe. Using the present north pole as the pivot, we rotated the North American pole path through about 45° of longitude, bringing Newfoundland about in contact with Scotland. [Do not be disconcerted by observing that the polar paths are overprinted on the modern map of eastern Asia and the northwestern Pacific

Ocean. This juxtaposition is explained in a later section.] The interpretation of the two polar wandering paths thus leads to the conclusion that, prior to about 200 Ma, North America and Europe must have been close together and may have moved over the asthenosphere as a single lithospheric plate. We may also conclude that subsequent to 200 Ma, which is in early Jurassic time, the single plate broke up into two plates, which gradually separated from one another.

Figure 13.9 is another exercise to show how paleomagnetic data can be used to fit two continents together. The map shows polar wandering paths of Africa and South America in their present positions. The shaded overlay shows South America as moved eastward and rotated so that the polar wander curves are superimposed. In rearranging the continents to a new fit, the latest and most reliable paleomagnetic data are used in this manner. Because of the range of error that exists in the data, some flexibility is allowed in order to match the continental plate boundaries in the most suitable manner and to align various structural trends in the bedrock geology.

At this point we need to consider that there are two modes of presenting polar wandering on hemispherical maps. Both of these modes have been shown in our figures. (A) Pole fixed, continent moving, as in Figure 13.6. An actual map of the continent is shown at successive latitudes for a series of ages, ending in the present geographic position. (The line segments on this map are added simply to allow the eye to follow the succession of continental outlines.) Of course, longitude is not known, so the placement is somewhat arbitrary. Except for the present position, the continent could be slid east or west along its parallel of latitude. In the absence of independent evidence, one would probably arrange them along a simple path of minimum length. (B) Continent fixed, pole moving, as in Figure 13.6. Since a paleopole is uniquely defined, there is no ambiguity of location. One pole point fits all longitudes. This presentation, shows the *apparent polar wander path* (APWP) (Van der Voo, 1983, p. 13-14). It is especially useful where two or more pole paths are plotted on one map. The paleopoles are shown by dot symbols, and these can be connected by straight-line segments or by smoothly curved lines.

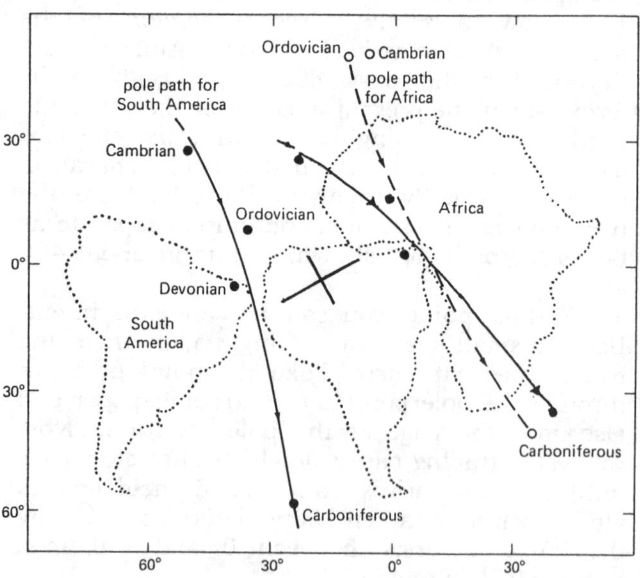

Figure 13.9 South-polar wandering paths during the Paleozoic for South America and Africa. South America has been rotated in a counterclockwise direction so as to bring the two paths into approximate coincidence. (Geographic coordinates of average paleomagnetic poles are from C.K. Seyfert and L.A. Sirkin, 1979, *Earth History and Plate Tectonics*, 2nd. Ed., New York, Harper & Row, p. 120-121, Table 7.1.)

13.5 Plotting a Paleopole

Locating a paleopole in terms of our present-day geographical grid system of latitude and longitude as depicted on world maps and globes requires that both the measured "fossil" declination and the inclination (dip) within the rock sample be used. Taking declination first, the observed paleodeclination is laid off as a spherical angle either to right or left of the meridian of the sample point. The ancient meridian, or *paleomeridian*, is projected in a northerly direction on a great circle (see Figure 13.12). Just how far to carry this line remains to be calculated.

Next, we must convert the measured "fossil" inclination (or magnetic "dip"), into its equivalent latitude. Figure 13.10A shows magnetic inclination of an ideal spherical globe. Inclination arrows are shown for every 10 degrees of latitude for both northern and southern hemispheres. Here, we need use only the northern hemisphere data. Figure 13.8B is an enlargement showing the dip arrow for latitude 30°N. A line has been drawn to show the plane of the horizon, which is tangent to the sphere. Inclination is defined as the angle of the dip arrow with respect to the tangent plane. This angle, I, is 49° (rounded off to nearest one degree). With respect to a line to the earth's center the angle of the dip needle is 41°.

Given the observed value of the inclination, the latitude can be obtained by solving the following equation: The tangent of the angle of inclination is equal to twice the value of the tangent of the paleolatitude:

$$\tan I = 2 \tan \lambda$$

where I is inclination and λ is the paleolatitude

Figure 13.11 is a graph showing the full

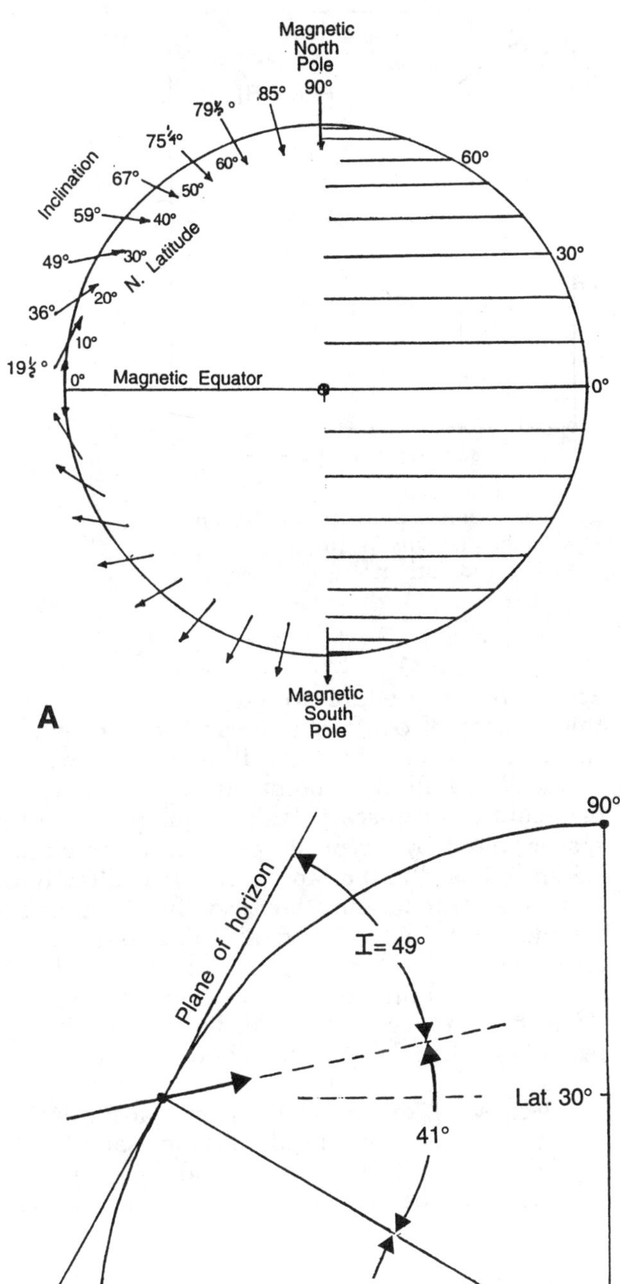

Figure 13.10 (A) Magnetic inclination at 10-degree intervals of latitude, north and south. (B) Detailed diagram of measurement of angle of inclination. (Copyright © by Arthur N. Strahler.)

relationship between inclination and latitude. The graph for reversed polarity is a mirror image of that for the normal polarity. Having converted the field measurement of inclination to one of latitude, the projected paleomeridian (PM) is terminated at a distance equal to the derived arc of latitude, as shown in Figure 13.12. Now the paleopole has been located in terms of both latitude and longitude on our geographic grid. (For full details, see Merrill and McElhinny, 1983, p. 79-94.) Figure 13.13 is a rough sketch of the final result in terms of a restored paleomagnetic grid.

Perhaps now you understand why, on a map of polar wandering paths such as Figure 13.8, those paths are superimposed on modern continents or oceans lying far distant from the continents which the paths represent. For example, in this illustration, the Permian paleopole for North America falls in eastern Siberia, while the Devonian paleopole for Eurasia lies far out over the northern Pacific Ocean.

At this point, you may ask how reversed polarity is handled. (See Chapter 7, Geomagnetic Polarity Reversals.) When the polarity of a rock sample has been determined, we do not know whether that pole is normal or reversed. For the major continents through Phanerozoic time, thousands of individual polarity readings have been taken and the major paleopole tracks leading to the present north magnetic pole are clearly established. When a new reversed sample is plotted, its position will stand out clearly from the established chain and we need only to flip it to the prevailing direction. For samples of Precambrian age, however, this hemispherical ambiguity may be difficult to establish, especially for terranes and microcontinents. For these, independent evidence not related to paleomagnetism may helpful. (See Van der Voo, 1993, p. 11-12.)

13.6 Problems of Apparent Polar Wandering

There is a complicating factor to be taken into consideration in plotting paleopoles and apparent polar wander paths. At the present time, the geomagnetic axis does not coincide with the earth's axis of rotation. One axis is presently inclined relative to the other by an angle of about 11.5°. As a result, the geomagnetic north pole is located at about latitude 70°N, which is a distance of about 2000 km from the geographic north pole. The north-seeking end of a magnetic compass needle points to the geomagnetic north pole. The horizontal angle between geographic (true) north and geomagnetic north indicated by the compass is called the *compass declination*. Records of compass declination have been kept at both Paris and London since about the year 1600. In London, between 1600 and 1820, compass declination changed in a westerly direction through a total angle of nearly 35°. Since 1820, the direction of change has reversed itself and shifted eastward about 20°. In Paris, from 1600 to 1915 inclination of the compass needle underwent a change amounting to 10° of latitude. Patterns of change at these two localities are quite similar, so it is reasonable to think that these changes follow a cyclic pattern and that

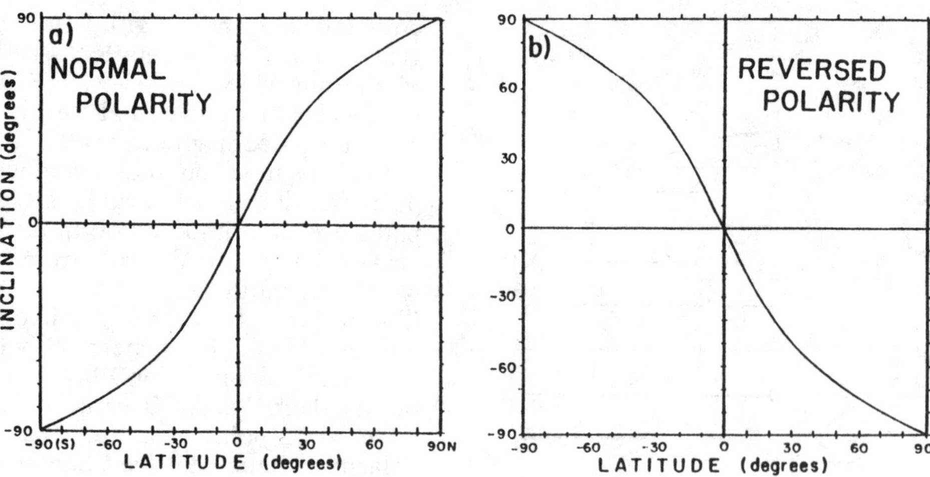

Figure 13.11 Graph of trigonometric relationship between magnetic inclination and latitude. (From Rob Van der Voo, 1993, *Paleomagnetism of the Atlantic, Tethys and Iapetus Oceans*, p. 10, Figure 2.1, New York, Cambridge Univ. Press. Used by permission of the publisher and author.)

over a time span of millions of years, the geomagnetic axis has, on the average, coincided rather closely with the axis of rotation.

Another source of error in paleomagnetic data lies in the place-to-place irregularities in the lines of magnetic force over the entire globe. These irregularities exist today and are known to be changing through time. There is no way that the pattern of these magnetic irregularities can be reconstructed for periods in the geologic past.

In the geophysical field of paleomagnetism, the earth's magnetism is said to be *dipolar*, meaning that the earth has a single two-ended magnetic axis and that the origin of the magnetism is in the earth's center (Van der Voo, 1993, p. 9). (See Chapter 7, Geomagnetism, and Figure 7.15.) The magnetism is said to be *geocentric*. This *dipole field* accounts for about 80% of the total value of the earth's magnetic field. It is thus a *geocentric dipole field*. The remaining 20% consists of a number of forms of magnetism other than that of the dipole field. Collectively, all of these non-dipole field components are lumped under the category of a *restfield*. The component of declination change described above, manifested in cycles with periods on the order of centuries, is referred to as a *secular cycle*. (In Latin, *secular* means "on a century-scale".) Now, a latitude circle of 20° diameter on the earth's surface is about 4,000 km in diameter—a huge error to allow for when plotting a paleopole from a single rock sample. The obvious remedial procedure is to take a series of rock samples, each separated from the next by a time span many times longer than a secular cycle. The sample locations would thus be randomly placed in terms of longitude on a fixed latitude circle, so that the mean of the declination observations would tend to sum to zero. This procedure would be feasible for a thick series of conformable sandstone beds or a thick succession of basalt flows. R.T. Merrill and M.W. McElhinny point out that in a typical drill-core of deep-sea pelagic sediment "the time span covered by a typical specimen of thickness 2.5 cm, as used in the laboratory, may already be more than a thousand years" so that "successive samples collected over great thicknesses could correspond to time spans of hundreds of thousands or millions of years (1983, p. 79).

Rob Van der Voo, a leading authority on paleomagnetism, states this concept as follows:

> Because of the rapid temporal variations of the restfield, we need only to sample the field for several centuries and the variations begin to be averaged out. Even the non-coaxial components of the dipole field, when averaged over a long time, cancel themselves in this way, resulting in a long-term average field nearly exclusively of geocentric, dipolar origin aligned with the rotation axis (coaxial field). (1993, p. 10)

Thus, the long-term coincidence of the two kinds of poles is made a fundamental assumption, or hypothesis, in paleomagnetic studies. The hypothesis goes by the name of the *geocentric axial dipole field hypothesis* (Merrill and McElhinny, 1983, p. 80). However, it has been a conservative practice to consider the difference between the two kinds of poles to be on the order of 5%.

13.7 True Polar Wander

Despite the seeming reasonableness of the fundamental hypothesis, attention must be given to an independent process called *true polar*

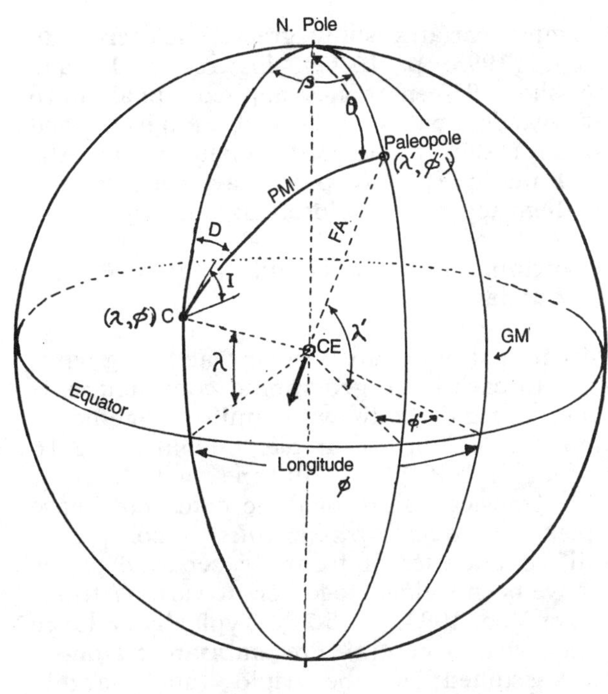

D: Declination of sample
I: Inclination of sample
S: Field site of sample
CE: Center of Earth
θ: Paleolatitude
φ: Longitude of S
PM: Paleomeridian
FA: Former axis
GM: Grenwich Meridian
λ': Paleolatitude
λ: Latitude of S
φ': Paleolelongitude

Figure 13.12 Angular relationships used in calculating the position of the paleopole from measured declination and inclination at the field site of of measurement. (From Rob Van der Voo, 1993, *Paleomagnetism of the Atlantic, Tethys,and Iapetus Oceans*, p. 12, Figure 2.3, New York, Cambridge Univ. Press.)

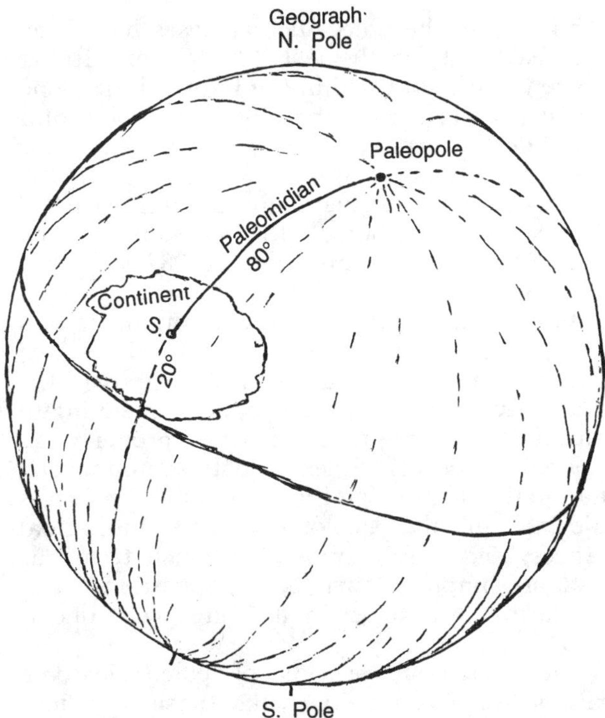

Figure 13.13 Sketch of the global paleocoordinates of the paleopole shown in Figure 13.12. (Copyright © by Arthur N. Strahler.)

wandering (TPW) in which the entire earth moves relative to the fixed pole of rotation. The pole of earth rotation (the *spin axis*) is determined in relation to the solar system coordinates and, neglecting precession, is fixed in relation to celestial coordinates. (The axis of the precessional cone points to the pole of the ecliptic. See Strahler, 1972, p. 32-34.) We shall dismiss as unimportant a spin axis that belongs to short-period and transient "wobbles," including the Chandler motion.

Our interest is in a long-term trend of earth motion in response to mass redistribution on or within the earth, and is unrelated to external forces (Gordon, 1987, p. 568-569). Data of very-long-baseline interferometry (VLBI) indicate that polar wandering is now occurring. Is this wandering now or has it in the past been of importance in interpretation of the apparent wandering paths?

A widely proposed theoretical cause of true polar wander would be the event of growth of a new large ice sheet centered on, say, the arctic circle (lat. 66°N.), causing the globe to rotate on a meridian. This "listing of the boat" would bring the growing ice sheet into lower latitudes and correspondingly move all other global features into either lower or higher latitudes. At the same time, the equatorial bulge would shift independently so as to remain centered on the spin equator. Deglaciation could also result in true polar wander, but in the opposite direction. Steepening or lessening of the angle of descent of subducting plates has been suggested as a potent form of change in mass distribution. Mantle convection has also been considered as a highly potent mechanism of true polar wander. All of these alternatives have been set forth in detail by Richard G. Gordon (1987, p. 587-589).

The question of whether true polar wander seriously affects the plotting of apparent pole wandering paths has attracted much attention, and at least three different kinds of tests have been devised and used. These are explained at length by Gordon (1987, p. 570-581). To sum up where we stand today on this question, we quote a few sentences by Rob Van der Voo:

> Given, therefore, the reality of moving tectonic elements, what about true polar wander? Might not the polar axis have shifted relative to the whole Earth? Once we know how every plate on earth moved with respect to this axis, as well as its movement with respect to other plates, we can try to determine whether the mosaic of plates that forms the earth's outer shell had indeed a common component of motion that was representative of general shift of the Earth

relative to the pole. Such analyses have been carried out for the last 100 Ma, and it has been found that within the limits of error no general shift and therefore no true polar wander occurred. The absence of true polar wander implies that—at least for the last 100 Ma—the paleomagnetically determined APW must be attributed to individual plate motions or continental drift. (1987, p. 16)

As in all cases where field measurements of a given property are repeated within a given area or rock zone, the purpose is to improve the probability that a reasonably meaningful quantitative description of that property is rendered. Basic principles of data sampling and data analysis are familiar to most students majoring in the geological and biological sciences, and it is assumed that such terms as "random sample," "variate," "population," and "standard error of estimate" are well understood.

The statistical aspects of paleopole data analysis are in some ways like those of a new rifle being tested. The rifle is firmly gripped in the vise of a test bench and bullets are fired at a distant target screen on which a blank grid has been fixed. The position of the first bullet hole could by chance be far off what eventually turns out to be the most likely spot. As the density of holes increases, we observe a radial density pattern emerging and we fit to it a circular-normal Gaussian distribution. A host of different forces act in concert to determine the flight of a single bullet. Although we like to think this is a strictly deterministic system, it defies complete description.

Fortunately, paleomagnetism got off to a good start when (as mentioned earlier in this chapter) Keith Runcorn's research group received advice from Ronald Fisher on how to apply statistical theory to the problem of significance of groups of plotted paleopoles (Van der Voo, 1993, p. 15). For a given set of determinations of declination and inclination from a single sedimentary formation or series of basaltic lava flows, a sample of, say, 25 variates will appear as a well-clustered group of paleopoles, such as that shown in Figure 13.14A. It would be typical of primary magnetization acquired over a long enough time to have averaged out secular motions of the restfield. Figure 13.14B, showing very close clustering is from a limestone in which new growth of magnetite occurred during later diagenesis (Van der Voo, 1993, p. 14-15).

A parameter commonly used to designate the closeness of clustering measures the semi-angle of a *cone of confidence* around an observed mean. The semi-angle designated as α_{95} defines a circle within which there is a 95 percent probability of finding the true mean of the population of variates. This circle will increase in diameter as the sample variates show greater scatter (Van der Voo, 1993, p. 16-17). Figures 13.15 and 13.16 show 95-cent cones applied apparent to polar wander paths on North America and Europe for the Middle Ordovician through the Early Jurassic. The two paths have been rotated to fit them together as closely as possible.

13.8 Tectonic Frameworks and Apparent Polar Wander

Our treatment of apparent polar wandering tends to refer to each large geographic continent as if it were a rigid body with uniform geologic composition. For example, Figure 13.16 compares the APWP of "Europe" with that of "North America." Both of these continents have complex *tectonic frameworks*, containing "fossil" boundaries of formerly separate plates that have been welded together at various times (Van der Voo, 1993, p. 25-26). Typically, a large continent has a central Precambrian craton—a shield—assumed to be rigid and largely unbroken by later major rifting or deformed by later compressional orogeny. (See Figures 13.1 and 13.2.) These cratons bear a partial covering platform of younger sedimentary strata that yield a full succession of Phanerozoic paleopoles. A disturbed marginal zone of the craton may exhibit folding and thrusting, for example, the Newer (Folded) Appalachians. Typically, the craton will have attached to its margins a zone accreted by subsequent orogeny in the form of arc-continent collisions. (See Chapter 9 and Figures 9.33 and 9.35).

Peripheral to (or including) that accreted zone may be a zone of accreted terranes—the Older Appalachians and the Alaska-British Columbia terranes, for example. Finally, there may exist some newer marginal zones of terranes in process of docking adjacent to active subduction margins. Each terrane provides unique paleopoles showing the region of origin and perhaps also its progress while it was carried along on an oceanic plate. Figure 13.17 is a graph on which paleopoles are plotted according to age and latitude, along with the apparent wandering paths. Paleopoles for Wrangellia are plotted for both north and south polarities, and either path can be selected as leading to docking with North America.

Another tectonic complication is the horizontal rotation of a lithospheric block, such as the Colorado Plateau or the Mojave block, and this feature may be located far inland. Another example is the blocks (or microplates) bearing the islands of Corsica and Sardinia in the Mediterranean basin. These blocks rotated, while at the same time they were moving away from the Mediterranean coast. This motion would have required a detachment under the block and the formation of new oceanic lithosphere in its "wake" (Van der Voo, 1993, p.

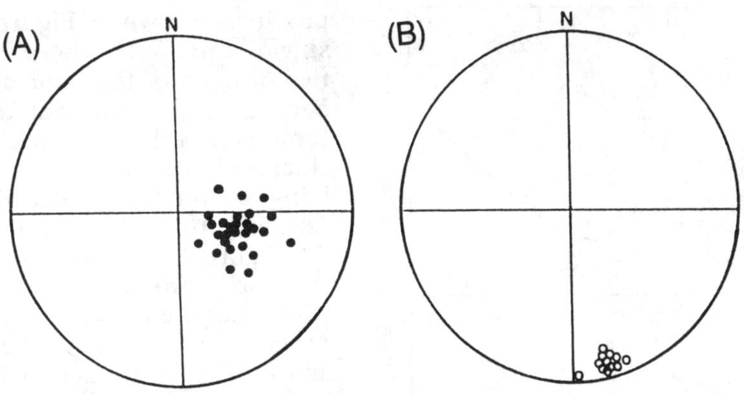

Figure 13.14 Samples of two clustered paleopoles. (A) Normal scatter pattern for primary magnetization acquired over a long span of time. (B) Very small scatter in a sample of limestone that has undergone secondary magnetization. (From Rob Van der Voo, 1992, *Paleomagnetism of the Atlantic, Tethys, and Iapetus Oceans*, p. 15, Figure 2.7. Cambridge, UK, and New York, Cambridge University Press. Used by permission of the author and the publisher.)

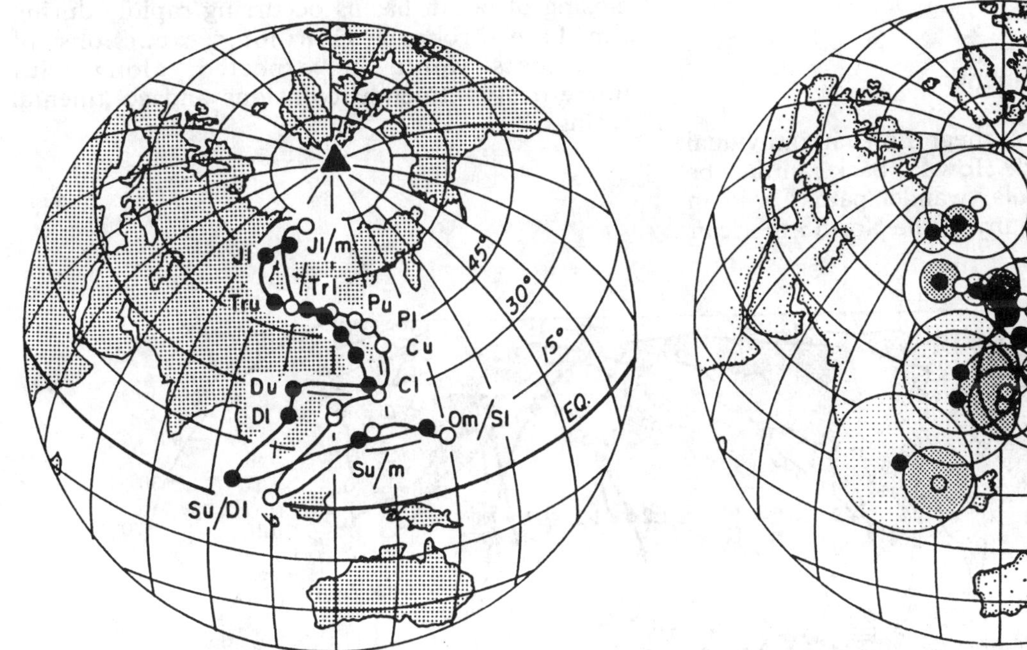

Figure 13.15 Apparent polar wander path for Euope and North America for Middle Ordovician through Early Jurassic. The path has been brought together by rotation.(From Rob Van der Voo, 1993, *Paleomagnetism of the Atlantic, Tethys and Iapetus oceans*. p. 112, Figure 5.28, Cambridge, UK, and New York, Cambridge University Press. Used by permission of the author 0.1and the publisher.)

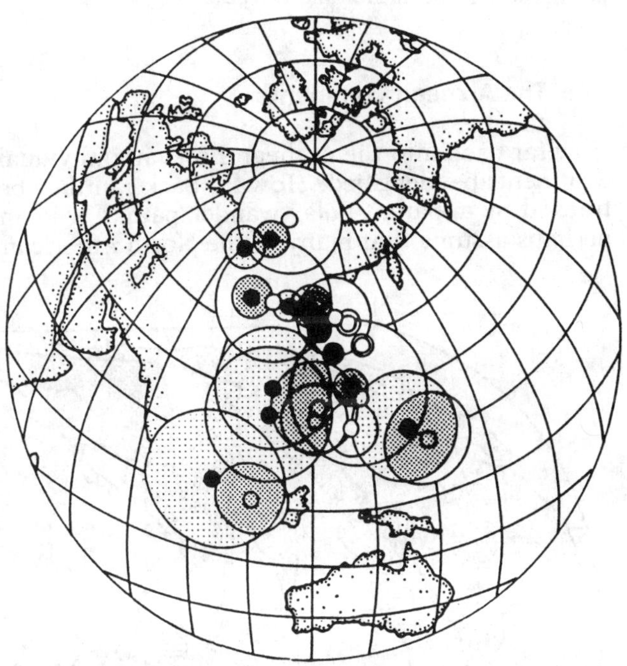

Figure 13.16 A similar set of of wander paths fitted with 95% confidence circles.(Same sources as in Figure 13.15; p.113. Used by permission of the author and the publisher.)

27). A rotating block may provide unique paleopoles of a series quite different from that of the main continent.

Although this brief overview of the application of paleomagnetism to plate tectonics omits many useful subtopics, the principles explained here, along with all aspects of plate tectonics presented in earlier chapters, will form the basis on which to understand and judge the historical review to follow.

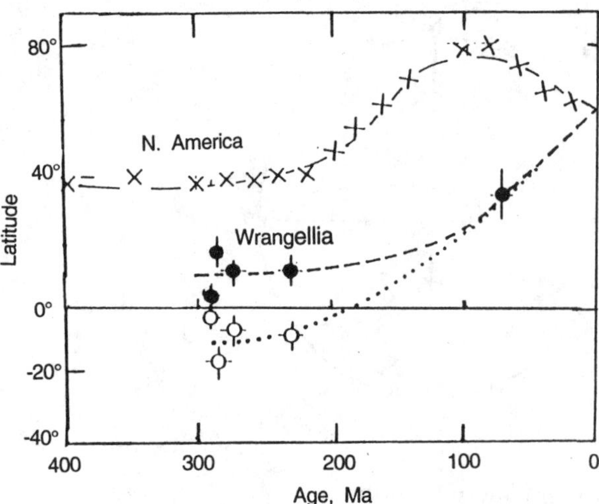

Figure 13.17 Graph of apparent polar wander paths for Wrangellia and North America. (Adapted from David G. Howell, 1989, *Tectonics of Suspect Terranes*. London, Chapman and Hall. Used by permission of the author and the publisher.)

13.9 The Archean Continents

How far back into the Archean Eon can individual continents be identified? How far back can they be tracked by apparent polar wander paths? We can perhaps assume that many of the North American provinces shown in Figure 13.2 were at one time single continents. There is a possibility that any two of them of the same age may have previously been a single continent that split into two. The same can perhaps be said for the other Archean shields shown on our world map (Figure 13.1) as lying in what are now Europe, Siberia, South America, Africa, India, China, and Australia.

Figure 13.18 shows the APW paths of two of the North American provinces: Superior and Slave (Cavanaugh and Seyfert, 1977). Both are of Late Archean age. The paths begin with the dates 2.75 and 2.7 Ga. First, trace each of these paths through its length until you reach the 1.8 Ga point. There, in the Early Proterozoic, you will find the paths to have joined, after which a single path follows a series of bends to arrive at 0.5 Ga. (The continuing path through the Phanerozoic is not shown on this map.) Joining of two paths signifies a continent-continent collision that welded the two together in the Early Proterozoic. Today, these two provinces are separated by four others. With the opening and closing of ocean basins occurring rapidly during the Late Archean such long excursions of continents would be expected, along with numerous continental collisions and continental riftings.

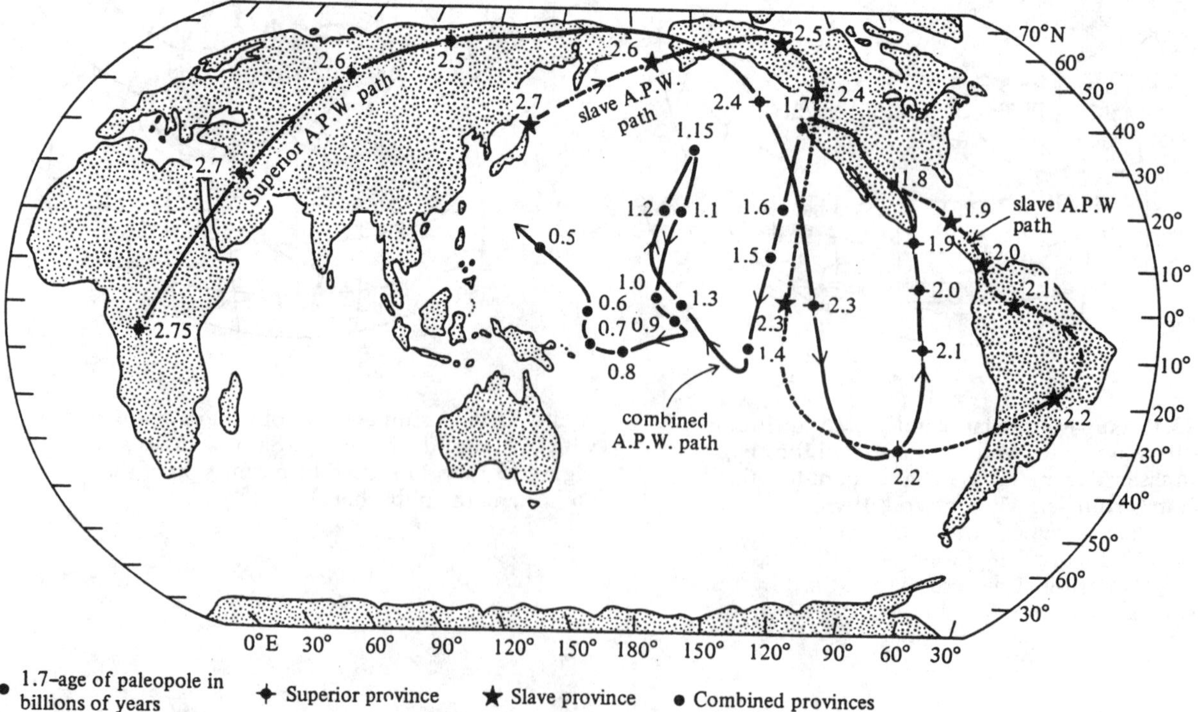

Figure 13.18 Apparent polar wander paths of the Superior and Slave provinces of ancestral North America from Late Archean to the start of the Phanerozoic. The two continents joined at about 1.8 Ga. (After Cavanaugh and Seyfert, 1977, *Geology*, v. 5, p. 207. From Carl K. Seyfert and Leslie A Serkin, 1979, *Earth History & Plate Tectonics*, 2nd. Ed., p. 205, Figure 9.22, New York, Harper & Row. Used by permission of of the authors and the publisher.)

13.10 Gondwana, Laurasia, and Pangea

We now jump ahead to the Late Proterozoic, for which the geographic relationships of continents is quite well documented and the continents are easy to recognize in terms of the continents of today. There was a group of ancestral southern continents which included core parts of today's South America, Africa, Antarctica, India, Malagasy, Australia, and New Zealand, as well as several other fragments of continental crust. By the Late Cambrian, these had joined together to form a *supercontinent* we call *Gondwana* (*Gondwanaland*). By the Late Proterozoic, there were also in existence the ancestral equivalents of all of today's northern continents: North America (including Greenland) and Eurasia (including Europe, Siberia, and China). By the end of the Paleozoic Era, these were also to become one supercontinent, to be called *Laurasia*.

What then, was "Pangea," described in Chapter 1? When did it exist? *Pangea* was (to coin a term) a *super-supercontinent* that consisted of virtually all the global continental lithosphere, including Gondawna and Laurasia. As such, it was essentially a single world-island surrounded by *Panthalassa*, the world-ocean. [At this point, we recommend that you read or reread in Chapter 2 the section headed "Wegener's Maps of Pangaea and Its Breakup," and examine Figures 2.7 through 2.10.]

The assembly of Pangea was not to become complete until near the end of the Paleozoic Era, when the two independent supercontinents, Gondawana and Laurasia, were finally joined by continent-continent collision in Permian time. Figure 13.19 is a schematic global map, published by the American Association of Petroleum Geologists and the University of Witwatersrand (de Wit, Jeffery, Bergh, and Nicolaysen, 1988). It shows Pangea at about 150 Ma (in the Late Jurassic) and includes the major continental units we have mentioned so far. Notice the subdivision of Panthalassa into four oceanic plates: Farallon, Kula, Phoenix, and Pacifica. Also shown are the two major classes of oceanic plate boundaries: subduction and spreading (with transforms).

13.11 Gondwana in the History of Geology

Gondwana, or Gondwanaland, is usually thought of as a southern hemisphere continent, since today its major parts lie largely south of the equator, and Antarctica is centered over the South Pole. The name *Gondwana* was introduced in 1872 by H.B.

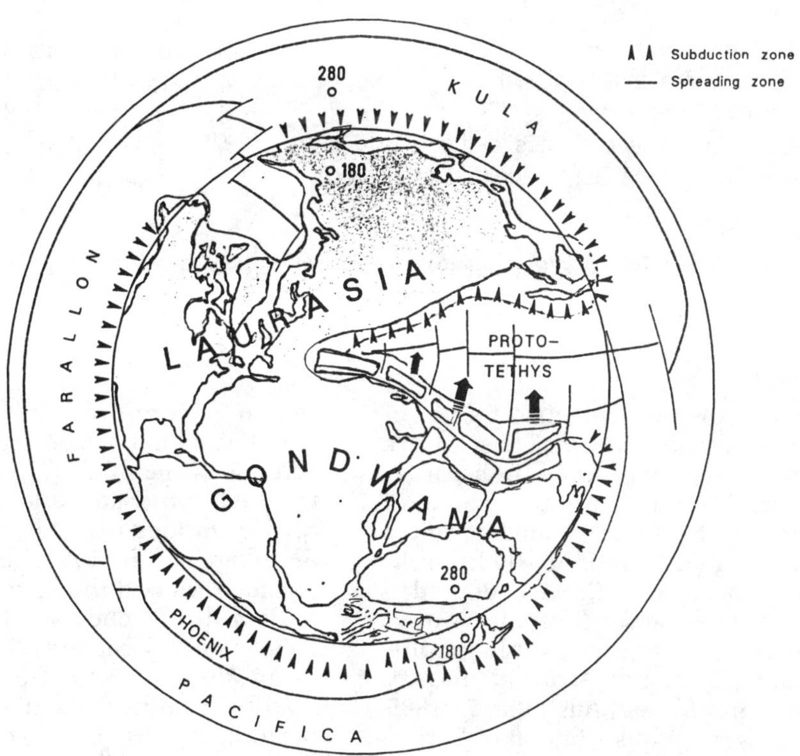

Figure 13.19 Schematic map of Gondwana, Laurasia, and the surrounding oceans. (From *Geological Map of Sectors of Gondwana ~150 Ma*, 1988, by de Wit, Jeffery, Berg, and Nicolaysen. Copyright © by the Amer. Assoc. of Petroleum Geologists and the University of Witwatersrand. Used by permission of the authors and the publishers.)

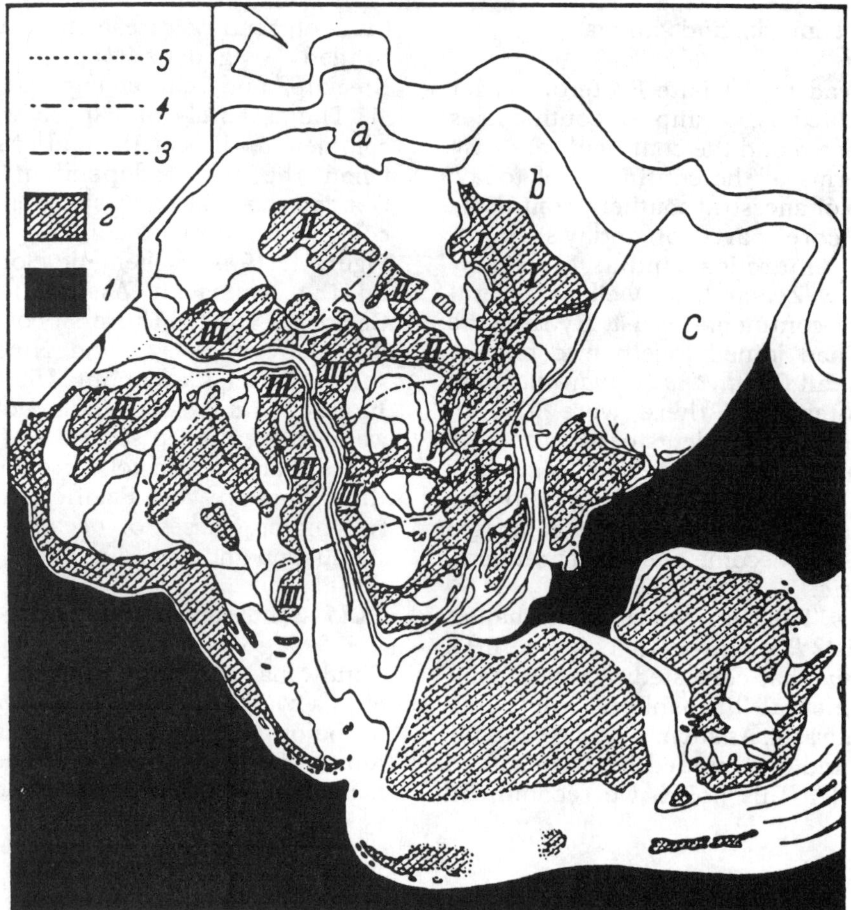

1 = Predominatly sima.
2 = Areas where anticlinial sial folding preponderates.
I, II, III = The three branches of the inner virgation of the Gondwanaland land block.
3 = Ridges of sial fold.
4 = Trough lines of sial fold.
5 = Joint land blocks.
a, b, c, = African, Arabian and Indian foothills of Gondwanaland.

Figure 13.20 Argand's 1924 *Tectonic Chart of Gondwanaland*, reproduced by Alfred Wegener in 1966. (See References Cited.)

Medlicott, a member of the Geological Survey of India. He applied the name Gondwana System to a sequence of sedimentary rocks found in a part of the Indian peninsula that bore the name of "ancient kingdom of the Gonds," an aboriginal tribe. The sequence extends continuously from the Upper Carboniferous to early Cretaceous and is characterized by the presence of *Glossopteris* fossil plants. Subsequently, the same stratigraphic sequence was found in South Africa, Malagasy, South America, Antarctica, and Australia. In 1885, Eduard Suess had used this distribution of flora as evidence of the former unity of these continents (de Wit et al., 1988). Alfred Wegener (1966, 1929) then used the same evidence to support the existence of a united continent which he, following Suess, called Gondwanaland.

At this point, a few words are needed about the recent dropping of "Gondwanaland" (or "Gondwana-Land"), entered in the first and second editions of the AGI's *Glossary of Geology*, from the third edition (Bates and Jackson, 1987). The two earlier editions had stated that "Gondwanaland is tautological." In 1991, tectonic geologist A.M.C. Sengor reviewed the historical use of these terms, finding that "Gondwana-Land," as used by Suess, is not tautological and should continue to be used as an alternative to "Gondwana." Here, we shall hold to "Gondwanaland" through the Wegenerian period, up to 1950, but favor "Gondwana" beginning in 1960.

As described in Chapter 2, matching of rock ages and structural patterns across the fitted edges of the nested continents provided strong evidence in favor of the former existence of Gondwanaland. Wegener showed this kind of matching on his 1915 map, reproduced in Figure 2.9. Wegener drew heavily for support on a 1927 treatise by a prominent South African geologist, Alexander du Toit, published by the Carnegie Institution of Washington. In his 1929 work, *The Origin of Continents and Oceans*, Wegener emphasized du Toit's observation that shield rocks in eastern Brazil are remarkably similar to those in western Africa (Wegener, 1966, p. 71 and Figure 18). Du Toit's 1927 map of the close relationship of these two continents is reproduced in our Figure 2.11.

Another strong supporter of Gondwanaland was E. Argand, a prominent geologist who made important contributions to the tectonics of the European Alps. Wegener reproduced Argand's 1924 map of Gondwanaland, which we present here as Figure 13.20. Compare it with our most recent version, Figure 13.25. The resemblance is striking! Opponents of Wegener argued that the matching of these structural features was merely coincidence or, if real, that intervening crustal blocks had since dropped down, leaving ocean gaps between.

Supporters of Wegener continued to document the similarities of rock types, ages, and structural patterns along closely fitted continental boundaries. In 1937, Du Toit traced a fold orogen called the "SAMFRAU Geosyncline" across Gondwanaland from South America, through South Africa and the Antarctic Peninsula, and across eastern Australia (see Figure 2.24). Du Toit further detailed the similarities of strata of comparable ages forming shield platforms on the landmasses of Gondwanaland. Figure 13.21 compares du Toit's 1937 map with the later rendition of Gondwanaland by the 1970 model by Smith and Hallam. A 1977 map by Barron, Harrison and Hay, exhibit here as Figure 13.22, showed a strong a gap between Africa and India.

As the unified theory of plate tectonics gained its wide acceptance in the late 1960s, a major research effort was launched by Patrick M. Hurley and colleagues at the Massachusetts Institute of Technology to make a detailed plot of rock types, ages, and orogenic structures of the continents (Hurley et al., 1967; Hurley and Rand, 1969). When those areas composed of rock older than 2 Ga on South America and Africa are enclosed by boundary lines, they clearly showed overlaps from one continental shield to the other. Structural trends based on fold axes also show excellent matching on the two continents (Hurley, 1968, p. 60).

At about this time, two prominent American geologists—Robert S. Dietz and John C. Holden—came forward with their strong support of the existence of Gondwana and Pangea, and the formation and subsequent breakup of both by the mechanisms of plate tectonics. Their technical paper appeared in the *Journal of Geophysics* (1970a) and a popular article in *Scientific American* (1970b). Both articles included a set of six global maps showing Pangea complete and its subsequent breakup and the dispersion of its continents. A

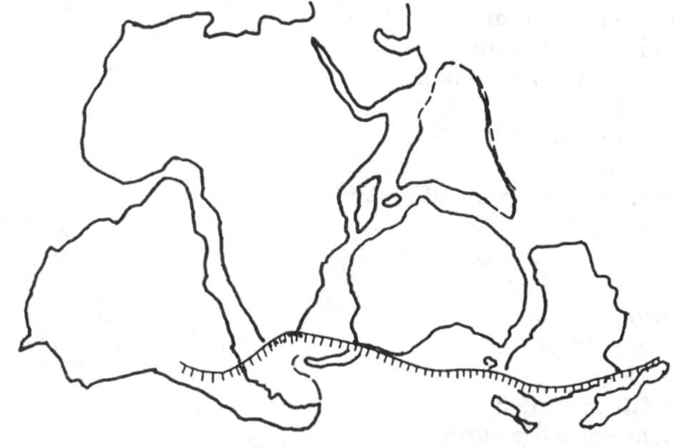

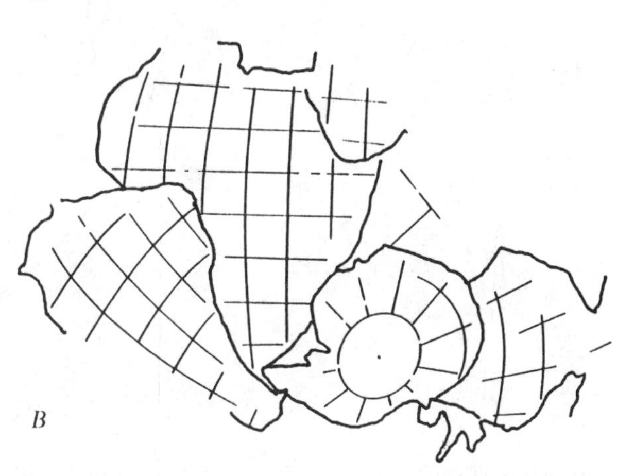

Figure 13.21 Two reconstructions of Gondwana (Gondwanalan:); (A) From Alexander du Toit, 1937, *Our Wandering Continents*, Edinburgh, Oliver & Boyd. (B) From A.G. Smith and A. Hallam, 1970, *Nature*, v. 225, p. 139. Reproduced by permission of Macmillan Magazines Ltd., London, England.

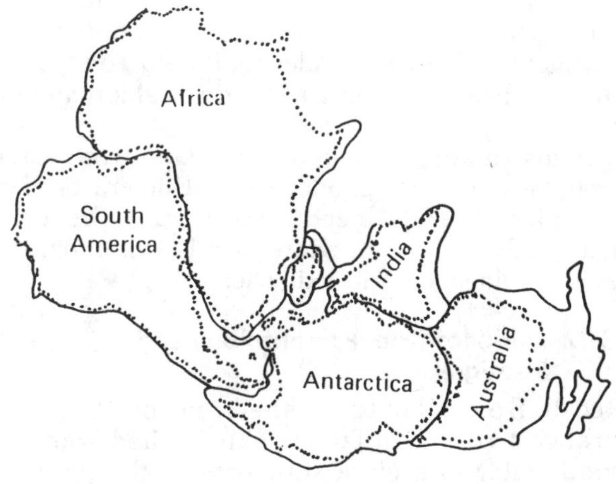

Figure 13.22. This rendition of Gondwana is from E.J. Barron, C.G.A Harrison, and W.W. Hay, 1977, *EOS*, v. 58, no. 9, p. 844, Figure 8. Reproduced by permission of the American Geophysical Union.

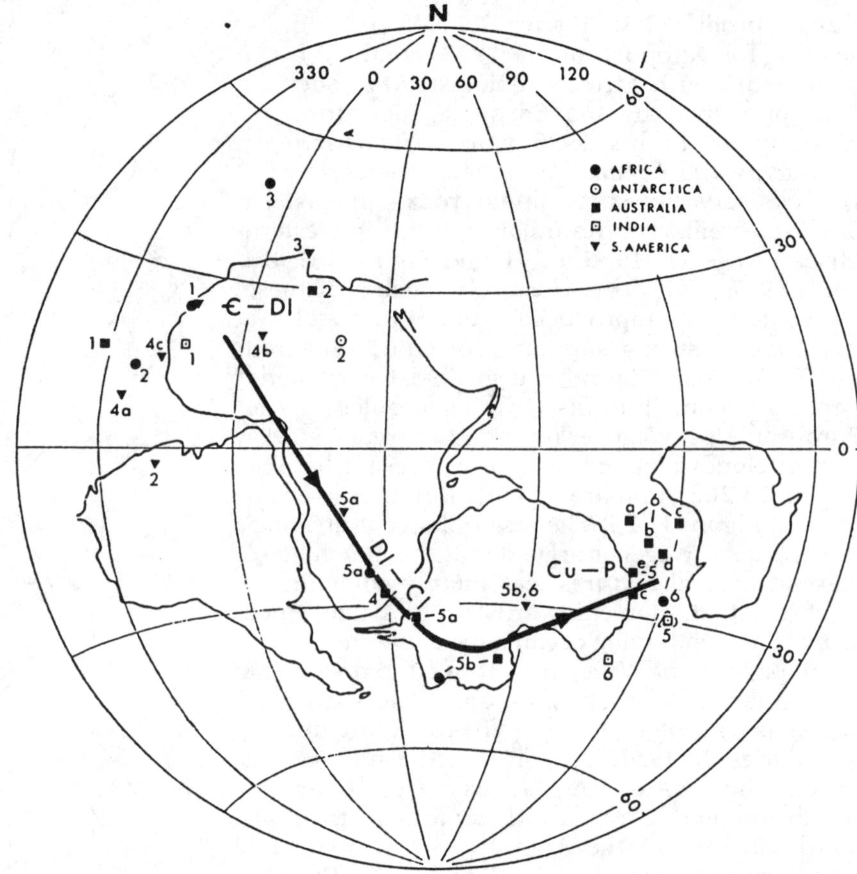

Figure 13.23 The common apparent polar wander path for the Gondwana continents. Africa is placed in its present position in this equal-area meridional projection. (From M.W. McElhinny and G.R. Luck, 1970, *Science*, v. 168, p. 831, Figure 1. Reproduced by permission of the American Association for the Advancement of Science and the authors.)

simplified version of this map series is reproduced in Chapter 1 as Figure 1.17. We have also reproduced a full set of the original drawings as Figure 13.34.

In a 1970 article in *Science*, M.W. McElhinny and G.R. Luck of the Australian National University reviewed the application of paleomagnetism and apparent polar wander paths to the reconstruction of Gondwana. They prepared a single APW path for Gondwana as a whole continent for the entire Paleozoic Era, reproduced here as Figure 13.23. The reconstruction of the continents closely resembles that of du Toit (1937), but has been derived only from paleomagnetic data.

This historical sketch of Gondwana has brought us into the modern scientific era of plate tectonics, but we need to reiterate the early historical period to review briefly other parallel lines of evidence for its existence.

13.12 Evidence from Paleontology and Stratigraphy

Recall from Chapter 2 that one of Wegener's strongest points in favor of the united southern continent was a close similarity in the platform strata lying on the cratons of the Gondwanaland. The strata he correlated span the range from the Carboniferous Period through the Mesozoic Era. A tillite is found in the upper Carboniferous sequence of all the Gondwanaland cratons. We shall emphasize in later paragraphs the significance of that tillite formation in connection with a Carboniferous glaciation that affected Gondwanaland.

Above the Carboniferous tillites lie Permian shales, interbedded with coal beds. The shales are of continental origin, deposited in shallow freshwater lakes and swamps, and contain fossil remains of a class of small freshwater reptiles, the mesosaurs. These creatures would probably not have been capable of swimming a wide ocean. Wegener was quick to realize that the finding of mesosaurs in the Permian strata of the several Gondwanaland units was strong evidence that they were formerly connected. On the other hand, it was argued by his opponents that land bridges then connected the Gondwanaland continents, enabling mesosaurs to move freely from one landmass to the other. Today the land-bridge argument has little force because we know from seismic data that there are no large sunken areas of continental crust beneath the ocean floor. As mentioned earlier, Wegener also noted that the Permian strata of all Gondwanaland units contain a similar assemblage of plant fossils; they were seed ferns belonging to the *Glossopteris* flora. The wide distribution of this flora strengthened the case for a single continent.

The Triassic strata of the Gondwanaland cratons consist of clastic rocks—sandstones and shales—containing fossil remains of a mammal-like reptile of the genus *Lystrosaurus*, a small animal with massive, wide-set legs. Fossil remains of *Lystrosaurus* are abundant in Triassic strata of southern Africa and are also found in India, Russia, and China. In the late 1960s, as the case for plate tectonics gained strength, paleontologists began an intensive search for *Lystrosaurus* fossils in Antarctica, for it was considered impossible for the animal to have migrated to Antarctica across the broad, deep ocean basin that now separates Antarctica from the other continents. The search met with success in December 1969, when remains of *Lystrosaurus* were found in the Transantarctic Mountains about 650 km from the south pole. This fossil find was hailed as one of the most significant in modern times, for it threw paleontologic evidence strongly in favor of the existence of a single continent of Gondwanaland as late as the Triassic Period (Elliot et al., 1970).

Another line of stratigraphic evidence was developed by Wegener through the interpretation of global climate zones prevailing at the time of deposition of platform sediments. *Paleoclimates*, which are climates of past geologic periods, are thought to have followed global patterns similar to those on the earth today. An equatorial belt of warm, wet climate is flanked by two great subtropical desert belts in the latitude range from 15° to 30°. Wegener reasoned that coal layers of Permian age would have been formed in the equatorial zone, where lush swamp forests would have grown. He supposed that Permian strata consisting in part of salt beds (halite) and gypsum would have been formed in the belt of the subtropical deserts. Sandstones representing lithified dunes of desert sand would also occur in this zone. When Wegener plotted the locations of these various kinds of sedimentary deposits on his map of Pangaea, he was able to show that they fell approximately into the expected latitude zones, but only if the position of the earth's polar axis and equator were rotated through about 30° latitude (Figure 2.1). The position of the south pole would then have fallen in the southern part of Gondwanaland, where a great glaciation was in progress through late Carboniferous and early Permian time.

13.13 The Glaciation of Gondwanaland

One of the most remarkable geological displays to be seen anywhere is the Dwyka tillite of South Africa, a lithified glacial till of late Carboniferous age. It contains striated boulders that clearly show the effects of strong abrasion beneath moving ice. Beneath the tillite is a floor of igneous rock that shows strong abrasion and gouging by the overriding ice. In Wegener's time, the evidences of a great glaciation in the Carboniferous and the Permian periods.were known from other parts of Gondwanaland, including South America, India, and Australia. You will notice that on Wegener's world map (Figure 2.17) the places where this evidence was found are shown as clustered around the position of the south pole in late Carboniferous time.

The glacial argument for a united continent was strong because it was difficult to explain how great ice sheets of subcontinental size could have formed near the margins of widely separated fragments of Gondwanaland. We know that a great ice sheet, several thousand meters thick at its center, requires a large landmass situated at high latitude, and these conditions were satisfied by a united Gondwanaland, but not by widely separated continents near their present latitudes.

Glaciation had strongly affected northern Africa in the late Proterozoic, and this was followed by a long, warm Cambrian period without glaciation. Glaciation resumed strongly in the Late Ordovician in northern Africa. If the South Pole lay in northwest Africa in late Ordovician time, we would expect to find evidence of glaciation in that area in exposed rocks of early Paleozoic age. As a matter of fact, in 1961 geologists had found in the Sahara Desert the distinctive markings of a glaciation—striations and grooves—enclosed in rocks of Upper Ordovician age. In 1970, an international expedition traveled to the central Sahara to evaluate this evidence. The visitors were convinced that a great glaciation had, indeed, occurred here, for not only were the glacial striations found, but also tillites and many other forms typical of such a glaciation (Fairbridge, 1970). Although the pole position was also favorable for glaciation of Gondwana in the Silurian and Early Devonian, there is no evidence of it in rocks of that age. For reasons not clear, widespread glaciation did not recur until the Carboniferous Period (Caputo and Crowell, 1985). A late Paleozoic Ice Age then set in, strongly affecting Antarctica, Australia, and India. In the Late Carboniferous, the glacial ice had reached its maximum extent—comparable to that of the Pleistocene. This condition has been attributed in part to an epeirogenic uplift of the Gondwana interior (Gonzales-Bonorina and Eyles, 1995, p. 1015).

Figure 13.24 is a reconstruction of Gondwana in the early Permian (Seyfert and Sirkin, 1979, p.340). It shows the inferred limits of ice sheets, while arrows show the directions of ice movements as interpreted from striations on the bedrock floor on which the tillites rest. On the same map we have shown the APW path from Figure 12.23. During its migration, the ice center followed closely the APW path we have shown (Caputo and Crowell, 1985, p. 1020).

13.14 An Updated Gondwana

In 1979, geoscientists from five different countries came together at a workshop dubbed "Reunite Gondwana" (de Wit et al., 1988). One task of the group was to test the consistency of apparent pole wander paths of the continental blocks of Gondwana with magnetic reversal data of the

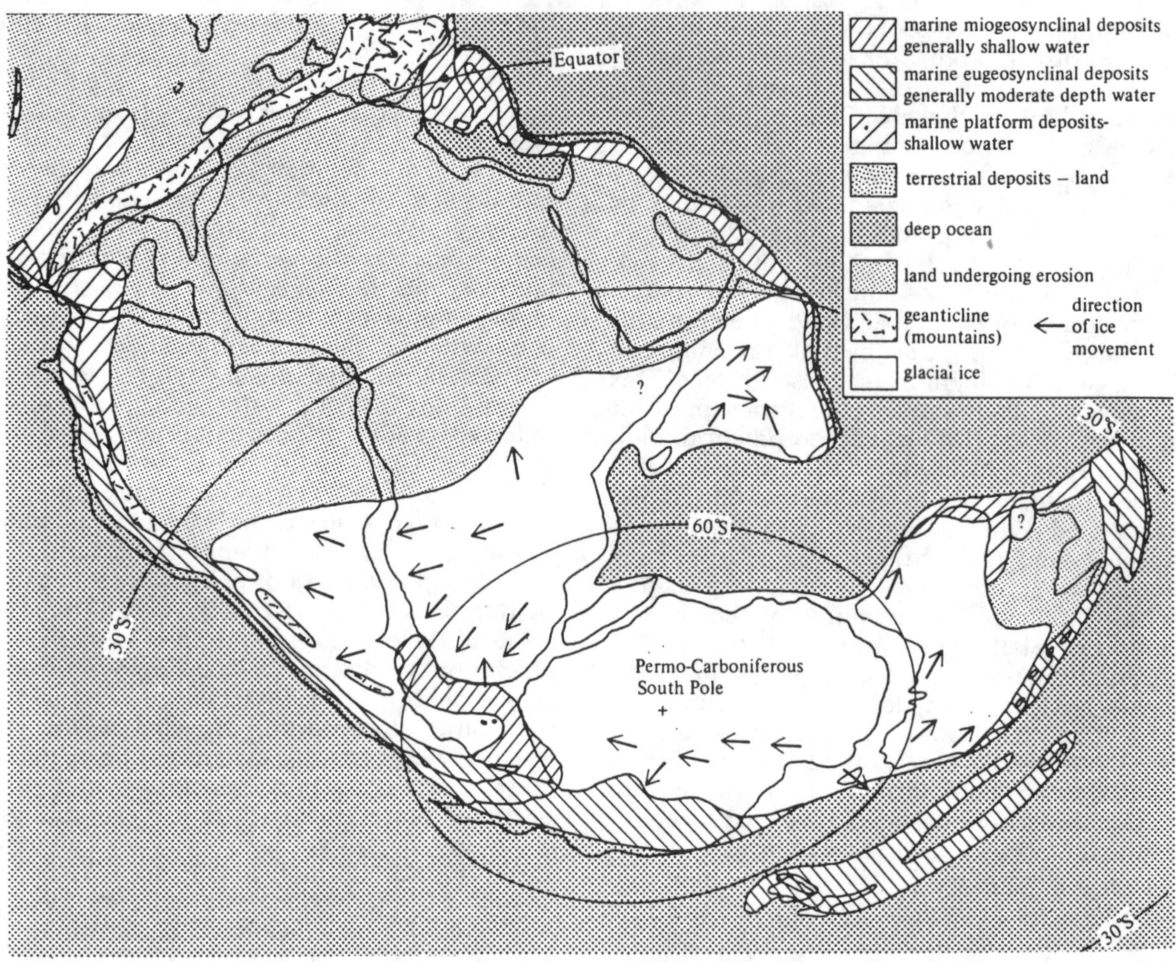

Figure 13.24 Paleogeographic map of Gondwana in early Permian time, showing areas covered by ice sheets. Apparent polar wander path as in Figure 13.23. (From C.K. Seyfert and L.A. Sirkin, 1979, *Earth History and Plate Tectonics*, p. 340, Figure 11.26, New York, Harper and Row. Used by permission of the publisher.)

surrounding ocean floors. Like reversing a movie film, they ran these geophysical data backward to obtain a new fit to the Gondwana components. Much of the effort went into the positioning of the numerous microcontinents that border the main continents along the southern margin of the map. India was chosen as the reference continent because its detailed APW pole had drifted through a distance of about 50 latitude degrees since the breakup occurred. The product of this procedure was a new map of Gondwana, described as "a tighter model." It is reproduced here as Figure 13.25. One unique feature of the map is the provision allowed for crustal extension (stretching) and transcurrent fault displacement within Africa, South America, and Antarctica. These zones of "intracontinental shear" are indicated on the map. The phase of extension is thought to have occurred around 350 Ma (Early Carboniferous).

An important new feature of the map is the recognition of two kinds of boundary zones. One is the southern boundary zone, set off on the map by a bold line running from Colombia in the west through Australia on the east. Perhaps you will recognize this line as resembling du Toit's "SAMFRAU geosyncline." This is the line of the earliest recognizable subduction-zone accretional orogens, named the *Gondwanides*. Several smaller continental fragments are among the Gondwanides. In contrast, the northern margin of Gondwana had been a passive margin since the early Paleozoic. A continental shelf (Cimmerian Shelf) and shallow seas dominated the northern margin. As shown on the Pangea map, Figure 13.19, the Proto-Tethys sea lay to the north; it contained an oceanic spreading boundary between the Kula and Pacifica oceans. Also shown schematically is a line of "calved" microcontinents that separated from Gondwana and migrated northward, eventually reaching Laurasia. The authors of the map summarized this new picture of Gondwana as follows: "On a broad scale a clear picture of tectonic-asymmetry has emerged from the study of Gondwana's margins: along the south, subduction tectonics was prominent; along the north a process of calving-tectonics dominated" (de Wit et al., 1988, Text on map).

When did Gondwana take form? As shown by

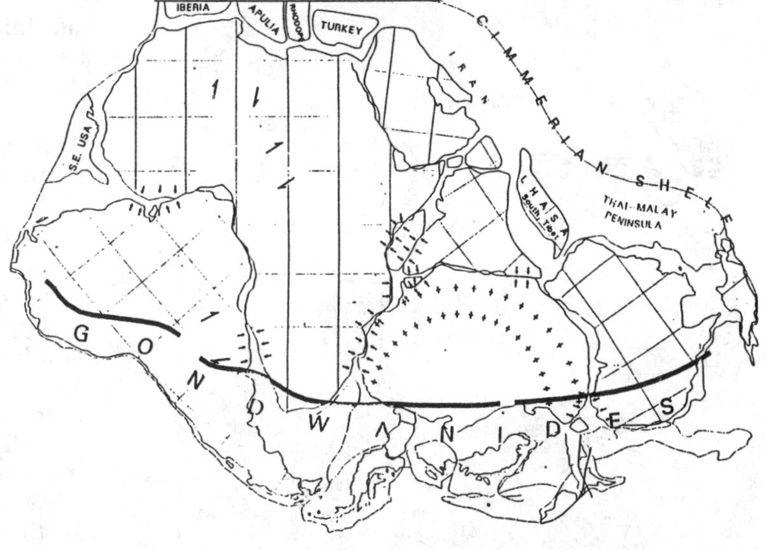

Figure 13.25 Map of Gondwana showing the Gonwdanides in relation to the original continents. (From *Geological Map of Sectors of Gondwana ~150 Ma*, 1988, by de Wit, Jeffery, Berg, and Nicolaysen. Copyright © by the Amer. Assoc. of Petroleum Geologists and the University of Witwatersrand. Used by permission of the publishers.)

intensive studies of the rock units that made up Gondwana in its completed form, it consists of four or more cores, or nuclei, of rocks older than 2 Ga, separated by orogenic belts of younger Precambrian rocks, as shown in Figure 13.22. This arrangement forces us to require an earlier time when the five nuclei were separate continents, and to conclude that their unification required the closing of the intervening oceans. We have already followed this model in analyzing the crustal provinces and sutures of North America, shown in Figure 13.2. According to the makers of our new map, the orogenic belts were active between 0.8 and 0.45 Ga, and that activity may have included suturing of the principal nuclei. "The orogenic belts may thus represent welds between large and small scale fragments that collided in the Late Proterozoic-Early Paleozoic and fused together to form Gondwana" (de Wit et al., 1988, Text on map).

When did Gondwana break up? While Gondwana remained intact through the Paleozoic, it was subjected to continual denudation that reduced the younger orogens to peneplanes. By the Early Permian (280 Ma), continental rifting began to occur, with rifts penetrating deep into the supercontinent. A major rift system was formed along what is today the east coast of Africa. The presence of marine sediments of Permian age in Malagasy requires a 1500 km penetration of ocean water into the Gondwana continent (de Wit et al., 1988). This rifting event was briefly mentioned in Chapter 10, as structures in the Permo-Triassic strata of Karroo age. (See map, Figure 10.14.) The rifting was evidently abortive and should not be confused with the Late Jurassic rifting (150 Ma) that began the breakup of Pangea. In the Late Permian (260 Ma) Gondwana had closed with Laurasia, and these two supercontinents were to remain joined for some 100 m.y, a time span that saw Pangea in place as the super-supercontinent.

13.15 New Light on the Early Continents

The 1990s brought an intensification of research on the history of the continents prior to the Paleozoic. This gives us an opportunity to enlarge our narrative of Gondwana farther back into time, before continuing forward again to examine the completion of Pangea from its two super-continents—Gondwana and Laurasia.

Two journal articles, published one month apart in 1991, raised suspicion that the northern continent Laurentia had switched its attachment from one southern continent to another. Moreover, neither of these connections—called *conjugate margins*—was reoccupied during the final assembly of Pangea, when Laurentia ended up in contact with northwestern Africa. Most maps of Pangea show the concave east coastline of Laurentia (North America) fitted into the convex coastline of northwestern Africa. (See Figures 13.34, 13.35, and 13.36).

In the May, 1991, issue of *Geology*, Eldredge M. Moores of the University of California-Davis wrote: "This paper presents the provocative hypothesis that the Late Proterozoic conjugate margin of the southwestern United States is present in the Precambrian region of East Antarctica" (p. 425). To understand what this juxtaposition means, you need to know that present-day Antarctica consists of two quite different geologic parts. The older and much larger part is the Precambrian shield. Divided from it by the Transantarctic Mountains is West Antarctica—the part with the "tail." Figure 13.25 shows that the lesser, younger fragment lies within the zone of Gondwanides, added at a later time. Moores's map, showing the continents in the "Late Precambrian" (Neoproterozoic) is reproduced here in simplified form as Figure 13.26. It shows Laurentia in position ~750 Ma alongside both Antarctica and Australia (i.e., alongside Gondwana). Moore listed many specific geological

Figure 13.26 A generalized paleomap showing North America (Laurentia) and early Gondwana units—Australia and East Antarctica—joined into one continent, ~0.75 Ga. (From E.M. Moores, 1991, *Geology*, v. 19, p. 427. Reproduced with the permission of the publisher, the Geological Society of America, Boulder, Colorado, USA. Copyright 1991.)

relationships that are involved in this arrangement. Using the acronym "SWEAT," he singled out the Southwestern United States-East Antarctic connection as distinct from the connection of the Northern Cordillera of British Columbia, Yukon, and Alaska (Wopmay province) with Australia. Laurentia was rifted apart from these Gondwana continents some 300 m.y. later and was to collide again with Gondwana, but only after having rotated a full turn (Moores, 1991, p. 425).

Ian W.D. Dalziel, a geologist on the faculty of the University of Texas, had independently devised a similar version of Moores's "prevocative theory" after the two had completed a field trip to the Transantarctic Mountains led by Dalziel in 1989 (Monastersky, 1991). Dalziel's presentation of the hypothesis and a map version of the continents ~675 Ma was published in *Geology* in June, 1991.

Another journal paper of June 1991—this one in *Science*—was authored by Paul F. Hoffman of the Geological Survey of Canada. It, too, had an intriguing title: "Did the breakout of Laurentia turn Gondwanaland inside-out?" Again, the time was the Late Proterozic, and Laurentia was surrounded by the other major continents. Hoffman had earlier identified this group as a supercontinent (1989), and it had been given the name of *Rodinia* in 1990 (McMenamin and McMenamin). Hoffman gives the time span of its breakup as 700 Ma (Vendian of the Late Proterozoic) to 500 Ma (end of the Cambrian).

The first of two of Hoffman's maps, shown here as Figure 13.27A can be approximately correlated with Moores's map, so far as the conjugate boundary of Laurentia and the Gondwana units are concerned. The age of the map is given as 700 Ma. Hoffman has included the missing continents of Gondwana, but they, too, are in earlier stages of growth, represented by Kalahari, Congo, West Africa and Amazonia. Baltica and Siberia are also included. Names of others are given: Tarim, Tibet, Kazakhstan, Mongolia, North China, South China, Indochina, Armorica. The most important new feature here is the conjugate boundary between the south side of Laurentia and the margins of Amazonia, Baltica, and Congo. Altogether, Laurentia appears "embedded" in a central position of the supercontinent.

By about 570 Ma, Laurentia had begun to break its way out of the supercontinent Rodinia. This stage is shown in Map A of Figure 13.28, a set of four maps presented by Dalziel, Dalla Salda, and Gahagan in 1994. As Map A shows, by 570 Ma, the initial rift had been formed between Laurentia and the three subcontinents of east Gondwana: Australia, East Antarctica, and Kalahari.

We continue now to the global continents at 500 Ma. Figure 13.27B shows Hoffman's map for the Late Cambrian. Laurentia and Baltica have moved far away "out into the open ocean," so to speak. Gondwana has been "fleshed out" with pan-African orogenic belts and appears (upside down on this map) complete in its development.

But the Rodinian merger was not to be the last time that Laurentia came back to mate with Gondwana. Long before plate tectonics was well established, geologists studying sedimentary rocks of middle and late Paleozoic age along the western margins of South America in Chile, Peru and Bolivia had found evidence that an "ancient landmass" had been attached to the present margin (Bahlburg, 1993, p. 909). Both sedimentary and

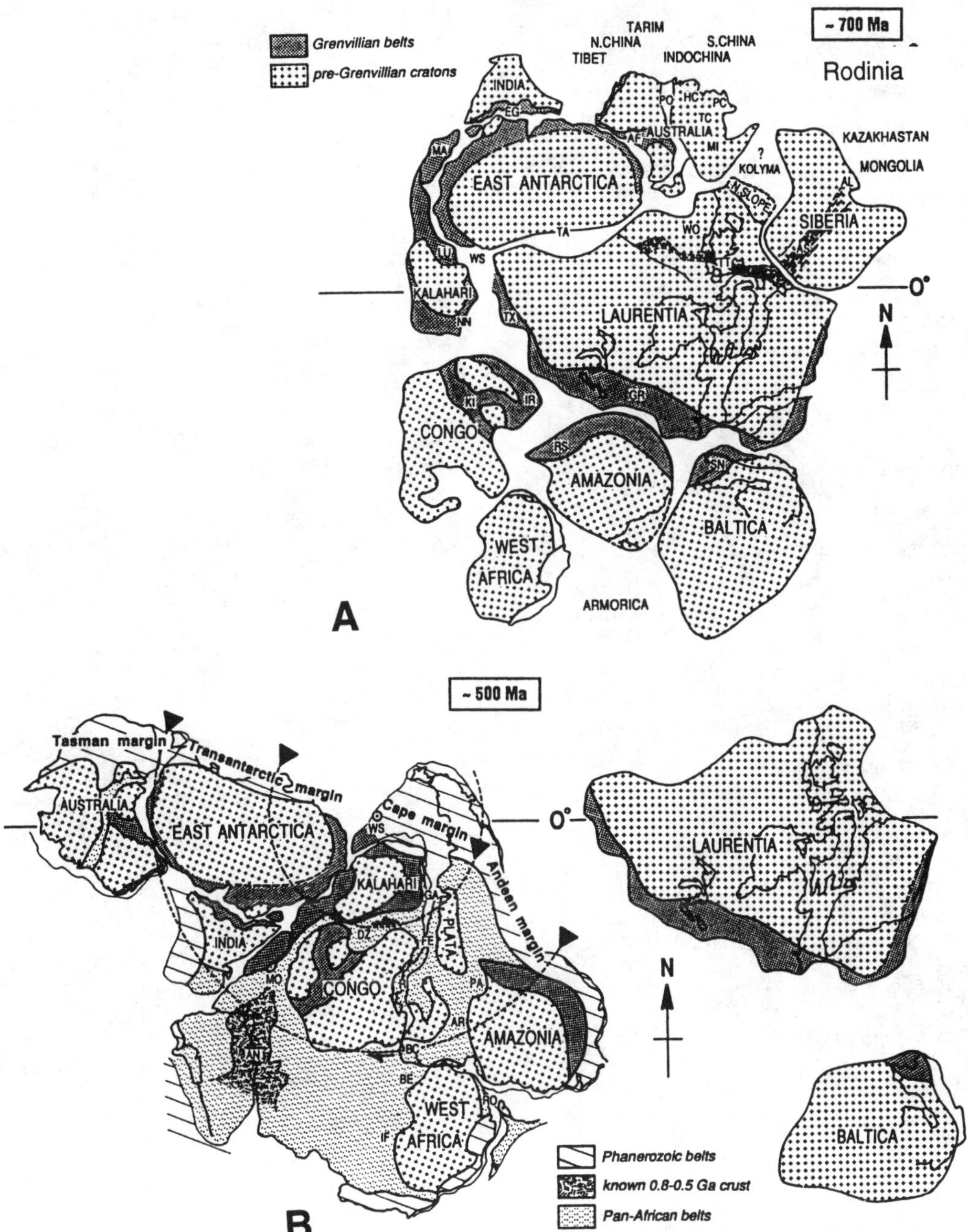

Figure 13.27 Maps showing ancestral Gondwana continents and Laurentia in the Late Proterozoic Era and in the Early Ordovician Period. (A) Reconstruction of Rodinia, ~0.7 Ga, showing Laurentia in contact with East Antarctica and other continental units that are later to become Gondwana. (B) Map showing Gondwana largely complete by ~0.5 Ga (Late Cambrian). Laurentia and Baltica have pulled away from Gondwana. (From Paul F. Hoffman, 1991, *Science*, v. 253, p. 1410, Figures 1A and 1B. Reproduced by permission of the American Association for the Advancement of Science and the author.)

tectonic evidence suggested this hypothesis. For example, clastic sedimentary units thickened and coarsened toward the west, suggesting the former existence to the west of sedimentary basins and upland sediment sources. Truncation of tectonic features striking to the northwest was also observed.

Dalziel, in the early 1990s, had proposed that Laurentia, after detaching and distancing itself from the Gondwana group, had rotated clockwise while moving back toward Gondwana. (Dalziel, Dalla Salda, and Gahagan, 1994; Dalziel, 1994). Map B of Figure 13.28 shows that at 520 Ma, Laurentia was presenting its leading margin (what

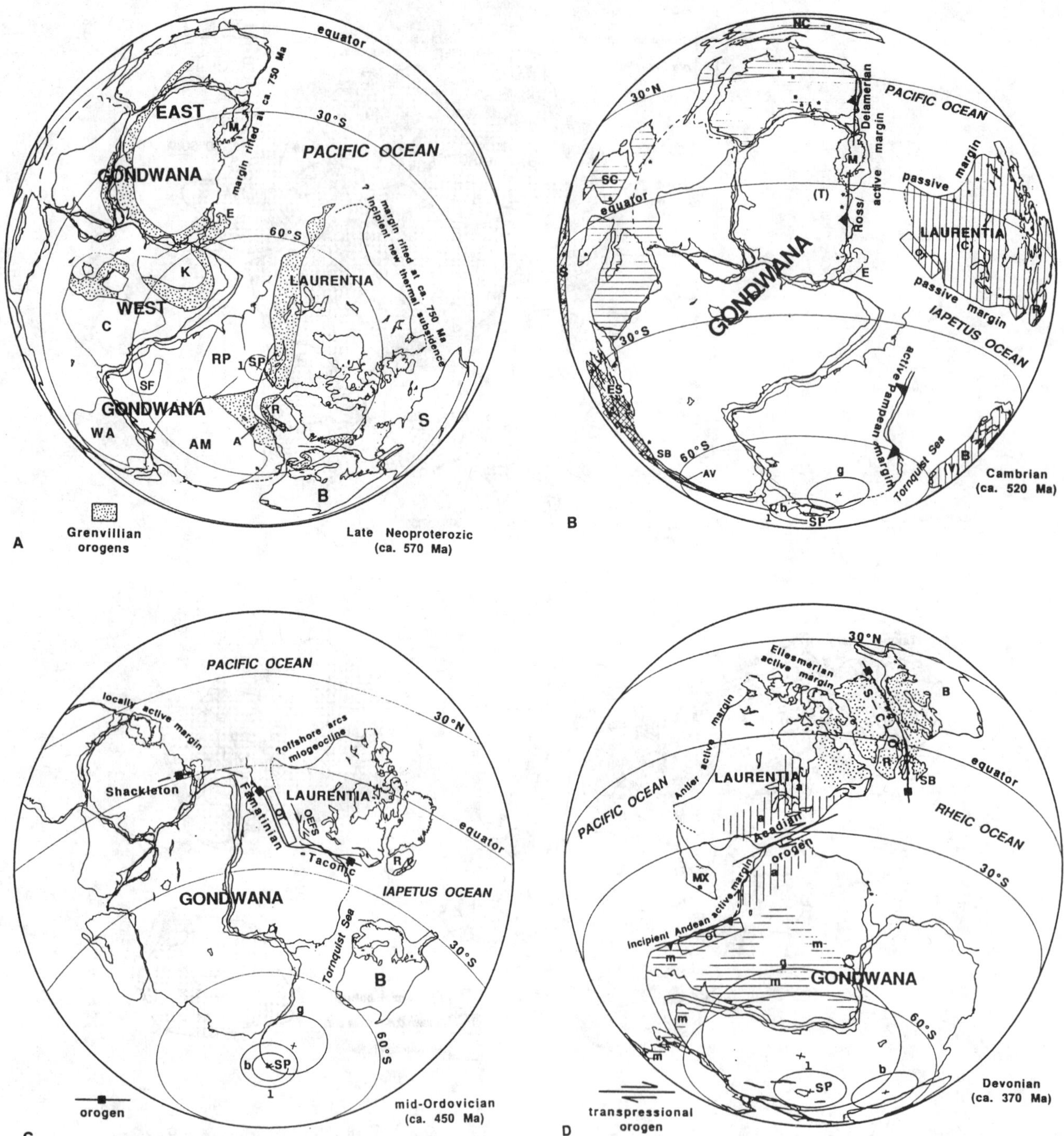

(A) Late Neoproterozoic (~570 Ma). Laurentia joined to ancestral Gondwana continent of Amazonia during the Caledonian orogeny.

(B) Mid-Cambrian (~520 Ma). Major continents of Gondwana in place. Laurentia isolated.

(C) Mid-Ordovician (~450 Ma). Laurentia rejoined to South America in the Taconic orogeny.

(D) Devonian (~370 Ma). Laurentia collides with northwestern margin of South America during later stages of the Acadian orogeny.

Figure 13.28 Four maps showing reconstructions of ancestral continents comprising Gondwana and Laurentia from Late Neoprotrerozoic through the Devonian Period. (Adapted from I.W.D. Dalziel, L.H. Dalla Salda, and L.M. Gagahan, 1994, *Bull., Geol. Soc. Amer.*, v. 106, p. 245, 247, 249, 250, Figures 1, 2, 3, 4. Reproduced with the permission of the publisher, the Geological Society of America, Boulder, Colorado, USA. Copyright 1994.)

is now the eastern seaboard of North America) toward what was the western margin of South America. By Mid-Ordovician (~450 Ma) Laurentia had collided with the Andean margin (Map C of Figure 13.28). The outward-bulging coastline of Laurentia fitted neatly into the concave coastline of the Andes. The orogen from this collision is known in classical stratigraphy as the Taconic Orogeny.

Some 50 m.y. later (by Mid-Silurian, 420 Ma), Laurentia had again rifted away from South America, and it had collided with Baltica. Then, in the Late Devonian (370 Ma) the Laurentia/Baltica continent closed with Gondwana. This time, it was a side-swiping encounter in which what is now the northern Appalachian margin grazed the northwest coast of South America, as shown in Map D of Figure 13.28. As indicated on the map, this was a transpressional orogen, largely of strike-slip motion. It is known in classical stratigraphy as the Acadian Orogeny.

Figure 13.29 is a schematic flow diagram attempting to track the changing relationships among the global continental units from the Neoproterozoic through the Paleozoic. Rodinia eventually evolves into Gondwana as Laurentia alternately joins and separates from the Gondwana group. The assembly of Gondwana in its final form, completed in the Silurian, saw a final joining

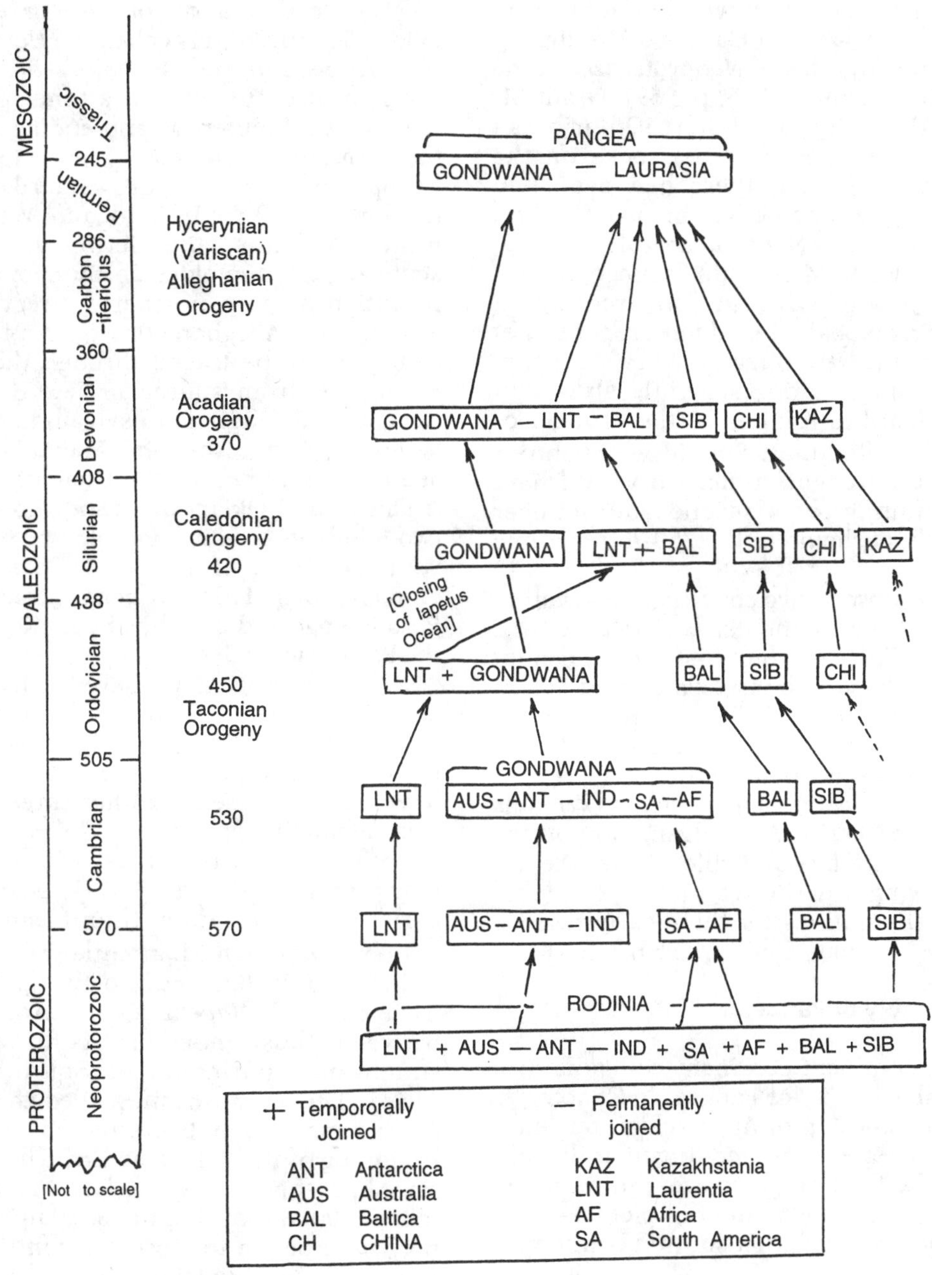

Figure 13.29 Diagram tracking the roles of the major individual continents from the Late Proterozoic to the Triassic. (Copyright © by Arthur N. Strahler.)

with Laurentia/Baltica (representing Laurasia) in the Devonian. The final union of Gondwana with Laurasia to form Pangea is achieved by the Late Permian.

Supercontinents older than Rodinia are postulated to have existed, despite the explanation of its namers (McMenamin and McMenamin, 1990, p. 5) that the name is derived from a Russian word meaning "to beget" (Dalziel and McMennamin, 1995, p. 959). The implication is, of course, that Rodinia begat all younger supercontinents. Now, there seems to be an ambiguity in this implication, since two versions of a "Rodinia" have been postulated. Rodinia as we described it above, in the 750-700 Ma range is the younger of the two. An older Rodinia was intended by McMenamin and McMenamin (1990), and it was assembled by continental collisions about 1 Ga (1000 Ma) during the Grenville orogeny, also of Neoproterozoic time (Dalziel and McMenamin, 1995, p. 959). Grant M. Young of the University of Western Ontario has offered evidence from glaciogenic rocks on the margins of Laurentia that there had been two "Rodinias." The older one he had named *Kanatia*. It, too, was within the Neoprotrerozoic (Young, 1995b). Dalziel and McMennamin "counsel retaining the name Rodinia for the supercontinent assembled during global Grenvillian orogenesis at the beginning of the Neoproterozoic Era" (1995, p. 959). To the contrary, our schedule shown in Figure 13.29 identifies Rodinia as the younger of the two supposed Rodinias. Should we push our Rodinia back to Grenville time, we would have made no accounting for a second and younger supercontinent that should fit the 750-700 Ma time slot.

Following a conservative course while awaiting newer research developments, we hold with a single Rodinia. To make our historical account even more remarkable, Young tells us that "there are published accounts of earlier supercontinents, going back as far as the Archean with the amalgamation of Kenorland before 2.5 Ga and three successive named supercontinents (Wiliams et al., 1991, Table 1) prior to amalgamation of [the first Rodinia] during the Grenville events. We are far from achieving a definitive picture of global continental configurations for these early periods of geologic time" (Young, 1995b, p. 960).

13.16 The Assembly of Pangea

Late Paleozoic continent-continent collisions led toward the final assembly of Pangea. In Chapter 9, we described the docking of Appalachian terranes punctuated by a series of arc-continent collisions that led up to the final orogenic event in Permian time. Here, we look only at the big picture—two major Paleozoic orogenies that sutured continents together.

Long before plate tectonics came on the scene, and even long before Wegener proposed that a Pangea existed, European and North American geologists had recognized two major orogenies that occurred in the late Paleozoic Era, each preceded by one or more lesser orogenies. The earlier of the two, named the *Caledonian Orogeny*, occurred about at the close of the Silurian Period (400 Ma) in what is now Western Europe. It produced a belt of nappes and overthrusts seen today in Ireland, Scotland, and Scandinavia. Part of the same belt is also found along the eastern coast of Greenland. This entire tectonic belt was referred to as the *Caledonides*. In North America, the former continuation of this orogen runs through Newfoundland, Nova Scotia, and New England. Figure 13.30 shows these orogenic belts aligned as a single continuous belt at the close of the Paleozoic Era.

The second and younger of the two great Paleozoic orogenies is called the *Hercynian orogeny* in Europe and the *Alleghany orogeny* in North America. It occurred over a time span starting in the Late Carboniferous and ending at the close of the Permian. As our map, Figure 13.30, shows, in Europe, the Hercynian orogen strikes west-to-east through southern Ireland and Wales, northern France, Belgium, and Germany, trending at an acute angle to the older Caledonian orogen, which trends in a more northerly direction. In North America, the Alleghany orogen is a fold-and-thrust belt that can be traced through the Appalachian Mountains from southern New England, southwestward through Pennsylvania, Maryland, the Virginias, Tennessee, and Alabama. Of the same age is the fold belt of the Ouachita Mountains in Arkansas and Oklahoma. (The gap between these two fold belts is now concealed by Cretaceous and younger strata of the Gulf Coast sedimentary embayment.) This orogeny affected strata of Permian age and can thus be thought of as closing the Paleozoic Era.

The two orogens we have briefly described are clearly the result of two different tectonic events separated in time by about 150 m.y. Both were, in their terminal phases, continent-continent collisions that sutured together three large slabs of continental lithosphere.

Turn now to the schematic paleogeographic maps shown in Figure 13.31. In Map A, during the early Paleozoic time (Cambrian, Ordovician, Silurian, Devonian), Laurentia was separated from Baltica (equivalent here to Europe) by an ocean basin called the *Iapetus Ocean*. Another ocean lay between those northern continents and the Gondwana continents of South America and Africa. This ocean basin, called the *Proto-Tethys Ocean*, may have been in existence from the beginning of the Paleozoic Era. The Iapetus Ocean may have opened up in late Precambrian time (about 600 Ma) during the breakup of Rodinia and may have begun to close early in the Ordovician. During the early closing stages, new subduction boundaries developed along one or both margins of the separated continental plates. Sedimentary basins formed as forearc and backarc basins, with

Figure 13.30 Sketch map of the Caledonian and Hercynian-Alleghany orogens. Continents are shown for Pangea at the beginning of the Mesozoic Era. (Copyright © by Arthur N. Strahler.)

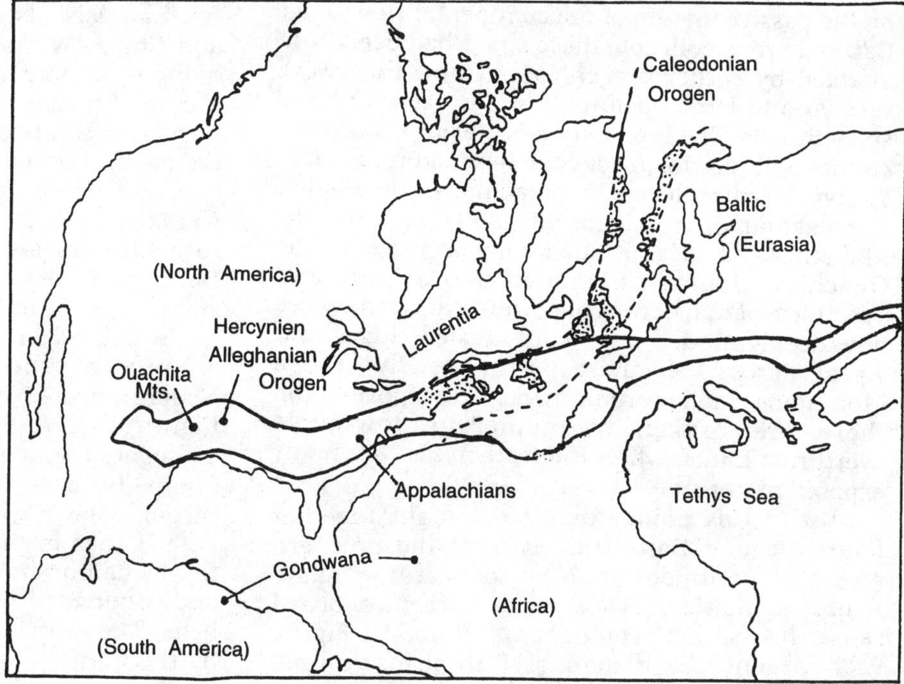

tectonic and volcanic arcs to provide sediment. By Silurian time, the Iapetus Ocean had begun to close in the northern section with a continent-collision that is now in the region of Greenland and Norway. As shown in Map B, collision had extended southward, and by the close of Silurian time was complete, welding Laurasia and Baltica together in what we have called the Caledonian orogeny.

Closure of the Iapetus Ocean welded Baltica to Laurentia to form the single continent of *Laurasia*. There remained, however, the narrow Proto-Tethys Ocean between Laurasia and Gondwana. (See Figure 13.19.) Followed eastward, this ocean widened into a broad ocean. An active subduction zone was probably present on one or both margins of the Proto-Tethys Ocean throughout nearly all of the Paleozoic Era. At intervals, arc-continent collisions impacted the Laurasian margin. Then, toward the end of the Paleozoic Era, closing of the Proto-Tethys began to take place (Map B of Figure 13.31).

That terminal continental collision began in Carboniferous time and was completed in the Permian Period; it was the Alleghany-Hercynian Orogeny we have already described. The roots of nappes produced in this collision have been identified in the Piedmont region of South Carolina (see Figure 9.12). Foreland folds were produced in Paleozoic strata that had accumulated

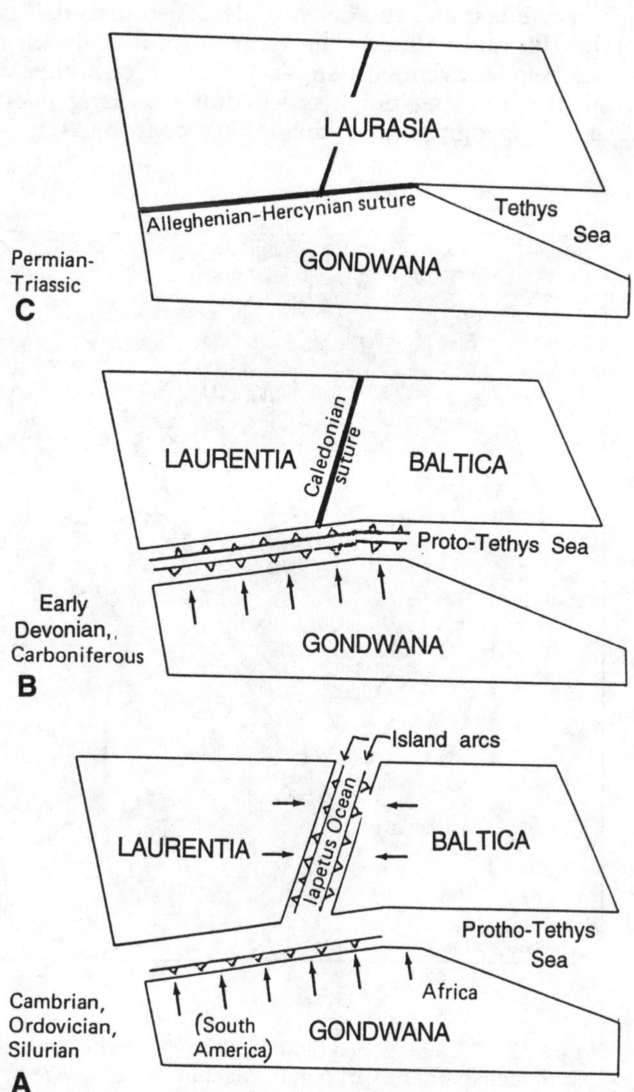

Figure 13.31 Schematic map-diagram showing the closing of the Paleozoic oceans, bringing together Laurasia and Gondwana into the single continent of of Pangea. (Copyright © by Arthur N. Strahler.)

on the passive margin of the continent. Prior to the Carboniferous collision, these strata had been little affected by earlier orogenies, but now they were thrown into large open folds and broken by large splay thrusts. The foreland folds die out toward the continental interior. Today the foreland fold belt is known as the Newer Appalachians (or Folded Appalachians); it extends from Pennsylvania to Alabama and is continued farther west as the Ouachita Mountains. Plunging anticlines and synclines of Carboniferous and older strata are now deeply eroded into sharp-crested ridges that zigzag across the landscape. In the Blue Ridge Mountains, metamorphic rocks are exposed, and these are broken by numerous low-angle overthrust faults, while still farther east are many exposed plutons.

Up to this point, we have brought together Laurentia and Baltica as parts of the northern group of continents that is to bear the name Laurasia. Baltica, as we use it here in a broad sense, has several components. Refer to Figure 9.37, a generalized map of European tectonic subdivisions. Baltica includes the Baltic Shield, the East European Platform (a covered shield), the Hercynides, and the Caledonides. Also included is the Ukranian shield. The eastern limit of Baltica has been conveniently set at the Ural Mountains, a suture trending north-south that has long been used by geographers to divide Europe from Asia.

Laurasia also included Kazakhstan, Siberia, and China. What are these continents and when did they become attached to Baltica? Figure 13.32, a map showing the main structural elements of northern Eurasia, outlines the east European craton. The Ural boundary is labeled as the Uralian orogenic belt. Bounding it on the east is Kazakhstan. It is triangular in outline, with major sutures of orogenic belts on all three sides. By Late Devonian time both Baltica and Kazakhstan were still isolated island continents.

Siberia as an ancient continent has been traced as one of the peripatetic players in the Neoproterozoic. It appears on the 700-Ma map in Figure 13.27A as part of Rodinia, sharing a conjugate boundary with Laurentia. Thereafter it seems to have been a loner, remaining free through the Early Paleozoic, and finally closed with Baltica in the Silurian. Figure 13.32 outlines the Precambrian craton of Siberia. It is bounded and subdivided by several Early Proterozoic fold belts. The Siberian craton is bounded on the west by the Central Asiatic orogenic belt, presumably formed of collision orogens produced as the Siberian craton closed with Kazakhstan. Siberia as an ancestral continent also includes a large Precambrian cratonic area to the south and east, and the younger Verkoyansk-Kolymian orogenic belt to the east. The southern boundary of the Siberian continent is indicated on the map as a

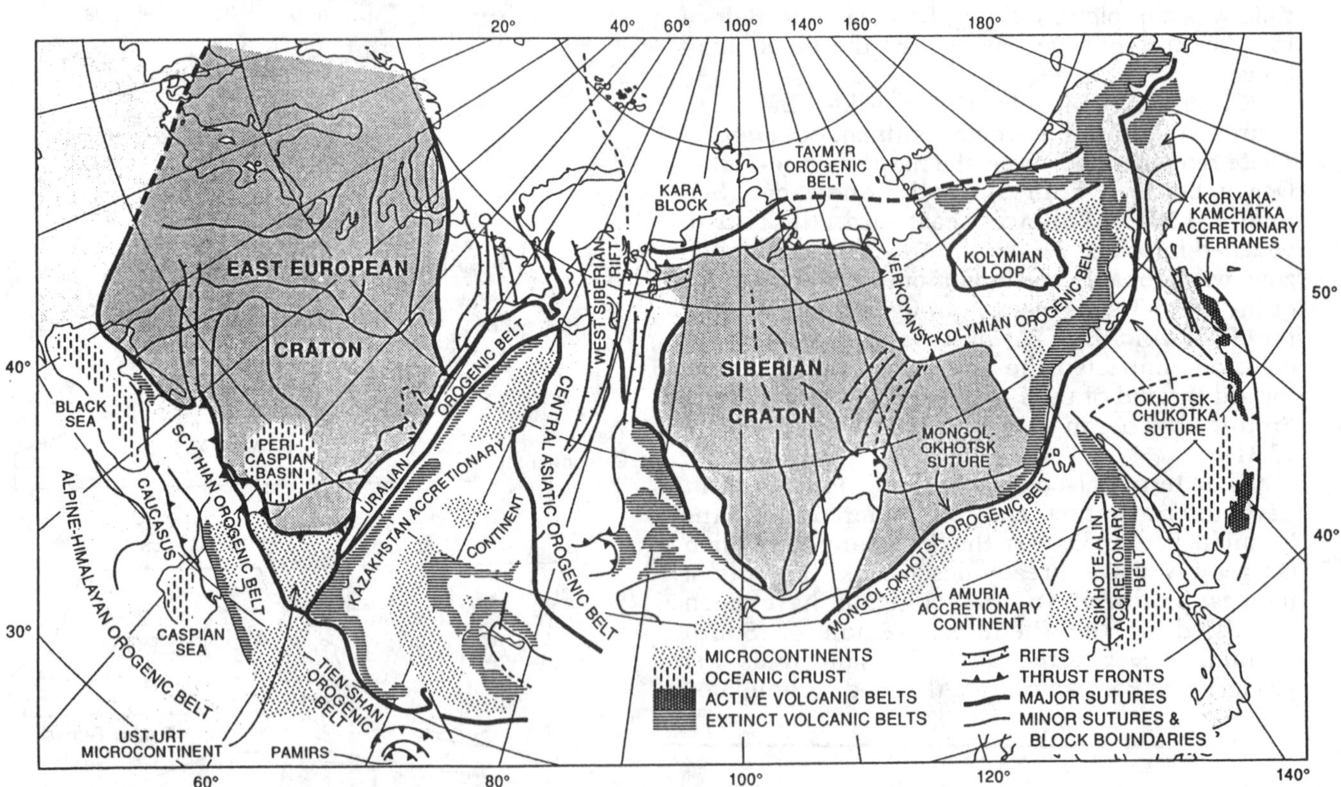

Figure 13.32 Generalized tectonic map of northern portion of the Eurasian continent. (Adapted from L. P. Zonenshain, F. Verhoef, R. Macnab, and H. Myers, 1991, *EOS*, v. 72, no. 29, p. 310, Figure 2. Copyright by the American Geophysical Union. Used by permission of the publisher and the authors.)

long major suture—the Mongol-Okhotsk orogenic belt—by which it is now joined to ancestral China and orogenic belts between the Siberian craton and Tibet.

The ancient continent known here simply as "China" is a large area extending from Siberia on the north to perhaps as far south as the eastern part of Indochina, where a shield area lies in Vietnam (Seyfert and Sirkin, 1979, p. 294). Figure 13.33 shows the three major cratons of China: Tarim, Sino-Korean, and Yangtze (Zhang, Liou, and Coleman, 1984). The last two named are often referred to as the North China block and the South China block. These two blocks were well separated in Late Carboniferous and Early Permian time, with joining occurring in Middle to Late Triassic (Yin and Nie, 1993, p. 810-811). Laurasia was fully put together by the end of the Triassic, finally completing Pangea, but that super-super continent was not destined to remain intact for long.

13.17 Maps of Pangea

New reconstructions of the completed Pangea began to occur in rapid succession as soon as the paradigm of plate tectonics was widely accepted. These showed Pangaea in Permian time (225 Ma), before its breakup began. Not surprisingly, the Gondwana half of Pangea looks familiar—much like those of Wegener and du Toit (see Figure 13.21). Those two scientists had already done a remarkably thorough job of marshaling the evidence for their versions of a retrofitting of the separated continental masses, based on several quite independent classes of evidence. That evidence was reviewed in this chapter and in Chapter 2.

Two of the pioneers of plate tectonics, Robert S. Dietz and John C. Holden, in their 1970 paper titled "Reconstruction of Pangaea," showed a five world maps, starting with the completed Pangea of late Permian time (~225 Ma). We reproduce this classic map set as Figure 13.34. Notice that Laurasia is shown with very little detail, as compared with Gondwana. Patrick Hurley's 1974 selected version, based on Briden et al., is shown in Figure 13.35. It gives information on the Precambrian shields and younger orogenic belts of all the assembled continents (Hurley, 1974, p. 373). Figure 13.36 is a full set of maps of Pangea starting with the assembly periods—Cambrian through Carboniferous—and continuing through to the present. These are reproduced from a 1979 work by Carl K, Seyfert and Leslie A. Sirkin, the first historical geology textbook to fully develop plate tectonics as its basic theme.

13.18 Stages in the Breakup of Pangaea

The breakup of Pangaea on a large scale probably began in the late Triassic, about 210 Ma. One reason to use this date is that the polar wandering paths of Africa and North America begin to diverge just after this time. The maps of Figure 13.36, starting with Map G show the breakup of Pangaea and changing pattern of separated continents for each geologic period. As shown on Map H (Jurassic), Laurasia had begun to separate from Gondwana and North America had become separated from Africa. South America and Africa remained in contact through the Jurassic, but India, Antarctica, and Australia were beginning to separate in an early phase of the opening of the Indian Ocean basin. At the same time, the Tethys Sea was beginning to close by a rotating motion of Eurasia, pivoting on the point of contact of Eurasia and Africa in the western Mediterranean.

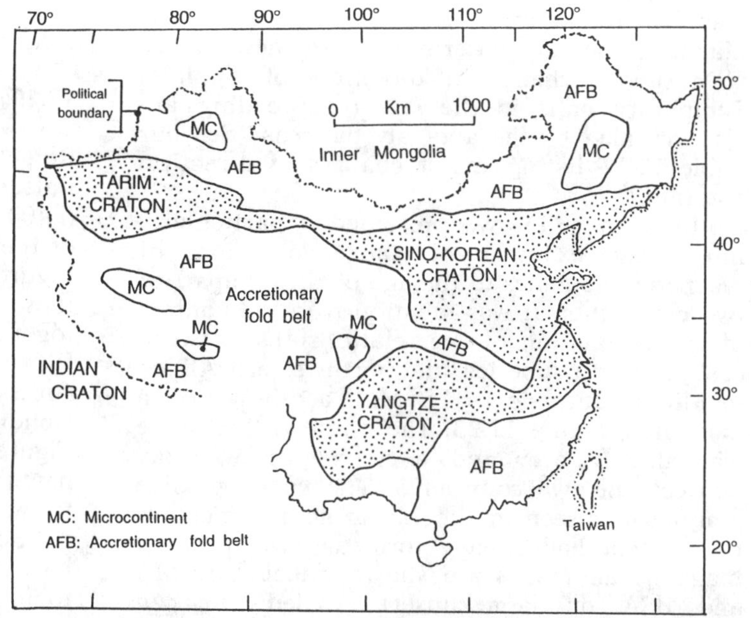

Figure 13.33 Generalized tectonic map of China. (Adapted from Z-H. M. Zhang, J.G. Liou, and G.G. Coleman, 1984, *Bull., Geol. Soc. Amer.*, v. 95, p. 296, Figure 1. Reproduced with the permission of the publisher, the Geological Society of America, Boulder, Colorado, USA. Copyright 1984.)

By the end of Jurassic time, 140 Ma, the North Atlantic basin was rather broadly opened up, and India was headed northward toward Asia. Two major transform faults bounded the sides of the Indian plate as it traveled rapidly northward away from the spreading boundary of the widening Indian Ocean basin. The trace of these transform boundaries is seen today in two long, narrow features of the Indian Ocean—the Owen Fracture Zone and the Ninety East Ridge (see Figure 5.28). Subduction of the oceanic portion of the plate north of India was continually taking place, so that an enormous volume of oceanic lithosphere was consumed before the Indian continental fragment finally collided with the Eurasian plate. (See Chapter 9, and Figures 9.46, 9.47.) In the late Jurassic, separation of South America and Africa had just begun, starting at the south and working north. By the end of Cretaceous time, 65 Ma, South America was well separated from Africa; the wide opening between them formed the South Atlantic basin. Table 13.1 lists for each period the beginning of separation of pairs of continents.

One of the great advantages of tracking the breakup of Pangea, as compared with deciphering the history of its earlier assembly, lies in the availability of a record of the magnetic anomalies on the seafloors. This subject was covered in Chapter 7. One has only to glance at the world geologic map of the ocean floors, Figure 7.31, to appreciate the value of the transforms (FZs) normal to the anomalies as displays of the paths of motion of the separating continents. The North and South Atlantic basins, especially, resemble an open book telling us when and where the breakup began, and at what rate it continued. Detailed information on the anomalies and transforms is available on another map: *Magnetic Lineations of the World's Ocean Basins*, 1989, prepared by Cande, LaBreque, Pitman, and others. A portion of this map is reproduced here as Figure 13.37. Magnetic anomaly patterns also provide evidence of a sudden change in direction of a plate. Temporary halts in the rate of spreading are also revealed by the anomaly patterns. See our Table 12.32 listing major changes of direction and rate.

In Chapter 11, we presented a particularly interesting example of the application of magnetic anomalies to the age of rifting apart of two continents. It was mentioned in the context of an examination of the relationships between eastern North America and northwestern Africa in Middle Jurassic (~175 Ma), as shown on a paleomap, Figure 11.23. The initial rifting stage was already over and a narrow seaway lay between the two continents. The young passive margins are seen in the Mesozoic sedimentary basins that had already formed. Two parallel magnetic anomalies are shown (labeled ECMA and BSA on large inset). Called *breakup anomalies*, these zones are in some way related to the axis of the Mid-Oceanic Ridge at the time the rift was formed. The seafloor that produced these anomalies is now buried, but the anomalies can still be detected. Figure 13.37 shows these breakup anomalies in their present locations. What seem to be corresponding breakup anomalies are shown and labeled along the west coast of Africa.

Table 13.1 Times of Commencement of Continental Separations

Period	Separation
Late Triassic (200 Ma)	
	North America and Eurasia from Gondwana
	Africa from India, Australia, and Antarctica
Late Jurassic (150 Ma)	
	Africa from South America
	Antarctica and Australia from India
	Malagasy from Africa
	Greenland from North America (Laurentia)
Late Cretaceous (70 Ma)	
	Greenland from Europe (Baltica)
	India from Seychelles Islands
Early Cenozoic (Paleocene) (54 Ma)	
	Australia from Antarctica
Late Cenozoic (Middle Miocene) (15 Ma)	
	Arabia from Africa
	Baja California from Mexico
	Sardinia and Corsica from Europe

Data from C.K. Seyfert and L.A. Sirkin, 1979, *Earth History and Plate Tectonics*, 2nd. Ed., p. 369, Table 12.1A.

13.19 The Rifting Apart of Laurasia

Refer back in the assembly of Pangea to the Caledonian orogeny at the close of the Silurian (~400 Ma) and the Hercynian/Alleghany orogeny of the Carboniferous/Permian (300 to 250 Ma). Figures 13.30 and 13.31 showed the result of these collisional orogenies, which was to weld together Laurentia (North America), Baltica (Europe), and Gondwana (Africa). By the Jurassic, Laurentia had separated from Gondwana and Baltica, as shown in Map H of Figure 13.36. The question now is this: Did this new rift follow the old sutures, and thus return to the same continental margins as before?

Suppose that you glue two blocks of soft balsa wood together, then later pull them apart to form a new break. The chances are that the

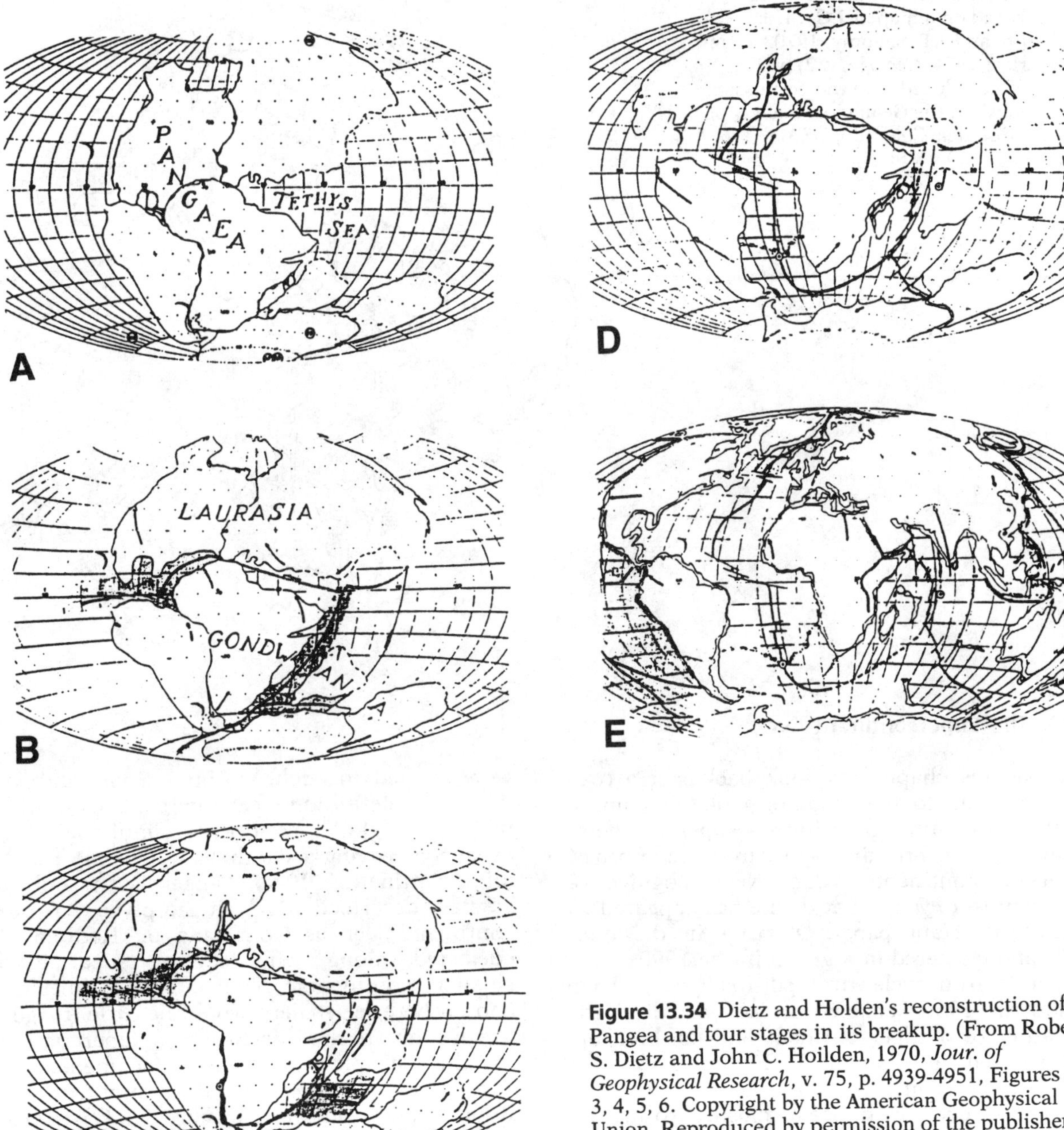

Figure 13.34 Dietz and Holden's reconstruction of Pangea and four stages in its breakup. (From Robert S. Dietz and John C. Hoilden, 1970, *Jour. of Geophysical Research*, v. 75, p. 4939-4951, Figures 2, 3, 4, 5, 6. Copyright by the American Geophysical Union. Reproduced by permission of the publisher and the authors.)

new break will not follow the glued contact very closely, Instead, some splinters will be pulled off one block and become a part of the other block, and vice versa. This is what seems to have happened when the final opening of the Atlantic began in Triassic time. Figure 13.38 shows this effect in a highly schematic way.

Without going into the details, which are very complex, we can point out a strange thing that resulted from the principle shown in Figure 13.38. When the Atlantic Ocean opened up in late Triassic time, a substantial strip of what was formerly the North American continent (Laurentia) on the western side of Iapetus Ocean adhered to the European plate and is now northern Ireland and the Highlands of Scotland (Figure 13.39). At the same time, a strip of what was formerly a part of the European continent on the east side of Iapetus Ocean adhered to the American plate and is now part of Newfoundland, Nova Scotia, and New England. So there was an exchange of crust between the two continents.

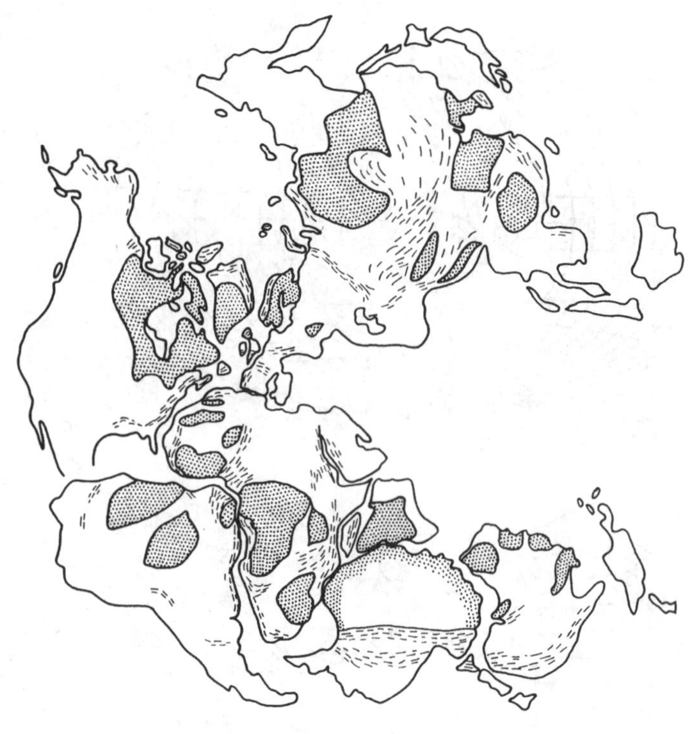

Figure 13.35 Patrick Hurley's map of Pangea, based on a map of J.C. Briden, A.G. Smith, and J.T. Sallomy, 1970. (From P.M. Hurley, 1974, *Geology*, v. 2, p. 373, Figure 1. Reproduced with the permission of the publisher, the Geological Society of America, Boulder, Colorado, USA. Copyright 1970.)

13.20 The Supercontinent Cycle

To close this chapter, we look back over a two-b.y. time span to find a pattern of the coming together of continents to form a supercontinent, followed by its breaking apart into a number of dispersed continents. Can we recognize a *supercontinent cycle*? That theme has appeared in several important papers starting in the mid-1980s and clustered in a group in the 1990s.

The Wilson cycle, first put forth by J. Tuzo Wilson in 1966, enabled us to visualize the formation of a supercontinent and its breakup. As reviewed in Chapter 1 (Figure 1.13), the Wilson cycle arbitrarily starts with continental rifting and ends with ocean closure following continental collision. A rational approach would, however, start a supercycle with the assembly of many continents into one and end with continental dispersion into many smaller continents.

In Chapter 1, in our brief mention of a supercontinent cycle, we presented a fanciful cartoon depicting the supercontinent cycle as a "dance" of its components (Figure 1.18). Each continent travels radially out during dispersal and then returns to a common meeting area. During this journey the lone continents accumulate orogens from impacting oceanic arcs. Some of the continents rotate, enabling them to accumulate orogens on all sides. When the cycle is completed the supercontinent will have been substantially enlarged.

How many supercontinent cycles have there been since the first scattered lithospheric plates were formed in Archean time? Some ambiguity lies in the definition of a supercontinent. Must it include all global continents simultaneously in existence, leaving a Panthalassa devoid of all but microcontinents? If so, Pangea is the only one we have described. Or is it simply a very large continent, such as Gondwana or Rodinia that coexisted along with several separate and smaller continents? The latter definition is chosen here, else there would be little to go on to substantiate the existence of a supercontinent. In this chapter we have documented two supercycles, those of the supercontinents Rodinia and Gondwana (Figure 13.39). Rodinia dates back to the Neoproterozoic, so there is ample time for more supercontinent cycles to have occurred during the 1 b.y. of the Early and Middle Proterozoic.

Canadian geologist Paul F. Hoffman (1989) took advantage of that huge gap, presenting evidence of the existence of a supercontinent about 1.6-1.3 Ga, which is at the start of the Middle Proterozoic. (Hoffman's evidence is reviewed below.) This supercontinent accumulated by collisional activity in the Early Proterozoic between 2.1 Ga and 1.8 Ga, and it included ancestral Laurentia along with other continents. Thus we see today in the shield of North America the core of this early supercontinent Hoffman suggested that supercontinents would not have formed at an earlier time (i.e., in the Archean Eon) because crustal thickness would have been insufficient (1989, p.

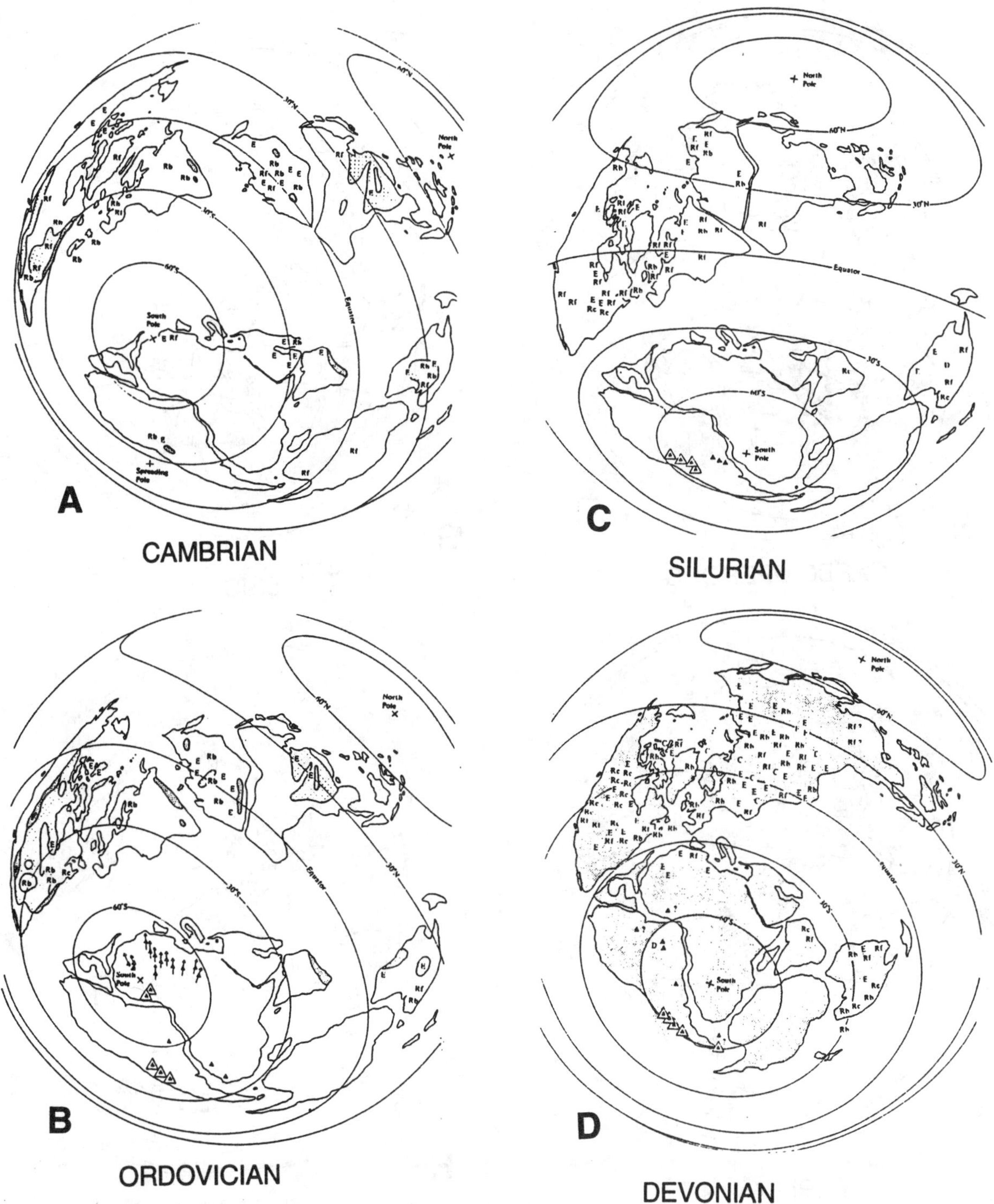

Figure 13.36 Set of 12 global maps showing the evolution of Gondwana and Laurasia from Cambrian time to the present, including the Pangean stage of Carboniferous and Permian time. (From Carl K. Seyfert and Leslie A. Sirkin, 1979, *Earth History and Plate Tectonics*, 2nd. Ed., New York, Harper & Row. Used by permission of of the authors and the publisher.)

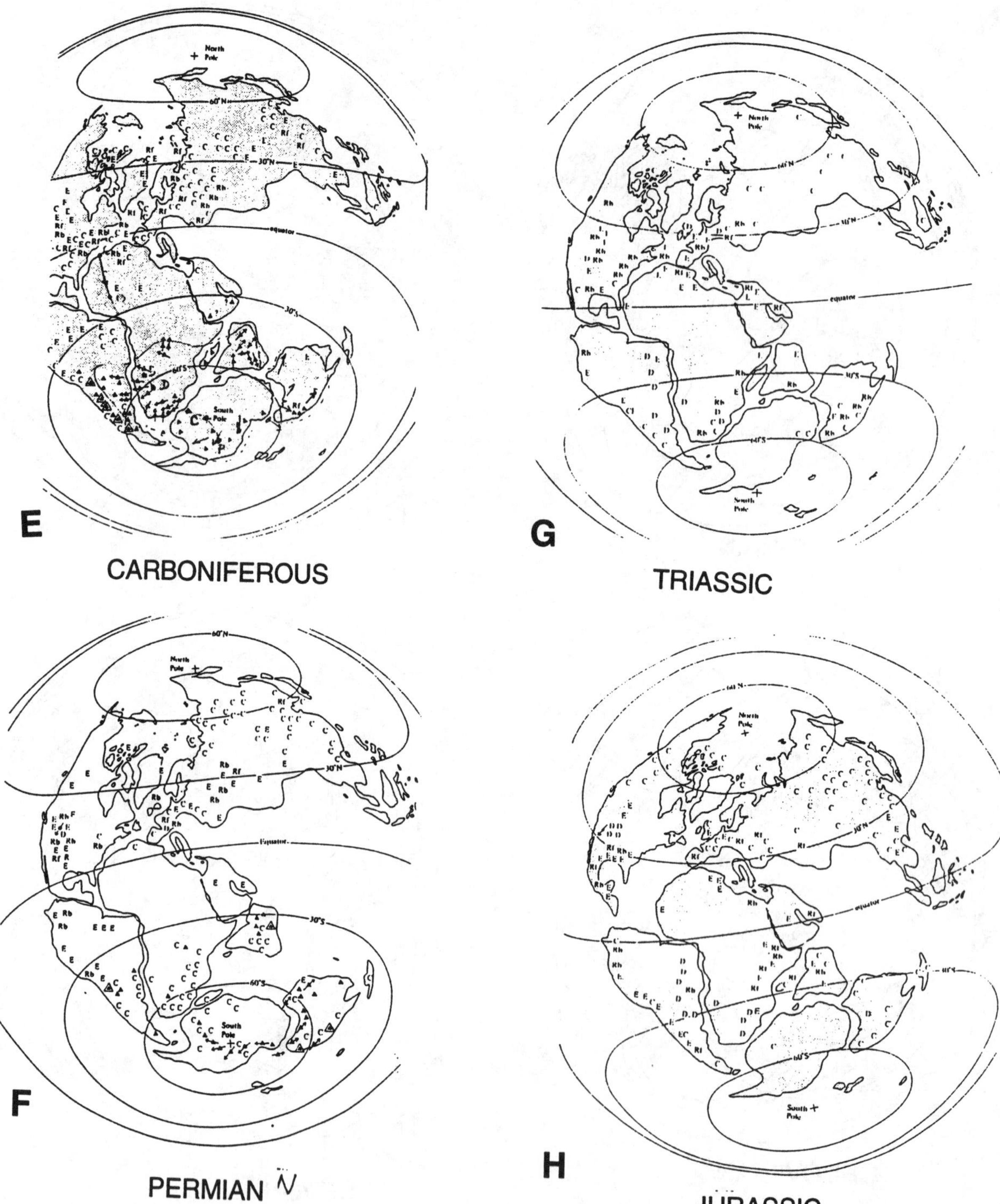
E
CARBONIFEROUS
G
TRIASSIC
F
PERMIAN
H
JURASSIC

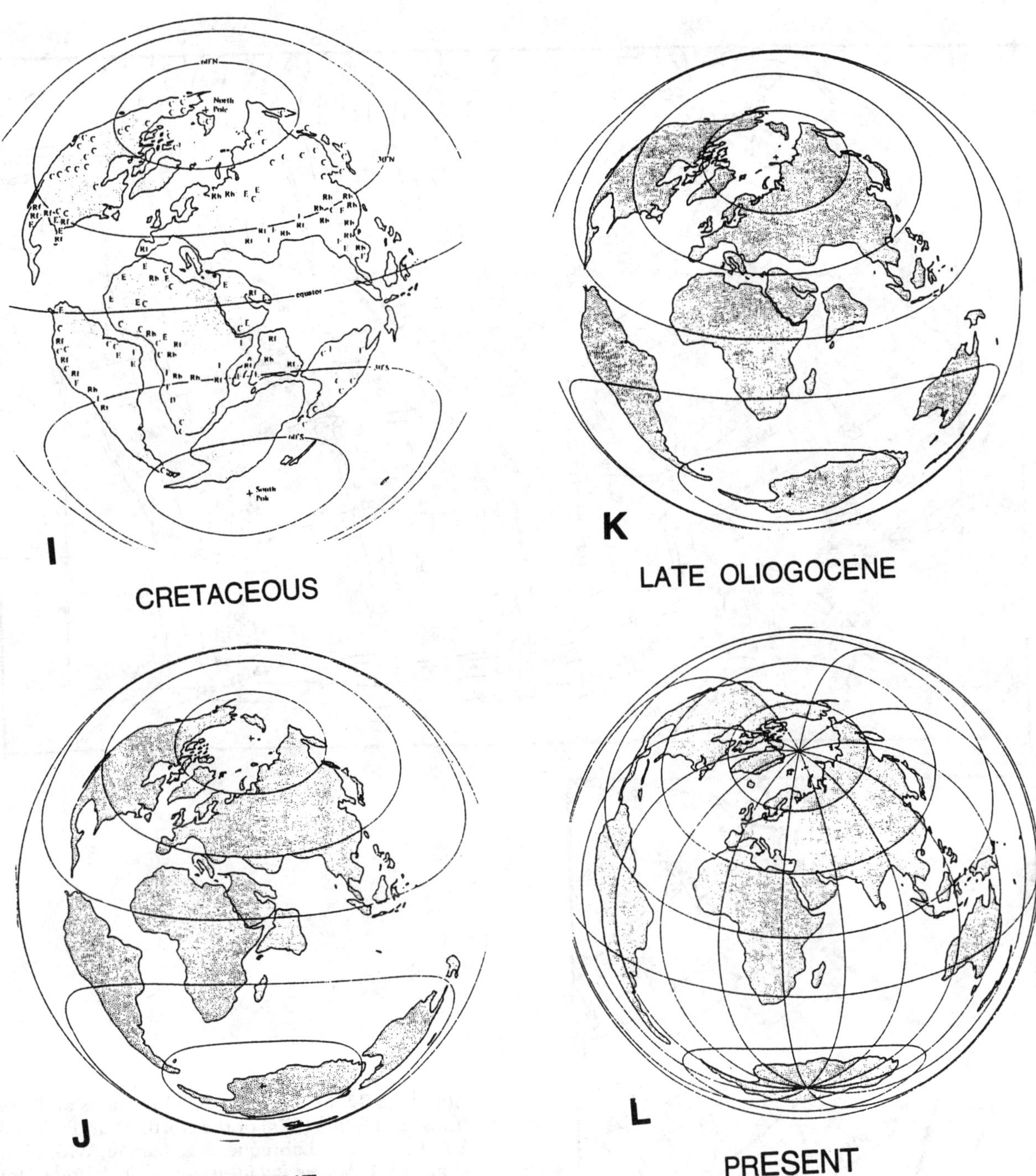
I
CRETACEOUS
K
LATE OLIOGOCENE
J
PALEOCENE
L
PRESENT

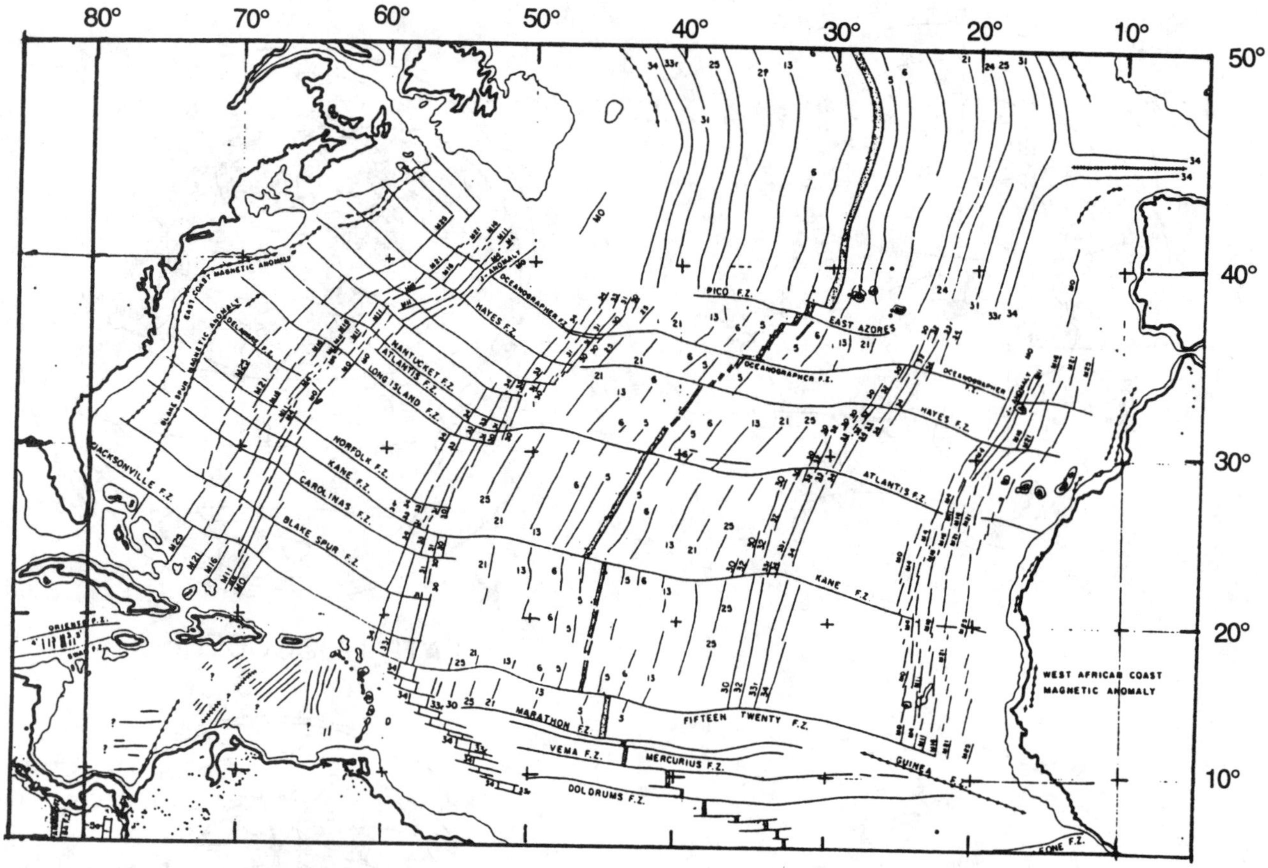

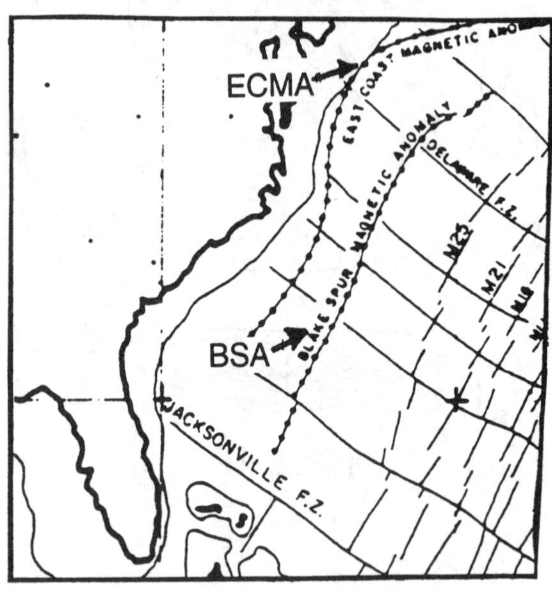

Figure 13.37 Map of magnetic lineations and healed transform faults (FZs) of the North Atlantic. (From S.C. Cande, J.L. Labreque, R.L. Larson, W.C. Pitman, et al., 1981, *Magnetic Lineations of the World's Ocean Basins* (Map). Copyright by the American Association of Petroleum Geologists. Used by permission of the publisher and the authors.)

135). This provision would mean that Archean provinces of North America, existed as separate continents until assembly started after 2.1 Ga.

We turn now to the mechanisms and energy sources that acted first to cause isolated continents to come together in collisions, building a supercontinent, and then to force continental rifting and breakup. The collision process is covered in Chapter 9. Collisions are inevitable as long as oceanic spreading plate boundaries are active, and spreading must be continuously active to dissipate internal heat. Where an ocean is bounded by continents having marginal subduction boundaries, as are those ringing the Pacific basin today, the trench-suction force tends to draw the continents toward the central oceanic spreading boundary, narrowing the ocean and bringing the continents

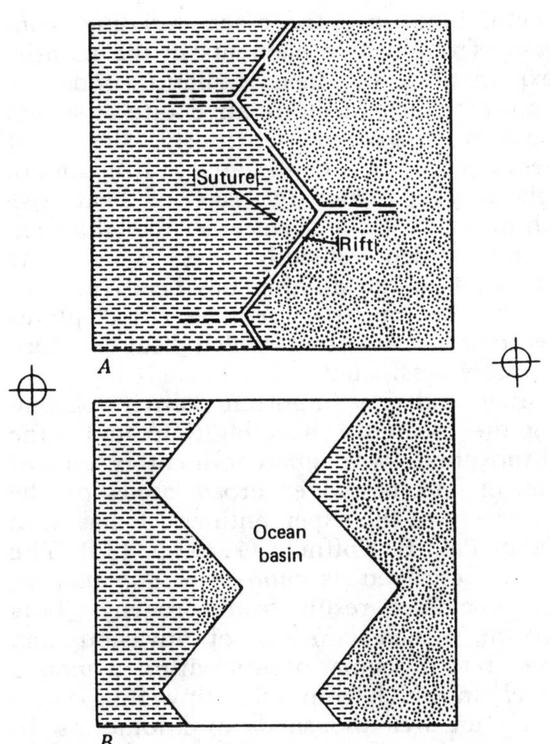

Figure 13.38 Schematic maps showing how a new continentral rift system may be superimposed on an older continental suture. (A) A new zigzag rift system lay across an old suture. (B) When the continents separated, portions of the former continent on the left adhered to the continent on the right, and vice versa. (Copyright © by Arthur N. Strahler.)

closer together. As indicated in Chapter 7, it seems inescapable that the Pacific basin is shrinking while the Atlantic basin is enlarging, so that the Americas are closing with Asia and Australia while the Atlantic Basin is widening.

This scenario may seem to account for the formation of a supercontinent, in theory at least. On the other hand, these processes act continuously and do not necessarily move all the continents along converging trajectories toward a common center. For a convergent force configuration to be present, a special agent would be needed. Mantle convection has been called upon as that agent by seismologist Don L. Anderson of the California Institute of Technology. In Chapter 3, we presented his pioneering contribution in 1962 to an understanding of the asthenosphere as a low-velocity layer (Figure 3.18). Anderson was also active in developing and interpreting seismic tomography of the mantle (1984). Anderson had developed the hypothesis that a downwelling motion of the mantle—the opposite of a rising mantle plume—would drag continents toward a common center in which the lithosphere is depressed (1984, p. 59). He had suggested "that stable downwelling mantle zones where large plates are captured tend to lie near the planetary poles" (Komnitz and Bond, 1991, p. 59).

We turn next to review briefly the problem of breakup of a supercontinent. The related subject of rifting is covered in some length in Chapter 10. The section titled *The Primary*

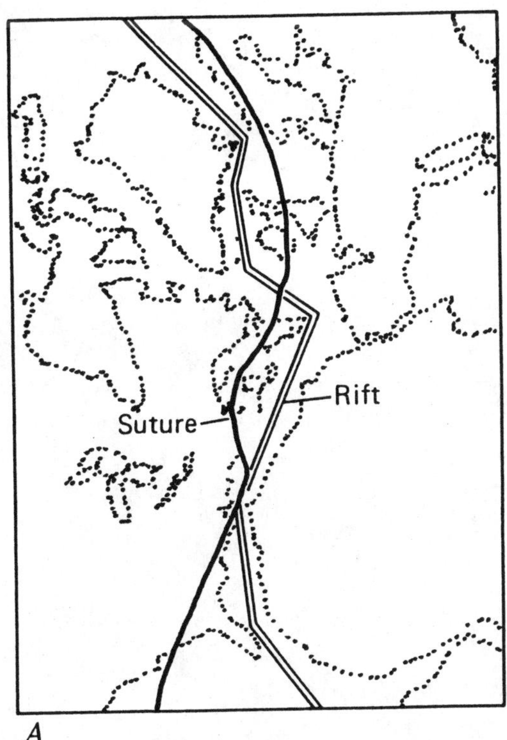

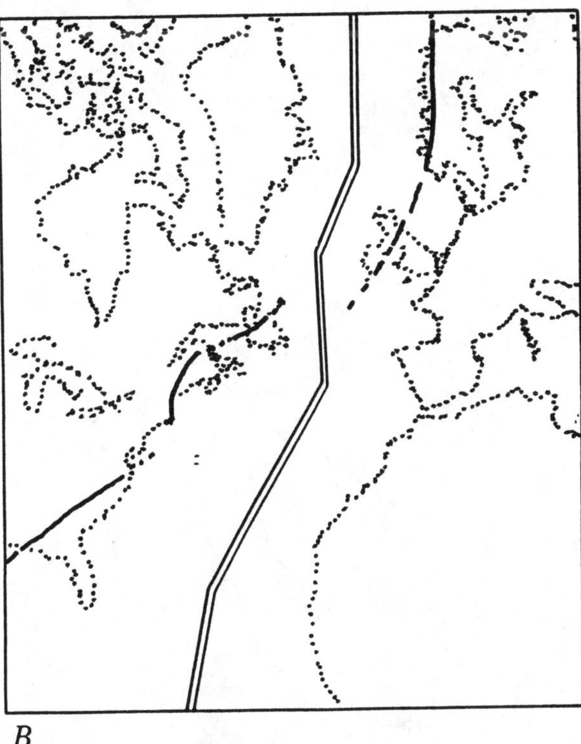

Figure 13.39 Maps showing conditions before and after the opening of the North Atlantic ocean basin. (A) Early Triassic time, immediately prior to rifting. (B) Later Mesozoic time. (Copyright © by Arthur N. Strahler.)

Cause of Intracontinental Extensional Stress describes the contribution of Anderson, Tanimato, and Zhang (1992) in interpreting seismic anomalies found in global mantle tomography. They revealed the possible existence of a convection system of broad, slowly rising columns within hot regions combined with broad sinking columns within cool regions (Figure 10.7). In such a convection system, plate lifting and cracking, and the rise of magma are provided by a powerful internal heat mechanism of long duration acting over broad continental areas. This information can now be directed to the problem of breakup of a supercontinent.

Anderson describes the supercontinent breakup as follows: "A supercontinent insulates the mantle and isolates it from subduction. Eventually the supercontinent breaks into pieces that move toward cold, downwelling mantle, overriding cold oceanic lithosphere in the process" (1994, p. 40). We assume that the rifting results from lifting of the lithosphere, creating a gradient outward from the continental interior and causing radially outward gravitational movement. This is analogous to the ridge-push force found in oceanic lithosphere on either side of a spreading rift (Chapter 7). In a popular article in *Scientific American* (1988), R. Damian Nance, Thomas R. Worsley, and Judith B. Moody explained the role of internal earth heat in Anderson's theory. While the dominant force in continental breakup is heat accumulating from the decay of radioactive elements in the mantle, the explanation of heat buildup under a supercontinent lies in the relative rate at which that heat is dissipated. Obviously, the great thickness of the continental lithosphere lithosphere will reduce the rate of heat loss through the crust to the surface, so that the rock temperature at depth steadily rises. When some critical point in the doming has been reached, rifting and the separation of the rifted plates exposes new oceans from which heat is much more rapidly dissipated.

Another and very important activity accompanying the escape of heat built up under the thick lithosphere of a supercontinent is that of the rise of magma under broad areas of the interior region of the supercontinent. It has been featured by Paul F. Hoffman (1989, p. 135). The process is described as *anorogenic magmatism*, since it does not result from orogeny. This magmatism, which consists of invasion and ponding of the magma, occurs within a *mantle superswell* in which convective upwelling takes place over an area thousands of kilometers in diameter. The silica-rich magmas are derived by melting of the lower crust. Lithologic types found in the superswell include granite, rhyolite, syenogranite, and anorthosite. These rocks are found today in large igneous provinces of ancient shields (Monastersky, 1989; Murphy and Nance, 1991).

References Cited

Abbott, D.H., and S.E. Hofman, 1984, Archean plate tectonics revisited. *Tectonics*, v. 3, no. 4, 429-448.

Anderson, Don L., 1962, The plastic layer of the earth's mantle. *Scientific American*, July 1962, p. 52-59.

Anderson, Don L., 1984. Hotspots, polar wander, Mesozoic convection and the geoid. *Science*, v. 223, p. 347-355.

Anderson, Don L., 1994, Superplumes or supercontinents? *Geology*, v. 22, p. 39-42.

Anderson, Don L., and Adam M. Dziewonsky, 1984, Seismic tomography. *Scientific American*, v. 251, no. 4, p. 60-68.

Anderson, Don L., T. Tanimoto, and Y.S. Zhang, 1992, Plate tectonics and hotspots. *Science*, v. 256, p. 1645-1651.

Argand, E., 1924, La tectonique de L'Asie. *Compte Rendus*, No. 5, p. 171-372. Brussels: Thirteenth International Geological Congress.

Balburg, Heinrich, 1993, Hypothetical southeast Pacific continent revisited: New evidence from the middle Paleozoic basins of northern Chile. *Geology*, v. 21, p. 909-912.

Barron, E.J., C.G.A. Harrison, and W.W. Hay 1978, A revised reconstruction of the southern continents, *EOS*, v. 59, p. 436-449.

Bates, Robert L., and Julia A. Jackson, Eds., 1987, *Glossary of Geology*, Alexandria, VA: American Geological Institute.

Bowring, Samuel A. and Todd Housh, 1995, The Earth's early revolution. *Science*, v. 269, p. 1535-1540.

Briden, J.C., A.G.Smith and J.T. Sallomy, 1970, The geomagnetic field in Permo-Triassic time. *Jour. of the Royal Astronomical Society*, v. 23, p. 101-120.

Caputo, Mário V., and John C. Crowell, 1985, Migration of glacial centers across Gondwana during Paleozoic Era. *Bull., Geol. Soc. Amer.*, v. 96, p. 1020-1036.

Card, K.D., and A. Ciesielski, 1986, Subdivisions of the Superior Provence of the Canadian Shield. *Geoscience Canada*, v. 13, 5-13.

Condie, Kent C., 1980, Origin and early development of the Earth's crust. *Precambrian Research*, v. 11, 183-197.

Condie, Kent C., 1989, 1993, *Plate Tectonics & Crustal Evolution*. Oxford, England: Pergamon Press Ltd.

Dalziel, Ian W.D., 1991, Pacific margins of Laurentia and East Antarctica-Australia as a conjugate rift pair: Evidence and implications for an Eocambrian supercontinent. *Geology*, v. 19, p. 598-601.

Dalziel, Ian W.D., 1994, Precambrian Scotland as a Laurentia-Gondwana link. *Geology*, v. 22, p., 589-592.

Dalziel, Ian W.D., 1995, Earth before Pangea. *Scientific American*, v. 272, no. 1, p. 58-63.

Dalziel, Ian W.D., and Mark A.S. McMenamin, 1995, Are Neoproterozoic glacial deposits preserved on the margins of Laurentia related to the fragmentation of two supercontinents?: Comment. *Geology*, v. 23, p. 959.

Dalziel, Ian W.D., Luis H. Dalla Salda, and Lisa M. Gahagan, 1994, Paleozoic Laurentian-Gondwana interaction and the origin of the Appalachian-Andean mountain system. *Bull., Geol. Soc. Amer.*, v. 106, p. 243-252.

de Wit, Maarten, Margaret Jeffery, Hugh Burgh, and Louis Nicolaysen, 1988, *Geological Map of Sectors of Gondwana*. Tulsa, OK: The American Association of Petroleum Geologists.

Deutsch, Ernst R., 1963, Polar wandering and continental drift: An evaluation of recent evidence. Pages 4-46 in Munyan Ed., 1963.

Dietz, Robert S., and John C. Holden, 1970a, Reconstruction of Pangea: Breakup and dispersion of continents, Permian to Present. *Jour. of Geophysical Research*, v. 75, p. 4939-4956.

Dietz, Robert S., and John C. Holden, 1970b, The Breakup of Pangaea. *Scientific American*, v. 233, no. 4, p. 30-41.

du Toit, Alexander L., 1927, *A Geological Comparison of South America with South Africa*. Publication No. 381. Washington, DC: Carnegie Institution of Washington.

du Toit, Alexander L., 1937, *Our Wandering Continents*. Edinburgh: Oliver & Boyd, Ltd.

Elliot, David H., Edwin H. Colbert, William J. Breed, James A Jensen, and Jon S. Powell, 1970, Triassic tetrapods from Antarctica: Evidence for continental drift. *Science*, v. 169, p. 1197-1201.

Fairbridge, Rhodes W., 1970, An ice age in the Sahara, *Geotimes*, v. 15, no. 6, p. 18-20

González-Bonorino, Gustavo, and Nicholas Eyles, 1995, Inverse relation between ice extent and the late Paleozoic glacial record of Gondwana. *Geology*, v. 23, p. 1015-1018.

Gordon, Richard G., 1987, Polar wander and paleomagnetism. *Ann. Reviews of Earth & Planetary Science*, v. 15, p. 567-593.
Hamilton, Warren, 1974, Antarctic tectonics and continental drift. Pages 74-93 in Munyon, Ed., 1963.

Hargraves, R.B., 1986, Faster spreading or greater ridge length in the Archean? *Geology*, v. 14, p. 750-752.

Hoffman, P.F., 1988, United plates of America, the birth of a craton. *Annual Reviews of Earth and Planetary Science*, v. 16.

Hoffman, Paul F., 1989, Speculations on Laurentia's first gigayear (2.0 to 1.0 Ga). *Geology*, v. 17, p. 135.

Hoffman, Paul F., 1991, Did the breakout of Laurentia turn Gondwanaland inside out? *Science*, v. 253, p. 1409-1412.

Howell, D.G., 1989, *Tectonics of Suspect Terranes*. London: Chapman and Hall.

Hurley Patrick M., and John R. Rand, 1969, Pre-drift continental nuclei. *Science*, V. 164, p. 1229-1242.

Hurley, Patrick M., 1968, The confirmation of continental drift. *Scientific American*, V. 218, no. 4, p. 53-64.

Hurley, Patrick M., 1974, Pangeaic orogenic system. *Geology*, v. 2, p. 373-376.

Hurley, Patrick, F.F.M. de Almeida, G.C. Melcher, U.G. Cordani, J.R. Rand, K. Kawashita, P. Vandoros, W.H. Pinson, Jr., and H.W. Fairbairn, 1967, Test of continental drift by comparison of radiometric ages. *Science*, v. 157, p. 495-500.

Irving, E., 1954, Paleomagnetism of the Torridonian Sandstone Series, N.W. Scotland. (Thesis) Univ. of Cambridge, England.

Irving, E., 1988, The paleomagnetic confirmation of continental drift. *EOS*, v. 69, no. 44, p. 994-1013.

Kerr, Richard A., 1985, Plate tectonics goes back 2 billion years. *Science*, v. 230, p. 1364-1367.

Kerr, Richard A., 1986, Plate tectonics is the key to the distant past. *Science*, V. 234, p. 670-672.

Kroner, A., and P.W. Layer, 1992, Crust formation and plate motion in the early Archean. *Science*, v. 256, p. 1405-1411.

Kroner, Alfred, 1985, Evolution of the Archean continental crust. *Annual Reviews of Earth and Planetary Sciences*, v. 13, p. 49-74.

Livermore, R.A., F.J. Vine, A.G. Smith, 1984, Plate motions and the geomagnetic field—II. Jurassic to Tertiary. *Geophysical Journal of the Royal Astronomical Society*, v. 79, p. 936-961.

Martin, H., 1986, Effect of steeper Archean geothermal gradient on geochemistry of subduction-zone magmas. *Geology*, v. 14, p. 753-756.

McElhinny, M.W., and G.R. Luck, 1970, Paleomagnetism and Gondwanaland. *Science*, v. 168, p. 830-832.

McMenamin, M.A.S., and D.L.S. McMenamin, 1990, *The Emergence of Animals: The Cambrian Breakthrough*. New York: Columbia Univ. Press.

Merrill, Ronald T., and Michael W. McElhinny, 1983, *The Earth's Magnetic Field: Its history, Origin and Planetary Perspectives*. London and New York: Academic Press.

Monastersky, Richard, 1989, Spinning the supercontinent cycle. *Science News*, v. 135, p. 344-346.

Monastersky, Richard, 1991, Married to Antarctica. *Science News*, v. 139, p. 266-267.

Moores, Eldredge M., 1986, The Proterozoic ophiolite problem, continental emergence, and the Venus connection. *Science*, vol. 234, p. 65-68.

Moores, Eldredge M., 1993, Neoproterozoic oceanic crustal thinning, emergence of continents, and origin of Phanerozoic ecosystem: A model. *Geology*, v. 21, p. 5-8.

Moores, Eldridge M., 1991, Southwest U.S.—East Antarctic (SWEAT) connection: A hypothesis. *Geology*, v. 19, p. 425-428.

Munyan, Arthur G., Ed., 1963, *Polar Wandering and Continental Drift*. Tulsa, OK: Soc. of Economic Paleontologists and Mineralogists.

Murphy, J. Brendan, and R. Damian Nance, 1991, Supercontinent model for the contrasting character of Late Proterozoic orogenic belts. *Geology*, v. 19, p. 469-472.

Nance, R. Damian, Thomas R. Worsley, and Judith B. Moody, 1988, The supercontinent cycle. *Scientific American*, v. 259, no. 1, p. 72-79.

Opdyke, N.D., and S.K. Runcorn, 1960, Wind directions in the western United States in the Late Paleozoic. *Bull., Geol. Soc. Amer.*, v. 71 , p. 959-972.

Renner, Rebecca, 1993, The hottest rocks on Earth. *New Scientist*, v. 139, no. 1883, p. 23-25.

Reymer, Arthur, and Gerald Schubert, 1984, Phanerozoic addition rates to the continental crust and crustal growth. *Tectonics*, v. 3, no. 1, p. 63-77.

Runcorn, S.K., 1959, Rock magnetism. *Science*, v. 129, p. 1002-1012.

Runcorn, S.K., 1963, Paleomagnetic methods of investigating polar wandering and continental drift. Pages 47-54 in Munyan, Ed., 1963.

Sengor, A.M.C., 1992, Difference between Gondwana and Gondwana-Land. *Geology*, v. 19, p. 287-288.

Seyfert, Carl K., 1987, Continental drift, paleomagnetic evidence. Pages 62-80 in Seyfert, Ed., 1987.

Seyfert, Carl K., and Leslie A. Sirkin, 1979, *Earth History and Plate Tectonics*. New York: Harper & Row, Publishers.

Seyfert, Carl K., Ed., 1987, *Encyclopedia of Structural Geology and Plate Tectonics*. New York: Van Nostrand Reinhold Co.

Smith, A.G., and A. Hallam, 1970, The fit of the southern continents. *Nature*, v. 225, p. 139-144.

Strahler, Arthur N., 1972, *The Earth Sciences*, New York: Harper & Row.

Van der Voo, Rob, 1987, Apparent polar wander. Pages 15-18 in Seyfert, Ed., 1987.

Van der Voo, Rob, 1993, *Paleomagnetism of the Atlantic, Tethys, and Iapetus Oceans*. Cambridge England and New York: Cambridge Univ. Press.

Veevers, J.J., 1995, Emergent, long-lived Gondwana vs. submergent, short-lived Laurasia: Supercontinental and Pan-African heat imparts long-term buoyancy by mafic underplating. *Geology*, v. 23, p. 1131-1134.

Wegener, Alfred, 1966, *The Origin of Continents and Oceans*, Translated from the 4th revised German edition (1929) by John Biram. New York: Dover Publications.

Wilks, M.E., 1988, The Himalayas—A modem analog for Archean crustal evolution. *Earth & Planetary Scientific Letters*, v. 87, p. 127-136.

Williams, H., P.F. Hoffman, J.F. Lewry, J.W.H. Monger, and T. Rivers, 1991, Anatomy of North America: Thematic geologic portrayals of the continent. *Tectonophysics*, v. 187, p. 117-134.

Wilson, J. Tuzo, 1966, Did the Atlantic close and then reopen? *Nature*, v. 211, p. 676-681.

Yin, An, and Shangyou Nie, 1993, An indentation model for the north and south China collision and the development of the Tan-Lu and Honam fault systems, eastern Asia. *Tectonics*, v. 12, no. 4, p. 801-813.

Young, Grant M., 1995a, Are Neoproterozoic glacial deposits preserved on the margins of Laurentia related to the fragmentation of two supercontinents? *Geology*, v. 23, p. 153-156.

Young, Grant M., 1995b, Are Neoproterozoic glacial deposits preserved on the margins of Laurentia related to the fragmentation of two supercontinents?: Reply. *Geology*, v. 23, p. 960.

Zhang, ZH. M., J.G. Liou, and R.G. Coleman, 1984, An outline of the plate tectonics of China. *Bull, Geol. Soc. Amer.*, v. 95, p 295-312.

Zonenshain, Lev P., Jacob Verhoef, Ron Macnab, and Herbert Meyers, 1991, Magnetic imprints of continental accretion in the U.S.S.R., *EOS* v. 72, no. 29, p. 305, 310.

GEOLOGICAL TIME SCALE

CENOZOIC

Period		Epoch		Age	Picks (Ma)
Quaternary		Holocene			0.01
		Pleistocene		Calabrian	1.6
Tertiary	Neogene	Pliocene	L	Piacenzian	3.4
			E	Zanclean	5.3
		Miocene	L	Messinian	6.5
				Tortonian	11.2
			M	Serravallian	15.1
				Langhian	16.6
			E	Burdigalian	21.8
				Aquitanian	23.7
	Paleogene	Oligocene	L	Chattian	30.0
			E	Rupelian	36.6
		Eocene	L	Priabonian	40.0
			M	Bartonian	43.6
				Lutetian	52.0
			E	Ypresian	57.8
		Paleocene	L	Selandian: Thanetian	60.6
				Selandian: Unnamed	63.6
			E	Danian	66.4

Age (Ma): 5, 10, 15, 20, 25, 30, 35, 40, 45, 50, 55, 60, 65

Magnetic polarity (Hist, Anom, Chron) — Anomalies: 1, 2, 2A, 3, 3A, 4, 4A, 5, 5A, 5B, 5C, 5D, 5E, 6, 6A, 6B, 6C, 7, 7A, 8, 9, 10, 11, 12, 13, 15, 16, 17, 18, 19, 20, 21, 22, 23, 24, 25, 26, 27, 28, 29. Chrons: C1, C2, C2A, C3, C3A, C4, C4A, C5, C5A, C5B, C5C, C5D, C5E, C6, C6A, C6B, C6C, C7, C7A, C8, C9, C10, C11, C12, C13, C15, C16, C17, C18, C19, C20, C21, C22, C23, C24, C25, C26, C27, C28, C29.

MESOZOIC

Period	Epoch	Age	Picks (Ma)	Uncert (m.y.)
			66.4	
Cretaceous	Late	Maastrichtian	74.5	4
		Campanian	84.0	4.5
		Santonian	87.5	
		Coniacian	88.5	2.5
		Turonian	91	
		Cenomanian	97.5	2.5
	Early	Albian	113	4
		Aptian	119	9
		Neocomian: Barremian	124	9
		Neocomian: Hauterivian	131	8
		Neocomian: Valanginian	138	5
		Neocomian: Berriasian	144	5
Jurassic	Late	Tithonian	152	12
		Kimmeridgian	156	6
		Oxfordian	163	15
	Middle	Callovian	169	15
		Bathonian	176	34
		Bajocian	183	34
		Aalenian	187	34
	Early	Toarcian	193	28
		Pliensbachian	198	32
		Sinemurian	204	18
		Hettangian	208	18
Triassic	Late	Norian	225	8
		Carnian	230	22
	Middle	Ladinian	235	10
		Anisian	240	22
	Early	Scythian	245	20

Age (Ma): 70, 80, 90, 100, 110, 120, 130, 140, 150, 160, 170, 180, 190, 200, 210, 220, 230, 240

Magnetic polarity (Hist, Anom, Chron) — Anomalies: 29, 30, 31, 32, 33, M0, M1, M3, M5, M10, M12, M14, M16, M18, M20, M22, M25, M29. Chrons: C29, C30, C31, C32, C33. RAPID POLARITY CHANGES

PALEOZOIC

Period		Epoch	Age	Picks (Ma)	Uncert (m.y.)
				245	20
Permian		Late	Tatarian	253	20
			Kazanian	258	24
			Ufimian	263	22
			Kungurian	268	12
		Early	Artinskian		
			Sakmarian		
			Asselian	286	12
Carboniferous	Pennsylvanian	Late	Gzelian (S.)		
			Kasimovian	296	10
			Moscovian (W.)		
			Bashkirian	315	20
			(N.)	320	
	Mississippian	Early	Serpukhovian	333	22
			Visean	352	8
			Tournaisian	360	10
Devonian		Late	Fammenian	367	12
			Frasnian	374	18
		Middle	Givetian	380	18
			Eifelian	387	28
		Early	Emsian	394	22
			Siegenian	401	18
			Gedinnian	408	12
Silurian		Late	Pridolian	414	12
			Ludlovian	421	12
		Early	Wenlockian	428	8
			Llandoverian	438	12
Ordovician		Late	Ashgillian	448	12
			Caradocian	458	16
		Middle	Llandeilan	468	16
			Llanvirnian	478	16
		Early	Arenigian	488	20
			Tremadocian	505	32
Cambrian		Late	Trempealeauan Franconian Dresbachian	523	36
		Middle		540	28
		Early		570	

Age (Ma): 260, 280, 300, 320, 340, 360, 380, 400, 420, 440, 460, 480, 500, 520, 540, 560

PRECAMBRIAN

Eon	Era	Bdy. Ages (Ma)
		570
Proterozoic	Late	900
	Middle	1600
	Early	2500
Archean	Late	3000
	Middle	3400
	Early	3800?

Age (Ma): 750, 1000, 1250, 1500, 1750, 2000, 2250, 2500, 2750, 3000, 3250, 3500, 3750

Index of Persons

Index of Subjects

Order Form

To:

Geo•Books Publishing
55 Fresh Pond Parkway
Cambridge, MA 02138-3348 USA
Phone: 617-864-1334
Fax: 617-876-9836

Order Information			
Copies	Title	Unit Price	Total Price
	Plate Tectonics by A. N. Strahler	$75.00*	
Shipping and handling at $4 for the first book and $2 for each additional book (UPS Ground):			
Total Due:			

*25% discount on quantities of 3 or more

❑ I enclose my check or money order for the total shown above.

❑ Please charge my ❑ Visa ❑ Mastercard account (credit card orders may be faxed directly to 617-876-9836).

Name on card ______________________________

Card number ______________________ Exp. Date ____/ ____

Ship my order to:

Name ______________________________

Address ______________________________

____

____

____

Daytime phone ______________________________